Table of Atomic Masses*

Element	Symbol	Atomic Number	Atomic Mass
Actinium	Ac	89	(227)†
Aluminum	Al	13	26.98
Americium	Am	95	(243)
Antimony	Sb	51	121.8
Argon	Ar	18	39.95
Arsenic	As	33	74.92
Astatine	At	85	(210)
Barium	Ba	56	137.3
Berkelium	Bk	97	(247)
Beryllium	Be	4	9.012
Bismuth	Bi	83	209.0
Bohrium	Bh	107	(264)
Boron	B	5	10.81
Bromine	Br	35	79.90
Cadmium	Cd	48	112.4
Calcium	Ca	20	40.08
Californium	Cf	98	(251)
Carbon	C	6	12.01
Cerium	Ce	58	140.1
Cesium	Cs	55	132.9
Chlorine	Cl	17	35.45
Chromium	Cr	24	52.00
Cobalt	Co	27	58.93
Copper	Cu	29	63.55
Curium	Cm	96	(247)
Darmstadtium	Ds	110	(281)
Dubnium	Db	105	(262)
Dysprosium	Dy	66	162.5
Einsteinium	Es	99	(252)
Erbium	Er	68	167.3
Europium	Eu	63	152.0
Fermium	Fm	100	(257)
Fluorine	F	9	19.00
Francium	Fr	87	(223)
Gadolinium	Gd	64	157.3
Gallium	Ga	31	69.72
Germanium	Ge	32	72.59
Gold	Au	79	197.0
Hafnium	Hf	72	178.5
Hassium	Hs	108	(265)
Helium	He	2	4.003
Holmium	Ho	67	164.9
Hydrogen	H	1	1.008
Indium	In	49	114.8
Iodine	I	53	126.9
Iridium	Ir	77	192.2
Iron	Fe	26	55.85
Krypton	Kr	36	83.80
Lanthanum	La	57	138.9
Lawrencium	Lr	103	(260)
Lead	Pb	82	207.2
Lithium	Li	3	6.941
Lutetium	Lu	71	175.0
Magnesium	Mg	12	24.31
Manganese	Mn	25	54.94
Meitnerium	Mt	109	(268)
Mendelevium	Md	101	(258)
Mercury	Hg	80	200.6
Molybdenum	Mo	42	95.94
Neodymium	Nd	60	144.2
Neon	Ne	10	20.18
Neptunium	Np	93	(237)
Nickel	Ni	28	58.69
Niobium	Nb	41	92.91
Nitrogen	N	7	14.01
Nobelium	No	102	(259)
Osmium	Os	76	190.2
Oxygen	O	8	16.00
Palladium	Pd	46	106.4
Phosphorus	P	15	30.97
Platinum	Pt	78	195.1
Plutonium	Pu	94	(244)
Polonium	Po	84	(209)
Potassium	K	19	39.10
Praseodymium	Pr	59	140.9
Promethium	Pm	61	(145)
Protactinium	Pa	91	(231)
Radium	Ra	88	226
Radon	Rn	86	(222)
Rhenium	Re	75	186.2
Rhodium	Rh	45	102.9
Rubidium	Rb	37	85.47
Ruthenium	Ru	44	101.1
Rutherfordium	Rf	104	(261)
Samarium	Sm	62	150.4
Scandium	Sc	21	44.96
Seaborgium	Sg	106	(263)
Selenium	Se	34	78.96
Silicon	Si	14	28.09
Silver	Ag	47	107.9
Sodium	Na	11	22.99
Strontium	Sr	38	87.62
Sulfur	S	16	32.07
Tantalum	Ta	73	180.9
Technetium	Tc	43	(98)
Tellurium	Te	52	127.6
Terbium	Tb	65	158.9
Thallium	Tl	81	204.4
Thorium	Th	90	232.0
Thulium	Tm	69	168.9
Tin	Sn	50	118.7
Titanium	Ti	22	47.88
Tungsten	W	74	183.9
Uranium	U	92	238.0
Vanadium	V	23	50.94
Xenon	Xe	54	131.3
Ytterbium	Yb	70	173.0
Yttrium	Y	39	88.91
Zinc	Zn	30	65.38
Zirconium	Zr	40	91.22

*The values given here are to four significant figures where possible.   †A value given in parentheses denotes the mass of the longest-lived isotope.

General Chemistry 162

Includes STUDENT SOLUTIONS MANUAL

Steven S. Zumdahl | Donald J. DeCoste

Australia • Brazil • Japan • Korea • Mexico • Singapore • Spain • United Kingdom • United States

CENGAGE
Learning·

General Chemistry 162: Includes STUDENT SOLUTIONS MANUAL

Executive Editors:
  Maureen Staudt
  Michael Stranz

Senior Project Development Manager:
  Linda deStefano

Marketing Specialist:
  Courtney Sheldon

Senior Production/Manufacturing Manager:
  Donna M. Brown

Production Editorial Manager:
  Kim Frv

Sr. Rights Acquisition Account Manager:
  Todd Osborne

Printed in the United States of America

Chemical Principles, 7th Edition
Steven S. Zumdahl | Donald J. DeCoste
© 2013, 2009 Brooks/Cole, Cengage Learning. All rights reserved.

Student Solutions Manual for Chemical Principles, 7th Edition
Steven S. Zumdahl | Donald J. DeCoste
© 2013 Brooks/Cole, Cengage Learning. All rights reserved.

Unless otherwise noted, all art is © Cengage Learning.

For product information and technology assistance, contact us at
Cengage Learning Customer & Sales Support, 1-800-354-9706
For permission to use material from this text or product,
submit all requests online at **cengage.com/permissions**
Further permissions questions can be emailed to
permissionrequest@cengage.com

This book contains select works from existing Cengage Learning resources and was produced by Cengage Learning Custom Solutions for collegiate use. As such, those adopting and/or contributing to this work are responsible for editorial content accuracy, continuity and completeness.

Compilation © 2012 Cengage Learning
ISBN-13: 978-1-285-13158-0

ISBN-10: 1-285-13158-4
Cengage Learning
5191 Natorp Boulevard
Mason, Ohio 45040
USA

Cengage Learning is a leading provider of customized learning solutions with office locations around the globe, including Singapore, the United Kingdom, Australia, Mexico, Brazil, and Japan. Locate your local office at:
international.cengage.com/region.
Cengage Learning products are represented in Canada by Nelson Education, Ltd.
For your lifelong learning solutions, visit **www.cengage.com/custom.**
Visit our corporate website at **www.cengage.com.**

GENERAL CHEMISTRY 162

CONTENTS

(*Note – this is a "custom" textbook that has been designed specifically for this course in a joint effort between your instructor and the publisher. Please note that some chapters may have been removed intentionally and some pages may be black & white as dictated by the changes and/or additions.)

STUDENT SOLUTIONS MANUAL

Bonding: General Concepts

Model of a buckyball with potassium ion.

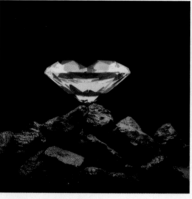

(top) Quartz grows in beautiful, regular crystals. (bottom) Two forms of carbon: graphite and diamond.

The world around us is composed almost entirely of compounds and mixtures of compounds: Rocks, coal, soil, petroleum, trees, and human bodies are all complex mixtures of chemical compounds in which different kinds of atoms are bound together. Substances composed of unbound atoms do exist in nature, but they are very rare. Examples are the argon in the atmosphere and the helium mixed with natural gas reserves.

The manner in which atoms are bound together in a given substance has a profound effect on its chemical and physical properties. For example, graphite is a soft, slippery material used as a lubricant in locks, and diamond is one of the hardest materials known, valuable both as a gemstone and in industrial cutting tools. Why do these materials, both composed solely of carbon atoms, have such different properties? The answer, as we will see, lies in the bonding within these substances.

Silicon and carbon are next to each other in Group 4A on the periodic table. From our knowledge of periodic trends, we might expect SiO_2 and CO_2 to be very similar. But SiO_2 is the empirical formula of silica, which is found in sand and quartz, whereas carbon dioxide is a gas, a product of respiration. Why are they so different? We will be able to answer this question after we have developed models for bonding.

Bonding and structure play a central role in determining the course of all chemical reactions, many of which are vital to our survival. Later in this book we will demonstrate the importance of bonding and structure by showing how enzymes facilitate complex chemical reactions, how genetic characteristics are transferred, and how hemoglobin in the blood carries oxygen throughout the body. All these fundamental biological reactions hinge on the geometric structures of molecules, sometimes depending on very subtle differences in molecular shape to channel the chemical reaction one way rather than another.

Many of the world's current problems require fundamentally chemical answers: disease and pollution control, the search for new energy sources, the development of new fertilizers to increase crop yields, the improvement of the protein content in various staple grains, and many more. To understand the behavior of natural materials, we must understand the nature of chemical bonding and the factors that control the structures of compounds. In this chapter we will present various classes of compounds that illustrate the different types of bonds and then develop models to describe the structure and bonding that characterize materials found in nature. Later these models will prove useful in understanding chemical reactions.

13.1 | Types of Chemical Bonds

What is a chemical bond? There is no simple and yet complete answer to this question. In Chapter 2 we defined bonds as forces that hold groups of atoms together and make the atoms function as a unit.

There are many types of experiments we can perform to determine the fundamental nature of materials. For example, we can study physical properties such as melting point, hardness, and electrical and thermal conductivity. We can also study solubility characteristics and the properties of the resulting solutions. To determine the charge distribution in a molecule, we can study its behavior in an electric field. We can obtain information about the strength of a bonding interaction by measuring the energy required to break the bond, the **bond energy.** Spectroscopy, the study of the interactions of electromagnetic radiation with matter, gives a wealth of information about molecular structure and energy level spacings.

There are several ways atoms can interact with one another to form aggregates. We will consider several specific examples to illustrate the various types of chemical bonds.

When solid sodium chloride is melted, it conducts electricity, a fact that convinces us that sodium chloride contains Na^+ and Cl^- ions. Thus, when sodium and chlorine react to form sodium chloride, electrons must be transferred from the sodium atoms to the chlorine atoms to form Na^+ and Cl^- ions, which then aggregate to form solid sodium chloride. Why does this happen? The best simple answer is that *the system can achieve the lowest possible energy by behaving in this way.* Part of the favorable energy change results from the attraction of a chlorine atom for an extra electron. Even more important are the very strong attractions between the oppositely charged ions. The resulting solid sodium chloride is a very sturdy material; it has a melting point of about 800°C. The bonding forces that produce this great thermal stability result from the electrostatic attractions of the closely packed, oppositely charged ions. This is an example of *ionic bonding.* Ionic substances are formed when an atom that loses electrons relatively easily reacts with an atom that has a high affinity for electrons. That is, an **ionic compound** results when a metal reacts with a nonmetal.

The energy of interaction between a pair of ions can be calculated by using **Coulomb's law:**

$$V = \frac{Q_1 Q_2}{4\pi\epsilon_0 r} = 2.31 \times 10^{-19} \text{ J nm}\left(\frac{Q_1 Q_2}{r}\right)$$

where V has units of joules, r is the distance between the ion centers in nanometers, Q_1 and Q_2 are the numerical ion charges, and ϵ_0 is the permittivity of the vacuum. For example, in solid sodium chloride, where the distance between the centers of the Na^+ and Cl^- ions is 276 picometers (0.276 nm), the ionic energy per pair of ions is

$$V = 2.31 \times 10^{-19} \text{ J nm} \left[\frac{(+1)(-1)}{0.276 \text{ nm}}\right] = -8.37 \times 10^{-19} \text{ J}$$

The negative sign indicates an attractive force. That is, *the ion pair has lower energy than the separated ions.* For a mole of pairs of Na^+ and Cl^- ions, the energy of interaction is

$$V = \left(-8.37 \times 10^{-19} \frac{\text{J}}{\text{ion pair}}\right)\left(6.022 \times 10^{23} \frac{\text{ion pair}}{\text{mol}}\right)$$

$$= -504 \text{ kJ/mol}$$

Note that this energy refers to a mole of $Na^+ \cdots Cl^-$ ion pairs in the gas phase where a given pair is far from any other pair. In solid sodium chloride, which contains a large array of closely packed Na^+ and Cl^- ions, where a given ion is close to many oppositely charged ions, the energy associated with ionic bonding is much greater than 504 kJ/mol because of the larger numbers of interacting ions.

Coulomb's law can also be used to calculate the repulsive energy when two like-charged ions are brought together. In this case the calculated energy value will have a positive sign.

We have seen that a bonding force develops when two very different atoms react to form oppositely charged ions. But how does a bonding force develop between two identical atoms? Let's explore this situation from a very simple point of view by considering the energy terms that result when two hydrogen atoms are brought close together, as shown in Fig. 13.1(a). For two closely spaced hydrogen atoms, there are two unfavorable energy terms, proton–proton

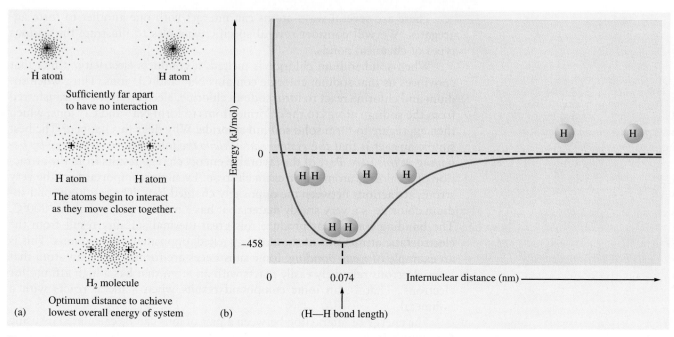

Figure 13.1
(a) The interaction of two hydrogen atoms. (b) Energy profile as a function of the distance between the nuclei of the hydrogen atoms. As the atoms approach each other, the energy decreases until the distance reaches 0.074 nm (0.74 Å) and then begins to increase again because of repulsions.

Bonding occurs if the energy of the aggregate is lower than that of the separated atoms.

The atoms in H_2 (and all other molecules) actually vibrate back and forth around the equilibrium internuclear distance.

repulsion and electron–electron repulsion, and one favorable term, proton–electron attraction. Under what conditions will the H_2 molecule be favored over the separated hydrogen atoms? That is, what conditions will favor bond formation? The answer lies in nature's strong tendency to achieve the lowest possible energy. A bond will form—that is, the two hydrogen atoms will exist as a molecular unit—if the system can lower its total energy in the process.

Therefore, the hydrogen atoms will assume the positions that give the lowest possible energy; the system will act to minimize the sum of the positive (repulsive) energy terms and the negative (attractive) energy terms. The distance at which the energy is minimum is called the equilibrium internuclear distance or, more commonly, the **bond length.** The total energy of this system as a function of distance between the hydrogen nuclei is shown in Fig. 13.1(b). Note four important features of this diagram:

1. The energy terms involved are the potential energy that results from the attractions and repulsions among the charged particles and the kinetic energy caused by the motions of the electrons.

2. The zero reference point for energy is defined for the atoms at infinite separation.

3. At very short distances the energy rises steeply because of the great importance of the internuclear repulsive forces at these distances.

4. The bond length is the distance at which the system has minimum energy, and the bond energy corresponds to the depth of the "well" at this distance.

In the H_2 molecule the electrons reside primarily in the space between the two nuclei, where they are attracted simultaneously by both protons. This positioning is precisely what leads to the stability of the H_2 molecule relative to two separated hydrogen atoms. The potential energy of each electron is lowered because of the increased attractive forces in this area. Although it is not usually discussed in connection with simple models of bonding, we should note that the kinetic energy of the electrons also changes when the individual atoms form the molecule. Thus the energy plotted in Fig. 13.1(b) is the total energy of the system, not just the potential energy. When we say that a bond is formed between the hydrogen atoms, we mean that the H_2 molecule is more stable

No Lead Pencils

Did you ever wonder why the part of a pencil that makes the mark is called the "lead"? Pencils have no lead in them now—and they never have. Apparently the association between writing and the element lead arose during the Roman Empire, when lead rods were used as writing utensils because they leave a gray mark on paper. Many centuries later, in 1564, a deposit of a black substance found to be very useful for writing was discovered in Borrowdale, England. This substance, originally called "black lead," was shown in 1879 by Swedish chemist Carl Sheele to be a form of carbon and was subsequently named graphite (after the Greek *graphein,* meaning "to write").

Originally, chunks of graphite from Borrowdale, called "marking stones," were used as writing instruments. Later, sticks of graphite were used. Because graphite is brittle, the sticks needed reinforcement. At first they were wrapped in string, which was unwound as the core wore down. Eventually, graphite rods were tied between two wooden slats or inserted into hollowed-out wooden sticks to form the first crude pencils.

Although Borrowdale graphite was pure enough to use directly, most graphite must be mixed with other materials to be useful for writing instruments. In 1795, French chemist Nicolas-Jaques Conté invented a process in which graphite is mixed with clay and water to produce pencil "lead," a recipe that is still used today. In modern pencil manufacture, graphite and clay are mixed and crushed into a fine powder to which water is added. After the gray sludge is blended for several days, it is dried, ground up again, and mixed with more water to give a gray paste. The paste is extruded through a metal tube to form thin rods, which are then cut into pencil-length pieces called "leads." These leads are heated in an oven to 1000°C until they are smooth and hard. The ratio of clay to graphite is adjusted to vary the hardness of the lead—the more clay in the mix, the harder the lead and the lighter the line it makes.

Pencils are made from a slat of wood with several grooves cut in it to hold the leads. A similar grooved slat is then placed on top and glued to form a "sandwich" from which individual pencils are cut, sanded smooth, and painted. Although many types of wood have been used over the years to make pencils, the current favorite is incense cedar from the Sierra Nevada Mountains of California.

Modern pencils are simple but amazing instruments. The average pencil can write approximately 45,000 words, which is equivalent to a line 35 miles long. The graphite in a pencil is easily transferred to paper because graphite contains layers of carbon atoms bound together in a "chicken-wire" structure. Although the bonding *within* each layer is very strong, the bonding *between* layers is weak, giving graphite its slippery, soft nature. In this way, graphite is much different from diamond, the other common elemental form of carbon. In diamond the carbon atoms are bound tightly in all three dimensions, making it extremely hard—the hardest natural substance.

Pencils are very useful—especially for doing chemistry problems—because we can erase our mistakes. Most pencils used in the United States have erasers (first attached to pencils in 1858), although most European pencils do not. Laid end to end, the number of pencils made in the United States each year would circle the earth about 15 times. Pencils illustrate how useful a simple substance like graphite can be.

than two separated hydrogen atoms by a certain quantity of energy (the bond energy).

We can also think of a bond in terms of forces. The simultaneous attraction for each electron by the two protons generates a force that pulls the protons toward each other. This attractive force just balances the proton–proton and electron–electron repulsive forces at the distance corresponding to the bond length.

The type of bonding we encounter in the hydrogen molecule and in many other molecules in which *electrons are shared by nuclei* is called **covalent bonding.**

Figure 13.2
The effect of an electric field on hydrogen fluoride molecules. (a) When no electric field is present, the molecules are randomly oriented. (b) When the field is turned on, the molecules tend to line up with their negative ends toward the positive pole and their positive ends toward the negative pole. (This illustration exaggerates the effect. Actually, only a small fraction of the molecules are lined up with the field at a given instant.)

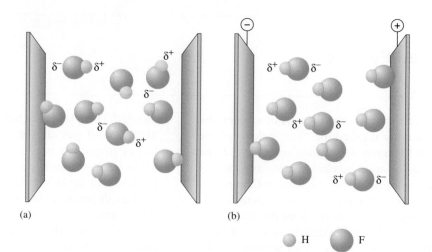

(a)   (b)

H   F

So far we have considered two extreme types of bonding. In ionic bonding the participating atoms are so different that one or more electrons are transferred to form oppositely charged ions. The bonding results from electrostatic interactions among the resulting ions. In covalent bonding two identical atoms share electrons equally. The bonding results from the mutual attraction of the two nuclei for the shared electrons. Between these extremes lie intermediate cases in which the atoms are not so different that electrons are completely transferred but are different enough so that unequal sharing results. These are called **polar covalent bonds.** An example of this type of bond occurs in the hydrogen fluoride (HF) molecule. When a sample of hydrogen fluoride gas is placed in an electric field, the molecules tend to orient themselves as shown in Fig. 13.2, with the fluoride end closest to the positive pole and the hydrogen end closest to the negative pole. This result implies that the HF molecule has the following charge distribution:

$$H\text{—}F$$
$$\delta+ \quad \delta-$$

where δ (delta) is used to indicate a fractional charge. This same effect was noted in Chapter 4, where many of water's unusual properties were attributed to the polar O—H bonds in the H_2O molecule.

The most logical explanation for the development of the partial positive and negative charges on the atoms (bond polarity) in such molecules as HF and H_2O is that the electrons in the bonds are not shared equally. For example, we can account for the polarity of the HF molecule by assuming that the fluorine atom has a stronger attraction for the shared electrons than the hydrogen atom. Similarly, in the H_2O molecule the oxygen atom appears to attract the shared electrons more strongly than the hydrogen atoms. Because bond polarity has important chemical implications, we find it useful to quantify the ability of an atom to attract shared electrons. In the next section we show how this is done.

13.2 | Electronegativity

The different affinities of atoms for the electrons in a bond are described by a property called **electronegativity:** *the ability of an atom in a molecule to attract shared electrons to itself.*

The most widely accepted method for determining electronegativity values is that of Linus Pauling (1901–1995), an American scientist who won Nobel Prizes for both chemistry and peace. To understand Pauling's model, consider a hypothetical molecule HX. The relative electronegativities of the H and X atoms are determined by comparing the measured H—X bond energy with the

Figure 13.3
The Pauling electronegativity values. Electronegativity generally increases across a period and decreases down a group.

"expected" H—X bond energy. The expected bond energy is an "average" (actually the geometric mean) of the H—H and X—X bond energies:

Expected H—X bond energy
$$= [(\text{H—H bond energy})(\text{X—X bond energy})]^{1/2}$$

The difference (Δ) between the actual (measured) and expected bond energies is

$$\Delta = (\text{H—X})_{\text{act}} - (\text{H—X})_{\text{exp}}$$

If H and X have identical electronegativities, $(\text{H—X})_{\text{act}}$ and $(\text{H—X})_{\text{exp}}$ are the same and Δ is 0. On the other hand, if X has a greater electronegativity than H, the shared electron(s) will tend to be closer to the X atom. The molecule will be polar, with the following charge distribution:

$$\underset{\delta+ \quad \delta-}{\text{H—X}}$$

Note that this bond can be viewed as having an ionic as well as a covalent component. The electrostatic attraction between the partially charged H and X atoms will lead to a greater bond strength. Thus $(\text{H—X})_{\text{act}}$ will be larger than $(\text{H—X})_{\text{exp}}$. The greater the difference in the electronegativities of the atoms, the greater is the ionic component of the bond and the greater is the value of Δ. Thus the relative electronegativities of H and X can be assigned from the Δ values.

The actual formula Pauling used to calculate electronegativity (EN) differences is

$$\text{EN(X)} - \text{EN(H)} = 0.102\sqrt{\Delta}$$

where all bond energies are in units of kJ/mol. Pauling then obtained absolute electronegativity values for the elements by assigning a value of 4.0 to fluorine (the element with the highest electronegativity).

Electronegativity values have been determined by this process for virtually all the elements; the results are given in Fig. 13.3. Note that for the representative elements, electronegativity generally increases from left to right across a period and decreases down a group. The range of electronegativity values is from 4.0 for fluorine to 0.7 for francium.

The relationship between electronegativity and bond type is shown in Table 13.1. For identical atoms (electronegativity difference of zero), the electrons in the bond are shared equally and no polarity occurs. When two atoms

The factor of 0.102 is a conversion factor between kJ and eV (the units originally used by Pauling).

Table 13.1

The Relationship Between Electronegativity and Bond Type

Electronegativity Difference in the Bonding Atoms	Bond Type
Zero	Covalent
↓	↓
Intermediate	Polar covalent
↓	↓
Large	Ionic

with widely differing electronegativities interact, electron transfer usually occurs, producing ions—an ionic substance is formed. Intermediate cases give polar covalent bonds with unequal electron sharing.

ⓌWL INTERACTIVE EXAMPLE 13.1

Arrange the following bonds according to increasing polarity: H—H, O—H, Cl—H, S—H, and F—H.

Solution The polarity of the bond increases as the difference in electronegativity increases. From the electronegativity values in Fig. 13.3, the following variation in bond polarity is expected (the Pauling electronegativity value appears in parentheses below each element):

$$H—H < S—H < Cl—H < O—H < F—H$$

(2.2)(2.2)   (2.6)(2.2)   (3.2)(2.2)   (3.4)(2.2)   (4.0)(2.2)

| Electronegativity difference | 0 | 0.4 | 1.1 | 1.2 | 1.8 |

Covalent bond ⎯⎯⎯⎯⎯⎯→ polar covalent bond
Polarity increases

Table 13.2

A Comparison of Pauling's and Allen's Electronegativity Values for Selected Representative Elements

Atom	Pauling	Allen
H	2.20	2.300
Li	0.98	0.912
Be	1.57	1.576
B	2.04	2.051
C	2.55	2.544
N	3.04	3.066
O	3.44	3.610
F	3.98	4.193
Ne	—	4.787
Cl	3.16	2.869
Br	2.96	2.685
I	2.66	2.359

Although Pauling's electronegativity values are the ones most commonly found in textbooks, several other systems for obtaining electronegativity values have been proposed. Recently, Leland C. Allen of Princeton University has pioneered an electronegativity scale based on the average ionization energies of the valence electrons for a given atom. Allen's system allows calculation of an electronegativity value for an atom that is independent of its bonding environment. In this system electronegativity becomes a property of the isolated atom. This approach is fundamentally different from Pauling's system, which is derived from the bond energies of atoms attached to one another.

Although we will not consider the details of Allen's quantum mechanical analysis, it is useful to compare Allen's and Pauling's values for some of the more important representative elements (Table 13.2). While many values are similar, some significant differences appear.

Allen has made a strong case that his system for obtaining electronegativities is more meaningful than that created by Pauling. Allen's values are now becoming accepted by the chemical community.

13.3 | Bond Polarity and Dipole Moments

We have seen that when hydrogen fluoride is placed in an electric field, the molecules have a preferential orientation (Fig. 13.2). This follows from the charge distribution in the HF molecule, which has a positive end and a negative end. A molecule such as HF that has a center of positive charge and a center of negative charge is said to be *dipolar*, or to have a **dipole moment**. A molecule that has a positive center of charge of magnitude Q and a negative center of charge of magnitude Q separated by a distance R has a dipole moment given by the expression

$$\text{Dipole moment} = \mu = QR$$

The debye is named after Peter Debye, who pioneered in the measurement of dipole moments.

which has SI units of coulomb meter (C m) but is most often given in units of debye [1 debye (D) = 3.336×10^{-30} C m]. The dipolar character of a molecule is often represented by an arrow pointing to the negative charge center, with the tail of the arrow indicating the positive center of charge:

$$\begin{array}{cc} \rightarrowtail \\ \delta+ \quad\ \delta- \end{array}$$

The dipole moment of a molecule gives useful information about its bonding and electron distribution. For example, the observed dipole moment for HF is 1.83 D. If HF were totally ionic (H^+F^-), the expected dipole moment (symbolized by μ) would be

$$\mu = \underset{\substack{\uparrow \\ \text{Electron} \\ \text{charge}}}{(1.60 \times 10^{-19}\ C)}\underset{\substack{\uparrow \\ \text{H—F bond} \\ \text{distance}}}{(9.17 \times 10^{-11}\ m)}$$

$$= 1.47 \times 10^{-29}\ C\ m = 4.40\ D$$

This calculation shows that HF is not fully ionic, since the measured dipole moment is much less than 4.40 D. We can estimate the ionic character of HF by assuming that the hydrogen has a charge $\delta+$ and the fluorine has a charge $\delta-$. Using the measured dipole moment, we have

$$1.83\ D = (\delta)(9.17 \times 10^{-11}\ m) \times \frac{1\ D}{3.336 \times 10^{-30}\ C\ m}$$

Solving for δ gives 6.66×10^{-20} C. Since the charge on an electron is 1.60×10^{-19} C, each atom in HF has a fractional charge of

$$\frac{6.66 \times 10^{-20}\ C}{1.60 \times 10^{-19}\ C} = 0.416$$

From this argument we might say that HF has 42% ionic bonding. Although this analysis is somewhat oversimplified (it assumes that charge distributions can be represented as point charges, for example), it does provide useful information about bonding. Recall that the dipolar character of a molecule is often represented by an arrow pointing to the negative charge center with the tail of the arrow indicating the positive center of charge:

$$\delta+ \qquad\qquad\qquad \delta-$$

Another way to represent the charge distribution in HF is by an electrostatic potential diagram (Fig. 13.4). For this representation the colors of visible light are used to show the variation in charge distribution. Red indicates the most electron-rich region of the molecule, and blue indicates the most electron-poor region.

From what has been said so far, we would expect any diatomic molecule with a polar bond (between atoms with different electronegativities) to exhibit a dipole moment. Although this is generally true, the observed dipole moments of diatomic molecules are sometimes smaller than expected. For example, the carbon monoxide molecule CO has a dipole moment of only 0.11 D, much smaller than expected from the polarity of the CO bond. This discrepancy is most likely caused by the lone pairs of electrons on the atoms, which make large contributions to the dipole moment in opposition to that from the bond polarity. We will not explore the details of this situation here. The dipole moments of some representative diatomic molecules are listed in Table 13.3.

Figure 13.4
An electrostatic potential diagram of HF. Red indicates the most electron-rich area (the fluorine atom) and blue indicates the most electron-poor region (the hydrogen atom).

Table 13.3

The Dipole Moments of Some Diatomic Molecules (gas phase)

Molecule	Dipole Moment (D)
CO	0.112
HF	1.83
HCl	1.11
HBr	0.78
HI	0.38
NaCl	9.00
LiF	6.33
KF	8.60
KBr	10.41

Figure 13.5
(a) The charge distribution in the water molecule. (b) The water molecule in an electric field. (c) The electrostatic potential diagram of the water molecule.

(a) (b) (c)

Figure 13.6
(a) The structure and charge distribution of the ammonia molecule. The polarity of the N—H bonds occurs because nitrogen has a greater electronegativity than hydrogen. (b) The dipole moment of the ammonia molecule oriented in an electric field. (c) The electrostatic potential diagram for ammonia.

(a) (b) (c)

Figure 13.7
(a) The carbon dioxide molecule.
(b) The opposed bond polarities cancel out, and the carbon dioxide molecule has no dipole moment. (c) The electrostatic potential diagram for carbon dioxide.

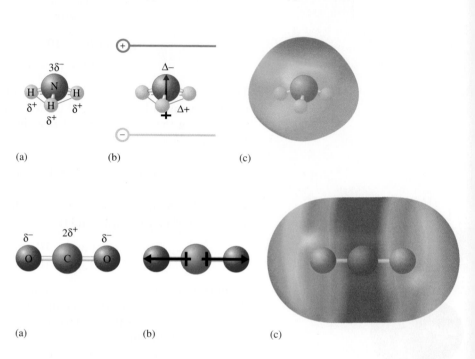

(a) (b) (c)

Polyatomic molecules can also exhibit dipolar behavior. For example, because the oxygen atom in the water molecule has a greater electronegativity than the hydrogen atoms, the molecular charge distribution is that shown in Fig. 13.5(a). This charge distribution causes the water molecule to behave in an electric field as if it had two centers of charge—one positive and one negative—as shown in Fig. 13.5(b). Thus the water molecule has a dipole moment. Similar behavior is observed for the NH_3 molecule (Fig. 13.6). Some molecules have polar bonds but do not have a dipole moment. This occurs when the individual bond polarities are arranged in such a way that they cancel. An example is the CO_2 molecule, a linear molecule that has the charge distribution shown in Fig. 13.7. In this case, since the opposing bond polarities cancel, the carbon dioxide molecule does not have a dipole moment. There is no preferential way for this molecule to line up in an electric field. (Try to find a preferred orientation.)

There are many cases where the bond polarities in molecules oppose and exactly cancel each other. Some common types of molecules with polar bonds but without dipole moments are shown in Table 13.4.

EXAMPLE 13.2

For each of the following molecules, show the direction of the bond polarities. Also indicate which ones have dipole moments: HCl, Cl_2, SO_3 (planar), CH_4 (tetrahedral), and H_2S (V-shaped).

Table 13.4

Types of Molecules with Polar Bonds but No Resulting Dipole Moment

Type		Cancellation of Polar Bonds	Example	Ball-and-Stick Model
Linear molecules with two identical bonds	B—A—B	←—+ +—→	CO_2	
Planar molecules with three identical bonds 120 degrees apart	B ⟋A⟍ B 120° B	↑ ⟋ ⟍	SO_3	
Tetrahedral molecules with four identical bonds 109.5 degrees apart	B ⟍A⟋ B B ⟍ B	↑ ⟋ ⟍ ↓	CCl_4	

Solution **The HCl molecule:** Because the electronegativity of chlorine (3.2) is greater than that of hydrogen (2.2), the chlorine is partially negative, and the hydrogen is partially positive. The HCl molecule has a dipole moment oriented as follows:

$\delta+$ $\delta-$

The Cl_2 molecule: Because the two chlorine atoms share the electrons equally, no bond polarity occurs. The Cl_2 molecule has no dipole moment.

The SO_3 molecule: Because the electronegativity of oxygen (3.4) is greater than that of sulfur (2.6), each oxygen has a partial negative charge, and the sulfur has a partial positive charge:

However, the bond polarities cancel, and the molecule has no dipole moment.

The CH_4 molecule: Carbon has a slightly higher electronegativity (2.6) than hydrogen (2.2). This leads to small partial positive charges on the hydrogen atoms and a small partial negative charge on the carbon:

This case is similar to the third type in Table 13.4. Since the bond polarities cancel, the molecule has no dipole moment.

The H₂S molecule: Since the electronegativity of sulfur (2.6) is greater than that of hydrogen (2.2), the sulfur has a partial negative charge, and the hydrogen atoms have a partial positive charge, which can be represented as follows:

$$\delta+ \; H \qquad\qquad H \; \delta+$$
$$S$$
$$2\delta-$$

This case is analogous to the water molecule. The polar bonds result in a dipole moment oriented as shown.

13.4 | **Ions: Electron Configurations and Sizes**

Atoms in stable compounds usually have a noble gas electron configuration.

The description of the electron arrangements in atoms that emerged from the quantum mechanical model has helped a great deal in our understanding of what constitutes a stable compound. For example, in a very large number of stable compounds, the atoms have noble gas arrangements of electrons. Non-metallic elements achieve a noble gas electron configuration either by sharing electrons with other nonmetals to form covalent bonds or by taking electrons from metals to form ions. In the latter case the nonmetals form anions and the metals form cations. The following generalizations can be applied to the electron configurations in most stable compounds:

As we will see later, there are exceptions to these rules, but they remain a useful place to start.

■ When *two nonmetals* react to form a covalent bond, they share electrons in a way that completes the valence electron configurations of both atoms. That is, both nonmetals attain noble gas electron configurations.

■ When *a nonmetal and a representative group metal* react to form a binary ionic compound, the ions form so that the valence electron configuration of the nonmetal is completed and the valence orbitals of the metal are emptied. In this way both ions achieve noble gas electron configurations.

Although there are some important exceptions, these generalizations apply to the vast majority of compounds and are important to remember. We will deal with covalent bonds more thoroughly later. Next, we will consider what implications these rules hold for ionic compounds.

Predicting Formulas of Ionic Compounds

At the beginning of this discussion, we should emphasize that when chemists use the term *ionic compound,* they are usually referring to the solid state of that compound. Solid ionic compounds contain a large collection of positive and negative ions packed together in a way that minimizes the $\ominus \cdot\cdot \ominus$ and $\oplus \cdot\cdot \oplus$ repulsions and maximizes the $\oplus \cdot\cdot \ominus$ attractions. This situation is in contrast to the gas phase of an ionic substance, where discrete ion pairs exist. Thus, when we speak in this text of the stability of an ionic compound, we are referring to the solid state, where the large attractive forces present among the oppositely charged ions tend to stabilize (favor the formation of) the ions. For example, as we mentioned in the previous chapter, the O^{2-} ion is not stable as

In the solid state of an ionic compound, the ions are relatively close together, and many ions are simultaneously interacting:

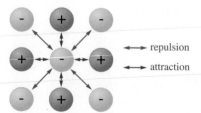

repulsion
attraction

In the gas phase of an ionic substance, the ions would be relatively far apart and would not contain large groups of ions:

an isolated gas-phase species but, of course, is very stable in many solid ionic compounds. That is, MgO(s), which contains Mg^{2+} and O^{2-} ions, is very stable, but the isolated gas-phase ion pair $Mg^{2+} \cdot \cdot O^{2-}$ is not energetically favorable in comparison with the separate neutral gaseous atoms. Thus you should keep in mind that in this section, and in most other cases in which we are describing the nature of ionic compounds, the discussion usually refers to the solid state, in which many ions are simultaneously interacting.

To illustrate the principles of electron configurations in stable, solid ionic compounds, we will consider the formation of an ionic compound from calcium and oxygen. We can predict what compound will form by considering the valence electron configurations of the two atoms:

$$Ca: \quad [Ar]4s^2$$

$$O: \quad [He]2s^22p^4$$

From Fig. 13.3 we see that the electronegativity of oxygen (3.4) is much greater than that of calcium (1.0). Because of this large difference, electrons will be transferred from calcium to oxygen to form oxygen anions and calcium cations in the compound. How many electrons are transferred? We can base our prediction on the observation that noble gas configurations are generally the most stable. Note that oxygen needs two electrons to fill its $2s$ and $2p$ valence orbitals and to achieve the configuration of neon ($1s^22s^22p^6$). And by losing two electrons, calcium can achieve the configuration of argon. Two electrons are therefore transferred:

$$Ca + O \longrightarrow Ca^{2+} + O^{2-}$$
$$\underbrace{}_{2e^-}$$

To predict the formula of the ionic compound, we simply recognize that chemical compounds are always electrically neutral—they have the same quantities of positive and negative charges. In this case we must have equal numbers of Ca^{2+} and O^{2-} ions, and the empirical formula of the compound is CaO.

The same principles can be applied to many other cases. For example, consider the compound formed between aluminum and oxygen. Because aluminum has the configuration $[Ne]3s^23p^1$, it must lose three electrons to form the Al^{3+} ion and thus achieve the neon configuration. Therefore, the Al^{3+} and O^{2-} ions form in this case. Since the compound must be electrically neutral, there must be three O^{2-} ions for every two Al^{3+} ions, and the compound has the empirical formula Al_2O_3.

Table 13.5 shows common elements that form ions with noble gas electron configurations in ionic compounds. In losing electrons to form cations, metals in Group 1A lose one electron, those in Group 2A lose two electrons, and those in Group 3A lose three electrons. In gaining electrons to form anions, nonmetals in Group 7A (the halogens) gain one electron, and those in Group 6A gain

Table 13.5

Common Ions with Noble Gas Electron Configurations in Ionic Compounds

Group 1A	Group 2A	Group 3A	Group 6A	Group 7A	Electron Configuration
H^-, Li^+	Be^{2+}				[He]
Na^+	Mg^{2+}	Al^{3+}	O^{2-}	F^-	[Ne]
K^+	Ca^{2+}		S^{2-}	Cl^-	[Ar]
Rb^+	Sr^{2+}		Se^{2-}	Br^-	[Kr]
Cs^+	Ba^{2+}		Te^{2-}	I^-	[Xe]

two electrons. Hydrogen typically behaves as a nonmetal and can gain one electron to form the hydride ion (H^-), which has the electron configuration of helium.

There are some important exceptions to the rules discussed here. For example, tin forms both Sn^{2+} and Sn^{4+} ions, and lead forms both Pb^{2+} and Pb^{4+} ions. Also, bismuth forms Bi^{3+} and Bi^{5+} ions, and thallium forms Tl^+ and Tl^{3+} ions. There are no simple explanations for the behavior of these ions. For now, just note them as exceptions to the very useful rule that ions generally adopt noble gas electron configurations in ionic compounds. Our discussion here refers to representative metals. The transition metals exhibit more complicated behavior, forming a variety of ions that will be considered in Chapter 19.

Sizes of Ions

Ion size plays an important role in determining the structure and stability of ionic solids, the properties of ions in aqueous solution, and the biological effects of ions. As with atoms, it is impossible to define precisely the sizes of ions. Most often, ionic radii are determined from the measured distances between ion centers in ionic compounds. This method, of course, involves an assumption about how the distance should be divided up between the two ions. Thus you will note considerable disagreement among ionic sizes given in various sources. Here we are mainly interested in trends and will be less concerned with absolute ion sizes.

Various factors influence ionic size. We will first consider the relative sizes of an ion and its parent atom. Since a positive ion is formed by removing electrons from a neutral atom, the resulting cation is smaller than its parent atom. The opposite is true for negative ions; the addition of electrons to a neutral atom produces an anion significantly larger than its parent atom.

It is also important to know how the sizes of ions vary depending on the positions of the parent elements in the periodic table. Figure 13.8 shows the sizes of the most important ions (each with a noble gas configuration) and their position in the periodic table. Note that ion size increases down a group. The changes that occur horizontally are complicated because of the change from predominantly metals on the left-hand side of the periodic table to nonmetals on the right-hand side. A given period thus contains both elements that give up electrons to form cations and ones that accept electrons to form anions.

One trend worth noting involves the relative sizes of a set of **isoelectronic ions**—*ions containing the same number of electrons.* Consider the ions O^{2-}, F^-, Na^+, Mg^{2+}, and Al^{3+}. Each of these ions has the neon electron configuration. How do the sizes of these ions vary? In general, there are two important facts to consider in predicting the relative sizes of ions: the number of electrons and the number of protons. Since these ions are isoelectronic, the number of electrons is 10 in each case. Electron repulsions should therefore be about the same in all cases. However, the number of protons increases from 8 to 13 as we go from the O^{2-} ion to the Al^{3+} ion. Thus, in going from O^{2-} to Al^{3+}, the 10 electrons experience a greater attraction as the positive charge on the nucleus increases. This causes the ions to become smaller. You can confirm this by looking at Fig. 13.8. In general, for a series of isoelectronic ions, the size decreases as the nuclear charge (Z) increases.

For isoelectronic ions, size generally decreases as Z increases.

ⓌWL INTERACTIVE EXAMPLE 13.3

Arrange the ions Se^{2-}, Br^-, Rb^+, and Sr^{2+} in order of decreasing size.

Solution This is an isoelectronic series of ions with the krypton electron configuration. Since these ions all have the same number of electrons, their sizes

Figure 13.8
Sizes of ions related to positions of elements in the periodic table. Note that size generally increases down a group. Also note that in a series of isoelectronic ions, size decreases with increasing atomic number. The ionic radii are given in units of picometers.

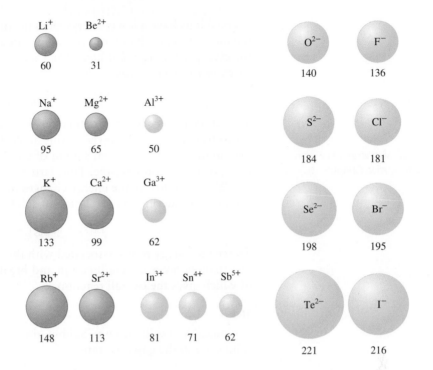

will depend on nuclear charge. The Z values are 34 for Se^{2-}, 35 for Br^-, 37 for Rb^+, and 38 for Sr^{2+}. Since the nuclear charge is greatest for Sr^{2+}, it is the smallest of these ions. The Se^{2-} ion is largest.

$$Se^{2-} > Br^- > Rb^+ > Sr^{2+}$$
↑   ↑
Largest   Smallest

◆WL INTERACTIVE EXAMPLE 13.4

Choose the largest ion in each of the following groups.

a. $Li^+, Na^+, K^+, Rb^+, Cs^+$ **b.** $Ba^{2+}, Cs^+, I^-, Te^{2-}$

Solution

a. The ions are all from Group 1A elements. Since size increases down a group (the ion with the greatest number of electrons is the largest), Cs^+ is the largest ion.

b. This is an isoelectronic series of ions, all of which have the xenon electron configuration. The ion with the smallest nuclear charge is the largest ion.

$$Te^{2-} > I^- > Cs^+ > Ba^{2+}$$
$Z = 52$ $Z = 53$ $Z = 55$ $Z = 56$

Ion size generally increases down a group.

13.5 | Formation of Binary Ionic Compounds

In this section we will introduce the factors that influence the stability and the structures of solid binary ionic compounds. We know that metals and nonmetals react by transferring electrons to form cations and anions that are mutually attractive. The resulting ionic solid forms because the aggregated oppositely charged ions have a lower energy than the original elements. Just how strongly the ions attract each other in the solid state is indicated by the **lattice energy**— *the change in energy that takes place when separated gaseous ions are packed together to form an ionic solid:*

$$M^+(g) + X^-(g) \longrightarrow MX(s)$$

The lattice energy is often defined as the energy *released* when an ionic solid forms from its ions. However, in this book the sign of an energy term is always determined from the system's point of view: negative if the process is exothermic; positive if endothermic. Thus lattice energy has a negative sign.

We can illustrate the energy changes involved in the formation of an ionic solid by considering the formation of solid lithium fluoride from its elements:

$$Li(s) + \tfrac{1}{2}F_2(g) \longrightarrow LiF(s)$$

To see the energy terms associated with this process, we take advantage of the fact that energy is a state function and break this reaction into steps, the sum of which gives the overall reaction.

The structures of ionic solids will be discussed in detail in Chapter 16.

Step 1

Sublimation of solid lithium. Sublimation involves taking a substance from the solid state to the gaseous state:

$$Li(s) \longrightarrow Li(g)$$

The enthalpy of sublimation for $Li(s)$ is 161 kJ/mol.

Step 2

Ionization of lithium atoms to form Li^+ ions in the gas phase:

$$Li(g) \longrightarrow Li^+(g) + e^-$$

This process corresponds to the first ionization energy for lithium, which is 520 kJ/mol.

Step 3

Dissociation of fluorine molecules. We need to form 1 mole of fluorine atoms by breaking the F—F bonds in 0.5 mole of F_2 molecules:

$$\tfrac{1}{2}F_2(g) \longrightarrow F(g)$$

The energy required to break this bond is 154 kJ/mol. In this case we are breaking the bonds in a half mole of fluorine, so the energy required for this step is 154 kJ/2, or 77 kJ.

Step 4

Formation of F^- ions from fluorine atoms in the gas phase:

$$F(g) + e^- \longrightarrow F^-(g)$$

The energy change for this process corresponds to the electron affinity of fluorine, which is -328 kJ/mol.

Step 5

Formation of solid lithium fluoride from the gaseous Li^+ and F^- ions:

$$Li^+(g) + F^-(g) \longrightarrow LiF(s)$$

This corresponds to the lattice energy for LiF, which is -1047 kJ/mol.

Figure 13.9
The energy changes involved in the formation of solid lithium fluoride from its elements. The numbers in parentheses refer to the reaction steps discussed in the text.

Since the sum of these five processes yields the desired overall reaction, the sum of the individual energy changes gives the overall energy change:

Process	Energy Change (kJ)
$Li(s) \rightarrow Li(g)$	161
$Li(g) \rightarrow Li^+(g) + e^-$	520
$\frac{1}{2}F_2(g) \rightarrow F(g)$	77
$F(g) + e^- \rightarrow F^-(g)$	−328
$Li^+(g) + F^-(g) \rightarrow LiF(s)$	−1047
Overall: $Li(s) + \frac{1}{2}F_2(g) \rightarrow LiF(s)$	−617 kJ (per mole of LiF)

In doing this calculation, we have ignored the small difference between ΔH_{sub} and ΔE_{sub}.

This process is summarized by the energy diagram in Fig. 13.9. Note that the formation of solid lithium fluoride from its elements is highly exothermic mainly because of the very large negative lattice energy. A great deal of energy is released when the ions combine to form the solid. In fact, note that the energy released when an electron is added to a fluorine atom to form the F^- ion (328 kJ/mol) is not enough to remove an electron from lithium (520 kJ/mol). That is, when a metallic lithium atom reacts with a nonmetallic fluorine atom to form *separated* ions,

$$Li(g) + F(g) \longrightarrow Li^+(g) + F^-(g)$$

the process is endothermic and thus unfavorable. Clearly, then, the main impetus for the formation of the ionic compound rather than a covalent compound results from the strong mutual attractions among the Li^+ and F^- ions in the solid. The lattice energy is the dominant energy term.

The structure of the solid lithium fluoride is represented in Fig. 13.10. Note the alternating arrangement of the Li^+ and F^- ions. Also note that each Li^+ is surrounded by six F^- ions and each F^- ion is surrounded by six Li^+ ions. This structure can be rationalized by assuming that the ions behave as hard spheres that pack together in a way that both maximizes the attractions among the oppositely charged ions and minimizes the repulsions among the identically charged ions.

All the binary ionic compounds formed by an alkali metal and a halogen have the structure shown in Fig. 13.10, except for the cesium salts. The ar-

(a)

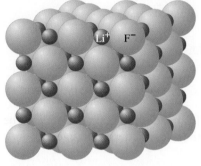

Li⁺   F⁻

(b)

Figure 13.10
The structure of lithium fluoride.
(a) Represented by a ball-and-stick
model. Note that each Li⁺ ion is surrounded by six F⁻ ions, and each
F⁻ ion is surrounded by six Li⁺ ions.
(b) Represented with the ions shown as
spheres. The structure is determined by
packing the spherical ions in a way that
both maximizes the ionic attractions
and minimizes the ionic repulsions.

Since the equation for lattice energy
contains the product Q_1Q_2, the lattice
energy for a solid with 2+ and 2− ions
should be four times that for a solid
with 1+ and 1− ions. That is,

$$\frac{(+2)(-2)}{(+1)(-1)} = 4$$

For MgO and NaF, the observed ratio
of lattice energies (Fig. 13.11) is

$$\frac{-3916 \text{ kJ}}{-923 \text{ kJ}} = 4.24$$

rangement of ions shown in Fig. 13.10 is often called the *sodium chloride structure,* after the most common substance that possesses it.

Lattice Energy Calculations

In discussing the energetics of the formation of solid lithium fluoride, we emphasized the importance of lattice energy in contributing to the stability of the ionic solid. Lattice energy can be represented by a modified form of Coulomb's law,

$$\text{Lattice energy} = k\left(\frac{Q_1Q_2}{r}\right)$$

where k is a proportionality constant that depends on the structure of the solid and the electron configurations of the ions, Q_1 and Q_2 are the charges on the ions, and r is the shortest distance between the centers of the cations and anions. Note that the lattice energy has a negative sign when Q_1 and Q_2 have opposite signs. This result is expected, since bringing cations and anions together is an exothermic process. Also note that the process becomes more exothermic as the ionic charges increase and as the distances between the ions in the solid decrease.

The importance of the charges in ionic solids can be illustrated by comparing the energies involved in the formation of NaF(*s*) and MgO(*s*). These solids contain the isoelectric ions Na⁺, F⁻, Mg²⁺, and O²⁻. The energy diagram for the formation of the two solids is given in Fig. 13.11. Note several important features:

The energy released when the gaseous Mg²⁺ and O²⁻ ions combine to form solid MgO is much greater (more than four times greater) than that released when the gaseous Na⁺ and F⁻ ions combine to form solid NaF.

The energy required to remove two electrons from the magnesium atom (735 kJ/mol for the first and 1445 kJ/mol for the second, yielding a total of 2180 kJ/mol) is much greater than the energy required to remove an electron from a sodium atom (495 kJ/mol).

Energy (737 kJ/mol) is required to add two electrons to the oxygen atom in the gas phase. Addition of the first electron is exothermic (−141 kJ/mol), but addition of the second electron is quite endothermic (878 kJ/mol). This latter energy must be obtained indirectly, since the O²⁻(*g*) is not stable.

Because twice as much energy is required to remove the second electron from magnesium as to remove the first, and because addition of an electron to the gaseous O⁻ ion is quite endothermic, it seems puzzling that magnesium oxide contains Mg²⁺ and O²⁻ ions rather than Mg⁺ and O⁻ ions. The answer lies in the lattice energy. Note that the lattice energy for combining gaseous Mg²⁺ and O²⁻ ions to form MgO(*s*) is 3000 kJ/mol more negative than that for combining gaseous Na⁺ and F⁻ ions to form NaF(*s*). Thus the energy released in forming a solid containing Mg²⁺ and O²⁻ ions rather than Mg⁺ and O⁻ ions more than compensates for the energies required for the processes that produce the Mg²⁺ and O²⁻ ions.

If there is so much lattice energy to be gained in going from singly charged to doubly charged ions in the case of magnesium oxide, why then does solid sodium fluoride contain Na⁺ and F⁻ ions rather than Na²⁺ and F²⁻ ions? We can answer this question by recognizing that both Na⁺ and F⁻ ions have the neon electron configuration. Removal of an electron from Na⁺ requires an extremely large quantity of energy (4560 kJ/mol) because a 2*p* electron must be removed. Conversely, the addition of an electron to F⁻ would require use of the relatively high-energy 3*s* orbital, which is also an unfavorable process. Thus we

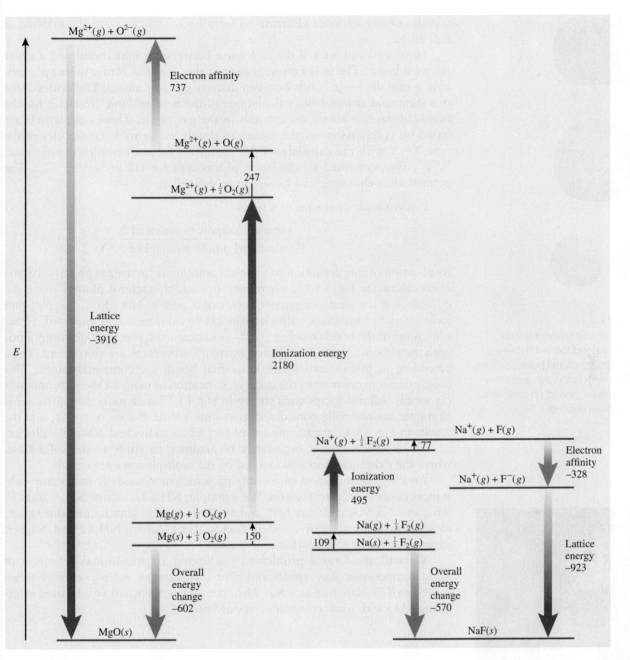

Figure 13.11

Comparison of the energy changes involved in the formation of solid sodium fluoride and solid magnesium oxide. Note the large lattice energy for magnesium oxide (where doubly charged ions are combining) compared with that for sodium fluoride (where singly charged ions are combining).

can say that for sodium fluoride the extra energy required to form the doubly charged ions is greater than the gain in lattice energy that would result.

This discussion of the energies involved in the formation of solid ionic compounds illustrates that a variety of factors operate to determine the composition and structure of these compounds. The most important of these factors involve the balancing of the energies required to form highly charged ions and the energy released when highly charged ions combine to form the solid.

13.6 | Partial Ionic Character of Covalent Bonds

Recall that when atoms with different electronegativities react to form molecules, the electrons are not shared equally. The possible result is a polar covalent bond or, in the case of a large electronegativity difference, a complete

(a)

(b)

(c)

Figure 13.12

The three possible types of bonds: (a) a covalent bond formed between identical F atoms; (b) the polar covalent bond of HF, with both ionic and covalent components; and (c) an ionic bond with no electron sharing.

Molten NaCl conducts an electric current, indicating the presence of mobile Na^+ and Cl^- ions.

transfer of one or more electrons to form ions. The cases are summarized in Fig. 13.12.

How well can we tell the difference between an ionic bond and a polar covalent bond? The only honest answer to this question is that there are probably no totally ionic bonds between *discrete pairs of atoms*. The evidence for this statement comes from calculations of the percent ionic character for the bonds of various binary compounds in the gas phase. These calculations are based on comparisons of the measured dipole moments for molecules of the type X—Y with the calculated dipole moments for the completely ionic case, X^+Y^-. We performed a calculation of this type for HF in Section 13.3. The percent ionic character of a bond can be defined as

Percent ionic character of a bond

$$= \left(\frac{\text{measured dipole moment of X—Y}}{\text{calculated dipole moment of } X^+Y^-} \right) \times 100\%$$

Application of this definition to various compounds (in the gas phase) gives the results shown in Fig. 13.13, where percent ionic character is plotted versus the difference in the electronegativity values of X and Y. Note from this plot that ionic character increases with electronegativity difference, as expected. However, none of the bonds reaches 100% ionic character, even though compounds with the maximum possible electronegativity differences are considered. Thus, according to this definition, no individual bonds are completely ionic. This conclusion is in contrast to the usual classification of many of these compounds (as solids). All the compounds shown in Fig. 13.13 with more than 50% ionic character are normally considered to be ionic solids. Recall, however, that the results in Fig. 13.13 are for the gas phase, where individual XY molecules exist. These results cannot necessarily be assumed to apply to the solid state, where the existence of ions is favored by the multiple ion interactions.

Another complication in identifying ionic compounds is that many substances contain polyatomic ions. For example, NH_4Cl contains NH_4^+ and Cl^- ions, and Na_2SO_4 contains Na^+ and SO_4^{2-} ions. The ammonium and sulfate ions are held together by covalent bonds. Thus, calling NH_4Cl and Na_2SO_4 ionic compounds is somewhat ambiguous.

We will avoid these problems by adopting an operational definition of ionic compounds: *Any compound that conducts an electric current when melted will be classified as ionic.* Also, the generic term *salt* will be used interchangeably with *ionic compound* in this book.

Figure 13.13

The relationship between the ionic character of a covalent bond and the electronegativity difference of the bonded atoms. The compounds normally considered to be ionic in the solid phase are shown in red.

13.7 | **The Covalent Chemical Bond: A Model**

Before we develop specific models for covalent chemical bonding, it will be helpful to summarize some of the concepts introduced in this chapter.

What is a chemical bond? Chemical bonds can be viewed as forces that cause a group of atoms to behave as a unit.

Why do chemical bonds occur? There is no principle of nature that states that bonds are favored or disfavored. Bonds are neither inherently "good" nor inherently "bad" as far as nature is concerned; they result from the tendency of a system to seek its lowest possible energy. From a simplistic point of view, bonds occur when collections of atoms are more stable (lower in energy) than the separate atoms. For example, about 1652 kJ of energy is required to break a mole of methane (CH_4) molecules into separate C and H atoms. Or, taking the opposite view, 1652 kJ of energy is released when 1 mole of methane is formed from 1 mole of gaseous C atoms and 4 moles of gaseous H atoms. Thus we can say that 1 mole of CH_4 molecules in the gas phase is 1652 kJ lower in energy than 1 mole of carbon atoms plus 4 moles of hydrogen atoms. Methane is therefore a stable molecule relative to its separated atoms.

We find it useful to interpret molecular stability in terms of a model called a chemical bond. To help understand why this model was invented, let's continue with methane, which consists of four hydrogen atoms arranged at the corners of a tetrahedron around a carbon atom:

A tetrahedron has four equal triangular faces.

Given this structure, it is natural to envision four individual C—H interactions (we call them bonds). The energy of stabilization of CH_4 is divided equally among the four bonds to give an average C—H bond energy per mole of C—H bonds:

$$\frac{1652 \text{ kJ}}{4} = 413 \text{ kJ}$$

Next, consider methyl chloride, which consists of CH_3Cl molecules having the structure

Experiments have shown that about 1578 kJ of energy is required to break down 1 mole of gaseous CH_3Cl molecules into gaseous carbon, chlorine, and hydrogen atoms. The reverse process can be represented as

$$C(g) + Cl(g) + 3H(g) \longrightarrow CH_3Cl(g) + 1578 \text{ kJ/mol}$$

A mole of gaseous methyl chloride is lower in energy by 1578 kJ than its separate gaseous atoms. Thus a mole of methyl chloride is held together by 1578 kJ of energy. Again, it is very useful to divide this energy into individual bonds. Methyl chloride can be visualized as containing one C—Cl bond and three C—H bonds. If we assume arbitrarily that a C—H interaction represents the same quantity of energy in any situation (that is, the strength of a

C—H bond is independent of its molecular environment), we can do the following bookkeeping:

$$1 \text{ mol of C—Cl bonds plus 3 mol of C—H bonds} = 1578 \text{ kJ}$$

$$\text{C—Cl bond energy} + 3(\text{average C—H bond energy}) = 1578 \text{ kJ}$$

$$\text{C—Cl bond energy} + 3(413 \text{ kJ/mol}) = 1578 \text{ kJ}$$

$$\text{C—Cl bond energy} = 1578 - 1239 = 339 \text{ kJ/mol}$$

These assumptions allow us to associate given quantities of energy with C—H and C—Cl bonds.

It is important to note that the bond concept is a human invention. Bonds provide a method for dividing up the energy evolved when a stable molecule is formed from its component atoms. Thus in this context *a bond represents a quantity of energy* obtained from the molecular energy of stabilization in a rather arbitrary way. This is not to say that the concept of individual bonds is a bad idea. In fact, the modern concept of the chemical bond, conceived by American chemists G. N. Lewis and Linus Pauling, is one of the most useful ideas chemists have ever developed.

Models: An Overview

The framework of chemistry, like that of any science, consists of models—attempts to explain how nature operates on the microscopic level based on experiences in the macroscopic world. To understand chemistry, one must understand its models and how they are used. We will use the concept of bonding to reemphasize the important characteristics of models, including their origin, structure, and uses.

Models originate from our observations of the properties of nature. For example, the concept of bonds arose from the observations that most chemical processes involve collections of atoms and that chemical reactions involve rearrangements of the ways in which the atoms are grouped. So to understand reactions, we must understand the forces that bind atoms together.

In natural processes there is a tendency toward lower energy. Collections of atoms therefore occur because the aggregated state has lower energy than

Bonding is a model proposed to explain molecular stability.

The concept of individual bonds makes it much easier to deal with complex molecules such as DNA. A small segment of a DNA molecule is shown here.

Will & Deni McIntyre/Photo Researchers

A ball-and-stick model of a protein segment illustrating the alpha helix.

the separated atoms. Why? As we have seen earlier in this chapter, the best explanations for the energy change involve atoms sharing electrons or atoms transferring electrons to become ions. In the case of electron sharing, we find it convenient to assume that individual bonds occur between pairs of atoms. Let's explore the validity of this assumption and see how it is useful.

In a diatomic molecule such as H_2, it is natural to assume that a bond exists between the atoms, holding them together. It is also useful to assume that individual bonds are present in polyatomic molecules such as CH_4. So instead of thinking of CH_4 as a unit with a stabilization energy of 1652 kJ per mole, we choose to think of CH_4 as containing four C—H bonds, each worth 413 kJ of energy per mole of bonds. Without this concept of individual bonds in molecules, chemistry would be hopelessly complicated. There are millions of different chemical compounds, and if each of these compounds had to be considered as an entirely new entity, the task of understanding chemical behavior would be overwhelming.

The bonding model provides a framework to systematize chemical behavior by enabling us to think of molecules as collections of common fundamental components. For example, a typical biomolecule, such as a protein, contains hundreds of atoms and might seem discouragingly complex. However, if we think of a protein as constructed of individual bonds, C—C, C—H, C—N, C—O, N—H, and so on, it helps tremendously in predicting and understanding the protein's behavior. The essential idea is that we expect a given bond to behave about the same in any molecular environment. Used in this way, the model of the chemical bond has helped chemists to systematize the reactions of the millions of existing compounds.

Fundamental Properties of Models

1. Models are human inventions, always based on an incomplete understanding of how nature works. *A model does not equal reality.*

2. Models are often wrong. This property derives from the first property. Models are based on speculation and are always oversimplifications.

3. Models tend to become more complicated as they age. As flaws are discovered in our models, we "patch" them and thus add more detail.

4. It is very important to understand the assumptions that are inherent in a particular model before you use it to interpret observations or to make predictions. Simple methods usually involve very restrictive assumptions and can be expected to yield only qualitative information. Asking for a sophisticated explanation from a simple model is like expecting to get an accurate mass for a diamond by using a bathroom scale.

   For a model to be used effectively, we must understand its strengths and weaknesses and ask only appropriate questions. An illustration of this point is the simple aufbau principle used to explain the electron configurations of the elements. Although this model correctly predicts the configuration for most atoms, chromium and copper do not agree with the predictions. Detailed studies show that the configurations of chromium and copper result from complex electron interactions that are not taken into account in the simple model. However, this does not mean that we should discard the simple model that is so useful for most atoms. Instead, we must apply it with caution and not expect it to be correct in every case.

5. When a model is wrong, we often learn much more than when it is right. If a model makes a wrong prediction, it usually means we do not understand some fundamental characteristics of nature. We often learn by making mistakes. (Try to remember that when you get back your next chemistry test.)

In addition to being very useful, the bonding model is physically sensible. It makes sense that atoms can form stable groups by sharing electrons; shared electrons give a lower energy state because they are simultaneously attracted by two nuclei.

Also, as we will see in the next section, bond energy data support the existence of discrete bonds that are relatively independent of the molecular environment. It is very important to remember, however, that the chemical bond is only a model. Although our concept of discrete bonds in molecules agrees with many of our observations, some molecular properties require that we think of a molecule as a whole, with the electrons free to move through the entire molecule. This is called *delocalization* of the electrons, a concept that will be discussed more completely in the next chapter.

13.8 | Covalent Bond Energies and Chemical Reactions

In this section we will consider the energies associated with various types of bonds and see how the bonding concept is useful in dealing with the energies of chemical reactions. One important consideration is to establish the sensitivity of a particular type of bond to its molecular environment. For example, consider the stepwise decomposition of methane:

Process	Energy Required (kJ/mol)
$CH_4(g) \rightarrow CH_3(g) + H(g)$	435
$CH_3(g) \rightarrow CH_2(g) + H(g)$	453
$CH_2(g) \rightarrow CH(g) + H(g)$	425
$CH(g) \rightarrow C(g) + H(g)$	339
	Total = 1652

$$\text{Average} = \frac{1652}{4} = 413$$

Although a C—H bond is broken in each case, the energy required varies in a nonsystematic way. This example shows that the C—H bond is somewhat sensitive to its environment. We use the *average* of these individual bond dissociation energies even though this quantity only approximates the energy associated with a C—H bond in a particular molecule. The degree of sensitivity of a bond to its environment can also be seen from experimental measurements of the energy required to break the C—H bond in the following molecules:

Molecule	Measured C—H Bond Energy (kJ/mol)
$HCBr_3$	380
$HCCl_3$	380
HCF_3	430
C_2H_6	410

These data show that the C—H bond strength varies significantly with its environment, but the concept of an average C—H bond strength remains useful to chemists. The average values of bond energies for various types of bonds are listed in Table 13.6.

So far we have discussed bonds in which one pair of electrons is shared. This type of bond is called a **single bond**. As we will see in more detail later, atoms sometimes share two pairs of electrons, forming a **double bond,** or share

Table 13.6

Average Bond Energies (kJ/mol)

				Single Bonds					Multiple Bonds	
H—H	432	N—H	391	I—I	149			C=C	614
H—F	565	N—N	160	I—Cl	208			C≡C	839
H—Cl	427	N—F	272	I—Br	175			O=O	495
H—Br	363	N—Cl	200					C=O*	745
H—I	295	N—Br	243			S—H	347	C≡O	1072
		N—O	201			S—F	327	N=O	607
C—H	413	O—H	467			S—Cl	253	N=N	418
C—C	347	O—O	146			S—Br	218	N≡N	941
C—N	305	O—F	190			S—S	266	C=N	615
C—O	358	O—Cl	203					C≡N	891
C—F	485	O—I	234			Si—Si	340		
C—Cl	339					Si—H	393		
C—Br	276	F—F	154			Si—C	360		
C—I	240	F—Cl	253			Si—O	452		
C—S	259	F—Br	237						
		Cl—Cl	239						
		Cl—Br	218						
		Br—Br	193						

*C=O (CO_2) = 799

three pairs of electrons, forming a **triple bond.** The bond energies for these *multiple bonds* are also given in Table 13.6.

A relationship also exists between the number of shared electron pairs and the bond length. As the number of shared electrons increases, the bond length shortens. This relationship is shown for selected bonds in Table 13.7.

Bond Energy and Enthalpy

Bond energy values can be used to calculate approximate energies for reactions. To illustrate how this is done, we will calculate the change in energy that accompanies the following reaction:

$$H_2(g) + F_2(g) \longrightarrow 2HF(g)$$

This reaction involves breaking one H—H and one F—F bond and forming two H—F bonds. For bonds to be broken, energy must be *added* to the system— an endothermic process. Consequently, the energy terms associated with bond breaking have *positive* signs. The formation of a bond *releases* energy, an exo-

Table 13.7

Bond Lengths for Selected Bonds

Bond	Bond Type	Bond Length (pm)	Bond Energy (kJ/mol)
C—C	Single	154	347
C=C	Double	134	614
C≡C	Triple	120	839
C—O	Single	143	358
C=O	Double	123	745
C—N	Single	143	305
C=N	Double	138	615
C≡N	Triple	116	891

thermic process, and the energy terms associated with bond making carry a *negative* sign. We can write the enthalpy change for a reaction as follows:

ΔH = sum of the energies required to break old bonds (positive signs) plus the sum of the energies released in the formation of new bonds (negative signs)

This leads to the expression

$$\Delta H = \underbrace{\Sigma\, D \text{ (bonds broken)}}_{\text{Energy required}} - \underbrace{\Sigma\, D \text{ (bonds formed)}}_{\text{Energy released}}$$

where Σ represents the sum of terms and D represents the bond energy per mole of bonds. (D *always* has a positive sign.)

In the case of the formation of HF,

$$\Delta H = D_{H-H} + D_{F-F} - 2D_{H-F}$$

$$= 1 \text{ mol} \times \frac{432 \text{ kJ}}{\text{mol}} + 1 \text{ mol} \times \frac{154 \text{ kJ}}{\text{mol}} - 2 \text{ mol} \times \frac{565 \text{ kJ}}{\text{mol}}$$

$$= -544 \text{ kJ}$$

Thus, when 1 mole of $H_2(g)$ and 1 mole of $F_2(g)$ react to form 2 moles of HF(g), 544 kJ of energy should be released.

This result can be compared with the calculation of ΔH for this reaction from the standard enthalpy of formation for HF (-271 kJ/mol):

$$\Delta H = 2 \text{ mol} \times (-271 \text{ kJ/mol}) = -542 \text{ kJ}$$

Thus the use of bond energies to calculate ΔH works quite well in this case.

Since bond energies are typically averages taken from several compounds, the ΔH calculated from bond energies is not expected to agree exactly with that calculated from enthalpies of formation.

OWL INTERACTIVE EXAMPLE 13.5

Using the bond energies listed in Table 13.6, calculate ΔH for the reaction of methane with chlorine and fluorine to give Freon-12 (CF_2Cl_2).

$$CH_4(g) + 2Cl_2(g) + 2F_2(g) \longrightarrow CF_2Cl_2(g) + 2HF(g) + 2HCl(g)$$

Solution The idea here is to break the bonds in the reactants to give individual atoms and then assemble these atoms into the products by forming new bonds:

$$\text{Reactants} \xrightarrow[\text{required}]{\text{Energy}} \text{atoms} \xrightarrow[\text{released}]{\text{Energy}} \text{products}$$

We then combine the energy changes to calculate ΔH:

$$\Delta H = \begin{matrix}\text{energy required}\\\text{to break bonds}\end{matrix} - \begin{matrix}\text{energy released}\\\text{when bonds form}\end{matrix}$$

where the minus sign gives the correct sign to the energy terms for the exothermic processes.

Reactant bonds broken:

CH_4	4 mol C—H	$4 \text{ mol} \times \dfrac{413 \text{ kJ}}{\text{mol}}$	= 1652 kJ
$2Cl_2$	2 mol Cl—Cl	$2 \text{ mol} \times \dfrac{239 \text{ kJ}}{\text{mol}}$	= 478 kJ
$2F_2$	2 mol F—F	$2 \text{ mol} \times \dfrac{154 \text{ kJ}}{\text{mol}}$	= 308 kJ

Total energy required = 2438 kJ

Product bonds formed:

CF_2Cl_2	2 mol C—F	$2 \text{ mol} \times \dfrac{485 \text{ kJ}}{\text{mol}}$ =	970 kJ
	and		
	2 mol C—Cl	$2 \text{ mol} \times \dfrac{339 \text{ kJ}}{\text{mol}}$ =	678 kJ
HF	2 mol H—F	$2 \text{ mol} \times \dfrac{565 \text{ kJ}}{\text{mol}}$ =	1130 kJ
HCl	2 mol H—Cl	$2 \text{ mol} \times \dfrac{427 \text{ kJ}}{\text{mol}}$ =	854 kJ

Total energy released = 3632 kJ

We now can calculate ΔH:

$$\Delta H = \begin{matrix} \text{energy required} \\ \text{to break bonds} \end{matrix} - \begin{matrix} \text{energy released} \\ \text{when bonds form} \end{matrix}$$

$$= 2438 \text{ kJ} - 3632 \text{ kJ} = -1194 \text{ kJ}$$

Since the sign of the value for the enthalpy change is negative, this means that 1194 kJ of energy is released per mole of CF_2Cl_2 formed. The value of ΔH calculated for this reaction using enthalpies of formation is −1126 kJ.

In performing the calculations in this section, we have made several approximations. Of course, we made the usual assumption that average bond energies apply regardless of the specific molecular environment. We also ignored the difference between enthalpy and internal energy in these calculations. Recall from Chapter 9 that at constant pressure $\Delta E = \Delta H - P\Delta V$. Thus, if a reaction involves a change in volume, a correction should be applied to the calculations of reaction enthalpies from bond energies. However, this correction is usually small compared with the uncertainties inherent in this method.

It should also be noted that the use of bond energies to estimate enthalpies of reaction should be limited to cases in which all the reactants and products are in the gas phase, where intermolecular interactions are expected to be minimal. Bond energies do not take these interactions into account.

13.9 | **The Localized Electron Bonding Model**

So far we have discussed the general characteristics of the chemical bonding model and have seen that properties such as bond strength and polarity can be assigned to individual bonds. In this section we introduce a specific model used to describe covalent bonds. We need a simple model that can be easily applied even to very complicated molecules and that can be used routinely by chemists to interpret and organize the wide variety of chemical phenomena. The model that serves this purpose is often called the **localized electron (LE) model**. This model assumes that *a molecule is composed of atoms that are bound together by using atomic orbitals to share electron pairs.* The electron pairs in the molecule are assumed to be localized on a particular atom or in the space between two atoms. Those pairs of electrons localized on an atom are called **lone pairs,** and those found in the space between the atoms are called **bonding pairs.**

As we will apply it, the LE model has three parts:

1. Description of the valence electron arrangement in the molecule using Lewis structures (will be discussed in the next section).

2. Prediction of the geometry of the molecule, using the valence shell electron-pair repulsion (VSEPR) model (will be discussed in Section 13.13).

3. Description of the types of atomic orbitals used by the atoms to share electrons or hold lone pairs (will be discussed in Chapter 14).

13.10 | Lewis Structures

The **Lewis structure** of a molecule represents the arrangement of valence electrons among the atoms in the molecule. These representations are named after G. N. Lewis (Fig. 13.14). The rules for writing Lewis structures are based on the observations of thousands of molecules, which show that *in most stable compounds the atoms achieve noble gas electron configurations*. Although this is not always the case, it is so common that it provides a very useful place to start.

We have already seen that when metals and nonmetals react to form solid binary ionic compounds, electrons are transferred, and the resulting ions typically have noble gas electron configurations. An example is the formation of KBr, where the K^+ ion has the [Ar] electron configuration and the Br^- ion has the [Kr] electron configuration. In writing Lewis structures, the rule is that *only the valence electrons are included*. Using dots to represent electrons, the Lewis structure for KBr is

No dots are shown in the K^+ ion since it has no valence electrons. The Br^- ion is shown with eight electrons since it has a filled valence shell.

Lewis structures show only valence electrons.

Figure 13.14

G. N. Lewis (above) conceived the octet rule while lecturing to a class of general chemistry students in 1902. He was also one of the two authors of a now classic work on thermodynamics, Lewis and Randall, *Thermodynamics and the Free Energy of Chemical Substances* (1923). (right) This is his original sketch. From G. N. Lewis, *Valence*, Dover Publications, Inc., New York, 1966.

The Bancroft Library

From G.N. Lewis, *Valence*, Dover Publications, Inc. New York, 1966

Next, we will consider Lewis structures for molecules with covalent bonds involving elements in the first and second periods. The principle of achieving a noble gas electron configuration applies to these elements as follows:

Hydrogen forms stable molecules where it shares two electrons. That is, it follows a **duet rule.** For example, when two hydrogen atoms, each with one electron, combine to form the H_2 molecule, we have

By sharing electrons, each hydrogen in H_2 has two electrons. This gives each hydrogen a filled valence shell.

Helium does not form bonds because its valence orbitals are already filled; it is a noble gas. Helium has the electron configuration $1s^2$ and can be represented by the Lewis structure

$$He:$$

The second-row nonmetals (carbon through fluorine) form stable molecules when they are surrounded by enough electrons to fill the valence orbitals—the $2s$ and the three $2p$ orbitals. Since eight electrons are required to fill the $2s$ and $2p$ orbitals, these elements typically obey the **octet rule;** they are surrounded by eight electrons. An example is the F_2 molecule, which has the following Lewis structure:

$$:\ddot{\underset{\cdot\cdot}{F}}\cdot \quad\longrightarrow\quad :\ddot{\underset{\cdot\cdot}{F}}:\ddot{\underset{\cdot\cdot}{F}}: \quad\longleftarrow\quad \cdot\ddot{\underset{\cdot\cdot}{F}}:$$

F atom with seven F_2 F atom with seven
valence electrons   molecule   valence electrons

Note that each fluorine atom in F_2 is, in effect, surrounded by eight electrons, two of which are shared with the other atom. Recall that the shared pair of electrons is called a *bonding pair*. Each fluorine atom also has three pairs of electrons not involved in bonding. These are the *lone pairs*.

Neon does not form bonds since it already has an octet of valence electrons (it is a noble gas). The Lewis structure is

$$:\ddot{\underset{\cdot\cdot}{Ne}}:$$

Note that only the valence electrons of the neon atom ($2s^2 2p^6$) are represented by the Lewis structure. The $1s^2$ electrons are core electrons and take no part in chemical reactions.

From the discussion above, we can formulate the following rules for writing Lewis structures of molecules containing atoms from the first two periods.

Carbon, nitrogen, oxygen, and fluorine almost always obey the octet rule in stable molecules.

STEPS | **Writing Lewis Structures**

1 Sum the valence electrons from all the atoms. Do not worry about keeping track of which electrons come from which atoms. It is the *total* number of electrons that is important.

2 Use a pair of electrons to form a bond between each pair of bound atoms.

3 Arrange the remaining electrons to satisfy the duet rule for hydrogen and the octet rule for the second-row elements.

To see how these rules are applied, we will construct the Lewis structures for a few molecules. We will first consider the water molecule and follow the rules above.

Step 1

We sum the *valence* electrons for H_2O as shown:

$$1 + 1 + 6 = 8 \text{ valence electrons}$$
$$\overset{\nearrow}{H} \quad \overset{\nearrow}{H} \quad \overset{\nearrow}{O}$$

Step 2

Using one pair of electrons per bond, we draw in the two O—H single bonds:

$$H—O—H$$

Note that *a line instead of a pair of dots is used to indicate each pair of bonding electrons*. This is the standard notation.

Step 3

We distribute the remaining electrons around the atoms to achieve a noble gas electron configuration for each atom. Since four electrons have been used in forming the two bonds, four electrons (8 − 4) remain to be distributed. Hydrogen is satisfied with two electrons (duet rule), but oxygen needs eight electrons to achieve a noble gas configuration. Thus the remaining four electrons are added to oxygen as two lone pairs. Dots are used to represent the lone pairs:

This is the correct Lewis structure for the water molecule. Each hydrogen has two electrons and the oxygen has eight:

As a second example, we will write the Lewis structure for carbon dioxide. Summing the valence electrons gives

$$4 + 6 + 6 = 16$$
$$\overset{\nearrow}{C} \quad \overset{\nearrow}{O} \quad \overset{\nearrow}{O}$$

After forming a bond between the carbon and each oxygen,

$$O—C—O$$

the remaining electrons are distributed to achieve noble gas configurations on each atom. In this case we have 12 electrons (16 − 4) remaining after the bonds are drawn. The distribution of these electrons is determined by a trial-and-error process. We have six pairs of electrons to distribute. Suppose we try three pairs on each oxygen to give

$$:\overset{..}{\underset{..}{O}}—C—\overset{..}{\underset{..}{O}}:$$

To see if this structure is correct, we need to check two things:

1. The total number of electrons. There are 16 valence electrons in this structure, which is the correct number.
2. The octet rule for each atom. Each oxygen has eight electrons, but the carbon has only four. This cannot be the correct Lewis structure.

H—O—H represents H:O:H

How can we arrange the 16 available electrons to achieve an octet for each atom? Suppose that there are two shared pairs between the carbon and each oxygen:

8 electrons   8 electrons   8 electrons

Now each atom is surrounded by 8 electrons, and the total number of electrons is 16, as required. Thus the correct Lewis structure for carbon dioxide has two double bonds.

Finally, let's consider the Lewis structure of the CN^- (cyanide) ion. Summing the valence electrons, we have

$$C \quad N \quad -$$
$$\uparrow \quad \uparrow \quad \uparrow$$
$$4 + 5 + 1 = 10$$

Note that the negative charge requires that an extra electron be added. After drawing a single bond (C—N), we distribute the remaining electrons to achieve a noble gas configuration for each atom. Eight electrons remain to be distributed. We can try various possibilities, for example:

$$\overset{..}{\underset{..}{C}}-\overset{..}{\underset{..}{N}}$$

This structure is incorrect because C and N have only six electrons each instead of eight. The correct arrangement is

$$[:C\equiv N:]^-$$

(Satisfy yourself that both carbon and nitrogen have eight electrons.)

⬙WL INTERACTIVE EXAMPLE 13.6

Give the Lewis structure for each of the following.

a. HF   **b.** N_2 **c.** NH_3 **d.** CH_4 **e.** CF_4 **f.** NO^+

Solution In each case we apply the three rules for writing Lewis structures. Recall that lines are used to indicate shared electron pairs and that dots are used to indicate nonbonding pairs (lone pairs). We have the following tabulated results:

	Total Valence Electrons	Draw Single Bonds	Calculate Number of Electrons Remaining	Use Remaining Electrons to Achieve Noble Gas Configurations
a. HF	$1 + 7 = 8$	H—F	6	H—$\ddot{\underset{..}{F}}$:
b. N_2	$5 + 5 = 10$	N—N	8	:N≡N:

c. NH_3	$5 + 3(1) = 8$	H—N—H
		    |
		    H
			2	H—$\overset{..}{N}$—H
				    |
				    H

d. CH_4	$4 + 4(1) = 8$	H
		    |
		H—C—H
		    |
		    H
			0	H
				    |
				H—C—H
				    |
				    H

(continued)

$\overset{..}{\underset{..}{O}}=C=\overset{..}{\underset{..}{O}}$ represents $\overset{..}{\underset{..}{O}}::C::\overset{..}{\underset{..}{O}}$

	Total Valence Electrons	Draw Single Bonds	Calculate Number of Electrons Remaining	Use Remaining Electrons to Achieve Noble Gas Configurations
e. CF_4	$4 + 4(7) = 32$	F—C—F with F	24	
f. NO^+	$5 + 6 - 1 = 10$	N—O	8	$[:N{\equiv}O:]^+$

When writing Lewis structures, don't worry about which electrons came from which atoms. The best way to look at a molecule is to regard it as a new entity that uses all of the available valence electrons of the atoms to achieve the lowest possible energy.* The valence electrons belong to the molecule rather than to the individual atoms. Simply distribute all valence electrons so that the various rules are satisfied, without regard to the origin of each particular electron.

13.11 | Resonance

A valid Lewis structure is one that obeys the rules we have outlined.

Sometimes more than one valid Lewis structure is possible for a given molecule. For example, consider the Lewis structure for the nitrate ion (NO_3^-), which has 24 valence electrons. So that an octet of electrons surrounds each atom, a structure like the following is required:

$$\left[\begin{array}{c} {:}\overset{..}{O}{:} \\ \| \\ N \\ \diagup \;\; \diagdown \\ {:}\overset{..}{O}{:} \quad {:}\overset{..}{O}{:} \end{array} \right]^-$$

If this structure accurately represents the bonding in NO_3^-, there should be two types of N—O bonds observed in the molecule: one shorter bond (the double bond) and two identical longer ones (the two single bonds). However, experiments clearly show that NO_3^- exhibits only *one* type of N—O bond with a length and strength between those expected for a single bond and a double bond. Thus, although the structure we have shown above is a valid Lewis structure, it does *not* correctly represent the bonding in NO_3^-. This is a serious problem, and it means that the model must be modified.

Look again at the proposed Lewis structure for NO_3^-. Because there is no reason for choosing a particular oxygen atom to have the double bond, there are really three valid Lewis structures:

Is any of these structures a correct description of the bonding in NO_3^-? No, because NO_3^- does not have one double and two single bonds—it has three

---

*In a sense this approach corrects for the fact that the LE model overemphasizes the point that a molecule is simply a sum of its parts—that is, that the atoms retain their individual identities in the molecule.

equivalent bonds. We can solve this problem by making the following assumption: The correct description of NO_3^- is *not given by any one* of the three Lewis structures individually but is given only by the *superposition of all three*.

The nitrate ion does not exist as any of the three extreme forms indicated by the individual Lewis structures but instead exists as an average of all three. **Resonance** *is invoked when more than one valid Lewis structure can be written for a particular molecule*. The resulting electron structure of the molecule is given by the average of these **resonance structures**. This situation is usually represented by double-headed arrows as follows:

Note that in all these resonance structures the arrangement of the nuclei is the same. Only the placement of the electrons differs. The arrows do not indicate that the molecule "flips" from one resonance structure to another. They simply show that the *actual structure is an average of the three resonance structures*.

The concept of resonance is necessary because the LE model postulates that electrons are localized between a given pair of atoms. However, nature doesn't really operate this way. Electrons are actually delocalized—they can move around the entire molecule. The valence electrons in the NO_3^- molecule distribute themselves to provide equivalent N—O bonds. Resonance is necessary to compensate for this defective assumption of the LE model. However, because this model is so useful, we retain the concept of localized electrons and add resonance to accommodate species like NO_3^-.

EXAMPLE 13.7

Describe the electron arrangement in the nitrite anion (NO_2^-) using the LE model.

Solution We will follow the usual procedure for obtaining the Lewis structure for the NO_2^- ion.

In NO_2^- there are $5 + 2(6) + 1 = 18$ valence electrons.
Indicating the single bonds gives the structure

$$O—N—O$$

The remaining 14 electrons $(18 - 4)$ can be distributed to produce these structures:

This is a resonance situation. Two equivalent Lewis structures can be drawn. *The electronic structure of the molecule is not correctly represented by either resonance structure but by the average of the two.* There are two equivalent N—O bonds, each one intermediate between a single and a double bond.

Equivalent Lewis structures contain the same numbers of single and multiple bonds. For example, the resonance structures for O_3,

and

are equivalent Lewis structures. They are equally important in describing the bonding in O_3. Nonequivalent Lewis structures contain different numbers of single and multiple bonds.

13.12 | Exceptions to the Octet Rule

The LE model is a simple but very successful model, and the rules we have used for Lewis structures apply to most molecules. To implement this model, we have relied heavily on the octet rule. So far we have treated molecules for which this rule is easily applied. However, inevitably, cases arise where the importance of an octet of electrons is called into question. Boron, for example, tends to form compounds in which the boron atom has fewer than eight electrons around it—it does not have a complete octet. Boron trifluoride (BF₃), a gas at normal temperatures and pressures, reacts very energetically with molecules such as water and ammonia that have available lone pairs. The violent reactivity of BF₃ with electron-rich molecules occurs because the boron atom is electron-deficient. Boron trifluoride has 24 valence electrons. The Lewis structure that seems most consistent with the properties of BF₃ is

Note that in this structure boron has only six electrons around it. The octet rule for boron can be satisfied by drawing a structure with a double bond, such as

and there are some theoretical studies that support such a structure for BF₃. However, since fluorine is so much more electronegative than boron, this structure seems questionable. In fact, some experiments indicate that each B—F bond is probably best described by the first Lewis structure, which is also consistent with the reactivity of BF₃ toward electron-rich molecules such as NH₃ with which it reacts to form H₃NBF₃:

In this stable compound, boron has an octet of electrons.

It is characteristic of boron to form molecules in which the boron atom is electron-deficient. On the other hand, carbon, nitrogen, oxygen, and fluorine do obey the octet rule.

Some atoms appear to exceed the octet rule. This behavior is observed only for those elements in Period 3 of the periodic table and beyond. To see how this arises, we will consider the Lewis structure for sulfur hexafluoride (SF₆). The sum of the valence electrons for SF₆ is

$$6 + 6(7) = 48 \text{ electrons}$$

Indicating the single bonds gives the structure on the left below:

A computer-generated representation of sulfur hexafluoride.

We have used 12 electrons to form the S—F bonds, which leaves 36 electrons. Since fluorine always follows the octet rule, we complete the six fluorine octets to give the structure on the right above. This structure uses all 48 valence electrons for SF_6, but sulfur has 12 electrons around it; that is, sulfur *exceeds* the octet rule. How can this happen? There are several ways to approach this situation. The classical explanation for molecules like SF_6 involves using the empty $3d$ orbitals on the third-period elements. Recall that the second-row elements have only $2s$ and $2p$ valence orbitals, whereas the third-row elements have $3s$, $3p$, and $3d$ orbitals. The $3s$ and $3p$ orbitals fill with electrons in going from sodium to argon, but the $3d$ orbitals remain empty. For example, the valence-orbital diagram for a sulfur atom is

Thus one way to account for the electronic structure of SF_6 is to assume that the empty $3d$ orbitals on sulfur can be used to accommodate extra electrons: The sulfur atom can have 12 electrons around it by using the $3s$ and $3p$ orbitals to hold 8 electrons, with the extra 4 electrons in the formerly empty $3d$ orbitals.

Lewis Structures and the Octet Rule

1. The second-row elements C, N, O, and F should always be assumed to obey the octet rule.

2. The second-row elements B and Be often have fewer than eight electrons around them in their compounds. These electron-deficient compounds are very reactive.

3. The second-row elements never exceed the octet rule, since their valence orbitals ($2s$ and $2p$) can accommodate only eight electrons.

4. Third-row and heavier elements often satisfy the octet rule but are assumed in the simplest model to exceed the octet rule by using their empty valence d orbitals.

5. When writing the Lewis structure for a molecule, first draw single bonds between all bonded atoms, and then satisfy the octet rule for all the atoms. If electrons remain after the octet rule has been satisfied, place them on the elements having available d orbitals (elements in the third period or beyond).

♥WL INTERACTIVE EXAMPLE 13.8

Write the Lewis structure for PCl_5.

Solution We can follow the same stepwise procedure we used previously for sulfur hexafluoride.

Step 1

Sum the valence electrons.

Step 2

Indicate single bonds between bound atoms.

Step 3

Distribute the remaining electrons. In this case, 30 electrons (40 − 10) remain. These are used to satisfy the octet rule for each chlorine atom. The final Lewis structure is

Note that phosphorus, a third-row element, exceeds the octet rule by two electrons.

In the PCl_5 and SF_6 molecules, the third-row central atoms (P and S, respectively) are assigned the extra electrons. However, in molecules having more than one atom that can exceed the octet rule, it is not always clear which atom should have the extra electrons. Consider the Lewis structure for the triiodide ion (I_3^-), which has

$$3(7) + 1 = 22 \text{ valence electrons}$$
$$\uparrow \qquad \uparrow$$
$$\text{I} \qquad -1 \text{ charge}$$

Indicating the single bonds gives I—I—I. At this point 18 electrons (22 − 4) remain. Trial and error will convince you that one of the iodine atoms must exceed the octet rule, but *which* one?

The rule we will follow is that *when it is necessary to exceed the octet rule for one of several third-row (or higher) elements, assume that the extra electrons are placed on the central atom.*

Thus for I_3^- the Lewis structure is

$$\left[: \ddot{I} - \dot{\ddot{I}} - \ddot{I} : \right]^-$$

where the central iodine exceeds the octet rule. This structure agrees with known properties of I_3^-.

EXAMPLE 13.9

Write the Lewis structure for each molecule or ion.

a. ClF_3 **b.** XeO_3 **c.** $RnCl_2$ **d.** $BeCl_2$ **e.** ICl_4^-

Solution

a. The chlorine atom (third row) accepts the extra electrons.

b. All atoms obey the octet rule.

c. Radon, a noble gas in Period 6, accepts the extra electrons.

$$:\overset{..}{\underset{..}{Cl}}-\overset{.}{\underset{..}{Rn}}\overset{.}{-}\overset{..}{\underset{..}{Cl}}:$$

d. Beryllium is electron-deficient.

$$:\overset{..}{\underset{..}{Cl}}-Be-\overset{..}{\underset{..}{Cl}}:$$

e. Iodine exceeds the octet rule.

So far we have assumed that third-row and heavier atoms can exceed the octet rule by using their valence *d* orbitals to accommodate the extra electrons. However, recent calculations* indicate that because the 3*d* orbitals are so much higher in energy than the 3*s* and 3*p* orbitals for a given atom, it is not feasible to use them. Researchers argue that satisfying the octet rule is a high priority for molecules and that there are ways to describe the bonding in molecules like SF_6 and PCl_5 without formally exceeding the octet rule. One such explanation depends on a concept called *hyperconjugation,* which is explained in the special feature "Hyperconjugation—The Octet Rules" on p. 632.

The main point that should be made here is that chemists disagree on the best way to explain molecules such as SF_6 and PCl_5. Researchers continue to try to find the best answers.

Odd-Electron Molecules

In addition to the question about the use of *d* orbitals in third-row and heavier atoms, another problem for the simple LE model involves molecules with odd numbers of electrons. Although relatively few molecules formed from nonmetals contain odd numbers of electrons, there are some notable examples. One such molecule is nitric oxide (NO), which is formed when nitrogen and oxygen gases react at the high temperatures present in automobile engines. Nitric oxide is emitted into the air, where it reacts with oxygen to form gaseous nitrogen dioxide (NO_2), another odd-electron molecule.

Since the LE model is based on pairs of electrons, it does not handle odd-electron cases in a natural way, although Lewis structures are sometimes written for these species. To treat odd-electron molecules accurately, we need a more sophisticated model.

Formal Charge

Molecules or polyatomic ions often have many nonequivalent Lewis structures, all which obey the rules for writing Lewis structures. For example, as we will see in detail, the sulfate ion has a Lewis structure with all single bonds and several Lewis structures that contain double bonds. How do we decide which of the many possible Lewis structures best describes the actual bonding in sulfate? One method involves estimating the charge on each atom in the various possible Lewis structures and using these charges to select the most appropriate structure(s). We will see below how this is done, but first we must decide on a method to evaluate atomic charges in molecules.

*L. Suidan, J. K. Bodenhopp, E. D. Glendening, and F. Weinhold, *J. Chem. Ed.* **72** (1995): 583.

Chemical Insights

Hyperconjugation—The Octet Rules

All our observations tell us that molecules such as SF_6 and PCl_5 are very stable, but what is the bonding like in these molecules? There are two extreme points of view: (1) The S and P atoms in these molecules exceed the octet rule, placing the extra electrons in $3d$ orbitals, and (2) the S and P atoms in these molecules obey the octet rule, resorting to hyperconjugation. *Hyperconjugation* involves binding n atoms to a central atom using fewer than n electron pairs around the central atom. To illustrate this model, consider SF_6. We know that there are six fluorine atoms around the central sulfur atom in this molecule. Can we explain the bonding without exceeding the octet rule? The answer is yes, by using Lewis structures such as the following:

Note that in each of these resonance structures (and the many other similar ones that can be drawn) the sulfur atom always has an octet of electrons around it. The "true" structure is a composite of these equivalent resonance structures. The overall bonding is described as a combination of covalent and ionic contributions. The covalent contribution to the bonding involves four electron pairs "spread out" over the six sulfur–fluorine bonds. The ionic contribution to the bonding arises as follows. Note that for each Lewis structure two of the fluorines have -1 formal charges and the sulfur has a $+2$ formal charge,

leading to ionic attractive forces. It is important to recall at this point that the description of the bonding in SF_6 by this model involves *all* the resonance structures similar to the one shown. Thus the F atoms are bound to the S atom by a combination of covalent bonding,

$$\frac{4 \text{ electron-pair bonds}}{6 \text{ S—F interactions}}$$

$$= \tfrac{2}{3} \text{ covalent bond per S—F interaction}$$

plus the ionic bonding described above.

A similar treatment can be given for PCl_5, using the following resonance structures,

each of which satisfies the octet rule.

Thus the use of hyperconjugation preserves the octet rule and does not require the central atom to use d orbitals, which this model's proponents argue are too high in energy to participate in the bonding of these types of molecules.

So honest disagreements exist among chemists as to the best Lewis structures for molecules that, at least at first glance, appear to exceed the octet rule. This uncertainty shows the limitations of the Lewis model with its localized electron pairs. Note, however, that even with its limitations, it is still very useful because of its simplicity. The ability to obtain a reasonable bonding picture with a "back-of-the-envelope" model has led to the enduring influence of the Lewis model.

In Chapter 4 we discussed one system for obtaining charges for atoms in molecules—oxidation states. However, in assigning oxidation states, we always count *both* of the shared electrons as belonging to the more electronegative atom in a bond. This practice leads to highly exaggerated estimates of charge. In other words, although oxidation states are useful for bookkeeping electrons in redox reactions, they are not realistic estimates of the actual charges on individual atoms in a molecule, and so they are not suitable for judging the appropriateness of Lewis structures. A second definition of atomic charges in a molecule, the **formal charge,** is more suitable for evaluating Lewis structures.

The concept of formal charge requires that we compare

1. the number of valence electrons on the free neutral atom (which has a charge of zero because the number of electrons equals the number of protons) and

2. the number of valence electrons "belonging" to a given atom in a molecule.

If an atom in a molecule has the same number of valence electrons as it does in the free state, the positive and negative charges just balance, and the atom has a formal charge of 0. If an atom has one more valence electron in a molecule than it has on a free atom, it has a formal charge of -1, and so on. Thus the formal charge on an atom in a molecule is defined as

$$\text{Formal charge} = \begin{pmatrix}\text{number of valence} \\ \text{electrons on a free atom}\end{pmatrix} - \begin{pmatrix}\text{number of valence electrons} \\ \text{assigned to the atom in the} \\ \text{molecule}\end{pmatrix}$$

To compute the formal charge of an atom in a molecule, we assign the valence electrons to the various atoms by making the following assumptions:

1. Lone pair electrons belong entirely to the atom in question.

2. Shared electrons are *divided equally* between the two sharing atoms.

Thus the number of valence electrons assigned to a given atom is calculated as follows:

$$(\text{Valence electrons})_{\text{assigned}} = \begin{pmatrix}\text{number of lone} \\ \text{pair electrons}\end{pmatrix} + \tfrac{1}{2}\begin{pmatrix}\text{number of} \\ \text{shared electrons}\end{pmatrix}$$

We will illustrate the procedures for calculating formal charges by considering two of the possible Lewis structures for the sulfate ion, which has 32 valence electrons. For the Lewis structure

each oxygen atom has six lone pair electrons and shares two electrons with the sulfur atom. Thus, according to the preceding assumptions, each oxygen is assigned seven valence electrons:

$$\text{Valence electrons assigned to each oxygen} = 6 \text{ plus } \tfrac{1}{2}(2) = 7$$

Lone pair electrons   Shared electrons

$$\text{Formal charge on oxygen} = 6 - 7 = -1$$

The formal charge on each oxygen is -1.

For the sulfur atom, there are no lone pair electrons, and eight electrons are shared with the oxygen atoms. Thus for sulfur,

$$\text{Valence electrons assigned to sulfur} = 0 + \tfrac{1}{2}(8) = 4$$

Lone pair electrons   Shared electrons

$$\text{Formal charge on sulfur} = 6 - 4 = 2$$

A second possible Lewis structure is

In this case the formal charges are as calculated below.

For oxygen atoms with single bonds:

$$\text{Valence electrons assigned} = 6 + \tfrac{1}{2}(2) = 7$$

$$\text{Formal charge} = 6 - 7 = -1$$

For oxygen atoms with double bonds:

$$\text{Valence electrons assigned} = 4 + \tfrac{1}{2}(4) = 6$$

Each double bond has 4 electrons

$$\text{Formal charge} = 6 - 6 = 0$$

For the sulfur atom:

$$\text{Valence electrons assigned} = 0 + \tfrac{1}{2}(12) = 6$$

$$\text{Formal charge} = 6 - 6 = 0$$

Now, having determined the formal charges for the various Lewis structures of the sulfate ion, can we use them to identify which of the resonance structures is closest to the actual electronic structure of the ion? There are two schools of thought on this issue. One position assumes that the atoms in a molecule or ion will try to achieve minimum formal charges. In other words, the assumption is that electrons will naturally flow from negatively charged parts of the molecule to positively charged parts, thus minimizing the charges on the atoms. From this point of view, the resonance structures of SO_4^{2-} with two double bonds (and minimum formal charges)

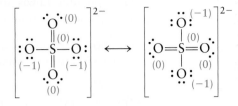

would be favored. Note that these structures exceed the octet rule, thus requiring the sulfur to use its $3d$ orbitals to hold electrons.

The other school of thought argues for the primacy of the octet rule and against the use of $3d$ orbitals. This position favors the single-bonded resonance structure of SO_4^{2-}

with its octet of electrons around the sulfur and its high formal charges.

Which point of view is correct? What do we know about the sulfate ion that might help us decide? One pertinent fact is that the sulfur–oxygen bonds in SO_4^{2-} are known by experiment to be shorter than expected for normal single bonds. This would seem to favor the resonance structures with double bonds. However, one can also argue that the high formal charges on the atoms in the single-bonded structure cause ionic attractions that pull the atoms closer together. Thus both schools of thought can adequately explain the short sulfur–oxygen bond lengths.

At this point the dispute continues about which position is correct. For second-row elements where the octet rule is never exceeded, it seems clear that the "best" Lewis structures conform to the following rules:

1. Atoms in molecules try to achieve formal charges as close to zero as possible.

2. Any negative formal charges are expected to reside on the most electronegative atoms.

However, for molecules or ions containing third-row or heavier atoms, the situation is still unclear.

Rules Governing Formal Charge

1. To calculate the formal charge on an atom:
   - Take the sum of the lone pair electrons and one-half of the shared electrons. This is the number of valence electrons assigned to a given atom in the molecule.
   - Subtract the number of assigned electrons from the number of valence electrons on the free, neutral atom to obtain the formal charge.

2. The sum of the formal charges of all atoms in a given molecule or ion must equal the overall charge on that species.

3. If nonequivalent Lewis structures exist for a species containing second-row atoms, those with formal charges closest to zero and with any negative formal charges on the most electronegative atoms are considered to best describe the bonding in the molecule or ion.

EXAMPLE 13.10

Give possible Lewis structures for XeO₃, an explosive compound of xenon. Determine the formal charges of each atom in the various Lewis structures.

Solution For XeO_3 (26 valence electrons) we can draw the following possible Lewis structures (formal charges are indicated in parentheses):

The concept of formal charge is most often used to evaluate the importance of various Lewis structures for molecules that exhibit resonance. However, formal charge arguments also can be helpful in predicting which, among a given group of atoms, is the central atom in a simple molecule. For example, why is carbon dioxide O—C—O rather than C—O—O? Although this question can be pursued at many different levels of sophistication, the simplest approach involves considering the formal charges in the two possible structures. Note that in the Lewis structure given previously for carbon dioxide,

$$\ddot{O}=C=\ddot{O}$$

all atoms have formal charges of 0. However, if the atoms are arranged as follows,

C—O—O

all the Lewis structures give unreasonable formal charges. Consider the following possibilities, where the formal charges are listed below each atom:

$$:C\equiv O-\ddot{O}:\qquad :\!\ddot{C}=O=\ddot{O}:\qquad :\ddot{C}-O\equiv O:$$
$$\;\;-1\;\;+2\;\;-1\qquad\;\;-2\;\;+2\;\;\;0\qquad\;\;\;-3\;\;+2\;\;+1$$

None of these Lewis structures (with their resulting formal charges) agrees with our observation that oxygen has a significantly greater electronegativity than carbon. That is, it doesn't make sense that a compound would contain a negatively charged carbon atom next to a positively charged oxygen atom.

As a final note, there are several cautions about formal charge to keep in mind. First, although formal charges are closer to actual atomic charges in molecules than are oxidation states, formal charges still are only estimates of charge—they should not be taken as actual atomic charges. Second, the evaluation of Lewis structures using formal charge ideas can lead to erroneous predictions.

In this same vein, note the difference between a "correct," or valid, Lewis structure and an electronic structure that accurately accounts for a molecule's observed properties. A valid Lewis structure is one that obeys the rules we have established for Lewis structures. However, this Lewis structure may or may not give an accurate picture of the molecule and its properties. Experiments must be carried out to make the final decisions on the correct description of the bonding in a molecule or polyatomic ion.*

---

*For a discussion of this issue, see Gordon H. Purser, *J. Chem. Ed.* **76** (1999): 1013.

13.13 | Molecular Structure: The VSEPR Model

The structures of molecules play a very important role in determining their chemical properties. As we will see later, structure is particularly important for biological molecules; a slight change in the structure of a large biomolecule can completely destroy its usefulness to a cell or may even change the cell from normal to cancerous.

Many accurate methods now exist for determining **molecular structure,** the three-dimensional arrangement of the atoms in a molecule. These methods must be used if precise information about structure is required. However, it is often useful to predict the approximate molecular structure of a molecule. In this section we consider a simple model that allows us to do this. This model, called the **valence shell electron-pair repulsion (VSEPR) model,** is useful in predicting the geometries of molecules formed from nonmetals. The main postulate of this model is that *the structure around a given atom is determined principally by minimizing electron-pair repulsions.* The idea is that the bonding and nonbonding pairs around a given atom should be positioned as far apart as possible. To see how this model works, we will first consider the molecule $BeCl_2$, which has the Lewis structure

$$:\ddot{C}l\!\!-\!\!Be\!\!-\!\!\ddot{C}l:$$

The origin of the "repulsions" among electron pairs probably results more from the operation of the Pauli exclusion principle than from electrostatic effects, but we will not be concerned with that in this text.

Note that there are two pairs of electrons around the beryllium atom. What arrangement of these electron pairs allows them to be as far apart as possible to minimize the repulsions? Clearly, the best arrangement places the pairs on opposite sides of the beryllium atom at 180 degrees:

This is the maximum possible separation for two electron pairs. Once we have determined the optimal arrangement of the electron pairs around the central atom, we can specify the molecular structure of $BeCl_2$ — that is, the positions of the atoms. Since each electron pair on beryllium is shared with a chlorine atom, the molecule has a **linear structure** with a bond angle of 180 degrees:

Next, let's consider BF_3, which has the Lewis structure

$$:\ddot{F}:$$
$$|$$
$$:\ddot{F}\!\!-\!\!B\!\!-\!\!\ddot{F}:$$

Here the boron atom is surrounded by three pairs of electrons. What arrangement will minimize the repulsions? The electron pairs are farthest apart at angles of 120 degrees:

Since each electron pair is shared with a fluorine atom, the molecular structure is

This is a planar (flat) and triangular molecule, which is commonly described as **trigonal planar.**

Next, let's consider the methane molecule, which has the Lewis structure

There are four pairs of electrons around the central carbon atom. What arrangement of these electron pairs best minimizes the repulsions? First, let's try a square planar arrangement:

The carbon atom and the electron pairs are centered in the plane of the paper, and the angles between the pairs are all 90 degrees.

Is there another arrangement with angles greater than 90 degrees that would put the electron pairs even farther away from each other? The answer is yes. The **tetrahedral arrangement** has angles of 109.5 degrees:

It can be shown that this is the maximum possible separation of four pairs around a given atom. This means that *whenever four pairs of electrons are present around an atom, they should always be arranged tetrahedrally.*

Now that we have obtained the electron-pair arrangement that gives the least repulsions, we can determine the positions of the atoms and thus the molecular structure of CH_4. In methane each of the four electron pairs is shared between the carbon atom and a hydrogen atom. Thus the hydrogen atoms are placed as shown in Fig. 13.15, giving the molecule a tetrahedral structure with the carbon atom at the center.

Recall that the fundamental idea of the VSEPR model is to find the arrangement of electron pairs around the central atom that minimizes the electron repulsions. Then we can determine the molecular structure from knowing how the electron pairs are shared with the peripheral atoms.

When four uniform balloons are tied together, they naturally form a tetrahedral shape.

Figure 13.15
The molecular structure of methane. The tetrahedral arrangement of electron pairs produces a tetrahedral arrangement of hydrogen atoms.

Steps for Using the VSEPR Model

1 Draw the Lewis structure for the molecule.

2 Count the electron pairs around the central atom, and arrange them in the way that minimizes repulsions (that is, put the pairs as far apart as possible).

3 Determine the positions of the atoms from the ways the electron pairs are shared.

4 Name the molecular structure from the positions of the *atoms*.

We will now predict the structure of ammonia (NH_3) using this approach.

■ **Draw the Lewis structure.**

$$H-\overset{\displaystyle ..}{N}-H$$
$$|$$
$$H$$

■ **Count the pairs of electrons, and arrange them to minimize repulsions.**

The NH_3 molecule has four pairs of electrons: three bonding pairs and one nonbonding pair. From the discussion of the methane molecule, we know that the best arrangement of four electron pairs is a tetrahedral array, as shown in Fig. 13.16(a).

■ **Determine the positions of the atoms.**

The three H atoms share electron pairs, as shown in Fig. 13.16(b).

■ **Name the molecular structure.**

It is very important to recognize that the *name* of the molecular structure is always based on the *positions of the atoms*. The placement of the electron pairs determines the structure, but the name is based on the positions of the atoms. Thus it is incorrect to say that the NH_3 molecule is tetrahedral. It has a tetrahedral arrangement of electron pairs but not a tetrahedral arrangement of atoms. The molecular structure of ammonia is a **trigonal pyramid** (one triangular side is different from the other three), rather than a tetrahedron, as shown in Fig. 13.16(c).

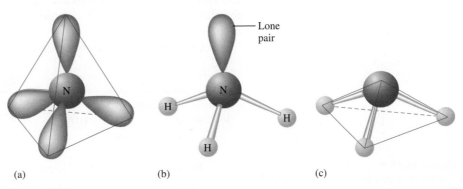

(a)   (b)   (c)

Figure 13.16

(a) The tetrahedral arrangement of electron pairs around the nitrogen atom in the ammonia molecule. (b) Three of the electron pairs around nitrogen are shared with hydrogen atoms, as shown, and the fourth is a lone pair. Although the arrangement of *electron pairs* is tetrahedral, as in the methane molecule, the hydrogen atoms in the ammonia molecule occupy only three corners of the tetrahedron. A lone pair occupies the fourth corner. (c) Note that molecular geometry is trigonal pyramidal, not tetrahedral.

Figure 13.17
(a) The tetrahedral arrangement of the four electron pairs around oxygen in the water molecule. (b) Two of the electron pairs are shared between oxygen and the hydrogen atoms, and two are lone pairs. (c) The V-shaped molecular structure of the water molecule.

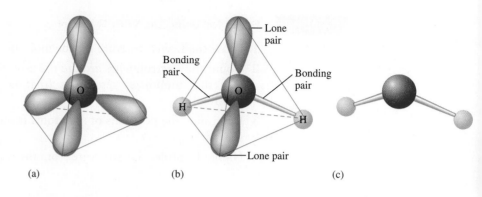

(a)   (b)   (c)

EXAMPLE 13.11

Describe the molecular structure of the water molecule.

Solution The Lewis structure for water is

$$H-\overset{\displaystyle ..}{\underset{\displaystyle ..}{O}}-H$$

There are four pairs of electrons: two bonding pairs and two nonbonding pairs. To minimize repulsions, these are best arranged in a tetrahedral array, as shown in Fig. 13.17(a). Although H_2O has a tetrahedral arrangement of electron pairs, it is not a tetrahedral molecule. The atoms in the H_2O molecule form a V-shape, as shown in Fig. 13.17(b) and (c).

From Example 13.11 we see that the H_2O molecule is V-shaped, or bent, because of the presence of the lone pairs. If no lone pairs were present, the molecule would be linear, the polar bonds would cancel, and the molecule would have no dipole moment. This would make water very different from the polar substance so familiar to us.

From the previous discussion, we would predict that the H—X—H bond angle (where X is the central atom) in CH_4, NH_3, and H_2O should be the tetrahedral angle (109.5 degrees). Experiments, however, show that the actual bond angles are those given in Fig. 13.18. What significance do these results have for the VSEPR model? One possible point of view is that the observed angles are close enough to the tetrahedral angle to be satisfactory. The opposite view is that the deviations are significant enough to require modification of the simple model so that it can more accurately handle similar cases. We will take the latter view.

Let's examine the following data:

	CH_4	NH_3	H_2O
Number of lone pairs	0	1	2
Bond angle	109.5°	107°	104.5°

Figure 13.18
The bond angles in the CH_4, NH_3, and H_2O molecules. Note that the bond angle between bonding pairs decreases as the number of lone pairs increases.

Methane   Ammonia   Water
109.5°   107°   104.5°

(a)

(b)

Figure 13.19
(a) In a bonding pair of electrons, the electrons are shared by two nuclei.
(b) In a lone pair, since both electrons must be close to a single nucleus, they tend to take up more of the space around that atom.

One interpretation of the trend observed here is that lone pairs require more space than bonding pairs; in other words, as the number of lone pairs increases, the bonding pairs are increasingly squeezed together.

This interpretation seems to make physical sense if we think in the following terms: A bonding pair is shared between two nuclei, and the electrons can be close to either nucleus. Therefore they are relatively confined between the two nuclei. A lone pair is localized on only one nucleus, so both electrons are close to that nucleus only, as shown schematically in Fig. 13.19. These pictures help us to understand why a lone pair may require more space near an atom than a bonding pair.

As a result of these observations, we make the following addition to the original postulate of the VSEPR model: *Lone pairs require more room than bonding pairs and tend to compress the angles between the bonding pairs.*

So far we have considered cases with two, three, and four electron pairs around the central atom. These are summarized in Table 13.8. Table 13.9 summarizes the structures possible for molecules in which there are four electron pairs around the central atom with various numbers of atoms bonded to it. Note that molecules with four pairs of electrons around the central atom can be tetrahedral (AB_4), trigonal pyramidal (AB_3), and V-shaped (AB_2). For five pairs

Table 13.8

Arrangements of Electron Pairs Around an Atom Yielding Minimum Repulsion

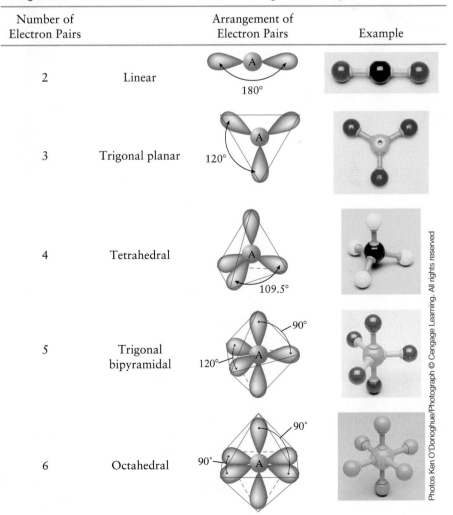

Number of Electron Pairs	Arrangement of Electron Pairs		Example
2	Linear	180°	
3	Trigonal planar	120°	
4	Tetrahedral	109.5°	
5	Trigonal bipyramidal	120° / 90°	
6	Octahedral	90° / 90°	

Table 13.9

Structures of Molecules That Have Four Electron Pairs Around the Central Atom

Table 13.10

Structures of Molecules with Five Electron Pairs Around the Central Atom

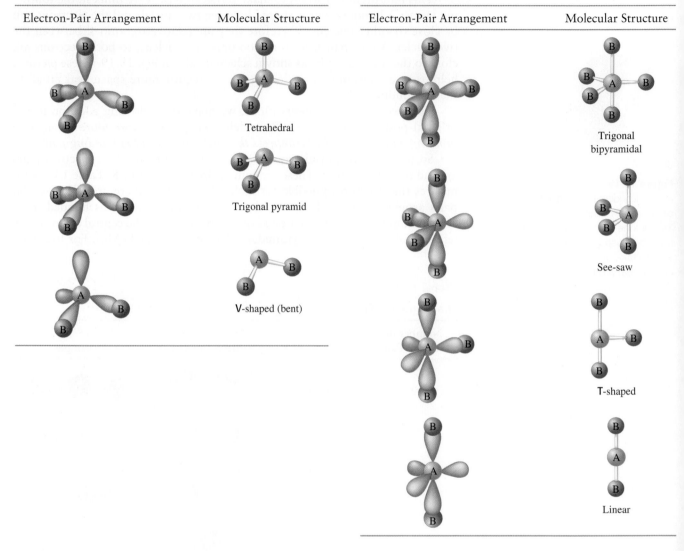

Electron-Pair Arrangement	Molecular Structure
	Tetrahedral
	Trigonal pyramid
	V-shaped (bent)

Electron-Pair Arrangement	Molecular Structure
	Trigonal bipyramidal
	See-saw
	T-shaped
	Linear

of electrons, there are several possible electron-pair arrangements. The one that produces minimum repulsion is a **trigonal bipyramid.** Note from Table 13.8 that this arrangement has two different angles, 90 degrees and 120 degrees. As the name suggests, the structure formed by this arrangement of pairs consists of two trigonal-based pyramids that share a common base. Table 13.10 summarizes the structures possible for molecules in which there are five electron pairs around the central atom with various numbers of atoms bonded to it. Note that molecules with five pairs of electrons around the central atom can be trigonal bipyramidal (AB_5), see-saw (AB_4), T-shaped (AB_3), and linear (AB_2). Six pairs of electrons can best be arranged around a given atom to form an **octahedral structure** with 90-degree angles, as shown in Table 13.8.

To use the VSEPR model to determine the geometric structures of molecules, you should memorize the relationships between the number of electron pairs and their best arrangement.

OWL INTERACTIVE EXAMPLE 13.12

When phosphorus reacts with excess chlorine gas, the compound phosphorus pentachloride (PCl_5) is formed. In the gaseous and liquid states, this substance consists of PCl_5 molecules, but in the solid state, it consists of a $1:1$ mixture of PCl_4^+ and PCl_6^- ions. Predict the geometric structures of PCl_5, PCl_4^+, and PCl_6^-.

Solution The traditional Lewis structure for PCl_5 is shown in the margin. Five pairs of electrons around the phosphorus atom require a trigonal bipyramidal arrangement (see Table 13.8). When the chlorine atoms are included, a trigonal bipyramidal molecule results.

Lewis structure for PCl₅

The Lewis structure for the PCl_4^+ ion $[5 + 4(7) - 1 = 32$ valence electrons] is shown in the margin. There are four pairs of electrons surrounding the phosphorus atom in the PCl_4^+ ion. This requires a tetrahedral arrangement of the pairs, as shown in the figure in the margin. Since each pair is shared with a chlorine atom, a tetrahedral PCl_4^+ cation results.

Lewis structure for PCl₄⁺

The traditional Lewis structure for PCl_6^- $[5 + 6(7) + 1 = 48$ valence electrons] is

Since phosphorus is surrounded by six pairs of electrons, an octahedral arrangement is required to minimize repulsions, as shown below on the left. Since each electron pair is shared with a chlorine atom, an octahedral PCl_6^- anion is predicted.

Tetrahedral PCl₄⁺ cation

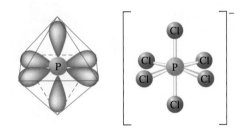

OWL INTERACTIVE EXAMPLE 13.13

Because the noble gases have filled s and p valence orbitals, they are not expected to be chemically reactive. In fact, for many years these elements were called *inert gases* because of this supposed inability to form any compounds. However, in the early 1960s, several compounds of krypton, xenon, and radon were synthesized. For example, a team at the Argonne National Laboratory produced the stable colorless compound xenon tetrafluoride (XeF_4). Predict its structure and determine whether it has a dipole moment.

Xenon tetrafluoride crystals.

Solution The traditional Lewis structure for XeF_4 is

The xenon atom in this molecule is surrounded by six pairs of electrons, requiring an octahedral arrangement:

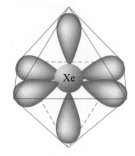

The structure predicted for this molecule depends on how the lone pairs and bonding pairs are arranged. Consider the two possibilities shown in Fig. 13.20. The bonding pairs are indicated by the presence of fluorine atoms. Since the structure predicted differs in the two cases, we must decide which of these arrangements is preferable. The key is to look at the lone pairs. In the structure in part (a), the lone pair–lone pair angle is 90 degrees; in the structure in part (b), the lone pairs are separated by 180 degrees. Since lone pairs require more room than bonding pairs, a structure with two lone pairs at 90 degrees is unfavorable. Thus the arrangement in Fig. 13.20(b) is preferred, and the molecular structure is predicted to be square planar. Note that this molecule is *not* described as being octahedral. There is an *octahedral arrangement of electron pairs,* but the *atoms* form a **square planar** structure.

Figure 13.20
Possible electron-pair arrangement for XeF_4. Since arrangement (a) has lone pairs 90 degrees apart, it is less favorable than arrangement (b), where the lone pairs are 180 degrees apart.

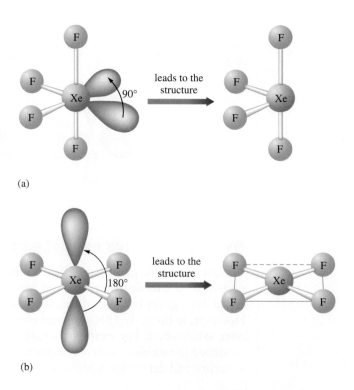

Although each Xe—F bond is polar (fluorine has a greater electronegativity than xenon), the square planar arrangement of these bonds causes the polarities to cancel.

Thus XeF_4 has no dipole moment.

We can further illustrate the use of the VSEPR model for molecules or ions with lone pairs by considering the triiodide ion (I_3^-). The Lewis structure for I_3^- is

$$[: \overset{..}{I} - \overset{..}{\underset{..}{I}} - \overset{..}{I} :]^-$$

The central iodine atom has five pairs around it, requiring a trigonal bipyramidal arrangement. Several possible arrangements of the lone pairs are shown in Fig. 13.21. Note that structures (a) and (b) have lone pairs at 90 degrees, whereas in (c) all lone pairs are at 120 degrees. Thus structure (c) is preferred. The resulting molecular structure for I_3^- is linear.

$$[I—I—I]^-$$

The VSEPR Model and Multiple Bonds

So far in our treatment of the VSEPR model, we have not considered any molecules with multiple bonds. To see how these molecules are handled by this model, let's consider the NO_3^- ion, which requires three resonance structures to describe its electronic structure:

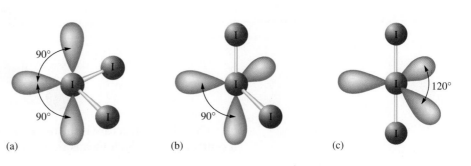

Figure 13.21

Three possible arrangements of the electron pairs in the I_3^- ion. Arrangement (c) is preferred because there are no 90-degree lone pair–lone pair interactions.

(a)   (b)   (c)

Chemical Insights

Chemical Structure and Communication: Semiochemicals

In this chapter we have stressed the importance of being able to predict the three-dimensional structure of a molecule. Molecular structure is important because of its effect on chemical reactivity. This is especially true in biological systems, where reactions must be efficient and highly specific. Among the hundreds of types of molecules in the fluids of a typical biological system, the appropriate reactants must find and react only with each other—they must be very discriminating. This specificity depends primarily on structure. The molecules are constructed so that only the appropriate partners can approach each other in a way that allows reaction.

Molecular structure is also central for those molecules used as a means of communication. Examples of chemical communication occurring in humans are the conduction of nerve impulses across synapses, the control of the manufacture and storage of key chemicals in cells, and the senses of smell and taste. Plants and animals also use chemical communication. For example, ants lay down a chemical trail so that other ants can find a certain food supply. Ants also warn their fellow workers of approaching danger by emitting certain chemicals.

Molecules convey messages by fitting into appropriate receptor sites in a very specific way, which is determined by their structure. When a molecule occupies a receptor site, chemical processes that produce the appropriate response are stimulated. Sometimes receptors can be fooled, as in the use of artificial sweeteners—molecules fit the sites on the taste buds that stimulate a "sweet" response in the brain, but they are not metabolized in the same way as natural sugars. Similar decep-

tion is useful in insect control. If an area is sprayed with synthetic female sex attractant molecules, the males of that species become so confused that mating does not occur.

A *semiochemical* is a molecule that delivers a message between members of the same or different species of plant or animal. There are three groups of these chemical messengers: allomones, kairomones, and pheromones. Each is of great ecological importance.

An *allomone* is defined as a chemical that gives adaptive advantage to the producer. For example, leaves of the black walnut tree contain an herbicide, juglone, that appears after the leaves fall to the ground. Juglone is not toxic to grass or certain grains, but it is effective against plants such as apple trees that would compete for the available water and food supplies.

Antibiotics are also allomones, since the microorganisms produce them to inhibit other species from growing near them.

Many plants produce bad-tasting chemicals to protect themselves from plant-eating insects and animals. The familiar compound nicotine deters animals from eating the tobacco plant. The millipede sends an unmistakable "back off" message by squirting a predator with benzaldehyde and hydrogen cyanide.

Defense is not the only use of allomones, however. Flowers use scent to attract pollinating insects. Honeybees, for instance, are guided to alfalfa flowers by a series of sweet-scented compounds.

Kairomones are chemical messengers that bring advantageous news to the receiver. For example,

The NO_3^- ion is known to be planar with 120-degree bond angles:

This planar structure is the one expected for three pairs of electrons around a central atom, which means that *a double bond should be counted as one ef-*

the floral scents are kairomones from the honeybees' viewpoint. Many predators are guided by kairomones emitted by their food. For example, apple skins exude a chemical that attracts the codling moth larva. In some cases kairomones help the underdog. Certain marine mollusks can pick up the "scent" of their predators, the sea stars, and make their escape.

Pheromones are chemicals that affect receptors of the same species as the donor. That is, they are specific within a species. *Releaser pheromones* cause an immediate reaction in the receptor, whereas *primer pheromones* cause long-term effects. Examples of releaser pheromones are the sex attractants of insects, generated in some species by the males and in others by the females. Sex pheromones have also been found in plants and mammals.

Alarm pheromones are highly volatile compounds (ones easily changed to a gas) released to warn of danger. Honeybees produce isoamyl acetate ($C_7H_{14}O_2$) in their sting glands. Because of its high volatility, this compound does not linger after the state of alert is over. Social behavior in insects is characterized by the use of *trail pheromones,* which are used to indicate a food source. Social insects such as bees, ants, wasps, and termites use these substances. Since trail pheromones are less volatile compounds, the indicators persist for some time.

Primer pheromones, which cause long-term behavioral changes, are harder to isolate and identify. One example, however, is the "queen substance" produced by queen honeybees. All the eggs in a colony are laid by one queen bee. If she is

Scott Camazine/Photo Researchers

Honeybees are attracted to these alfalfa flowers by sweet-scented compounds the flowers emit.

removed from the hive or dies, the worker bees are activated by the absence of the queen substance and begin to feed royal jelly to bee larvae to raise a new queen. The queen substance also prevents the development of the workers' ovaries so that only the queen herself can produce eggs.

Many studies of insect pheromones are now under way in the hope that they will provide a method of controlling insects that is more efficient and safer than the current chemical pesticides.

fective pair in using the VSEPR model. This makes sense because the two pairs of electrons involved in the double bond are *not* independent pairs. Both of the electron pairs must be in the space between the nuclei of the two atoms to form the double bond. In other words, the double bond acts as one center of electron density to repel the other pairs of electrons. The same holds true for triple bonds. This leads us to another general rule: *For the VSEPR model, multiple bonds count as one effective electron pair.*

The molecular structure of nitrate also illustrates one more important point: *When a molecule exhibits resonance, any one of the resonance structures can be used to predict the molecular structure using the VSEPR model.* These rules are illustrated in Example 13.14.

Chemical Insights   Smelling and Tasting Electronically

The human nose and tongue are excellent quality-control sensors. For example, we can tell whether food is spoiled by its disagreeable odor and taste. Because it's impractical to use humans as sensors in industrial settings, several companies are now developing electronic noses.

Cyrano Sciences has developed a hand-held electronic nose (called a Cyranose) that can identify specific odors by the "smell print" they create in the 32 sensors of the instrument. Each sensor is composed of conductive carbon black combined with a nonconducting polymer. In the presence of the chemicals associated with an odor, the polymer swells, thereby disrupting the conductive pathways and increasing the resistance. The device is "trained" to detect particular odors by subjecting it to known sources of those odors and storing the electrical signals in the machine's database. When the "nose" is then exposed to an odor in an industrial setting, it identifies the odor by comparing the input signals with its database. The Cyranose is used in the food and beverage industries to monitor the condition of raw materials and the quality of the finished product. In the chemical industry, it is used to pinpoint leaks and to identify manufacturing odors.

Other artificial noses are now being developed that can furnish early detection of diseases. Various researchers are now developing "noses" that can detect different types of bacteria and can provide early diagnosis of lung cancer.

A company called Alpha M.O.S. has recently introduced what it calls the "world's first commercial electronic tongue," a device used to identify various tastes associated with liquids. Like the Cyranose, the electronic tongue must first be "trained" by exposing its probe to known liquid characteristics to record their "fingerprints." Once programmed, the "tongue" can recognize tastes such as sweetness, sourness, bitterness, and salti-

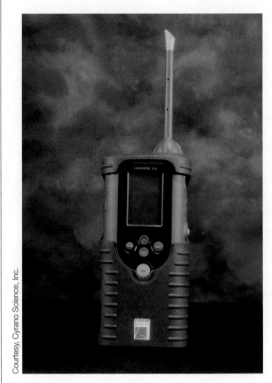

A Cyranose sensor (an "electronic nose").

ness and can detect rancidity and various types of contamination. The electronic tongue is of particular interest to the pharmaceutical industry, where it is hoped it can reduce the need for human tasting panels.

Artificial tasters are also being developed for sensing diseases. For example, Eric V. Anslyn and his coworkers at the University of Texas at Austin have reported a system that can recognize the "taste of heart disease" by analyzing the "taste" of blood samples.

Humans and animals are still the best "smellers" and tasters, but computers are rapidly catching up.

Courtesy, Cyrano Science, Inc.

⦿WL INTERACTIVE EXAMPLE 13.14

Predict the molecular structure of the sulfur dioxide molecule. Is this molecule expected to have a dipole moment?

Solution First, we must determine the Lewis structure for the SO_2 molecule, which has 18 valence electrons. The expected resonance structures are

To determine the molecular structure, we must count the electron pairs around the sulfur atom. In each resonance structure, the sulfur has one lone pair, one pair in a single bond, and one double bond. Counting the double bond as one pair yields three effective pairs around the sulfur. According to Table 13.8, a trigonal planar arrangement is required, yielding a V-shaped molecule:

$$O \underset{S}{\overset{120°}{\diagdown \diagup}} O$$

Thus the structure of the SO_2 molecule is expected to be V-shaped with a 120-degree bond angle. The molecule has a dipole moment directed as shown:

$$O \underset{\underset{+}{S}}{\diagdown \uparrow \diagup} O$$

Since the molecule is V-shaped, the polar bonds do not cancel.

It should be noted at this point that lone pairs oriented at least 120 degrees from other pairs do not produce significant distortions of bond angles. For example, the angle in the SO_2 molecule is actually quite close to 120 degrees. We will follow the general principle that *an angle of 120 degrees provides lone pairs with enough space so that distortions do not occur. Angles less than 120 degrees are distorted when lone pairs are present.*

Molecules Containing No Single Central Atom

So far we have considered molecules consisting of one central atom surrounded by other atoms. The VSEPR model can be readily extended to more complicated molecules, such as methanol (CH_3OH). This molecule is represented by the following Lewis structure:

The VSEPR Model

The following rules are helpful in using the VSEPR model to predict molecular structure.

1. Determine the Lewis structure(s) for the molecule.

2. For molecules with resonance structures, use any of the structures to predict the molecular structure.

3. Sum the electron pairs around the central atom.

(continued)

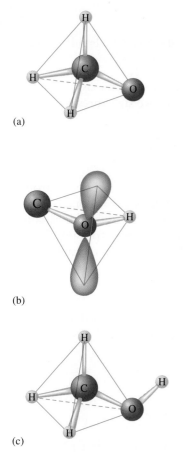

(a)

(b)

(c)

Figure 13.22
The molecular structure of methanol.
(a) The arrangement of electron pairs and atoms around the carbon atom.
(b) The arrangement of bonding and lone pairs around the oxygen atom.
(c) The molecular structure.

> *The VSEPR Model (Continued)*
>
> 4. When counting pairs, count each multiple bond as a single effective pair.
> 5. Determine the arrangement of the pairs that minimizes electron-pair repulsions. These arrangements are shown in Table 13.8.
> 6. Lone pairs require more space than bonding pairs. Choose an arrangement that gives the lone pairs as much room as possible, although it appears that an angle of at least 120 degrees between lone pairs provides enough space. Recognize that lone pairs at angles less than 120 degrees may produce distortions from the idealized structure.

The molecular structure can be predicted from the arrangement of pairs around the carbon and oxygen atoms. Note that there are four pairs of electrons around the carbon, which calls for a tetrahedral arrangement, as shown in Fig. 13.22(a). The oxygen also has four pairs, requiring a tetrahedral arrangement. However, in this case the tetrahedron will be slightly distorted by the space requirements of the lone pairs [Fig. 13.22(b)]. The overall geometric arrangement for the molecule is shown in Fig. 13.22(c).

The VSEPR Model—How Well Does It Work?

The VSEPR model is very simple. There are only a few rules to remember, yet the model correctly predicts the molecular structures of most molecules formed from nonmetallic elements. Molecules of any size can be treated by applying the VSEPR model to each appropriate atom (those bonded to at least two other atoms) in the molecule. Thus we can use this model to predict the structures of molecules with hundreds of atoms. It does, however, fail in a few instances. For example, phosphine (PH_3), which has a Lewis structure analogous to that of ammonia,

would be predicted to have a molecular structure similar to that for NH_3 with bond angles of about 107 degrees. However, the bond angles of phosphine are actually 94 degrees. There are ways of explaining this structure, but more rules have to be added to the model.

This example again illustrates the point that simple models will certainly have exceptions. In introductory chemistry we want to use simple models that fit the majority of cases; we are willing to accept a few failures rather than complicate the model. The amazing thing about the VSEPR model is that such a simple model correctly predicts the structures of so many molecules.

Key Terms

Section 13.1
bond energy
ionic compound
Coulomb's law
bond length
covalent bonding
polar covalent bond

Section 13.2
electronegativity

Section 13.3
dipole moment

Section 13.4
isoelectronic ions

Section 13.5
lattice energy

Section 13.8
single bond
double bond
triple bond

Section 13.9
localized electron (LE) model
lone pair
bonding pair

Section 13.10
Lewis structure
duet rule
octet rule

Section 13.11
resonance
resonance structure

Section 13.12
formal charge

Section 13.13
molecular structure
valence shell electron-pair
 repulsion (VSEPR) model
linear structure
trigonal planar
tetrahedral arrangement
trigonal pyramid
trigonal bipyramid
octahedral structure
square planar

For Review

⭕WL and **go Chemistry**

Sign in at **www.cengage.com/owl** to:
• View tutorials and simulations, develop problem-solving skills, and complete online homework assigned by your professor.
• Download Go Chemistry mini lecture modules for quick review and exam prep from OWL (or purchase them at **www.cengagebrain.com**)

Chemical bonds
■ Hold groups of atoms together
■ Occur when a group of atoms can lower its total energy by aggregating
■ Types of chemical bonds
 ■ Ionic: electrons are transferred to form ions
 ■ Covalent: equal sharing of electrons
 ■ Polar covalent: unequal electron sharing
■ Percent ionic character of a bond X—Y

$$\frac{\text{Measured dipole moment of X—Y}}{\text{Calculated dipole moment for X}^+ \text{Y}^-} \times 100\%$$

■ Electronegativity: the relative ability of an atom to attract shared electrons
 ■ The polarity of a bond depends on the electronegativity difference of the bonded atoms
■ The spatial arrangement of polar bonds in a molecule determines whether the molecule has a dipole moment

Ionic bonding
■ An ion has a different size than its parent atom
 ■ An anion is larger than its parent ion
 ■ A cation is smaller than its parent atom
■ Lattice energy: the change in energy when ions are packed together to form an ionic solid

Bond energy
■ The energy necessary to break a covalent bond
■ Increases as the number of shared pairs increases
■ Can be used to estimate the enthalpy change for a chemical reaction

Lewis structures
■ Show how the valence electron pairs are arranged among the atoms in a molecule or polyatomic ion
■ Stable molecules usually contain atoms that have their valence orbitals filled
 ■ Leads to a duet rule for hydrogen
 ■ Leads to an octet rule for second-row elements
 ■ The atoms of elements in the third row and beyond can exceed the octet rule
■ Several equivalent Lewis structures can be drawn for some molecules, a concept called resonance
■ When several nonequivalent Lewis structures can be drawn for a molecule, formal charge is often used to choose the most appropriate structure(s)

VSEPR model
■ Based on the idea that electron pairs will be arranged around a central atom in a way that minimizes the electron repulsions
■ Can be used to predict the geometric structure of most molecules

Discussion Questions

These questions are designed to be considered by groups of students in class. Often these questions work well for introducing a particular topic in class.

1. Explain the electronegativity trends across a row and down a column of the periodic table. Compare these trends with those of ionization energy and atomic radii. How are they all related?

2. The ionic compound AB is formed. The charges on the ions may be +1, −1; +2, −2; +3, −3; or even larger. What are the factors that determine the charge for an ion in an ionic compound?

3. Using only the periodic table, predict the most stable ion for Na, Mg, Al, S, Cl, K, Ca, and Ga. Arrange these from largest to smallest radius, and explain why the radius varies as it does. Compare your predictions with Fig. 13.8.

4. The bond energy for the C—H bond is about 413 kJ/mol in CH_4 but 380 kJ/mol in $CHBr_3$. Although these values are relatively close in magnitude, they are different. Explain why they are different. Does the fact that the C—H bond energy in $CHBr_3$ is lower make any sense? Why?

5. Consider the following statement: "Because oxygen seems to prefer a negative two charge, the second electron affinity is more negative than the first." Indicate everything that is correct in this statement. Indicate everything that is incorrect. Correct the incorrect information, and explain.

6. Which has the greater bond lengths: NO_2^- or NO_3^-? Explain.

7. The following ions are best described with resonance structures. Draw the resonance structures, and using formal charge arguments, predict the "best" Lewis structure for each ion.
   a. NCO^-
   b. CNO^-

8. Would you expect the electronegativity of titanium to be the same in the species Ti, Ti^{2+}, Ti^{3+}, and Ti^{4+}? Explain.

9. The second electron affinity values for both oxygen and sulfur are unfavorable (endothermic). Explain.

10. Arrange the following molecules from most to least polar, and explain your order: CH_4, CF_2Cl_2, CF_2H_2, CCl_4, and CCl_2H_2.

Exercises

WL Interactive versions of these problems may be assigned in OWL.

A blue exercise number indicates that the answer to that exercise appears at the back of this book and a solution appears in the *Solutions Guide*.

Chemical Bonds and Electronegativity

11. Distinguish between the terms *electronegativity* and *electron affinity*, *covalent bond* and *ionic bond*, and *pure covalent bond* and *polar covalent bond*. Characterize the types of bonds in terms of electronegativity difference. Energetically, why do ionic and covalent bonds form?

12. The following electrostatic potential diagrams represent H_2, HCl, or NaCl. Label each, and explain your choices.

13. An alternative definition of electronegativity is

$$\text{Electronegativity} = \text{constant (I.E.} - \text{E.A.)}$$

where I.E. is the ionization energy and E.A. is the electron affinity using the sign conventions of this book. Use data in Chapter 12 to calculate the (I.E. − E.A.) term for F, Cl, Br, and I. Do these values show the same trend as the electronegativity values given in this chapter? The first ionization energies of the halogens are 1678, 1255, 1138, and 1007 kJ/mol, respectively. (*Hint:* Choose a constant so that the electronegativity of fluorine equals 4.0. Using this constant, calculate relative electronegativities for the other halogens and compare to values given in the text.)

14. Use Coulomb's law,

$$V = \frac{Q_1Q_2}{4\pi\epsilon_0 r} = 2.31 \times 10^{-19} \text{ J nm}\left(\frac{Q_1Q_2}{r}\right)$$

to calculate the energy of interaction for the following two arrangements of charges, each having a magnitude equal to the electron charge.

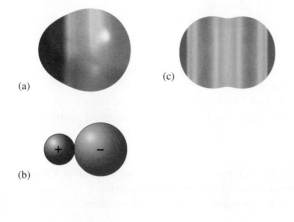

(a)

(b)

(c)

a. 1×10^{-10} m $\quad 1 \times 10^{-10}$ m
   $(+1) \longleftrightarrow (-1) \longleftarrow \infty \longrightarrow (+1) \longleftrightarrow (-1)$

b. 1×10^{-10} m (-1) 1×10^{-10} m
   $(+1) \quad (+1)$
   1×10^{-10} m (-1) 1×10^{-10} m

15. Without using Fig. 13.3, predict the order of increasing electronegativity in each of the following groups of elements.
    a. C, N, O
    b. S, Se, Cl
    c. Si, Ge, Sn
    d. Tl, S, Ge
    e. Na, K, Rb
    f. B, O, Ga

16. Without using Fig. 13.3, predict which bond in each of the following groups is the most polar.
    a. C—F, Si—F, Ge—F
    b. P—Cl, S—Cl
    c. S—F, S—Cl, S—Br
    d. Ti—Cl, Si—Cl, Ge—Cl
    e. C—H, Si—H, Sn—H
    f. Al—Br, Ga—Br, In—Br, Tl—Br

17. Repeat Exercises 15 and 16. This time use the values of the electronegativities of the elements given in Fig. 13.3. Are there any differences among your answers?

18. Hydrogen has an electronegativity value between boron and carbon and identical to phosphorus. With this in mind, rank the following bonds in order of decreasing polarity: P—H, O—H, N—H, F—H, C—H.

19. Rank the following bonds in order of increasing ionic character: N—O, Ca—O, C—F, Br—Br, K—F.

20. List all the possible bonds that can occur between the elements P, Cs, O, and H. Predict the type of bond (ionic, covalent, or polar covalent) one would expect to form for each bond.

21. Some plant fertilizer compounds are $(NH_4)_2SO_4$, $Ca_3(PO_4)_2$, K_2O, P_2O_5, and KCl. Which of these compounds contain both ionic and covalent bonds?

22. The following electrostatic potential diagrams represent CH_4, NH_3, or H_2O. Label each, and explain your choices.

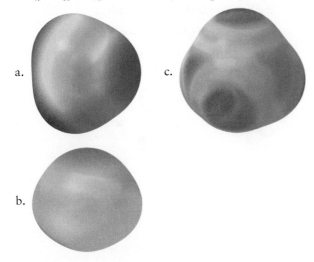

a.

c.

b.

Ions and Ionic Compounds

23. When an element forms an anion, what happens to the radius? When an element forms a cation, what happens to the radius? Why? Define the term *isoelectronic*. When comparing sizes of ions, which ion has the largest radius, and which ion has the smallest radius in an isoelectronic series? Why?

24. Consider the ions Sc^{3+}, Cl^-, K^+, Ca^{2+}, and S^{2-}. Match these ions to the following pictures that represent the relative sizes of the ions.

25. For each of the following groups, place the atoms and ions in order of decreasing size.
    a. Cu, Cu^+, Cu^{2+}
    b. Ni^{2+}, Pd^{2+}, Pt^{2+}
    c. O, O^-, O^{2-}
    d. La^{3+}, Eu^{3+}, Gd^{3+}, Yb^{3+}
    e. Te^{2-}, I^-, Cs^+, Ba^{2+}, La^{3+}

26. Write electron configurations for each of the following.
    a. the cations: Mg^{2+}, Sn^{2+}, K^+, Al^{3+}, Tl^+, As^{3+}
    b. the anions: N^{3-}, O^{2-}, F^-, Te^{2-}

27. Write electron configurations for the most stable ion formed by each of the elements Rb, Ba, Se, and I (when in stable ionic compounds).

28. Give an example of an ionic compound where both the anion and the cation are isoelectronic with each of the following noble gases.
    a. Ne
    b. Ar
    d. Kr
    e. Xe

29. What noble gas has the same electron configuration as each of the ions in the following compounds?
    a. cesium sulfide
    b. strontium fluoride
    c. calcium nitride
    d. aluminum bromide

30. Which of the following ions have noble gas electron configurations?
    a. Fe^{2+}, Fe^{3+}, Sc^{3+}, Co^{3+}
    b. Tl^+, Te^{2-}, Cr^{3+}
    c. Pu^{4+}, Ce^{4+}, Ti^{4+}
    d. Ba^{2+}, Pt^{2+}, Mn^{2+}

31. Give three ions that are isoelectronic with krypton. Place these ions in order of increasing size.

32. Which compound in each of the following pairs of ionic substances has the most exothermic lattice energy? Justify your answers.
    a. LiF, CsF
    b. NaBr, NaI
    c. $BaCl_2$, BaO
    d. Na_2SO_4, $CaSO_4$
    e. KF, K_2O
    f. Li_2O, Na_2S

33. Predict the empirical formulas of the ionic compounds formed from the following pairs of elements. Name each compound.
    a. Al and S
    b. K and N
    c. Mg and Cl
    d. Cs and Br

34. Following are some important properties of ionic compounds:
    i. low electrical conductivity as solids, and high conductivity in solution or when molten
    ii. relatively high melting and boiling points
    iii. brittleness

    How does the concept of ionic bonding discussed in this chapter account for these properties?

35. Use the following data to estimate ΔH_f° for potassium chloride.

$$K(s) + \tfrac{1}{2}Cl_2(g) \longrightarrow KCl(s)$$

Lattice energy	−690. kJ/mol
Ionization energy for K	419 kJ/mol
Electron affinity of Cl	−349 kJ/mol
Bond energy of Cl_2	239 kJ/mol
Enthalpy of sublimation for K	90. kJ/mol

36. Use the following data to estimate ΔH_f° for magnesium fluoride.

$$Mg(s) + F_2(g) \longrightarrow MgF_2(s)$$

Lattice energy	−2913 kJ/mol
First ionization energy of Mg	735 kJ/mol
Second ionization energy of Mg	1445 kJ/mol
Electron affinity of F	−328 kJ/mol
Bond energy of F_2	154 kJ/mol
Enthalpy of sublimation of Mg	150. kJ/mol

37. Consider the following: $Li(s) + \tfrac{1}{2}I_2(g) \rightarrow LiI(s)$ $\Delta H = -292$ kJ. $LiI(s)$ has a lattice energy of −753 kJ/mol. The ionization energy of $Li(g)$ is 520. kJ/mol, the bond energy of $I_2(g)$ is 151 kJ/mol, and the electron affinity of $I(g)$ is −295 kJ/mol. Use these data to determine the heat of sublimation of $Li(s)$.

38. In general, the higher the charge on the ions in an ionic compound, the more favorable is the lattice energy. Why do some stable ionic compounds have +1 charged ions even though +4, +5, and +6 charged ions would have a more favorable lattice energy?

39. Consider the following energy changes:

	ΔE (kJ/mol)
$Mg(g) \longrightarrow Mg^+(g) + e^-$	735
$Mg^+(g) \longrightarrow Mg^{2+}(g) + e^-$	1445
$O(g) + e^- \longrightarrow O^-(g)$	−141
$O^-(g) + e^- \longrightarrow O^{2-}(g)$	878

a. Magnesium oxide exists as $Mg^{2+}O^{2-}$, not as Mg^+O^-. Explain.
b. What experiment could be done to confirm that magnesium oxide does not exist as Mg^+O^-?

40. Use the following data (in kJ/mol) to estimate ΔH for the reaction $S^-(g) + e^- \rightarrow S^{2-}(g)$. Include an estimate of uncertainty.

	ΔH_f°	Lattice Energy	IE of M	ΔH_{sub} of M
Na_2S	−365	−2203	495	109
K_2S	−381	−2052	419	90.
Rb_2S	−361	−1949	409	82
Cs_2S	−360.	−1850.	382	78

$$S(s) \longrightarrow S(g) \qquad \Delta H = 277 \text{ kJ/mol}$$

$$S(g) + e^- \longrightarrow S^-(g) \qquad \Delta H = -200. \text{ kJ/mol}$$

41. Rationalize the following lattice energy values:

Compound	Lattice Energy (kJ/mol)
CaSe	−2862
Na_2Se	−2130
CaTe	−2721
Na_2Te	−2095

42. The lattice energies of $FeCl_3$, $FeCl_2$, and Fe_2O_3 are (in no particular order) −2631 kJ/mol, −5339 kJ/mol, and −14,774 kJ/mol. Match the appropriate formula to each lattice energy.

Bond Energies

43. Use bond energy values in Table 13.6 to estimate ΔH for each of the following reactions in the gas phase.
a. $H_2(g) + Cl_2(g) \rightarrow 2HCl(g)$
b. $N{\equiv}N(g) + 3H_2(g) \rightarrow 2NH_3(g)$

c. $H-C{\equiv}N(g) + 2H_2(g) \longrightarrow H-\underset{\underset{\displaystyle H}{|}}{\overset{\overset{\displaystyle H}{|}}{C}}-\underset{\underset{\displaystyle H}{|}}{\overset{\overset{\displaystyle H}{|}}{N}}(g)$

d. $\underset{H}{\overset{H}{>}}N-N\underset{H}{\overset{H}{<}}(g) + 2F_2(g) \longrightarrow N{\equiv}N(g) + 4HF(g)$

44. Compare your answers from parts a and b of Exercise 43 with ΔH values calculated for each reaction using standard enthalpies of formation in Appendix 4. Do enthalpy changes calculated from bond energies give a reasonable estimate of the actual values?

45. Use bond energies to predict ΔH for the isomerization of methyl isocyanide to acetonitrile.

$$CH_3N{\equiv}C(g) \longrightarrow CH_3C{\equiv}N(g)$$

46. Use data from Table 13.6 to estimate ΔH for the combustion of methane (CH_4), as shown below:

47. Use bond energies to estimate ΔH for the combustion of 1 mole of acetylene:

$$C_2H_2(g) + \tfrac{5}{2}O_2(g) \longrightarrow 2CO_2(g) + H_2O(g)$$

48. Consider the following reaction:

$$A_2 + B_2 \longrightarrow 2AB \qquad \Delta H = -285 \text{ kJ}$$

The bond energy for A_2 is one-half the amount of the AB bond energy. The bond energy of $B_2 = 432$ kJ/mol. What is the bond energy of A_2?

49. The space shuttle orbiter uses the oxidation of methyl hydrazine by dinitrogen tetroxide for propulsion:

$$5N_2O_4(g) + 4N_2H_3CH_3(g)$$
$$\longrightarrow 12H_2O(g) + 9N_2(g) + 4CO_2(g)$$

Use bond energies to estimate ΔH for this reaction. The structures for the reactants are

50. Following are three processes that have been used for the industrial manufacture of acrylonitrile—an important chemical used in the manufacture of plastics, synthetic rubber, and fibers. Use bond energy values (Tables 13.6 and 13.7) to estimate ΔH for each of the reactions.

b. $4CH_2{=}CHCH_3 + 6NO \xrightarrow[\text{Ag}]{700°C}$
$$4CH_2{=}CHCN + 6H_2O + N_2$$

The nitrogen–oxygen bond energy in nitric oxide (NO) is 630. kJ/mol.

c. $2CH_2{=}CHCH_3 + 2NH_3 + 3O_2 \xrightarrow[\text{425–510°C}]{\text{Catalyst}}$
$$2CH_2{=}CHCN + 6H_2O$$

51. Is the elevated temperature noted in parts b and c of Exercise 50 needed to provide energy to endothermic reactions?

52. Acetic acid is responsible for the sour taste of vinegar. It can be manufactured using the following reaction:

$$CH_3OH(g) + C{\equiv}O(g) \longrightarrow CH_3\overset{\displaystyle O}{\overset{\displaystyle \|}{C}}{-}OH(l)$$

Use tabulated values of bond energies (Table 13.6) to estimate ΔH for this reaction. Compare this result to the ΔH value calculated using standard enthalpies of formation in Appendix 4. Explain any discrepancies.

53. Use bond energies (Table 13.6), values of electron affinities (Table 12.8), and the ionization energy of hydrogen (1312 kJ/mol) to estimate ΔH for each of the following reactions.
   a. $HF(g) \longrightarrow H^+(g) + F^-(g)$
   b. $HCl(g) \longrightarrow H^+(g) + Cl^-(g)$
   c. $HI(g) \longrightarrow H^+(g) + I^-(g)$
   d. $H_2O(g) \longrightarrow H^+(g) + OH^-(g)$
   (Electron affinity of $OH(g) = -180.$ kJ/mol.)

54. The standard enthalpies of formation of $S(g)$, $F(g)$, $SF_4(g)$, and $SF_6(g)$ are $+278.8$ kJ/mol, $+79.0$ kJ/mol, -775 kJ/mol, and -1209 kJ/mol, respectively.
   a. Use these data to estimate the energy of an S—F bond.
   b. Compare the value that you calculated in part a with the value given in Table 13.6. What conclusions can you draw?
   c. Why are the ΔH_f° values for $S(g)$ and $F(g)$ not equal to zero, even though sulfur and fluorine are elements?

55. Use the following standard enthalpies of formation to estimate the N—H bond energy in ammonia. Compare this with the value in Table 13.6.

$N(g)$	472.7 kJ/mol
$H(g)$	216.0 kJ/mol
$NH_3(g)$	-46.1 kJ/mol

56. The standard enthalpy of formation for $NO(g)$ is 90. kJ/mol. Use this and the values for the $O{=}O$ and $N{\equiv}N$ bond energies to estimate the bond strength in NO.

Lewis Structures and Resonance

57. Write Lewis structures that obey the octet rule for each of the following. Except for HCN and H_2CO, the first atom listed is the central atom. For HCN and H_2CO, carbon is the central atom.
   a. HCN   d. NH_4^+ g. CO_2
   b. PH_3 e. H_2CO h. O_2
   c. $CHCl_3$ f. SeF_2 i. HBr

58. Draw a Lewis structure that obeys the octet rule for each of the following molecules and ions. In each case the first atom listed is the central atom.
   a. $POCl_3$, SO_4^{2-}, XeO_4, PO_4^{3-}, ClO_4^-
   b. NF_3, SO_3^{2-}, PO_3^{3-}, ClO_3^-
   c. ClO_2^-, SCl_2, PCl_2^-

59. Considering your answers to Exercise 58, what conclusions can you draw concerning the structures of species containing the same number of atoms and the same number of valence electrons?

60. Draw Lewis structures for the following. Show all resonance structures, where applicable. Carbon is the central atom in OCN^- and SCN^-.
   a. NO_2^-, NO_3^-, N_2O_4(N_2O_4 exists as $O_2N{-}NO_2$.)
   b. OCN^-, SCN^-, N_3^-

61. Some of the pollutants in the atmosphere are ozone, sulfur dioxide, and sulfur trioxide. Draw Lewis structures for these three molecules. Show all resonance structures.

62. Peroxyacetyl nitrate, or PAN, is present in photochemical smog. Draw Lewis structures (including resonance forms) for PAN. The skeletal arrangement is

63. A toxic cloud covered Bhopal, India, in December 1984 when water leaked into a tank of methyl isocyanate, and the product escaped into the atmosphere. Methyl isocya-

nate is used in the production of many pesticides. Draw the Lewis structures for methyl isocyanate, CH_3NCO, including resonance forms.

64. Explain the terms *resonance* and *delocalized electrons*. When a substance exhibits resonance, we say that none of the individual Lewis structures accurately portrays the bonding in the substance. Why do we draw resonance structures?

65. Benzene (C_6H_6) consists of a six-membered ring of carbon atoms with one hydrogen bonded to each carbon. Draw Lewis structures for benzene, including resonance structures.

66. An important observation supporting the need for resonance in the LE model is that there are only three different structures of dichlorobenzene ($C_6H_4Cl_2$). How does this fact support the need for the concept of resonance?

67. Borazine ($B_3N_3H_6$) has often been called "inorganic" benzene. Draw Lewis structures for borazine. Borazine is a six-membered ring of alternating boron and nitrogen atoms.

68. Draw all the possible Lewis structures for dimethylborazine [$(CH_3)_2B_3N_3H_4$]. (See Exercise 67.) Would there be a different number of structures if there was no resonance?

69. Which of the following statements is(are) true? Correct the false statements.
   a. It is impossible to satisfy the octet rule for all atoms in XeF_2.
   b. Because SF_4 exists, OF_4 should also exist because oxygen is in the same family as sulfur.
   c. The bond in NO^+ should be stronger than the bond in NO^-.
   d. As predicted from the two Lewis structures for ozone, one oxygen–oxygen bond is stronger than the other oxygen–oxygen bond.

70. Lewis structures can be used to understand why some molecules react in certain ways. Write the Lewis structures for the reactants and products in the reactions described below.
   a. Nitrogen dioxide dimerizes to produce dinitrogen tetroxide.
   b. Boron trihydride accepts a pair of electrons from ammonia, forming BH_3NH_3.

   Give a possible explanation for why these two reactions occur.

71. The most common type of exception to the octet rule are compounds or ions with central atoms having more than eight electrons around them. PF_5, SF_4, ClF_3, and Br_3^- are examples of this type of exception. Draw the Lewis structures for these compounds or ions. Which elements, when they have to, can have more than eight electrons around them? How is this rationalized?

72. SF_6, ClF_5, and XeF_4 are three compounds whose central atoms do not follow the octet rule. Draw Lewis structures for these compounds.

73. Consider the following bond lengths:

   C—O   1.43 Å   C=O   1.23 Å   C≡O   1.09 Å

   In the CO_3^{2-} ion, all three C—O bonds have identical bond lengths of 1.36 Å. Why?

74. Order the following species with respect to the carbon–oxygen bond length (longest to shortest):

   $$CO, CO_2, CO_3^{2-}, CH_3OH$$

   What is the order from the weakest to the strongest carbon–oxygen bond?

75. Place the species below in order of the shortest to the longest nitrogen–oxygen bond.

   $$H_2NOH, \quad N_2O, \quad NO^+, \quad NO_2^-, \quad NO_3^-$$

   (H_2NOH exists as $H_2N—OH$.)

Formal Charge

76. Use the formal charge arguments to rationalize why BF_3 would not follow the octet rule.

77. Use formal charge arguments to explain why CO has a much smaller dipole moment than would be expected on the basis of electronegativity.

78. Nitrous oxide (N_2O) has three possible Lewis structures:

   $$:N{=}N{=}\ddot{O}: \longleftrightarrow :N{\equiv}N{-}\ddot{\ddot{O}}: \longleftrightarrow :\ddot{N}{-}N{\equiv}O:$$

   Given the following bond lengths,

N—N	167 pm	N=O	115 pm
N=N	120 pm	N—O	147 pm
N≡N	110 pm		

   rationalize the observations that the N—N bond length in N_2O is 112 pm and that the N—O bond length is 119 pm. Assign formal charges to the resonance structures for N_2O. Can you eliminate any of the resonance structures on the basis of formal charges? Is this consistent with observation?

79. Draw Lewis structures that obey the octet rule for the following species. Assign the formal charge to each central atom.
   a. $POCl_3$ c. ClO_4^- e. SO_2Cl_2 g. ClO_3^-
   b. SO_4^{2-} d. PO_4^{3-} f. XeO_4 h. NO_4^{3-}

80. Draw the Lewis structures that involve minimum formal charges for the species in Exercise 79.

81. When molten sulfur reacts with chlorine gas, a vile-smelling orange liquid forms that has an empirical formula of SCl. The structure of this compound has a formal charge of zero on all elements in the compound. Draw the Lewis structure for the vile-smelling orange liquid.

82. Oxidation of the cyanide ion produces the stable cyanate ion (OCN^-). The fulminate ion (CNO^-), on the other hand, is very unstable. Fulminate salts explode when struck; $Hg(CNO)_2$ is used in blasting caps. Write the Lewis structures and assign formal charges for the cyanate and fulminate ions. Why is the fulminate ion so unstable? (C is the central atom in OCN^-, and N is the central atom in CNO^-.)

83. Write the Lewis Structure for O_2F_2 (O_2F_2 exists as F—O—O—F). Assign oxidation states and formal charges to the atoms in O_2F_2. This compound is a vigorous and

potent oxidizing and fluorinating agent. Are oxidation states or formal charges more useful in accounting for these properties of O_2F_2?

84. Benzoic acid is a food preservative. The space-filling model for benzoic acid is shown below.

- ● C
- ○ H
- ● O

Benzoic acid
($C_6H_5CO_2H$)

Draw the Lewis structure for benzoic acid, including all resonance structures in which all atoms have a formal charge of zero.

Molecular Structure and Polarity

85. Write the name of each of the following molecular structures.

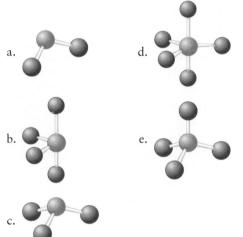

a.

b.

c.

d.

e.

86. State whether or not each of the following has a permanent dipole moment.

a.

b.

c.

d.

e.

f.

87. Predict the molecular structure and the bond angles for each molecule or ion in Exercises 57, 58, and 60.

88. Predict the molecular structure and the bond angles for each of the following.
   a. SeO_3 b. SeO_2 c. PCl_3 d. SCl_2 e. SiF_4

89. There are several molecular structures based on the trigonal bipyramid geometry. Three such structures are

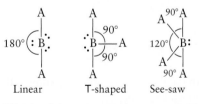

Linear   T-shaped   See-saw

Which of the compounds or ions in Exercises 71 and 72 have these molecular structures?

90. Two variations of the octahedral geometry are illustrated below.

Square planar   Square pyramid

Which of the compounds or ions in Exercises 71 and 72 have these molecular structures?

91. Predict the molecular structure and the bond angles for each of the following. (See Exercises 89 and 90.)
    a. $XeCl_2$ b. ICl_3 c. TeF_4 d. PCl_5

92. Predict the molecular structure and the bond angles for each of the following. (See Exercises 89 and 90.)
    a. ICl_5 b. $XeCl_4$ c. $SeCl_6$

93. Which of the molecules in Exercise 88 have net dipole moments (are polar)?

94. Which of the molecules in Exercises 91 and 92 have net dipole moments (are polar)?

95. Give two requirements that should be satisfied for a molecule to be polar. Explain why CF_4 and XeF_4 are nonpolar compounds (have no net dipole moments), whereas SF_4 is polar (has a net dipole moment). Is CO_2 polar? What about COS? Explain.

96. What do each of the following sets of compounds/ions have in common with each other? Reference your Lewis structures for Exercises 88, 91, and 92.
    a. $XeCl_4$, $XeCl_2$
    b. ICl_5, TeF_4, ICl_3, PCl_3, SCl_2, SeO_2

97. Which of the following statements is(are) true? Correct the false statements.
    a. The molecules SeS_3, SeS_2, PCl_5, $TeCl_4$, ICl_3, and $XeCl_2$ all exhibit at least one bond angle which is approximately 120 degrees.
    b. The bond angle in SO_2 should be similar to the bond angle in CS_2 or SCl_2.
    c. Of the compounds CF_4, KrF_4, and SeF_4, only SeF_4 exhibits an overall dipole moment (is polar).
    d. Central atoms in a molecule adopt a geometry of the bonded atoms and lone pairs about the central atom in order to maximize electron repulsions.

98. Consider the following Lewis structure, where E is an unknown element:

What are some possible identities for element E? Predict the molecular structure (including bond angles) for this ion.

99. Consider the following Lewis structure, where E is an unknown element:

What are some possible identities for element E? Predict the molecular structure (including bond angles) for this ion. (See Exercises 89 and 90.)

100. Although the VSEPR model is correct in predicting that CH_4 is tetrahedral, NH_3 is pyramidal, and H_2O is bent, the model in its simplest form does not account for the fact that these molecules do not have exactly the same bond angles (< HCH is 109.5 degrees, as expected for a tetrahedron, but < HNH is 107.3 degrees and < HOH is 104.5 degrees). Explain these deviations from the tetrahedral angle.

101. Draw Lewis structures and predict the molecular structures of the following. (See Exercises 89 and 90.)
    a. OCl_2, KrF_2, BeH_2, SO_2 c. CF_4, SeF_4, KrF_4
    b. SO_3, NF_3, IF_3 d. IF_5, AsF_5

    Which of the above compounds have net dipole moments (are polar)?

102. Which of the following molecules have net dipole moments? For the molecules that are polar, indicate the polarity of each bond and the direction of the net dipole moment of the molecule.
    a. CH_2Cl_2, $CHCl_3$, CCl_4
    b. CO_2, N_2O
    c. PH_3, NH_3

103. The molecules BF_3, CF_4, CO_2, PF_5, and SF_6 are all nonpolar, even though they contain polar bonds. Why?

Additional Exercises

104. Although both the Br_3^- and I_3^- ions are known, the F_3^- ion does not exist. Explain.

105. Write Lewis structures for CO_3^{2-}, HCO_3^-, and H_2CO_3. When acid is added to an aqueous solution containing carbonate or bicarbonate ions, carbon dioxide gas is formed. We generally say that carbonic acid (H_2CO_3) is unstable. Use bond energies to estimate ΔH for the reaction (in the gas phase):

$$H_2CO_3 \longrightarrow CO_2 + H_2O$$

Specify a possible cause for the instability of carbonic acid.

106. The structure of TeF_5^- is

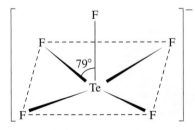

Draw a complete Lewis structure for TeF_5^-, and explain the distortion from the ideal square pyramidal structure. (See Exercise 90.)

107. The compound NF_3 is quite stable, but NCl_3 is very unstable (NCl_3 was first synthesized in 1811 by P. L. Dulong, who lost three fingers and an eye studying its properties). The compounds NBr_3 and NI_3 are unknown, although the explosive compound $NI_3 \cdot NH_3$ is known. Account for the instability of these halides of nitrogen.

108. There are two possible structures of XeF_2Cl_2, where Xe is the central atom. Draw them, and describe how measurements of dipole moments might be used to distinguish among them.

109. Which member of the following pairs would you expect to be more energetically stable? Justify each choice.
    a. NaBr or $NaBr_2$ c. SO_4 or XeO_4
    b. ClO_4 or ClO_4^- d. OF_4 or SeF_4

110. Many times, extra stability is characteristic of a molecule or ion in which resonance is possible. How could this feature be used to explain the acidities of the following compounds? (The acidic hydrogen is marked by an asterisk.) Part c shows resonance in the phenyl ring (C_6H_5).

    a.
    $$\overset{\displaystyle O}{\underset{\displaystyle \shortparallel}{H-C-OH^*}}$$

    b.
    $$CH_3-\overset{\displaystyle O}{\underset{\displaystyle \shortparallel}{C}}-CH=\overset{\displaystyle OH^*}{C}-CH_3$$

    c.
    OH*
    (benzene ring with OH* substituent)

111. Arrange the following in order of increasing radius and increasing ionization energy.
    a. N^+, N, N^-
    b. Se, Se^-, Cl, Cl^+
    c. Br^-, Rb^+, Sr^{2+}

112. Draw a Lewis structure for the N,N-dimethylformamide molecule. The skeletal structure is

$$H-\overset{\displaystyle O}{\underset{\displaystyle \mid}{C}}-\overset{\displaystyle \mid}{N}-CH_3$$
$$\underset{\displaystyle CH_3}{\mid}$$

Various types of evidence lead to the conclusion that there is some double-bond character to one of the C—N bonds. Draw one or more resonance structures that support this observation.

113. A compound, XF_5, is 42.81% fluorine by mass. Identify the element X. What is the molecular structure of XF_5?

114. The study of carbon-containing compounds and their properties is called organic chemistry. Besides carbon atoms, *organic compounds* also can contain hydrogen, oxygen, and nitrogen atoms (as well as other types of atoms). A common trait of simple organic compounds is to have Lewis structures in which all atoms have a formal charge of zero. Consider the following incomplete Lewis structure for an organic compound called *histidine* (one of the amino acids, which are the building blocks of proteins found in human bodies):

Draw a complete Lewis structure for histidine in which all atoms have a formal charge of zero. What are the approximate bond angles about the carbon atom labeled 1 and the nitrogen atom labeled 2?

115. Do the Lewis structures obtained in Exercises 79 and 80 predict the same molecular structure for each case?

116. Predict the molecular structure for each of the following. (See Exercises 89 and 90.)
    a. $BrFI_2$ b. XeO_2F_2 c. $TeF_2Cl_3^-$

    For each formula, there are at least two different structures that can be drawn using the same central atom. Draw the possible structures for each formula.

Challenge Problems

117. Predict the molecular structure of KrF_2. Using hyperconjugation, draw the Lewis structures for KrF_2 that obey the octet rule. Show all resonance forms.

118. Consider the following computer-generated model of caffeine.

    ● H
    ● O
    ● N
    ● C

    Draw a Lewis structure for caffeine in which all atoms have a formal charge of zero.

119. Given the following information:

    Heat of sublimation of Li(s) = 166 kJ/mol
    Bond energy of HCl = 427 kJ/mol
    Ionization energy of Li(g) = 520. kJ/mol
    Electron affinity of Cl(g) = −349 kJ/mol
    Lattice energy of LiCl(s) = −829 kJ/mol
    Bond energy of H_2 = 432 kJ/mol

    Calculate the net change in energy for the following reaction:

    $$2Li(s) + 2HCl(g) \longrightarrow 2LiCl(s) + H_2(g)$$

120. Use data in this chapter and Chapter 12 to discuss why MgO is an ionic compound but CO is not an ionic compound.

121. A promising new material with great potential as a fuel in solid rocket motors is ammonium dinitramide $[NH_4N(NO_2)_2]$.
    a. Draw Lewis structures (including resonance forms) for the dinitramide ion $[N(NO_2)_2^-]$.
    b. Predict the bond angles around each nitrogen in the dinitramide ion.
    c. Ammonium dinitramide can decompose explosively to nitrogen, water, and oxygen. Write a balanced equation for this reaction, and use bond energies to estimate ΔH for the explosive decomposition of this compound.
    d. To estimate ΔH from bond energies, you made several assumptions. What are some of your assumptions?

122. Think of forming an ionic compound as three steps (this is a simplification, as with all models): (1) removing an electron from the metal, (2) adding an electron to the nonmetal, and (3) allowing the metal cation and non-metal anion to come together.
    a. What is the sign of the energy change for each of these three processes?
    b. In general, what is the sign of the sum of the first two processes? Use examples to support your answer.
    c. What must be the sign of the sum of the three processes?
    d. Given your answer to part c, why do ionic bonds occur?
    e. Given your explanations to part d, why is NaCl stable but not Na_2Cl and $NaCl_2$? What about MgO compared to MgO_2 and Mg_2O?

123. The compound hexaazaisowurtzitane is one of the highest-energy explosives known (*C & E News*, p. 26, Jan. 17, 1994). The compound, also known as CL-20, was first synthesized in 1987. The method of synthesis and detailed performance data are still classified information because of CL-20's potential military application in rocket boosters and in warheads of "smart" weapons. The structure of CL-20 is

In such shorthand structures, each point where lines meet represents a carbon atom. In addition, the hydrogens attached to the carbon atoms are omitted. Each of the six carbon atoms has one hydrogen atom attached. Three possible reactions for the explosive decomposition of CL-20 are

  i. $C_6H_6N_{12}O_{12}(s) \longrightarrow$
$$6CO(g) + 6N_2(g) + 3H_2O(g) + \tfrac{3}{2}O_2(g)$$
  ii. $C_6H_6N_{12}O_{12}(s) \longrightarrow$
$$3CO(g) + 3CO_2(g) + 6N_2(g) + 3H_2O(g)$$
  iii. $C_6H_6N_{12}O_{12}(s) \longrightarrow$
$$6CO_2(g) + 6N_2(g) + 3H_2(g)$$

  a. Use bond energies to estimate ΔH for these three reactions.
  b. Which of the above reactions releases the largest amount of energy per kilogram of CL-20?

124. In molecules of the type X—O—H, as the electronegativity of X increases, the acid strength increases. In addition, if the electronegativity of X is a very small value, the molecule acts like a base. Explain these observations and provide examples.

125. Calculate the standard heat of formation of the compound $ICl(g)$ at 25°C. (*Hint:* Use Table 13.6 and Appendix 4 data.)

126. An ionic compound made from the metal M and the diatomic gas X_2 has the formula M_aX_b, in which $a = 1$ or 2 and $b = 1$ or 2. Use the data provided to determine the most likely values for a and b, along with the most likely charges for each of the ions in the ionic compound.

Data (in units of kJ/mol)

Successive ionization energies of M: 480., 4750.

Successive electron affinity values for X: -175, 920.

Enthalpy of sublimation for $M(s) \rightarrow M(g)$: 110.

Bond energy of X_2: 250.

Lattice energy for MX (M^+ and X^-): -1200. kJ/mol

Lattice energy for MX_2 (M^{2+} and X^-): -3500. kJ/mol

Lattice energy for M_2X (M^+ and X^{2-}): -3600. kJ/mol

Lattice energy for MX (M^{2+} and X^{2-}): -4800. kJ/mol

Marathon Problem

127. Identify the following five compounds of H, N, and O. For each compound, write a Lewis structure that is consistent with the information given.
    a. All the compounds are electrolytes, although not all are strong electrolytes. Compounds C and D are ionic and compound B is covalent.
    b. Nitrogen occurs in its highest possible oxidation state in compounds A and C; nitrogen occurs in its lowest possible oxidation state in compounds C, D, and E. The formal charge on both nitrogens in compound C is +1; the formal charge on the only nitrogen in compound B is 0.

c. Compounds A and E exist in solution. Both solutions give off gases. Commercially available concentrated solutions of compound A are normally 16 M. The commercial, concentrated solution of compound E is 15 M.

d. Commercial solutions of compound E are labeled with a misnomer that implies that a binary, gaseous compound of nitrogen and hydrogen has reacted with water to produce ammonium ions and hydroxide ions. Actually, this reaction occurs to only a slight extent.

e. Compound D is 43.7% N and 50.0% O by mass. If compound D were a gas at STP, it would have a density of 2.86 g/L.

f. A formula unit of compound C has one more oxygen than a formula unit of compound D. Compounds C and A have one ion in common when compound A is acting as a strong electrolyte.

g. Solutions of compound C are weakly acidic; solutions of compound A are strongly acidic; solutions of compounds B and E are basic. The titration of 0.726 g of compound B requires 21.98 mL of 1.000 M HCl for complete neutralization.

Covalent Bonding: Orbitals

14

chapter

A stylized model of a nitrogen molecule.

In Chapter 13 we discussed the fundamental concepts of bonding and introduced the most widely used simple model for covalent bonding: the localized electron (LE) model. We saw the usefulness of a bonding model as a means for systematizing chemistry by allowing us to look at molecules in terms of individual bonds. We also saw that the approximate molecular structure can be predicted using a model that focuses on minimizing electron-pair repulsions. In this chapter we will examine bonding models in more detail, particularly focusing on the role of orbitals.

14.1 | Hybridization and the Localized Electron Model

Recall that the LE model views a molecule as a collection of atoms bound together by sharing electrons between atomic orbitals. The arrangement of valence electrons is represented by the Lewis structure (or structures, where resonance occurs), and the approximate molecular geometry can be predicted using the VSEPR model. In this section we will describe what types of atomic orbitals are used by this model to share the electrons and hence to form the bonds.

sp^3 Hybridization

Let's reconsider the bonding in methane, which has the Lewis structure and molecular geometry shown in Fig. 14.1. In general, we assume that bonding involves only the valence orbitals. This means that the hydrogen atoms in methane use $1s$ orbitals. The valence orbitals of a carbon atom are the $2s$ and $2p$ orbitals shown in Fig. 14.2. Thinking about how carbon can use these orbitals to bond to the hydrogen atoms reveals two related problems:

1. Using the $2p$ and $2s$ atomic orbitals will lead to two different types of C—H bonds: (a) those from the overlap of a $2p$ orbital of carbon and a $1s$ orbital of hydrogen (there will be three of these) and (b) those from the overlap of a $2s$ orbital of carbon and a $1s$ orbital of hydrogen (there will be one of these). This presents a problem because the experimental evidence indicates that methane has four identical C—H bonds.

2. Since the carbon $2p$ orbitals are mutually perpendicular, we might expect the three C—H bonds formed with these orbitals to be oriented at 90-degree angles:

However, the methane molecule is known by experiment to be tetrahedral with bond angles of 109.5 degrees.

This analysis suggests that carbon adopts a set of atomic orbitals other than its "native" $2s$ and $2p$ orbitals to bond to the hydrogen atoms in forming the methane molecule. In fact, it is not surprising that the $2s$ and $2p$ orbitals present on an *isolated* carbon atom might not be the best set of orbitals for bonding. That is, a different set of atomic orbitals might better serve the carbon atom to form the most stable CH_4 molecule.

To account for the known structure of methane in terms of this model, we need a set of four equivalent atomic orbitals, arranged tetrahedrally. In fact, such a set of orbitals can be obtained quite readily by combining the carbon $2s$ and $2p$ orbitals, as shown schematically in Fig. 14.3. This mixing of the na-

Figure 14.1

(a) The Lewis structure of the methane molecule. (b) The tetrahedral molecular geometry of the methane molecule.

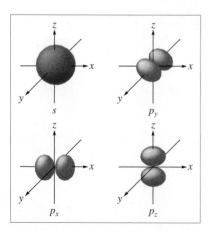

Figure 14.2

The valence orbitals on a free carbon atom: $2s$, $2p_x$, $2p_y$, and $2p_z$.

Hybridization is a modification of the LE model to account for the observation that atoms often seem to use special atomic orbitals in forming molecules.

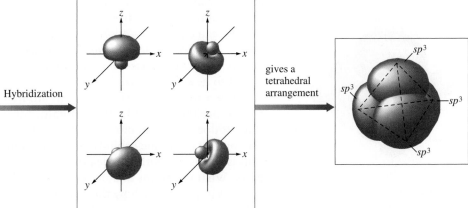

Figure 14.3
The "native" 2s and three 2p atomic orbitals characteristic of a free carbon atom are combined to form a new set of four sp³ orbitals. The small lobes of the orbitals are usually omitted from diagrams for clarity.

Figure 14.4
Cross section of an sp³ orbital. Generated from a program by Robert Allendoerfer on Project SERAPHIM disk PC 2402; reprinted with permission.

sp³ hybridization gives a tetrahedral set of orbitals.

tive atomic orbitals to form special orbitals for bonding is called **hybridization.** The four new orbitals are called sp^3 orbitals since they are formed from one 2s and three 2p orbitals (s^1p^3). Similarly, we say that the carbon atom undergoes sp^3 **hybridization** or is described to be sp^3 hybridized. The four sp^3 orbitals are identical in shape, each one having a large lobe and a small lobe (Fig. 14.4). The four orbitals are oriented in space so that the large lobes form a tetrahedral arrangement, as shown in Fig. 14.3.

The linear combinations of the 2s and 2p orbitals that give the four sp^3 hybrid orbitals are listed below:

$$\phi_1 = \tfrac{1}{2}[(s) + (p_x) + (p_y) + (p_z)]$$

$$\phi_2 = \tfrac{1}{2}[(s) + (p_x) - (p_y) - (p_z)]$$

$$\phi_3 = \tfrac{1}{2}[(s) - (p_x) + (p_y) - (p_z)]$$

$$\phi_4 = \tfrac{1}{2}[(s) - (p_x) - (p_y) + (p_z)]$$

where (s) and (p) represent 2s and 2p atomic orbital functions, and where the factor of $\tfrac{1}{2}$ is present to satisfy the boundary condition that the total probability is 1 for each orbital. Each of the functions ϕ_1, ϕ_2, ϕ_3, and ϕ_4 represents a separate sp^3 hybrid orbital.

The hybridization of the carbon 2s and 2p orbitals can also be represented by an orbital energy-level diagram, as shown in Fig. 14.5. Note that electrons have been omitted because we are not concerned with the electron arrangements on the individual atoms—it is the total number of valence electrons and the arrangement of those electrons in the *molecule* that are important.

In summary, the experimentally known structure of methane can be explained by the LE model if we assume that carbon adopts a special set of sp^3

Figure 14.5
An energy-level diagram showing the formation of four sp³ orbitals.

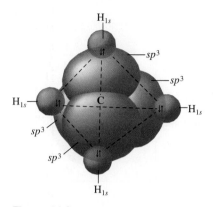

Figure 14.6
The tetrahedral set of four sp^3 orbitals on the carbon atom is used to share electron pairs with the four 1s orbitals of the hydrogen atoms to form the four equivalent C—H bonds. This accounts for the known tetrahedral structure of the CH_4 molecule.

atomic orbitals oriented toward the corners of a tetrahedron, which are then used to bond to the hydrogen atoms, as shown in Fig. 14.6.

We can extend this analysis to any molecule that forms a tetrahedral set of bonds: *Whenever a set of equivalent tetrahedral atomic orbitals is required by an atom, this model assumes that the atom forms a set of sp^3 orbitals; the atom is said to be sp^3 hybridized.*

It is really not surprising that an atom in a molecule might adopt a set of atomic orbitals, called **hybrid orbitals,** different from those it has in the free state. It does not seem unreasonable that to achieve minimum energy, an atom uses one set of atomic orbitals in the free state and a different set in a molecule. This is consistent with the idea that a molecule is more than simply a sum of its parts. What the atoms in a molecule were like before the molecule was formed is not as important as how the electrons are best arranged in the molecule. The individual atoms are assumed to respond as needed to achieve the minimum energy for the molecule. However, although hybridization enables us to account for the known structures of molecules, its predictions about the energies of the electrons in molecules are often incorrect. For example, the sp^3 model for methane predicts that all four pairs of electrons have identical energies. Experiments show, however, that in methane two of the electrons are present at a lower energy than the other six. This situation reminds us again that we must be cautious when we use models. Models are *always* oversimplifications and will give misleading predictions if used incorrectly. The LE model using hybridization does a very good job of accounting for molecular structures but does not accurately describe electron energies.

EXAMPLE 14.1

Describe the bonding in the ammonia molecule using the LE model.

Solution A complete description of the bonding involves three steps:

1. Write the Lewis structure.
2. Determine the arrangement of electron pairs using the VSEPR model.
3. Determine the hybrid atomic orbitals used for bonding in the molecule.

The Lewis structure for NH_3 is

The four electron pairs around the nitrogen atom require a tetrahedral arrangement. We have seen that a tetrahedral set of sp^3 hybrid orbitals is obtained by combining the 2s and three 2p orbitals. In the NH_3 molecule, three of the sp^3 orbitals are used to form bonds to the three hydrogen atoms, and the fourth sp^3 orbital is used to hold the lone pair, as shown in Fig. 14.7.

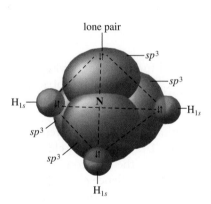

Figure 14.7
The nitrogen atom in ammonia is sp^3 hybridized.

sp^2 Hybridization

Ethylene (C_2H_4) is an important starting material in the manufacture of plastics. The C_2H_4 molecule has 12 valence electrons and the following Lewis structure:

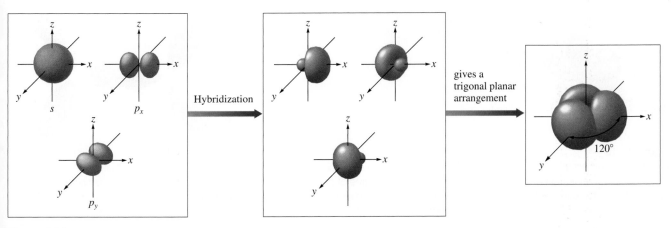

Figure 14.8
The hybridization of the s, p_x, and p_y atomic orbitals results in the formation of three sp^2 orbitals centered in the xy plane. The large lobes of the orbitals lie in the plane at angles of 120 degrees and point toward the corners of a triangle.

The assumption that a double bond acts as one effective electron pair, equivalent to a single bonding pair, works well to give the *approximate* molecular structure.

sp^2 hybridization gives a trigonal planar arrangement of atomic orbitals.

The plastics shown here were manufactured with a polymer based on ethylene.

Recall that in the VSEPR model a double bond acts as one effective pair. Thus in the ethylene molecule each carbon is surrounded by three effective pairs. This model requires a trigonal planar arrangement with bond angles of 120 degrees. What orbitals do the carbon atoms use in this molecule? The molecular geometry requires a planar set of orbitals at angles of 120 degrees. Since the 2s and 2p valence orbitals of carbon do not have the required arrangement, we need a set of hybrid orbitals.

The sp^3 orbitals we have just considered will not work because they exhibit angles of 109.5 degrees rather than the required 120 degrees. Therefore, in ethylene the carbon atom must hybridize in a different manner. A set of three orbitals arranged at 120-degree angles in the same plane can be obtained by combining one s orbital and two p orbitals, as shown schematically in Fig. 14.8. The orbital energy-level diagram for this arrangement is shown in Fig. 14.9. Since one 2s and two 2p orbitals are used to form these hybrid orbitals, this is called sp^2 **hybridization**. Note from Fig. 14.8 that the plane of the sp^2 hybridized orbitals is determined by which p orbitals are used. Since in this case we have arbitrarily decided to use the p_x and p_y orbitals, the hybrid orbitals are centered in the xy plane. We will not show the detailed forms of these functions.

In the formation of the sp^2 orbitals, one 2p orbital on carbon has not been used. This remaining p orbital (p_z) is oriented perpendicular to the plane of the sp^2 orbitals, as shown in Fig. 14.10.

Now we will see how these orbitals can be used to account for the Lewis structure of ethylene. The three sp^2 orbitals on each carbon are used to share electrons, as shown in Fig. 14.11. In each of these bonds, the electron pair is shared in an area centered on a line running between the atoms. This type of

Figure 14.9
An orbital energy-level diagram for sp^2 hybridization. Note that one p orbital remains unchanged.

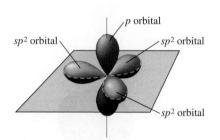

Figure 14.10
When one *s* and two *p* orbitals are mixed to form a set of three *sp*² orbitals, one *p* orbital remains unchanged and is perpendicular to the plane of the hybrid orbitals. Note that in this figure and those that follow, the hybrid orbitals are drawn with narrowed lobes to show their orientations more clearly.

Figure 14.11
The σ bonds in ethylene. Note that for each bond the shared electron pair occupies the region directly between the atoms.

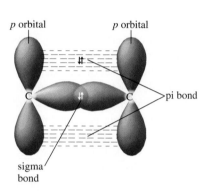

Figure 14.12
A carbon–carbon double bond consists of a σ bond and a π bond. In the σ bond, the shared electrons occupy the space directly between the atoms. The π bond, is formed from the unhybridized *p* orbitals on the two carbon atoms. In a π bond, the shared electron pair occupies the space above and below a line joining the atoms.

covalent bond is called a **sigma (σ) bond.** In the ethylene molecule, the σ bonds are formed using the *sp*² orbitals on each carbon atom and the 1*s* orbital on each hydrogen atom.

How can we explain the double bond between the carbon atoms? In the σ bond, the electron pair occupies the space between the carbon atoms. The second bond must therefore result from sharing an electron pair in the space *above and below* the σ bond. This type of bond can be formed using the 2*p* orbital perpendicular to the *sp*² hybrid orbitals on each carbon atom (refer to Fig. 14.10). These parallel *p* orbitals can share an electron pair, which occupies the space above and below a line joining the atoms, to form a **pi (π) bond,** as shown in Fig. 14.12.

Note that σ bonds are formed from orbitals whose lobes point toward each other, but π bonds result from parallel orbitals. A *double bond consists of one σ bond*, where the electron pair is located directly between the atoms, *and one π bond*, where the shared pair occupies the space above and below the σ bond.

We can now completely specify the orbitals used to form the bonds in the ethylene molecule. As shown in Fig. 14.13, the carbon atoms are described as using *sp*² hybrid orbitals to form the σ bonds to the hydrogen atoms and to each other and using *p* orbitals to form the π bond with each other. Note that we have accounted fully for the Lewis structure of ethylene with its carbon–carbon double bond and carbon–hydrogen single bonds.

This example illustrates an important general principle of this model: *Whenever an atom is surrounded by three effective pairs, a set of sp² hybrid orbitals is required.*

sp Hybridization

Another type of hybridization occurs in carbon dioxide, which has the following Lewis structure:

$$\ddot{O}=C=\ddot{O}$$

Figure 14.13
(a) The orbitals used to form the bonds in ethylene. (b) The Lewis structure for ethylene.

(a)

(b)

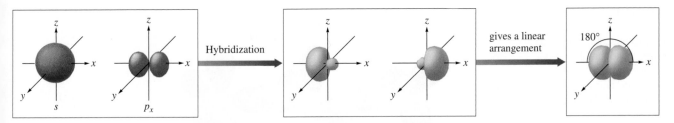

Figure 14.14
When one *s* orbital and one *p* orbital are hybridized, a set of two *sp* orbitals oriented at 180 degrees results.

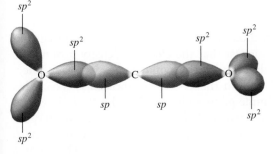

Figure 14.15
The hybrid orbitals in the CO_2 molecule.

Figure 14.16
The orbital energy-level diagram for the formation of *sp* hybrid orbitals of carbon.

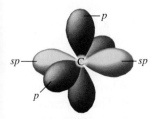

Figure 14.17
The orbitals of an *sp* hybridized carbon atom.

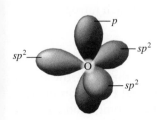

Figure 14.18
The orbital arrangement for an *sp²* hybridized oxygen atom.

In the CO_2 molecule, the carbon atom has two effective pairs that are arranged at an angle of 180 degrees. We therefore need a pair of atomic orbitals oriented in opposite directions. This requires a new type of hybridization, since neither sp^3 nor sp^2 hybrid orbitals fit this case. Obtaining two hybrid orbitals arranged at 180 degrees requires **sp hybridization,** involving one *s* orbital and one *p* orbital, as shown schematically in Fig. 14.14.

In terms of this model, *two effective pairs around an atom will always require* sp *hybridization of that atom.* The *sp* orbitals of carbon in carbon dioxide are shown in Fig. 14.15, and the corresponding orbital energy-level diagram for their formation is given in Fig. 14.16. The *sp* hybrid orbitals are used to form the σ bonds between carbon and the oxygen atoms. Note that two $2p$ orbitals remain unchanged on the *sp* hybridized carbon. They are used to form the π bonds to the oxygen atoms.

In the CO_2 molecule, each oxygen atom has three effective pairs around it, requiring a trigonal planar arrangement of the pairs. Since a trigonal set of hybrid orbitals corresponds to sp^2 hybridization, each oxygen atom can be assumed to be sp^2 hybridized. The orbital on each oxygen left unchanged by the hybridization process is used for the π bond to the carbon atom.

Now we are ready to account for the Lewis structure of carbon dioxide. The *sp* orbitals on carbon form σ bonds with the sp^2 orbitals on the two oxygen atoms (Fig. 14.15). The remaining sp^2 orbitals on the oxygen atoms hold lone pairs. The π bonds between the carbon atom and each oxygen atom are formed by the overlap of parallel $2p$ orbitals. The *sp* hybridized carbon atom has two unhybridized *p* orbitals, pictured in Fig. 14.17. Each of these *p* orbitals is used to form a π bond with an oxygen atom (Fig. 14.18). The total bonding picture predicted by the LE model for the CO_2 molecule is shown in Fig. 14.19. Note that this picture of the bonding neatly explains the arrangement of electrons predicted by the Lewis structure.

It is useful to remind ourselves at this point that because we are using a very simple bonding model, the picture of a molecule we get from this model is

Figure 14.19
(a) The orbitals predicted by the LE model to describe the bonds in carbon dioxide. Note that the carbon–oxygen double bonds each consist of one σ bond and one π bond. (b) The Lewis structure for carbon dioxide.

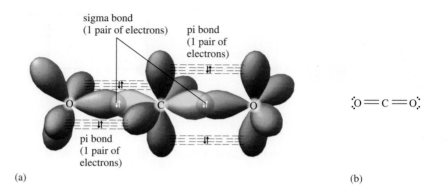

(a)

(b)

an approximate one. The carbon dioxide molecule provides a good case in point. Various types of evidence suggest that the electron density around the two C—O bonds in CO_2 is actually cylindrically symmetric—that is, the electron density is homogeneous all around the O—C—O molecular axis. This result is not consistent with the simple picture given in Fig. 14.19(a), in which the two C—O bonds have their π electron densities centered in two perpendicular planes. The model can be corrected in a straightforward manner to remove this difficulty, but we will not pursue this correction here. The point is that a very simple model is quite useful to us because it is so easy to apply. Simple models help us to organize our observations and often provide a place to start as we pursue the answer to a problem. However, we must be wary of simple models—they often provide a significantly distorted picture.

EXAMPLE 14.2

Describe the bonding in the N_2 molecule.

Solution The Lewis structure for the nitrogen molecule is

$$:N\equiv N:$$

where each nitrogen atom is surrounded by two effective pairs. (Remember that multiple bonds count as one effective pair.) This gives a linear arrangement (180 degrees) requiring a pair of oppositely directed orbitals. Therefore, this situation requires sp hybridization. Each nitrogen atom in the nitrogen molecule has two sp hybrid orbitals and two unchanged p orbitals, as shown in Fig. 14.20(a). The sp orbitals are used to form the σ bond between the nitrogen atoms and to hold lone pairs, as shown in Fig. 14.20(b). The p orbitals are used to form the two π bonds [Fig. 14.20(c)]; each pair of overlapping, parallel p orbitals holds one electron pair. Such bonding accounts for the electron arrangement given by the Lewis structure. The triple bond consists of a σ bond (overlap of two sp orbitals) and two π bonds (each from an overlap of two p orbitals). In addition, a lone pair occupies an sp orbital on each nitrogen atom.

dsp^3 Hybridization

In Section 13.12 we considered the dispute about whether the third-row atoms actually exceed the octet rule in compounds such as SF_6 and PCl_5. This dispute hinges on the use of the $3d$ orbitals for bonding in these compounds. In this section we will describe the hybrid orbitals that are involved when the $3d$ orbitals are assumed to participate in the bonding.

Figure 14.20

(a) An *sp* hybridized nitrogen atom. There are two *sp* hybrid orbitals and two unhybridized *p* orbitals. (b) The σ bond in the N₂ molecule. (c) The two π bonds in N₂ are formed when electron pairs are shared between two sets of parallel *p* orbitals. (d) The total bonding picture for N₂.

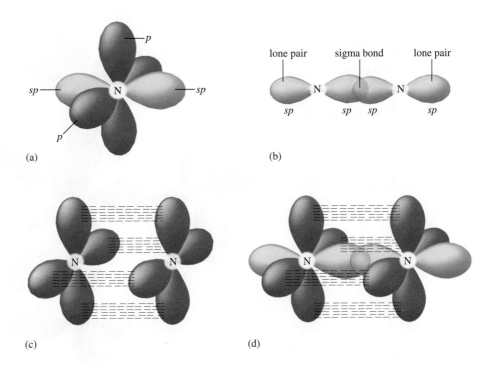

Figure 14.21

A set of *dsp³* hybrid orbitals on a phosphorus atom. Note that the set of five *dsp³* orbitals has a trigonal bipyramidal arrangement. (Each *dsp³* orbital also has a small lobe that is not shown in this diagram.)

First we will consider phosphorus pentachloride (PCl₅). The traditional Lewis structure for PCl₅ (assuming *d* orbital participation)

shows that the phosphorus atom is surrounded by five electron pairs. Since in the VSEPR model five pairs require a trigonal bipyramidal arrangement, we need a trigonal bipyramidal set of atomic orbitals on phosphorus. Such a set of orbitals is formed by *dsp³* **hybridization** of one *d* orbital, one *s* orbital, and three *p* orbitals, as shown in Fig. 14.21.

Although it will not be important for our purposes, the *dsp³* hybrid orbital set is different from the hybrids we have considered so far in that the hybrid orbitals pointing to the vertices of the triangle (often called the three equatorial hybrid orbitals) are slightly different in shape than the other two (the *axial* orbitals). This situation stands in contrast to the *sp*, *sp²*, and *sp³* hybrid sets in which each orbital in a particular set is identical in shape to the others.

The *dsp³* hybridized phosphorus atom in the PCl₅ molecule uses its five *dsp³* orbitals to share electrons with the five chlorine atoms. Note that according to this model *a set of five effective pairs around a given atom always requires a trigonal bipyramidal arrangement, which in turn involves dsp³ hybridization of that atom.*

The Lewis structure for PCl₅ shows that each chlorine atom is surrounded by four electron pairs. This requires a tetrahedral arrangement, which in turn requires a set of four *sp³* orbitals on each chlorine atom.

Now we can describe the bonding in the PCl₅ molecule. The five P—Cl σ bonds are formed by sharing electrons between a *dsp³* orbital on the phos-

Figure 14.22

The orbitals used to form the bonds in the PCl_5 molecule. The phosphorus atom uses a set of five dsp^3 orbitals to share electron pairs with sp^3 orbitals on the five chlorine atoms. The other sp^3 orbitals on each chlorine atom hold lone pairs.

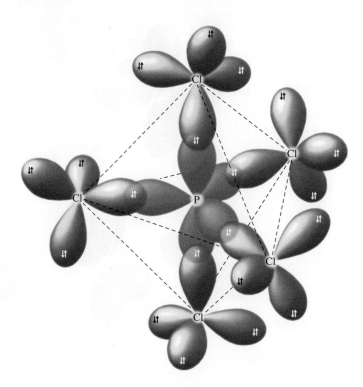

Although in its simplest form the LE model of bonding invokes the use of hybrids involving d orbitals for trigonal bipyramidal and octahedral structures, there is considerable disagreement about the actual participation of d orbitals in such molecules. For a discussion, see A. E. Reed and F. Weinhold, *J. Am. Chem. Soc.* 108 (1986): 3586, and references therein.

phorus atom and an sp^3 orbital on each chlorine.* The other sp^3 orbitals on each chlorine hold lone pairs. This arrangement is shown in Fig. 14.22.

EXAMPLE 14.3

Describe the bonding in the triiodide ion (I_3^-).

Solution The traditional Lewis structure for I_3^-

$$\left[: \overset{..}{\underset{..}{I}} - \overset{.}{\underset{..}{I}} - \overset{..}{\underset{..}{I}} : \right]^-$$

shows that the central iodine atom has five pairs of electrons. A set of five pairs requires a trigonal bipyramidal arrangement, which in turn requires a set of dsp^3 orbitals. The outer iodine atoms have four pairs of electrons, which calls for a tetrahedral arrangement and sp^3 hybridization.

Thus the central iodine is dsp^3 hybridized. Three of these hybrid orbitals hold lone pairs, and two of them overlap with sp^3 orbitals from the other two iodine atoms to form σ bonds.

d^2sp^3 Hybridization

Next, we consider sulfur hexafluoride (SF_6), which has the traditional Lewis structure

---

*Although we have no way of proving conclusively that each chlorine atom is sp^3 hybridized, we assume that minimizing electron-pair repulsions is as important for peripheral atoms as for the central atom. Thus we will apply the VSEPR model and hybridization to both central and peripheral atoms.

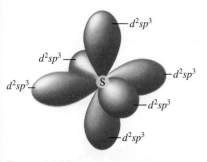

Figure 14.23
An octahedral set of d^2sp^3 orbitals on a sulfur atom. The small lobe of each hybrid orbital has been omitted for clarity.

This requires an octahedral arrangement of pairs and, in turn, an octahedral set of six hybrid orbitals. This leads to d^2sp^3 **hybridization,** in which two d orbitals, one s orbital, and three p orbitals are combined (Fig. 14.23). Note that *six electron pairs around an atom are always arranged octahedrally, requiring d^2sp^3 hybridization of the atom.* Each d^2sp^3 orbital on the sulfur atom is used to bond to a fluorine atom. Since there are four pairs on each fluorine atom, the fluorine atoms are assumed to be sp^3 hybridized.

EXAMPLE 14.4

How is the xenon atom in XeF_4 hybridized?

Solution The Lewis structure for XeF_4 has six pairs of electrons around xenon that are arranged octahedrally to minimize repulsions. An octahedral set of six atomic orbitals is required to hold these electrons, and the xenon atom is assumed to be d^2sp^3 hybridized.

Lewis structure

Octahedral arrangement of six electron pairs.

Xenon uses six d^2sp^3 hybrid atomic orbitals to bond to the four fluorine atoms and to hold the two lone pairs.

The description of a molecule using the LE model involves three distinct steps.

STEPS	**Describing a Molecule with the Localized Electron Model**
	1 Draw the Lewis structure(s).
	2 Determine the arrangement of electron pairs using the VSEPR model.
	3 Specify the hybrid orbitals needed to accommodate the electron pairs.

It is important to perform the steps in this order. For a model to be successful, it must follow nature's priorities. In the case of bonding, it seems clear that the tendency for a molecule to minimize its energy is more important than maintenance of the characteristics of atoms as they exist in the free state. The atoms adjust to meet the "needs" of the molecule. When considering the bonding in a particular molecule, therefore, we always start with the molecule rather than the component atoms. In the molecule the electrons are arranged to give each atom a noble gas configuration where possible and to minimize electron-pair repulsions. We then assume that the atoms adjust their orbitals by hybridization to allow the molecule to adopt the structure that gives the minimum energy.

In applying the LE model, we must not overemphasize the characteristics of the separate atoms. The particular atom on which the valence electrons originated is not important; what is important is where they are needed in the molecule to achieve maximum stability. In the same vein, the forms of the orbitals on the isolated atoms are relatively unimportant; what really matters are

Figure 14.24
The relationship among the number of effective pairs, their spatial arrangement, and the hybrid orbital set required.

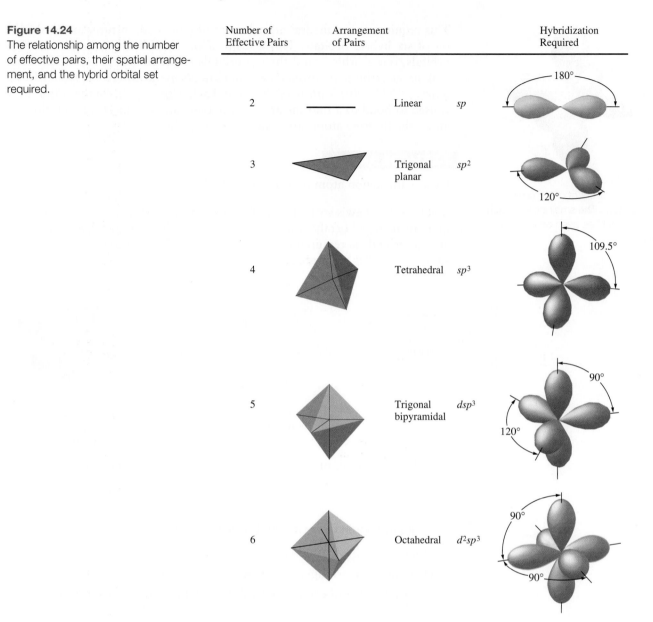

Number of Effective Pairs	Arrangement of Pairs		Hybridization Required
2	Linear	sp	180°
3	Trigonal planar	sp^2	120°
4	Tetrahedral	sp^3	109.5°
5	Trigonal bipyramidal	dsp^3	90° 120°
6	Octahedral	d^2sp^3	90° 90°

the forms needed by the molecule to achieve minimum energy. The requirements for the various types of hybridization are summarized in Fig. 14.24.

❤WL INTERACTIVE EXAMPLE 14.5

For each of the following molecules or ions, describe the molecular structure, and predict the hybridization of each atom.

a. CO   **b.** BF_4^- **c.** XeF_2

Solution

a. The CO molecule has 10 valence electrons, and its Lewis structure is

$$:C{\equiv}O:$$

Each atom has two effective pairs, which means that both are sp hybridized. The triple bond consists of a σ bond produced by the overlap of an sp orbital from each atom and two π bonds produced by the overlap of

$2p$ orbitals from each atom. The lone pairs are in sp orbitals. Since the CO molecule has only two atoms, it must be linear.

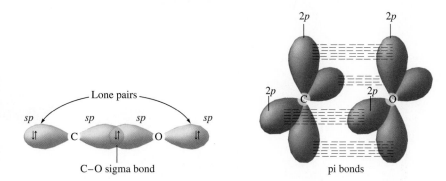

b. The BF_4^- ion has 32 valence electrons. The Lewis structure shows four pairs of electrons around the boron atom, requiring a tetrahedral arrangement:

This requires sp^3 hybridization of the boron atom. Each fluorine atom also has four electron pairs and can be assumed to be sp^3 hybridized (only one sp^3 orbital is shown for each fluorine atom). The BF_4^- ion's molecular structure is tetrahedral.

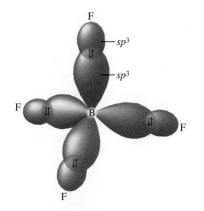

c. The XeF_2 molecule has 22 valence electrons. The Lewis structure shows five electron pairs on the xenon atom, which requires a trigonal bipyramidal arrangement:

Note that the lone pairs are placed in the plane where they are 120 degrees apart. Accommodating five pairs at the vertices of a trigonal bipyramid can be explained if the xenon atom adopts a set of five dsp^3 orbitals. Each fluorine atom has four electron pairs and can be assumed to be sp^3 hybridized. The XeF_2 molecule has a linear arrangement of atoms.

14.2 | The Molecular Orbital Model

It should be clear by now that the LE model is of great value in interpreting the structures and bonding of molecules. However, there are some problems with this model at this level of approximation. For example, since it incorrectly assumes that electrons are localized, the concept of resonance must be added. Also, the model does not deal easily with molecules containing unpaired electrons. And finally, the model in this form gives no direct information about bond energies.

Another model often used to describe bonding is the **molecular orbital model.** To introduce the assumptions, methods, and results of this model, we will consider the simplest of all molecules, H_2, which consists of two protons and two electrons. A very stable molecule, H_2 is lower in energy than the separated hydrogen atoms by 432 kJ/mol.

Since the hydrogen molecule consists of protons and electrons, the same components found in separated hydrogen atoms, it seems reasonable to use a theory similar to the atomic theory discussed in Chapter 12, which assumes that the electrons in an atom exist in orbitals of a given energy. Can we apply this same type of model to the hydrogen molecule? Yes; in fact, describing the H_2 molecule in terms of quantum mechanics is quite straightforward.

However, even though it is formulated rather easily, this problem cannot be solved exactly. The difficulty is the same as that encountered in dealing with polyelectronic atoms—the electron correlation problem. Since we cannot account for the details of the electron movements, we cannot deal with the electron–electron interactions in a specific way. We need to make approximations that allow the solution of the problem but that do not destroy the model's physical integrity. The success of these approximations can be measured only by comparing predictions from the theory with experimental observations. In this case we will see that the simplified model works well.

Just as atomic orbitals are solutions to the quantum mechanical treatment of atoms, **molecular orbitals (MOs)** are solutions to the molecular problem. MOs have many of the same characteristics as atomic orbitals. Two of the most important are (1) they can hold two electrons with opposite spins and (2) the square of the molecular orbital wave function indicates the electron probability.

As in the application of quantum mechanics to isolated atoms, the MO orbital treatment can be carried out at various levels of sophistication. In our description of the model, we will assume that the MOs for H_2 are constructed

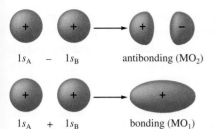

Figure 14.25
The combination of hydrogen $1s$ atomic orbitals to form MOs. The phases of the orbitals are shown by signs inside the boundary surfaces. When the orbitals are added, the matching phases produce constructive interference, which gives enhanced electron probability between the nuclei. This results in a bonding molecular orbital. When one orbital is subtracted from the other, destructive interference occurs between the opposite phases, leading to a node between the nuclei. This is an antibonding MO.

using hydrogen $1s$ orbitals. We say that the $1s$ orbitals form the "basis set" for the MOs. A more detailed treatment would use a different basis set—one in which the radial part of the atomic orbitals would be allowed to vary to achieve the lowest-energy MOs for the hydrogen molecule. However, to avoid as many complications as possible, as we discuss the fundamental ideas of the MO description of molecules, we will use the simplest version of this model.

We will now describe the bonding in the hydrogen molecule using the MO model. The first step is to obtain the hydrogen molecule's orbitals, a process that is greatly simplified if we assume that the MOs can be constructed from the hydrogen $1s$ orbitals.

In this approximate treatment of the hydrogen molecule, two MOs result:

$$MO_1 = 1s_A + 1s_B$$
$$MO_2 = 1s_A - 1s_B$$

where $1s_A$ and $1s_B$ represent the $1s$ orbitals from the two separated hydrogen atoms. This process is shown schematically in Fig. 14.25 along with the phases of the orbitals.

The orbital properties of greatest interest are size, shape (described by the electron probability distribution), and energy. These properties for the hydrogen MOs are represented in Fig. 14.26. From this figure we can note several important points:

1. The electron probability of both MOs is centered along the line passing through the two nuclei. For MO_1, the greatest electron probability is *between* the nuclei. In this case the matching phases of the orbitals produce constructive interference and enhanced electron probability between the two nuclei. For MO_2, it is centered along the molecular axis but outside the area between the two nuclei. In this case the mismatched phases produce destructive interference leading to a node in the electron probability between the two nuclei. In both MOs the electron density has cylindrical symmetry with respect to the molecular axis. That is, the electron probability is the same along any line drawn perpendicular to the bond axis at a given point on the axis. This type of cylindrically symmetric electron distribution is described as *sigma* (σ), as in the localized electron model. Accordingly, we refer to MO_1 and MO_2 as **sigma (σ) MOs.**

2. In the molecule, only the MOs are available for occupation by electrons. The $1s$ atomic orbitals of the hydrogen atoms no longer exist because the H_2 molecule—a new entity—has its own set of new orbitals.

3. MO_1 is lower in energy than the $1s$ orbitals of free hydrogen atoms, but MO_2 is higher in energy than the $1s$ orbitals. This fact has very important implications for the stability of the H_2 molecule: If the two electrons (one from each hydrogen atom) occupy the lower-energy MO, they will have

Figure 14.26
(a) The MO energy-level diagram for the H_2 molecule. (b) The shapes of the MOs are obtained by squaring the wave functions for MO_1 and MO_2. The positions of the nuclei are indicated by •.

Bonding will result if the molecule has lower energy than the separated atoms.

lower energy than they have in the two separate hydrogen atoms. This situation favors molecule formation because nature tends to seek the lowest energy state. That is, the driving force for molecule formation here is that the MO available to the two electrons has lower energy than the atomic orbitals these electrons occupy in the separated atoms. This situation is *"pro" bonding.*

On the other hand, if the two electrons were forced to occupy the higher-energy MO, they would be definitely *"anti" bonding.* In this case these electrons would have lower energy in the separated atoms than in the molecule; thus the separated state would be favored. Of course, since the lower-energy MO_1 *is* available, the two electrons occupy that MO and the resulting molecule is stable.

We have seen that the MOs of the hydrogen molecule fall into two classes: bonding and antibonding. A **bonding MO** is *lower in energy than the atomic orbitals of which it is composed.* Electrons in this type of orbital favor the molecule; that is, they will favor bonding. An **antibonding MO** is *higher in energy than the atomic orbitals of which it is composed.* Electrons in this type of orbital will favor the separated atoms (they are antibonding). Figure 14.27 illustrates these ideas.

4. Figure 14.26 shows that for the bonding MO in the H_2 molecule, the electrons have the greatest probability of being between the nuclei. This is exactly what we would expect, since the electrons can lower their energies by being simultaneously attracted by both nuclei. On the other hand, the electron distribution for the antibonding MO is such that the electrons are mainly outside the space between the nuclei. This type of distribution is not expected to provide any bonding force. In fact, it causes the electrons to be higher in energy than in the separated atoms. Thus the MO model produces electron distributions and energies that agree with our basic ideas of bonding. This fact reassures us that the model is physically reasonable.

5. The labels on MOs indicate their symmetries (shapes), their parent atomic orbitals, and whether they are bonding or antibonding. Antibonding character is indicated by an asterisk. For the H_2 molecule, both MOs have σ symmetry and both are constructed from hydrogen $1s$ atomic orbitals. The molecular orbitals for H_2 are therefore labeled as follows:

$$MO_1 = \sigma_{1s}$$

$$MO_2 = \sigma_{1s}{}^*$$

6. Molecular electron configurations can be written in much the same way as atomic configurations. Since the H_2 molecule has two electrons in the σ_{1s} molecular orbital, the electron configuration is $\sigma_{1s}{}^2$.

Figure 14.27
Bonding and antibonding MOs.

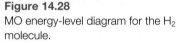

Atomic orbitals in
a free H atom

σ_{1s}^{*}

E

H_{1s} H_{1s}

σ_{1s}

σ_{1s}^{*} and σ_{1s} are
molecular orbitals
in the H_2 molecule

Figure 14.28
MO energy-level diagram for the H_2
molecule.

7. Each MO can hold two electrons, but the electrons' spins must be opposite.

8. Orbitals are conserved. The number of MOs is always the same as the number of atomic orbitals used to construct them.

Many of these points are summarized in Fig. 14.28.

Bond Order

Fundamentally, a molecule forms because it has lower energy than the separated atoms. In the simple MO model, this is reflected by the number of bonding electrons (those that achieve lower energy in going from the free atoms to the molecule) versus the number of antibonding electrons (those that are higher in energy in the molecule than in the free atoms). If the number of bonding electrons is greater than the number of antibonding electrons in a given molecule, the molecule is predicted to be stable.

The quantitative indicator of molecular stability (bond strength) for a diatomic molecule is the **bond order**: *the difference between the number of bonding electrons and the number of antibonding electrons, divided by 2.*

$$\text{Bond order} = \frac{\text{number of bonding electrons} - \text{number of antibonding electrons}}{2}$$

We divide by 2 because we are used to thinking of bonds in terms of *pairs* of electrons.

Bond order is an indication of bond strength because it reflects the difference between the number of bonding electrons and the number of antibonding electrons, which in turn reflects the quantity of energy released when the molecule is formed from its atoms. *Therefore, larger bond order indicates greater bond strength.*

Since the H_2 molecule has two bonding electrons and no antibonding electrons, the bond order is 1:

$$\text{Bond order} = \frac{2 - 0}{2} = 1$$

σ_{1s}^{*}

E He_{1s} He_{1s}

σ_{1s}

Figure 14.29
The MO energy-level diagram for the
He_2 molecule.

We will now apply the MO model to the helium molecule (He_2). Does this model predict that this molecule is stable? Since the He atom has a $1s^2$ configuration, $1s$ orbitals are used to construct the MOs. Therefore, the molecules will have four electrons. From the diagram shown in Fig. 14.29, it is apparent that two electrons are raised in energy and two are lowered in energy. Thus the bond order is zero:

$$\frac{2 - 2}{2} = 0$$

This implies that the He_2 molecule is *not* stable with respect to the two free He atoms, which agrees with the observation that helium gas consists of individual He atoms.

σ_{1s}^{*}

E He_{1s} He_{1s}

σ_{1s}

He He_2^{+} He^{+}

Figure 14.30
The MO energy-level diagram for the
He_2^{+} ion. Note that in this case the
components from which He_2^{+} is "constructed" are He and He^{+}.

Next, we will apply the simple MO model to diatomic ions, starting with He_2^{+}. Is this ion expected to be stable? Examination of Fig. 14.30 shows that when He is combined with He^{+} to form He_2^{+}, two electrons are lowered in energy and only one is raised in energy. That is, the bond order is $(2 - 1)/2 = \frac{1}{2}$, and He_2^{+} is predicted to be stable. Experiments have shown that He_2^{+} does indeed exist with a bond energy of 250 kJ/mol.

Figure 14.31
The MO energy-level diagram for the H_2^+ ion.

Figure 14.32
The MO energy-level diagram for the H_2^- ion.

Similarly, the H_2^+ ion is known to exist with a bond energy of 255 kJ/mol. This result is in agreement with the simple MO model (Fig. 14.31), which predicts a bond order of $(1 - 0)/2 = \frac{1}{2}$.

Figure 14.32 shows the MO diagram for the H_2^- ion, which is predicted to have a bond order of $(2 - 1)/2 = \frac{1}{2}$. However, in this case the prediction of the model does not agree with experimental results. The H_2^- ion is not known, and all indications are that it is unstable, immediately decomposing to H_2 and a free electron. Thus, again, we are reminded about the perils of simple models. The reasons for the instability of the H_2^- ion are beyond the scope of this treatment.

14.3 | Bonding in Homonuclear Diatomic Molecules

In this section we consider *homonuclear diatomic molecules* (those composed of two identical atoms) formed by elements in Period 2 of the periodic table. The lithium atom has a $1s^2 2s^1$ electron configuration, and from our discussion in the preceding section, it would seem logical to use the Li $1s$ and $2s$ orbitals to form the MOs of the Li_2 molecule. However, the $1s$ orbitals on the lithium atoms are much smaller than the $2s$ orbitals and therefore do not overlap in space to any appreciable extent (Fig. 14.33). Thus the two electrons in each $1s$ orbital can be assumed to be localized on a given atom, which means that they do not participate in the bonding. The following general principle applies: *To participate in molecular orbitals, atomic orbitals must overlap in space.* This means that only the valence orbitals of atoms contribute significantly to the MOs of a particular molecule.

The MO diagram of the Li_2 molecule and the shapes of its bonding and antibonding MOs are shown in Fig. 14.34. The electron configuration for Li_2 (valence electrons only) is σ_{2s}^2, and the bond order is 1:

$$\frac{2 - 0}{2} = 1$$

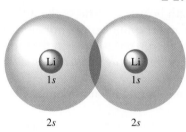

Figure 14.33
The relative sizes of the lithium $1s$ and $2s$ atomic orbitals.

Figure 14.34
The MO energy-level diagram for the Li_2 molecule.

(a)

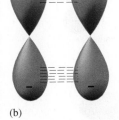

(b)

(c)

(d)

Figure 14.35

(a) The three mutually perpendicular $2p$ orbitals on two adjacent boron atoms. The signs indicate the orbital phases. Two pairs of parallel p orbitals can overlap, as shown in (b) and (c), and the third pair can overlap head-on, as shown in (d).

Only valence atomic orbitals contribute significantly to MOs.

Thus Li_2 is expected to be a stable molecule (has lower energy than two separated lithium atoms). However, this does not mean that Li_2 is the most stable form of elemental lithium. In fact, at normal temperature and pressure, lithium exists as a solid containing many lithium atoms bonded together.

For the beryllium molecule (Be_2), the bonding and antibonding orbitals both contain two electrons. In this case the bond order is $(2 - 2)/2 = 0$. Thus the model predicts that since Be_2 is not more stable than two separated Be atoms, no molecule should form. However, experiments indicate that $Be_2(g)$ does exist, although it has a *very* weak bond (bond energy ≈ 10 kJ/mol). In contrast, beryllium metal contains many beryllium atoms bonded to each other and is stable for reasons we will discuss in Chapter 16.

Since the boron atom has a $1s^2 2s^2 2p^1$ configuration, we describe the B_2 molecule by considering how p atomic orbitals combine to form MOs. Recall that p orbitals have two lobes and that they occur in sets of three mutually perpendicular orbitals [Fig. 14.35(a)]. When two B atoms approach each other, two pairs of p orbitals can overlap in a parallel manner [Figs. 14.35(b) and (c)] and one pair can overlap head-on [Fig. 14.35(d)].

First, let's consider the MOs formed by the head-on overlap, as shown in Fig. 14.36(a). If the two orbitals are combined directly (added together), the positive phase of the left orbital overlaps with the negative phase of the right orbital. This destructive interference of the orbitals produces a node between the nuclei that leads to decreased electron probability. Therefore, this results in an antibonding MO. On the other hand, when the phase of the right orbital is reversed (its sign is reversed by subtracting it from the left orbital), constructive interference results, giving enhanced electron probability between the nuclei. This is a bonding MO. Note that the electrons in the bonding MO are, as expected, concentrated between the nuclei, and the electrons in the antibonding MO are concentrated outside the area between the two nuclei. Both of these MOs are σ MOs.

The p orbitals that overlap in a parallel manner also produce bonding and antibonding orbitals [Fig. 14.36(b)]. When the parallel p orbitals are added

Figure 14.36
(a) The two *p* orbitals on the boron atoms that overlap head-on combine to form *σ* bonding and antibonding orbitals. The bonding orbital is formed by reversing the sign of the right orbital so that the positive phases of both orbitals match between the nuclei to produce constructive interference. This leads to enhanced electron probability between the nuclei. The antibonding orbital is formed by the direct combination of the orbitals, which gives destructive interference of the positive phase of one orbital with the negative phase of the second orbital. This produces a node between the nuclei, which gives decreased electron probability. (b) When the parallel *p* orbitals are combined with the positive and negative phases matched, constructive interference occurs, giving a bonding *π* orbital. When the orbitals have opposite phases (the signs of one orbital are reversed), destructive interference occurs, resulting in an antibonding *π* orbital.

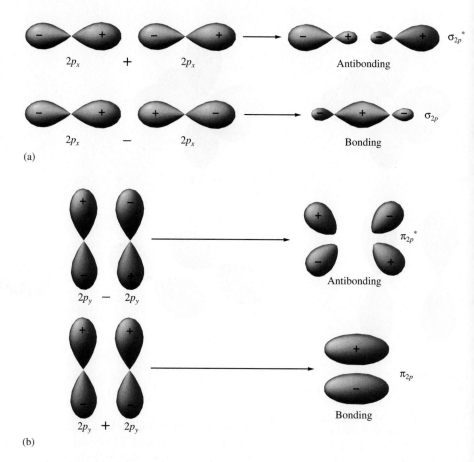

together, the phases match, and constructive interference occurs, giving a bonding orbital. When the phase of the right orbital is reversed and combined with the left orbital, destructive interference occurs, giving an antibonding orbital. Since the electron probability lies above and below the line between the nuclei, both the orbitals are **pi (π) MOs.** They are designated as π_{2p} for the bonding MO and π_{2p}^* for the antibonding MO.

Let's try to make an educated guess about the relative energies of the σ and π MOs formed from the $2p$ atomic orbitals. Would we expect the electrons to prefer the σ bonding orbital (where the electron probability is concentrated in the area between the nuclei) or the π bonding orbital? The σ orbital would seem to have the lower energy since the electrons are closest to the two nuclei. This agrees with the observation that σ interactions are typically stronger than π interactions.

Figure 14.37 gives the MO energy-level diagram *expected* when the two sets of $2p$ orbitals on the two borom atoms combine to form MOs. Note that there are two π bonding orbitals at the same energy (degenerate orbitals) formed from the two pairs of parallel p orbitals, and there are two degenerate π antibonding orbitals. The energy of the π_{2p} orbitals is expected to be higher than that of the σ_{2p} orbital because σ interactions are generally stronger than π interactions.

To construct the total MO diagram for the B_2 molecule, we make the assumption that the $2s$ and $2p$ orbitals combine separately (in other words, there is no $2s$–$2p$ mixing). The resulting diagram is shown in Fig. 14.38. Note that B_2 has six *valence* electrons. (Remember that the $1s$ orbitals and electrons are

Figure 14.37
The *expected* MO energy-level diagram for the combination of the $2p$ orbitals on two boron atoms.

Figure 14.38

The *expected* MO energy-level diagram for the B_2 molecule.

Figure 14.39

An apparatus used to measure the paramagnetism of a sample. A paramagnetic sample will appear heavier when the electromagnet is turned on because the sample is attracted into the inducing magnetic field.

assumed not to participate in the bonding.) This diagram predicts a bond order of 1:

$$\frac{4-2}{2} = 1$$

Therefore, B_2 should be a stable molecule.

Paramagnetism

At this point we need to discuss an additional molecular property—magnetism. Most materials have no magnetism until they are placed in a magnetic field. However, in the presence of such a field, magnetism of two types can be induced. **Paramagnetism** causes the substance to be attracted toward the inducing magnetic field. **Diamagnetism** causes the substance to be repelled from the inducing magnetic field. Figure 14.39 illustrates how paramagnetism is measured. The sample is weighed with the electromagnet turned off and then weighed again with the electromagnet turned on. An increase in weight when the field is turned on indicates that the sample is paramagnetic. Studies have shown that *paramagnetism is associated with unpaired electrons,* and diamagnetism is associated with paired electrons.* Any substance that has both paired and unpaired electrons will exhibit net paramagnetism, since the effect of paramagnetism is much stronger than that of diamagnetism. Thus the phenomenon of paramagnetism provides a ready means for testing whether a substance contains unpaired electrons.

The MO energy-level diagram given in Fig. 14.38 predicts that the B_2 molecule will be diamagnetic, since the MOs contain only paired electrons. However, experiments show that B_2 is actually paramagnetic with two unpaired electrons. Why does the model yield the wrong prediction? This is yet another illustration of how models are developed and used. In general, we try to use the simplest possible model that accounts for all of the important observations. In this case, although the simplest model has been relatively successful in describing all the diatomic molecules up to B_2, it certainly is suspect if it cannot describe the B_2 molecule correctly.

Let's reconsider one of our previous assumptions. In our treatment of B_2, we have assumed that the s and p orbitals combine separately to form MOs. Calculations show that when the s and p orbitals are allowed to mix (participate) in the same MO, a different energy-level diagram results for B_2 (Fig. 14.40). Note that even though the s and p contributions to the MOs are no longer separate, we retain the simple orbital designations. The mixing of p and s atomic orbitals occurs only in the σ MOs (σ_{2s}, σ_{2s}^*, σ_{2p}, and σ_{2p}^*). Because the energy of the σ_{2p} orbital is changed by p–s mixing, the energies of π_{2p} and σ_{2p} orbitals are reversed. Also, the p–s mixing changes the energies of the σ_{2s} and σ_{2s}^* such that they are no longer equally spaced relative to the energy of the free $2s$ orbital.

Perhaps an easier way to understand the effects of p–s mixing is to think in terms of electron repulsions. Note from Figs. 14.34 and 14.36 that both the σ_{2s} and the σ_{2p} orbitals show significant electron probability in the area between the nuclei of the bonded atoms. This means that electrons in the σ_{2s} orbital will repel any electrons placed in the σ_{2p} orbital, thus making this orbital "less attractive" (higher in energy) to electrons. Therefore, the σ_{2p} orbital is pushed to a higher energy level than the π_{2p} orbitals, which do not have electron probability between the nuclei and are not affected by electrons in the σ_{2s} orbital. This situation applies to B_2, C_2, and N_2, as shown in Fig. 14.41.

---

*This is an oversimplification but one that will not concern us here.

Figure 14.40
The *correct* MO energy-level diagram for the B_2 molecule. When *p–s* mixing is allowed, the energies of the σ_{2p} and π_{2p} orbitals are reversed. The two electrons from the B 2p orbitals now occupy separate, degenerate π_{2p} MOs and thus have parallel spins. Therefore, this diagram explains the observed paramagnetism of B_2.

Bond energy increases with bond order; bond length decreases with increasing bond order.

Figure 14.41
The MO energy-level diagrams, bond orders, bond energies, and bond lengths for the diatomic molecules B_2 through F_2. Note that for O_2 and F_2 the σ_{2p} orbital is lower in energy than the π_{2p} orbitals.

The repulsion effects between σ_{2s} and σ_{2p} electrons decrease in going across the period because the increasing nuclear charge pulls the σ_{2s} electrons in closer, effectively making the σ_{2s} orbital smaller and decreasing the σ_{2s}–σ_{2p} interactions. This causes the energy of the σ_{2p} orbital to drop below the π_{2p} orbital in O_2 and F_2, as indicated in Fig. 14.41.

When the six valence electrons of the B_2 molecule are placed in the modified energy-level diagram, each of the last two electrons goes into one of the degenerate π_{2p} orbitals. This produces a paramagnetic molecule in agreement with experimental results. Thus, when the model is extended to allow *p–s* mixing in MOs, it predicts the correct magnetism. Note that the bond order is $(4 - 2)/2 = 1$, as before.

The diatomic molecules C_2 and N_2 can be described using the same MOs as for B_2 (Fig. 14.40) and inserting the correct number of electrons. Because *p–s* mixing is less important in O_2 and F_2, the σ_{2p} orbital is lower in energy than the π_{2p} orbitals. The MO diagrams for the homonuclear diatomic molecules for the Period 2 elements are summarized in Fig. 14.41, together with experimentally obtained bond strengths and lengths. Several significant points arise from these results.

1. There are definite correlations between bond order, bond energy, and bond length. As the bond order predicted by the MO model increases, the bond energy increases, and the bond length decreases. This is a clear indication that the bond order predicted by the model accurately reflects bond strength, and it strongly supports the reasonableness of the MO model.

2. Comparison of the bond energies of the B_2 and F_2 molecules indicates that bond order cannot automatically be associated with a particular bond energy. Although both molecules have a bond order of 1, the bond in B_2 appears to be about twice as strong as the bond in F_2. As we will see in our later discussion of the halogens, F_2 has an unusually weak single bond because of larger-than-usual electron–electron repulsions (there are 14 valence electrons on the small F_2 molecule).

	B_2	C_2	N_2	O_2	F_2
Magnetism	Para–magnetic	Dia–magnetic	Dia–magnetic	Para–magnetic	Dia–magnetic
Bond order	1	2	3	2	1
Observed bond dissociation energy (kJ/mol)	290	620	942	495	154
Observed bond length (pm)	159	131	110	121	143

3. Note the very large bond energy associated with the N_2 molecule, which the MO model predicts will have a bond order of 3, a triple bond. The very strong bond in N_2 is the principal reason that many nitrogen-containing compounds are used as explosives. The reactions involving these explosives give the very stable N_2 molecule as a product, thus releasing large quantities of energy.

4. The O_2 molecule is known to be paramagnetic. This can be very convincingly demonstrated by pouring liquid oxygen between the poles of a strong magnet, as shown in Fig. 14.42. Because of its paramagnetism, the oxygen is attracted to the magnet gap, where it remains until it evaporates. Significantly, the MO model correctly predicts oxygen's paramagnetism, but the simplest form of the LE model predicts a diamagnetic molecule.

Figure 14.42
When liquid oxygen is poured into the space between the poles of a strong magnet, it remains there until it boils away. This attraction of liquid oxygen for the magnetic field demonstrates the paramagnetism of the O_2 molecule.

⏻WL INTERACTIVE EXAMPLE 14.6

For the species O_2, O_2^+, and O_2^-, give the electron configuration and the bond order for each. Which has the strongest bond?

Solution The O_2 molecule has 12 valence electrons (6 + 6), O_2^+ has 11 valence electrons (6 + 6 − 1), and O_2^- has 13 valence electrons (6 + 6 + 1). We will assume that the ions can be treated using the same MO diagram used for the neutral diatomic molecule:

	O_2	O_2^+	O_2^-
σ_{2p}^*	—	—	—
π_{2p}^*	↑ ↑	↑ —	↑↓ ↑
π_{2p}	↑↓ ↑↓	↑↓ ↑↓	↑↓ ↑↓
σ_{2p}	↑↓	↑↓	↑↓
σ_{2s}^*	↑↓	↑↓	↑↓
σ_{2s}	↑↓	↑↓	↑↓

The electron configuration for each species can then be taken from the diagram:

$$O_2 \quad (\sigma_{2s})^2(\sigma_{2s}^*)^2(\sigma_{2p})^2(\pi_{2p})^4(\pi_{2p}^*)^2$$

$$O_2^+ \quad (\sigma_{2s})^2(\sigma_{2s}^*)^2(\sigma_{2p})^2(\pi_{2p})^4(\pi_{2p}^*)^1$$

$$O_2^- \quad (\sigma_{2s})^2(\sigma_{2s}^*)^2(\sigma_{2p})^2(\pi_{2p})^4(\pi_{2p}^*)^3$$

The bond orders are as follows:

$$\text{For } O_2: \quad \frac{8-4}{2} = 2$$

$$\text{For } O_2^+: \quad \frac{8-3}{2} = 2.5$$

$$\text{For } O_2^-: \quad \frac{8-5}{2} = 1.5$$

Thus O_2^+ is expected to have the strongest bond of the three species.

Experimental evidence supports these predictions. The bond energies for O_2^+, O_2, and O_2^- are 643, 495, and 395 kJ/mol, respectively.

ⓦWL INTERACTIVE EXAMPLE 14.7

Use the MO model to predict the bond order and magnetism of each molecule.

a. Ne_2 **b.** P_2

Solution

a. The valence orbitals for Ne are $2s$ and $2p$. Thus we can use the MOs we have already constructed for the diatomic molecules of the Period 2 elements. The Ne_2 molecule has 16 valence electrons (8 from each atom). Placing these electrons in the appropriate MOs produces the following diagram:

The bond order is $(8 - 8)/2 = 0$, so Ne_2 should not exist.

b. The P_2 molecule found in "brown phosphorus," which is stable only at very low temperatures, contains phosphorus atoms from the third row of the periodic table. We will assume that diatomic molecules of the Period 3 elements can be treated very similarly to those from Period 2. The only change will be that the MOs are formed from $3s$ and $3p$ atomic orbitals. The P_2 molecule has 10 valence electrons (5 from each phosphorus atom). The resulting molecular orbital diagram follows.

The molecule has a bond order of 3 and is expected to be diamagnetic.

It should be noted that phosphorus exists in nature as P_4 molecules (and as other, more complex forms).

Figure 14.43

The MO energy-level diagram for the NO molecule. We assume that orbital order is the same as that for N_2. The bond order is 2.5.

14.4 | Bonding in Heteronuclear Diatomic Molecules

In this section we will deal with selected examples of **heteronuclear diatomic molecules**—those containing two different atoms. A special case involves molecules containing atoms adjacent to each other in the periodic table. Since the atoms involved in such a molecule are so similar, we can use the MO diagram for homonuclear molecules. For example, we can predict the bond order and magnetism of nitric oxide (NO) by placing its 11 valence electrons (5 from nitrogen and 6 from oxygen) in the MO energy-level diagram shown in Fig. 14.43. The molecule should be paramagnetic with a bond order of

$$\frac{8 - 3}{2} = 2.5$$

Figure 14.44
The MO energy-level diagram for both the NO^+ and CN^- ions.

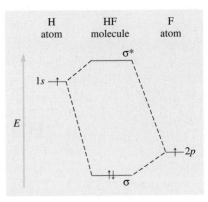

Figure 14.45
A partial MO energy-level diagram for the HF molecule.

Experimentally, nitric oxide is indeed found to be paramagnetic. Note that this odd-electron molecule is described very naturally by the MO model. In contrast, the LE model, in the simple form used in this text, does not readily describe such molecules.

⚘WL INTERACTIVE EXAMPLE 14.8

Use the MO model to predict the magnetism and bond order of the NO^+ and CN^- ions.

Solution The NO^+ ion has 10 valence electrons $(5 + 6 - 1)$. The CN^- ion also has 10 valence electrons $(4 + 5 + 1)$. Both ions are therefore diamagnetic and have a bond order of 3:

$$\frac{8 - 2}{2} = 3$$

The MO diagram for these two ions is the same (Fig. 14.44).

When the two atoms of a diatomic molecule are very different, the energy-level diagram for homonuclear molecules can no longer be used. A new diagram must be devised for each molecule. We will illustrate such a case by considering the hydrogen fluoride (HF) molecule. The electron configurations of the hydrogen and fluorine atoms are $1s^1$ and $1s^22s^22p^5$, respectively. To keep things as simple as possible, we will assume that fluorine uses only one of its $2p$ orbitals to bond to hydrogen. Thus the MOs for HF will be composed of fluorine $2p$ and hydrogen $1s$ orbitals. Figure 14.45 gives the partial MO energy-level diagram for HF, focusing only on the orbitals involved in the bonding. We are assuming that fluorine's other valence electrons remain localized on the fluorine atom. The $2p$ orbital of fluorine is shown at a lower energy than the $1s$ orbital of hydrogen on the diagram because fluorine binds its valence electrons more tightly. Thus the $2p$ electron on a free fluorine atom is at lower energy than the $1s$ electron on a free hydrogen atom. The diagram predicts that the HF molecule should be stable since both electrons are lowered in energy relative to their energies in the free hydrogen and fluorine atoms, and this is the driving force for bond formation.

Because the fluorine $2p$ orbital is lower in energy than the hydrogen $1s$ orbital, the electrons prefer to be closer to the fluorine atom. That is, the σ MO containing the bonding electron pair shows greater electron probability close to the fluorine (Fig. 14.46). The electron pair is not shared equally. This causes

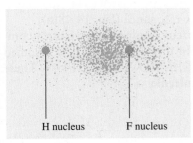

Figure 14.46
The electron probability distribution in the bonding MO of the HF molecule. Note the greater electron density close to the fluorine atom.

the fluorine atom to have a slight excess of negative charge and leaves the hydrogen atom partially positive. This is exactly the bond polarity observed for HF. Thus the MO model accounts in a straightforward way for the different electronegativities of hydrogen and fluorine and the resulting unequal charge distribution.

14.5 | Combining the Localized Electron and Molecular Orbital Models

In this text we have treated bonding in terms of simple models not only because we are presenting the material at an introductory level but also because a lot of first-order thinking by chemists uses these simple "back-of-the-envelope" models. Thus, as long as we are aware of the pitfalls of oversimplified models, we can use them to our benefit.

In this section we will attempt to make these simple models even more useful by addressing a particular shortcoming of the LE model—its assumption that electrons are localized (restricted to the space between a given pair of atoms). This problem is most apparent for molecules where several valid Lewis structures can be drawn. Recall that none of the resonance structures taken alone adequately describes the electronic structure of the molecule. The concept of resonance was invented to solve this problem. However, even with resonance included, the LE model does not describe molecules and ions such as O_3 and NO_3^- in a very satisfying way.

It would seem that the ideal bonding model would be one with the simplicity of the LE model but with the delocalization characteristics of the MO model. We can achieve this by combining the two models to describe molecules that require resonance. Note that for species such as O_3 and NO_3^- the double bond changes position in the resonance structures (Fig. 14.47). Since a double bond involves one σ bond and one π bond, there is a σ bond between all bound atoms in each resonance structure. It is really the π bond that has different locations in the various resonance structures.

> In molecules that require resonance, it is the π bonding that is most clearly delocalized.

We conclude that the σ electrons in a molecule can be described as being localized with no apparent problems. It is the π electrons that must be treated as being delocalized. Thus, for molecules that require resonance, we will use the LE model to describe the σ bonding and the MO model to describe the π bonding. This allows us to keep the bonding model as simple as possible and yet give a more physically accurate description of such molecules.

We will illustrate this procedure by considering the bonding in benzene, an important industrial chemical that must be handled carefully because it is a known carcinogen. The benzene molecule (C_6H_6) consists of a planar hexagon of carbon atoms with one hydrogen atom bound to each carbon atom, as shown in Fig. 14.48(a). In the molecule all six C—C bonds are known to be equivalent. To explain this fact, the LE model must invoke resonance [Fig. 14.48(b)].

A better description of the bonding in benzene results when we use a combination of the models, as described above. In this description it is assumed that the σ bonds to carbon involve sp^2 orbitals, as shown in Fig. 14.49. These σ bonds are all centered in the plane of the molecule.

Figure 14.47

The resonance structures for O_3 and NO_3^-. Note that it is the double bond that occupies various positions in the resonance structures.

The Always Interesting NO

Nitrogen monoxide (commonly called nitric oxide) is a compound with a dual personality. Produced by the reaction of N_2 and O_2 at the high temperatures associated with combustion in automobiles and conventional power plants, NO immediately reacts with O_2 to form NO_2, a major air pollutant. Nitric oxide has also been implicated as a cause of brain damage in people with strokes. During a stroke, relatively large amounts of NO are produced by the body, leading to nerve damage in the brain. On the other hand, NO has in recent years been shown to be an essential regulator of many body processes, including controlling blood pressure, aiding in penile erection, assisting digestion, and battling tumor cells.

Recent findings indicate additional important roles for NO. For example, researchers in the United States and Tanzania have discovered that the presence of NO in the blood seems to aid in the body's battle against infectious diseases. These results indicate that patients with relatively high blood levels of NO are much more successful in fighting off malaria. However, the situation is complicated: NO's dual personality may again be evident. The studies indicate that while NO may bolster the body's resistance to malaria, the release of excess NO in the brain in people with certain forms of malaria may in fact be responsible for major brain damage. The role of NO in malaria and other infectious diseases continues to be the focus of much current research.

On a related front, studies at the Karolinska Institute in Stockholm, Sweden, seem to indicate that NO furnishes protection against sinus infections. Unlike the nose, where bacteria thrive, the sinuses—the air-filled cavities in the head surrounding the nose—are surprisingly microbe-free. In trying to discern the reason for the lack of bacteria in the sinuses—a warm, moist, seemingly bacteria-friendly environment—Swedish scientists found that the cavities contain NO concentrations close to the maximum levels allowed in polluted air. They discovered that cells in the walls of the sinuses produce NO, presumably to protect against bacterial infection—the NO binds to vital enzymes in microbes, stopping their growth and reproduction. But the importance of NO goes beyond its antibacterial role. It also behaves as a powerful vasodilator, a substance that dilates blood vessels. The researchers postulate that some of the NO in the sinuses travels through the airways into the lungs, where it dilates blood vessels in areas well supplied with O_2, thus increasing the amount of oxygen absorbed into the blood.

The powers of NO are also apparent in the operation of hemoglobin, the protein that delivers O_2 to the tissues and returns CO_2 to be exhaled in the lungs. Recent studies at Duke University indicate that hemoglobin has a dangling side chain that binds NO. As the hemoglobin releases O_2 to the tissues it also sheds some of its bound NO, which dilates blood vessels and helps the oxygen get to the tissues. The hemoglobin then picks up CO_2 and any circulating NO and returns them to the lungs to be exhaled. Thus hemoglobin not only exchanges O_2 for CO_2 at the tissues but also regulates blood pressure in the process.

Thus NO continues to show its dual personality—sometimes positive, sometimes negative, always interesting.

Figure 14.48

(a) The benzene molecule consists of a ring of six carbon atoms with one hydrogen atom bound to each carbon; all atoms are in the same plane. All the C—C bonds are known to be equivalent. (b) Two of the resonance structures for the benzene molecule. The LE model must invoke resonance to account for the six equal C—C bonds.

Figure 14.49
The σ bonding system in the benzene molecule.

Figure 14.50
(a) The π MO system in benzene is formed by combining the six p orbitals from the six sp^2 hybridized carbon atoms. (b) The electrons in the resulting π MO are delocalized over the entire ring of carbon atoms, giving six equivalent bonds. A composite of these orbitals is represented here.

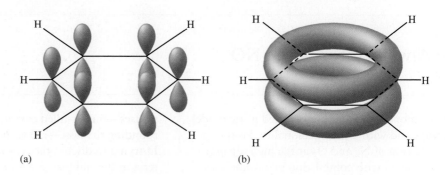

(a)   (b)

Since each carbon atom is sp^2 hybridized, a p orbital perpendicular to the plane of the ring remains on each carbon atom. These six p orbitals can be used to form π molecular orbitals, as shown in Fig. 14.50(a). The electrons in the resulting π molecular orbitals are delocalized above and below the plane of the ring, as shown in Fig. 14.50(b). This gives six equivalent C—C bonds, as required by the known structure of the benzene molecule. The benzene structure is often written as

to indicate the **delocalized π bonding** in the molecule.

Very similar treatments can be applied to other planar molecules for which resonance is required by the LE model. For example, the NO_3^- ion can be described using the π MO system shown in Fig. 14.51. In this molecule each atom is assumed to be sp^2 hybridized. This leaves one p orbital on each atom perpendicular to the plane of the ion. These p orbitals can combine to form the π MO system.

Figure 14.51
(a) The p orbitals used to form the π bonding system in the NO_3^- ion.
(b) A representation of the delocalization of the electrons in the π MO system of the NO_3^- ion.

(a)   (b)

14.6 | Orbitals: Human Inventions

In the treatment of the bonding and structure in molecules we have stressed that the descriptions we have given are models—and simple ones, at that. These models are extraordinarily valuable because they provide pictures in our minds of what molecules might look like and how they might behave. This helps us decide what questions to ask (what experiments to do) as we try to understand more completely the complicated behavior of matter. However, as valuable as these pictures are, we must remember that they greatly oversimplify a very complex situation. We must realize that these models can give us a rather superficial view that is often highly misleading.

For example, after all of the talk about orbitals in the last several chapters, you probably have the distinct impression that orbitals actually exist. The truth is, they do not—at least not in the physical sense. Orbitals are mathematical functions—solutions to a modified Schrödinger equation (the changes made to allow separation into independent electron equations).

Thus orbitals are mathematical tools we use to describe atoms and molecules. However, they have no physical reality in the sense that if you could look at a water molecule, you would probably not "see" anything like the pictures we have shown in this book. These pictures merely help us visualize the theoretical information we have accumulated for water.

We should also make clear that much more sophisticated treatments of atoms and molecules than we have considered here do exist and are carried out quite routinely by chemists who specialize in this area. These quantum mechanical calculations involve many fewer approximations than are made to obtain the models we have discussed here. However, although these treatments produce accurate mathematical descriptions of atomic and molecular properties, they are usually very difficult to interpret physically.

In contrast, the simple, highly pictorial models we have considered in this text are extremely useful because they help us do first-order chemical thinking and organize the information about matter that we gather from experiments. For example, there is a great deal of experimental evidence to suggest that methane has a tetrahedral structure. We have seen that the VSEPR model predicts this structure and that sp^3 hybrid orbitals on the carbon atom are consistent with this structure. Of course, this does not mean that methane really has four localized pairs of electrons, all with the same energy. In fact, the electrons in methane are delocalized and do not all have the same energy. However, the fact that methane is more complicated than these models indicate does not destroy the usefulness of the models. They still help us greatly as we organize the vast amount of information we collect about molecules. For example, chemists have learned to expect certain behaviors of "sp^3 carbon atoms" no matter what molecule contains them. A similar statement also applies to "sp^2 carbon atoms," "sp carbon atoms," and so on.

There is another point that should be made in connection with the theories of atoms and molecules. Even the experts in the field disagree (sometimes violently) about what the mathematical descriptions of atoms and molecules mean.*

---

*References to some interesting and provocative papers on this subject follow. These articles are probably too sophisticated to be read with great understanding now, but you can try to read them and then put copies of them in your files to be reread as your knowledge of chemistry increases. They raise some interesting questions.

L. Pauling, "The Nature of the Chemical Bond—1992," *J. Chem. Ed.* **69** (1992): 519.

J. F. Ogilvie, "The Nature of the Chemical Bond—1990," *J. Chem. Ed.* **67** (1990): 280.

M. Laing, "No Rabbit Ears on Water," *J. Chem. Ed.* **64** (1987): 124.

R. B. Martin, "Localized and Spectroscopic Orbitals: Squirrel Ears on Water," *J. Chem. Ed.* **65** (1988): 688.

E. R. Scerri, "Have Orbitals Really Been Observed?" *J. Chem. Ed.* **77** (2000): 1492.

Chemistry Explorers

Jonathan Kenny Looks at Spectroscopy in the Real World

Professor Jonathan Kenny, who has been on the faculty at Tufts University in Medford, Massachusetts, since 1981, earned his B.S. degree at the University of Notre Dame and his Ph.D. at the University of Chicago.

Professor Kenny's research focuses on the use of spectroscopy to analyze samples in the real world. One project involves a vehicle that uses a hydraulic press to insert a small-diameter rod into the ground to depths of 50 m or more. A sapphire window near the tip of the rod allows spectroscopic signals to pass through. The goal is to detect and analyze groundwater contaminants. This type of analysis presents major challenges because of the number of species present and the complex nature of the soil.

Another project of Kenny's is the development of a fingerprinting method for ballast water in ships based on multidimensional fluorescence spectroscopy. Ships involved in international trade often transport aquatic nuisance species in their ballast water, and the U.S. Coast Guard must enforce existing regulations that require all ships entering U.S. ports to exchange their ballast water in the deep ocean. Kenny and his students demonstrated that their fluorescence-based method can accurately identify water samples from different ports. Professor Kenny is also interested in developing innovative ways to help students learn chemistry in the context of related sciences such as astrophysics and biology. He teaches an environmental chemistry course for liberal arts students organized around the cosmic evolution time line.

Jonathan Kenny.

And even the most fundamental ideas about bonding that we have discussed in this text are subject to controversy. For example, Bacskay, Reimers (University of Sydney, Australia), and Nordholm (Göteburg University, Sweden) have suggested* that the simple "electrostatic model" presented here neglects the significance of changes in electron kinetic energies and atomic orbital contractions. The point here is not to present these more complex concepts but to make sure that you appreciate the nature of models and that you recognize the difference between the information learned about matter from experiments and the information learned from theories. Because matter is so complex, we often tailor our theories to explain a limited area of nature so as to keep the theories simple enough to understand and use. However, it is very dangerous to assume that such a limited theory can then be used in a wider sense. We must be very careful to ask proper questions of our theories or we face the danger of being greatly misled.

14.7 | Molecular Spectroscopy: An Introduction

Spectroscopy can be defined as the study of the interaction of electromagnetic radiation with matter. Spectroscopy provides a nondestructive and highly sensitive method for obtaining information about the identity, structure, and properties of substances. We have already discussed the emission spectrum of the hydrogen atom (Chapter 12) and the importance of the information it provides about hydrogen's quantized energy levels. Spectroscopy is also very useful for the study of molecules. Molecules can absorb electromagnetic radiation

---

*Bacskay, Reimers, and Nordholm, *J. Chem. Ed.* **74** (1997), 1494.

Figure 14.52

A schematic representation of two electronic energy levels in a molecule, with the vibrational (in red) and rotational (in blue) energy levels shown for each electronic state.

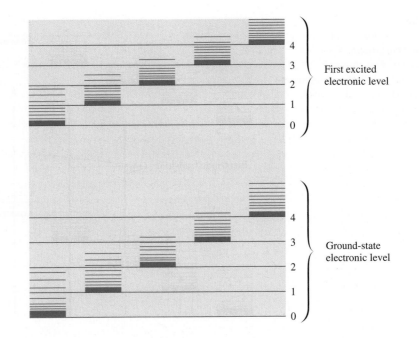

First excited electronic level

Ground-state electronic level

to furnish energy for many different processes, all which have quantized energy levels. For example, a molecule can absorb or emit a photon and go from a lower electronic energy state to a higher electronic energy state, or vice versa. This so-called *electronic transition* can be described approximately as a change from one electron arrangement to another. Typically, electronic transitions require photons in the ultraviolet or visible regions of the spectrum. In addition to undergoing electronic transitions, molecules can undergo vibrational and rotational energy transitions. For example, the atoms in a molecule vibrate around their equilibrium positions, giving rise to quantized vibrational energy levels whose spacings correspond to the energies of photons in the infrared region of the electromagnetic spectrum. Molecules also rotate and have quantized rotational energy levels whose spacings correspond to the energies of photons in the microwave region. In fact, it is the rotational excitation of the water molecules in food and the transfer of this energy to other molecules that form the basis for microwave cooking.

A schematic representation of two molecular electronic states with the accompanying vibrational and rotational energy levels is given in Fig. 14.52. Note that each electronic energy level has a set of quantized vibrational states and that each vibrational state has a set of rotational states.

Depending on the energy of the photons interacting with it, a molecule can undergo a pure rotational transition (change rotational levels but remain in the same vibrational and electronic states), a vibrational transition that may also involve a simultaneous rotational transition (Fig. 14.53), or an electronic transition that may involve a simultaneous vibrational and/or rotational change. The details of the geometric structure and electronic structure of the molecule determine exactly what types of transitions can occur. We will not deal with these issues here because they are beyond the scope of this text.

14.8 | Electronic Spectroscopy

The electronic spectrum of a molecule, which typically occurs in the ultraviolet or visible region of the electromagnetic spectrum, provides information about the spacings of the electronic energy levels in the molecule. The electronic spec-

Figure 14.53
The various types of transitions are shown by vertical arrows. Note that rotational changes are lowest in energy, followed by vibrational changes and then electronic changes, which require the highest-energy photons.

trum plots the quantity of radiation absorbed versus the wavelength of the radiation, showing peaks (maxima) at wavelengths where the photons have an energy that matches an energy gap in the molecule. The electronic spectrum corresponding to the electronic transitions shown in Fig. 14.53 is represented* in Fig. 14.54.

Electronic transitions from bonding to antibonding molecular orbitals are often encountered. In this case the potential energy curve for the ground state will be quite different from that for the excited state because less bonding electron density is found in the excited state. An example is the transition from the ground state of NO^+ ion to the first excited state, as shown in Fig. 14.55.

The majority of electronic transitions in molecules occurs in the UV region of the spectrum because the energy separations of electron states typically cor-

A technician using an electron spectroscopy unit used for chemical analysis.

---

*In the gas phase, various rotational levels in the ground vibrational state will be populated, and transitions to various rotational levels in the excited state will occur, giving rise to a fine structure in the spectrum. This fine structure is absent in solutions because collision of the solute with a solvent molecule occurs before a rotation is completed. Rotational fine structure will not be discussed here.

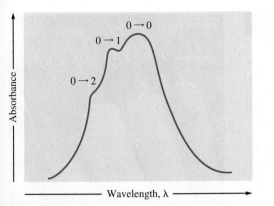

Figure 14.54
Spectrum corresponding to the changes indicated in Fig. 14.53. The transitions correspond to the vibrational changes $\nu = 0 \rightarrow \nu' = 0$, $\nu = 0 \rightarrow \nu' = 1$, and $\nu = 0 \rightarrow \nu' \rightarrow 2$.

Figure 14.55
The molecular orbital diagram for the ground state of NO^+ (on the left) and the first excited state of NO^+ (on the right). This transition involves a bonding electron being transferred to an antibonding orbital.

Figure 14.56
The molecular structure of beta-carotene. The double bonds alternate with single bonds in this molecule, called a conjugated bonding system.

respond to the energies of photons in the UV region. However, some molecules have electronic energy separations that correspond to radiation in the visible region (Fig. 12.3). One such class of compounds includes the coordination compounds that contain transition metal ions (see Section 19.6). Another class of compounds that absorbs in the visible region of the spectrum involves molecules with long chains of carbon molecules that have alternating double bonds, such as carotene (Fig. 14.56). Substances with alternating double bonds are called conjugated molecules. As a first approximation, these molecules can be described in terms of a particle in a box (Section 12.6). Note from Section 12.6 that the energy of the particle (in this case an electron in a conjugated *pi* system) is inversely proportional to the length of the box L. As the box gets longer, the energy separations decrease. This is exactly what happens with a conjugated molecule. As the conjugated system gets longer, the electron energies get closer together, and the light absorbed corresponds to longer wavelengths.

White light consists of all of the colors of the rainbow (Fig. 12.3), so when particular colors are absorbed by a given molecule, the substance appears colored. The color that results is the one given by the "sum" of the colors that remain unabsorbed. For example, carotene absorbs visible light in the violet and blue regions (Fig. 14.57). It appears orange in color because the colors not absorbed "add up" to produce orange. In fact, carotene is the substance that give carrots their bright orange color.

Often when a molecule absorbs a photon, the resulting excited state is much more chemically reactive than is the molecule in its ground state. The study of the chemistry of these electronically excited molecules is called *photochemistry*. A particularly important area of photochemistry concerns the study of the reactions that occur in the earth's atmosphere. For example, photochemical smog depends to a large extent on the photodecomposition of nitrogen dioxide to form very reactive oxygen atoms that combine with oxygen molecules in the air to form ozone, which then goes on to react with other pollutants. Ironically, the problems of ozone *depletion* in the upper atmosphere also result from a photochemical reaction—in this case the photodecomposition of chlorofluorocarbons such as CF_2Cl_2 to produce reactive chlorine atoms, which catalyze ozone decomposition. We will discuss this situation in more detail in Chapter 15.

Lasers, which are discussed in more detail in Chapter 16, have assumed a very important role in electronic spectroscopy in recent years for two reasons: They can deliver large quantities of energy at very precise wavelengths, and the

Figure 14.57

The electronic absorption spectrum of beta-carotene. The molecule absorbs strongly in the blue-violet region. The colors that remain give carotene its characteristic orange color (the dye in carrots).

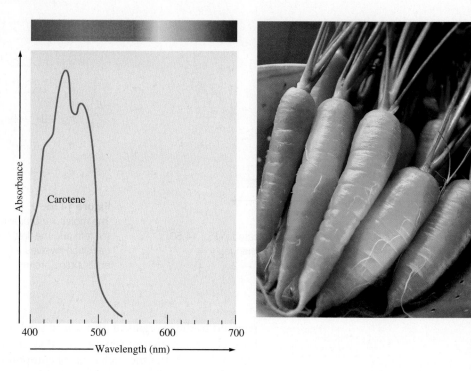

power can be delivered in very short bursts—on the order of only 10^{-15} second (one femtosecond) in duration. This allows the excitation of molecules with an ultrashort pulse of energy, after which the molecule can be observed as it decays back to the ground state by various pathways. These techniques are now being used to elucidate the mechanisms of chemical reactions, as we will discuss in Chapter 15.

Electronic spectroscopy also provides a sensitive and accurate method for determining the amount of absorbing species present in a sample (quantitative analysis). This technique is described in Appendix 3.

14.9 | Vibrational Spectroscopy

As we have seen, a molecule can be approximated as a collection of atoms held together by bonds. In describing the vibrations in a molecule, we can compare the bond between a given pair of atoms to a spring attached to two masses. As the atoms move apart in a vibrational motion, the bond—like a spring—provides a restoring force that pulls the atoms back toward each other.

For example, for a diatomic molecule, the potential energy of the system as a function of the distance between the atoms can be represented as shown in Fig. 14.58. In this figure R_e represents the equilibrium bond distance, which occurs at the minimum potential energy. The potential energy increases if the atoms are moved closer together than R_e because of the repulsive forces generated by the positively charged nuclei. The increase in the potential energy as the bond is stretched represents the energy needed to overcome the bonding force generated by the shared electrons. For small displacements from R_e, the bond can be treated as a harmonic oscillator (red curve in Fig. 14.58) in which the force F is given by

$$F = -k(R - R_e)$$

where k is the force constant and R is the actual bond length. When the stretched bond is released, if the system behaves like a classical harmonic os-

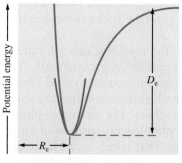

Figure 14.58

The potential curve for a diatomic molecule (blue) where R_e represents the equilibrium bond distance and D_e is the bond dissociation energy. The parabolic curve (red) represents the behavior of a true harmonic oscillator.

cillator, the atoms will oscillate around R_e with a frequency v given by the equation

$$v = \frac{1}{2\pi}\sqrt{\frac{k}{\mu}}$$

in which μ is the reduced mass:

$$\mu = \frac{(m_1)(m_2)}{m_1 + m_2}$$

where m_1 and m_2 represent the masses of the atoms connected by the bond. In classical physics the oscillations could have any frequency. However, like all of the energies in a molecule, the vibrational energy levels are actually quantized. As a consequence, only certain, discrete frequencies are allowed. The energy levels that correspond to the allowed frequencies are given by the following equation:

$$E_v = hv_0\left(v + \frac{1}{2}\right)$$

where v_0 = the characteristic frequency of the vibration*

v = the vibrational quantum number, which can assume only the values: 0, 1, 2, 3, . . .

This equation assumes harmonic behavior where the vibrational levels are equally spaced (separated by an energy equivalent to v_0). However, bonds do not behave exactly like springs (for example, the restoring force is weaker for a bond than is predicted for a spring at greatly stretched bond lengths). The actual potential energy curve (called the Morse potential) for a bond is represented by the blue curve in Fig. 14.58 and is shown in detail in Fig. 14.59. Note that the vibrational energy spacings on the Morse potential get smaller with increasing v, leading to "anharmonic" behavior.

For purposes of determining the force constant for a particular bond, the energy required for the $v = 0$ to $v = 1$ transition is used (this is assumed to be v_0). This procedure is illustrated in Example 14.9. Vibrational transitions in molecules typically require energies that correspond to the infrared region of the electromagnetic spectrum. The data are often represented in "wave numbers"; a wave number is the reciprocal of the wavelength (in cm) required to cause the vibrational transition.

Figure 14.59
Morse energy curve for a diatomic molecule.

---

*Notice that the vibrational energy is not zero when $v = 0$. The energy $hv_0/2$ corresponding to $v = 0$ is the "zero-point energy" of the molecule.

EXAMPLE 14.9

The infrared spectrum of gaseous HCl ($^1H^{35}Cl$) shows the $v = 0$ to $v = 1$ transition at 2885 cm^{-1}. Calculate the vibrational force constant for the HCl molecule.

Solution The fundamental vibrational frequency for HCl is

$$\frac{1}{2\pi}\sqrt{\frac{k}{\mu}} = v_0 = \frac{c}{\lambda} = (2.998 \times 10^{10} \text{ cm s}^{-1})(2885 \text{ cm}^{-1})$$

so

$$\frac{1}{2\pi}\sqrt{\frac{k}{\mu}} = 8.649 \times 10^{13} \text{ s}^{-1}$$

where

$$\mu = 1.627 \times 10^{-27} \text{ kg for } ^1H^{35}Cl \text{ (See Example 14.10.)}$$

Thus

$$k = 4\pi^2(1.627 \times 10^{-27} \text{ kg})(8.649 \times 10^{13} \text{ s}^{-1})^2$$

$$= 4.80 \times 10^2 \text{ kg s}^{-2} = 4.80 \times 10^2 \text{ J m}^{-2}$$

$$= \text{force constant for the H—Cl bond}$$

The determination of the force constant for a particular bond can give information about the bond strength. Strong springs have relatively large force constants, and the same holds true for strong bonds.

The analysis given thus far applies to diatomic molecules. For simple polyatomic molecules, several characteristic vibrational motions, called normal modes, are possible. As an example, the normal modes of vibration for the SO_2 molecule are shown in Fig. 14.60.

A particular bonded pair of atoms has a characteristic vibrational frequency (wave number) that is relatively insensitive to its molecular environment. Thus a signal that appears in the infrared (IR) spectrum at that characteristic frequency provides good evidence that this particular atom pair is present in the molecule. For example, a C—H pair in a molecule will always show a vibrational signal at about 3000 cm^{-1} (the range of wave numbers is actually 2850–3300 cm^{-1}, depending on the specific molecular environment). On the other hand, the O—H group in a molecule will show a vibrational bond at about 3600 cm^{-1}. Likewise, a carbonyl group

$$\begin{array}{c} \diagdown \\ \diagup \end{array} C{=}O$$

Figure 14.60

The three fundamental vibrations for sulfur dioxide. Note that the two structures for each fundamental vibration show the extremes of the motions of the atoms. (The amplitudes are exaggerated to illustrate the motion.)

Transmittance (%)

3500   3000   2500   2000   1500   1000   500

Wave number (cm⁻¹)

Figure 14.61

The infrared spectrum of CH_2Cl_2. (The wave number scale changes on this spectrum at 2000 cm⁻¹.)

always shows a distinctively shaped vibrational band at about 1700 cm⁻¹. A carbon–carbon double bond

$$\text{C=C}$$

shows a vibration at about 1650 cm⁻¹, and so on. The IR spectrum of a molecule can be a great aid in identifying which atom groupings are present in a molecule and thus can provide valuable information for identifying a specific molecule. A typical IR spectrum is shown in Fig. 14.61. Note that for this spectrum percent transmittance (%T) is plotted instead of absorbance. Absorbance (A) and %T are related as follows:

$$A = -\log\left(\frac{\%T}{100}\right)$$

This causes the "peaks" in a vibrational spectrum to be pointed in the opposite direction as those for an electronic spectrum.

Typical frequency ranges for the stretching motions of several common bonds are shown in Table 14.1. The exact frequency for a given bond in a molecule depends on its molecular environment.

Table 14.1

Characteristic Stretching Frequency Ranges for Several Common Types of Bonds

Bond	Frequency Range (cm⁻¹)
C—H	2850–3300
C=C	1640–1680
C≡C	2100–2260
C—O	1080–1300
C=O	1690–1760
O—H	3610–3640

14.10 | Rotational Spectroscopy

Because the spacings of the quantized rotational energy levels for a molecule depend on its molecular structure, the experimental determination of a molecule's rotational energy levels provides information about its structure. That is, determination of the specific energies of microwave radiation that a given molecule absorbs yields direct information about the rotational energy spacings, which in turn gives information about the details of the molecule's structure. For example, for a linear molecule, the energies of the rotational states are given by the formula

$$E_J = \frac{h^2}{8\pi^2 I} J(J + 1) = hBJ(J + 1)$$

where J = the rotational quantum number, which can assume only integer values and zero ($J = 0, 1, 2, 3, \ldots$)

h = Planck's constant = 6.626×10^{-34} J s

I = the moment of inertia of the molecule

$B = h/(8\pi^2 I)$

For a heteronuclear diatomic molecule containing atoms with masses m_1 and m_2, the moment of inertia is given by the relationship

$$I = \mu R_e^2$$

where
$$\mu = \text{reduced mass} = \frac{m_1 m_2}{m_1 + m_2}$$

R_e = average (equilibrium) bond length

Let's now consider how rotational spectroscopy can give information about the structure of a molecule. For example, if the energy of the photon necessary to promote a heteronuclear diatomic molecule from E_0 ($J = 0$) to E_1 ($J = 1$) is determined, the value of I for the molecule can be calculated, which in turn allows the calculation of R_e. Thus the rotational spectrum of a diatomic molecule provides an accurate method for measuring its average bond length.

Rotational energy levels are very close together. As a consequence, rotational energy transitions are initiated by relatively low-energy (long-wavelength) radiation. Typically, rotational changes are produced by radiation in the microwave region. To absorb radiation and thereby change its rotational energy, a molecule must have a permanent dipole moment. Also, heteronuclear diatomic molecules can change only one rotational level at a time—for example, from a level with $J = 1$ to a level with $J = 2$, from $J = 2$ to $J = 3$, and so on. That is, for these molecules, $\Delta J = +1$.

Thus the allowed absorption frequencies can be derived (in terms of J, B, and I) as follows: Recall that for an energy-level change ΔE,

$$\Delta E = h\upsilon = E_f - E_i$$

where E_f and E_i are the final and initial energies, respectively. Using the equation above for E_J, we have

$$E_f = hBJ_f(J_f + 1)$$
and
$$E_i = hBJ_i(J_i + 1)$$

Therefore,

$$\Delta E = E_f - E_i = hB[J_f(J_f + 1) - J_i(J_i + 1)]$$

Since J_f and J_i can differ only by 1, we know that

$$J_f = J_i + 1$$

Thus
$$\Delta E = hB[(J_i + 1)(J_i + 2) - J_i(J_i + 1)]$$
and
$$\Delta E = 2hB(J_i + 1)$$

We can convert to frequency υ as follows:

$$\upsilon = \frac{\Delta E}{h} = 2B(J_i + 1)$$

Thus, for a given heteronuclear diatomic molecule, the frequencies for the various rotational transitions are separated by $2B$, as shown in Table 14.2.

Example 14.10 illustrates the use of the rotational transition energy to calculate the bond length of a diatomic molecule.

Table 14.2

Several Allowed Rotational Transitions for a Heteronuclear Diatomic Molecule

Transition	Frequency
$J = 0 \rightarrow J = 1$	$2B$
$J = 1 \rightarrow J = 2$	$4B$
$J = 2 \rightarrow J = 3$	$6B$
$J = 3 \rightarrow J = 4$	$8B$
$J = 4 \rightarrow J = 5$	$10B$

EXAMPLE 14.10

The microwave spectrum of $^1H^{35}Cl$ shows that the transition from $J = 0$ to $J = 1$ requires electromagnetic radiation with a wavelength of 4.85×10^{-4} m. Calculate the bond length of the $^1H^{35}Cl$ molecule. (The masses of ^1H and ^{35}Cl are 1.0078 amu and 34.9689 amu, respectively.)

Solution We know that

$$\Delta E = 2hB(J_i + 1) = h\nu = \frac{hc}{\lambda}$$

so

$$\frac{c}{\lambda} = 2B(J_i + 1)$$

where

$$\lambda = 4.85 \times 10^{-4} \text{ m}$$

$$c = 2.998 \times 10^8 \text{ m/s}$$

$$J_i = 0$$

Then

$$\frac{c}{\lambda} = 2B(1) = \frac{2.998 \times 10^8 \text{ ms}^{-1}}{4.85 \times 10^{-4} \text{ m}}$$

and

$$B = 3.09 \times 10^{11} \text{ s}^{-1}$$

Since

$$B = \frac{h}{8\pi^2 I}$$

then

$$I = \frac{h}{8\pi^2 B} = \frac{6.626 \times 10^{-34} \text{ J s}}{8\pi^2(3.09 \times 10^{11} \text{ s}^{-1})} = 2.57 \times 10^{-47} \text{ kg m}^2$$

where

$$I = \mu R_e^2$$

For $^1\text{H}^{35}\text{Cl}$,

$$\mu = \frac{m_H m_{Cl}}{m_H + m_{Cl}} = \frac{(1.0078)(34.9689)}{1.0078 + 34.9689} = 0.9796 \text{ amu}$$

Since one amu = 1.661×10^{-27} kg,

$$\mu = 0.9796 \text{ amu} \times 1.661 \times 10^{-27} \frac{\text{kg}}{\text{amu}} = 1.627 \times 10^{-27} \text{ kg}$$

then

$$R_e^2 = \frac{I}{\mu} = \frac{2.57 \times 10^{-47} \text{ kg m}^2}{1.627 \times 10^{-27} \text{ kg}}$$

and

$$R_e = 1.26 \times 10^{-10} \text{ m} = 126 \text{ pm}$$

This represents the measured bond length of the $^1\text{H}^{35}\text{Cl}$ molecule.

As might be expected, the rotational spectra of polyatomic molecules are more complex than those for diatomic molecules. For example, depending on their structures, polyatomic molecules can have as many as three different moments of inertia. Although more complicated, the analysis of the structures of polyatomic molecules using rotational spectra follows the same principles as we have discussed for diatomic molecules.

14.11 | Nuclear Magnetic Resonance Spectroscopy

Nuclear magnetic resonance (NMR) spectroscopy has risen to the same level of importance as electronic, vibrational, and rotational spectroscopy as a tool for studying molecular properties, particularly structural properties. Certain nuclei, such as the hydrogen nucleus (proton), have a nuclear "spin." The "spinning" nucleus* generates a small magnetic field that we will call μ. When placed

---

*The nucleus does not literally spin, although we often picture it that way. Nuclear "spin," like electron "spin," is simply a name for a property called spin angular momentum.

Figure 14.62

Representations of the two spin states of the proton interacting with a large, steady magnetic field B.

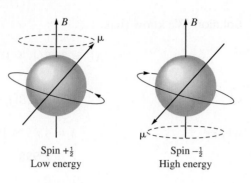

Spin $+\frac{1}{2}$
Low energy

Spin $-\frac{1}{2}$
High energy

in a strong, external magnetic field (B), the nucleus can exist in two distinct states: a low-energy state in which μ is aligned with the external magnetic field B and a high-energy state in which μ is opposed to the external magnetic field (Fig. 14.62). A transition from the more stable alignment (with the field) to the less stable alignment (against the field) occurs when the nucleus absorbs electromagnetic energy that is exactly equal to the energy separation between the states (ΔE). This energy gap is very small and corresponds to the radiofrequency range of the electromagnetic spectrum. Because the net absorption energies are so small, a special technique is needed to detect the signal, a condition called resonance. We will not discuss the details of the instrumentation here.

We will focus on three features of the NMR spectrum: the number and size of the signals, the chemical shift, and spin–spin coupling.

Number and Size of Signals

First, we will consider how the NMR spectrometer can distinguish between hydrogen nuclei in different molecular environments and produce multiple signals. Magnetically equivalent protons (hydrogen nuclei in the same local environment) produce one signal. For example, in a molecule such as bromoethane (Fig. 14.63), there are two sets of magnetically equivalent hydrogens. The hydrogens labeled a are the three magnetically equivalent methyl hydrogens, and the hydrogens labeled b are the two magnetically equivalent methylene hydrogens. Magnetically equivalent protons sense the same local magnetic environment. That is, they occupy equivalent positions in the molecule.

a b

Figure 14.63

The molecular structure of bromoethane. The molecule has two distinct magnetic environments labeled a and b.

Because of rapid rotations about sigma bonds and molecular symmetry, the three methyl hydrogens are all equivalent to each other. For the same reasons, the two methylene protons are also equivalent to each other. In summary, the methyl hydrogens (a) all exist in the same magnetic environment but experience a different magnetic field than the methylene hydrogens (b) because of different local magnetic fields. As a result, the resonance energy ΔE corresponding to the frequency of absorption v will be different for these two groups of hydrogen nuclei, producing two distinct signals. Thus the NMR spectrometer can distinguish between groups of hydrogen nuclei that experience different local magnetic fields.

The areas of the signals are directly proportional to the number of hydrogens. In the case of bromoethane, the two peaks have an area ratio of 3:2 because there are three methyl hydrogens (a) and two methylene hydrogens (b). We would expect a spectrum that looks like the idealized version shown in Fig. 14.64. We will look at an actual spectrum presently.

Chemical Shift

When a molecule is placed in an external magnetic field B, each hydrogen nucleus experiences a total field that is the sum of B and two other local magnetic fields: one produced by the electrons (H_e) and the other produced by neighbor-

Figure 14.64
The expected NMR spectrum for bromoethane.

Area ratios   2   3

Figure 14.65
(a) The spin of proton H_y can be "up" or "down." (b) This leads to a "doublet" (two peaks with equal areas) as the signal for proton H_x.

(a)   (b)

Figure 14.66
(a) The spins for protons H_y can both be "up," can be opposed (in two ways), or can both be "down." (b) This leads to a "triplet" signal for proton H_x, with areas 1:2:1 reflecting the ways of achieving the various states shown in (a).

(a)   (b)

ing protons that possess a nuclear spin (H_h). Thus the applied magnetic field (B) is constant, whereas the magnetic fields H_e and H_h depend on the molecular environment. The magnetic field produced by the neighboring electrons (H_e) determines the position (relative frequency) of an NMR signal, called the chemical shift. The magnetic fields produced by neighboring nuclei (H_h) are smaller than H_e and can cause splitting of the NMR signal, called spin–spin coupling. This effect will be discussed in the next subsection.

The position of an NMR signal is typically recorded relative to the position of the signal of an internal standard. This standard is commonly tetramethyl silane (TMS) [(CH_3)$_4$Si]. Assuming the difference in frequency between TMS and the hydrogen nucleus of interest is Δ, the spectrometer will record a signal at

$$\frac{\Delta}{v_0} \times 10^6 = \delta$$

where v_0 is the spectrometer frequency. The symbol δ (delta) represents the position of the signal, the chemical shift, expressed as parts per million (ppm) on a scale of 1–10 ppm. The signal for TMS occurs at 0.0 ppm, whereas the signals for most nuclei are "downfield" toward 10 ppm.

Spin–Spin Coupling

Next, we will consider how the magnetic field produced by neighboring protons (H_h) can cause the splitting of the NMR signal. First, we will consider the signal due to a hydrogen atom (H_x) with only one neighboring hydrogen atom (H_y) (Fig. 14.65). The neighboring hydrogen nucleus will have approximately equal probability of existing in either the "up" or "down" orientation. In other words, half the molecules exist with proton H_y "up" and half will exist with the H_y proton "down." As a result, two different peaks are observed, because H_h for H_x adds and subtracts from the local field "felt" by H_y. This pattern is called a doublet, and we say that the neighboring hydrogen nucleus (H_y) splits the signal of H_x into a doublet. The intensity of the two lines is equal because the probability of the neighboring hydrogen nucleus (H_y) existing in either spin state is approximately equal.

When there are two magnetically equivalent adjacent hydrogen nuclei, three possibilities exist for their combined magnetic fields (Fig. 14.66). Both can have spin "up," one can have spin "up" and the other have spin "down," (there are two ways to achieve this), or both can have spin "down" [Fig. 14.66(a)]. These three possibilities have a probability ratio of 1:2:1, which corresponds to three different signal frequencies. The appearance of the resulting NMR signal for H_x is a three-line pattern, called a triplet, with intensities 1:2:1 [Fig. 14.66(b)].

When there are three magnetically equivalent neighboring hydrogen nuclei (Fig. 14.67), the H_x signal splits into a quartet with intensity pattern 1:3:3:1 for similar reasons to those discussed for the other cases.

Figure 14.67
The spins for protons H_y can be arranged as shown in (a), leading to four different magnetic environments for proton H_x. This arrangement leads to a "quartet" signal (b) for proton H_x, with areas 1:3:3:1 reflecting the ways of achieving the various states shown in (a).

(a)   (b)

Next, we will examine the actual NMR spectrum for bromoethane (CH_3CH_2Br), shown in Fig. 14.68. This spectrum consists of a triplet [the CH_3 protons (*a*), split by the two adjacent CH_2 protons] and a quartet [the CH_2 protons (*b*) split by the adjacent CH_3 protons].

Spin–spin coupling is transmitted through the covalent bonds of the molecule by causing polarization of the electron spins. That is, when the proton of a hydrogen bonded to a carbon has spin "up," it causes a slight "unpairing" of the electrons in the bond between the hydrogen and the carbon. As a result, the "spin down" electron is favored in the neighborhood of the proton; the "spin up" electron spends more time near the carbon. This spin polarization, which continues through neighboring bonds, decreases as it gets farther from the original proton spin. Thus spin–spin coupling gets weaker (attenuates) with the number of bonds. In general, spin–spin coupling is observed for hydrogen nuclei that are separated by no more than three sigma bonds. For example, in the molecule 2-butanone (Fig. 14.69), hydrogens from groups *a* and *b* split one

Figure 14.68
The NMR spectrum of CH_3CH_2Br (bromoethane) with TMS as reference.

NMR and Oenology

Serious wine collectors can pay many thousands of dollars for a rare vintage wine. For example, a 1946 Chateau Petrus might bring as much as $7000. Buying such a bottle of wine can be risky. It is not uncommon for a wine exposed to oxygen through a bad cork to be spoiled through decomposition of the alcohol to vinegar (acetic acid) or acetaldehyde. In the past, the only way to find out whether the wine was still good was to open the bottle and taste it. Now, however, there is a new technology based on NMR that should allow the detection of excess acetic acid without opening the bottle.

Wine collector Gene Mulvihill has funded the construction of a special NMR spectrometer by chemistry professor Matthew Augstine of the University of California at Davis. The special NMR spectrometer, which costs about $100,000, uses a superconducting magnet that operates near 0 K. The bottle of wine to be evaluated is placed in the magnetic field and the resulting NMR spectrum is analyzed for signals characteristic of the protons in the hydrogen atoms in acetic acid.

Mulvihill has formed a company, Wine Scanner, Inc., to market the services of the wine-analyzing NMR machine to wine collectors and upscale restaurants with expensive wine inventories. *In vino veritas.*

Gene Mulvihill and his wine-analyzing NMR spectrometer.

Figure 14.69

(a) The molecule (2-butanone)

CH₃CH₂CCH₃
‖
O

has the NMR spectrum shown in (b).

(a)

(b)

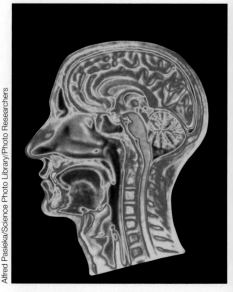

Figure 14.70

A technician speaks to a patient before he is moved into the cavity of a magnetic resonance imaging (MRI) machine.

Figure 14.71

A colored magnetic resonance imaging (MRI) scan through a human head, showing a healthy brain in side view.

another because they are separated by only three bonds. However, hydrogens from group *c* are not split by any other hydrogens because they are separated from the other hydrogens by more than three sigma bonds. Note also that the coupling is never observed between magnetically equivalent hydrogen atoms. That is, magnetically equivalent protons do not split each other.

NMR spectroscopy has assumed a major role in our attempts to understand the structures and functions of molecules. For example, NMR has developed to the stage where it is possible to determine the three-dimensional structures of protein molecules containing thousands of atoms. One reason that this feat is possible is that other nuclei such as ^{13}C and ^{31}P have spin states that respond to an external magnetic field in much the same way as does ^{1}H. Therefore, NMR spectra of these nuclei can also be obtained, thus providing more structural information. The use of NMR to study protein structure was deemed so important that a Nobel Prize was recently awarded for this work.

Another very important application of NMR, called magnetic resonance imaging (MRI), is widely used as a medical diagnosis tool. In using this technique, the patient is placed in a strong magnetic field (Fig. 14.70) and the responses of protons in the water contained in the various types of tissues are measured and mapped into an image of the part of the body under study (Fig. 14.71). This sensitive and nondestructive method for providing images of various parts of the body has revolutionized medical diagnosis. The discoverers of this technique, Paul Lauterbur of the University of Illinois and Peter Mansfield of the University of Nottingham, were awarded the Nobel Prize for medicine in 2003.

Key Terms

Section 14.1
hybridization
sp^3 hybridization
hybrid orbitals
sp^2 hybridization
sigma (σ) bond
pi (π) bond
sp hybridization
dsp^3 hybridization
d^2sp^3 hybridization

Section 14.2
molecular orbital model
molecular orbital (MO)
sigma (σ) molecular orbital
bonding molecular orbital
antibonding molecular orbital
bond order

Section 14.3
pi (π) molecular orbital
paramagnetism
diamagnetism

Section 14.4
heteronuclear diatomic molecule

Section 14.5
delocalized π bonding

Section 14.7
spectroscopy

For Review

◯WL and **go Chemistry**

Two widely used bonding models
- Localized electron model
- Molecular orbital model

Localized electron model
- Molecule is pictured as a group of atoms sharing electron pairs between atomic orbitals
- Hybrid orbitals, which are combinations of the "native" atomic orbitals, are often required to account for the molecular structure
  - Six electron pairs (octahedral arrangement) requires d^2sp^3 orbitals
  - Five electron pairs (trigonal bipyramidal arrangement) requires dsp^3 orbitals
  - Four electron pairs (tetrahedral arrangement) require sp^3 orbitals
  - Three electron pairs (trigonal planar arrangement) require sp^2 orbitals
  - Two electron pairs (linear arrangement) requires sp orbitals

Two types of bonds
- Sigma: electrons are shared in the area centered on a line joining the atoms
- Pi: a shared electron pair occupies the space above and below the line joining the atoms

Molecular orbital model
- A molecule is assumed to be a new entity consisting of positively charged nuclei and electrons
- The electrons in the molecule are contained in molecular orbitals, which in the simplest form of the model are constructed from the atomic orbitals of the constituent atoms
- The model correctly predicts relative bond strength, magnetism, and bond polarity
- It correctly portrays electrons as being delocalized in polyatomic molecules
- The main disadvantage of the model is that it is difficult to apply qualitatively to polyatomic molecules

Molecular orbitals are classified in two ways: energy and shape
- Energy
  - A bonding MO is lower in energy than the atomic orbitals from which it is constructed. Electrons in this type of MO are lower in energy in the molecule than in the separated atoms and thus favor molecule formation.
  - An antibonding MO is higher in energy than the atomic orbitals from which it is constructed. Electrons in this type of MO are higher in energy in the molecule than in the separated atoms and thus do not favor molecule formation.
- Shape (symmetry)
  - Sigma (σ) MOs have their electron probability centered on a line passing through the nuclei
  - Pi (π) MOs have their electron probability concentrated above and below the line connecting the nuclei

Bond order is an index of bond strength

Bond order

$$= \frac{\text{number of bonding electrons} - \text{number of antibonding electrons}}{2}$$

Molecules that require the concept of resonance in the localized electron model can be more accurately described by combining the localized electron and molecular orbital models

- The σ bonds are localized
- The π bonds are delocalized

Spectroscopy

- Provides a method for obtaining information about the identity, structure, and properties of substances.
- Electronic spectroscopy: provides information about the spacings of the electronic energy levels.
- Vibrational spectroscopy: typically in the infrared region (IR spectroscopy); gives evidence for a particular atom pair in a molecule.
- Rotational spectroscopy: provides information about the structure of a given molecule.
- Nuclear magnetic resonance (NMR) spectroscopy: allows for the understanding of the structures and functions of molecules.

Discussion Questions

These questions are designed to be considered by groups of students in class. Often these questions work well for introducing a particular topic in class.

1. What are molecular orbitals? How do they compare with atomic orbitals? Can you tell by the shape of bonding orbitals and antibonding orbitals which is lower in energy? Explain.

2. Explain the difference between the σ and π MOs for homonuclear diatomic molecules. How are bonding orbitals and antibonding orbitals different? Why are there two π MOs and one σ MO? Why are the π MOs degenerate?

3. Compare Figs. 14.38 and 14.40. Why are they different? Because B_2 is known to be paramagnetic, the π_{2p} and σ_{2p} MOs must be switched from our first prediction. What is the rationale for this? Why might one expect the σ_{2p} to be lower in energy than the π_{2p}? Why can't we use diatomic oxygen to help us decide whether the σ_{2p} or π_{2p} is lower in energy?

4. Which of the following would you expect to be more favorable energetically? Explain.
   a. An H_2 molecule in which enough energy is added to excite one electron from a bonding to an antibonding MO
   b. Two separate H atoms

5. Draw the Lewis structure for HCN. Indicate the hybrid orbitals, and draw a picture showing all the bonds between the atoms, labeling each bond as σ or π.

6. Which is the more correct statement: "The methane molecule (CH_4) is a tetrahedral molecule because it is sp^3 hybridized" or "The methane molecule (CH_4) is sp^3 hybridized because it is a tetrahedral molecule"? What, if anything, is the difference between these two statements?

7. Compare and contrast the MO model with the LE model. When is each useful?

8. What are the relationships among bond order, bond energy, and bond length? Which of these quantities can be measured?

Exercises

OWL Interactive versions of these problems may be assigned in OWL.

A blue exercise number indicates that the answer to that exercise appears at the back of this book and a solution appears in the *Solutions Guide*.

The LE Model and Hybrid Orbitals

9. Why do we hybridize atomic orbitals to explain the bonding in covalent compounds? What type of bonds form from hybrid orbitals, σ or π? Explain.

10. What hybridization is required for central atoms that have a tetrahedral arrangement of electron pairs? A trigonal planar arrangement of electron pairs? A linear arrangement of electron pairs? How many unhybridized p atomic orbitals are present when a central atom exhibits tetrahedral geometry? Trigonal planar geometry? Linear geometry? What are the unhybridized p atomic orbitals used for?

11. Why are d orbitals sometimes used to form hybrid orbitals? Which period of elements does not use d orbitals for hybridization? If necessary, which d orbitals ($3d$, $4d$, $5d$, or $6d$) would sulfur use to form hybrid orbitals requiring d atomic orbitals? Answer the same question for arsenic and for iodine.

12. The atoms in a single bond can rotate about the internuclear axis without breaking the bond. The atoms in a double bond and a triple bond cannot rotate about the internuclear axis unless the bond is broken. Why?

13. Use the LE model to describe the bonding in H_2O.

14. Use the LE model to describe the bonding in H_2CO and C_2H_2. Carbon is the central atom in H_2CO, and C_2H_2 exists as HCCH.

15. The space-filling models of ethane and ethanol are shown below.

Ethane   Ethanol
(C_2H_6)   (C_2H_5OH)

C
H
O

Use the LE model to describe the bonding in ethane and ethanol.

16. The space-filling models of hydrogen cyanide and phosgene are shown below.

Hydrogen cyanide   Phosgene
(HCN)   ($COCl_2$)

C
H
O
N
Cl

Use the LE model to describe the bonding in hydrogen cyanide and phosgene.

17. Give the expected hybridization of the central atom for the molecules or ions in Exercises 57, 58, and 60 from Chapter 13.

18. Give the expected hybridization of the central atom for the molecules in Exercises 91 and 92 from Chapter 13.

19. Urea, a compound formed in the liver, is one of the ways humans excrete nitrogen. The Lewis structure for urea is

$$\begin{array}{ccccc} H & :\!O\!: & H \\ | & \| & | \\ H-N-C-N-H \\ \cdot\cdot & & \cdot\cdot \end{array}$$

Using hybrid orbitals for carbon, nitrogen, and oxygen, determine which orbitals overlap to form the various bonds in urea.

20. Give the expected hybridization for the molecular structures illustrated below.

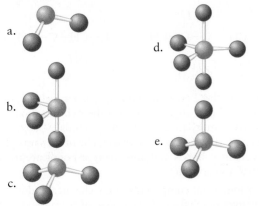

a.

b.

c.

d.

e.

21. For each of the following molecules, write a Lewis structure, predict the molecular structure (including bond angles), give the expected hybrid orbitals on the central atom, and predict the overall polarity.
   a. CF_4 g. AsF_5
   b. NF_3 h. KrF_2
   c. OF_2 i. KrF_4
   d. BF_3 j. SeF_6
   e. BeH_2 k. IF_5
   f. TeF_4 l. IF_3

22. Predict the hybrid orbitals used by the sulfur atom(s) in each of the following. Also predict the molecular structure, including bond angle(s).
   a. SO_2
   b. SO_3

   c. $S_2O_3^{2-}$ $\left[\begin{array}{c} O \\ | \\ S-S-O \\ | \\ O \end{array} \right]^{2-}$

   d. $S_2O_8^{2-}$ $\left[\begin{array}{c} O \qquad\qquad O \\ | \qquad\qquad | \\ O-S-O-O-S-O \\ | \qquad\qquad | \\ O \qquad\qquad O \end{array} \right]^{2-}$

   e. SO_3^{2-} h. SF_4
   f. SO_4^{2-} i. SF_6
   g. SF_2 j. F_3S-SF

23. Why must all six atoms in C_2H_4 be in the same plane?

24. The allene molecule has the following Lewis structure:

Must all four hydrogen atoms lie in the same plane? If not, what is the spatial relationship among them? Why?

25. Biacetyl and acetoin are added to margarine to make it taste more like butter.

Biacetyl   Acetoin

Complete the Lewis structures, predict values for all C—C—O bond angles, and give the hybridization of all the carbon atoms in these two compounds. Must the four carbons and two oxygens in biacetyl lie in the same plane? How many σ bonds and how many π bonds are there in biacetyl and acetoin?

26. Many important compounds in the chemical industry are derivatives of ethylene (C_2H_4). Two of them are acrylonitrile and methyl methacrylate.

Acrylonitrile   Methyl methacrylate

Complete the Lewis structures for these molecules, showing all lone pairs. Give approximate values for bond angles *a* through *f*, and give the hybridization of all carbon atoms. In acrylonitrile and methyl methacrylate indicate which atoms in each molecule must lie in the same plane. How many σ bonds and how many π bonds are there in acrylonitrile and methyl methacrylate?

27. One of the first drugs to be approved for use in treatment of acquired immune deficiency syndrome (AIDS) was azidothymidine (AZT). Complete the Lewis structure of AZT.

a. How many carbon atoms use sp^3 hybridization?
b. How many carbon atoms use sp^2 hybridization?
c. Which atom is sp hybridized?
d. How many σ bonds are in the molecule?
e. How many π bonds are in the molecule?
f. What is the N—N—N bond angle in the azide ($-N_3$) group?
g. What is the H—O—C bond angle in the side group attached to the five-membered ring?

h. What is the hybridization of the oxygen atom in the $-CH_2OH$ group?

28. Hot and spicy foods contain molecules that stimulate pain-detecting nerve endings. Two such molecules are piperine and capsaicin:

Piperine

Capsaicin

Piperine is the active compound in white and black pepper, and capsaicin is the active compound in chili peppers. The ring structures in piperine and capsaicin are shorthand notation. Each point where lines meet represents a carbon atom.

a. Complete the Lewis structures for piperine and capsaicin, showing all lone pairs of electrons.
b. How many carbon atoms are sp, sp^2, and sp^3 hybridized in each molecule?
c. Which hybrid orbitals are used by the nitrogen atoms in each molecule?
d. Give approximate values for the bond angles marked *a* through *l* in the above structures.

29. Two molecules used in the polymer industry are azodicarbonamide and methyl cyanoacrylate. Their structures are

Azodicarbonamide   Methyl cyanoacrylate

Azodicarbonamide is used in forming polystyrene. When added to the molten plastic, it decomposes to nitrogen, carbon monoxide, and ammonia gases, which are captured as bubbles in the molten polymer. Methyl cyanoacrylate is the main ingredient in super glue. As the glue sets, methyl cyanoacrylate polymerizes across the carbon–carbon double bond. (See Chapter 21.)

a. Complete the Lewis structures showing all lone pairs of electrons.
b. Which hybrid orbitals are used by the carbon atoms in each molecule and the nitrogen atoms in azodicarbonamide?

c. How many π bonds are present in each molecule?

d. Give approximate values for the bond angles marked *a* through *h* in the above structures.

30. The antibiotic thiarubin-A was discovered by studying the feeding habits of wild chimpanzees in Tanzania. The structure for thiarubin-A is

a. Complete the Lewis structures showing all lone pairs of electrons.

b. Indicate the hybrid orbitals used by the carbon and sulfur atoms in thiarubin-A.

c. How many σ and π bonds are present in this molecule?

31. The three most stable oxides of carbon are carbon monoxide (CO), carbon dioxide (CO_2), and carbon suboxide (C_3O_2). The space-filling models for these three compounds are

For each oxide, draw the Lewis structure, predict the molecular structure, and describe the bonding (in terms of the hybrid orbitals for the carbon atoms).

The MO Model

32. Consider the following molecular orbitals formed from the combination of two hydrogen 1*s* orbitals:

a. Which is the bonding molecular orbital, and which is the antibonding molecular orbital? Explain how you can tell by looking at their shapes.

b. Which of the two molecular orbitals is lower in energy? Why is this true?

33. Sketch the molecular orbital and label its type (σ or π; bonding or antibonding) that would be formed when the following atomic orbitals overlap. Explain your labels.

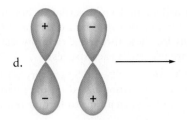

34. What are the relationships among bond order, bond energy, and bond length? Which of these can be measured? Distinguish between the terms *paramagnetic* and *diamagnetic*. What type of experiment can be done to determine if a material is paramagnetic?

35. What modification to the molecular orbital model was made from the experimental evidence that B_2 is paramagnetic?

36. A Lewis structure obeying the octet rule can be drawn for O_2 as follows:

$$:\overset{..}{O}=\overset{..}{O}:$$

Use the molecular orbital energy-level diagram for O_2 to show that the above Lewis structure corresponds to an excited state.

37. How does molecular orbital theory explain the following observations?

a. H_2 is stable, whereas He_2 is unstable.

b. B_2 and O_2 are paramagnetic, whereas C_2, N_2, and F_2 are diamagnetic.

c. N_2 has a very large bond energy associated with it.

d. NO^+ is more stable than NO^-.

38. Why does the molecular orbital model do a better job in explaining the bonding in NO^- and NO than the hybrid orbital model?

39. Show how a hydrogen 1*s* atomic orbital and a fluorine 2*p* atomic orbital overlap to form bonding and antibonding MOs in the hydrogen fluoride molecule. Are they σ or π MOs?

40. Which of the following are predicted by the molecular orbital model to be stable diatomic species?

a. H_2^+, H_2, H_2^-, H_2^{2-}

b. N_2^{2-}, O_2^{2-}, F_2^{2-}

c. Be_2, B_2, Ne_2

41. Which charge(s) for the N_2 molecule would give a bond order of 2.5?

42. In which of the following diatomic molecules would the bond strength be expected to weaken as an electron is removed?

a. H_2 b. B_2 c. C_2^{2-} d. OF

43. In terms of the molecular orbital model, which species in each of the following two pairs will most likely be the one to gain an electron? Explain.

CN or NO O_2^{2+} or N_2^{2+}

44. Using the molecular orbital model to describe the bonding in CO, CO^+, and CO^{2+}, predict the bond orders and the relative bond lengths for these three species. How many unpaired electrons are present in each species?

45. As compared with CO and O_2, CS and S_2 are very unstable molecules. Give an explanation based on the relative abilities of the sulfur and oxygen atoms to form π bonds.

46. Consider the following electron configuration:

$$(\sigma_{3s})^2(\sigma_{3s}^*)^2(\sigma_{3p})^2(\pi_{3p})^4(\pi_{3p}^*)^4$$

Give four species that, in theory, would have this electron configuration.

47. What type of molecular orbital would result from the combination of two d_{xz} atomic orbitals shown below? Assume the x axis is the internuclear axis.

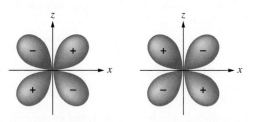

48. Using an MO energy-level diagram, would you expect O_2 to have a lower or higher first ionization energy than atomic oxygen? Why?

49. Use Figs. 14.45 and 14.46 to answer the following questions.
    a. Would the bonding MO in HF place greater electron density near the H or the F atom? Why?
    b. Would the bonding MO have greater fluorine $2p$ character, greater hydrogen $1s$ character, or an equal contribution from both? Why?
    c. Answer parts a and b for the antibonding MO in HF.

50. The diatomic molecule OH exists in the gas phase. OH plays an important part in combustion reactions and is a reactive oxidizing agent in polluted air. The bond length and bond energy have been measured to be 97.06 pm and 424.7 kJ/mol, respectively. Assume that the OH molecule is analogous to the HF molecule discussed in the chapter and that the MOs result from the overlap of a p_z orbital from oxygen and the $1s$ orbital of hydrogen (the O—H bond lies along the z axis).
    a. Draw pictures of the sigma bonding and antibonding molecular orbitals in OH.
    b. Which of the two MOs has the greater hydrogen $1s$ character?
    c. Can the $2p_x$ orbital of oxygen form MOs with the $1s$ orbital of hydrogen? Explain.
    d. Knowing that only the $2p$ orbitals of oxygen interact significantly with the $1s$ orbital of hydrogen, complete the MO energy-level diagram for OH. Place the correct number of electrons in the energy levels.
    e. Estimate the bond order for OH.
    f. Predict whether the bond order of OH^+ is greater than, less than, or the same as that of OH. Explain.

51. What is delocalized π bonding, and what does it explain? Explain the delocalized π bonding system in C_6H_6 (benzene) and SO_2.

52. Describe the bonding in the O_3 molecule and the NO_2^- ion using the LE model. How would the molecular orbital model describe the π bonding in these two species?

53. Describe the bonding in the CO_3^{2-} ion using the LE model. How would the molecular orbital model describe the π bonding in this species?

54. The space-filling model for benzoic acid is shown below.

Benzoic acid
$(C_6H_5CO_2H)$

Describe the bonding in benzoic acid using the LE model combined with the molecular orbital model.

Spectroscopy

55. The infrared spectrum of $^1H^{79}Br$ shows the $v = 0$ to $v = 1$ transition at 2650. cm^{-1}. Determine the vibrational force constant for the HBr molecule. The atomic mass of ^1H is 1.0078 amu, and the atomic mass of ^{79}Br is 78.918 amu.

56. If the force constant of $^{14}N^{16}O$ is 1550. N m^{-1}, determine the wave number of a line in the infrared spectrum of NO. The atomic mass of ^{14}N is 14.003 amu, and the atomic mass of ^{16}O is 15.995 amu.

57. The microwave spectrum of $^{12}C^{16}O$ shows that the transition from $J = 0$ to $J = 1$ requires electromagnetic radiation with a wavelength of 2.60×10^{-3} m.
    a. Calculate the bond length of CO. See Exercise 56 for the atomic mass of ^{16}O.
    b. Calculate the frequency of radiation absorbed in a rotational transition from the second to the third excited state of CO.

58. Draw the idealized NMR spectra for the following compounds.
    a.

Assume that the five hydrogen atoms in the benzene ring are equivalent with no spin–spin coupling.

b.

c.

59. Consider the following idealized NMR multiplets.

i.   ii.   iii.   iv.

Which is the correct multiplet for the underlined group in the following molecules?

a. CH_3—$\underline{CH_2}$—O—CH_2—CH_3

b. $\underline{CH_3}$—O—$\overset{\overset{\textstyle O}{\|}}{C}$—$CH_2$—$CH_3$

c. $(CH_3)_3C$—O—$\overset{\overset{\textstyle O}{\|}}{C}$—$\underline{CH_2}$—$CH_2$—$CH_3$

d. $H_2\underline{C}$—$\overset{\overset{\textstyle F}{|}}{C}H$—$CH_2$—$\overset{\overset{\textstyle O}{\|}}{C}$—O—$CH_2$—$CH_3$ (with F F on first two carbons)

60. The NMR spectra below are for the organic compounds C_6H_{12} and $C_4H_{10}O$. Deduce the structures for these compounds. See Exercise 70 for a discussion of the bonding in organic compounds. The structure of C_6H_{12} has one double bond, with the rest being single bonds, and the structure of $C_4H_{10}O$ has only single bonds. Note that the TMS reference has been omitted in each spectrum.

C_6H_{12}

$C_4H_{10}O$

Additional Exercises

61. Draw the Lewis structures, predict the molecular structures, and describe the bonding (in terms of the hybrid orbitals for the central atom) for the following.
  a. XeO_3 c. $XeOF_4$ e. XeO_3F_2
  b. XeO_4 d. $XeOF_2$

62. $FClO_2$ and F_3ClO can both gain a fluoride ion to form stable anions. F_3ClO and F_3ClO_2 can also lose a fluoride ion to form stable cations. Draw Lewis structures and describe the hybrid orbitals used by chlorine in these four ions.

63. Two structures can be drawn for cyanuric acid:

a. Are these two structures the same molecule? Why or why not?
b. Give the hybridization of the carbon and nitrogen atoms in each structure.
c. Use bond energies (Table 13.6) to predict which form is more stable; that is, which contains the strongest bonds?

64. Using bond energies from Table 13.6, estimate the barrier to rotation around a carbon–carbon double bond. To do this, consider what must happen to go from

to

in terms of making and breaking chemical bonds; that is, what happens to the π bond?

65. Show how a d_{xz} atomic orbital and a p_z atomic orbital combine to form a bonding molecular orbital. Assume the x axis is the internuclear axis. Is a σ or a π molecular orbital formed? Explain.

66. Describe the bonding in the first excited state of N_2 (the one closest in energy to the ground state) using the MO model. What differences do you expect in the properties of the molecule in the ground state and in the first excited state? (An excited state of a molecule corresponds to an electron arrangement other than that giving the lowest possible energy.)

67. Consider three molecules: A, B, and C. Molecule A has a hybridization of sp^3. Molecule B has two more effective pairs (electron pairs around the central atom) than molecule A. Molecule C consists of two σ bonds and two π bonds. Give the molecular structure, hybridization, bond angles, and an example for each molecule.

68. Complete the following resonance structures for $POCl_3$:

(A)   (B)

a. Would you predict the same molecular structure from each resonance structure?
b. What is the hybridization of P in each structure?
c. What orbitals can the P atom use to form the π bond in structure B?
d. Which resonance structure would be favored on the basis of formal charges?

69. Complete the Lewis structures of the following molecules. Predict the molecular structure, polarity, bond angles, and hybrid orbitals used by the atoms marked by asterisks for each molecule.

a. BH_3
$$\begin{array}{c} \text{H} \\ | \\ \overset{*}{\text{B}} \\ \diagup \quad \diagdown \\ \text{H} \quad \text{H} \end{array}$$

b. N_2F_2 F—N*—N*—F

c. C_4H_6 $$\begin{array}{c} \text{H} \qquad \text{H} \\ | \qquad | \\ \text{H}-\overset{*}{\text{C}}-\overset{*}{\text{C}}-\overset{*}{\text{C}}-\overset{*}{\text{C}}-\text{H} \\ | \qquad | \\ \text{H} \qquad \text{H} \end{array}$$

d. ICl_3 $$\begin{array}{c} \text{Cl}-\overset{*}{\text{I}}-\text{Cl} \\ | \\ \text{Cl} \end{array}$$

70. Vitamin B_6 is an organic compound whose deficiency in the human body can cause apathy, irritability, and an increased susceptibility to infections. Below is an incomplete Lewis structure, for vitamin B_6. Complete the Lewis structure and answer the following questions. [*Hint:* Vitamin B_6 can be classified as an organic compound (a compound based on carbon atoms). The majority of Lewis structures for simple organic compounds have all atoms with a formal charge of zero. Therefore, add lone pairs and multiple bonds to the structure below to give each atom a formal charge of zero.]

a. How many σ bonds and π bonds exist in vitamin B_6?
b. Give approximate values for the bond angles marked a through g in the structure.
c. How many carbon atoms are sp^2 hybridized?
d. How many carbon, oxygen, and nitrogen atoms are sp^3 hybridized?
e. Does vitamin B_6 exhibit delocalized π bonding? Explain.

71. Consider the following computer-generated model of caffeine:

Complete a Lewis structure for caffeine in which all atoms have a formal charge of zero (as is typical with most organic compounds). How many C and N atoms are sp^2 hybridized? How many C and N atoms are sp^3 hybridized? sp hybridized? How many σ and π bonds are there?

72. Aspartame is an artificial sweetener marketed under the name Nutra-Sweet. A partial Lewis structure for aspartame is shown below:

Note that the six-sided ring is shorthand notation for a benzene ring ($—C_6H_5$). Benzene is discussed in Section 14.5. Complete the Lewis structure for aspartame. How many C and N atoms exhibit sp^2 hybridization? How many C and O atoms exhibit sp^3 hybridization? How many σ and π bonds are in aspartame? Aspartame is an organic compound, and the Lewis structure follows the guidelines outlined in Exercise 70.

73. The N_2O molecule is linear and polar.
a. On the basis of this experimental evidence, which arrangement is correct, NNO or NON? Explain your answer.

b. On the basis of your answer in part a, write the Lewis structure of N_2O (including resonance forms). Give the formal charge on each atom and the hybridization of the central atom.

c. How would the multiple bonding in :N≡N—Ö: be described in terms of orbitals?

74. Values of measured bond energies may vary greatly depending on the molecule studied. Consider the following reactions:

$$NCl_3(g) \longrightarrow NCl_2(g) + Cl(g) \qquad \Delta H = 375 \text{ kJ/mol}$$

$$ONCl(g) \longrightarrow NO(g) + Cl(g) \qquad \Delta H = 158 \text{ kJ/mol}$$

Rationalize the difference in the values of ΔH for these reactions, even though each reaction appears to involve the breaking of only one N—Cl bond. (*Hint:* Consider the bond order of the NO bond in ONCl and in NO.)

Challenge Problems

75. Given that the ionization energy of F_2^- is 290. kJ/mol, do the following.
   a. Calculate the bond energy of F_2^-. You will need to look up the bond energy of F_2 and ionization energy of F^-.
   b. Explain the difference in bond energy between F_2^- and F_2 using MO theory.

76. Bond energy has been defined in the text as the amount of energy required to break a chemical bond, so we have come to think of the addition of energy as breaking bonds. However, in some cases the addition of energy can cause the formation of bonds. For example, in a sample of helium gas subjected to a high-energy source, some He_2 molecules exist momentarily and then dissociate. Use MO theory (and diagrams) to explain why He_2 molecules can come to exist and why they dissociate.

77. a. A flask containing gaseous N_2 is irradiated with 25-nm light. Using the following information, indicate what species can form in this flask during irradiation.

$$N_2(g) \longrightarrow 2N(g) \qquad \Delta H = 941 \text{ kJ/mol}$$

$$N_2(g) \longrightarrow N_2^+(g) + e^- \qquad \Delta H = 1501 \text{ kJ/mol}$$

$$N(g) \longrightarrow N^+(g) + e^- \qquad \Delta H = 1402 \text{ kJ/mol}$$

   b. What range of wavelengths will produce atomic nitrogen in the flask but will not produce any ions?
   c. Explain why the first ionization energy of N_2 (1501 kJ/mol) is greater than the first ionization energy of atomic nitrogen (1402 kJ/mol).

78. Use the MO model to determine which of the following has the smallest ionization energy: N_2, O_2, N_2^{2-}, N_2^-, O_2^+. Explain your answer.

79. Cholesterol ($C_{27}H_{46}O$) has the following structure:

In such shorthand structures, each point where lines meet represents a carbon atom, and most H atoms are not shown. Draw the complete structure, showing all carbon and hydrogen atoms. (There will be four bonds to each carbon atom.) Indicate which carbon atoms use sp^2 or sp^3 hybrid orbitals. Are all carbon atoms in the same plane, as implied by the structure?

80. Arrange the following from lowest to highest ionization energy: O, O_2, O_2^-, O_2^+. Explain your answer.

81. Carbon monoxide (CO) forms bonds to a variety of metals and metal ions. Its ability to bond to iron in hemoglobin is the reason that CO is so toxic. The bond carbon monoxide forms to metals is through the carbon atom:

$$M—C≡O$$

   a. On the basis of electronegativities, would you expect the carbon atom or the oxygen atom to form bonds to metals?
   b. Assign formal charges to the atoms in CO. Which atom would you expect to bond to a metal on this basis?
   c. In the MO model, bonding MOs place more electron density near the more electronegative atom. (See the HF molecule, Figs. 14.45 and 14.46.) Antibonding MOs place more electron density near the less electronegative atom in the diatomic molecule. Use the MO model to predict which atom of carbon monoxide should form bonds to metals.

82. Use the MO model to explain the bonding in BeH_2. When constructing the MO energy-level diagram, assume that the Be $1s$ electrons are not involved in bond formation.

83. In Exercise 65 in Chapter 13, the Lewis structures for benzene (C_6H_6) were drawn. Using one of the Lewis structures, estimate $\Delta H°_f$ for $C_6H_6(g)$ using bond energies and given the standard enthalpy of formation of $C(g)$ is 717 kJ/mol. The experimental $\Delta H°_f$ value for $C_6H_6(g)$ is 83 kJ/mol. Explain the discrepancy between the experimental value and the calculated $\Delta H°_f$ value for $C_6H_6(g)$.

84. For each chemical formula below, an NMR spectrum is described, including relative overall areas (intensities) for the various signals given in parentheses. Draw the structure of a compound having the specific formula that would give the described NMR spectrum. (*Hint:* All of

these formulas represent organic compounds. Lewis structures for organic compounds typically have all atoms in the compound with a formal charge of zero. This is the case in this problem.)

a. $C_2H_3Cl_3$; NMR has one singlet signal.

b. $C_3H_6Cl_2$; NMR has a triplet (4) and a quintet (2) signal.

c. $C_3H_6O_2$; NMR has a singlet (1), a quartet (2), and a triplet (3) signal.

d. $C_5H_{10}O$; NMR has a heptet (1), a singlet (3), and a doublet (6) signal.

e. C_3H_6O; NMR has a triplet (3), a quintet (2), and a triplet (1) signal.

85. Structural isomers are compounds that have the same chemical formula but the atoms are bonded together differently giving different compounds. Consider the two structural isomers having the formula C_2H_6O. Draw the two isomers, and describe what should be seen in the NMR spectrum for each isomer (types of signals and relative overall intensities). (*Hint:* Both of the isomers are organic compounds. Lewis structures for organic compounds typically have all atoms in the compound with a formal charge of zero. This is the case in this problem.)

Marathon Problem

86. The sp^2 hybrid atomic orbitals have the following general form:

$$\Phi_1 = \sqrt{1/3}\,\Phi_s + 2A\Phi_{px}$$

$$\Phi_2 = \sqrt{1/3}\,\Phi_s - A\Phi_{px} + B\Phi_{py}$$

$$\Phi_3 = \sqrt{1/3}\,\Phi_s - A\Phi_{px} - B\Phi_{py}$$

where Φ_s, Φ_{px}, and Φ_{py} represent orthonormal (normalized and orthogonalized) atomic orbitals. Calculate the values of A and B.

Chemical Kinetics

15

chapter

Soccer goalie catching a ball.

Mike Powell/Allsports Concepts/Getty Images

The applications of chemistry focus primarily on chemical reactions, and the commercial use of a reaction requires knowledge of several of its characteristics. A reaction is defined by its reactants and products, whose identities must be learned by experiment. Once the reactants and products are known, the equation for the reaction can be written and balanced, and stoichiometric calculations can be carried out. Another very important characteristic of a reaction is its spontaneity. Spontaneity refers to the *inherent tendency* for the process to occur; however, it implies nothing about speed. *Spontaneous does not mean fast.* There are many spontaneous reactions that are so slow that no apparent reaction occurs over a period of weeks or years at normal temperatures. For example, there is a strong inherent tendency for gaseous hydrogen and oxygen to combine to form water,

$$2H_2(g) + O_2(g) \longrightarrow 2H_2O(l)$$

but in fact the two gases can coexist indefinitely at 25°C. Similarly, the gaseous reactions

$$H_2(g) + Cl_2(g) \longrightarrow 2HCl(g)$$

$$N_2(g) + 3H_2(g) \longrightarrow 2NH_3(g)$$

are both highly likely to occur from a thermodynamic standpoint, but we observe no product formation under normal conditions. In addition, the process of changing diamond to graphite is spontaneous but is so slow that it is not detectable.

To be useful, reactions must occur at a reasonable rate. To produce the 20 million tons of ammonia needed each year for fertilizer, we cannot simply mix nitrogen and hydrogen gases at 25°C and wait for them to react. It is not enough to understand the stoichiometry and thermodynamics of a reaction; we must also understand the factors that govern the rate of the reaction. The area of chemistry that concerns reaction rates is called **chemical kinetics.**

One of the main goals of chemical kinetics is to understand the steps by which a reaction takes place. This series of steps is called the *reaction mechanism.* Understanding the mechanism allows us to find ways to facilitate the reaction. For example, the Haber process for the production of ammonia requires high temperatures to achieve commercially feasible reaction rates. However, even higher temperatures (and more cost) would be required without the use of iron oxide, which speeds up the reaction.

In this chapter we will consider the fundamental ideas of chemical kinetics. We will explore rate laws, reaction mechanisms, and simple models for chemical reactions.

15.1 | Reaction Rates

The kinetics of air pollution is discussed in Section 15.9.

To introduce the concept of reaction rate, we will consider the decomposition of nitrogen dioxide, a gas that causes air pollution. Nitrogen dioxide decomposes to nitric oxide and oxygen as follows:

$$2NO_2(g) \longrightarrow 2NO(g) + O_2(g)$$

Suppose in a particular experiment we start with a flask of nitrogen dioxide at room temperature, where it is stable indefinitely, and quickly heat it to 300°C, where it decomposes according to the preceding equation. We then measure the concentrations of nitrogen dioxide, nitric oxide, and oxygen over time as the nitrogen dioxide decomposes. The results of this experiment are summarized in Table 15.1, and the data are plotted in Fig. 15.1.

Table 15.1

Concentrations of Reactant and Products as a Function of Time for the Reaction $2NO_2(g) \longrightarrow 2NO(g) + O_2(g)$ (at 300°C)

Time (±1 s)	Concentration (mol/L)		
	NO_2	NO	O_2
0	0.0100	0	0
50	0.0079	0.0021	0.0011
100	0.0065	0.0035	0.0018
150	0.0055	0.0045	0.0023
200	0.0048	0.0052	0.0026
250	0.0043	0.0057	0.0029
300	0.0038	0.0062	0.0031
350	0.0034	0.0066	0.0033
400	0.0031	0.0069	0.0035

Figure 15.1
Starting with pure nitrogen dioxide at 300°C, the concentrations of nitrogen dioxide, nitric oxide, and oxygen are plotted versus time.

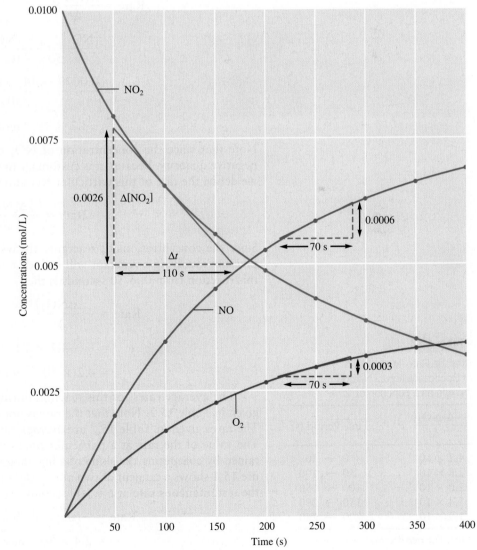

This definition of reaction rate assumes that the volume remains constant. A more general definition of reaction rate is the change in the number of moles per unit of volume per unit of time.

Note from these results that the concentration of the reactant (NO_2) decreases with time and that the concentrations of the products (NO and O_2) increase with time. Chemical kinetics deals with the speed at which these changes occur. The speed, or *rate*, of a process is defined as the change in a given quantity over a specific period of time. For chemical reactions the quantity that changes is the amount or concentration of a reactant or product. So the **reaction rate** of a chemical reaction is defined as the *change in concentration of a reactant or product per unit time*:

$$\text{Rate} = \frac{\text{concentration of A at time } t_2 - \text{concentration of A at time } t_1}{t_2 - t_1}$$

$$= \frac{\Delta[A]}{\Delta t}$$

where A represents a specific reactant or product and the square brackets indicate concentration in mol/L. As usual, the symbol Δ indicates a *change* in a given quantity.

Now let's calculate the average rate at which the concentration of NO_2 changes over the first 50 seconds of the reaction, using the data given in Table 15.1.

$$\text{Rate} = \frac{\Delta[NO_2]}{\Delta t}$$

$$= \frac{[NO_2]_{t=50} - [NO_2]_{t=0}}{50 \text{ s} - 0 \text{ s}}$$

$$= \frac{0.0079 \text{ mol/L} - 0.0100 \text{ mol/L}}{50 \text{ s}}$$

$$= -4.2 \times 10^{-5} \text{ mol L}^{-1} \text{ s}^{-1}$$

Note that since the concentration of NO_2 decreases with time, $\Delta[NO_2]$ is a negative quantity. Because it is customary to work with *positive* reaction rates, we define the rate of this particular reaction as

$$\text{Rate} = -\frac{\Delta[NO_2]}{\Delta t}$$

Since the concentrations of reactants always decrease with time, any rate expression involving a reactant will include a negative sign. The average rate of this reaction from 0 to 50 seconds is then

$$\text{Rate} = -\frac{\Delta[NO_2]}{\Delta t}$$

$$= -(-4.2 \times 10^{-5} \text{ mol L}^{-1} \text{ s}^{-1})$$

$$= 4.2 \times 10^{-5} \text{ mol L}^{-1} \text{ s}^{-1}$$

The average rates for this reaction during several other time intervals are given in Table 15.2. Note that the rate is not constant but decreases with time. The rates given in Table 15.2 are *average* rates over 50-second time intervals. The value of the rate at a particular time (the **instantaneous rate**) can be obtained by computing the slope of a line tangent to the curve at that point. Figure 15.1 shows a tangent drawn at $t = 100$ seconds. The *slope* of this line gives the instantaneous rate at $t = 100$ seconds:

$$\text{Rate} = -(\text{slope of the tangent line})$$

$$= 2.4 \times 10^{-5} \text{ mol L}^{-1} \text{ s}^{-1}$$

Table 15.2

Average Rate (in mol L^{-1} s^{-1}) of Decomposition of Nitrogen Dioxide as a Function of Time

$-\dfrac{\Delta[NO_2]}{\Delta t}$	Time Period (s)
4.2×10^{-5}	$0 \rightarrow 50$
2.8×10^{-5}	$50 \rightarrow 100$
2.0×10^{-5}	$100 \rightarrow 150$
1.4×10^{-5}	$150 \rightarrow 200$
1.0×10^{-5}	$200 \rightarrow 250$

Note: The *rate* decreases with time.

Femtochemistry

Some reactions occur very slowly, such as when a nail rusts. Others occur very rapidly, such as when methane is combusted in a Bunsen burner. Studying very fast reactions requires very special techniques, usually involving lasers—devices that produce high-energy bursts of light with very precise frequencies. The study of very fast reactions is one of the most important areas of chemical research, as demonstrated by the fact that the 1999 Nobel Prize in chemistry was awarded to Ahmed H. Zewail of the California Institute of Technology in Pasadena, California. Zewail's studies involve reactions that occur on the femtosecond (10^{-15} s) time scale—the time scale for molecular vibrations.

In Zewail's laboratory a strong laser flash of a few femtoseconds' duration shines on beams of molecules streaming into a vacuum chamber. The laser beam is tuned to excite all of the molecules to the same state, where they are vibrating in unison. Subsequent, weaker laser pulses monitor the concentrations of the reactants, intermediates, and products as the reaction occurs.

One reaction studied by Zewail is the decomposition of cyclobutane to two ethylene molecules:

Ahmed Zewail/California Institute of Technology

A laser spectroscopy laboratory at the California Institute of Technology.

The intermediate exists for approximately 700 fs (700×10^{-15} s) and then decomposes into two ethylene molecules. Techniques similar to Zewail's approach (commonly called femtochemistry) are now widely used in chemical research and are being applied to problems such as elucidating the mechanism for energy conversion in chlorophyll (photosynthesis) and understanding the way human eyes detect light.

Zewail has shown that the reaction mechanism involves the breaking of one of the carbon–carbon bonds in cyclobutane to produce a tetramethylene intermediate:

Unpaired electrons

So far we have discussed the rate of this reaction only in terms of the reactant. The rate can also be defined in terms of the products. However, in doing so, we must take into account the coefficients in the balanced equation for the reaction because the stoichiometry determines the relative rates of the consumption of reactants and the generation of products. For example, in the reaction

$$2NO_2(g) \longrightarrow 2NO(g) + O_2(g)$$

both NO_2 and NO have a coefficient of 2, so NO is produced at the same rate as NO_2 is consumed. We can verify this from Fig. 15.1. Note that the curve for NO is the same shape as the curve for NO_2 except that it is inverted. This means that at any point in time the slope of the tangent to the curve for NO will be the negative of the slope to the curve for NO_2. (Verify this at the point $t = 100$ seconds on both curves.) In contrast, O_2 has a coefficient of 1, which means it is produced half as fast as NO, which has a coefficient of 2. That is, the rate of NO production is twice the rate of O_2 production.

We can also verify this fact from Fig. 15.1. For example, at $t = 250$ seconds,

Slope of the tangent to the NO curve $= 8.6 \times 10^{-6}$ mol L^{-1} s^{-1}

Slope of the tangent to the O_2 curve $= 4.3 \times 10^{-6}$ mol L^{-1} s^{-1}

The slope at $t = 250$ seconds on the NO curve is twice the slope of that point on the O_2 curve, showing that the rate of production of NO is twice that of O_2. The rate information can be summarized as follows:

$$\boxed{\begin{array}{c}\text{Rate of consumption}\\\text{of } NO_2\end{array}} = \boxed{\begin{array}{c}\text{rate of production}\\\text{of NO}\end{array}} = \boxed{2(\text{rate of production of } O_2)}$$

Because the reaction rate changes with time, and because the rate may be different for the various reactants and products (by factors that depend on the coefficients in the balanced equation), we must be very specific when we describe a rate for a chemical reaction.

15.2 | Rate Laws: An Introduction

Note that the term *reversible* has different meanings in kinetics and thermodynamics.

Chemical reactions are *reversible*. In our discussion of the decomposition of nitrogen dioxide, we have so far considered only the forward reaction:

$$2NO_2(g) \longrightarrow 2NO(g) + O_2(g)$$

However, the reverse reaction can also occur. As NO and O_2 accumulate, they can react to re-form NO_2:

$$O_2(g) + 2NO(g) \longrightarrow 2NO_2(g)$$

When gaseous NO_2 is placed in an otherwise empty container, the dominant reaction initially is

$$2NO_2(g) \longrightarrow 2NO(g) + O_2(g)$$

and the change in the concentration of NO_2 ($\Delta[NO_2]$) depends only on the forward reaction. However, after a period of time, enough products accumulate so that the reverse reaction becomes important. Now $\Delta[NO_2]$ depends on the *difference in the rates of the forward and reverse reactions*. This complication can be avoided if we study the rate of a reaction under conditions where the reverse reaction makes only a negligible contribution. Typically, this means that we study a reaction at a point soon after the reactants are mixed, before the products have had time to build up to significant levels.

Under conditions such that the reverse reaction can be neglected, the *reaction rate depends only on the concentrations of the reactants.* For the decomposition of nitrogen dioxide, we can write

$$\text{Rate} = k[NO_2]^n \tag{15.1}$$

Such an expression, which shows how the rate depends on the concentrations of reactants, is called a **rate law.** The proportionality constant k, called the **rate constant,** and n, called the **order** of the reactant, must both be determined by experiment. The order of a reactant can be positive or negative and can be an integer or a fraction. For the relatively simple reactions we will consider in this book, the orders will generally be positive integers.

Note two important points about Equation (15.1):

1. The concentrations of the products do not appear in the rate law because the reaction rate is being studied under conditions where the reverse reaction does not contribute to the overall rate.

2. The value of the exponent n must be determined by experiment; it cannot be written from the balanced equation.

Before we go further, we must define exactly what we mean by the term *rate* in Equation (15.1). In Section 15.1 we saw that reaction rate means a change in concentration per unit time. However, which reactant or product concentration do we choose in defining the rate? For example, for the decomposition of NO_2 to produce O_2 and NO considered in Section 15.1, we could define the rate in terms of any of these three species. However, since O_2 is produced only half as fast as NO_2, we must be careful to specify which species we are talking about in a given case. For instance, we might choose to define the reaction rate in terms of the consumption of NO_2:

$$\text{Rate} = -\frac{\Delta[NO_2]}{\Delta t} = -\frac{d[NO_2]}{dt} = k[NO_2]^n$$

where d indicates an infinitesimally small change. On the other hand, we could define the rate in terms of the production of O_2:

$$\text{Rate}' = \frac{d[O_2]}{dt} = k'[NO_2]^n$$

Note that because $2NO_2$ molecules are consumed for every O_2 molecule produced,

$$\text{Rate} = 2 \times \text{rate}'$$

or

$$k[NO_2]^n = 2k'[NO_2]^n$$

and

$$k = 2 \times k'$$

Thus the value of the rate constant depends on how the rate is defined.

In this text we will always be careful to define exactly what is meant by the rate for a given reaction so that there will be no confusion about which specific rate constant is being used.

Types of Rate Laws

Notice that the rate law we have used to this point expresses rate as a function of concentration. For example, for the decomposition of NO_2 we have defined the rate as

$$\text{Rate} = -\frac{d[NO_2]}{dt} = k[NO_2]^n$$

The terms *differential rate law* and *rate law* will be used interchangeably in this text.

which tells us (once we have determined the value of *n*) exactly how the rate depends on the concentration of the reactant NO_2. A rate law that expresses how the *rate depends on concentration* is called the **differential rate law,** but it is often simply called the **rate law.** Thus, when we use the term *rate law* in this text, we mean the expression that gives the rate as a function of concentration.

A second kind of rate law, the **integrated rate law,** will also be important in our study of kinetics. The integrated rate law expresses how the *concentrations depend on time.* As we will see, a given differential rate law is always related to a certain type of integrated rate law, and vice versa. That is, if we determine the differential rate law for a given reaction, we automatically know the form of the integrated rate law for the reaction. This means that once we determine either type of rate law for a reaction, we also know the other one.

Which rate law we choose to determine by experiment often depends on what types of data are easiest to collect. If we can conveniently measure how the rate changes as the concentrations are changed, we can readily determine the differential (rate/concentration) rate law. On the other hand, if it is more convenient to measure the concentration as a function of time, we can determine the form of the integrated (concentration/time) rate law. We will discuss how rate laws are actually determined in the next several sections.

Why are we interested in determining the rate law for a reaction? How does it help us? It helps us because we can work backward from the rate law to find the steps by which the reaction occurs. Most chemical reactions do not take place in a single step but result from a series of sequential steps. To understand a chemical reaction, we must learn what these steps are. For example, a chemist who is designing an insecticide may study the reactions involved in the process of insect growth to see what type of molecule may interrupt this series of reactions. Or an industrial chemist may be trying to make a reaction occur faster, using less expensive conditions. To accomplish this, he or she must know which step is slowest because it is that step that must be speeded up. Thus a chemist is usually not interested in a rate law for its own sake but for what it tells about the steps by which a reaction occurs. We will develop a process for finding the reaction steps later in this chapter.

Rate Laws

1. There are two types of rate laws:
   - The differential rate law (often called simply the rate law) shows how the rate of a reaction depends on concentrations.
   - The integrated rate law shows how the concentrations of species in the reaction depend on time.
2. Because we will typically consider reactions under conditions where the reverse reaction is unimportant, our rate laws will involve concentrations of reactants.
3. Because the differential and integrated rate laws for a given reaction are related in a well-defined way, the experimental determination of *either* of the rate laws is sufficient.
4. Experimental convenience usually dictates which type of rate law is determined experimentally.
5. Knowing the rate law for a reaction is important mainly because we can usually infer the individual steps involved in the reaction from the specific form of the rate law.

15.3 | Determining the Form of the Rate Law

The first step in understanding how a given chemical reaction occurs is to determine the *form* of the rate law. In this section we will explore ways to obtain the differential rate law for a reaction. First, we will consider the decomposition of dinitrogen pentoxide in carbon tetrachloride solution:

$$2N_2O_5(soln) \longrightarrow 4NO_2(soln) + O_2(g)$$

Data for this reaction at 45°C are listed in Table 15.3 and plotted in Fig. 15.2. In this reaction the oxygen gas escapes from the solution and thus does not react with the nitrogen dioxide, so we do not have to be concerned about the effects of the reverse reaction at any time over the life of the reaction. In other words, the reverse reaction is negligible at all times over the course of this reaction.

Evaluation of the reaction rates at N_2O_5 concentrations of 0.90 *M* and 0.45 *M*, by taking the slopes of the tangents to the curve at these points (Fig. 15.2), yields the following data:

$[N_2O_5]$	Rate (mol L^{-1} s^{-1})
0.90 *M*	5.4×10^{-4}
0.45 *M*	2.7×10^{-4}

Note that when $[N_2O_5]$ is halved, the rate is also halved. This means that the rate of this reaction depends on the concentration of N_2O_5 to the *first power*. In other words, the (differential) rate law for this reaction is

$$\text{Rate} = -\frac{d[N_2O_5]}{dt} = k[N_2O_5]$$

Thus the reaction is *first order* in N_2O_5. Note that for this reaction the order is *not* the same as the coefficient of N_2O_5 in the balanced equation for the reaction. This reemphasizes the fact that the order of a particular reactant must be obtained by *observing* how the reaction rate depends on the concentration of that reactant.

We have seen that determining the instantaneous rate at two different reactant concentrations gives the following rate law for the decomposition of N_2O_5:

$$\text{Rate} = -\frac{d[A]}{dt} = k[A]$$

where A represents N_2O_5.

Table 15.3

Concentration/Time Data for the Reaction $2N_2O_5(soln) \longrightarrow 4NO_2(soln) + O_2(g)$ (at 45°C)

$[N_2O_5]$ (mol/L)	Time (s)
1.00	0
0.88	200
0.78	400
0.69	600
0.61	800
0.54	1000
0.48	1200
0.43	1400
0.38	1600
0.34	1800
0.30	2000

First order: Rate = *k*[A]. Doubling the concentration of A doubles the reaction rate.

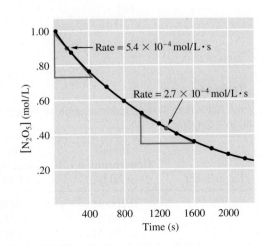

Figure 15.2

A plot of the concentration of N_2O_5 as a function of time for the reaction $2N_2O_5(soln) \longrightarrow 4NO_2(soln) + O_2(g)$ (at 45°C). Note that the reaction rate at $[N_2O_5] = 0.90$ *M* is twice that at $[N_2O_5] = 0.45$ *M*.

The value of the initial rate is determined for each experiment at the same value of t as close to $t = 0$ as possible.

Method of Initial Rates

The most common method for directly determining the form of the differential rate law for a reaction is the **method of initial rates**. The **initial rate** of a reaction is the instantaneous rate determined just after the reaction begins (just after $t = 0$). The idea is to determine the instantaneous rate before the initial concentrations of reactants have changed significantly. Several experiments are carried out using different initial concentrations, and the initial rate is determined for each run. The results are then compared to see how the initial rate depends on the initial concentrations. This procedure allows the form of the rate law to be determined. We will illustrate the method of initial rates by using the following reaction:

$$NH_4^+(aq) + NO_2^-(aq) \longrightarrow N_2(g) + 2H_2O(l)$$

Table 15.4 gives initial rates obtained from three experiments involving different initial concentrations of reactants.

The general form of the rate law for this reaction is

$$Rate = -\frac{d[NH_4^+]}{dt} = k[NH_4^+]^n[NO_2^-]^m$$

We can determine the values of n and m by observing how the initial rate depends on the initial concentrations of NH_4^+ and NO_2^-. In Experiments 1 and 2, where the initial concentration of NH_4^+ remains the same but where the initial concentration of NO_2^- doubles, the observed initial rate also doubles. Since

$$Rate = k[NH_4^+]^n[NO_2^-]^m$$

we have, for Experiment 1,

$$Rate = 1.35 \times 10^{-7} \text{ mol L}^{-1} \text{ s}^{-1} = k(0.100 \text{ mol/L})^n(0.0050 \text{ mol/L})^m$$

and for Experiment 2,

$$Rate = 2.70 \times 10^{-7} \text{ mol L}^{-1} \text{ s}^{-1} = k(0.100 \text{ mol/L})^n(0.010 \text{ mol/L})^m$$

Rates 1, 2, and 3 were determined at the same value of t (very close to $t = 0$).

The ratio of these rates is

$$\frac{Rate\ 2}{Rate\ 1} = \underbrace{\frac{2.70 \times 10^{-7} \text{ mol L}^{-1} \text{ s}^{-1}}{1.35 \times 10^{-7} \text{ mol L}^{-1} \text{ s}^{-1}}}_{2.00} = \frac{k\cancel{(0.100 \text{ mol/L})^n}(0.010 \text{ mol/L})^m}{k\cancel{(0.100 \text{ mol/L})^n}(0.0050 \text{ mol/L})^m}$$

$$= \underbrace{\frac{(0.010 \text{ mol/L})^m}{(0.0050 \text{ mol/L})^m}}_{(2.0)^m}$$

Table 15.4

Initial Rates from Three Experiments for the Reaction $NH_4^+(aq) + NO_2^-(aq) \longrightarrow N_2(g) + 2H_2O(l)$

Experiment	Initial Concentration of NH_4^+	Initial Concentration of NO_2^-	Initial Rate (mol L^{-1} s^{-1})
1	0.100 M	0.0050 M	1.35×10^{-7}
2	0.100 M	0.010 M	2.70×10^{-7}
3	0.200 M	0.010 M	5.40×10^{-7}

Thus
$$\frac{\text{Rate 2}}{\text{Rate 1}} = 2.00 = (2.0)^m$$

which means the value of m is 1. The rate law for this reaction is first order in the reactant NO_2^-.

A similar analysis of the results for Experiments 2 and 3 yields the following ratio:

$$\frac{\text{Rate 3}}{\text{Rate 2}} = \frac{5.40 \times 10^{-7} \text{ mol L}^{-1} \text{ s}^{-1}}{2.70 \times 10^{-7} \text{ mol L}^{-1} \text{ s}^{-1}} = \frac{(0.200 \text{ mol/L})^n}{(0.100 \text{ mol/L})^n}$$

$$= 2.00 = \left(\frac{0.200}{1.100}\right)^n = (2.00)^n$$

The value of n is also 1.

We have shown that the values of n and m are both 1. Therefore, the rate law is

$$\text{Rate} = k[NH_4^+][NO_2^-]$$

This rate law is first order in both NO_2^- and NH_4^+. Note that it is merely a coincidence that n and m have the same values as the coefficients of NH_4^+ and NO_2^- in the balanced equation for the reaction.

Overall reaction order is the sum of the orders for each reactant. For a discussion of how this term can be misleading, see John C. Reeve, "Some Provocative Opinions on the Terminology of Chemical Kinetics," *J. Chem. Ed.* 68 (1991): 278.

The **overall reaction order** is the sum of n and m. For this reaction, $n + m = 2$. The reaction is second order overall.

The value of the rate constant (k) can now be calculated by using the results of *any* of the three experiments shown in Table 15.4. From the data for Experiment 1, we know that

$$\text{Rate} = k[NH_4^+][NO_2^-]$$

$$1.35 \times 10^{-7} \text{ mol L}^{-1} \text{ s}^{-1} = k(0.100 \text{ mol/L})(0.0050 \text{ mol/L})$$

Then

$$k = \frac{1.35 \times 10^{-7} \text{ mol L}^{-1} \text{ s}^{-1}}{(0.100 \text{ mol/L})(0.0050 \text{ mol/L})} = 2.7 \times 10^{-4} \text{ L mol}^{-1} \text{ s}^{-1}$$

EXAMPLE 15.1

The reaction between bromate ions and bromide ions in acidic aqueous solution is given by the following equation:

$$BrO_3^-(aq) + 5Br^-(aq) + 6H^+(aq) \longrightarrow 3Br_2(l) + 3H_2O(l)$$

Table 15.5 gives the results of four experiments involving this reaction. Using these data, determine the orders for all three reactants, the overall reaction order, and the value of the rate constant.

Table 15.5

The Results from Four Experiments to Study the Reaction
$BrO_3^-(aq) + 5Br^-(aq) + 6H^+(aq) \longrightarrow 3Br_2(l) + 3H_2O(l)$

Experiment	Initial Concentration of BrO_3^- (mol/L)	Initial Concentration of Br^- (mol/L)	Initial Concentration of H^+ (mol/L)	Measured Initial Rate (mol L^{-1} s^{-1})
1	0.10	0.10	0.10	8.0×10^{-4}
2	0.20	0.10	0.10	1.6×10^{-3}
3	0.20	0.20	0.10	3.2×10^{-3}
4	0.10	0.10	0.20	3.2×10^{-3}

A solution containing BrO_3^- ions being added to a solution containing Br^- ions to form Br_2.

Solution The general form of the rate law for this reaction is

$$\text{Rate} = k[BrO_3^-]^n[Br^-]^m[H^+]^p$$

We can determine the values of n, m, and p by comparing the rates from the various experiments. To determine the value of n, we use the results from Experiments 1 and 2, in which only $[BrO_3^-]$ changes:

$$\frac{\text{Rate 2}}{\text{Rate 1}} = \frac{1.6 \times 10^{-3} \text{ mol L}^{-1}\text{ s}^{-1}}{8.0 \times 10^{-4} \text{ mol L}^{-1}\text{ s}^{-1}}$$

$$= \frac{k(0.20 \text{ mol/L})^n(0.10 \text{ mol/L})^m(0.10 \text{ mol/L})^p}{k(0.10 \text{ mol/L})^n(0.10 \text{ mol/L})^m(0.10 \text{ mol/L})^p}$$

$$2.0 = \left(\frac{0.20 \text{ mol/L}}{0.10 \text{ mol/L}}\right)^n = (2.0)^n$$

Thus n is equal to 1.

To determine the value of m, we use the results from Experiments 2 and 3, in which only $[Br^-]$ changes:

$$\frac{\text{Rate 3}}{\text{Rate 2}} = \frac{3.2 \times 10^{-3} \text{ mol L}^{-1}\text{ s}^{-1}}{1.6 \times 10^{-3} \text{ mol L}^{-1}\text{ s}^{-1}}$$

$$= \frac{k(0.20 \text{ mol/L})^n(0.20 \text{ mol/L})^m(0.10 \text{ mol/L})^p}{k(0.20 \text{ mol/L})^n(0.10 \text{ mol/L})^m(0.10 \text{ mol/L})^p}$$

$$2.0 = \left(\frac{0.20 \text{ mol/L}}{0.10 \text{ mol/L}}\right)^m = (2.0)^m$$

Thus m is equal to 1.

To determine the value of p, we use the results from Experiments 1 and 4, in which $[BrO_3^-]$ and $[Br^-]$ are constant but $[H^+]$ changes:

$$\frac{\text{Rate 4}}{\text{Rate 1}} = \frac{3.2 \times 10^{-3} \text{ mol L}^{-1}\text{ s}^{-1}}{8.0 \times 10^{-4} \text{ mol L}^{-1}\text{ s}^{-1}}$$

$$= \frac{k(0.10 \text{ mol/L})^n(0.10 \text{ mol/L})^m(0.20 \text{ mol/L})^p}{k(0.10 \text{ mol/L})^n(0.10 \text{ mol/L})^m(0.10 \text{ mol/L})^p}$$

$$4.0 = \left(\frac{0.20 \text{ mol/L}}{0.10 \text{ mol/L}}\right)^p$$

$$4.0 = (2.0)^p = (2.0)^2$$

Thus p is equal to 2.

The rate of this reaction is first order in BrO_3^- and Br^- and second order in H^+. The overall reaction order is $n + m + p = 4$.

The rate law can now be written:

$$\text{Rate} = k[BrO_3^-][Br^-][H^+]^2$$

The value of the rate constant k can be calculated from the results of any of the four experiments. For Experiment 1 the initial rate is $8.0 \times 10^{-4} \text{ mol L}^{-1}\text{ s}^{-1}$, and $[BrO_3^-] = 0.100 \ M$, $[Br^-] = 0.100 \ M$, and $[H^+] = 0.100 \ M$. Using these values in the rate law gives

$$8.00 \times 10^{-4} \text{ mol L}^{-1}\text{ s}^{-1} = k(0.10 \text{ mol/L})(0.10 \text{ mol/L})(0.10 \text{ mol/L})^2$$

$$8.00 \times 10^{-4} \text{ mol L}^{-1}\text{ s}^{-1} = k(1.0 \times 10^{-4} \text{ mol}^4/\text{L}^4)$$

$$k = \frac{8.0 \times 10^{-4} \text{ mol L}^{-1}\text{ s}^{-1}}{1.0 \times 10^{-4} \text{ mol}^4/\text{L}^4}$$

$$= 8.00 \text{ L}^3 \text{ mol}^{-3} \text{ s}^{-1}$$

Check: Verify that the same value of k can be obtained from the results of the other experiments.

15.4 | The Integrated Rate Law

In the field of kinetics, the rate for this type of reaction is usually defined as

$$\text{Rate} = -\frac{1}{a}\frac{d[A]}{dt}$$

where a is the coefficient of A in the balanced equation. However, to avoid complications, we will leave out the factor of $1/a$, which simply changes the value of the rate constant by a factor of a.

The rate laws we have considered so far express the rate as a function of the reactant concentrations. It is also useful to be able to express the reactant concentrations as a function of time, given the (differential) rate law for the reaction. In this section we will show how this is done.

We will proceed by first looking at reactions involving a single reactant:

$$aA \longrightarrow \text{products}$$

all of which have a rate law of the form

$$\text{Rate} = -\frac{d[A]}{dt} = k[A]^n$$

We will develop the integrated rate laws individually for the cases $n = 1$ (first order), $n = 2$ (second order), and $n = 0$ (zero order).

First-Order Rate Laws

For the reaction

$$2N_2O_5(soln) \longrightarrow 4NO_2(soln) + O_2(g)$$

experiments show that the rate law is

$$\text{Rate} = -\frac{d[N_2O_5]}{dt} = k[N_2O_5]$$

The decomposition of N_2O_5 in solution to form NO_2 plus O_2 (bubbles). The brown gas above the solution is escaping NO_2.

An integrated rate law relates concentration to reaction time.

Since the rate of this reaction depends on the concentration of N_2O_5 to the first power, it is a **first-order reaction**. This means that if the concentration of N_2O_5 in a flask were suddenly doubled, the rate of production of NO_2 and O_2 would also double. Using calculus, this differential rate law can be integrated, which yields the expression

$$\ln[N_2O_5] = -kt + \ln[N_2O_5]_0$$

where ln indicates the natural logarithm, t is the time, $[N_2O_5]$ is the concentration of N_2O_5 at time t, and $[N_2O_5]_0$ is the initial concentration of N_2O_5 (at $t = 0$, the start of the experiment). Note that such an equation, called the integrated rate law, expresses the *concentration of the reactant as a function of time*.

For a chemical reaction of the form

$$aA \longrightarrow \text{products}$$

where the kinetics are first order in [A], the differential rate law is of the form

$$\text{Rate} = -\frac{d[A]}{dt} = k[A]$$

and the **integrated first-order rate law** is

$$\ln[A] = -kt + \ln[A]_0 \tag{15.2}$$

There are three important things to note about Equation (15.2):

1. The equation shows how the concentration of A depends on time. If the initial concentration of A and the value of the rate constant k are known, the concentration of A at any time can be calculated.

2. Equation (15.2) is of the form $y = mx + b$, where a plot of y versus x is a straight line with slope m and intercept b. In this case

$$y = \ln[A] \qquad x = t \qquad m = -k \qquad b = \ln[A]_0$$

For a first-order reaction, a plot of ln[A] versus t is a straight line.

Thus, for a first-order reaction, plotting the natural logarithm of concentration versus time always gives a straight line. This fact is often used to test whether a reaction is first order. For the reaction of the type

$$aA \longrightarrow products$$

the *reaction is first order in A if a plot of ln[A] versus t is a straight line.* Conversely, if the plot is not a straight line, the reaction is not first order.

3. The integrated rate law for a first-order reaction can also be expressed in terms of the *ratio* of [A] and $[A]_0$ as follows:

$$\ln\left(\frac{[A]_0}{[A]}\right) = kt$$

EXAMPLE 15.2

The decomposition of N_2O_5 in the gas phase was studied at constant temperature:

$$2N_2O_5(g) \longrightarrow 4NO_2(g) + O_2(g)$$

The following results were collected:

$[N_2O_5]$ (mol/L)	Time (s)
0.1000	0
0.0707	50
0.0500	100
0.0250	200
0.0125	300
0.00625	400

Using these data, verify that the rate law is first order in $[N_2O_5]$, and calculate the value of the rate constant, where the rate $= -d[N_2O_5]/dt$.

Solution We can verify that the rate law is first order in $[N_2O_5]$ by constructing a plot of $\ln[N_2O_5]$ versus time. The values of $\ln[N_2O_5]$ at various times are given below, and the plot of $\ln[N_2O_5]$ versus time is shown in Fig. 15.3.

$\ln[N_2O_5]$	Time (s)
−2.303	0
−2.649	50
−2.996	100
−3.689	200
−4.382	300
−5.075	400

The plot is a straight line, confirming that the reaction is first order in N_2O_5, since it follows the equation $\ln[N_2O_5] = -kt + \ln[N_2O_5]_0$.

Since the reaction is first order, the slope of the line equals $-k$. In this case

$$k = -(slope) = 6.93 \times 10^{-3} \text{ s}^{-1}$$

Figure 15.3
A plot of $\ln[N_2O_5]$ versus time.

EXAMPLE 15.3

Using the data given in Example 15.2, calculate $[N_2O_5]$ 150. s after the start of the reaction.

Solution We know from Example 15.2 that $[N_2O_5] = 0.0500$ mol/L at 100 s and $[N_2O_5] = 0.0250$ mol/L at 200 s. Since 150 s is halfway between 100 s and

200 s, it is tempting to assume that we can use a simple average to obtain $[N_2O_5]$ at that time. This is incorrect because it is $\ln[N_2O_5]$, not $[N_2O_5]$, that depends directly on t. To calculate $[N_2O_5]$ after 150 s, we must use Equation (15.2):

$$\ln[N_2O_5] = -kt + \ln[N_2O_5]_0$$

where $t = 150.$ s, $k = 6.93 \times 10^{-3}$ s^{-1} (as determined in Example 15.2), and $[N_2O_5]_0 = 0.100$ mol/L.

$$\ln([N_2O_5])_{t=150} = -(6.93 \times 10^{-3} \text{ s}^{-1})(150. \text{ s}) + \ln(0.100)$$

$$= -1.040 - 2.303 = -3.343$$

$$[N_2O_5]_{t=150} = \text{antilog}(-3.343) = 0.0353 \text{ mol/L}$$

Note that this value of $[N_2O_5]$ is *not* halfway between 0.0500 mol/L and 0.0250 mol/L.

Half-Life of a First-Order Reaction

The time required for a reactant to reach half of its original concentration is called the **half-life of a reaction** and is designated by $t_{1/2}$. To illustrate this idea, we can calculate the half-life of the decomposition reaction discussed in Example 15.2. The data plotted in Fig. 15.4 show that the half-life for this reaction is 100 seconds. We can see this by considering the following numbers:

$[N_2O_5]$ (mol/L)	Time (s)		
0.1000	0		
		$\Delta t = 100$ s;	$\dfrac{[N_2O_5]_{t=100}}{[N_2O_5]_{t=0}} = \dfrac{0.050}{0.100} = \dfrac{1}{2}$
0.0500	100		
		$\Delta t = 100$ s;	$\dfrac{[N_2O_5]_{t=200}}{[N_2O_5]_{t=100}} = \dfrac{0.025}{0.050} = \dfrac{1}{2}$
0.0250	200		
		$\Delta t = 100$ s;	$\dfrac{[N_2O_5]_{t=300}}{[N_2O_5]_{t=200}} = \dfrac{0.0125}{0.0250} = \dfrac{1}{2}$
0.0125	300		

Note that it *always* takes 100 seconds for $[N_2O_5]$ to be halved in this reaction.

Figure 15.4
A plot of $[N_2O_5]$ versus time for the decomposition reaction of N_2O_5.

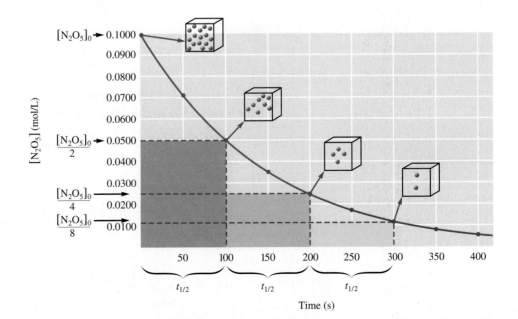

A general formula for the half-life of a first-order reaction can be derived from the integrated rate law for the general reaction,

$$aA \longrightarrow \text{products}$$

If the reaction is first order in [A],

$$\ln\left(\frac{[A]_0}{[A]}\right) = kt$$

By definition, when $t = t_{1/2}$, $\qquad [A] = \dfrac{[A]_0}{2}$

Then for $t = t_{1/2}$, the integrated rate law becomes

$$\ln\left(\frac{[A]_0}{[A]_0/2}\right) = kt_{1/2}$$

or $\qquad\qquad\qquad\qquad\qquad \ln(2) = kt_{1/2}$

Substituting the value of $\ln(2)$ and solving for $t_{1/2}$ gives

$$t_{1/2} = \frac{0.693}{k} \tag{15.3}$$

For a first-order reaction, $t_{1/2}$ is independent of the initial concentration.

This is the *general equation for the half-life of a first-order reaction.* Equation (15.3) can be used to calculate $t_{1/2}$ if k is known, or k if $t_{1/2}$ is known. Note that for a first-order reaction *the half-life does not depend on concentration.*

⬢WL INTERACTIVE EXAMPLE 15.4

A certain first-order reaction has a half-life of 20.0 minutes.

a. Calculate the rate constant for this reaction.

b. How much time is required for this reaction to be 75% complete?

Solution

a. Solving Equation (15.3) for k gives

$$k = \frac{0.692}{t_{1/2}} = \frac{0.693}{20.0 \text{ min}} = 3.47 \times 10^{-2} \text{ min}^{-1}$$

b. We use the integrated rate law in the form

$$\ln\left(\frac{[A]_0}{[A]}\right) = kt$$

If the reaction is 75% complete, 75% of the reactant has been consumed. This leaves 25% in the original form:

$$\frac{[A]}{[A]_0} \times 100 = 25$$

This means that

$$\frac{[A]}{[A]_0} = 0.25 \qquad \text{and} \qquad \frac{[A]_0}{[A]} = 4.0$$

Therefore,

$$\ln\left(\frac{[A]_0}{[A]}\right) = \ln(4.0) = kt = \left(\frac{3.47 \times 10^{-2}}{\text{min}}\right)t$$

and $t = 40.$ min

Thus it takes 40. minutes for this particular reaction to reach 75% completion.
Let's consider another way of solving this problem by using the definition of half-life. After one half-life the reaction has gone 50% to completion. If the initial concentration were 1.0 mol/L, after one half-life the concentration would be 0.50 mol/L. One more half-life would produce a concentration of 0.25 mol/L. Comparing 0.25 mol/L with the original 1.0 mol/L shows that 25% of the reactant is left after two half-lives. This is a general result. (What percentage of reactant remains after three half-lives?) Two half-lives for this reaction is 2(20.0 min), or 40.0 minutes, which agrees with the above answer.

Second-Order Rate Laws

For a general reaction involving a single reactant,

$$aA \longrightarrow \text{products}$$

Second order: Rate = $k[A]^2$. Doubling the concentration of A quadruples the reaction rate; tripling the concentration of A increases the rate by nine times.

which is second order in A, the rate law can be defined as

$$\text{Rate} = -\frac{d[A]}{dt} = k[A]^2 \qquad (15.4)$$

Integration of this differential rate law yields the **integrated second-order rate law:**

$$\frac{1}{[A]} = kt + \frac{1}{[A]_0} \qquad (15.5)$$

Note the following characteristics of Equation (15.5):

For a second-order reaction, a plot of $1/[A]$ versus t is linear.

1. A plot of $1/[A]$ versus t will produce a straight line with a slope equal to k.
2. Equation (15.5) shows how [A] depends on time and can be used to calculate [A] at any time t, provided k and $[A]_0$ are known.

When one half-life of a second-order reaction has elapsed ($t = t_{1/2}$), by definition, $[A] = [A]_0/2$. Equation (15.5) then becomes

$$\frac{1}{\dfrac{[A]_0}{2}} = kt_{1/2} + \frac{1}{[A]_0}$$

and $$\frac{1}{[A]_0} = kt_{1/2}$$

Solving for $t_{1/2}$ gives *the expression for the half-life of a second-order reaction:*

$$t_{1/2} = \frac{1}{k[A]_0} \qquad (15.6)$$

EXAMPLE 15.5

When two identical molecules combine, the resulting molecule is called a *dimer*.

Butadiene reacts to form its dimer according to the equation

$$2C_4H_6(g) \longrightarrow C_8H_{12}(g)$$

The following data were collected for this reaction at a given temperature:

$[C_4H_6]$ (mol/L)	Time (± 1 s)
0.01000	0
0.00625	1000
0.00476	1800
0.00370	2800
0.00313	3600
0.00270	4400
0.00241	5200
0.00208	6200

a. Is this reaction first order or second order?

b. What is the value of the rate constant for the reaction?

c. What is the half-life for the reaction under the conditions of this experiment?

Solution

a. To decide whether the rate law for this reaction is first order or second order, we must see whether the plot of $\ln[C_4H_6]$ versus time is a straight line (first order) or the plot of $1/[C_4H_6]$ versus time is a straight line (second order). The data necessary to make these plots are as follows:

t (s)	$\dfrac{1}{[C_4H_6]}$	$\ln[C_4H_6]$
0	100	-4.605
1000	160	-5.075
1800	210	-5.348
2800	270	-5.599
3600	319	-5.767
4400	370	-5.915
5200	415	-6.028
6200	481	-6.175

The resulting plots are shown in Fig. 15.5. Since the $\ln[C_4H_6]$ versus t plot is not a straight line, the reaction is *not* first order. The reaction is,

Butadiene (C_4H_6)

Figure 15.5
(a) A plot of $\ln[C_4H_6]$ versus t.
(b) A plot of $1/[C_4H_6]$ versus t.

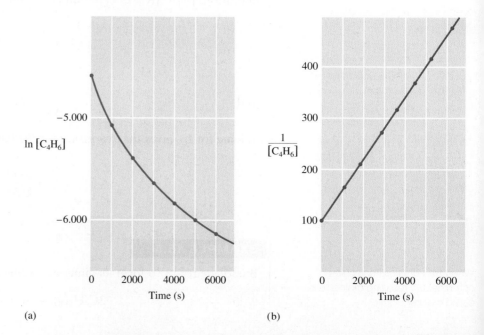

however, second order, as shown by the linearity of the $1/[C_4H_6]$ versus t plot. Thus we can now write the rate law for this second-order reaction:

$$\text{Rate} = -\frac{d[C_4H_6]}{dt} = k[C_4H_6]^2$$

b. For a second-order reaction, a plot of $1/[C_4H_6]$ versus t produces a straight line with slope k. In terms of the standard equation for a straight line, $y = mx + b$, we have $y = 1/[C_4H_6]$ and $x = t$. In this case,

$$k = \text{slope} = 6.14 \times 10^{-2} \text{ L mol}^{-1} \text{ s}^{-1}$$

c. The expression for the half-life of a second-order reaction is

$$t_{1/2} = \frac{1}{k[A]_0}$$

In this case $k = 6.14 \times 10^{-2} \text{ L mol}^{-1} \text{ s}^{-1}$ (from part b) and $[A]_0 = [C_4H_6]_0 = 0.01000 \text{ }M$ (the concentration at $t = 0$). Thus

$$t_{1/2} = \frac{1}{(6.14 \times 10^{-2} \text{ L mol}^{-1} \text{ s}^{-1})(1.000 \times 10^{-2} \text{ mol/L})}$$

$$= 1.63 \times 10^3 \text{ s}$$

The initial concentration of C_4H_6 is halved in 1630 s.

For a second-order reaction, $t_{1/2}$ depends on $[A]_0$. For a first-order reaction, $t_{1/2}$ is independent of $[A]_0$.

It is important to recognize the difference between the half-life for a first-order reaction and the half-life for a second-order reaction. For a second-order reaction, $t_{1/2}$ depends on both k and $[A]_0$; for a first-order reaction, $t_{1/2}$ depends only on k. For a first-order reaction, a constant time is required to reduce the concentration of the reactant by half, and then by half again, and so on, as the reaction proceeds. In Example 15.5 we saw that this is *not* true for a second-order reaction. For that second-order reaction, we found that the first half-life (the time required to go from $[C_4H_6] = 0.010 \text{ }M$ to $[C_4H_6] = 0.0050 \text{ }M$) is 1630 seconds. We can estimate the second half-life from the concentration data as a function of time. Note that to reach $0.0024 \text{ }M$ C_4H_6 (approximately $0.0050/2$) requires 5200 seconds of reaction time. Thus, to get from $0.0050 \text{ }M$ C_4H_6 to $0.0024 \text{ }M$ C_4H_6 takes 3570 seconds ($5200 - 1630$). The second half-life is much longer than the first. This pattern is characteristic of second-order reactions. In fact, *for a second-order reaction, each successive half-life is double the preceding one* (provided the effects of the reverse reaction can be ignored, as we are assuming here). Prove this to yourself by examining the equation $t_{1/2} = 1/(k[A]_0)$.

For each successive half-life, $[A]_0$ is halved. Since $t_{1/2} = 1/k[A]_0$, $t_{1/2}$ doubles.

Zero-Order Rate Laws

Most reactions involving a single reactant show either first-order or second-order kinetics. However, sometimes such a reaction can be a **zero-order reaction**. The rate law for a zero-order reaction is

$$\text{Rate} = k[A]_0 = k(1) = k$$

A zero-order reaction has a constant rate.

For a zero-order reaction, the rate is a constant. It does not change with concentration as it does for first-order or second-order reactions.

The **integrated rate law for a zero-order reaction** is

$$[A] = -kt + [A]_0 \tag{15.7}$$

In this case a plot of $[A]$ versus t gives a straight line of slope $-k$, as shown in Fig. 15.6.

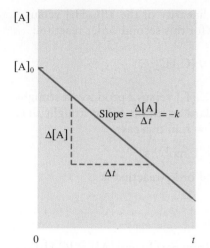

Figure 15.6
A plot of [A] versus t for a zero-order reaction.

The expression for the half-life of a zero-order reaction can be obtained from the integrated rate law. By definition, $[A] = [A]_0/2$ when $t = t_{1/2}$, so

$$\frac{[A]_0}{2} = -kt_{1/2} + [A]_0$$

or

$$kt_{1/2} = \frac{[A]_0}{2}$$

Solving for $t_{1/2}$ gives

$$t_{1/2} = \frac{[A]_0}{2k} \tag{15.8}$$

Zero-order reactions are most often encountered when a substance such as a metal surface or an enzyme is required for the reaction to occur. For example, the decomposition reaction

$$2N_2O(g) \longrightarrow 2N_2(g) + O_2(g)$$

occurs on a hot platinum surface. When the platinum surface is completely covered with N_2O molecules, an increase in the concentration of N_2O has no effect on the rate, since only those N_2O molecules on the surface can react. Under these conditions, *the rate is a constant* because it is controlled by what happens on the platinum surface rather than by the total concentration of N_2O, as illustrated in Fig. 15.7. This reaction can also occur at high temperatures with no platinum surface present, but under these conditions it is not zero order.

Integrated Rate Laws for Reactions with More Than One Reactant

So far we have considered the integrated rate laws for simple reactions with only one reactant. Special techniques are required to deal with more complicated reactions. For example, consider the reaction

$$BrO_3^-(aq) + 5Br^-(aq) + 6H^+(aq) \longrightarrow 3Br_2(l) + 3H_2O(l)$$

From experimental evidence we know that the rate law is

$$\text{Rate} = -\frac{d[BrO_3^-]}{dt} = k[BrO_3^-][Br^-][H^+]^2$$

Suppose we run this reaction under conditions where $[BrO_3^-]_0 = 1.0 \times 10^{-3}\ M$, $[Br^-]_0 = 1.0\ M$, and $[H^+]_0 = 1.0\ M$. As the reaction proceeds, $[BrO_3^-]$

Figure 15.7
The decomposition reaction $2N_2O(g) \longrightarrow 2N_2(g) + O_2(g)$ takes place on a platinum surface. Although $[N_2O]$ is twice as great in (b) as in (a), the rate of decomposition of N_2O is the same in both cases since the platinum surface can accommodate only a certain number of molecules. As a result, this reaction is zero order.

$\bullet\bullet\bullet$ N_2O

(a)   (b)

decreases significantly, but because the Br^- ion and H^+ ion concentrations are so large initially, relatively little of either of these two reactants is consumed. Thus $[Br^-]$ and $[H^+]$ remain *approximately constant*. In other words, under the conditions where the Br^- ion and H^+ ion concentrations are much larger than the BrO_3^- ion concentration, we can assume that throughout the reaction

$$[Br^-] = [Br^-]_0 \quad \text{and} \quad [H^+] = [H^+]_0$$

This means that the rate law can be written as

$$\text{Rate} = k[Br^-]_0[H^+]_0^2[BrO_3^-] = k'[BrO_3^-]$$

where, since $[Br^-]_0$ and $[H^+]_0$ are constant,

$$k' = k[Br^-]_0[H^+]_0^2$$

The rate law $\qquad\qquad \text{Rate} = k'[BrO_3^-]$

is first order. However, since this rate law was obtained by simplifying a more complicated one, it is called a **pseudo-first-order rate law.** Under the conditions of this experiment, a plot of $\ln[BrO_3^-]$ versus t gives a straight line with a slope equal to $-k'$. Since $[Br^-]_0$ and $[H^+]_0$ are known, the value of k can be calculated from the equation

$$k' = k[Br^-]_0[H^+]_0^2$$

which can be rearranged to give

$$k = \frac{k'}{[Br^-]_0[H^+]_0^2}$$

Note that the kinetics of complicated reactions can be studied by observing the behavior of one reactant at a time. If the concentration of one reactant is much smaller than the concentrations of the others, then the amounts of those reactants present in large concentrations will not change significantly and can be regarded as constant. The change in concentration with time of the reactant present in a relatively small amount can then be used to determine the order of the reaction in that component. This technique allows us to determine rate laws for complex reactions.

15.5 | Rate Laws: A Summary

In the last several sections, we have developed the following important points:

1. To simplify the rate laws for reactions, we have always assumed that the rate is being studied under conditions where only the forward reaction is important. This produces rate laws that contain only reactant concentrations.

2. There are two types of rate laws.

   a. The differential rate law (often called *the rate law*) shows how the rate depends on the concentrations. The forms of the rate laws for zero-order, first-order, and second-order kinetics of reactions with a single reactant are shown in Table 15.6.

   b. The integrated rate law shows how concentration depends on time. The integrated rate laws corresponding to zero-order, first-order, and second-order kinetics of reactions with a single reactant are given in Table 15.6.

3. Whether we determine the differential rate law or the integrated rate law depends on the type of data that can be collected conveniently and accurately. Once we have experimentally determined either type of rate law for a given reaction, we can write the other rate law.

Table 15.6

Summary of the Kinetics for Reactions of the Type $aA \longrightarrow$ Products That Are Zero, First, or Second Order in [A]

	Order		
	Zero	First	Second
Rate law	Rate $= k$	Rate $= k[A]$	Rate $= k[A]^2$
Integrated rate law	$[A] = -kt + [A]_0$	$\ln[A] = -kt + \ln[A]_0$	$\dfrac{1}{[A]} = kt + \dfrac{1}{[A]_0}$
Plot needed to give a straight line	$[A]$ versus t	$\ln[A]$ versus t	$\dfrac{1}{[A]}$ versus t
Relationship of rate constant to the slope of the straight line	Slope $= -k$	Slope $= -k$	Slope $= k$
Half-life	$t_{1/2} = \dfrac{[A]_0}{2k}$	$t_{1/2} = \dfrac{0.693}{k}$	$t_{1/2} = \dfrac{1}{k[A]_0}$

4. The most common method for experimentally determining the differential rate law is the method of initial rates. In this method several experiments are run at different initial concentrations, and the instantaneous rates are determined for each at the same value of t as close to $t = 0$ as possible. The point is to evaluate the rate before the concentrations change significantly from the initial values. From a comparison of the initial rates and the initial concentrations, the dependence of the rate on the concentrations of various reactants can be obtained—that is, the order in each reactant can be determined.

5. To experimentally determine the integrated rate law for a reaction, we measure concentrations at various values of t as the reaction proceeds. Then we see which integrated rate law correctly fits the data. Typically, this is done by ascertaining which type of plot gives a straight line. This information is described for reactions with a single reactant in Table 15.6. Once the correct straight-line plot is found, the correct integrated rate law can be chosen and the value of k obtained from the slope. Also, the (differential) rate law for the reaction can then be written.

6. The integrated rate law for a reaction that involves several reactants can be treated by choosing conditions such that the concentration of only one reactant varies in a given experiment. This is done by having the concentration of one reactant be small compared with the concentrations of all the others, causing a rate law such as

$$\text{Rate} = k[A]^n[B]^m[C]^p$$

to reduce to $\qquad\qquad \text{Rate} = k'[A]^n$

where $k' = k[B]_0^m[C]_0^p$, $[B]_0 \gg [A]_0$, and $[C]_0 \gg [A]_0$. The value of n is obtained by determining whether a plot of $[A]$ versus t is linear ($n = 0$), a plot of $\ln[A]$ versus t is linear ($n = 1$), or a plot of $1/[A]$ versus t is linear ($n = 2$). The value of k' is determined from the slope of the appropriate plot. The values of m, p, and k are found by determining the value of k' at several different concentrations of B and C.

15.6 | Reaction Mechanisms

Most chemical reactions occur by a *series of steps* called the **reaction mechanism.** To understand a reaction, we must know its mechanism, and one of the main purposes for studying kinetics is to learn as much as possible about the steps involved in a reaction. In this section we explore some of the fundamental characteristics of reaction mechanisms.

Consider the reaction between nitrogen dioxide and carbon monoxide:

$$NO_2(g) + CO(g) \longrightarrow NO(g) + CO_2(g)$$

The rate law for this reaction is known from experiment to be

$$\text{Rate} = k[NO_2]^2$$

As we will see below, this reaction is more complicated than it appears from the balanced equation. This is quite typical; the balanced equation for a reaction tells us the reactants, the products, and the stoichiometry but gives no direct information about the reaction mechanism.

For the reaction between nitrogen dioxide and carbon monoxide, the mechanism is thought to involve the steps shown in Fig. 15.8, where k_1 and k_2 are the rate constants of the individual reactions. In this mechanism gaseous NO_3 is an **intermediate,** a species that is neither a reactant nor a product but that is formed and consumed during the reaction sequence (Fig. 15.8).

Each of these reactions is called an **elementary step,** *a reaction whose rate law can be written from its molecularity.* **Molecularity** is defined as the number of species that must collide to produce the reaction indicated by that step. A reaction involving one molecule is called a **unimolecular step.** Reactions involving the collision of two and three species are termed **bimolecular** and **termolecular,** respectively. Termolecular steps are quite rare because the probability of three molecules colliding simultaneously is very small. Examples of these three types of elementary steps and the corresponding rate laws are shown in Table 15.7. Note from Table 15.7 that the rate law for an elementary step follows *directly* from the molecularity of that step. For example, for a bimolecular step, the rate law is always second order, either of the form $k[A]^2$ for a step with a single reactant or of the form $k[A][B]$ for a step involving two reactants.

We can now define a reaction mechanism more precisely. It is a *series of elementary steps that must satisfy two requirements:*

1. The sum of the elementary steps must give the overall balanced equation for the reaction.

2. The mechanism must agree with the experimentally determined rate law.

A balanced equation does not tell us how the reactants become products.

An intermediate is formed in one step and consumed in a subsequent step and so is never seen as a product.

The prefix uni- means "one," bi- means "two," and ter- means "three."

A unimolecular elementary step is always first order, a bimolecular step is always second order, and so on.

Figure 15.8
A molecular representation of the elementary steps in the reaction of NO_2 and CO.

Step 1

Step 2

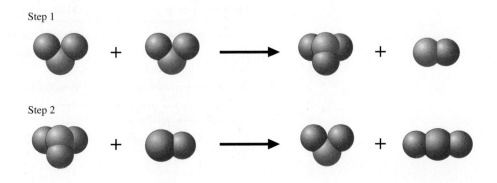

Chemical Insights | Ultracold Reactions

More than 200 years ago the work of Charles Gay-Lussac led to the suspicion that an absolute low temperature exists for matter. In recent years scientists have come close to cooling matter to 0 K. Temperatures of about 10^{-7} K have been achieved by *laser cooling* in which a laser beam is directed against a beam of atoms, dramatically slowing the movement of atoms to near zero.

It is extremely difficult to slow atoms to near absolute zero, but it is even harder to cool molecules to these temperatures. One strategy is to begin with "hot" diatomic molecules and then cool them down using lasers. However, as the velocities of these molecules decrease, they retain high levels of vibrational energy that ultimately cause the molecules to break apart. The other strategy is to cool atoms and then try to get them to form molecules. This is the approach used by physicist Jun Ye and his coworkers at the University of Colorado in Boulder. Ye and his research group were able to form molecules of potassium and rubidium at ultracold temperatures and then encourage the molecules to emit their excess vibrational energy using a laser pulse to produce stable molecules at about 2×10^{-7} K. Because the K-Rb molecule is slightly polar (the potassium atom has a slightly greater electronegativity value than the rubidium atom, which leads to a dipole $^{\delta-}$K-Rb$^{\delta+}$), the mole-

cules can be manipulated by an electric field. Ye and his coworkers have observed the reaction

$$2K\text{-}Rb \longrightarrow K_2 + Rb_2$$

at these ultralow temperatures. Because the motions of the molecules are so slow at these temperatures, the researchers have been able to study the details of this reaction. For example, they found that the reaction occurs only when the molecules are head to tail and that the reaction is greatly speeded up when the electric field around the molecule is increased. They also observed that the molecules react with greater certainty when they are within 1 nm of each other.

Theoretical studies by Paul Julienne at the National Institute of Standards and Technology in Maryland and Zbigniew Idziaczek at the University of Warsaw predict how the molecules find each other so that they can react. At these low temperatures, the molecules behave more like diffuse waves than discrete spots, and the waves can spread beyond the individual molecules for hundreds of nanometers. These waves affect how the molecules close in on each other to react. As more of these studies are done at ultracold temperatures, we are certain to learn a lot more about how molecules react with each other.

Table 15.7

Examples of Elementary Steps and Corresponding Rate Laws

Elementary Step	Molecularity	Rate Law
A $\longrightarrow$ products	*Uni*molecular	Rate = $k[A]$
A + A $\longrightarrow$ products (2A $\longrightarrow$ products)	*Bi*molecular	Rate = $k[A]^2$
A + B $\longrightarrow$ products	*Bi*molecular	Rate = $k[A][B]$
A + A + B $\longrightarrow$ products (2A + B $\longrightarrow$ products)	*Ter*molecular	Rate = $k[A]^2[B]$
A + B + C $\longrightarrow$ products	*Ter*molecular	Rate = $k[A][B][C]$

Christopher Rose-Petruck Studies Ultrafast X-ray Spectroscopy

Christopher Rose-Petruck, Associate Professor of Chemistry at Brown University, was educated in Germany, receiving his Ph.D. at the Ludwig-Maximilians University in Munich.

Professor Rose-Petruck's research focuses on the detailed mechanisms of certain important reactions that occur in solution. Because molecules undergo structural changes as they react on the timescale of picoseconds (10^{-12} s) and femtoseconds (10^{-15} s), "seeing" these changes occur requires ultrafast spectroscopic techniques. Professor Rose-Petruck and his group use ultrafast X-ray spectroscopy to study reactions as they occur in solutions. As part of their research, they have designed a reliable laboratory instrument that delivers the ultrashort X-ray pulses needed for ultrafast X-ray spectroscopy. To do this Professor Rose-Petruck developed a high power laser–driven X-ray source.

One system that Professor Rose-Petruck has been investigating involves the reactions of the iron carbonyl compound $Fe(CO)_5$ in solution. He and his students have found that $Fe(CO)_5$ rearranges in solution in a way that allows a solvent molecule to directly attach to the iron atom. This knowledge is important in understanding how $Fe(CO)_5$ and similar compounds react in solution.

Christopher Rose-Petruck with his children.

Professor Rose-Petruck plans to continue his studies of chemical reactions with the goal of "seeing" the reactants approach each other, form some sort of activated complex, and follow the products as they separate.

To see how these requirements are applied, we will consider the mechanism given above for the reaction of nitrogen dioxide with carbon monoxide. First, note that the sum of the two steps gives the overall balanced equation:

$$NO_2(g) + NO_2(g) \longrightarrow NO_3(g) + NO(g)$$

$$NO_3(g) + CO(g) \longrightarrow NO_2(g) + CO_2(g)$$

$$\cancel{NO_2(g)} + NO_2(g) + \cancel{NO_3(g)} + CO(g) \longrightarrow \cancel{NO_3(g)} + NO(g) + \cancel{NO_2(g)} + CO_2(g)$$

Overall reaction: $NO_2(g) + CO(g) \longrightarrow NO(g) + CO_2(g)$

The first requirement for a correct mechanism is met. To see whether the mechanism meets the second requirement, we need to introduce a new concept: the **rate-determining step.**[*] Multistep reactions may have one step that is much slower than all the others. Reactants can become products only as fast as they can complete this slowest step. That is, the overall reaction can be no faster than the slowest or rate-determining step in the sequence. An analogy for this situation is the rapid pouring of water through a funnel into a container. The water collects in the container at a rate that is essentially determined by the size of the funnel opening and not by the rate of pouring.

A reaction is only as fast as its slowest step.

---

[*]The concept of a rate-controlling step in a reaction mechanism is complex and often misleading. For a comprehensive discussion of this issue, see "Rate-Controlling Step: A Necessary or Useful Concept," by Keith J. Laidler, *J. Chem. Ed.* **65** (1988): 250.

The rate at which this colored solution enters the flask is determined by the size of the funnel stem, not how fast the solution is poured.

Which is the rate-determining step in the reaction of nitrogen dioxide with carbon monoxide? Let's *assume* that the first step is rate determining and the second step is relatively fast:

$$NO_2(g) + NO_2(g) \longrightarrow NO_3(g) + NO(g) \qquad \text{Slow (rate determining)}$$
$$NO_3(g) + CO(g) \longrightarrow NO_2(g) + CO_2(g) \qquad \text{Fast}$$

What we have really assumed here is that the formation of NO_3 occurs much more slowly than its reaction with CO. The rate of CO_2 production is then controlled by the rate of formation of NO_3 in the first step. Since this is an elementary step, we can write the rate law from the molecularity. The bimolecular first step has the rate law

$$\text{Rate of formation of } NO_3 = \frac{d[NO_3]}{dt} = k_1[NO_2]^2$$

Since the overall reaction rate can be no faster than the slowest step,

$$\text{Overall rate} = k_1[NO_2]^2$$

Note that this rate law agrees with the experimentally determined rate law given earlier. Since the mechanism we assumed above satisfies the two requirements stated earlier, it *may* be the correct mechanism for the reaction.

EXAMPLE 15.6

The balanced equation for the reaction of gaseous nitrogen dioxide and fluorine is

$$2NO_2(g) + F_2(g) \longrightarrow 2NO_2F(g)$$

The experimentally determined rate law is

$$\text{Rate} = k[NO_2][F_2]$$

A suggested mechanism for this reaction is

$$NO_2 + F_2 \xrightarrow{k_1} NO_2F + F \qquad \text{Slow}$$
$$F + NO_2 \xrightarrow{k_2} NO_2F \qquad \text{Fast}$$

Is this an acceptable mechanism? That is, does it satisfy the two requirements?

Solution The first requirement for an acceptable mechanism is that the sum of the steps give the balanced equation:

$$NO_2 + F_2 \longrightarrow NO_2F + F$$
$$\underline{F + NO_2 \longrightarrow NO_2F}$$
$$2NO_2 + F_2 + \cancel{F} \longrightarrow 2NO_2F + \cancel{F}$$

Overall reaction: $\qquad 2NO_2 + F_2 \longrightarrow 2NO_2F$

The first requirement is met.

The second requirement is that the mechanism must agree with the experimentally determined rate law. Since the proposed mechanism states that the first step is rate determining, the overall reaction rate must be that of the first step. The first step is bimolecular, so the rate law is

$$\text{Rate} = k_1[NO_2][F_2]$$

This has the same form as the experimentally determined rate law. The proposed mechanism is acceptable because it satisfies both requirements. (Note that we have not proved it is *the correct* mechanism.)

How does a chemist deduce the mechanism for a given reaction? The rate law is always determined first. Then, using chemical intuition and following the two rules given above, the chemist constructs a possible mechanism. Until recently, we could not prove a mechanism absolutely. We could only say that a mechanism that satisfies the two requirements is *possibly* correct. Recent advances in spectroscopy, however, such as those pioneered by Professor Ahmed Zewail (see "Femtochemistry" on page 721) and the use of STM techniques to study reactions, have provided the means for identifying mechanisms exactly (see "Seeing Reaction Mechanisms" on page 744). Deducing the mechanism for a chemical reaction is difficult; it requires skill and experience. We will only touch on this process in this text.

Mechanisms with Fast Forward and Reverse First Steps

A common type of reaction mechanism is one involving a first step in which *both* the forward and reverse reactions are very fast compared with the reactions in the second step. An example of this type of mechanism is that for the decomposition of ozone to oxygen. The balanced reaction is

$$2O_3(g) \longrightarrow 3O_2(g)$$

The observed rate law is

$$\text{Rate} = k\frac{[O_3]^2}{[O_2]}$$

Note that this rate law is unusual in that it contains the concentration of a *product*. The mechanism proposed for this process is

$$O_3 \underset{k_{-1}}{\overset{k_1}{\rightleftharpoons}} O_2 + O$$

$$O + O_3 \overset{k_2}{\longrightarrow} 2O_2$$

The double arrows in the first step indicate that both the forward and reverse reactions are important. They have the rate constants k_1 and k_{-1}, respectively.

For this mechanism we will assume that *both* the forward and reverse reactions of the first step are very fast compared with the reaction in the second step. This means that the second step is rate determining. Therefore, the rate for the overall reaction is equal to the rate of the second step:

The second step is relatively slow because of the very small concentration of O_3 molecules.

$$\text{Rate} = k_2[O][O_3]$$

This rate law does not have the same form as the experimentally determined rate law. For one thing, it contains the concentration of the intermediate, an oxygen atom. We can remove [O] and obtain a rate law that agrees with the experiment results by making an additional assumption. We assume that the rates of the forward and reverse reactions in the first step are equal. That is, we assume that the initial reversible fast step is at equilibrium. This makes sense because the rates of both the forward and reverse reactions for the first step are so much faster than the rate of the second step. For the first step,

$$\text{Rate of forward reaction} = k_1[O_3]$$

and $$\text{Rate of reverse reaction} = k_{-1}[O_2][O]$$

At equilibrium we have

$$k_1[O_3] = k_{-1}[O_2][O]$$

Chemical Insights   Seeing Reaction Mechanisms

Until very recently chemists could only guess at the details of reaction mechanisms. New developments such as femtosecond spectroscopy (see "Femtochemistry" on page 721) and scanning tunneling microscopy (STM; see "Seeing Atoms" on page 22) have enabled scientists to begin to see the details of chemical reactions.

A perfect example of these new techniques is furnished by the study of the oxidation of carbon monoxide by oxygen to form carbon dioxide by Professor Wilson Ho and his coworkers at the University of California at Irvine. Taking advantage of the single-molecule dexterity of the tip of an STM instrument, Ho and his colleagues maneuvered a single CO molecule on a silver surface until it was near an adsorbed O_2 molecule (Fig. 15.9). At this point an O—CO—O intermediate formed on the surface. A little shot of energy from the STM tip caused the intermediate to form CO_2, which exited the surface while leaving a lone O atom behind. In another study Ho and his coworkers found that CO_2 could be formed by depositing a CO molecule from the STM tip onto an oxygen atom on the surface.

The new techniques of femtosecond spectroscopy and STM are revolutionizing the way chemistry is carried out. We are now at the point where we can "see" the detailed pathways of chemical reactions.

Figure 15.9
The STM images of the reaction of CO and O_2. (a) An O_2 molecule (oval) and a CO molecule (circle) on a surface. As the two molecules approach each other, a reaction occurs (b) to form an O—CO—O complex (c). After an electron pulse is applied to the complex, a newly formed CO_2 molecule exits the surface, leaving behind a single O atom (d).

We solve for [O]:

$$[O] = \frac{k_1[O_3]}{k_{-1}[O_2]}$$

Now we substitute the expression for [O] into the rate law for the second step:

$$\text{Rate} = k_2[O][O_3] = k_2\left(\frac{k_1[O_3]}{k_{-1}[O_2]}\right)[O_3] = \frac{k_2k_1[O_3]^2}{k_{-1}[O_2]}$$

$$= k\frac{[O_3]^2}{[O_2]}$$

where k is a composite constant representing k_2k_1/k_{-1}.

This rate law, *derived* by postulating the two elementary steps and making assumptions about the relative rates of these steps, agrees with the experimental rate law. Since this mechanism (the elementary steps *plus* the assumptions) also gives the correct overall stoichiometry, it is an acceptable mechanism for the decomposition of ozone to oxygen.

EXAMPLE 15.7

The gas-phase reaction of chlorine with chloroform is described by the equation

$$Cl_2(g) + CHCl_3(g) \longrightarrow HCl(g) + CCl_4(g)$$

The rate law determined from experiment has a noninteger order:

$$\text{Rate} = k[Cl_2]^{1/2}[CHCl_3]$$

A proposed mechanism for this reaction follows:

$$Cl_2(g) \underset{k_{-1}}{\overset{k_1}{\rightleftharpoons}} 2Cl(g) \qquad \text{Both fast with equal rates (fast equilibrium)}$$

$$Cl(g) + CHCl_3(g) \xrightarrow{k_2} HCl(g) + CCl_3(g) \qquad \text{Slow}$$

$$CCl_3(g) + Cl(g) \xrightarrow{k_3} CCl_4(g) \qquad \text{Fast}$$

Is this an acceptable mechanism for the reaction?

Solution Two questions must be answered. First, does the mechanism give the correct overall stoichiometry? Adding the three steps does yield the correct balanced equation:

$$Cl_2(g) \rightleftharpoons 2Cl(g)$$

$$Cl(g) + CHCl_3(g) \longrightarrow HCl(g) + CCl_3(g)$$

$$CCl_3(g) + Cl(g) \longrightarrow CCl_4(g)$$

$$\overline{Cl_2(g) + \cancel{Cl}(g) + CHCl_3(g) + \cancel{CCl_3}(g) + \cancel{Cl}(g) \longrightarrow 2\cancel{Cl}(g) + HCl(g) + \cancel{CCl_3}(g) + CCl_4(g)}$$

Overall reaction: $Cl_2(g) + CHCl_3(g) \longrightarrow HCl(g) + CCl_4(g)$

Second, does the mechanism agree with the observed rate law? Since the overall reaction rate is determined by the rate of the slowest step,

$$\text{Overall rate} = \text{rate of second step} = k_2[Cl][CHCl_3]$$

Since the chlorine atom is an intermediate, we must find a way to eliminate [Cl] in the rate law. This can be done by recognizing that since the first step is at equilibrium, its forward and reverse rates are equal:

$$k_1[Cl_2] = k_{-1}[Cl]^2$$

Solving for $[Cl]^2$ gives

$$[Cl]^2 = \frac{k_1[Cl_2]}{k_{-1}}$$

Taking the square root of both sides yields

$$[Cl] = \left(\frac{k_1}{k_{-1}}\right)^{1/2} [Cl_2]^{1/2}$$

and

$$\text{Rate} = k_2[Cl][CHCl_3] = k_2\left(\frac{k_1}{k_{-1}}\right)^{1/2} [Cl_2]^{1/2}[CHCl_3] = k[Cl_2]^{1/2}[CHCl_3]$$

where

$$k = k_2\left(\frac{k_1}{k_{-1}}\right)^{1/2}$$

The rate law derived from the mechanism agrees with the experimentally observed rate law. This mechanism satisfies the two requirements and thus is an acceptable mechanism.

15.7 | The Steady-State Approximation

In the simplest reaction mechanisms, one particular step is usually rate determining. However, it is not unusual in complex, multistep reaction mechanisms for different steps to be rate determining under different sets of conditions.

In cases where a specific rate-determining step cannot be chosen, an analysis called the **steady-state approximation** is often used. The central feature of this method is the assumption that the concentration of any intermediate remains constant as the reaction proceeds. An intermediate is neither a reactant nor a product but something that is formed and then consumed as the reaction proceeds.

For example, the reaction between nitric oxide and hydrogen,

$$2NO(g) + H_2(g) \longrightarrow N_2O(g) + H_2O(g)$$

may proceed via the following mechanism:

1. $2NO \underset{k_{-1}}{\overset{k_1}{\rightleftharpoons}} N_2O_2$

2. $N_2O_2 + H_2 \xrightarrow{k_2} N_2O + H_2O$

In this mechanism the intermediate is N_2O_2. To apply the steady-state approximation to this mechanism, we assume the concentration of N_2O_2 remains constant. That is,

$$\frac{d[N_2O_2]}{dt} = 0$$

Next, we will identify the steps that produce N_2O_2 and those that consume N_2O_2 and write the rate law for each. Then we will apply the condition that the concentration of N_2O_2 is constant by setting the total rate of production of N_2O_2 equal to the total rate of consumption of N_2O_2. That is, if

Rate of production of N_2O_2 = rate of consumption of N_2O_2

then
$$\frac{d[N_2O_2]}{dt} = 0$$

Rate of Production of N₂O₂

In this mechanism N_2O_2 is produced only in the forward part of the first elementary step,

$$2NO \xrightarrow{k_1} N_2O_2$$

and the rate law for this step is

$$\frac{d[N_2O_2]}{dt} = k_1[NO]^2$$

Rate of Consumption of N₂O₂

In this mechanism N_2O_2 is consumed in the reverse part of the first step,

$$2NO \xleftarrow{k_{-1}} N_2O_2$$

and in the second step,

$$N_2O_2 + H_2 \xrightarrow{k_2} N_2O + H_2O$$

The rate laws for these steps are

$$-\frac{d[N_2O_2]}{dt} = k_{-1}[N_2O_2] \quad \text{and} \quad -\frac{d[N_2O_2]}{dt} = k_2[N_2O_2][H_2]$$

The Steady-State Condition

Now we equate the rates of production and consumption of N_2O_2:

$$k_1[NO]^2 = k_{-1}[N_2O_2] + k_2[N_2O_2][H_2]$$

Rate of production   Total rate of consumption

The Rate Law for the Overall Reaction

Next, we will write the rate law for the overall reaction,

$$2NO + H_2 \longrightarrow N_2O + H_2O$$

We can do this in several ways, depending on which reactant or product we use to represent the rate. In this case we will choose the decomposition of H_2 to define the rate:

$$\text{Rate of reaction} = -\frac{d[H_2]}{dt}$$

Note that H_2 is consumed only in the second step of the mechanism:

$$N_2O_2 + H_2 \xrightarrow{k_1} N_2O + H_2O$$

Thus the rate law is

$$-\frac{d[H_2]}{dt} = k_2[N_2O_2][H_2]$$

However, this is not the final form of the rate law for the overall reaction because it contains the concentration of an intermediate. We can remove this concentration from the rate law by solving the steady-state expression

$$k_1[NO]^2 = k_{-1}[N_2O_2] + k_2[N_2O_2][H_2]$$

for $[N_2O_2]$:

$$[N_2O_2] = \frac{k_1[NO]^2}{k_{-1} + k_2[H_2]}$$

We substitute this expression into the rate law,

$$\text{Rate} = -\frac{d[H_2]}{dt} = k_2[N_2O_2][H_2]$$

to give

$$\text{Rate} = -\frac{d[H_2]}{dt} = k_2[H_2]\left(\frac{k_1[NO]^2}{k_{-1} + k_2[H_2]}\right)$$

or

$$\text{Rate} = -\frac{d[H_2]}{dt} = \frac{k_2 k_1[H_2][NO]^2}{k_{-1} + k_2[H_2]}$$

This is the overall rate law for the proposed mechanism based on the steady-state analysis. Note that this rate law is quite complicated, which is common for rate laws obtained by assuming steady-state conditions. The usual practice for testing the validity of a complicated rate law involves choosing concentration conditions that produce a simpler form of the rate law. For example, if the reaction between NO and H_2 is studied under conditions where the concentration of H_2 is large enough so that

$$k_2[H_2] \gg k_{-1}$$

then the full rate law

$$\frac{k_2 k_1 [H_2][NO]^2}{k_{-1} + k_2[H_2]}$$

reduces to

$$\frac{k_2 k_1 [H_2][NO]^2}{k_2[H_2]} = k_1[NO]^2$$

Thus, at sufficiently high concentrations of H_2, the reaction should show second-order dependence on the concentration of nitric oxide if the suggested mechanism is valid.

On the other hand, at low concentrations of H_2, such that

$$k_{-1} \gg k_2[H_2]$$

the rate law reduces to the form

$$\text{Rate} = \frac{k_2 k_1}{k_{-1}}[H_2][NO]^2 = k[H_2][NO]^2$$

Studies of the reaction under these conditions should show first-order dependence on $[H_2]$, as well as second-order dependence on $[NO]$, if the suggested mechanism is valid.

The ideas we have developed above for a specific mechanism can be generalized as follows.

STEPS | **Analyzing a Mechanism Using the Steady-State Approximation**

1 Write the proposed mechanism (the elementary steps).

2 Construct a steady-state expression for each intermediate I by applying the criterion

$$\frac{d[I]}{dt} = 0$$

which means that

Rate of production of I = rate of consumption of I

This condition is implemented by identifying each step that produces or consumes I and writing the appropriate rate law for each. The sum of the rate laws that produce I are then set equal to the sum of the rate laws that consume I.

3 From the steady-state approximation for each intermediate $I_1, I_2, \ldots$, solve for $[I_1], [I_2], \ldots$.

4 Construct the rate law for the overall reaction in terms of one of the reactants or products. The decision about which reactant or product to use in constructing the rate law is based on convenience.

5 Use the expressions from step 3 for $[I_1], [I_2], \ldots$ to substitute for the concentrations of intermediates found in the rate law for step 4. The goal is to obtain an overall rate law that contains only reactant and/or product concentrations.

15.8 | A Model for Chemical Kinetics

How do chemical reactions occur? We already have given some indications. For example, we have seen that the rates of chemical reactions depend on the concentrations of the reacting species. The initial rate for the reaction

$$a\text{A} + b\text{B} \longrightarrow \text{products}$$

can be described by the rate law

$$\text{Rate} = k[\text{A}]^n[\text{B}]^m$$

where the order of each reactant depends on the detailed reaction mechanism. This explains why reaction rates depend on concentration. But what about some of the other factors affecting reaction rates? For example, how does temperature affect the speed of a reaction?

We can answer this question qualitatively from our experience. We use refrigerators because food spoilage is retarded at low temperatures. The combustion of wood occurs at a measurable rate only at high temperatures. An egg cooks in boiling water much faster at sea level than in Leadville, Colorado (elevation 10,000 feet), where the boiling point of water is about 90°C. These observations and others lead us to conclude that *chemical reactions speed up when the temperature is increased.* Experiments have shown that virtually all rate constants show an exponential increase with absolute temperature, as represented in Fig. 15.10.

In this section we will introduce a model that can be used to account for the observed characteristics of reaction rates. This model, the **collision model,** is built around the central idea that *molecules must collide to react.* We have already seen that this assumption can explain the concentration dependence of reaction rates. Now we need to consider whether this model can also account for the observed temperature dependence of reaction rates.

The kinetic molecular theory of gases predicts that an increase in temperature increases molecular velocities and so increases the frequency of intermolecular collisions. This agrees with the observation that reaction rates are greater at higher temperatures. Thus there is qualitative agreement between the collision model and experimental observations. However, it is found that the rate of reaction is much smaller than the calculated collision frequency in a given collection of gas particles. This must mean that *only a small fraction of the collisions produces a reaction.* Why?

This question was first addressed in the 1880s by Svante Arrhenius. He proposed the existence of a *threshold energy,* called the **activation energy,** that must be overcome to produce a chemical reaction. We can see that this proposal makes sense by considering the decomposition of BrNO in the gas phase:

$$2\text{BrNO}(g) \longrightarrow 2\text{NO}(g) + \text{Br}_2(g)$$

In this reaction two Br—N bonds must be broken and one Br—Br bond must be formed. Breaking a Br—N bond requires considerable energy (243 kJ/mol), which must come from somewhere. The collision model postulates that the energy required to break the bonds comes from the kinetic energies possessed by the reacting molecules before the collision. This kinetic energy is changed into potential energy as the molecules are distorted during a collision, breaking bonds and rearranging the atoms into the product molecules.

We can envision the reaction progress as shown in Fig. 15.11. The arrangement of atoms found at the top of the potential energy "hill," or barrier, is called the **activated complex,** or **transition state.** The conversion of BrNO to NO and Br_2 is exothermic, as indicated by the fact that the products have

k

$T\,(\text{K})$

Figure 15.10

A plot showing the exponential dependence of the rate constant on absolute temperature. The exact temperature dependence of k is different for each reaction. This plot represents the behavior of a rate constant that doubles for every increase in temperature of 10 K.

The higher the activation energy, the slower is the reaction at a given temperature.

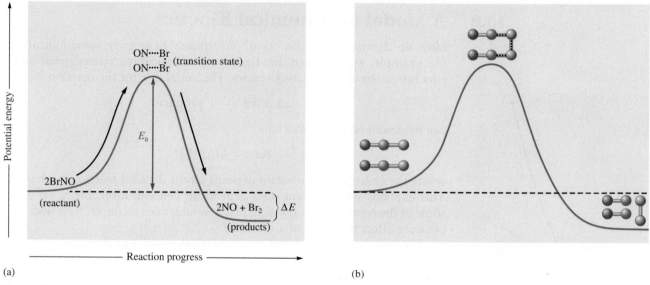

(a)   (b)

Figure 15.11

(a) The change in potential energy as a function of reaction progress for the reaction 2BrNO $\longrightarrow$ 2NO + Br$_2$. The activation energy E_a represents the energy needed to disrupt the BrNO molecules so that they can form products. The quantity ΔE represents the net change in energy in going from reactant to products. (b) A molecular representation of the reaction.

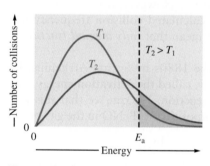

Figure 15.12

Plot showing the number of collisions with a particular energy at T_1 and T_2, where $T_2 > T_1$.

lower energy than the reactant. However, ΔE has no effect on the rate of the reaction. Rather, the rate depends on the size of the activation energy E_a.

The main point here is that a certain minimum energy is required for two BrNO molecules to "get over the hill" so that products can form. This is furnished by the collision energy. A collision between two BrNO molecules with small kinetic energies will not have enough energy to get over the barrier, and no reaction occurs. At a given temperature, only a certain fraction of the collisions possess enough energy to be effective and thus to result in product formation.

We can be more precise by recalling from Chapter 5 that a distribution of velocities occurs in a sample of gas molecules. Therefore, a distribution of collision energies also occurs, as shown in Fig. 15.12 for two different temperatures. Figure 15.12 also shows the activation energy for the reaction in question. Only collisions with energy greater than the activation energy are able to react (get over the barrier). At the lower temperature T_1, the fraction of effective collisions is quite small. However, as the temperature is increased to T_2, the fraction of collisions with the required activation energy increases dramatically. When the temperature is doubled, the fraction of effective collisions much more than doubles. In fact, the fraction of effective collisions increases *exponentially* with temperature. This agrees with the observation that rates of reactions increase exponentially with temperature.

Arrhenius postulated that the number of collisions having an energy equal to or greater than the activation energy is given by the expression

Number of collisions with at least the activation energy

$$= (\text{total number of collisions})e^{-E_a/RT}$$

where E_a is the activation energy, R is the universal gas constant, and T is the Kelvin temperature. The factor $e^{-E_a/RT}$ represents the fraction of collisions with energy E_a or greater at temperature T.

We have seen that not all molecular collisions are effective in producing chemical reactions because a minimum energy is required for the reaction to occur. There is, however, another complication. Experiments show that the

Figure 15.13
Several possible orientations for a collision between two BrNO molecules. Orientations (a) and (b) can lead to a reaction, but orientation (c) cannot.

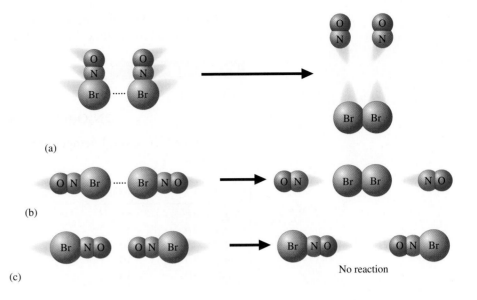

(a)

(b)

(c)

No reaction

observed reaction rate is considerably smaller than the rate of collisions with enough energy to surmount the barrier. This means that many collisions, even though they have the required energy, still do not produce a reaction. Why not?

The answer lies in the **molecular orientations** during collisions. We can illustrate this effect by using the reaction between two BrNO molecules, as shown in Fig. 15.13. Some collision orientations can lead to reaction, and others cannot. Therefore, we must include a correction factor to allow for collisions with nonproductive molecular orientations.

To summarize, two requirements must be satisfied for reactants to collide successfully (to rearrange to form products):

1. The collision must involve enough energy to produce the reaction; that is, the collision energy must equal or exceed the activation energy.

2. The relative orientations of the reactants must allow formation of any new bonds necessary to produce products.

Taking these factors into account, we can represent the rate constant as

$$k = zpe^{-E_a/RT}$$

where z is the collision frequency (the total number of collisions per second). The factor p in this expression, called the **steric factor**, reflects the fraction of collisions with effective orientations. Recall that the factor $e^{-E_a/RT}$ represents the fraction of collisions with sufficient energy to produce a reaction. This expression is most often written in the form

$$k = Ae^{-E_a/RT} \qquad (15.9)$$

which is called the **Arrhenius equation**. In this equation A, which replaces zp, is called the **pre-exponential factor**, or **frequency factor**, for the reaction.

Taking the natural logarithm of each side of the Arrhenius equation yields

$$\ln(k) = -\frac{E_a}{R}\left(\frac{1}{T}\right) + \ln(A) \qquad (15.10)$$

Equation (15.10) is a linear equation of the type $y = mx + b$, where $y = \ln(k)$, $m = -E_a/R = $ slope, $x = 1/T$, and $b = \ln(A) = $ intercept. Thus, for a reaction where the rate constant obeys the Arrhenius equation, a plot of $\ln(k)$ versus $1/T$ gives a straight line. The slope and intercept can be used to determine the values of E_a and A characteristic of that reaction. The fact that most rate constants obey the Arrhenius equation to a good approximation indicates that the collision model for chemical reactions is physically reasonable.

EXAMPLE 15.8

The reaction

$$2N_2O_5(g) \longrightarrow 4NO_2(g) + O_2(g)$$

was studied at several temperatures and the following values of k were obtained:

k (s⁻¹)	T (°C)
2.0×10^{-5}	20
7.3×10^{-5}	30
2.7×10^{-4}	40
9.1×10^{-4}	50
2.9×10^{-3}	60

Calculate the value of E_a for this reaction.

Solution To obtain the value of E_a, we need to construct a plot of $\ln(k)$ versus $1/T$. First, we must calculate values of $\ln(k)$ and $1/T$:

T (°C)	T (K)	$1/T$ (K)	k (s⁻¹)	$\ln(k)$
20	293	3.41×10^{-3}	2.0×10^{-5}	-10.82
30	303	3.30×10^{-3}	7.3×10^{-5}	-9.53
40	313	3.19×10^{-3}	2.7×10^{-4}	-8.22
50	323	3.10×10^{-3}	9.1×10^{-4}	-7.00
60	333	3.00×10^{-3}	2.9×10^{-3}	-5.84

The plot of $\ln(k)$ versus $1/T$ is shown in Fig. 15.14. The slope is found to be -1.2×10^4 K. Since

$$\text{Slope} = -\frac{E_a}{R}$$

Figure 15.14
Plot of $\ln(k)$ versus $1/T$ for the reaction $2N_2O_5(g) \longrightarrow 4NO_2(g) + O_2(g)$. The value of the activation energy for this reaction can be obtained from the slope of the line, which equals $-E_a/R$.

then

$$E_a = -R(\text{slope}) = -(8.3145 \text{ J K}^{-1} \text{ mol}^{-1})(-1.2 \times 10^4 \text{ K})$$

$$= 1.0 \times 10^5 \text{ J/mol}$$

Thus the value of the activation energy for this reaction is 1.0×10^5 J/mol.

The most common procedure for finding E_a for a reaction involves measuring the rate constant k at several temperatures and then plotting $\ln(k)$ versus $1/T$, as shown in Example 15.8. However, E_a can also be calculated from the values of k at only two temperatures using a formula that can be derived as follows from Equation (15.10).

At temperature T_1, the rate constant is k_1; thus

$$\ln(k_1) = -\frac{E_a}{RT_1} + \ln(A)$$

At temperature T_2, the rate constant is k_2; thus

$$\ln(k_2) = -\frac{E_a}{RT_2} + \ln(A)$$

Subtracting the first equation from the second gives

$$\ln\left(\frac{k_2}{k_1}\right) = \frac{E_a}{R}\left(\frac{1}{T_1} - \frac{1}{T_2}\right) \tag{15.11}$$

Therefore, the values of k_1 and k_2 measured at temperatures T_1 and T_2 can be used to calculate E_a.

15.9 | Catalysis

We have seen that the rate of a reaction increases dramatically with temperature. If a particular reaction does not occur fast enough at normal temperatures, we can speed it up by raising the temperature. However, sometimes this is not feasible. For example, since living cells can survive only in a rather narrow temperature range, the human body is designed to operate at an almost constant temperature of 98.6°F. But the many complicated biochemical reactions keeping us alive would be much too slow at this temperature without intervention. We survive only because the body contains many substances called **enzymes** that increase the rates of these reactions even though body temperature remains constant. In fact, almost every biologically important reaction is assisted by a specific enzyme. An important example involves the enzyme carbonic anhydrase, which catalyzes the reaction of carbon dioxide with water:

$$CO_2 + H_2O \rightleftharpoons HCO_3^- + H^+$$

This crucial reaction allows the carbon dioxide that forms in the cells during metabolism to be removed. If the carbon dioxide were allowed to accumulate, it would poison the cell. Carbonic anhydrase is so efficient that one molecule of enzyme can catalyze the reaction of over *600,000 carbon dioxide molecules in one second!*

Although it is possible to use higher temperatures to speed up commercially important reactions, such as the Haber process for synthesizing ammonia, this is very expensive. In a chemical plant an increase in temperature means significantly increased energy costs. The use of an appropriate catalyst allows a reaction to proceed rapidly at a relatively low temperature and therefore can hold down production costs.

Chemical Insights

TiO₂—One of Nature's Most Versatile Materials

Titanium(IV) oxide (commonly called titanium dioxide) is a compound with an amazing array of talents. It is a widely used white pigment for paint, paper, vinyl floor coverings, sunscreens, and synthetic fibers. However, it is much more than a simple pigment. TiO₂, it appears, has an almost unlimited ability to catalyze the breakdown of organic materials. In Japan, scores of companies are scrambling to take advantage of this remarkable talent. TiO₂-impregnated paint used on buildings and in automobile and rail tunnels prevents the buildup of oily dust, TiO₂-impregnated glass prevents oily buildup on chandeliers and automobile windows, and a TiO₂-impregnated fan belt can help break down grease that often clogs kitchen exhaust fans. TiO₂ catalysis can also be used to break down air pollutants such as cigarette smoke and nitrogen oxides. In addition to all these talents, TiO₂ kills bacteria.

TiO₂ is a photocatalyst—it requires light for its catalytic activity. It also requires the presence of oxygen and water. The mechanism for the catalytic behavior of TiO₂ results from its behavior as a semiconductor. When light is absorbed by TiO₂, free electrons and "holes" are created that cause adsorbed water and oxygen molecules to form hydroxyl (OH) and superoxide (O₂⁻) radicals,

© Anteromite/Shutterstock.com

A white paint pigment that contains TiO₂.

species with unpaired electrons. These extremely reactive radicals can react with and destroy virtually all organic materials. The formation of these radicals also explains the ability of TiO₂ to catalyze the reactions of nitrogen oxides to form nitric acid. These radicals are lethal to microorganisms and explain the ability of TiO₂ to behave as a bactericide.

New uses are being found daily for the many talents of TiO₂.

Figure 15.15
Energy plots for catalyzed and uncatalyzed pathways for a given reaction. Note that although the shapes of the catalyzed and uncatalyzed energy profiles are shown here the same for simplicity, they do not have identical shapes for actual reactions.

A **catalyst** is *a substance that speeds up a reaction without being consumed itself.* Just as virtually all vital biological reactions are assisted by enzymes (biological catalysts), almost all industrial processes also benefit from the use of catalysts. For example, the production of sulfuric acid uses vanadium(V) oxide, and the Haber process uses a mixture of iron and iron oxide.

How does a catalyst work? Remember that for each reaction a certain energy barrier must be surmounted. How can we make a reaction occur faster without raising the temperature to increase the molecular kinetic energies? The solution is to provide a new pathway for the reaction, one with a *lower activation energy.* That is what a catalyst does, as shown in Fig. 15.15. Because the catalyst allows the reaction to occur along a pathway with a lower activation energy, a much larger fraction of collisions is effective at a given temperature. Thus the reaction rate is increased. This effect is illustrated in Fig. 15.16. Note from this diagram that although a catalyst lowers the activation energy (E_a) for a reaction, it does not affect the energy difference (ΔE) between products and reactants.

Catalysts are classified as homogeneous or heterogeneous. A **homogeneous catalyst** is one that is *present in the same phase (physical state) as the reacting molecules.* A **heterogeneous catalyst** exists *in a different phase,* usually as a solid.

Figure 15.16

Effect of a catalyst on the number of reaction-producing collisions. Because a catalyst provides a reaction pathway with a lower activation energy, a much greater fraction of the collisions is effective for the catalyzed pathway (b) than for the uncatalyzed pathway (a) (at a given temperature). This allows reactants to become products at a much higher rate, even though there is no temperature increase.

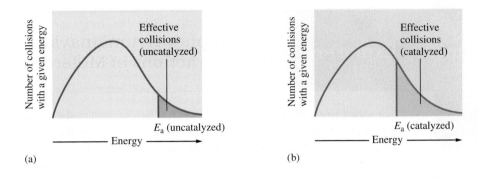

Heterogeneous Catalysis

Heterogeneous catalysis most often involves gaseous reactants being adsorbed on the surface of a solid catalyst. **Adsorption** refers to the collection of one substance on the surface of another substance; **absorption** refers to the penetration of one substance into another. Water is *absorbed* by a sponge.

One of the earliest examples of heterogeneous catalysis involves the synthesis of ammonia from nitrogen and hydrogen. This process was developed in 1909 by German chemist Fritz Haber—who tested more than 1000 possible catalysts before settling on iron as the best choice. (Today, ammonia manufacturers use a solid catalyst consisting of a mixture of iron, potassium, and calcium that performs better than iron alone.) Although Haber had no means for determining why iron was a good catalyst, it is now understood that the key to iron's effectiveness is that the strong nitrogen–nitrogen and hydrogen–hydrogen bonds are weakened when the H_2 and N_2 molecules are bound to iron atoms on the surface of the metal. Iron turns out to be an ideal catalyst because the iron–nitrogen bond is sufficiently strong that the nitrogen atoms on the surface do not recombine to form N_2 but is weak enough to allow nitrogen and hydrogen atoms on the surface to combine to form ammonia.

An important example of heterogeneous catalysis occurs in the hydrogenation of unsaturated hydrocarbons, compounds composed mainly of carbon and hydrogen and containing some carbon–carbon double bonds. Hydrogenation is an important industrial process used to change unsaturated fats, occurring as oils, to saturated fats (solid shortenings such as Crisco). In this process the C=C bonds are converted to C—C bonds through the addition of hydrogen.

A simple example of hydrogenation involves ethylene:

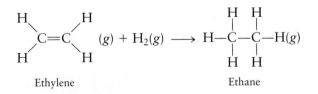

This reaction is quite slow at normal temperatures mainly because the strong bond in the hydrogen molecule results in a large activation energy for the reaction. However, the reaction rate can be greatly increased by using a solid catalyst of platinum, palladium, or nickel. The hydrogen and ethylene adsorb on the catalyst surface, where the reaction occurs. The main function of the catalyst apparently is to allow formation of metal–hydrogen interactions that weaken the H—H bonds and facilitate the reaction. The mechanism is illustrated in Fig. 15.17.

Chemistry Explorers

Christopher Arumainayagam Researches the Interactions of Molecules with Surfaces

Professor Christopher Arumainayagam, who has been on the faculty of Wellesley College since 1990, received his B.A. degree from Harvard University and his Ph.D. from Stanford University.

One goal of Professor Arumainayagam's research is to understand the interactions of molecules with solid surfaces in order to learn more about the reaction mechanisms of heterogeneous catalysis. In experiments conducted using molecular beams (narrow streams of molecules that are undisturbed by collisions with other gas molecules), Professor Arumainayagam has studied how adsorption on a solid surface depends on the velocity and angle of approach of the incident molecule. In collaboration with Professor John Yates, Professor Arumainayagam has also studied the production and removal of surface defects (irregularities) that are thought to play a critical role in the performance of heterogeneous catalysts.

In his current research at Wellesley College, Professor Arumainayagam and his undergraduate students are using surface science techniques and low-energy electron beams to understand how high-energy particles (e.g., electrons, protons, alpha particles) and high-energy photons (e.g., X rays and gamma rays) interact with matter, causing ionization. Results of their studies may provide information that could further cost-efficient destruction of hazardous chemicals and improve our understanding of the electron-induced decomposition of feed gases used in the processing of semiconductor devices.

Christopher Arumainayagam and a student.

Figure 15.17

Heterogeneous catalysis of the hydrogenation of ethylene. (a) Hydrogen is adsorbed on the metal surface, forming metal–hydrogen bonds and breaking the H—H bonds. (b) During adsorption, the C—C π bond in ethylene is broken and metal–carbon bonds are formed. (c) The adsorbed molecules and atoms migrate toward each other on the metal surface, forming new C—H bonds. (d) The C atoms in ethane (C_2H_6) have completely saturated bonding capacities and so cannot bind strongly to the metal surfaces. The C_2H_6 molecule thus escapes.

(a)

Metal surface

(b)

(c)

(d)

Carbon

Hydrogen

Typically, heterogeneous catalysis involves four steps:

1. Adsorption and activation of the reactants
2. Migration of the adsorbed reactants on the surface
3. Reaction among the adsorbed substances
4. Escape, or *desorption,* of the products

Heterogeneous catalysis also occurs in the oxidation of gaseous sulfur dioxide to gaseous sulfur trioxide. This process is especially interesting because it illustrates both positive and negative consequences of chemical catalysis.

The negative side is the formation of damaging air pollutants. Recall that sulfur dioxide, a toxic gas with a choking odor, is formed when sulfur-containing fuels are burned. However, it is sulfur trioxide that causes most of the environmental damage, mainly through the production of acid rain. When sulfur trioxide combines with a droplet of water, sulfuric acid is formed:

$$H_2O(l) + SO_3(g) \longrightarrow H_2SO_4(aq)$$

This sulfuric acid can cause considerable damage to vegetation, buildings and statues, and fish populations.

Sulfur dioxide is *not* rapidly oxidized to sulfur trioxide in clean, dry air. Why, then, is there a problem? The answer is catalysis. Dust particles and water droplets catalyze the reaction between SO_2 and O_2 in the air.

On the positive side, the heterogeneous catalysis of the oxidation of SO_2 is used to advantage in the manufacture of sulfuric acid, where the reaction of O_2 and SO_2 to form SO_3 is catalyzed by a solid mixture of platinum and vanadium(V) oxide.

Heterogeneous catalysis is also used in the catalytic converters of automobile exhaust systems. The exhaust gases, containing compounds such as nitric oxide, carbon monoxide, and unburned hydrocarbons, are passed through a converter containing beads of solid catalyst (Fig. 15.18). The catalyst promotes the conversion of carbon monoxide to carbon dioxide, hydrocarbons to carbon dioxide and water, and nitric oxide to nitrogen gas, to lessen the environmental impact of the exhaust gases. This beneficial catalysis can, unfortunately, be accompanied by the unwanted catalysis of the oxidation of SO_2 to SO_3, the latter reacting with the moisture present to form sulfuric acid.

Because of the complex nature of the reactions that take place in the converter, a mixture of catalysts is used. The most effective catalytic materials are transition metal oxides and noble metals such as palladium and platinum. A catalytic converter typically consists of platinum and rhodium particles deposited on a ceramic honeycomb, a configuration that maximizes the contact between the metal particles and the exhaust gases. In studies performed during the last ten years, researchers at General Motors have shown that rhodium

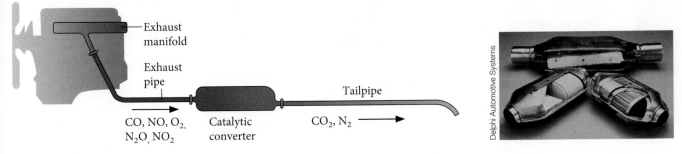

Figure 15.18
The exhaust gases from an automobile engine are passed through a catalytic converter to minimize environmental damage.

Chemical Insights Enzymes: Nature's Catalysts

The most impressive examples of homogeneous catalysis occur in nature, where the complex reactions necessary for plant and animal life are made possible by enzymes. Enzymes are large molecules specifically tailored to facilitate a given type of reaction. Usually enzymes are proteins, an important class of biomolecules constructed from α-amino acids that have the general structure

where R represents any one of 20 different substituents. These amino acid molecules can be "hooked together" to form a polymer (a word meaning "many parts") called a *protein*. The general structure of a protein can be represented as follows:

| Many amino acid fragments | Fragment from an amino acid with substituent R | Fragment from an amino acid with substituent R' | Fragment from an amino acid with substituent R'' |

Since specific proteins are needed by the human body, the proteins in food must be broken into their constituent amino acids, which are then used to construct new proteins in the body's cells. The reaction in which a protein is broken down one amino acid at a time is shown in Fig. 15.19. Note that in this reaction a water molecule reacts with a protein molecule to produce an amino acid and a new protein containing one fewer amino acid. Without the help of the enzymes found in human cells, this reaction would be much too slow to be useful. One of these enzymes is *carboxypeptidase-A*, a zinc-containing protein (Fig. 15.20).

Carboxypeptidase-A captures the protein to be acted on (called the *substrate*) in a special groove

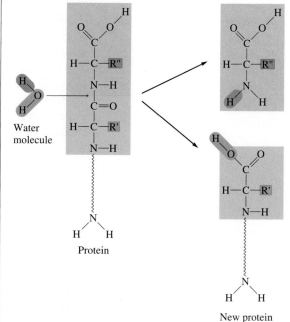

Figure 15.19
The removal of the end amino acid from a protein by reaction with a molecule of water. The products are an amino acid and a new, smaller protein.

and positions the substrate so that the end is in the *active site*, where the catalysis occurs (Fig. 15.21). Note that the Zn^{2+} ion bonds to the oxygen of the C=O (carbonyl) group. This polarizes the electron density in the carbonyl group, allowing the neighboring C—N bond to be broken much more easily. When the reaction is completed, the remaining portion of the substrate protein and the newly formed amino acid are released by the enzyme.

The process just described for carboxypeptidase-A is characteristic of the behavior of other enzymes. Enzyme catalysis can be represented by the series of reactions shown below:

$$E + S \underset{k_{-1}}{\overset{k_1}{\rightleftharpoons}} E \cdot S$$

$$E \cdot S \overset{k_2}{\rightleftharpoons} E + P$$

Figure 15.20
The structure of the enzyme carboxypeptidase-A, which contains 307 amino acids.

where E represents the enzyme, S represents the substrate, E · S represents the enzyme–substrate complex, and P represents the products. The enzyme and substrate form a complex where the reaction occurs. The enzyme then releases the products and is ready to repeat the process. The most amazing thing about enzymes is their efficiency. Because an enzyme plays its catalytic role over and over and very rapidly, only a tiny amount of enzyme is required. This makes the isolation of enzymes for study quite difficult.

Figure 15.21
Protein–substrate interaction. The substrate is shown in black and red, with the red representing the terminal amino acid. Blue indicates side chains from the enzyme that help bind the substrate.

promotes the dissociation of NO molecules adsorbed on its surface, thereby enhancing the conversion of NO, a serious air pollutant, to N_2, a natural component of pure air.

One consequence of the widespread use of catalytic converters has been the need to remove lead from gasoline. Tetraethyl lead was used for more than 50 years as a very effective "octane booster" because of its antiknocking characteristics. However, lead quickly destroys much of a converter's catalytic efficiency. This poisoning effect, along with health concerns about the toxicity of lead, has necessitated the removal of lead from gasoline, which has caused a search for other antiknock additives and the redesigning of engines to run on lower-octane gasoline.

Yet another application of solid-state catalysis occurs in the desulfurization of petroleum. Natural petroleum includes various molecules that contain sulfur atoms. Combustion of this petroleum produces SO_2, which must be removed from the exhaust to prevent air pollution. One way to prevent pollution by SO_2 is to remove the sulfur from the petroleum before it is used for fuel—the desulfurization of petroleum. One type of sulfur-containing molecules found in petroleum are thiols, which can be written R—SH, where R represents a molecular fragment containing a long chain of carbon atoms. In desulfurization the goal is to remove the sulfur from this molecule to produce a hydrocarbon (R—H):

$$R—SH \longrightarrow R—H + S$$

Oil chemists have found that this process is catalyzed by a mixture of molybdenum, cobalt, and sulfur. Because this catalyst is a very complicated substance, we are not certain how it works. It is thought that the desulfurization reaction involves the thiol binding to the catalytic surface. In this process the S—H bond is broken, with the R—S and the H being bound to metal atoms on the surface of the catalyst. The H atom is then transferred to the R fragment to form R—H, which migrates away, leaving the S behind.

Homogeneous Catalysis

A homogeneous catalyst exists in the same phase as the reacting molecules. There are many examples in both the gas and liquid phases. One such example is the unusual catalytic behavior of nitric oxide toward ozone. In the troposphere, the part of the atmosphere closest to earth, nitric oxide catalyzes ozone production. However, in the upper atmosphere, it catalyzes the decomposition of ozone. Both of these effects are unfortunate environmentally.

In the lower atmosphere, NO is produced in any high-temperature combustion process where N_2 is present. The reaction

$$N_2(g) + O_2(g) \longrightarrow 2NO(g)$$

is very slow at normal temperatures because of the very strong N≡N and O=O bonds. However, at elevated temperatures, such as those found in the internal combustion engines of automobiles, significant quantities of NO form. Some of this NO is converted back to N_2 in the catalytic converter, but significant amounts escape into the atmosphere to react with oxygen:

$$2NO(g) + O_2(g) \longrightarrow 2NO_2(g)$$

In the atmosphere NO_2 can absorb light and decompose as follows:

$$NO_2(g) \xrightarrow{\text{Light}} NO(g) + O(g)$$

The oxygen atom formed in this process is very reactive and can combine with oxygen molecules to form ozone:

$$O_2(g) + O(g) \longrightarrow O_3(g)$$

Although O_2 is represented here as the oxidizing agent for NO, the actual oxidizing agent is probably some type of peroxide compound produced by the reaction of oxygen with pollutants. The direct reaction of NO with O_2 is very slow.

Hot, New Enzymes

Enzymes, nature's catalysts, are very attractive to chemical companies: Enzymes are very efficient catalysts and as natural products they tend to be easier on the environment than human-made catalysts. However, one disadvantage of most enzymes is that they can function only near room temperature and at pH values near 7. Because of these limitations, scientists are now looking at the enzymes that occur in organisms that exist in extreme conditions.

The exotic microorganisms that thrive in the scalding temperatures of hot springs, the freezing temperatures of the Arctic, or extremes in pH or salinity are called *extremophiles* and their enzymes are called *extremozymes*. Although the extremozymes are attractive to industry because they can survive in the extreme conditions that often characterize industrial processes, the parent extremophiles are difficult to grow "in captivity" because of the unusual conditions they require. Because of the difficulties in culturing these microorganisms, biotechnology companies are now "shotgun" cloning the DNA from a mix of these extremophiles. The steps in this process are represented below.

A micrograph of the extremophile *Archaeoglobus fulgidis,* an organism that lives in the hot sediments near submarine hydrothermal vents.

Alfred Pasieka/Science Photo Library/Photo Researchers, Inc.

Collect samples of extremophiles from their natural habitats.

Extract and purify the DNA.

Cut the DNA into fragments and clone the fragments.

Use the DNA fragments to make proteins (expression products).

Screen the expression products for enzyme activity.

The DNA fragments are expressed (proteins are made from the genes contained in the fragments) most commonly using *Escherichia coli.* Interestingly, even though *E. coli* must be cultured under the mild conditions necessary for them to survive, the extremozymes formed seem to have their characteristic catalytic activities, indicating that they have the same structures as when they are formed in their native extreme conditions.

The mixtures of extremozymes produced by the expression process are then tested to see if they have catalytic activity for the industrial processes of interest. If a given mixture shows catalytic activity, it is then usually subjected to random DNA mutagenesis or "molecule breeding" to see whether random evolution of the enzymes will lead to improved activities.

The potential market for the extremozymes is huge. Currently, the global market for industrial enzymes is more than $7 billion. The companies developing the extremozymes hope that their products can replace existing industrial catalysts, making processes more efficient by lowering costs and minimizing the formation of by-products.

Ozone is a powerful oxidizing agent that can react with other air pollutants to form substances irritating to the eyes and lungs.

In this series of reactions, nitric oxide is acting as a true catalyst because it assists the production of ozone without being consumed itself. This can be seen by summing the reactions:

$$NO(g) + \tfrac{1}{2}O_2(g) \longrightarrow NO_2(g)$$

$$NO_2(g) \xrightarrow{\text{Light}} NO(g) + O(g)$$

$$O_2(g) + O(g) \longrightarrow O_3(g)$$

$$\overline{\tfrac{3}{2}O_2(g) \longrightarrow O_3(g)}$$

In the upper atmosphere, the presence of nitric oxide has the opposite effect—the depletion of ozone. The series of reactions involved is

$$NO(g) + O_3(g) \longrightarrow NO_2(g) + O_2(g)$$

$$O(g) + NO_2(g) \longrightarrow NO(g) + O_2(g)$$

$$\overline{O(g) + O_3(g) \longrightarrow 2O_2(g)}$$

Nitric oxide is again catalytic, but here its effect is to change O_3 to O_2. This is a potential problem because O_3, which absorbs ultraviolet light, is necessary to protect us from the harmful effects of this high-energy radiation. That is, we want O_3 in the upper atmosphere to block ultraviolet radiation from the sun. However, we do not want it in the lower atmosphere where we have to breathe it and its oxidation products.

Over the last decade, research has shown that the ozone layer in the upper atmosphere is also threatened by *Freons,** a group of stable, noncorrosive compounds long used as refrigerants and propellants in aerosol cans. The most commonly used substance of this type was Freon-12 (CCl_2F_2). The chemical inertness of Freons makes them more useful but also creates a problem, since they remain for a long time in the environment. Eventually, they migrate into the upper atmosphere to be decomposed by high-energy light. Among the decomposition products are chlorine atoms:

$$CCl_2F_2(g) \xrightarrow{\text{Light}} CClF_2(g) + Cl(g)$$

These chlorine atoms can catalyze the decomposition of ozone:

$$Cl(g) + O_3(g) \longrightarrow ClO(g) + O_2(g)$$

$$O(g) + ClO(g) \longrightarrow Cl(g) + O_2(g)$$

$$\overline{O(g) + O_3(g) \longrightarrow 2O_2(g)}$$

The problem of Freons has been brought strongly into focus by the discovery of a mysterious "hole" in the ozone layer in the stratosphere over Antarctica. Studies to find the reason for the hole have found unusually high levels of chlorine monoxide (ClO) in the atmosphere over Antarctica. This strongly implicates the Freons in the atmosphere as being at least partially responsible for the ozone destruction in the area.

Because they pose environmental problems, Freons were banned years ago by the U.S. government for use in aerosol cans, and they have recently been banned for use in air conditioners and refrigerators.

---

*For more information, see S. Elliott and F. S. Rowland, "Chlorofluorocarbons and Stratospheric Ozone," *J. Chem. Ed.* 64 (1987): 387, and P. S. Zurer, "Ozone Depletion's Recurring Surprises Challenge Atmospheric Scientists," *Chem. Eng. News,* May 24, 1993: 8.

Key Terms

chemical kinetics

Section 15.1
reaction rate
instantaneous rate

Section 15.2
rate law
rate constant
order
differential rate law (rate law)
integrated rate law

Section 15.3
method of initial rates
initial rate
overall reaction order

Section 15.4
first-order reaction
integrated first-order rate law
half-life of a reaction
integrated second-order rate law
zero-order reaction
integrated rate law for a
   zero-order reaction
pseudo-first-order rate law

Section 15.6
reaction mechanism
intermediate
elementary step
molecularity
unimolecular step
bimolecular step
termolecular step
rate-determining step

Section 15.7
steady-state approximation

Section 15.8
collision model
activation energy
activated complex (transition
   state)
molecular orientations
steric factor
Arrhenius equation
pre-exponential (frequency)
   factor

Section 15.9
enzyme
catalyst
homogeneous catalyst
heterogeneous catalyst
adsorption
absorption

For Review

OWL and go Chemistry

Sign in at **www.cengage.com/owl** to:
- View tutorials and simulations, develop problem-solving skills, and complete online homework assigned by your professor.
- Download Go Chemistry mini lecture modules for quick review and exam prep from OWL (or purchase them at **www.cengagebrain.com**)

Chemical kinetics
- The study of the factors that control the rate (speed) of a chemical reaction
  - Rate is defined in terms of the change in concentration of a given reaction component per unit time
  - Kinetic measurements are often made under conditions where the reverse reaction is insignificant
- The kinetic and thermodynamic properties of a reaction are not fundamentally related

Rate laws
- Differential rate law: describes the rate as a function of concentration

$$\text{Rate} = -\frac{\Delta[A]}{\Delta t} = k[A]^n$$

  - k is the rate constant
  - n is the order; not related to the coefficients in the balanced equation
- Integrated rate law: describes the concentration as a function of time
  - For a reaction of the type

$$aA \longrightarrow \text{products}$$

for which

$$\text{Rate} = k[A]^n$$

$n = 0:$ $\quad [A] = -kt + [A]_0$

$$t_{1/2} = \frac{[A]_0}{2k}$$

$n = 1:$ $\quad \ln[A] = -kt + \ln[A]_0$

$$t_{1/2} = \frac{0.693}{k}$$

$n = 2:$ $\quad \dfrac{1}{[A]} = kt + \dfrac{1}{k[A]_0}$

$$t_{1/2} = \frac{1}{k[A]_0}$$

- The value of k can be determined from the plot of the appropriate function of [A] versus t

Reaction mechanism
- Series of elementary steps by which an overall reaction occurs
  - Elementary step: rate law for the step can be written from the molecularity of the reaction
- Two requirements for an acceptable mechanism:
  - The elementary steps sum to give the correct overall balanced equation
  - The mechanism agrees with the experimentally determined rate law

- Simple reactions can have an elementary step that is slower than all of the other steps; which is called the rate-determining step.

Steady state approximation
- Used when a specific rate-determining step cannot be chosen.
- Assumes the concentration of any intermediate remains constant as the reaction proceeds.

Kinetic models
- The simplest model to account for reaction kinetics is the collision model
  - Molecules must collide to react
  - The collision kinetic energy furnishes the potential energy needed to enable the reactants to rearrange to form products
  - A certain threshold energy called the activation energy (E_a) is necessary for a reaction to occur
  - The relative orientations of the colliding reactants are also a determining factor in the reaction rate
  - This model leads to the Arrhenius equation:

$$k = Ae^{-E_a/RT}$$

  - A depends on the collision frequency and relative orientation of the molecules
  - The value of E_a can be found by obtaining the values of k at several temperatures

Catalyst
- Speeds up a reaction without being consumed
- Works by providing a lower-energy pathway for the reaction
- Enzymes are biological catalysts
- Catalysts can be classified as homogeneous or heterogeneous
  - Homogeneous: exist in the same phase as the reactants
  - Heterogeneous: exist in a different phase than the reactants

Discussion Questions*

These questions are designed to be considered by groups of students in class. Often these questions work well for introducing a particular topic in class.

1. Define the term *stability* from both a kinetic and a thermodynamic perspective. Give examples to show the differences in these concepts.

2. Describe at least two experiments you could perform to determine a rate law.

3. Make a graph of [A] versus time for zero-, first-, and second-order reactions. From these graphs, compare successive half-lives.

4. How does temperature affect k, the rate constant? Explain.

5. Consider the following statements: "In general, the rate of a chemical reaction increases at first. After that the rate of the reaction decreases because its rate is depen-

dent on the concentrations of the reactants, and these are decreasing." Indicate everything that is correct in these statements, and indicate everything that is incorrect. Correct the incorrect statements, and explain.

6. For the reaction A + B $\longrightarrow$ C, explain at least two ways in which the rate law could be zero order in chemical A.

7. A friend of yours states, "A balanced equation tells us how chemicals interact. Therefore, we can determine the rate law directly from the balanced equation." What do you tell your friend?

8. The rate constant (k) depends on which of the following? (There may be more than one answer.)
   a. the concentration of the reactants
   b. the nature of the reactants
   c. the temperature
   d. the order of the reaction
   Explain.

9. Provide a conceptual rationale for the differences in the half-lives of zero-, first-, and second-order reactions.

*In the Questions and the Exercises the term *rate law* always means differential rate law.

Exercises*

⚙**WL** Interactive versions of these problems may be assigned in OWL.
A blue exercise number indicates that the answer to that exercise appears at the back of this book and a solution appears in the *Solutions Guide*.

Reaction Rates

10. Define *reaction rate*. Distinguish between the initial rate, average rate, and instantaneous rate of a chemical reaction. Which of these rates is usually fastest? The initial rate is the rate used by convention. Give a possible explanation as to why.

11. Consider the general reaction

$$aA + bB \longrightarrow cC$$

and the following average rate data over a specific time period Δt:

$$-\frac{\Delta A}{\Delta t} = 0.0080 \text{ mol L}^{-1} \text{ s}^{-1}$$

$$-\frac{\Delta B}{\Delta t} = 0.0120 \text{ mol L}^{-1} \text{ s}^{-1}$$

$$\frac{\Delta C}{\Delta t} = 0.0160 \text{ mol L}^{-1} \text{ s}^{-1}$$

Determine a set of possible coefficients to balance this general reaction.

12. Consider the reaction

$$4PH_3(g) \longrightarrow P_4(g) + 6H_2(g)$$

If, in a certain experiment, over a specific time period, 0.0048 mole of PH_3 is consumed in a 2.0-L container during each second of the reaction, what are the rates of production of P_4 and H_2 in this experiment?

13. In the Haber process for the production of ammonia,

$$N_2(g) + 3H_2(g) \longrightarrow 2NH_3(g)$$

what is the relationship between the rate of production of ammonia and the rate of consumption of hydrogen?

14. What are the units for each of the following if concentrations are expressed in moles per liter and time in seconds?
    a. rate of a chemical reaction
    b. rate constant for a zero-order rate law
    c. rate constant for a first-order rate law
    d. rate constant for a second-order rate law
    e. rate constant for a third-order rate law

15. The rate law for the reaction

$$Cl_2(g) + CHCl_3(g) \longrightarrow HCl(g) + CCl_4(g)$$

is

$$\text{Rate} = k[Cl_2]^{1/2}[CHCl_3]$$

What are the units for k assuming time in seconds?

----

*In the Questions and the Exercises, the term *rate law* always means differential rate law.

16. The hydroxyl radical (OH) is an important oxidizing agent in the atmosphere. At 298 K the rate constant for the reaction of OH with benzene is 1.24×10^{-12} cm³ molecule^{-1} s^{-1}. Calculate the value of the rate constant in L mol^{-1} s^{-1}.

Rate Laws from Experimental Data: Initial-Rates Method

17. The reaction

$$2NO(g) + Cl_2(g) \longrightarrow 2NOCl(g)$$

was studied at $-10°C$. The following results were obtained, where

$$\text{Rate} = -\frac{d[Cl_2]}{dt}$$

$[NO]_0$ (mol/L)	$[Cl_2]_0$ (mol/L)	Initial Rate (mol L^{-1} min^{-1})
0.10	0.10	0.18
0.10	0.20	0.36
0.20	0.20	1.45

a. What is the rate law?
b. What is the value of the rate constant?

18. The following data were obtained for the gas-phase decomposition of dinitrogen pentoxide,

$$2N_2O_5(g) \longrightarrow 4NO_2(g) + O_2(g)$$

$[N_2O_5]_0$ (mol/L)	Initial Rate (mol L^{-1} s^{-1})
0.0750	8.90×10^{-4}
0.190	2.26×10^{-3}
0.275	3.26×10^{-3}
0.410	4.85×10^{-3}

where $\quad \text{Rate} = \dfrac{-d[N_2O_5]}{dt}$

Write the rate law and calculate the value of the rate constant.

19. The decomposition of nitrosyl chloride was studied:

$$2NOCl(g) \rightleftharpoons 2NO(g) + Cl_2(g)$$

The following data were obtained, where

$$\text{Rate} = \frac{-d[NOCl]}{dt}$$

$[NOCl]_0$ (molecules/cm³)	Initial Rate (molecules cm^{-3} s^{-1})
3.0×10^{16}	5.98×10^4
2.0×10^{16}	2.66×10^4
1.0×10^{16}	6.64×10^3
4.0×10^{16}	1.06×10^5

a. What is the rate law?

b. Calculate the rate constant.

c. Calculate the rate constant for the concentrations given in moles per liter.

20. The rate of the reaction between hemoglobin (Hb) and carbon monoxide (CO) was studied at 20°C. The following data were collected, with all concentration units in $\mu mol/L$. (A hemoglobin concentration of 2.21 $\mu mol/L$ is equal to 2.21×10^{-6} mol/L.)

$[Hb]_0$ ($\mu mol/L$)	$[CO]_0$ ($\mu mol/L$)	Initial Rate ($\mu mol\ L^{-1}\ s^{-1}$)
2.21	1.00	0.619
4.42	1.00	1.24
4.42	3.00	3.71

a. Determine the orders of this reaction with respect to Hb and CO.

b. Determine the rate law.

c. Calculate the value of the rate constant.

d. What would be the initial rate for an experiment with $[Hb]_0 = 3.36\ \mu mol/L$ and $[CO]_0 = 2.40\ \mu mol/L$?

21. The following data were obtained for the reaction

$$2ClO_2(aq) + 2OH^-(aq)$$
$$\longrightarrow ClO_3^-(aq) + ClO_2^-(aq) + H_2O(l)$$

where

$$Rate = -\frac{d[ClO_2]}{dt}$$

$[ClO_2]_0$ (mol/L)	$[OH^-]_0$ (mol/L)	Initial Rate (mol $L^{-1}\ s^{-1}$)
0.0500	0.100	5.75×10^{-2}
0.100	0.100	2.30×10^{-1}
0.100	0.0500	1.15×10^{-1}

a. Determine the rate law and the value of the rate constant.

b. What would be the initial rate for an experiment with $[ClO_2]_0 = 0.175$ mol/L and $[OH^-]_0 = 0.0844$ mol/L?

22. The reaction

$$2NO(g) + O_2(g) \longrightarrow 2NO_2(g)$$

was studied, and the following data were obtained, where

$$Rate = -\frac{d[O_2]}{dt}$$

$[NO]_0$ (molecules/cm³)	$[O_2]_0$ (molecules/cm³)	Initial Rate (molecules cm^{-3} s^{-1})
1.00×10^{18}	1.00×10^{18}	2.00×10^{16}
3.00×10^{18}	1.00×10^{18}	1.80×10^{17}
2.50×10^{18}	2.50×10^{18}	3.13×10^{17}

What would be the initial rate for an experiment where $[NO]_0 = 6.21 \times 10^{18}$ molecules/cm³ and $[O_2]_0 = 7.36 \times 10^{18}$ molecules/cm³?

23. The reaction

$$H_2SeO_3(aq) + 6I^-(aq) + 4H^+(aq)$$
$$\longrightarrow Se(s) + 2I_3^-(aq) + 3H_2O(l)$$

was studied at 0°C, and the following data were obtained:

$[H_2SeO_3]_0$ (mol/L)	$[H^+]_0$ (mol/L)	$[I^-]_0$ (mol/L)	Initial Rate (mol $L^{-1}\ s^{-1}$)
1.0×10^{-4}	2.0×10^{-2}	2.0×10^{-2}	1.66×10^{-7}
2.0×10^{-4}	2.0×10^{-2}	2.0×10^{-2}	3.33×10^{-7}
3.0×10^{-4}	2.0×10^{-2}	2.0×10^{-2}	4.99×10^{-7}
1.0×10^{-4}	4.0×10^{-2}	2.0×10^{-2}	6.66×10^{-7}
1.0×10^{-4}	1.0×10^{-2}	2.0×10^{-2}	0.42×10^{-7}
1.0×10^{-4}	2.0×10^{-2}	4.0×10^{-2}	13.2×10^{-7}
1.0×10^{-4}	1.0×10^{-2}	4.0×10^{-2}	3.36×10^{-7}

These relationships hold only if there is an insignificant amount of I_3^- present. What is the rate law and the value of the rate constant? $\left(\text{Assume that rate} = -\frac{d[H_2SeO_3]}{dt}.\right)$

24. The initial rate of a reaction doubles as the concentration of one of the reactants is quadrupled. What is the order of this reactant? If a reactant has a -1 order, what happens to the initial rate when the concentration of that reactant increases by a factor of two?

25. A study was made of the effect of the hydroxide concentration on the rate of the reaction

$$I^-(aq) + OCl^-(aq) \longrightarrow IO^-(aq) + Cl^-(aq)$$

The following data were obtained:

$[I^-]_0$ (mol/L)	$[OCl^-]_0$ (mol/L)	$[OH^-]_0$ (mol/L)	Initial Rate (mol $L^{-1}\ s^{-1}$)
0.0013	0.012	0.10	9.4×10^{-3}
0.0026	0.012	0.10	18.7×10^{-3}
0.0013	0.0060	0.10	4.7×10^{-3}
0.0013	0.018	0.10	14.0×10^{-3}
0.0013	0.012	0.050	18.7×10^{-3}
0.0013	0.012	0.20	4.7×10^{-3}
0.0013	0.018	0.20	7.0×10^{-3}

Determine the rate law and the value of the rate constant for this reaction.

Integrated Rate Laws

26. The initial rate for a reaction is equal to the slope of the tangent line at $t \approx 0$ in a plot of [A] versus time. From calculus,

$$Initial\ rate = \frac{-d[A]}{dt}$$

Therefore, the differential rate law for a reaction is

$$Rate = \frac{-d[A]}{dt} = k[A]^n$$

Assuming you have some calculus in your background, derive the zero-, first-, and second-order integrated rate laws using the differential rate law.

27. If the half-life for a reaction is 20. seconds, what would be the second half-life, assuming the reaction is either zero, first, or second order?

28. A certain reaction has the following general form:

$$aA \longrightarrow bB$$

At a particular temperature and $[A]_0 = 2.80 \times 10^{-3}$ M, concentration versus time data were collected for this reaction, and a plot of $1/[A]$ versus time resulted in a straight line with a slope value of $+3.60 \times 10^{-2}$ L mol^{-1} s^{-1}.
   a. Determine the rate law, the integrated rate law, and the value of the rate constant for this reaction.
   b. Calculate the half-life for this reaction.
   c. How much time is required for the concentration of A to decrease to 7.00×10^{-4} M?

29. A certain reaction has the following general form:

$$aA \longrightarrow bB$$

At a particular temperature and $[A]_0 = 2.00 \times 10^{-2}$ M, concentration versus time data were collected for this reaction, and a plot of $\ln[A]$ versus time resulted in a straight line with a slope value of -2.97×10^{-2} min^{-1}.
   a. Determine the rate law, the integrated rate law, and the value of the rate constant for this reaction.
   b. Calculate the half-life for this reaction.
   c. How much time is required for the concentration of A to decrease to 2.50×10^{-3} M?

30. The decomposition of ethanol (C_2H_5OH) on an alumina (Al_2O_3) surface,

$$C_2H_5OH(g) \longrightarrow C_2H_4(g) + H_2O(g)$$

was studied at 600 K. Concentration versus time data were collected for this reaction, and a plot of $[A]$ versus time resulted in a straight line with a slope value of -4.00×10^{-5} mol L^{-1} s^{-1}.
   a. Determine the rate law, the integrated rate law, and the value of the rate constant for this reaction.
   b. If the initial concentration of C_2H_5OH was 1.25×10^{-2} M, calculate the half-life for this reaction.
   c. How much time is required for all of the 1.25×10^{-2} M C_2H_5OH to decompose?

31. The decomposition of hydrogen peroxide was studied at a particular temperature. The following data were obtained, where

$$Rate = -\frac{d[H_2O_2]}{dt}$$

Time (s)	$[H_2O_2]$ (mol/L)
0	1.00
120 ± 1	0.91
300 ± 1	0.78
600 ± 1	0.59
1200 ± 1	0.37
1800 ± 1	0.22
2400 ± 1	0.13
3000 ± 1	0.082
3600 ± 1	0.050

Determine the integrated rate law, the differential rate law, and the value of the rate constant. Calculate the $[H_2O_2]$ at 4000. s after the start of the reaction.

32. The dimerization of butadiene was studied at 500. K:

$$2C_4H_6(g) \longrightarrow C_8H_{12}(g)$$

The following data were obtained, where

$$Rate = -\frac{d[C_4H_6]}{dt}$$

Time (s)	$[C_4H_6]$ (mol/L)
195	1.6×10^{-2}
604	1.5×10^{-2}
1246	1.3×10^{-2}
2180	1.1×10^{-2}
6210	0.68×10^{-2}

Determine the forms of the integrated rate law, the differential rate law, and the value of the rate constant for this reaction.

33. The rate of the reaction

$$NO_2(g) + CO(g) \longrightarrow NO(g) + CO_2(g)$$

depends only on the concentration of nitrogen dioxide at temperatures below 225°C. At a temperature below 225°C, the following data were collected:

Time (s)	$[NO_2]$ (mol/L)
0	0.500
1.20×10^3	0.444
3.00×10^3	0.381
4.50×10^3	0.340
9.00×10^3	0.250
1.80×10^4	0.174

Determine the integrated rate law, the differential rate law, and the value of the rate constant at this temperature. Calculate $[NO_2]$ at 2.70×10^4 s after the start of the reaction.

34. The rate of the reaction

$$O(g) + NO_2(g) \longrightarrow NO(g) + O_2(g)$$

was studied at a certain temperature. This reaction is one step of the nitric oxide–catalyzed destruction of ozone in the upper atmosphere.
   a. In one experiment, NO_2 was in large excess at a concentration of 1.0×10^{13} molecules/cm^3 with the following data collected:

Time (s)	$[O]$ (atoms/cm^3)
0	5.0×10^9
1.0×10^{-2}	1.9×10^9
2.0×10^{-2}	6.8×10^8
3.0×10^{-2}	2.5×10^8

What is the order of the reaction with respect to oxygen atoms?

b. The reaction is known to be first order with respect to NO_2. Determine the overall rate law and the value of the rate constant.

35. At 500 K in the presence of a copper surface, ethanol decomposes according to the equation

$$C_2H_5OH(g) \longrightarrow CH_3CHO(g) + H_2(g)$$

The pressure of C_2H_5OH was measured as a function of time, and the following data were obtained:

Time (s)	$P_{C_2H_5OH}$ (torr)
0	250.
100.	237
200.	224
300.	211
400.	198
500.	185

Since the pressure of a gas is directly proportional to the concentration of the gas, we can express the rate law for a gaseous reaction in terms of partial pressures. Using the preceding data, deduce the rate law, the integrated rate law, and the value of the rate constant, all in terms of pressure units in atm and time in seconds. Predict the pressure of C_2H_5OH after 900. s from the start of the reaction. (*Hint:* To determine the order of the reaction with respect to C_2H_5OH, compare how the pressure of C_2H_5OH decreases with each time listing.)

36. Experimental data for the reaction

$$A \longrightarrow 2B + C$$

have been plotted in the following three different ways (with concentration units in mol/L):

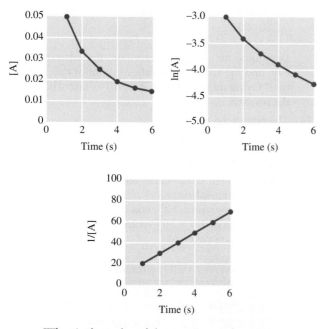

a. What is the order of the reaction with respect to A, and what is the initial concentration of A?
b. What is the concentration of A after 9 s?
c. What are the first three half-lives for this experiment?

37. The reaction

$$NO(g) + O_3(g) \longrightarrow NO_2(g) + O_2(g)$$

was studied by performing two experiments. In the first experiment (results shown in following table), the rate of disappearance of NO was followed in a large excess of O_3. (The $[O_3]$ remains effectively constant at 1.0×10^{14} molecules/cm³.)

Time (ms)	[NO] (molecules/cm³)
0	6.0×10^8
100 ± 1	5.0×10^8
500 ± 1	2.4×10^8
700 ± 1	1.7×10^8
1000 ± 1	9.9×10^7

In the second experiment, [NO] was held constant at 2.0×10^{14} molecules/cm³. The data for the disappearance of O_3 were as follows:

Time (ms)	$[O_3]$ (molecules/cm³)
0	1.0×10^{10}
50 ± 1	8.4×10^9
100 ± 1	7.0×10^9
200 ± 1	4.9×10^9
300 ± 1	3.4×10^9

a. What is the order with respect to each reactant?
b. What is the overall rate law?
c. What is the value of the rate constant obtained from each set of experiments?

$$\text{Rate} = k'[NO]^x \qquad \text{Rate} = k''[O_3]^y$$

d. What is the value of the rate constant for the overall rate law?

$$\text{Rate} = k[NO]^x[O_3]^y$$

38. Determine the forms of the integrated and the differential rate laws for the decomposition of benzene diazonium chloride,

$$C_6H_5N_2Cl(aq) \longrightarrow C_6H_5Cl(l) + N_2(g)$$

from the following data, which were collected at 50.°C and 1.00 atm:

Time (s)	N_2 Evolved (mL)
6	19.3
9	26.0
14	36.0
22	45.0
30.	50.4
∞	58.3

The total solution volume was 40.0 mL.

39. You and a coworker have developed a molecule that has shown potential as cobra antivenom (AV). This antivenom

works by binding to the venom (V), thereby rendering it nontoxic. This reaction can be desrcibed by the rate law

$$\text{Rate} = k[AV]^1[V]^1$$

You have been given the following data from your coworker:

$$[V]_0 = 0.20 \ M$$

$$[AV]_0 = 1.0 \times 10^{-4} \ M$$

A plot of ln[AV] versus time gives a straight line with a slope of $-0.32 \ s^{-1}$. What is the value of the rate constant (k) for this reaction?

40. Consider the following representation of the reaction $2NO_2(g) \rightarrow 2NO(g) + O_2(g)$.

(a) time = 0 minutes   (b) time = 10 minutes   (c) time = ? minutes

Time

Determine the time for the final representation above if the reaction is
a. first order
b. second order
c. zero order

41. The rate law for the decomposition of phosphine (PH_3) is

$$\text{Rate} = -\frac{d[PH_3]}{dt} = k[PH_3]$$

It takes 120. s for the concentration of 1.00 M PH_3 to decrease to 0.250 M. How much time is required for 2.00 M PH_3 to decrease to a concentration of 0.350 M?

42. The radioactive isotope ^{32}P decays by first-order kinetics and has a half-life of 14.3 days. How long does it take for 95.0% of a given sample of ^{32}P to decay?

43. Consider the following initial rate data for the decomposition of compound AB to give A and B:

$[AB]_0$ (mol/L)	Initial Rate (mol L^{-1} s^{-1})
0.200	3.20×10^{-3}
0.400	1.28×10^{-2}
0.600	2.88×10^{-2}

Determine the half-life for the decomposition reaction initially having 1.00 M AB present.

44. The rate law for the reaction

$$2NOBr(g) \longrightarrow 2NO(g) + Br_2(g)$$

at some temperature is

$$\text{Rate} = -\frac{d[NOBr]}{dt} = k[NOBr]^2$$

a. If the half-life for this reaction is 2.00 s when $[NOBr]_0 = 0.900 \ M$, calculate the value of k for this reaction.
b. How much time is required for the concentration of NOBr to decrease to 0.100 M?

45. A first-order reaction is 75.0% complete in 320. s.
a. What are the first and second half-lives for this reaction?
b. How long does it take for 90.0% completion?

46. For the reaction A $\rightarrow$ products, successive half-lives are observed to be 10.0, 20.0, and 40.0 min for an experiment in which $[A]_0 = 0.10 \ M$. Calculate the concentration of A at the following times.
a. 80.0 min   b. 30.0 min

47. The decomposition of hydrogen iodide on finely divided gold at 150°C is zero order with respect to HI. The rate defined below is constant at 1.20×10^{-4} mol/L · s.

$$2HI(g) \xrightarrow{\text{Au}} H_2(g) + I_2(g)$$

$$\text{Rate} = -\frac{d[HI]}{dt} = k = 1.20 \times 10^{-4} \ \text{mol/L} \cdot s$$

a. If the initial HI concentration was 0.250 mol/L, calculate the concentration of HI at 25 minutes after the start of the reaction.
b. How long will it take for all of the 0.250 M HI to decompose?

48. Consider two reaction vessels, one containing A and the other containing B, with equal concentrations at $t = 0$. If both substances decompose by first-order kinectics, where

$$k_A = 4.50 \times 10^{-4} \ s^{-1}$$

$$k_B = 3.70 \times 10^{-3} \ s^{-1}$$

how much time must pass to reach a condition such that $[A] = 4.00[B]$?

49. Theophylline is a phamaceutical drug that is sometimes used to help with lung function. You observe a case where the initial lab results indicate that the concentration of theophylline in a patient's body decreased from 2.0×10^{-3} M to 1.0×10^{-3} M in 24 hours. In another 12 hours, the drug concentration was found to be 5.0×10^{-4} M. What is the value of the rate constant for the metabolism of this drug in the body?

50. Consider the hypothetical reaction

$$A + B + 2C \longrightarrow 2D + 3E$$

where the rate law is

$$\text{Rate} = -\frac{d[A]}{dt} = k[A][B]^2$$

An experiment is carried out where $[A]_0 = 1.0 \times 10^{-2}$ M, $[B]_0 = 3.0$ M, and $[C]_0 = 2.0$ M. The reaction is started, and after 8.0 seconds, the concentration of A is 3.8×10^{-3} M.

a. Calculate the value of k for this reaction.
b. Calculate the half-life for this experiment.
c. Calculate the concentration of A after 13.0 seconds.
d. Calculate the concentration of C after 13.0 seconds.

51. Consider the reaction

$$3A + B + C \longrightarrow D + E$$

where the rate law is defined as

$$-\frac{d[A]}{dt} = k[A]^2[B][C]$$

An experiment is carried out where $[B]_0 = [C]_0 = 1.00$ M and $[A]_0 = 1.00 \times 10^{-4}$ M.

a. If after 3.00 minutes $[A] = 3.26 \times 10^{-5}$ M, calculate the value of k.
b. Calculate the half-life for this experiment.
c. Calculate the concentration of B and the concentration of A after 10.0 minutes.

Reaction Mechanisms

52. Define each of the following.
a. elementary step
b. molecularity
c. reaction mechanism
d. intermediate
e. rate-determining step

53. Define what is meant by unimolecular and bimolecular steps. Why are termolecular steps infrequently seen in chemical reactions?

54. What two requirements must be met to call a mechanism plausible? Why say a "plausible" mechanism instead of the "correct" mechanism? Is it true that most reactions occur by a one-step mechanism? Explain.

55. Write the rate laws for the following elementary reactions.
a. $CH_3NC(g) \longrightarrow CH_3CN(g)$
b. $O_3(g) + NO(g) \longrightarrow O_2(g) + NO_2(g)$
c. $O_3(g) \longrightarrow O_2(g) + O(g)$

d. $O_3(g) + O(g) \longrightarrow 2O_2(g)$
e. $^{14}_{6}C \longrightarrow ^{14}_{7}N + \beta$ particle (nuclear decay)

56. A possible mechanism for the decomposition of hydrogen peroxide is

$$H_2O_2 \longrightarrow 2OH$$

$$H_2O_2 + OH \longrightarrow H_2O + HO_2$$

$$HO_2 + OH \longrightarrow H_2O + O_2$$

Using your results fom Exercise 31, specify which step is the rate-determining step. What is the overall balanced equation for the reaction?

57. A proposed mechanism for a reaction is

$$C_4H_9Br \longrightarrow C_4H_9^+ + Br^- \qquad \text{Slow}$$

$$C_4H_9^+ + H_2O \longrightarrow C_4H_9OH_2^+ \qquad \text{Fast}$$

$$C_4H_9OH_2^+ + H_2O \longrightarrow C_4H_9OH + H_3O^+ \qquad \text{Fast}$$

Write the rate law expected for this mechanism. What is the overall balanced equation for the reaction? What are the intermediates in the proposed mechanism?

58. Is the mechanism

$$NO + Cl_2 \xrightarrow{k_1} NOCl_2$$

$$NOCl_2 + NO \xrightarrow{k_2} 2NOCl$$

consistent with the results you obtained in Exercise 17? If so, which step is the rate-determining step?

59. The reaction

$$2NO(g) + O_2(g) \longrightarrow 2NO_2(g)$$

exhibits the rate law

$$\text{Rate} = k[NO]^2[O_2]$$

Which of the following mechanisms is consistent with this rate law?
a. $NO + O_2 \longrightarrow NO_2 + O$ Slow
   $O + NO \longrightarrow NO_2$ Fast
b. $NO + O_2 \rightleftharpoons NO_3$ Fast equilibrium
   $NO_3 + NO \longrightarrow 2NO_2$ Slow
c. $2NO \longrightarrow N_2O_2$ Slow
   $N_2O_2 + O_2 \longrightarrow N_2O_4$ Fast
   $N_2O_4 \longrightarrow 2NO_2$ Fast
d. $2NO \rightleftharpoons N_2O_2$ Fast equilibrium
   $N_2O_2 \longrightarrow NO_2 + O$ Slow
   $O + NO \longrightarrow NO_2$ Fast

60. The gas-phase reaction between Br_2 and H_2 to form HBr is assumed to proceed by the following mechanism:

$$Br_2 \underset{k_{-1}}{\overset{k_1}{\rightleftharpoons}} 2Br$$

$$Br + H_2 \underset{k_{-2}}{\overset{k_2}{\rightleftharpoons}} HBr + H$$

$$H + Br_2 \xrightarrow{k_3} HBr + Br$$

$$2Br \xrightarrow{k_4} Br_2$$

a. Under what conditions does the rate law have the form rate $= k'[Br_2]$?

b. Under what conditions does the rate law have the form rate $= k''[H_2][Br_2]^{1/2}$?

c. Give expressions for k' and k'' in terms of the rate constants used to define the mechanism.

61. The reaction

$$5Br^-(aq) + BrO_3^-(aq) + 6H^+(aq) \longrightarrow 3Br_2(l) + 3H_2O(l)$$

is expected to obey the mechanism

$$BrO_3^-(aq) + H^+(aq) \underset{k_{-1}}{\overset{k_1}{\rightleftharpoons}} HBrO_3(aq)$$
Fast equilibrium

$$HBrO_3(aq) + H^+(aq) \underset{k_{-2}}{\overset{k_2}{\rightleftharpoons}} H_2BrO_3^+(aq)$$
Fast equilibrium

$$Br^-(aq) + H_2BrO_3^+(aq) \overset{k_3}{\longrightarrow} (Br\!-\!BrO_2)(aq) + H_2O(l)$$
Slow

$$(Br\!-\!BrO_2)(aq) + 4H^+(aq) + 4Br^-(aq) \longrightarrow \text{products}$$
Fast

Write the rate law for this reaction.

62. The rate law for the reaction

$$BrO_3^-(aq) + 3SO_3^{2-}(aq) \longrightarrow Br^-(aq) + 3SO_4^{2-}(aq)$$

is $\text{Rate} = k[BrO_3^-][SO_3^{2-}][H^+]$

The first step in a proposed mechanism is

$$SO_3^{2-}(aq) + H^+(aq) \overset{k_1}{\longrightarrow} HSO_3^-(aq) \quad \text{Fast}$$

The second step is rate determining. Write a possible second step for the mechanism.

63. The reaction

$$I^-(aq) + OCl^-(aq) \longrightarrow IO^-(aq) + Cl^-(aq)$$

is believed to occur by the following mechanism:

$$OCl^- + H_2O \underset{k_{-1}}{\overset{k_1}{\rightleftharpoons}} HOCl + OH^- \quad \text{Fast equilibrium}$$

$$I^- + HOCl \overset{k_2}{\longrightarrow} HOI + Cl^- \quad \text{Slow}$$

$$HOI + OH^- \overset{k_1}{\longrightarrow} H_2O + IO^- \quad \text{Fast}$$

Write the rate law for this reaction. *Note:* Since the reaction is in aqueous solution, the effective concentration of water remains constant. Thus the rate of the forward reaction in the first step can be written as

$$\text{Rate} = k[H_2O][OCl^-] = k_1[OCl^-]$$

64. In the gas phase, the production of phosgene from chlorine and carbon monoxide is assumed to proceed by the following mechanism:

$$Cl_2 \underset{k_{-1}}{\overset{k_1}{\rightleftharpoons}} 2Cl \quad \text{Fast equilibrium}$$

$$Cl + CO \underset{k_{-2}}{\overset{k_2}{\rightleftharpoons}} COCl \quad \text{Fast equilibrium}$$

$$COCl + Cl_2 \overset{k_3}{\longrightarrow} COCl_2 + Cl \quad \text{Slow}$$

$$2Cl \overset{k_4}{\longrightarrow} Cl_2 \quad \text{Fast}$$

Overall
reaction: $CO + Cl_2 \longrightarrow COCl_2$

a. Write the rate law for this reaction.

b. Which species are intermediates?

65. The following mechanism is proposed for the reduction of NO_3^- by $MoCl_6^{2-}$:

$$MoCl_6^{2-} \underset{k_{-1}}{\overset{k_1}{\rightleftharpoons}} MoCl_5^- + Cl^-$$

$$NO_3^- + MoCl_5^- \overset{k_2}{\longrightarrow} OMoCl_5^- + NO_2^-$$

a. What is the intermediate?

b. Derive an expression for the rate law (rate $= d[NO_2^-]/dt$) for the overall reaction using the steady-state approximation.

66. The following mechanism has been proposed to account for the rate law of the decomposition of ozone to $O_2(g)$:

$$O_3 + M \underset{k_{-1}}{\overset{k_1}{\rightleftharpoons}} O_2 + O + M$$

$$O + O_3 \overset{k_2}{\longrightarrow} 2O_2$$

Apply the steady-state hypothesis to the concentration of atomic oxygen, and derive the rate law for the decomposition of ozone. (M stands for an atom or molecule that can exchange kinetic energy with the particles undergoing the chemical reaction.)

67. Consider the hypothetical reaction

$$B \longrightarrow E + F$$

which is assumed to occur by the mechanism

$$B + B \underset{k_{-1}}{\overset{k_1}{\rightleftharpoons}} B^* + B$$

$$B^* \overset{k_2}{\longrightarrow} E + F$$

where B^* represents a B molecule with enough energy to surmount the reaction energy barrier.

a. Derive the rate law for the production of E using the steady-state approximation.

b. Assume that this reaction is known to be first order. Under what conditions does your derived rate law (from part a) agree with this observation?

c. Explain how a chemical reaction can be first order, since even in a simple case ($B \longrightarrow E + F$) molecules must collide to build up enough energy to get over the energy barrier. Why aren't all reactions at least second order? In other words, explain the physical significance of the result from part b.

Temperature Dependence of Rate Constants and the Collision Model

68. How is the rate of a reaction affected by each of the following.
a. activation energy
b. temperature
c. frequency of collisions
d. orientation of collisions

69. The central idea of the collision model is that molecules must collide in order to react. Give two reasons why not all collisions of reactant molecules result in product formation.

70. Consider the following potential energy plots

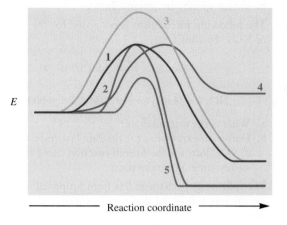

E

Reaction coordinate

a. Rank the reactions from fastest to slowest, and explain your answer. If any reactions have equal rates, explain why.
b. Label the reactions as endothermic or exothermic, and supply your answer.
c. Rank the exothermic reactions from greatest to least change in potential energy, and support your answer.

71. The graph below shows the number of collisions with a particular energy for two different temperatures.

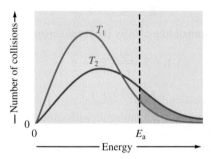

Number of collisions →

T_1

T_2

E_a

Energy →

a. Which is greater, T_2 or T_1? How can you tell?
b. What does this graph tell us about the temperature dependence of the rate of a chemical reaction? Explain your answer.

72. Which of the following reactions would you expect to have the larger rate at room temperature? Why? (*Hint:* Think of which would have the lower activation energy.)

$$2Ce^{4+}(aq) + Hg_2^{2+}(aq) \longrightarrow 2Ce^{3+}(aq) + 2Hg^{2+}(aq)$$

$$H_3O^+(aq) + OH^-(aq) \longrightarrow 2H_2O(l)$$

73. The activation energy for the decomposition of $HI(g)$ to $H_2(g)$ and $I_2(g)$ is 186 kJ/mol. The rate constant at 555 K is 3.52×10^{-7} L mol^{-1} s^{-1}. What is the rate constant at 645 K?

74. The decomposition of iodoethane in the gas phase proceeds according to the following equation:

$$C_2H_5I(g) \longrightarrow C_2H_4(g) + HI(g)$$

At 660. K, $k = 7.2 \times 10^{-4}$ s^{-1}; at 720. K, $k = 1.7 \times 10^{-2}$ s^{-1}. What is the rate constant for this first-order

decomposition at 325°C? If the initial pressure of iodoethane is 894 torr at 245°C, what is the pressure of iodoethane after three half-lives?

75. A certain reaction has an activation energy of 54.0 kJ/mol. As the temperature is increased from 22°C to a higher temperature, the rate constant increases by a factor of 7.00. Calculate the higher temperature.

76. Chemists commonly use a rule of thumb that an increase of 10 K in temperature doubles the rate of a reaction. What must the activation energy be for this statement to be true for a temperature increase from 25°C to 35°C?

77. The reaction

$$(CH_3)_3CBr + OH^- \longrightarrow (CH_3)_3COH + Br^-$$

in a certain solvent is first order with respect to $(CH_3)_3CBr$ and zero order with respect to OH^-. In several experiments the rate constant k was determined at different temperatures. A plot of $\ln(k)$ versus $1/T$ was constructed that resulted in a straight line with a slope of -1.10×10^4 K and a y intercept of 33.5. Assume that k has units of s^{-1}.
a. Determine the activation energy for this reaction.
b. Determine the value of the frequency factor A.
c. Calculate the value of k at 25°C.

78. The rate constant for the gas-phase decomposition of N_2O_5,

$$N_2O_5 \longrightarrow 2NO_2 + \tfrac{1}{2}O_2$$

has the following temperature dependence:

T (K)	k (s^{-1})
338	4.9×10^{-3}
318	5.0×10^{-4}
298	3.5×10^{-5}

Make the appropriate graph using these data, and determine the activation energy for this reaction.

79. Experimental values for the temperature dependence of the rate constant for the gas-phase reaction

$$NO(g) + O_3(g) \longrightarrow NO_2(g) + O_2(g)$$

are as follows:

T (K)	k (L mol^{-1} s^{-1})
195	1.08×10^9
230.	2.95×10^9
260.	5.42×10^9
298	12.0×10^9
369	35.5×10^9

Make the appropriate graph using these data, and determine the activation energy for this reaction.

80. Draw a rough sketch of the energy profile for each of the following cases.
a. $\Delta E = +10$ kJ/mol, $E_a = 25$ kJ/mol
b. $\Delta E = -10$ kJ/mol, $E_a = 50$ kJ/mol
c. $\Delta E = -50$ kJ/mol, $E_a = 50$ kJ/mol

Which reaction will have the greatest rate at 298 K? Assume the frequency factor A is the same for all three reactions.

81. For the following reaction profiles, indicate
   a. the positions of reactants and products.
   b. the activation energy.
   c. ΔE for the reaction.

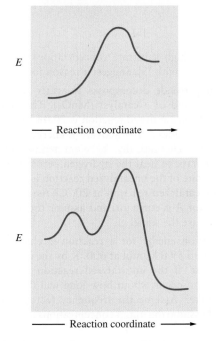

   ─── Reaction coordinate ──→

   ─── Reaction coordinate ──→

   d. The second reaction profile is representative of a reaction that occurs by a two-step mechanism. Which point on the plot represents the energy of the intermediate in the two-step reaction? Which step in the mechanism is rate determining, the first or the second step? Explain.

82. The activation energy for the reaction

$$NO_2(g) + CO(g) \longrightarrow NO(g) + CO_2(g)$$

   is 125 kJ/mol, and ΔE for the reaction is -216 kJ/mol. What is the activation energy for the reverse reaction $[NO(g) + CO_2(g) \longrightarrow NO_2(g) + CO(g)]$?

83. The activation energy for the reaction

$$A_2(g) + B_2(g) \longrightarrow 2AB(g)$$

   is 167 kJ/mol, and ΔE for the reaction is $+28$ kJ/mol. What is the activation energy for the decomposition of AB?

Catalysis

84. Why does a catalyst increase the rate of a reaction? What is the difference between a homogeneous and a heterogeneous catalyst? Would a given reaction necessarily have the same rate law for both a catalyzed and an uncatalyzed pathway? Explain.

85. Consider the following potential energy plots for a chemical reaction when answering the questions below.

   a. Which plot (red or blue) is the catalyzed pathway? How do you know?
   b. What does ΔE_1 represent?
   c. What does ΔE_2 represent?
   d. Is the reaction endothermic or exothermic?

86. Would the slope of a $\ln(k)$ versus $1/T$ (K) plot for a catalyzed reaction be more or less negative than the slope of a $\ln(k)$ versus $1/T$ (K) plot for the uncatalyzed reaction? Assume that both rate laws are first order. Explain.

87. The decomposition of NH_3 to N_2 and H_2 was studied on two surfaces:

Surface	E_a (kJ/mol)
W	163
Os	197

   Without a catalyst, the activation energy is 335 kJ/mol.
   a. Which surface is the better heterogeneous catalyst for the decomposition of NH_3? Why?
   b. How many times faster is the reaction at 298 K on the W surface compared with the reaction with no catalyst present? Assume that the frequency factor A is the same for each reaction.
   c. The decomposition reaction on the two surfaces obeys a rate law of the form

$$\text{Rate} = k\frac{[NH_3]}{[H_2]}$$

   How can you explain the inverse dependence of the rate on the H_2 concentration?

88. One pathway for the destruction of ozone in the upper atmosphere is

$$O_3(g) + NO(g) \longrightarrow NO_2(g) + O_2(g) \qquad \text{Slow}$$
$$NO_2(g) + O(g) \longrightarrow NO(g) + O_2(g) \qquad \text{Fast}$$

   Overall reaction: $O_3(g) + O(g) \longrightarrow 2O_2(g)$

   a. Which species is a catalyst?
   b. Which species is an intermediate?
   c. E_a for the uncatalyzed reaction

$$O_3(g) + O(g) \longrightarrow 2O_2(g)$$

is 14.0 kJ. E_a for the same reaction when catalyzed is 11.9 kJ. What is the ratio of the rate constant for the catalyzed reaction to that for the uncatalyzed reaction at 25°C? Assume the frequency factor A is the same for each reaction.

89. One of the concerns about the use of Freons is that they will migrate to the upper atmosphere, where chlorine atoms can be generated by the reaction

$$CCl_2F_2 \xrightarrow{h\nu} CF_2Cl + Cl$$

Freon-12

Chlorine atoms can also act as a catalyst for the destruction of ozone. The activation energy for the reaction

$$Cl + O_3 \longrightarrow ClO + O_2$$

is 2.1 kJ/mol. Which is the more effective catalyst for the destruction of ozone, Cl or NO? (See Exercise 88.)

90. Assuming that the mechanism for the hydrogenation of C_2H_4 given in Section 15.9 is correct, would you predict that the product of the reaction of C_2H_4 with D_2 would be CH_2D—CH_2D or CHD_2—CH_3?

91. For enzyme-catalyzed reactions that follow the mechanism

$$E + S \rightleftharpoons E \cdot S$$

$$E \cdot S \rightleftharpoons E + P$$

a graph of the rate as a function of [S], the concentration of the substrate, has the following general appearance:

[S]

Note that at high substrate concentrations the rate no longer changes with [S]. Suggest a reason for this.

92. Hydrogen peroxide decomposes to water and oxygen gas with the aid of a catalyst (MnO_2). The activation energy of the uncatalyzed reaction is 70.0 kJ/mol. When the catalyst is added, the activation energy at 20.°C is 42.0 kJ/mol. Theoretically, to what temperature (°C) would one have to heat the hydrogen peroxide solution so that the rate of the uncatalyzed reaction is equal to the rate of the catalyzed reaction at 20.°C? Assume the frequency factor A is constant, and assume the initial concentrations are the same.

93. The activation energy for a reaction is changed from 184 kJ/mol to 59.0 kJ/mol at 600. K by the introduction of a catalyst. If the uncatalyzed reaction takes about 2400 years to occur, about how long will the catalyzed reaction take? Assume the frequency factor A is constant, and assume the initial concentrations are the same.

Additional Exercises

94. The rate law for a reaction can be determined only from experiment and not from the balanced equation. Two experimental procedures were outlined in this chapter. What are these two procedures? Explain how each method is used to determine rate laws.

95. The type of rate law for a reaction, either the differential rate law or the integrated rate law, is usually determined by which data are easiest to collect. Explain.

96. a. Using the free energy profile for a simple one-step reaction, show that at equilibrium $K = k_f/k_r$, where k_f and k_r are the rate constants for the forward and reverse reactions. *Hint:* Use the relationship $\Delta G° = -RT \ln(K)$, and represent k_f and k_r using the Arrhenius equation ($k = Ae^{-E_a/RT}$).

b. Why is the following statement false? "A catalyst can increase the rate of a forward reaction but not the rate of the reverse reaction."

97. Iodomethane (CH_3I) is a commonly used reagent in organic chemistry. When used properly, this reagent allows chemists to introduce methyl groups in many different, useful applications. The chemical does pose a risk as a carcinogen, possibly owing to iodomethane's ability to react with portions of the DNA strand (if they were to come in contact). Consider the following hypothetical initial rates data:

$[DNA]_0$ (μmol/L)	$[CH_3I]_0$ (μmol/L)	Initial Rate (μmol L^{-1} s^{-1})
0.100	0.100	3.20×10^{-4}
0.100	0.200	6.40×10^{-4}
0.200	0.200	1.28×10^{-3}

Which of the following could be a possible mechanism to explain the initial rate data?

Mechanism I DNA + $CH_3I \longrightarrow$ DNA—$CH_3^+ + I^-$

Mechanism II $CH_3I \longrightarrow CH_3^+ + I^-$ Slow

                    DNA + $CH_3^+ \longrightarrow$ DNA—CH_3^+ Fast

98. Two isomers (A and B) of a given compound dimerize as follows:

$$2A \xrightarrow{k_1} A_2$$

$$2B \xrightarrow{k_2} B_2$$

Both processes are known to be second order in the reactant, and k_1 is known to be 0.250 L mol^{-1} s^{-1} at 25°C. In a particular experiment A, and B were placed in separate containers at 25°C, where $[A]_0 = 1.00 \times 10^{-2}$ M and $[B]_0 = 2.50 \times 10^{-2}$ M. After each reaction had progressed for 3.00 min, $[A] = 3.00[B]$. In this case the rate laws are defined as follows:

$$\text{Rate} = -\frac{d[A]}{dt} = k_1[A]^2$$

$$\text{Rate} = -\frac{d[B]}{dt} = k_2[B]^2$$

a. Calculate the concentration of A_2 after 3.00 min.
b. Calculate the value of k_2.
c. Calculate the half-life for the experiment involving A.

99. The thermal degradation of silk was studied by Kuruppillai, Hersh, and Tucker ("Historic Textile and Paper Materials," *ACS Advances in Chemistry Series*, No. 212, 1986) by measuring the tensile strength of silk fibers at various times of exposure to elevated temperature. The loss of tensile strength follows first-order kinetics,

$$-\frac{ds}{dt} = ks$$

where s is the strength of the fiber retained after heating and k is the first-order rate constant. The effects of adding a deacidifying agent and an antioxidant to the silk were studied, and the following data were obtained:

Heating Time (days)	Strength Retained (%)		
	Untreated	Deacidifying Agent	Antioxidant
0.00	100.0	100.1	114.6
1.00	67.9	60.8	65.2
2.00	38.9	26.8	28.1
3.00	16.1	—	11.3
6.00	6.8	—	—

a. Determine the first-order rate constants for the thermal degradation of silk for each of the three experiments.
b. Does either of the two additives appear to retard the degradation of silk?
c. Calculate the half-life for the thermal degradation of silk for each of the three experiments.

100. Sulfuryl chloride (SO_2Cl_2) decomposes to sulfur dioxide (SO_2) and chlorine (Cl_2) by reaction in the gas phase. The following data were obtained when a sample containing 5.00×10^{-2} mole of sulfuryl chloride was heated to 600 K ± 1 K in a 5.00×10^{-1} L container.

Time (h)	0.00	1.00	2.00	4.00	8.00	16.00
Pressure (atm)	4.93	5.60	6.34	7.33	8.56	9.52

Define the rate as $-d[SO_2Cl_2]/dt$.
a. Determine the value of the rate constant for the decomposition of sulfuryl chloride at 600 K.
b. What is the half-life of the reaction?
c. What would be the pressure in the vessel after 0.500 h and after 12.0 h?
d. What fraction of the sulfuryl chloride remains after 20.0 h?

101. One reason suggested for the instability of long chains of silicon atoms is that the decomposition involves the following transition state:

The activation energy for such a process is 210 kJ/mol, which is less than either the Si—Si or the Si—H bond energy. Why would a similar mechanism not be expected to play a very important role in the decomposition of long chains of carbon atoms as seen in organic compounds?

102. The following results were obtained at 600 K for the decomposition of ethanol on an alumina (Al_2O_3) surface,

$$C_2H_5OH(g) \longrightarrow C_2H_4(g) + H_2O(g)$$

t (s)	P_{Total} (torr)
0	250.
10.	265
20.	280.
30.	295
40.	310.
50.	325

a. Predict P_{Total} in torr at $t = 80.$ s.
b. What is the value of the rate constant, and what are its units?
c. What is the order of the reaction?
d. Calculate P_{Total} at $t = 300.$ s.

103. At 620. K butadiene dimerizes at a moderate rate. The following data were obtained in an experiment involving this reaction:

t (s)	$[C_4H_6]$ (mol/L)
0	0.01000
1000.	0.00629
2000.	0.00459
3000.	0.00361

a. Determine the order of the reaction in butadiene.
b. In how many seconds is the dimerization 1.0% complete?
c. In how many seconds is the dimerization 2.0% complete?
d. What is the half-life for the reaction if the initial concentration of butadiene is 0.0200 M?
e. Use the results from this problem and Exercise 32 to calculate the activation energy for the dimerization of butadiene.

104. The decomposition of $NO_2(g)$ occurs by the following bimolecular elementary reaction:

$$2NO_2(g) \longrightarrow 2NO(g) + O_2(g)$$

The rate constant at 273 K is 2.3×10^{-12} L mol^{-1} s^{-1}, and the activation energy is 111 kJ/mol. How long will it take for the concentration of $NO_2(g)$ to decrease from an initial partial pressure of 2.5 atm to 1.5 atm at 500. K? Assume ideal gas behavior.

105. The activation energy for a certain uncatalyzed biochemical reaction is 50.0 kJ/mol. In the presence of a catalyst at 37°C, the rate constant for the reaction increases by a factor of 2.50×10^3 as compared with the uncatalyzed reaction. Assuming that the frequency factor A is the same for both the catalyzed and uncatalyzed reactions, calculate the activation energy for the catalyzed reaction.

106. For the reaction

$$2N_2O_5(g) \longrightarrow 4NO_2(g) + O_2(g)$$

the following data were collected, where

$$\text{Rate} = -\frac{d[N_2O_5]}{dt}$$

	$T = 338$ K	$T = 318$ K
t (s)	$[N_2O_5]$	$[N_2O_5]$
0	1.00×10^{-1} M	1.00×10^{-1} M
100.	6.14×10^{-2} M	9.54×10^{-2} M
300.	2.33×10^{-2} M	8.63×10^{-2} M
600.	5.41×10^{-3} M	7.43×10^{-2} M
900.	1.26×10^{-3} M	6.39×10^{-2} M

Calculate E_a for this reaction.

107. Experiments have shown the average frequency of chirping of individual snowy tree crickets (*Oecanthus fultoni*) to be 178 min^{-1} at 25.0°C, 126 min^{-1} at 20.3°C, and 100. min^{-1} at 17.3°C.

a. What is the apparent activation energy of the reaction that controls the chirping?
b. What chirping rate would be expected at 15.0°C?
c. Compare the observed rates and your calculated rate from part b to the rule of thumb that the Fahrenheit temperature is 42 plus 0.80 times the number of chirps in 15 s.

108. Experiments during a recent summer on a number of fireflies (small beetles, *Lampyridae photinus*) showed that the average interval between flashes of individual insects was 16.3 s at 21.0°C and 13.0 s at 27.8°C.

a. What is the apparent activation energy of the reaction that controls the flashing?
b. What would be the average interval between flashes of an individual firefly at 30.0°C?
c. Compare the observed intervals and the one you calculated in part b to the rule of thumb that the Celsius temperature is 54 minus twice the interval between flashes.

109. The compound NO_2Cl is thought to decompose to NO_2 and Cl_2 by the following mechanism:

$$NO_2Cl \underset{k_{-1}}{\overset{k_1}{\rightleftharpoons}} NO_2 + Cl$$

$$NO_2Cl + Cl \overset{k_2}{\longrightarrow} NO_2 + Cl_2$$

Derive the rate law for the production of Cl_2 using the steady-state approximation.

110. Many biochemical reactions are catalyzed by large protein molecules called enzymes. A typical mechanism for the conversion of a biochemical substrate (S) to product (P) catalyzed by an enzyme (E) involves the following steps:

$$E + S \underset{k_{-1}}{\overset{k_1}{\rightleftharpoons}} ES$$

$$ES \overset{k_2}{\longrightarrow} P$$

The rate-determining step is the decomposition of the intermediate enzyme–substrate complex (ES) to products (P). Under these conditions, show that the overall rate of product formation is

$$\text{Rate} = \frac{d[P]}{dt} = \frac{k_1 k_2 [E]_T [S]}{k_{-1} + k_2 + k_1[S]}$$

where $[E]_T$ equals the total enzyme concentration:

$$[E]_T = [E] + [ES]$$

Challenge Problems

111. Consider the following reaction:

$$CH_3X + Y \longrightarrow CH_3Y + X$$

At 25°C the following two experiments were run, yielding the following data:

Experiment 1: [Y]$_0$ = 3.0 M

[CH$_3$X]	Time (h)
7.08×10^{-3} M	1.0
4.52×10^{-3} M	1.5
2.23×10^{-3} M	2.3
4.76×10^{-4} M	4.0
8.44×10^{-5} M	5.7
2.75×10^{-5} M	7.0

Experiment 2: [Y]$_0$ = 4.5 M

[CH$_3$X]	Time (h)
4.50×10^{-3} M	0
1.70×10^{-3} M	1.0
4.19×10^{-4} M	2.5
1.11×10^{-4} M	4.0
2.81×10^{-5} M	5.5

Experiments were also run at 85°C. The value of the rate constant at 85°C was found to be 7.88×10^8 (with the time in units of hours), where [CH$_3$X]$_0$ = 1.0×10^{-2} M and [Y]$_0$ = 3.0 M.
a. Determine the rate law and the value of k for this reaction at 25°C.
b. Determine the half-life at 85°C.
c. Determine E_a for the reaction.
d. Given that the C—X bond energy is known to be about 325 kJ/mol, suggest a mechanism that explains the results in parts a and c.

112. The following data were collected in two studies of the reaction

$$2A + B \longrightarrow C + D$$

where

$$Rate = \frac{-d[A]}{dt}$$

Time (s)	Experiment 1 [A] (M) $\times 10^{-2}$	Experiment 2 [A] (M) $\times 10^{-2}$
0	10.0	10.0
20.	6.67	5.00
40.	5.00	3.33
60.	4.00	2.50
80.	3.33	2.00
100.	2.86	1.67
120.	2.50	1.43

In experiment 1, [B]$_0$ = 5.0 M. In experiment 2, [B]$_0$ = 10.0 M.
a. Why is [B] much greater than [A]?
b. Give the rate law and value for k for this reaction.
c. Which of the following mechanisms could be correct for this reaction? Justify your choice.
   i. A + B $\rightleftharpoons$ E (fast equilibrium)
      E + B $\longrightarrow$ C + D (slow)
   ii. A + B $\rightleftharpoons$ E (fast equilibrium)
      E + A $\longrightarrow$ C + D (slow)
   iii. A + A $\longrightarrow$ E (slow)
      E + B $\longrightarrow$ C + D (fast)

113. Consider a reaction of the type aA → products, in which the rate law is found to be rate = $k[A]^3$ (termolecular reactions are improbable but possible). If the first half-life of the reaction is found to be 40. s, what is the time for the second half-life? *Hint:* Using your calculus knowledge, derive the integrated rate law from the differential rate law for a termolecular reaction:

$$Rate = \frac{-d[A]}{dt} = k[A]^3$$

114. For the reaction

$$2A + B \longrightarrow products$$

a friend proposes the following mechanism:

$$A + B \rightleftharpoons M$$

$$A + M \longrightarrow products$$

a. Assuming that the second step is the rate-determining step and the first step is a fast equilibrium step, determine the rate law. Represent the rate constant in terms of k_1, k_{-1}, and k_2.
b. Using the steady-state approximation, determine the rate law.
c. Under what conditions of [A] and [B] do you get the same rate law in parts a and b?

115. Consider the hypothetical reaction

$$A + B + 2C \longrightarrow 2D + 3E$$

In a study of this reaction, three experiments were run at the same temperature. The rate is defined as $-d[B]/dt$.

Experiment 1:
[A]$_0$ = 2.0 M   [B]$_0$ = 1.0×10^{-3} M   [C]$_0$ = 1.0 M

[B] (mol/L)	Time (s)
2.7×10^{-4}	1.0×10^5
1.6×10^{-4}	2.0×10^5
1.1×10^{-4}	3.0×10^5
8.5×10^{-5}	4.0×10^5
6.9×10^{-5}	5.0×10^5
5.8×10^{-5}	6.0×10^5

Experiment 2:

$[A]_0 = 1.0 \times 10^{-2} M \quad [B]_0 = 3.0 M \quad [C]_0 = 1.0 M$

[A] (mol/L)	Time (s)
8.9×10^{-3}	1.0
7.1×10^{-3}	3.0
5.5×10^{-3}	5.0
3.8×10^{-3}	8.0
2.9×10^{-3}	10.0
2.0×10^{-3}	13.0

Experiment 3:

$[A]_0 = 10.0 M \quad [B]_0 = 5.0 M \quad [C]_0 = 5.0 \times 10^{-1} M$

[C] (mol/L)	Time (s)
0.43	1.0×10^{-2}
0.36	2.0×10^{-2}
0.29	3.0×10^{-2}
0.22	4.0×10^{-2}
0.15	5.0×10^{-2}
0.08	6.0×10^{-2}

Write the rate law for this reaction, and calculate the rate constant.

116. A reaction represented by the equation

$$3O_2(g) \longrightarrow 2O_3(g)$$

was studied at a specific temperature, and the following data were collected:

Time (s)	Total Pressure (atm)
0	1.000
46.89	0.9500
98.82	0.9033
137.9	0.8733
200.0	0.8333
286.9	0.7900
337.9	0.7700
511.3	0.7233

a. Determine the rate law for this reaction.
b. Determine the value of the rate constant (including units).
c. Calculate the time it would take for the total pressure to be 0.7133 atm.

117. The gas-phase decomposition $2N_2O_5 \rightarrow 4NO_2 + O_2$ is first order but not unimolecular. A possible mechanism is

$$M + N_2O_5 \underset{k_{-1}}{\overset{k_1}{\rightleftharpoons}} NO_3 + NO_2 + M$$

$$NO_3 + NO_2 \xrightarrow{k_2} NO + O_2 + NO_2$$

$$NO_3 + NO \xrightarrow{k_3} 2NO_2$$

Apply the steady-state approximation to the concentrations of the intermediates NO_3 and NO, and derive the rate law for the decomposition of N_2O_5.

118. You are studying the kinetics of the reaction $H_2(g) + F_2(g) \rightarrow 2HF(g)$ and you wish to determine a mechanism for the reaction. You run the reaction twice by keeping one reactant at a much higher pressure than the other reactant (this lower-pressure reactant begins at 1.000 atm). Unfortunately, you neglect to record which reactant was at the higher pressure, and you forget it later. Your data for the first experiment are as follows:

Pressure of HF (atm)	Time (min)
0	0
0.300	30.0
0.600	65.8
0.900	110.4
1.200	169.1
1.500	255.9

When you run the second experiment (in which the higher-pressure reactant is run at a much higher pressure), you determine the values of the apparent rate constants to be the same. It also turns out that you find data taken from another person in the lab. This individual found that the reaction proceeds 40.0 times faster at 55°C than at 35°C. You also know, from the energy-level diagram, that there are three steps to the mechanism, and the first step has the highest activation energy. You look up the bond energies of the species involved and they are (in kJ/mol): H—H (432), F—F (154), and H—F (565).

a. Sketch an energy-level diagram (qualitative) that is consistent with the one described.
b. Develop a reasonable mechanism for the reaction. Support your answer and explain the significance of each piece of information.
c. Which reactant was limiting in the experiments?

119. Hydrogen peroxide and the iodide ion react in acidic solution as follows:

$$H_2O_2(aq) + 3I^-(aq) + 2H^+(aq) \longrightarrow I_3^-(aq) + 2H_2O(l)$$

The kinetics of this reaction were studied by following the decay of the concentration of H_2O_2 and constructing plots of $\ln[H_2O_2]$ versus time. All the plots were linear and all solutions had $[H_2O_2]_0 = 8.0 \times 10^{-4}$ mol/L. The slopes of these straight lines depended on the initial concentrations of I^- and H^+. The results follow:

$[I^-]_0$ (mol/L)	$[H^+]_0$ (mol/L)	Slope (min^{-1})
0.1000	0.0400	−0.120
0.3000	0.0400	−0.360
0.4000	0.0400	−0.480
0.0750	0.0200	−0.0760
0.0750	0.0800	−0.118
0.0750	0.1600	−0.174

The rate law for this reaction has the form

$$\text{Rate} = \frac{-d[H_2O_2]}{dt} = (k_1 + k_2[H^+])[I^-]^m[H_2O_2]^n$$

a. Specify the orders of this reaction with respect to $[H_2O_2]$ and $[I^-]$.
b. Calculate the values of the rate constants k_1 and k_2.
c. What reason could there be for the two-term dependence of the rate on $[H^+]$?

Marathon Problem

120. Consider the following hypothetical data collected in two studies of the reaction

$$2A(g) + 2B(g) \longrightarrow C(g) + 2D(g)$$

Time (s)	Experiment 1 [A] (mol/L)	Experiment 2 [A] (mol/L)
0.	1.0×10^{-2}	1.0×10^{-2}
10.	8.4×10^{-3}	5.0×10^{-3}
20.	7.1×10^{-3}	2.5×10^{-3}
30.	?	1.3×10^{-3}
40.	5.0×10^{-3}	6.3×10^{-4}

In experiment 1, [B] = 10.0 M. In experiment 2, [B] = 20.0 M.

$$\text{Rate} = \frac{-d[A]}{dt}$$

a. Use the concentration versus time data to determine the rate law for the reaction.

b. Solve for the rate constant k for the reaction. Include units.

c. Calculate the concentration of A in experiment 1 at $t = 30.$ s.

d. The following three mechanisms are proposed for this reaction:

  i. 2B $\rightleftharpoons$ B$_2$ (Fast equilibrium)
     B$_2$ + A $\longrightarrow$ E + D (Slow)
     E + A $\longrightarrow$ C + D (Fast)
  ii. A + B $\longrightarrow$ D + F (Slow)
      F + B $\longrightarrow$ C + G (Fast)
      G + A $\longrightarrow$ D (Fast)
  iii. A + 2B $\longrightarrow$ E + D (Slow)
       E + A $\longrightarrow$ C + D (Fast)

Choose the best mechanism(s). Include an explanation of which mechanism(s) you exclude and why. If you believe two (or even all three) mechanisms are equally good, explain why.

Liquids and Solids

16

chapter

A flexible statue of a robot made of stainless steel and bronze.

You have only to think about water to appreciate how different the three states of matter are. Flying, swimming, and ice skating are all done in contact with water in its various forms. Clearly, the arrangements of the water molecules must be significantly different in its gas, liquid, and solid forms.

Recall that a gas can be pictured as a substance whose component particles are far apart and are in rapid, random motion, exerting relatively small forces on each other. The kinetic molecular model was constructed to account for the ideal behavior that real gases approach at high temperatures and low pressures.

Solids are obviously very different from gases. Gases have low densities and high compressibilities and completely fill a container. Solids have much greater densities, are compressible only to a very slight extent, and are rigid—a solid maintains its shape irrespective of its container. These properties indicate that the components of a solid are close together and exert large attractive forces on each other.

The properties of liquids lie somewhere between those of solids and those of gases, but not midway between, as can be seen from some of the properties of the three states of water. For example, compare the enthalpy change for the melting of ice at 0°C (the heat of fusion) with that for vaporizing liquid water at 100°C (the heat of vaporization):

$$H_2O(s) \longrightarrow H_2O(l) \qquad \Delta H^\circ_{fus} = 6.02 \text{ kJ/mol}$$

$$H_2O(l) \longrightarrow H_2O(g) \qquad \Delta H^\circ_{vap} = 40.7 \text{ kJ/mol}$$

These values show a much greater change in structure in going from the liquid to the gas than in going from the solid to the liquid. This suggests that there are extensive attractive forces among the molecules in liquid water, similar to but not as strong as those in the solid state.

The relative similarity of the liquid and solid states can also be seen in the densities of the three states of water. As shown in Table 16.1, the densities for liquid and solid water are quite close. Compressibilities can also be used to explore the relationship among water's states. At 25°C the density of liquid water changes from 0.99707 g/cm³ at a pressure of 1 atm to 1.046 g/cm³ at 1065 atm. Given the large change in pressure, this is a very small variation in the density. Ice also shows little variation in density with increased pressure. On the other hand, at 400°C the density of gaseous water changes from 3.26×10^{-4} g/cm³ at 1 atm pressure to 0.157 g/cm³ at 242 atm—a huge variation.

The conclusion is clear. The liquid and solid states show many similarities and are strikingly different from the gaseous state (Fig. 16.1). We must bear this in mind as we develop models for the structures of solids and liquids.

Table 16.1

Densities of the Three States of Water

State	Density (g/cm³)
Solid (0°C, 1 atm)	0.9168
Liquid (25°C, 1 atm)	0.9971
Gas (400°C, 1 atm)	3.26×10^{-4}

Gas   Liquid   Solid

Figure 16.1

Schematic representations of the three states of matter.

16.1 | # Intermolecular Forces

Recall that atoms can form stable units called molecules by sharing electrons. This is called *intramolecular* (within the molecule) bonding. In this chapter we will consider the properties of the **condensed states of matter** (liquids and solids) and the forces that cause the aggregation of the components of a substance to form a liquid or a solid. These forces may involve covalent or ionic bonding, or they may involve weaker interactions usually called **intermolecular forces** (because they occur between, rather than within, molecules).

It is important to recognize that when a substance like water changes from solid to liquid to gas, *the molecules remain intact*. The changes of state are caused by changes in the forces *among* the molecules rather than those *within* the molecules. In ice, as we will see later in this chapter, the molecules are virtually locked in place, although they can vibrate about their positions. If energy is added, the motions of the molecules increase, and they eventually achieve the greater movement and disorder characteristic of liquid water; the ice has melted. As more energy is added, the gaseous state is eventually reached, where the individual molecules are far apart and thus interacting relatively little. However, the gas still consists of water molecules. It would take much more energy to overcome the covalent bonds and decompose the water molecules into their component atoms. This can be seen by comparing the energy needed to vaporize 1 mole of liquid water (40.7 kJ) with that needed to break the O—H bonds in 1 mole of water molecules (934 kJ).

Remember that temperature is a measure of the random motions of the particles in a substance.

Dipole–Dipole Forces

Recall that molecules with polar bonds often behave in an electric field as if they had a center of positive charge and a center of negative charge; that is, they exhibit a dipole moment. Molecules with dipole moments can attract each other electrostatically by lining up so that the positive and negative ends are close to each other, as shown in Fig. 16.2(a). This is called a **dipole–dipole attraction**. In a condensed state such as a liquid, the dipoles find the best compromise between attraction and repulsion, as shown in Fig. 16.2(b).

Dipole–dipole forces are typically only about 1% as strong as covalent or ionic bonds, and they rapidly become weaker as the distance between the dipoles increases. At low pressures in the gas phase, where the molecules are far apart, these forces are relatively unimportant.

Particularly strong dipole–dipole forces are seen among molecules in which hydrogen is bound to a highly electronegative atom, such as nitrogen, oxygen, or fluorine. Two factors account for the strengths of these interactions: the great polarity of the bond and the close approach of the dipoles, allowed by the very small size of the hydrogen atom. Because dipole–dipole attractions of this type are so unusually strong, they are given a special name—**hydrogen bonding**. Figure 16.3 shows hydrogen bonding among water molecules.

Hydrogen bonding has a very important effect on various physical properties. For example, the boiling points for the covalent hydrides of the elements in Groups 4A, 5A, 6A, and 7A are shown in Fig. 16.4. Note that the nonpolar tetrahedral hydrides of Group 4A show a steady increase in boiling point with molar mass (that is, in going down the group), whereas for the other groups the lightest member has an unexpectedly high boiling point. Why? The answer lies in the especially large hydrogen-bonding interactions that exist among the smallest molecules with the most polar X—H bonds. These unusually strong hydrogen-bonding forces are due primarily to two factors. One factor is the relatively large electronegativity values of the lightest elements in each group, which leads to especially polar X—H bonds. The second factor is the small size

(a)

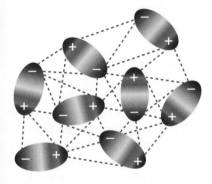

Attraction - - - - - - - - -
Repulsion   - - - - - - - - -

(b)

Figure 16.2

(a) The electrostatic interaction of two polar molecules. (b) The interaction of many dipoles in a condensed state.

Figure 16.3
(a) The polar water molecule. (b) Hydrogen bonding among water molecules. Note that the small size of the hydrogen atom allows for close interactions.

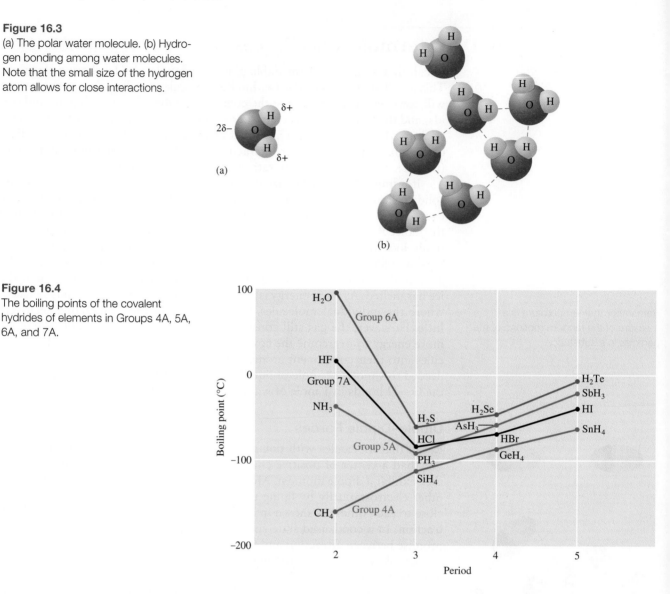

(a)

(b)

Figure 16.4
The boiling points of the covalent hydrides of elements in Groups 4A, 5A, 6A, and 7A.

Boiling point will be defined precisely in Section 16.10.

The dipole–dipole and London dispersion forces are sometimes called van der Waals forces after Johannes van der Waals. See Section 5.10.

of the first element of each group. This allows for the close approach of the dipoles, further strengthening the intermolecular forces. Because the interactions among the molecules containing the lightest elements in Groups 5A, 6A, and 7A are so strong, an unusually large quantity of energy must be supplied to overcome these interactions and separate the molecules to produce the gaseous state—hence the very high boiling points.

London Dispersion Forces

Even molecules without dipole moments must exert forces on each other. We know they do because all substances—even the noble gases—exist in the liquid and solid states under certain conditions. The relatively weak forces that exist among noble gas atoms and nonpolar molecules are called **London dispersion forces.** To understand the origin of these forces, let's consider a pair of noble gas atoms. Although we usually assume that the electrons of an atom are uniformly distributed about the nucleus, this is apparently not true at every instant. Atoms can develop a momentary nonsymmetrical electron distribution that produces a temporary dipolar arrangement of charge. This *instantaneous dipole* can then *induce* a similar dipole in a neighboring atom, as shown in Fig. 16.5(a). This phenomenon leads to an interatomic attraction that is both weak

Figure 16.5

(a) An instantaneous polarization can occur on atom A, creating an instantaneous dipole. This dipole creates an induced dipole on neighboring atom B. (b) Nonpolar molecules such as H_2 can develop instantaneous and induced dipoles.

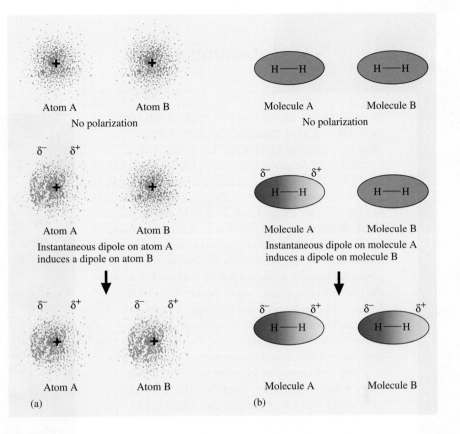

Table 16.2

The Freezing Points of the Group 8A Elements

Element	Freezing Point (°C)
Helium*	−269.7
Neon	−248.6
Argon	−189.4
Krypton	−157.3
Xenon	−111.9

*Helium is the only liquid that does not freeze when the temperature is lowered at 1 atm. It will freeze only if more pressure is applied.

The dispersion forces in molecules with large atoms are quite significant and are often actually more important than dipole–dipole forces.

and short-lived but that can be very significant for large atoms, as we will discuss later. For these interactions to become strong enough to produce a solid, the motions of the atoms must be greatly reduced. This explains, for instance, why the noble gas elements have such low freezing points (Table 16.2).

Note from Table 16.2 that the freezing point rises going down the group. The principal cause for this trend is that as the mass (and the atomic number) increases, the number of electrons increases, so there is an increased chance of the occurrence of momentary dipoles. We say that large atoms with many electrons exhibit a higher *polarizability* than small atoms. Thus the importance of London dispersion forces greatly increases as atomic size increases.

These same ideas also apply to nonpolar molecules such as H_2, CH_4, CCl_4, and CO_2 [Fig. 16.5(b)]. Since none of these molecules has a permanent dipole moment, their principal means of attraction for each other is through London dispersion forces.

16.2 | The Liquid State

Liquids and liquid solutions are vital to our lives. Of course, water is the most important liquid. Besides being essential to life, it provides a medium for food preparation, for transportation, for cooling in many types of machines and industrial processes, for recreation, for cleaning, and for a myriad of other uses.

Liquids exhibit many characteristics that help us to understand their natures. We have already mentioned their low compressibility, lack of rigidity, and high density compared with gases. Many of the properties of liquids give us direct information about the forces that exist among the particles. For example, when a liquid is poured onto a solid surface, it tends to bead as drop-

Chemical Insights   Getting a Grip

Geckos are tiny lizards that can easily climb vertical walls and hang from the ceiling by a single toe. How they accomplish this feat has befuddled humans since Aristotle wrote about it 2300 years ago. The astonishing fact is that a 2-inch gecko can support 90 pounds—the weight of a typical eight- or nine-year-old child. How does it do this?

A recent study suggests that London dispersion forces—typically thought of as very weak interactions—may be responsible for geckos' sticking power. A team of scientists led by Robert J. Full of the University of California at Berkeley and Kellar Autumn at Lewis and Clark College in Portland, Oregon, has studied the sticking force of the tiny "hairs" called *setae* (pronounced "see-tee") on gecko feet. Close examination shows that each seta contains tiny curved pads called spatulae. When a gecko's foot fastens onto a surface, the billion or so spatulae that cover the sole come into close contact with the surface. The scientists' calculations show that the dispersion forces from these billions of interactions can explain the amazing gecko grip. Gecko adhesion also works in a vacuum, which eliminates the possibility that "suction" is involved in the process.

The West Coast team was tipped off to the nature of the adhesion forces by the unusual way in which a gecko walks—by setting its toes down like tongues uncurling and lifting its toes as if peeling up adhesive tape. The downward step seems to both press the setae against the surface and tug them parallel to the surface, ensuring that maximum contact is made. Tests show that the setae hold fast until the angle between them and the surface reaches about 30 degrees. To remove its toes from the surface, the gecko presumably raises the setae beyond the critical angle of 30 degrees.

Figuring out how geckos stick is not just an issue of pure scientific interest but could lead to

The feet and toes of a variety of gecko lizards.

products such as super sticky tape and robots that could climb any surface. The gecko's adhesive system never leaves a residue, never gets dirty, never wears out, and works on any surface. Many useful products can be visualized if scientists can find a way to artificially replicate gecko adhesion. It might even take all of the danger (and fun) out of rock climbing!

lets, a phenomenon that depends on the intermolecular forces. Although molecules in the interior of the liquid are completely surrounded by other molecules, those at the liquid's surface are subject to attractions only from the side and from below (Fig. 16.6). The effect of this uneven pull on the surface molecules tends to draw them into the body of the liquid and causes a droplet of liquid to assume the shape that has the minimum surface area—a sphere.

To increase a liquid's surface area, molecules must move from the interior of the liquid to the surface. This requires energy, since some intermolecular

For a given volume, a sphere has a smaller surface area than any other shape.

Surface

Figure 16.6
A molecule in the interior of a liquid is attracted to the molecules surrounding it, whereas a molecule at the surface of a liquid is attracted only by molecules below it and on each side of it.

The composition of glass is discussed in Section 16.5.

Figure 16.7
(top left) Nonpolar liquid mercury forms a convex meniscus in a glass tube. (top right) Polar water forms a concave meniscus. (bottom) Beads of water on a waxed car finish.

forces must be overcome. The resistance of a liquid to an increase in its surface area is called the **surface tension** of the liquid. As we would expect, liquids with relatively large intermolecular forces tend to have relatively high surface tensions.

Polar liquids also exhibit **capillary action,** the spontaneous rising of a liquid in a narrow tube. Two different types of forces are responsible for this property: *cohesive forces,* the intermolecular forces among the molecules of the liquid, and *adhesive forces,* the forces between the liquid molecules and their container. We have already seen how cohesive forces operate among polar molecules. Adhesive forces between a polar liquid and a given surface are strongest when the surface is made of a substance that has polar bonds. For example, glass contains many oxygen atoms with partial negative charges that are attractive to the positive end of a polar molecule such as water. This ability of water to "wet" glass makes it creep up the walls of the tube where the water surface touches the glass. This, however, tends to increase the surface area of the water, which is opposed by the cohesive forces that try to minimize the surface area. Thus, because water has both strong cohesive (intermolecular) forces and strong adhesive forces to glass, it "pulls itself" up a glass capillary tube (a tube with a small diameter) to a height where the weight of the column of water just balances the water's tendency to be attracted to the glass surface. The concave shape of the meniscus (Fig. 16.7) shows that water's adhesive forces toward the glass are stronger than its cohesive forces. A nonpolar liquid such as mercury shows a convex meniscus in a glass tube. This behavior is characteristic of a liquid in which the cohesive forces are stronger than the adhesive forces toward the glass.

Another property of liquids that is strongly dependent on intermolecular forces is **viscosity,** a measure of a liquid's resistance to flow. As might be expected, liquids with large intermolecular forces tend to be highly viscous. For example, glycerol, whose structure is

$$
\begin{array}{c}
\quad\quad\ \overset{\displaystyle H}{|} \\
H-\overset{|}{C}-O-H \\
H-\overset{|}{C}-O-H \\
H-\overset{|}{C}-O-H \\
\quad\quad\ \overset{|}{H}
\end{array}
$$

has an unusually high viscosity mainly because of its high capacity to form hydrogen bonds.

Molecular complexity also leads to higher viscosity because very large molecules can become entangled with each other. For example, nonviscous gasoline contains molecules of the type $CH_3-(CH_2)_n-CH_3$, where n varies from about 3 to 8. However, grease, which is very viscous, contains much larger molecules in which n varies from 20 to 25.

In many respects the development of a structural model for liquids presents greater challenges than the development of such a model for the other two states of matter. In the gaseous state, the particles are so far apart and are moving so rapidly that intermolecular forces are negligible under most circumstances. This means we can use a relatively simple model for gases. In the solid state, although the intermolecular forces are large, the molecular motions are minimal, and fairly simple models are again possible. The liquid state, however, has both strong intermolecular forces *and* significant molecular motions. Such a situation precludes the use of really simple models for liquids. Recent advances in spectroscopy—the study of the manner in which substances interact with electromagnetic radiation—make it possible to follow the very rapid

Chemical Insights   Smart Fluids

Matter seems to be getting smarter these days. Increasingly, we have discovered materials that can remember their initial shape after being deformed or can sense and respond to their environment. In particular, valuable new materials have been formulated whose properties can be changed instantly by applying a magnetic or electric field.

One example of such a substance is a fluid whose flow characteristics (rheology) can be changed from free flowing to almost solid in about 0.01 second by the application of an electromagnetic field. This magnetorheological (MR) fluid was developed by Lord Corporation. Working in collaboration with Delphi Corporation, the company is applying the fluid in suspension control of General Motors automobiles such as Cadillacs and Corvettes. The so-called Magneride system has sensors that monitor the road surface and provide information about what suspension damping is needed. In response, a message is instantly sent to an electromagnetic coil in the shock absorbers, which adjusts the viscosity of the MR fluid to provide continuously variable damping. The result: an amazingly smooth ride and unerring road-holding ability.

The MR fluid is composed of a synthetic oil in which particles of an iron-containing compound are suspended. When the magnetic field is turned off,

Magnetic field off
Magnetic particles flow randomly

Magnetic field on
Applied field (*H*) creates structure that increases viscosity

these particles flow freely in all directions (see the figure above). When the field is turned on, the particles aggregate into chains that line up perpendicular to the flow of the fluid, thereby increasing its viscosity in proportion to the strength of the applied field.

Many other applications of MR fluids besides auto suspensions are under development. For example, this technology is being used in a prosthesis (see below) for above-the-knee amputees, which gives them a more natural gait and improves stair climbing. One very large-scale application is in Japan's National Museum of Emerging Science and Innovation, where an MR fluid is being used in dampers to protect the building against earthquake damage. Large MR fluid dampers are also being used for stabilizing bridges such as the Dong Ting Lake Bridge in China's Hunan province to steady it in high winds.

Photos Courtesy, Lord Corporation

This High Intelligence Prosthesis for the knee uses an MR fluid damper to provide motion that closely duplicates the natural movement of the knee joint.

changes that occur in liquids. As a result, our models of liquids are becoming more accurate. As a starting point, a typical liquid might best be viewed as containing a large number of regions where the arrangements of the components are similar to those found in the solid, but with more disorder. In addition, a smaller number of regions exist in the liquid where gaps ("holes") occur among the molecules. The situation is highly dynamic, with rapid fluctuations occurring in both types of regions.

16.3   An Introduction to Structures and Types of Solids

There are many ways to classify solids, but the broadest categories are **crystalline solids,** those with a highly regular arrangement of their components, and **amorphous solids,** those with considerable disorder in their structures.

The regular arrangement of the components of a crystalline solid at the microscopic level produces the beautiful, characteristic shapes of crystals, such as those shown in Fig. 16.8. The positions of the components in a crystalline solid are usually represented by a **lattice,** a three-dimensional array of points designating the centers of the components (atoms, ions, or molecules) that shows the repetitious pattern of the components. The *smallest repeating unit* of

Figure 16.8
Several crystalline solids. (clockwise from upper left) Rhodochrosite, fluorite, pyrite, amethyst.

the lattice is called the **unit cell.** Thus a particular lattice can be generated by repeating (translating) the unit cell in all three dimensions to form the extended structure. Three common unit cells and their lattices are shown in Fig. 16.9.

Although we will concentrate on crystalline solids in this book, there are many important noncrystalline (amorphous) materials. An example is common glass, which is best pictured as a solution whose components are "frozen in place" before they can achieve an ordered arrangement. Although glass is a solid (it has a rigid shape), a great deal of disorder exists in its structure.

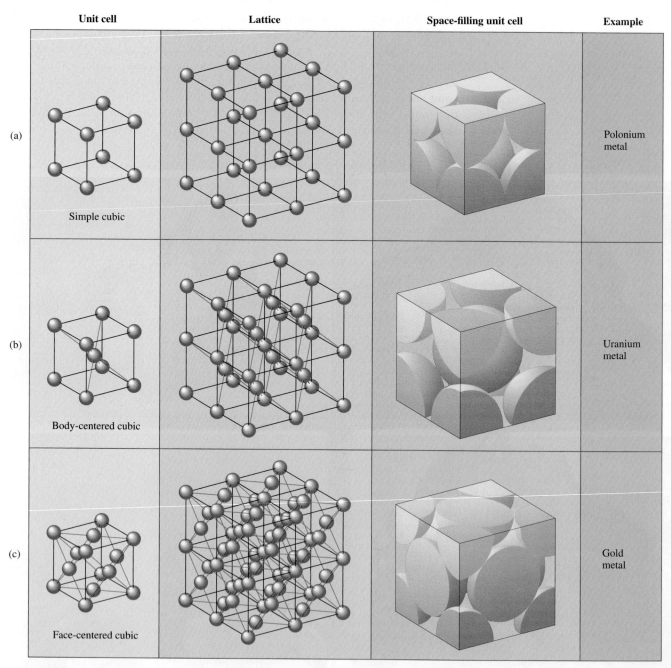

Unit cell	Lattice	Space-filling unit cell	Example
(a) Simple cubic			Polonium metal
(b) Body-centered cubic			Uranium metal
(c) Face-centered cubic			Gold metal

Figure 16.9

Three cubic unit cells and the corresponding lattices. Note that only parts of spheres on the corners and faces of the unit cells reside inside the unit cell, as shown by the cutoff versions.

Conch Clues

Nature is an excellent source of ideas for making materials that are useful in the human world. A recent example involves the shell of the giant pink queen conch (*Strombus gigas*). The shell of the Caribbean conch (pronounced "conk") is 100 to 1000 times stronger than the aragonite mineral that makes up 99% of the shell. Since aragonite is a form of calcium carbonate, which in its pure form breaks like chalk, why is the conch shell so tough?

Arthur Heuer and his colleagues at Case Western Reserve University in Cleveland have used microscopy to show that the secret of the conch shell's strength lies in the protein that surrounds strands of aragonite in the shell. These strands are bundled into larger strands, which are in turn packed into still larger structures. At each level of organization, adjacent structures are oriented perpendicular to one another. This arrangement allows fractures to spread without shattering the shell.

The conch shell, which is 99% calcium carbonate, is therefore really a composite material in which proteins provide the toughness that makes the shell so resistant to shattering. Although the conch shell itself is not useful (except to the conch), it illustrates how composites may offer much greater strength than the individual substances involved.

Scientists are studying many other natural materials* that are especially strong yet very light.

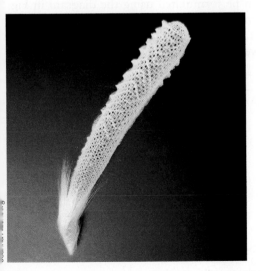

Silica sea sponge.

Examples include the silica sea sponge, which has an intricate cylindrical glass skeleton approximately 20 cm long and a few centimeters in diameter. Another interesting natural structure is the 20-cm-long beak of the Toco toucan, which makes up one-third of the bird's length but accounts for only 1/20 of its mass.

Lessons learned from these natural materials may well lead to high-performance materials that may prove useful in aerospace vehicles, bridges, and construction materials.

(top) Toco toucan. (bottom) Scanning electron microscope (SEM) image of the layered and staggered keratin tiles that make up the outer shell of a Toco toucan's beak.

*For more information, see "Making the Most of It," *Sci. News* **169** (2006): 184.

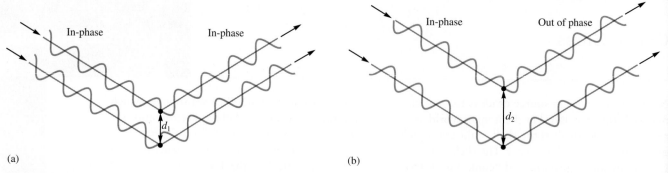

(a)   (b)

Figure 16.10

X rays scattered from two different atoms may reinforce (constructive interference) or cancel (destructive interference) one another. (a) Both the incident rays and the reflected rays are also in phase. In this case d_1 is such that the difference in the distances traveled by the two rays is a whole number of wavelengths. (b) The incident rays are in phase, but the reflected rays are exactly out of phase. In this case d_2 is such that the difference in distances traveled by the two rays is an odd number of half wavelengths.

X-Ray Analysis of Solids

The structures of crystalline solids are most commonly determined by **X-ray diffraction.** Diffraction occurs when beams of light are scattered from a regular array of points or lines where the spacings between the components are comparable to the wavelength of the light. Diffraction is caused by constructive interference when the waves of parallel beams are in phase and by destructive interference when the waves are out of phase.

When X rays of a single wavelength are directed at a crystal, a diffraction pattern is obtained, as we saw in Fig. 12.7. The light and dark areas on the photographic plate occur because the waves scattered from various atoms may reinforce or cancel each other (see Fig. 16.10). The key to whether the waves reinforce or cancel is the difference in distance traveled by the waves after they strike the atoms. The waves are in phase before they are reflected; thus, if the difference in distance traveled after reflection is an *integral number of wavelengths,* the waves will still be in phase when they meet again.

Since the distance traveled after reflection depends on the distance between the atoms, the diffraction pattern can be used to determine the interatomic spacings. The exact relationship can be formulated using the diagram in Fig. 16.11, which shows two in-phase waves being reflected by atoms in two different layers of a crystal. The extra distance traveled by the lower wave is the sum of the distances xy and yz. The waves will be in phase after reflection if

$$xy + yz = n\lambda \tag{16.1}$$

where n is an integer and λ is the wavelength of the X rays. Using trigonometry (Fig. 16.11), we can show that

$$xy + yz = 2d \sin \theta \tag{16.2}$$

Figure 16.11

Reflection of X rays of wavelength λ from a pair of atoms in two different layers of a crystal. The lower wave travels an extra distance equal to the sum of xy and yz. If this distance is an integral number of wavelengths ($n = 1$, 2, 3, . . .), the waves will reinforce each other when they exit the crystal.

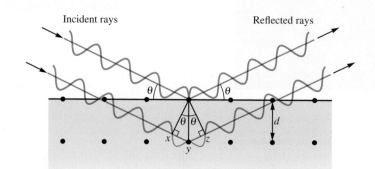

Incident rays   Reflected rays where d is the distance between the atoms and θ is the angle of incidence and reflection. Combining Equation (16.1) and Equation (16.2) gives

$$n\lambda = 2d \sin \theta \qquad (16.3)$$

Equation (16.3) is called the **Bragg equation,** after William Henry Bragg (1862–1942) and his son William Lawrence Bragg (1890–1972). They shared the Nobel Prize in physics in 1915 for their pioneering work in X-ray crystallography.

A diffractometer is a computer-controlled instrument used for carrying out the X-ray analysis of crystals. It rotates the crystal with respect to the X-ray beam and collects the data produced by the scattering of the X rays from the various planes of atoms in the crystal. The results are then analyzed by computer. The techniques for crystal structure analysis have reached a level of sophistication that allows the determination of very complex structures, such as those important in biological systems. Using X-ray diffraction, we can gather data on bond lengths and angles and, in doing so, can test the predictions of our models of molecular geometry.

Types of Crystalline Solids

There are many different types of crystalline solids. For example, although both sugar and salt dissolve readily in water, the properties of the resulting solutions are quite different. The salt solution readily conducts an electric current, but the sugar solution does not. This behavior arises from the nature of the components of these two solids. Common salt (NaCl) is an ionic solid; it contains Na^+ and Cl^- ions. When solid sodium chloride dissolves in the polar water, sodium and chloride ions are distributed throughout the resulting solution and are free to conduct an electric current. Table sugar (sucrose), on the other hand, is composed of neutral molecules that are dispersed throughout the water when the solid dissolves. Since no ions are present in the solid, the resulting solution does not conduct electricity. These examples illustrate two important types of solids: **ionic solids,** represented by sodium chloride, and **molecular solids,** represented by sucrose.

A third type of solid is illustrated by elements such as graphite, diamond, and buckminsterfullerene (all pure carbon), boron, silicon, and all metals. These substances all have atoms occupying the lattice points; we will call them **atomic solids.** Examples of the three types of solids are shown in Fig. 16.12.

Figure 16.12

Examples of three types of crystalline solids. Only part of the structure is shown in each case. (a) An atomic solid. (b) An ionic solid. (c) A molecular solid. The dashed lines show the hydrogen bonding among the polar water molecules.

Cl$^-$

Na$^+$

H$_2$O

C

Diamond

(a)

Sodium chloride

(b)

Ice

(c)

The internal forces in a solid determine the properties of the solid.

The properties of a solid are determined primarily by the nature of the forces that hold the solid together. For example, although argon, copper, and diamond all form atomic solids, they have strikingly different properties. Argon has a very low melting point ($-189°C$), whereas diamond and copper melt at high temperatures (about $3500°C$ and $1083°C$, respectively). Copper is an excellent conductor of electricity, but argon and diamond are both insulators. Copper can be easily changed in shape; it is both malleable (can form thin sheets) and ductile (can be pulled into a wire). Diamond, on the other hand, is the hardest natural substance known. The marked differences in properties among these three atomic solids are caused by bonding differences. We will explore the bonding in solids in the next two sections.

16.4 | Structure and Bonding in Metals

The closest packing model for metallic crystals assumes that metal atoms are uniform, hard spheres.

Metals are characterized by high thermal and electrical conductivity, malleability, and ductility. As we will see, these properties can be traced to the nondirectional covalent bonding found in metallic crystals.

A metallic crystal can be pictured as containing spherical atoms packed together and bonded to each other equally in all directions. We can model such a structure by packing uniform, hard spheres in a manner that most efficiently uses the available space. Such an arrangement is called **closest packing** (Fig. 16.13). The spheres are packed in layers in which each sphere is surrounded by six others. In the second layer, the spheres do not lie directly over those in the first layer. Instead, each one occupies an indentation (or dimple) formed by three spheres in the first layer. In the third layer, the spheres can occupy the dimples of the second layer in two possible ways. They can occupy positions so that each sphere in the third layer lies directly over a sphere in the first layer (the *aba* arrangement), or they can occupy positions so that no sphere in the third layer lies over one in the first layer (the *abc* arrangement).

The *aba* arrangement has the *hexagonal* unit cell shown in Fig. 16.14, and the resulting structure is called the **hexagonal closest packed (hcp) structure.** The *abc* arrangement has a *face-centered cubic* unit cell, as shown in Fig. 16.15,

Figure 16.13
The closest packing arrangement of uniform spheres. In each layer a given sphere is surrounded by six others. (a) *aba* packing: The second layer is like the first, but it is displaced so that each sphere in the second layer occupies a dimple in the first layer. The spheres in the third layer occupy dimples in the second layer so that the spheres in the third layer lie directly over those in the first layer (*aba*). (b) *abc* packing: The spheres in the third layer occupy dimples in the second layer so that no spheres in the third layer lie above any in the first layer (*abc*). The fourth layer is like the first.

(a) *abab* — Closest packing

Top view   Top view   Side view

(b) *abca* — Closest packing

Top view   Top view   Top view   Side view

Figure 16.14
When spheres are closest packed so that the spheres in the third layer are directly over those in the first layer (*aba*), the unit cell is the hexagonal prism illustrated here in red.

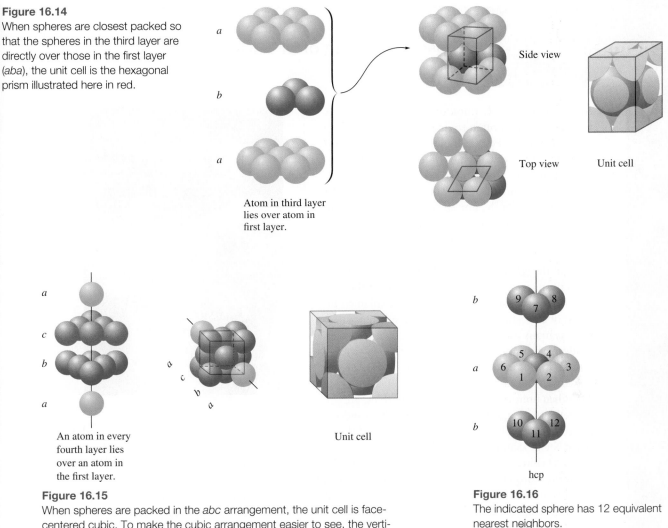

Atom in third layer lies over atom in first layer.

Side view

Top view

Unit cell

An atom in every fourth layer lies over an atom in the first layer.

Unit cell

hcp

Figure 16.15
When spheres are packed in the *abc* arrangement, the unit cell is face-centered cubic. To make the cubic arrangement easier to see, the vertical axis has been tilted as shown.

Figure 16.16
The indicated sphere has 12 equivalent nearest neighbors.

and the resulting structure is called the **cubic closest packed (ccp) structure.** Note that in the hcp structure the spheres in every other layer occupy the same vertical position (*ababab* . . .), whereas in the ccp structure the spheres in every fourth layer occupy the same vertical position (*abcabca* . . .). A characteristic of both structures is that each sphere has 12 equivalent nearest neighbors: 6 in the same layer, 3 in the layer above, and 3 in the layer below (that form the dimples). This is illustrated for the hcp structure in Fig. 16.16.

Knowing the *net* number of spheres (atoms) in a particular unit cell is important for many applications involving solids. To illustrate the procedure for finding the net number of spheres in a unit cell, let's consider a face-centered cubic unit cell (Fig. 16.17). Note that this unit cell is defined by the *centers* of the spheres on the cube's corners. Thus 8 cubes share a given sphere, so $\frac{1}{8}$ of this sphere lies inside each unit cell. Since a cube has 8 corners, there are $8 \times \frac{1}{8}$ pieces, or enough to put together 1 whole sphere. The spheres at the center of each face are shared by 2 unit cells, so $\frac{1}{2}$ of each lies inside a particular unit cell. Since the cube has 6 faces, we have $6 \times \frac{1}{2}$ pieces, or enough to construct 3 whole spheres. Thus the net number of spheres in a face-centered cubic unit cell is

$$\left(8 \times \frac{1}{8}\right) + \left(6 \times \frac{1}{2}\right) = 4$$

Chemical Insights

Closest Packing of M & Ms

Although we usually think of scientists as dealing with esoteric and often toxic materials, sometimes they surprise us. For example, scientists at several prestigious universities have lately shown a lot of interest in M & M candies.

To appreciate the scientists' interest in M & Ms, we must consider the importance of packing atoms, molecules, or microcrystals in understanding the structures of solids. The most efficient use of space is the closest packing of uniform spheres, where 74% of the space is occupied by the spheres and 26% of space is left unoccupied. Although the structures of most pure metals can be explained in terms of closest packing, most other substances—such as many alloys and ceramics—consist of random arrays of microscopic particles. For this reason, it is of interest to study how such objects pack in a random way.

When uniform spheres, such as marbles, are poured into a large container, the resulting random packing of the spheres results in only 64% of the space being occupied by the spheres. Thus it was very surprising when Princeton University chemist Salvatore Torquato and his colleagues at Cornell and North Carolina Central Universities discovered that when the ellipsoidal-shaped M & Ms are poured into a large container, the candies occupy 73.5% of the available space. In other words, the randomly packed M & Ms occupy space with almost the same efficiency as closest packed spheres do.

Why do randomly packed ellipsoids occupy space so much more efficiently than randomly

Denise Applewhite/Princeton University

packed spheres? The scientists speculate that because the ellipsoids can tip and rotate in ways that spheres cannot, they can pack more closely to their neighbors.

According to Torquato, these results are important because they will help us to better understand the properties of disordered materials ranging from powders to glassy solids. He also says that M & Ms make ideal test objects because they are inexpensive and uniform and "you can eat the experiment afterward."

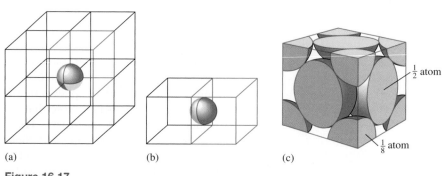

(a)   (b)   (c)

Figure 16.17
The net number of spheres in a face-centered cubic unit cell. (a) Note that the sphere on a corner of the colored cell is shared with 7 other unit cells. Thus $\frac{1}{8}$ of such a sphere lies within a given unit cell. Since there are 8 corners in a cube, there are 8 of these $\frac{1}{8}$ pieces, the equivalent of 1 net sphere. (b) The sphere on the center of each face is shared by two unit cells, and thus each unit cell has $\frac{1}{2}$ of each of these types of spheres. There are 6 of these $\frac{1}{2}$ spheres, yielding 3 net spheres. (c) Thus the face-centered cubic unit cell contains 4 net spheres.

Seething Surfaces

When we picture a solid, we think of the particles as being packed closely together with relatively little motion. The particles are thought to vibrate randomly about their positions but stay in nearly the same place. Recent research, however, indicates surface particles are a great deal more mobile than was previously thought. Independent teams of scientists from the University of Leiden in the Netherlands and Sandia National Laboratory in New Mexico have found a surprising amount of atom swapping occurring on the surface of a copper crystal.

Dutch scientist Raoul van Gastel and his colleagues used a scanning tunneling microscope (STM) to study the surface of a copper crystal containing indium atom impurities. They noted that a given patch of surface would stay the same for several scans and then, suddenly, the indium atoms would appear at different places. Surprisingly, the indium atoms seemed to make "long jumps," moving as many as five atom positions between scans. The most likely explanation for these movements is a "hole" created by a copper atom escaping the surface. This hole moves around as other atoms shift to fill it in succession (see accompanying figure). The best analogy to the movement of the hole is the toy slide puzzle with 15 numbered pieces and one missing piece in a 4 × 4 array. The object of the game is to slide a piece into the hole and then repeat the process until the numbers appear in order.

The hole on the copper surface moves very fast—up to 100 million times per second—shuffling copper atoms and allowing the indium atoms to change positions. Van Gastel believes that all of the observed motion results from just a few fast-moving holes. In fact, he suggests that just one in 6 billion copper atoms is missing at a given time, analogous to one person in the entire earth's population. Its absence causes a given atom on the surface to move every 30 or 40 seconds. Brian Swartzentruber of Sandia National Laboratories came to similar conclusions using an STM to track the movement of palladium atoms on a copper surface.

These results have important implications. For example, metal surfaces are often used to speed up particular reactions. The motions on the metal surface could significantly influence the way that reactants interact with the surface. Also, a lot of effort is now being expended to construct tiny "machines" (called nanoscale devices) by assembling individual atoms on a solid surface. These devices could be literally torn apart by excess surface motions.

A toy slide puzzle.

A section of a surface containing copper atoms (red) and an indium atom (yellow). A hole due to a missing copper atom is shown on the left. The blue line on the right shows the movement of this hole. As an atom moves to fill the hole, the hole moves as well. In the process, the indium atom jumps to a new position.

Illustration from R. van Gastel, et al., *Physical Review Letters,* Feb. 19, 2001, Vol. 86, Issue 5, pp. 1562–1565. Copyright 2001 by the American Physical Society.

In Example 16.1 we will see how the density of a closest packed solid can be calculated.

OWL INTERACTIVE EXAMPLE 16.1

Silver crystallizes in a cubic closest packed structure. The radius of a silver atom is 1.44 Å (144 pm). Calculate the density of solid silver.

Solution

■ What are we trying to solve?

In this problem we are asked to solve for the density of solid silver. Density is the mass per unit volume, so we will need to determine the mass of silver atoms that occupy a given volume in the crystal. This will require us to determine the number of silver atoms in this volume. With the number of atoms of silver and the atomic mass of silver, we can determine the mass of silver.

The structure is cubic closest packed, which means the unit cell is face-centered cubic, as shown in the figure at left.

We must find the volume of this unit cell and the net number of atoms it contains. Note that in this structure the atoms touch along the diagonals of each face and not along the edges of the cube. Thus the length of the diagonal is $r + 2r + r$, or $4r$, where r represents the radius of a silver atom. We next find the length of the edge of the cube by the Pythagorean theorem:

$$e^2 + e^2 = (4r)^2$$

$$2e^2 = 16r^2$$

$$e^2 = 8r^2$$

$$e = \sqrt{8r^2} = r\sqrt{8}$$

Since $r = 1.44$ Å for a silver atom,

$$e = (1.44 \text{ Å})(\sqrt{8}) = 4.07 \text{ Å}$$

The volume of the unit cell is e^3, which is $(4.07 \text{ Å})^3$ or 67.4 Å^3. We convert this to cubic centimeters as follows:

$$67.4 \text{ Å}^3 \times \left(\frac{1.00 \times 10^{-8} \text{ cm}}{\text{Å}}\right)^3 = 6.74 \times 10^{-23} \text{ cm}^3$$

Since the net number of atoms in a face-centered cubic unit cell is 4, there are 4 silver atoms in a volume of $6.74 \times 10^{-23} \text{ cm}^3$. Therefore,

$$\text{Density} = \frac{\text{mass}}{\text{volume}}$$

$$= \frac{(4 \text{ atoms})(107.9 \text{ g/mol})(1 \text{ mol}/6.022 \times 10^{23} \text{ atoms})}{6.74 \times 10^{-23} \text{ cm}^3}$$

$$= 10.6 \text{ g/cm}^3$$

Closest packing describes the most efficient method for arranging uniform spheres. We can calculate the fraction of the space actually occupied by the spheres (f_v),

$$f_v = \frac{\text{volume occupied by spheres in the unit cell}}{\text{volume of the unit cell}}$$

by using ideas we have developed in the preceding discussion.

Figure 16.18
In the body-centered cubic unit cell, the spheres touch along the body diagonal.

Figure 16.19
The body-centered cubic unit cell with the center sphere deleted.

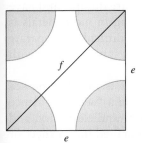

Figure 16.20
One face of the body-centered cubic unit cell. By the Pythagorean theorem, $f^2 = e^2 + e^2$.

Figure 16.21
The relationship of the body diagonal (b) to the face diagonal (f) and edge (e) for the body-centered cubic unit cell.

Recall that in the cubic closest packing arrangement, the unit cell is face-centered cubic and contains four net spheres. Thus the volume occupied by spheres in the unit cell is four times the volume of each sphere:

$$4 \times \tfrac{4}{3}\pi r^3$$

In Example 16.1 we found that the edge of the unit cell (e) is related to the radius of the packed spheres (r) as follows:

$$e = r\sqrt{8}$$

Therefore, the volume of the unit cell is e^3, where

$$e^3 = (r\sqrt{8})^3$$

and the fraction of space occupied by the spheres is

$$f_v = \underbrace{\frac{\overbrace{4 \times \tfrac{4}{3}\pi r^3}^{\text{Volume of spheres}}}{(r\sqrt{8})^3}}_{\text{Volume of unit cell}} = 0.740$$

This result means that in a cubic closest packed solid 74.0% of the space is occupied by spheres (26.0% is open space). This result also applies to hexagonal closest packing, although we will not prove it here.

In contrast, for simple cubic packing (spheres stacked on top of each other in successive layers), the spheres occupy only 52.4% of the space (verify this for yourself).

Examples of metals that are cubic closest packed are aluminum, iron, copper, cobalt, and nickel. Magnesium and zinc exhibit hexagonal closest packing. Calcium and certain other metals can crystallize in either structure.

Body-Centered Cubic Packing

Although most metals assume one of the closest packed structures in the solid state, some metallic elements have structures that are not closest packed. For example, the structures of the alkali metals are characterized by a **body-centered cubic (bcc) unit cell** (Fig. 16.9). In this structure each sphere has 8 nearest neighbors (count the number of atoms around the atom at the center of the unit cell), as compared with 12 in the closest packed structures.

Note that in body-centered cubic packing the unit cell is a cube with one sphere at its center. In this structure the spheres touch along the body diagonal (Fig. 16.18). For clarity, the cube for this unit cell is shown in Fig. 16.19 with the center sphere deleted.

The body-centered arrangement of spheres is not a closest packed structure, as we can show by calculating the fraction of space occupied by the spheres. To express the volume of the cube in terms of the radius of the packed spheres, we must use the Pythagorean theorem twice. First, we express the face diagonal f in terms of the edge e (Fig. 16.20):

$$f^2 = e^2 + e^2 = 2e^2$$

Because the spheres touch along the body diagonal, the length of the body diagonal b is $4r$. We can relate the body diagonal, the face diagonal, and the cube edge as follows (Fig. 16.21):

$$b^2 = (4r)^2 = e^2 + f^2$$

and

$$(4r)^2 = e^2 + 2e^2 = 3e^2$$

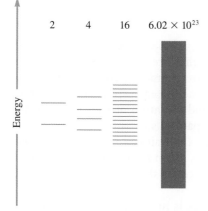

Figure 16.22
The electron sea model for metals postulates a regular array of cations in a "sea" of valence electrons. (a) Representation of an alkali metal (Group 1A) with one valence electron. (b) Representation of an alkaline earth metal (Group 2A) with two valence electrons.

Figure 16.23
The molecular orbital energy levels produced when various numbers of atomic orbitals interact. Note that for two atomic orbitals two rather widely spaced energy levels result. (Recall the description of H_2 in Section 14.2.) As more atomic orbitals become available to form MOs, the resulting energy levels become more closely spaced, finally producing a band of very closely spaced orbitals.

Thus

$$e = \frac{4r}{\sqrt{3}}$$

The body-centered cubic unit cell contains 2 net spheres:

$$8(\tfrac{1}{8}) + 1 = 2$$

$\quad\quad\quad\uparrow\quad\quad\uparrow$
Corners Center

Thus we can compute the fraction of space occupied by the spheres:

Volume occupied
by spheres

$$\frac{2 \times \frac{4}{3}\pi r^3}{\left(\dfrac{4r}{\sqrt{3}}\right)^3} = \frac{\sqrt{3}\,\pi}{8} = 0.680$$

Cube volume

So in the body-centered cubic arrangement, 68.0% of the space is actually occupied by spheres. This is somewhat less than the space occupied in the closest packed structures (74.0%). That is, in contrast to cubic closest packing and hexagonal closest packing, the body-centered cubic method of packing spheres does not represent a closest packed structure.

The reasons why some metals adopt a body-centered cubic structure rather than a closest packed structure are complex and are often not apparent in particular cases.

Bonding in Metals

Any successful bonding model for metals must account for the typical physical properties of metals: malleability, ductility, and the efficient and uniform conduction of heat and electricity in all directions. Although the shapes of most pure metals can be changed relatively easily, most metals are durable and have high melting points. These facts indicate that the bonding in most metals is both *strong* and *nondirectional*. That is, although it is difficult to separate metal atoms, it is relatively easy to move them, if the atoms stay in contact with each other.

The simplest picture that explains these observations is the **electron sea model,** which envisions a regular array of metal cations in a "sea" of valence electrons (Fig. 16.22). The mobile electrons conduct heat and electricity, and the cations are easily moved around as the metal is hammered into a sheet or pulled into a wire.

A related model that gives a more detailed view of the electron energies and motions is the **band model,** or the molecular orbital (MO) model, for metals. In this model the electrons are assumed to travel around the metal crystal in MOs formed from the valence atomic orbitals of the metal atoms (Fig. 16.23).

Recall that in the MO model for the gaseous Li_2 molecule (Section 14.3), two widely spaced MO energy levels (bonding and antibonding) result when two identical atomic orbitals interact. However, when many metal atoms interact, as in a metal crystal, the large number of resulting MOs become closely spaced, forming a virtual continuum of levels, called **bands** (Fig. 16.23).

As an illustration, picture a magnesium metal crystal, which has an hcp structure. Since each magnesium atom has one $3s$ and three $3p$ valence atomic orbitals, a crystal with n magnesium atoms has available $n(3s)$ and $3n(3p)$ orbitals to form the MOs, as illustrated in Fig. 16.24. Note that the core electrons are localized, as shown by their presence in the energy "well" around each magnesium atom produced by its nuclear charge. However, the valence electrons occupy closely spaced MOs, which are only partially filled.

Crystals of magnesium grown from a vapor.

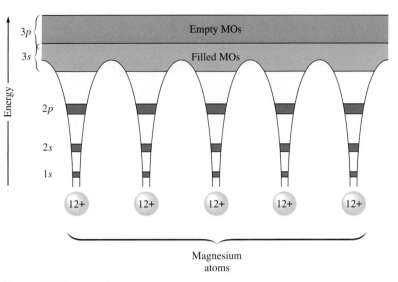

Figure 16.24

A representation of the energy levels (bands) in a magnesium crystal. The electrons in the 1s, 2s, and 2p orbitals are close to the nuclei and thus are localized on each magnesium atom as shown. However, the 3s and 3p valence orbitals overlap and mix to form MOs. Electrons in these energy levels can travel throughout the crystal.

The existence of empty MOs close in energy to filled MOs explains the thermal and electrical conductivity of metal crystals. Metals conduct electricity and heat very efficiently because of the availability of highly mobile electrons. For example, when an electrical potential is placed across a strip of metal, for current to flow, electrons must be free to move from the negative to the positive areas of the metal. In the band model for metals, mobile electrons are furnished when electrons in filled MOs are excited into empty ones. The conduction electrons are free to travel throughout the metal crystal as dictated by the potential imposed on the metal. The MOs occupied by these conducting electrons are called **conduction bands.** These mobile electrons also account for the efficiency of the conduction of heat through metals. When one end of a metal rod is heated, the mobile electrons can rapidly transmit the thermal energy to the other end.

Metal Alloys

Because of the nature of the structure and bonding of metals, other elements can be introduced into a metallic crystal relatively easily to produce substances called **alloys.** An alloy is best defined as *a substance that contains a mixture of elements and has metallic properties.* Alloys can be conveniently classified into two types.

In a **substitutional alloy,** some of the host metal atoms are *replaced* by other metal atoms of similar size. For example, in brass about one-third of the atoms in the host copper metal are replaced by zinc atoms, as shown in Fig. 16.25(a). Sterling silver (93% silver and 7% copper), pewter (85% tin, 7% copper, 6% bismuth, and 2% antimony), and plumber's solder (67% lead and 33% tin) are other examples of substitutional alloys.

An **interstitial alloy** is formed when some of the interstices (holes) in the closest packed metal structure are occupied by small atoms, as shown in Fig. 16.25(b). Steel, the best known interstitial alloy, contains carbon atoms in the holes of an iron crystal. The presence of the interstitial atoms changes the properties of the host metal. Pure iron is relatively soft, ductile, and malleable because of the absence of strong directional bonding. The spherical metal atoms can be rather easily moved with respect to each other. However, when

(a)

Brass

○ copper
◯ zinc

(b)

Steel

◯ iron
• carbon

Figure 16.25

Two types of alloys.

Table 16.3

The Composition of the Two Brands of Steel Tubing Most Commonly Used to Make Lightweight Racing Bicycles

Brand of Tubing	% C	% Si	% Mn	% Mo	% Cr
Reynolds	0.25	0.25	1.3	0.20	—
Columbus	0.25	0.30	0.65	0.20	1.0

carbon, which forms strong directional bonds, is introduced into an iron crystal, the presence of the directional carbon–iron bonds makes the resulting alloy harder, stronger, and less ductile than pure iron. The amount of carbon present directly affects the properties of steel. *Mild steels,* containing less than 0.2% carbon, are relatively ductile and malleable. These steels are used for nails, cables, and chains. *Medium steels,* containing 0.2–0.6% carbon, are harder than mild steels and are used in rails and structural steel beams. *High-carbon steels,* containing 0.6–1.5% carbon, are tough and hard and are used for springs, tools, and cutlery.

Many types of steel contain elements in addition to iron and carbon. Such steels are often called *alloy steels* and can be viewed as being mixed interstitial (carbon) and substitutional (other metals) alloys. Bicycle frames, for example, are constructed from a wide variety of alloy steels. The compositions of the two brands of steel tubing used in high-quality racing bicycles are given in Table 16.3.

16.5 | Carbon and Silicon: Network Atomic Solids

Many atomic solids contain strong directional covalent bonds. We will call these substances **network solids.** In contrast to metals, these materials are typically brittle and do not efficiently conduct heat or electricity. To illustrate network solids, in this section we will discuss two very important elements, carbon and silicon, and some of their compounds.

Carbon occurs in the *allotropes* (different forms) diamond, graphite, and the fullerenes. The fullerenes are molecular solids (see Section 16.6), but diamond and graphite are typically network solids. In diamond, the hardest naturally occurring substance, each carbon atom is surrounded by a tetrahedral arrangement of other carbon atoms, as shown in Fig. 16.26(a). This structure is stabilized by covalent bonds, which, in terms of the localized electron model, are formed by the overlap of sp^3 hybridized atomic orbitals on each carbon atom.

Figure 16.26

The structures of (a) diamond and (b) graphite. In each case only a small part of the entire structure is shown.

(a)   Diamond   (b)   Graphite

Weak bonding between layers

Figure 16.27
Partial representation of the MO energies in (a) diamond and (b) a typical metal.

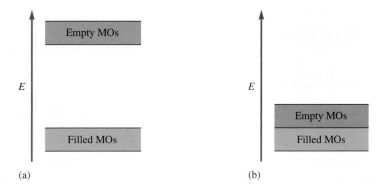

(a)

(b)

It is also useful to consider the bonding among the carbon atoms in diamond in terms of the MO model. Energy-level diagrams for diamond and a typical metal are given in Fig. 16.27. Recall that the conductivity of metals can be explained by postulating that electrons are excited from filled levels into the very near empty levels—the conduction bands. However, note that in the energy-level diagram for diamond there is *a large gap between the filled and the empty levels.* This means that electrons cannot be easily transferred to the empty conduction bands. As a result, diamond is not expected to be a good electrical conductor. In fact, this prediction of the model agrees exactly with the observed behavior of diamond, which is known to be an electrical *insulator*—it does not conduct an electric current.

Graphite is very different from diamond. Diamond is hard, basically colorless, and an insulator; graphite is slippery, black, and a conductor. These differences, of course, arise from the differences in bonding in the two types of solids. In contrast to the tetrahedral arrangement of carbon atoms in diamond, the structure of graphite is based on layers of carbon atoms arranged in fused six-membered rings, as shown in Fig. 16.26(b). Each carbon atom in a particular layer of graphite is surrounded by three other carbon atoms in a trigonal planar arrangement with 120-degree bond angles. The localized electron model predicts sp^2 hybridization in this case. The three sp^2 orbitals on each carbon are used to form σ bonds to three other carbon atoms. One $2p$ orbital remains unhybridized on each carbon and is perpendicular to the plane of carbon atoms, as shown in Fig. 16.28. These orbitals combine to form a group of closely spaced π MOs that are important in two ways. First, they contribute significantly to the stability of the graphite layers because of the π bonding. Second,

Graphite consists of layers of carbon atoms.

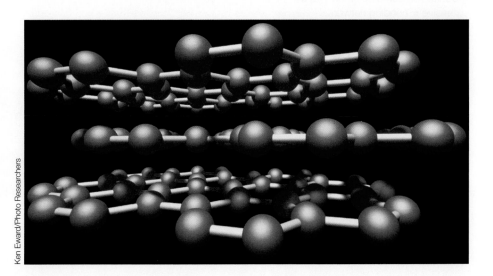

Chemical Insights

Graphene—Miracle Substance?

Graphite is a fascinating substance consisting of "chicken-wire" layers of carbon atoms. Due to the strong carbon–carbon bonds in each of its layers, graphite is even more thermodynamically stable than diamond. Because of the unusual stability of graphite, scientists have long wondered whether the individual chicken-wire layers could exist independently. This question was answered only recently by Andre Gein and Konstantin Novoselov, two scientists working at the University of Manchester in the United Kingdom, when they were able to pull layers a single atom thick from graphite using Scotch tape. This work was deemed so important that Gein and Novoselov were awarded the Nobel Prize in physics in 2010.

Since the isolation of sheets of graphene by Gein and Novoselov, research in the properties and possible uses of this material has virtually exploded. Graphene has truly amazing properties. For example, it is believed to be the strongest material known, more than 100 times stronger than steel. Also, it is stiffer than diamond, yet it can be stretched like rubber.

Much of the interest in graphene centers on the fact that it is the best conductor of heat and electricity known. Electrons travel through graphene at ultrafast speeds. In fact, electrons in graphene exhibit the fractional quantum Hall effect: The electrons act collectively as if they are particles with only a fraction of the charge of an electron. Because of its exceptional thermal and electrical conductivities, graphene appears to be an ideal candidate for future electronic devices. Scientists at IBM have already built graphene-based transistors that can switch on and off 26 billion times per second, far faster than conventional silicon-based devices.

One problem that has hampered the development of graphene-based devices is the difficulty in producing large sheets of graphene. Byung Hee Hong and his team, from South Korea, have recently reported making rectangular sheets of graphene measuring 30 inches along the diagonal. It appears that we are very close to making commercial electronic devices based on the amazing properties of graphene.

the π MOs with their delocalized electrons account for the electrical conductivity of graphite. These closely spaced orbitals are exactly analogous to the conduction bands found in metal crystals.

Graphite is often used as a lubricant in locks (where oil is undesirable because it collects dirt). The characteristic slipperiness of graphite can be explained by noting that graphite has very strong bonding *within* the layers of

Figure 16.28

The *p* orbitals (a) perpendicular to the plane of the carbon ring system in graphite can combine to form (b) an extensive π bonding network.

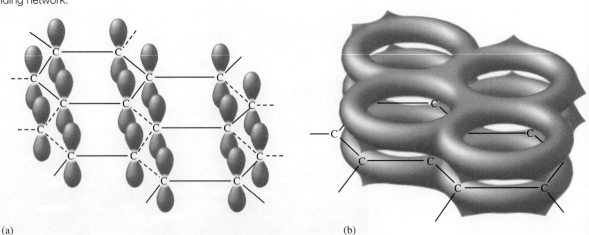

(a)   (b)

carbon atoms but little bonding *between* the layers (the valence electrons are all used to form σ or π bonds among carbons within a given layer). This arrangement allows the layers to slide past one another quite readily. Graphite's layered structure is quite obvious when viewed with a high-magnification electron microscope. This structure is in contrast to that of diamond, which has uniform bonding in all directions in the crystal.

Because of their extreme hardness, diamonds are extensively used in industrial cutting implements. Thus it is desirable to convert inexpensive graphite to diamond. As we might expect from the high density of diamond (3.5 g/cm^3) compared with that of graphite (2.2 g/cm^3), this transformation can be accomplished by applying very high pressures to graphite. The application of 150,000 atm of pressure at 2800°C converts graphite virtually completely to diamond. (The high temperature is required to break the strong bonds in graphite so that the rearrangement can occur.)

Silicon is an important constituent of the compounds that make up the earth's crust. In fact, silicon is to geology what carbon is to biology. Just as carbon compounds are the basis for most biologically significant systems, silicon compounds are fundamental to most of the rocks, sands, and soils found in the earth's crust. Although carbon and silicon are next to each other in Group 4A of the periodic table, the carbon-based compounds of biology and the silicon-based compounds of geology have markedly different structures. Carbon compounds typically contain long strings of carbon–carbon bonds, but the most stable silicon compounds involve chains with silicon–oxygen bonds. *The most important silicon compounds contain silicon and oxygen.*

The fundamental silicon–oxygen compound is **silica,** which has the empirical formula SiO_2. Knowing the properties of the apparently similar compound carbon dioxide, one might expect silica to be a gas that contains discrete SiO_2 molecules. In fact, nothing could be further from the truth—quartz and some types of sand are typical of the materials composed of silica. What accounts for this difference? The answer lies in the bonding.

Recall that the Lewis structure for CO_2 is

$$\ddot{\text{O}}\!=\!\text{C}\!=\!\ddot{\text{O}}$$

and that each C=O bond is described as a combination of a σ bond, involving a carbon sp hybrid orbital, and a π bond, involving a carbon $2p$ orbital. On the contrary, silicon cannot use its valence $3p$ orbitals to form strong π bonds to oxygen; the larger size of the silicon atom and its orbitals results in a less effective overlap with the smaller oxygen orbitals. Therefore, instead of forming π bonds, the silicon atom satisfies the octet rule by forming single bonds to four oxygen atoms, as shown in the representation of the structure of quartz in Fig. 16.29. Note that in this structure each silicon atom is at the center of a tetrahedral arrangement of oxygen atoms, which are shared with other silicon atoms. Although the empirical formula for quartz is SiO_2, the structure is based on a *network* of SiO_4 tetrahedra with shared oxygen atoms rather than discrete SiO_2 molecules. Thus the differing abilities of carbon and silicon to form π bonds with oxygen have profound effects on the structures and properties of CO_2 and SiO_2.

Compounds closely related to silica that are found in most rocks, soils, and clays are the **silicates.** Like silica, the silicates are based on interconnected SiO_4 tetrahedra. However, in contrast to silica, where the O:Si ratio is 2:1, silicates have O:Si ratios greater than 2:1 and contain silicon–oxygen *anions.* This means that for the formation of the neutral solid silicates, cations are needed to balance the excess negative charge. In other words, silicates are salts con-

Artificial diamonds are discussed in more detail in Section 16.11.

The bonding in the CO_2 molecule was described in Section 14.1.

Figure 16.29
(Top) The structure of quartz (empirical formula SiO_2). Quartz contains chains of SiO_4 tetrahedra (bottom) that share oxygen atoms.

Chemical Insights   Superconductivity

Although metals such as copper and aluminum are good conductors of electricity, up to 20% of the total energy is wasted in the transmission of a current by resistance heating of the wires. However, this loss of energy may be avoidable. Certain kinds of materials undergo a remarkable transition as they are cooled; their electrical resistance changes virtually to zero. These substances, called **superconductors,** conduct electricity with no wasted heat energy.

There is, of course, a catch. In the past superconductivity has been observed only at very low temperatures and is thus very expensive to maintain. In 1911 mercury was observed to exhibit superconductivity, but only at approximately 4 K, the boiling point of liquid helium. In the next 75 years, several niobium alloys showed superconductivity at temperatures as high as 23 K. However, in 1986 researchers realized that certain metallic oxides are superconductors at temperatures well above 23 K. The graph shows how rapidly our knowledge of superconductors is increasing.

The current class of high-temperature superconductors is called *perovskites*, a well-known class of compounds that contain copper, an alkaline earth metal, a lanthanide metal, and oxygen. In the unit cell for the compounds with formula $YBa_2Cu_3O_x$, in which $x = 6.527$, the small open circles (see figure) indicate the expected oxygen positions, but some of these positions are vacant in the known materials—thus the variable oxygen content.

In addition to exhibiting superconductivity at temperatures above the boiling point of liquid nitrogen (77 K), these ceramic materials can sustain very high currents, an important characteristic necessary for any large-scale application. More recent results have shown that materials containing thallium and calcium ions in place of the lanthanide ions superconduct at 125 K. In early 1993 researchers in Zurich, Switzerland, discov-

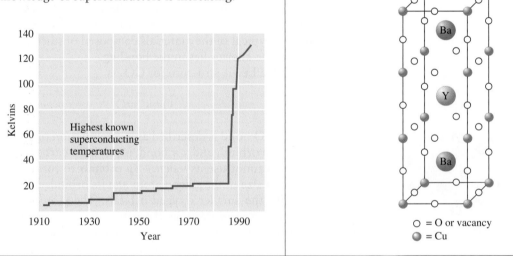

○ = O or vacancy
● = Cu

taining metal cations and polyatomic silicon–oxygen anions. Examples of important silicate anions are shown in Fig. 16.30.

When silica is heated above its melting point (about 1600°C) and then cooled rapidly, an amorphous solid called a **glass** results (Fig. 16.31). Note that a glass contains a good deal of disorder, in contrast to the crystalline nature of quartz. Glass more closely resembles a very viscous solution than a crystalline solid. Common glass results when substances such as Na_2CO_3 are added to the silica melt, which is then cooled. The properties of glass can be varied greatly by varying the additives. For example, addition of B_2O_3 produces a glass (called borosilicate glass) that expands and contracts little under ered a mercury-containing compound that is super-conducting at 133 K.

What does all this mean for the future? Super-conducting materials could easily cause a revolution similar to that brought about by solid-state electronics. For example, one can envision electrical power transmitted with virtually no loss of energy. Also, new generations of superconducting electromagnets could lead to the operation of particle accelerators at unprecedented energies, the development of nuclear fusion power, the ability to produce incredibly accurate three-dimensional images of the human body for diagnosis of disease, and the development of superfast, magnetically levitated trains.

After a great surge of progress in the late 1980s, the pace slowed greatly in the early 1990s as theory tried to catch up with the results from experiments. We need to develop an understanding of why these ceramic materials are superconducting so that we can design better materials that superconduct at even higher temperatures. And there are many practical problems. For example, metal conductors can be easily bent into coils to allow construction of electromagnets, but anyone who has ever dropped a plate knows how brittle ceramic materials are. Another question concerns how current can be conducted over long distances by superconducting materials. However, there seems to be little doubt that ingenious solutions eventually will be found to the problems. The answers are already beginning to appear.

For example, American Superconductor (ASC) of Westborough, Massachusetts, in conjunction with Pirelli Cable of Milan, Italy, has produced a prototype high-temperature superconducting

Yoav Levy/Phototake

A magnet is levitated over a superconducting ceramic immersed in liquid nitrogen.

"wire" that exceeds the current-carrying threshold required for commercial underground power transmission cables. The 1-m-long conductor, based on a bismuth–strontium–calcium–copper oxide superconductor, carries over 2300 amps of direct current at liquid nitrogen temperatures (77 K). This is more than twice the current-carrying capability of conventional copper cables.

ASC manufactures superconducting cables by pouring powdered reactants into a silver tube, drawing the tube into a wire, and then heating to produce the superconducting ceramic. Tens to hundreds of these fine conductors are then combined to form superconducting cable. Although ASC is now capable of producing individual superconducting wire filaments that are 1 km in length, much work remains to find a way to automate the multifilament cable manufacturing process.

large temperature changes. Thus it is useful for labware and cooking utensils. The most common brand name for this glass is Pyrex. The addition of K_2O produces an especially hard glass that can be ground to the precise shapes needed for eyeglasses and contact lenses. The compositions of several types of glass are shown in Table 16.4.

Ceramics

Ceramics are typically made from clays (which contain silicates) that are hardened by firing at high temperatures. Ceramics are a class of nonmetallic materials that are strong, brittle, and resistant to heat and attack by chemicals.

Chemical Insights   Greenhouse Glass

We have emphasized in this section how the different bonding tendencies of carbon and silicon with oxygen lead to very different types of covalent oxides. Carbon and oxygen form CO_2, a gas under normal conditions, and silicon and oxygen form silica, a network solid. However, Professors Mario Santoro and Federico Gorelli of the University of Florence in Italy have discovered that when carbon dioxide is subjected to extreme temperatures and pressures, it forms a glass very similar to that formed by SiO_2. Using a diamond anvil press inside a furnace, the Italian scientists found that at 640,000 atm and 700 kelvins a solid forms that is 10 times as hard as quartz but softer than diamond.

This substance, which they named "carbonia," is the hardest amorphous substance known.

Carbonia is transparent and similar in structure to amorphous silica in windows but much harder. Another nonmolecular form of carbon dioxide, called carbon dioxide 5, was made by different researchers several years ago.

Carbonia and carbon dioxide 5 are mostly of theoretical interest now because they immediately disappear when the pressure is decreased. It is very interesting that although carbon and silicon show very different bonding properties to oxygen under normal conditions, under pressure carbon becomes much more like silicon.

Like glass, ceramics are based on silicates, but with that the resemblance ends. Glass can be melted and remelted as often as desired, but once a ceramic has been hardened, it is resistant to extremely high temperatures. This behavior results from the very different structures of glasses and ceramics. A glass is a *homogeneous,* noncrystalline "frozen solution," whereas a ceramic is *heterogeneous.* A ceramic contains two phases: minute crystals of silicates that are suspended in a glassy cement.

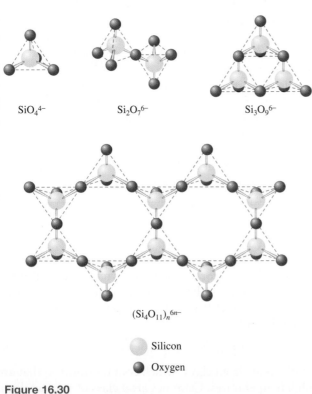

SiO_4^{4-} $Si_2O_7^{6-}$ $Si_3O_9^{6-}$

$(Si_4O_{11})_n^{6n-}$

○ Silicon

● Oxygen

Figure 16.30

Examples of silicate anions, all of which are based on SiO_4^{4-} tetrahedra.

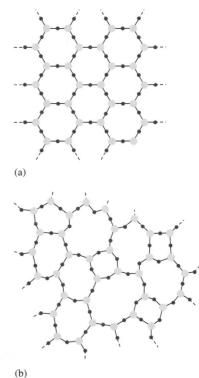

(a)

(b)

Figure 16.31

Two-dimensional representations of (a) a quartz crystal and (b) a quartz glass.

Explosive Sniffer

These days security is at the top of everyone's list of important concerns, especially for the people who are responsible for the safety of our transportation systems. In particular, airports need speedy and sensitive detectors for explosives. Plastic explosives are especially tricky to detect because they do not respond to metal detectors, and they can be shaped into innocent-looking objects to avoid X-ray detection. However, a team of scientists at Oak Ridge National Laboratory led by Thomas Thundat has just published a description of an inexpensive device that is extremely sensitive to two N-containing compounds found in plastic explosives. The key part of this detection device is a tiny (180-micrometer), V-shaped cantilever made of silicon. The cantilever is shown in the accompanying photo next to a human hair for size comparison.

The upper surface of the cantilever was first coated with a layer of gold and then a one-molecule-thick layer of an acid that binds to each of the two N-containing molecules to be detected: pentaerythritol tetranitrate (PETN) and hexahydro-1,3,5-triazine (RDX). When a stream of air containing tiny amounts of PETN or RDX passes over the cantilever, these molecules bind to the cantilever, causing it to bend "like a diving board." This bending is not due to the added mass of the attached PETN and RDX. Rather, the deformation occurs because the area of the cantilever surface where binding takes place stretches relative to the unbound areas. A laser pointed at the cantilever detects the bending motion when PETN or RDX

When explosive compounds bind to these V-shaped cantilevers, the microscopic structures, which are about the width of a hair, bend and produce a signal.

(or both) is present. The device's sensitivity is quite remarkable: 14 parts per trillion of PETN and 30 parts per trillion of RDX.

All in all, this device appears very promising for detecting plastic explosives in luggage. The cantilevers are inexpensive to construct (approximately $1), and the entire device is about the size of a shoe box. Also, the Oak Ridge team can fabricate thousands of cantilevers in one device. By putting different coatings on the cantilever arms, it should be possible to detect many other types of chemicals and possible biological agents.

This detector looks like a very promising addition to our arsenal of security devices.

Table 16.4

Compositions of Some Common Types of Glass

Type of Glass	Percentages of Various Components						
	SiO_2	CaO	Na_2O	B_2O_3	Al_2O_3	K_2O	MgO
Window (soda-lime glass)	72	11	13	—	0.3	3.8	—
Cookware (aluminosilicate glass)	55	15	—	—	20	—	10
Heat-resistant (borosilicate glass)	76	3	5	13	2	0.5	—
Optical	69	12	6	0.3	—	12	—

Chemical Insights | Gallium Arsenide Lasers

Lasers are an essential part of modern life, providing the most efficient way to carry telephone communications by cable, the best-quality music using compact disc players, and the most accurate method for reading grocery prices. The laser (the word *lase* is an acronym for "light amplification by stimulated emission") is a device for producing an intense, coherent beam of light that results when excited electrons release photons as they change to a lower energy state. Excited electrons can return to a lower energy level by spontaneous, random emission of light. However, there is another mechanism in which the emission process is actually stimulated by a passing photon that has the same energy as the emitted photon. This is the phenomenon on which the laser is based. We will have more to say about this presently.

Gallium arsenide is a prominent member of the so-called 3–5 class of semiconductors, those containing elements from Groups 3A and 5A of the periodic table. An n-type semiconductor results when the arsenic-to-gallium ratio is greater than 1. A p-type semiconductor results when gallium is in excess. By carefully controlling the conditions under which a Ga–As semiconductor is made, one can design p–n junctions into the material. At each p–n junction, electrons from the n-type region are available to "fall into" holes in the p-type region, producing photons (see the accompanying figure). As the emitted photons travel through the solid, they *stimulate* the emission of additional photons. A mirror at the edge of the solid reflects these photons back through the substance, where they stimulate even more emission events. All these stimulated emissions produce photons with their waves in phase. Thus this process leads to a large number of coherent (in-phase) photons, which proceed out the other end of the solid where a "half-mirror" is placed. This mirror reflects some of the photons and allows the rest to leave as an intense, coherent "laser beam" of light. A current driven through the substance by an applied potential difference provides a continuous supply of electrons (and removes electrons to make new holes) so that the process occurs continuously while the power is on.

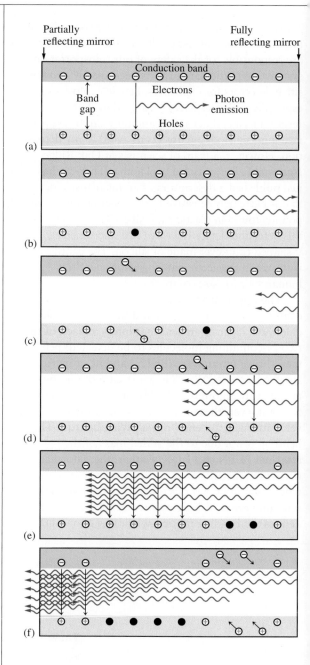

Suggested Reading
Ron Cowen, "Inventing the Light Fantastic," *Sci. News* May 8 (2010): 18.

n-type semiconductor

(a)

p-type semiconductor

(b)

Figure 16.32

(a) A silicon crystal doped with arsenic, which has one extra valence electron. (b) A silicon crystal doped with boron, which has one less electron than silicon.

[Energy-level diagram (a): Empty MOs (Conduction bands); "Excess" valence electrons (•) from donor impurity; Filled MOs; axis labeled E]

(a)

[Energy-level diagram (b): Empty MOs (Conduction bands); Electron vacancies (○) due to the doping atoms; axis labeled E]

(b)

Figure 16.33

Energy-level diagrams for (a) an n-type semiconductor and (b) a p-type semiconductor.

To understand how ceramics harden, one must know something about the structure of clays. Clays are formed by the weathering action of water and carbon dioxide on the mineral feldspar, which is a mixture of silicates with empirical formulas such as $K_2O \cdot Al_2O_3 \cdot 6SiO_2$ and $Na_2O \cdot Al_2O_3 \cdot 6SiO_2$. Feldspar is really an **aluminosilicate** in which aluminum as well as silicon atoms are part of the oxygen-bridged polyanion. The weathering of feldspar produces kaolinite, consisting of tiny thin platelets with the empirical formula $Al_2Si_2O_5(OH)_4$. When dry, the platelets cling together, but when water is present, they can slide over one another, giving clay its plasticity. As clay dries, the platelets begin to interlock again. When the remaining water is driven off during firing, the silicates and cations form a "glass" that binds the tiny crystals of kaolinite.

Ceramics have a very long history. Rocks, which are natural ceramic materials, served as the earliest tools. Later, clay vessels dried in the sun or baked in fires served as containers for food and water. These early vessels were crude and quite porous. With the discovery of glazing, which probably occurred about 3000 B.C. in Egypt, pottery became more serviceable as well as more beautiful. Prized porcelain is essentially the same material as crude earthenware, but specially selected clays and glazings are used for porcelain, which is also fired at a very high temperature.

Semiconductors

Elemental silicon has the same structure as diamond, as might be expected from its position in the periodic table (in Group 4A directly under carbon). Recall that in diamond there is a large energy gap between the filled and empty MOs (Fig. 16.27). This gap prevents excitation of electrons to the empty MOs (conduction bands) and makes diamond an insulator. In silicon the situation is similar but the energy gap is smaller. A few electrons can cross the gap at 25°C, making silicon a *semiconducting element*, or **semiconductor.** In addition, at higher temperatures, where more energy is available to excite electrons into the conduction bands, the conductivity of silicon increases. This is typical behavior for a semiconducting element and is in contrast to the behavior of metals. In metals, the conductivity decreases with increasing temperature.

The small conductivity of silicon can be enhanced at normal temperatures if the silicon crystal is *doped* with certain other elements. For example, when a small fraction of silicon atoms is replaced by arsenic atoms, each having *one more* valence electron than silicon, extra electrons become available for conduction, as shown in Fig. 16.32(a). This produces an **n-type semiconductor,** a substance whose conductivity is increased by doping it with atoms having more valence electrons than the atoms in the host crystal. These extra electrons lie close in energy to the conduction bands and can easily be excited into these levels, where they can conduct an electric current [Fig. 16.33(a)].

We can also enhance the conductivity of silicon by doping the crystal with an element such as boron, which has only three valence electrons, one *less* than silicon. Because boron has one less electron than is required to form the bonds to the surrounding silicon atoms, an electron vacancy, or *hole,* is created, as shown in Fig. 16.33(b). As an electron moves to fill this hole, it leaves a new hole. As this process is repeated, the hole advances through the crystal in a direction opposite to the movement of the electrons jumping to fill the hole. Another way of thinking about this phenomenon is that in pure silicon each atom has four valence electrons, so the low-energy MOs are exactly filled. Replacing silicon atoms with boron atoms leaves vacancies in these MOs, as shown in Fig. 16.33(b). This means that there is only one electron in some of the MOs, and these unpaired electrons can function as conducting electrons.

Chemical Insights | Transistors and Integrated Circuits

Transistors have had an immense impact on the technology of electronic devices for which signal amplification is needed, such as communications equipment and computers. Before the invention of the transistor at Bell Laboratories in 1947, amplification was provided exclusively by vacuum tubes, which were both bulky and unreliable. The first electronic digital computer, ENIAC, built at the University of Pennsylvania, had 19,000 vacuum tubes and consumed 150,000 watts of electricity. Because of the discovery and development of the transistor and the printed circuit, a hand-held calculator run by a small battery has the same computing power as ENIAC.

A *junction transistor* is made by joining n-type and p-type semiconductors to form an n–p–n or a p–n–p junction. The former type is shown in the diagram below. The input signal (to be amplified) occurs in circuit 1, which has a small resistance and a forward-biased n–p junction (junction 1). As the voltage of the input signal to this circuit varies, the current in the circuit varies. This means there is a change in the number of electrons crossing the n–p junction. Circuit 2 has a relatively large resistance and is under reverse bias. The key to the operation of the transistor is that current flows in circuit 2 only when electrons crossing junction 1

also cross junction 2 and travel to the positive terminal. Since the current in circuit 1 determines the number of electrons crossing junction 1, the number of electrons available to cross junction 2 is also directly proportional to the current in circuit 1. The current in circuit 2 therefore varies depending on the current in circuit 1.

The voltage (V), current (I), and resistance (R) in a circuit are related by the equation

$$V = IR$$

Since circuit 2 has a large resistance, a given current in circuit 2 produces a larger voltage than the same current in circuit 1, which has a small resistance. Thus a signal of variable voltage in circuit 1, such as might be produced by a human voice on a telephone, is reproduced in circuit 2, but with much greater voltage changes. That is, the input signal has been *amplified* by the junction transistor. This device replaces the large vacuum tube and is a tiny component of a printed circuit on a silicon chip.

Silicon chips are really "planar" transistors constructed from thin layers of n-type and p-type regions connected by conductors. A chip less than 1 cm wide can contain hundreds of printed circuits and can be used in computers, radios, and televisions.

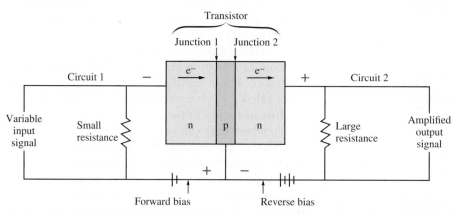

A schematic of two circuits connected by a transistor. The signal in circuit 1 is amplified in circuit 2.

Wax   Silicon dioxide

(a)

(b)

(c)

(d)

(e)

(f)

(g)

(h)

Electrical connection

Template

The steps for forming a transistor in a crystal of initially pure silicon. An integrated circuit has many n–p–n junction transistors. This figure illustrates the formation of one transistor area. The chip begins as a thin wafer of silicon that has been doped with an n-type impurity. A protective layer of silicon dioxide is then produced on the wafer by exposing it in a furnace to an oxidizing atmosphere. The next step is to produce a p-type semiconductor. In this step the surface of the oxide is covered by a light-sensitive wax, as shown in part (a). A template that allows light to shine through only in selected areas is then placed on top [part (b)], and the chip is exposed to light. The wax that has been exposed to light undergoes a chemical change that causes its solubility to be different from the unexposed wax. The unexposed wax is dissolved by using selective solvents [part (c)], and the exposed area is treated with an etching solution to dissolve the oxide coating [part (d)]. When the remaining wax is dissolved, the silicon wafer has its oxide coating intact except at the one spot (of diameter x), as shown in part (d).

Template

Exposing the wafer to a p-type impurity such as boron at about 1000°C causes a p-type semiconductor area to be formed in the exposed spot as the boron atoms diffuse into the silicon crystal [part (e)]. Next, for the formation of a small n-type area in the center of the p-type region, the wafer is again placed in the oxidizing furnace to be recoated over its entire surface with oxide. Then a new wax covering is applied, which is illuminated through a template with a transparent area indicated by y [part (f)]. The wax and oxide are then removed from the illuminated area, and the wafer is exposed to an n-type impurity to form a small n-type region, as shown in part (g). Next, conductors are layered onto the chip, giving the finished transistor [part (h)], which has two circuits connected through an n–p–n junction (see diagram on page 812). This transistor then becomes a part of a larger circuit layered onto the chip and interconnected by conductors.

The method given here for producing an integrated circuit does not represent the latest technology in this field. The manufacture of integrated circuits is a highly competitive business and changes in methodology occur almost daily.

Thus the substance becomes a better conductor. When semiconductors are doped with atoms having fewer valence electrons than the atoms of the host crystal, they are called **p-type semiconductors,** so named because the positive holes can be viewed as the charge carriers.

Most important applications of semiconductors involve the connection of a p-type and an n-type to form a **p–n junction.** Figure 16.34(a) shows a typical junction; the red circles represent excess electrons in the n-type semiconductor, and the white circles represent holes (electron vacancies) in the p-type semiconductor. At the junction a small number of electrons migrate from the n-type region into the p-type region, where there are vacancies in the low-energy MOs. The effect of these migrations is to place a negative charge on the p-type region (since it now has a surplus of electrons) and a positive charge on the n-type region (since it has lost electrons, leaving holes in its low-energy MOs). This charge buildup, called the *contact potential,* or *junction potential,* prevents further migration of electrons.

Now suppose an external electrical potential is applied by connecting the negative terminal of a battery to the p-type region and the positive terminal to the n-type region. The situation represented in Fig. 16.34(b) results. Electrons are drawn toward the positive terminal, and the resulting holes move toward the negative terminal—exactly opposite to the natural flow of electrons at the p–n junction. The junction resists the imposed current flow in this direction and is said to be under *reverse bias.* No current flows through the system.

On the other hand, if the battery is connected so that the negative terminal is connected to the n-type region and the positive terminal is connected to the p-type region [Fig. 16.34(c)], the movement of electrons (and holes) is in the

Electrons must be in singly occupied MOs to conduct a current.

Figure 16.34

The p–n junction involves the contact of a p-type and an n-type semiconductor. (a) The charge carriers of the p-type region are holes (⬤). In the n-type region, the charge carriers are electrons (⬤). (b) No current flows (reverse bias). (c) Current readily flows (forward bias). Note that each electron that crosses the boundary leaves a hole behind. Thus the electrons and the holes move in opposite directions.

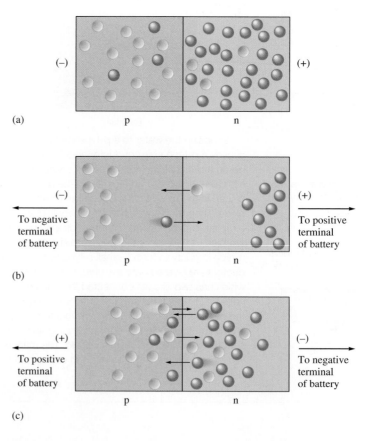

A new IBM microchip featuring silicon on a "blanket" of insulating material to protect it from temperature changes.

favored direction. The junction has low resistance, and a current flows easily. The junction is said to be under *forward bias.*

A p–n junction makes an excellent *rectifier,* a device that produces direct current (flows in one direction) from an alternating current (flows in both directions alternately). When placed in a circuit where the potential is constantly reversing, a p–n junction transmits current only under forward bias, thus converting the alternating current to a direct current. Radios, computers, and other electrical devices formerly used bulky, unreliable vacuum tubes as rectifiers. The p–n junction has revolutionized electronics; modern solid-state components contain p–n junctions in printed circuits.

16.6 | Molecular Solids

So far we have considered solids in which atoms occupy the lattice positions. In most cases such crystals can be considered to consist of one giant molecule. However, there are many types of solids that contain discrete molecular units at each lattice position. A common example is ice, where the lattice positions are occupied by water molecules [see Fig. 16.12(c)]. Other examples are dry ice (solid carbon dioxide), some forms of sulfur that contain S_8 molecules [Fig. 16.35(left)], certain forms of phosphorus that contain P_4 molecules [Fig. 16.35(right)], and the fullerenes, which are all carbon-containing molecules such as C_{60}, C_{70}, and others. These substances are characterized by

Figure 16.35

(left) Sulfur crystals (yellow) contain S_8 molecules. (right) White phosphorus contains P_4 molecules. It is so reactive with the oxygen in air that it must be stored under water.

Table 16.5

Comparison of Atomic Separations Within Molecules (Covalent Bonds) and Between Molecules (Intermolecular Interactions)

Solid	Distance Between Atoms in Molecule*	Closest Distance Between Molecules in the Solid
P_4	2.20 Å	3.8 Å
S_8	2.06 Å	3.7 Å
Cl_2	1.99 Å	3.6 Å

*The shorter distances within the molecules indicate stronger bonding.

strong covalent bonding *within* the molecules but relatively weak forces *between* the molecules. For example, it takes only 6 kJ of energy to melt 1 mole of solid water (ice) because only intermolecular (H_2O—H_2O) interactions must be overcome. However, 470 kJ of energy is required to break a mole of covalent O—H bonds. The differences between the covalent bonds within the molecules and the forces between the molecules are apparent from the comparison of the interatomic and intermolecular distances in solids shown in Table 16.5.

The forces that exist among the molecules in a molecular solid depend on the nature of the molecules. Many molecules such as CO_2, I_2, P_4, and S_8 have zero dipole moments, and the intermolecular forces are London dispersion forces. Because these forces are usually small, we might expect all these substances to be gaseous at 25°C, as is the case for carbon dioxide. However, as the size of the molecules increases, the London forces become quite large, causing many of these substances to be solids at 25°C.

When molecules do have dipole moments, their intermolecular forces are typically greater, especially when hydrogen bonding is possible. Water molecules are particularly well suited to interact with each other because each molecule has two polar O—H bonds and two lone electron pairs on the oxygen atom. This can lead to the association of four hydrogen atoms with each oxygen: two by covalent bonds and two by dipole forces, as shown in the figure in the margin. Note the two relatively short covalent oxygen–hydrogen bonds and the two longer oxygen–hydrogen dipole interactions that can be seen in the ice structure in Fig. 16.12(c).

16.7 | Ionic Solids

Ionic solids are stable, high-melting-point substances held together by the strong electrostatic forces that exist between oppositely charged ions. The principles governing the structures of ionic solids were introduced in Section 13.5. In this section we will review and extend these principles.

The structures of most binary ionic solids, such as sodium chloride, can be explained by the closest packing of spheres. Typically, the large ions, which are usually the anions, are packed in one of the closest packing arrangements (hcp or ccp), whereas the smaller cations fit into holes among the closest packed anions. The packing is done in a way that maximizes the electrostatic attractions among oppositely charged ions while minimizing the repulsions among ions with like charges.

There are three types of holes in closest packed structures:

1. Trigonal holes are formed by three spheres in the same layer [Fig. 16.36(a)].

2. Tetrahedral holes are formed when a sphere sits in the dimple of three spheres in an adjacent layer [Fig. 16.36(b)].

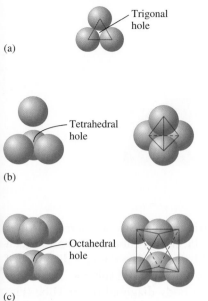

(a)

(b)

(c)

Figure 16.36
The holes that exist among closest packed uniform spheres. (a) The trigonal hole formed by three spheres in a given plane. (b) The tetrahedral hole formed when a sphere occupies a dimple in an adjacent layer. (c) The octahedral hole formed by six spheres in two adjacent layers.

3. Octahedral holes are formed between two sets of three spheres in adjoining layers of the closest packed structures [Fig. 16.36(c)].

For spheres of a given diameter, the holes increase in size as follows:

$$\text{Trigonal} < \text{tetrahedral} < \text{octahedral}$$

In fact, trigonal holes are so small that they are never occupied in binary ionic compounds. Whether the tetrahedral or octahedral holes in a given binary ionic solid are occupied depends mainly on the *relative* sizes of the anion and cation. Next, we will determine the sizes of the octahedral and tetrahedral holes and consider guidelines for their occupation by ions.

Octahedral Holes

An octahedral hole lies at the center of six equidistant spheres whose centers define an octahedron. Three of these six spheres lie in one closest packed layer and three lie in the adjacent layer [Fig. 16.36(c)]. These six spheres can be rotated to show the octahedron more clearly (Fig. 16.37).

Since the edges of all six spheres are exactly the same distance from the center of the octahedral hole, we can calculate the radius of this hole most easily by focusing on the four spheres whose centers form a square (Fig. 16.37). Note from Fig. 16.37 that R is the radius of the packed spheres, r is the radius of the octahedral hole, and d is the length of the diagonal of the square. From the Pythagorean theorem,

$$(2R)^2 + (2R)^2 = d^2$$

where
$$d = R + 2r + R = 2R + 2r = 2(R + r)$$

So we have
$$8R^2 = d^2$$

and
$$d = \sqrt{8}R = 2\sqrt{2}\,R = 2(R + r)$$

Solving for r yields

$$r = \sqrt{2}\,R - R = 1.414R - R = 0.414R$$

This result shows that an octahedral hole in a closest packed structure has a radius that is 0.414 times the radius of the packed spheres (ions).

Tetrahedral Holes

A tetrahedral hole lies at the center of four spheres whose centers form a tetrahedron [Fig. 16.37(b)]. Three of the spheres are in a given closest packed layer, and the fourth is in the next layer, nestling into the dimple formed by the other three.

Figure 16.37
(a) The octahedral hole (shown in yellow) lies at the center of six spheres that touch along the edge (e) of the square. The packed spheres (in blue) are shown smaller than actual size for clarity. (b) The diagonal of the square (d) equals $R + 2r + R$, where r is the radius of the octahedral hole and R is the radius of the packed spheres.

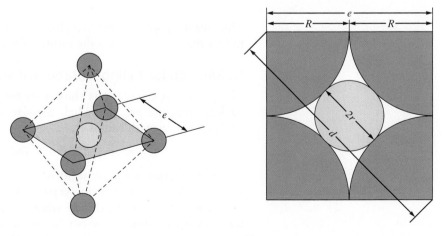

(a)

(b)

Figure 16.38
The tetrahedral hole. (a) The four spheres around a tetrahedral hole are shown inscribed in a cube. The spheres are shown much smaller than actual size. They actually touch along the face diagonal f. (b) The center of the tetrahedral hole (shown in red) is at the center of the body diagonal b (shown in purple).

(a)   (b)

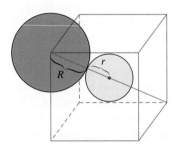

Figure 16.39
One packed sphere and its relationship to the tetrahedral hole. Note that (body diagonal)/2 = $R + r$.

The most convenient way to do geometric calculations on a tetrahedron is to inscribe it in a cube, as shown in Fig. 16.38. In this cube two spheres touch along the face diagonal of any cube face. This means that the face diagonal of the cube has length $2R$, where R is the radius of the packed spheres. The center of the tetrahedral hole is at the center of the body diagonal of the cube (Fig. 16.39). Now we will use the Pythagorean theorem twice to express the length of the body diagonal in terms of R. First, we express the face diagonal f in terms of the edge of the cube e:

$$f^2 = e^2 + e^2 = (2R)^2$$

Thus
$$e = \sqrt{2}\,R$$

Now we express the body diagonal b in terms of f and e:

$$b^2 = f^2 + e^2 = (2R)^2 + (\sqrt{2}\,R)^2$$

which leads to
$$b = \sqrt{6}\,R$$

Now the distance from the center of the body diagonal to the corner of the cube ($b/2$) is

$$r + R = \frac{b}{2} = \frac{\sqrt{6}\,R}{2} = \sqrt{\frac{3}{2}}\,R$$

   ↑   ↖

Radius of   Radius of
tetrahedral packed
hole   spheres

So
$$r = \sqrt{\frac{3}{2}}\,R - R = 1.225R - R = 0.225R$$

Thus we have shown that in a closest packed structure a tetrahedral hole has a radius that is 0.225 times the radius of the packed spheres.

Guidelines for Filling Octahedral and Tetrahedral Holes

The preceding calculations show that the tetrahedral holes in a given closest packed structure are about half the size of the octahedral holes. That is, for packed spheres with radius R,

$$r^{\text{tet}} = 0.225R \quad \text{and} \quad r^{\text{oct}} = 0.414R$$

Now picture an ionic solid MX containing M^+ cations and X^- anions, where the X^- ions form a closest packed array. Assuming that the X^- ions have radius $R-$, how do we decide where to put the smaller cations? That is, do they occupy tetrahedral or octahedral holes? To obtain the most stable solid, we want to maximize the $M^+ \cdots X^-$ interactions and minimize the $X^- \cdots X^-$

Figure 16.40

(a) A simple cubic array with X⁻ ions, with an M⁺ ion in the center (in the cubic hole). (b) The body diagonal b equals $R + 2r + R$, since X⁻ and M⁺ touch along this body diagonal.

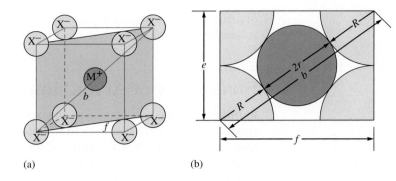

(a)   (b)

In the closest packed arrangement, the X⁻ ions are touching. However, if M⁺ ions are forced into holes in the structure that are smaller than the M⁺ ions, the X⁻ ions are forced apart, decreasing the X⁻···X⁻ repulsions. On the other hand, M⁺ and X⁻ will be in direct contact, maximizing the M⁺···X⁻ interactions.

repulsions. We can do this by putting the M⁺ ions into holes that are slightly smaller than the size of the M⁺ ions. This causes the closest packed X⁻ ions to be pushed apart slightly. Assuming that the ions behave as hard spheres, this will result in a structure where the M⁺ and X⁻ ions touch but where the X⁻ ions will no longer be touching.

With this idea in mind, we can now establish guidelines for filling the tetrahedral and octahedral holes. In terms of $r+$ (radius of M⁺) and $R-$ (radius of X⁻), if

$$0.225R- < r+ < 0.414R-$$

Size of tetrahedral holes ↑   ↑ Size of octahedral holes

then the M⁺ ions are placed in the tetrahedral holes. That is, this condition ensures that the M⁺ ions are larger than the tetrahedral holes in the closest packed array of X⁻ ions. This is what we want.

As we consider MX solids with larger and larger M⁺ ions, at some point the M⁺ ions become large enough to fill (and exceed the size of) the octahedral holes. Specifically, a cation with radius larger than $0.414R-$ should be placed in the octahedral holes rather than in the tetrahedral holes in the closest packed structure. As we continue to consider larger and larger M⁺ ions, what happens? Is there an upper limit to the size of M⁺ ions that can be forced into the octahedral holes? The answer is yes. For very large cations, the solid switches from a closest packed array of X⁻ ions to a simple cubic arrangement of X⁻ ions with an M⁺ ion in the center of each cube (Fig. 16.40).

This structure can be described as M⁺ occupying a *cubic hole*. Use of geometric arguments similar to those we have used for the tetrahedral and octahedral holes shows that for a cubic hole,

$$r+^{cubic} = 0.732R-$$

This means that for the solid MX, the M⁺ ions occupy the octahedral holes in the range where

$$0.414R- < r+ < 0.732R-$$

For large M⁺ ions ($r+ > 0.732R-$), the solid switches to the simple cubic arrangement just described.

The guidelines for filling the tetrahedral, octahedral, and cubic holes are summarized in Table 16.6.

A few more points need to be considered. The guidelines just given assume that the ions behave as hard spheres and that only ionic forces occur. Therefore, it is not surprising that these guidelines *are not always obeyed*. They just give us a starting point for describing the structures of ionic solids. In addition, although we have considered only solids of the type MX containing a 1:1 ratio

Table 16.6

Guidelines for Filling Various Types of Holes for the Ionic Solid MX

Size of M⁺	Type of Hole Filled
$0.225R- < r+ < 0.414R-$	Tetrahedral
$0.414R- < r+ < 0.732R-$	Octahedral
$0.732R- < r+$	Cubic

of cations and anions, these guidelines also apply to other types of binary ionic solids. We will consider some specific solids in the next section.

16.8 | Structures of Actual Ionic Solids

In this section we will consider some specific binary ionic solids to show how these solids illustrate the ideas of ion packing. Because an ionic solid must be neutral overall, the stoichiometry of the compound (the ratio of the numbers of anions to cations) is determined by the ion charges. On the other hand, the structure of the compound (the placement of the ions in the solid) is determined, at least to a first approximation, by the relative sizes of the ions.

Before we consider specific compounds, we need to consider the locations and relative numbers of tetrahedral and octahedral holes in the closest packed structures. The location of the tetrahedral holes in the face-centered cubic unit cell of the ccp structure is shown in Fig. 16.41(a). Note from this figure that there are eight tetrahedral holes in the unit cell. Recall from the discussion in Section 16.4 that there are four net spheres in the face-centered cubic unit cell. Thus there are *twice as many tetrahedral holes as there are packed spheres* in the closest packed structure.

The location of the octahedral holes in the face-centered cubic unit cell is shown in Fig. 16.42(a). The easiest octahedral hole to find in this structure is the one at the center of the cube. Note that this hole is surrounded by six spheres, as is required to form an octahedron. Since the remaining octahedral holes are shared with other unit cells, they are more difficult to visualize. However, it can be shown that the number of octahedral holes in the ccp structure is the *same* as the number of packed spheres.

Using these ideas, we will now consider the structures of some specific ionic solids.

The Structures of the Alkali Halides

The structure of sodium chloride, which is the prototype for most of the alkali halides, is best described as a cubic closest packed array of Cl^- ions with the Na^+ ions in all of the octahedral holes [Fig. 16.42(b)]. The relative sizes of these ions are such that $r_{Na+} = 0.66R_{Cl-}$, so this solid obeys the guidelines given previously. Note that the Cl^- ions are forced apart by the Na^+ ions, which are too large for the octahedral holes in the closest packed array of Cl^- ions. Since the number of octahedral holes is the same as the number of packed spheres, all the octahedral holes must be filled with Na^+ ions to achieve the required 1:1 stoichiometry. Most other alkali halides also have the sodium chloride structure. In fact, all the halides of lithium, sodium, potassium, and rubidium have this structure. Cesium fluoride has the sodium chloride struc-

Closest packed structures contain twice as many tetrahedral holes as packed spheres. Closest packed structures contain the same number of octahedral holes as packed spheres.

Figure 16.41
(a) The location (red ×) of a tetrahedral hole in the face-centered cubic unit cell. (b) One of the tetrahedral holes. (c) The unit cell for ZnS, where the S^{2-} ions (yellow) are closest packed, with the Zn^{2+} ions (purple) filling alternate tetrahedral holes. (d) The unit cell for CaF_2, where the Ca^{2+} ions (purple) form a face-centered cubic arrangement, with the F^- ions (yellow) in all of the tetrahedral holes.

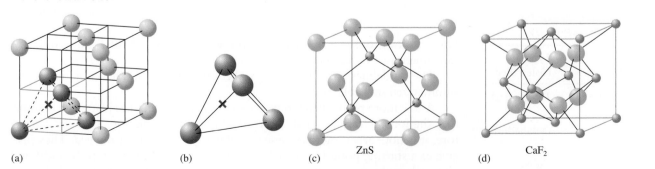

(a)   (b)   (c) ZnS   (d) CaF₂

(a)

(b)

Figure 16.42

(a) The locations (gray ×) of the octahedral holes in the face-centered cubic unit cell. (b) Representation of the unit cell for solid NaCl. The Cl⁻ ions (green spheres) have a ccp arrangement, with Na⁺ ions (gray spheres) filling all the octahedral holes. This representation shows the idealized closest packed structure of NaCl. In the actual structure, the Cl⁻ ions do not quite touch.

ture, but because of the large size of Cs^+ ions, in this case the Cs^+ ions form a cubic closest packed arrangement with the F^- ions in all the octahedral holes. On the other hand, cesium chloride, in which the Cs^+ and Cl^- ions are almost the same size, has a simple cubic structure of Cl^- ions, with each Cs^+ ion in the cubic hole in the center of each cube. The compounds cesium bromide and cesium iodide also have this latter structure.

The Structure of Zinc Sulfide

The compound ZnS illustrates another important general type of structure. In ZnS the ion sizes are such that $r_{Zn^{2+}} \approx 0.35 R_{S^{2-}}$. According to the guidelines, this should mean that the Zn^{2+} ions occupy the tetrahedral holes among the closest packed S^{2-} ions. This is exactly what is found in ZnS. However, because there are twice as many tetrahedral holes as closest packed ions, only one-half of the tetrahedral holes are occupied in zinc sulfide, producing the required 1:1 ratio of Zn^{2+} and S^{2-} ions [Fig. 16.41(c)]. Zinc sulfide has two forms: zinc blende, where the S^{2-} ions are cubic closest packed, and wurtzite, where the S^{2-} ions are hexagonal closest packed. In both cases the Zn^{2+} ions occupy half of the tetrahedral holes. The substances ZnO and CdS also show both the zinc blende and wurtzite structures.

The Structure of Calcium Fluoride

The structure of the compound CaF_2 can be described as a face-centered cubic array of Ca^{2+} ions with the F^- ions in all the tetrahedral holes.* This gives the required 1:2 ratio of Ca^{2+} and F^- ions. This structure is called the fluorite structure [Fig. 16.41(d)] and is also observed in the compounds SrF_2, $BaCl_2$, PbF_2, and CdF_2, among others.

16.9 | Lattice Defects

So far we have assumed that crystalline compounds are perfect—that is, that all the atoms, ions, or molecules are present and occupy the correct sites. Although crystalline materials are highly ordered and most of the components are where they are expected to be, all real crystals have imperfections called *lattice defects*.

Point defects refer to totally missing particles (atoms, ions, or molecules) or to cases where the particle is in a nonstandard location. A crystal with missing particles is said to have *Schottky defects* [Fig. 16.43(a)]. When ions are missing from an ionic compound, they must be missing in a way that preserves the overall electrical neutrality of the substance. For example, for every missing Ca^{2+} ion in CaF_2, there must be two missing F^- ions.

Crystals in which particles have migrated to nonstandard positions are said to exhibit *Frenkel defects* [Fig. 16.43(b)]. One group of compounds where Frenkel defects are present to the extreme is the silver halides—AgCl, AgBr, and AgI. In these compounds the anion positions are mostly those expected from closest packing ideas; however, the silver ions are distributed almost randomly in the various holes and can easily travel within the solid structure. This property is a major reason that the silver halides are so useful in photographic films.

---

*The structure of CaF_2 is not a closest packed structure because the Ca^{2+} ions that occupy the face-centered cubic sites are smaller than the F^- ions. An alternative description of this structure is a simple cubic array of F^- ions, with Ca^{2+} ions in half of the cubic holes.

Figure 16.43
Defects in crystalline ionic solids.
(a) Schottky defects, in which there are vacant sites. (b) Frenkel defects, in which an atom or an ion of either sign is present at an inappropriate site.

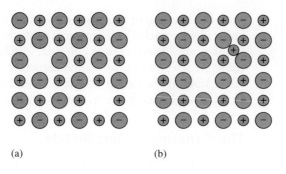

(a)   (b)

In some cases the crystal defects involve impurities that lead to *nonstoichiometric compounds*. For example, wüstite, which has the idealized formula FeO, actually varies from $Fe_{1.0}O_{1.0}$ to $Fe_{0.95}O_{1.0}$. These variations occur when some of the Fe^{2+} ions in the compound are replaced by Fe^{3+} ions in a way that preserves the electrical neutrality of the solid. There are many other examples of nonstoichiometric compounds. One extreme case involves TiO, which can vary from $Ti_{1.0}O_{0.7}$ to $Ti_{0.8}O_{1.0}$.

16.10 | Vapor Pressure and Changes of State

Now that we have considered the general properties of the three states of matter, we can explore the processes by which matter changes state. One very familiar example of a change in state occurs when a liquid evaporates from an open container. This is clear evidence that the molecules of a liquid can escape from the liquid's surface and form a gas. Called **vaporization,** or *evaporation,* this process is endothermic because energy is required to overcome the relatively strong intermolecular forces in the liquid. The energy required to vaporize 1 mole of a liquid at a pressure of 1 atm is called the standard **heat of vaporization** or the standard **enthalpy of vaporization** and is usually symbolized as $\Delta H°_{vap}$.

The endothermic nature of vaporization has great practical significance; in fact, one of the most important roles that water plays in our world is to act as a coolant. Because of the strong hydrogen bonding among its molecules in the liquid state, water has an unusually large heat of vaporization (40.7 kJ/mol). A significant portion of the sun's energy that reaches earth is spent evaporating water from the oceans, lakes, and rivers rather than warming the earth. The vaporization of water is also crucial to the body's temperature control system through evaporation of perspiration.

Vapor is the usual term for the gas phase of a substance that exists as a solid or liquid at 25°C and 1 atm.

(a)   (b)

Figure 16.44
Behavior of a liquid in a closed container. (a) Initially, net evaporation occurs as molecules are transferred from the liquid to the vapor phase, so the amount of liquid decreases. (b) As the number of vapor molecules increases, the rate of return to the liquid (condensation) increases, until finally the rate of condensation equals the rate of evaporation. The system is at equilibrium, and no further changes occur in the amounts of vapor or liquid.

Vapor Pressure

When a liquid is placed in a closed container, the amount of liquid at first decreases but eventually becomes constant. The decrease occurs because there is an initial net transfer of molecules from the liquid to the vapor phase (Fig. 16.44). However, as the number of vapor molecules increases, so does the rate of return of these molecules to the liquid. The process by which vapor molecules re-form a liquid is called **condensation**. Eventually, enough vapor molecules are present above the liquid so that the rate of condensation equals the rate of evaporation (Fig. 16.45). At this point no further net change occurs in the amount of liquid or vapor because the two opposite processes exactly balance each other; the system is at equilibrium. Note that this system is highly dynamic on the molecular level—molecules are constantly escaping from and entering the liquid at a high rate. However, there is no net change because the two opposite processes just balance each other.

Figure 16.45
The rates of condensation and evaporation over time for a liquid sealed in a closed container. The rate of evaporation remains constant, whereas the rate of condensation increases as the number of molecules in the vapor phase increases, until the two rates become equal. At this point the equilibrium vapor pressure is attained.

The pressure of the vapor present at equilibrium is called the *equilibrium vapor pressure* or, more commonly, the **vapor pressure** of the liquid. A simple barometer can measure the vapor pressure of a liquid, as shown in Fig. 16.46. The liquid is injected at the bottom of the tube of mercury and floats to the surface because the mercury is so dense. A portion of the liquid evaporates at the top of the column, producing a vapor whose pressure pushes some mercury out of the tube. When the system reaches equilibrium, the vapor pressure can be determined from the change in the height of the mercury column, since

$$P_{atm} = P_{vapor} + P_{Hg\ column}$$

Thus

$$P_{vapor} = P_{atm} - P_{Hg\ column}$$

The vapor pressures of liquids vary widely [Fig. 16.46(b)]. Liquids with high vapor pressures are said to be *volatile*—they evaporate readily from an open dish.

The vapor pressure of a liquid is principally determined by the size of the *intermolecular forces* in the liquid. Liquids in which the intermolecular forces are large have relatively low vapor pressures because the molecules need high energies to escape to the vapor phase. For example, although water has a much lower molar mass than diethyl ether, the strong hydrogen bonding forces that

Figure 16.46
(a) The vapor pressure of a liquid can be measured easily using a simple barometer of the type shown here. (b) The three liquids, water, ethanol (C_2H_5OH), and diethyl ether [($C_2H_5)_2O$], have quite different vapor pressures. Ether is by far the most volatile of the three. Note that in each case a little liquid remains (floating on the mercury).

Figure 16.47
The number of molecules in a liquid with a given energy versus kinetic energy at two temperatures ($T_1 < T_2$). Note that the proportion of molecules with enough energy to escape the liquid to the vapor phase (indicated by shaded areas) increases dramatically with temperature. This causes vapor pressure to increase markedly with temperature.

Table 16.7

The Vapor Pressure of Water as a Function of Temperature

T (°C)	P (torr)
0.0	4.579
10.0	9.209
20.0	17.535
25.0	23.756
30.0	31.824
40.0	55.324
60.0	149.4
70.0	233.7
90.0	525.8

exist among water molecules in the liquid cause water's vapor pressure to be much lower than that of diethyl ether [Fig. 16.46(b)]. In general, substances with large molar masses have relatively low vapor pressures mainly because of the large dispersion forces. The more electrons a substance has, the more polarizable it is, and the greater are the dispersion forces.

Measurements of the vapor pressure for a given liquid at several temperatures show that *vapor pressure increases significantly with temperature.* Figure 16.47 illustrates the distribution of molecular kinetic energies present in a liquid at two different temperatures. To overcome the intermolecular forces in a liquid, a molecule must have a minimum kinetic energy. As the temperature of the liquid is increased, the fraction of molecules having sufficient energy to overcome these forces and escape to the vapor phase increases markedly. Thus the vapor pressure of a liquid increases dramatically with temperature. The vapor pressure values for water at several temperatures are given in Table 16.7.

The quantitative nature of the temperature dependence of vapor pressure can be illustrated graphically. Plots of vapor pressure versus temperature for water, ethanol, and diethyl ether are shown in Fig. 16.48(a). Note the nonlinear increase in vapor pressure for all the liquids as the temperature is increased.

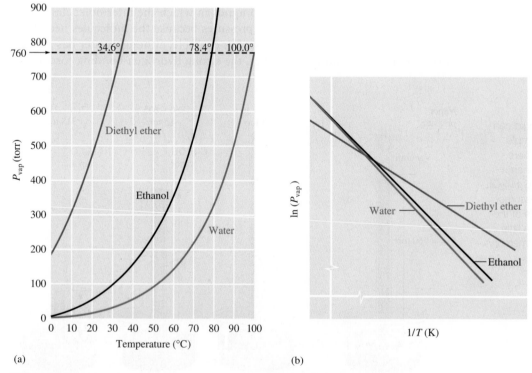

(a)

(b)

Figure 16.48
(a) The vapor pressure of water, ethanol, and diethyl ether as a function of temperature. (b) Plots of $\ln(P_{vap})$ versus $1/T$ (Kelvin temperature) of water, ethanol, and diethyl ether.

A straight line can be obtained from these data by plotting $\ln(P_{vap})$ versus $1/T$, where T is the Kelvin temperature [Fig. 16.48(b)]. We can represent this behavior by the equation

$$\ln(P_{vap}) = -\frac{\Delta H_{vap}}{R}\left(\frac{1}{T}\right) + C \tag{16.4}$$

where ΔH_{vap} is the enthalpy of vaporization, R is the universal gas constant, and C is a constant characteristic of a given liquid. Note that this equation is a simplified version of the equation obtained in Section 10.11 for the temperature dependence of an equilibrium constant:

$$\ln K = -\frac{\Delta H°}{R}\left(\frac{1}{T}\right) + \frac{\Delta S°}{R}$$

The similarity is not unexpected, since vapor pressure is an equilibrium phenomenon. Note that we can now interpret the constant C in terms of ΔS, the entropy of vaporization for a given liquid.

EXAMPLE 16.2

Using the plots in Fig. 16.48(b), determine whether water or diethyl ether has the smaller enthalpy of vaporization.

Solution When $\ln(P_{vap})$ is plotted versus $1/T$, the slope of the resulting straight line is

$$-\frac{\Delta H_{vap}}{R}$$

Note from Fig. 16.48(b) that the slopes of the lines for water and diethyl ether are both negative, as expected. Also note that the line for ether has the smaller slope. Thus ether has the smaller value of ΔH_{vap}. This makes sense because the hydrogen bonding in water causes it to have a relatively large enthalpy of vaporization.

Equation (16.4) is important for several reasons. For example, we can determine the heat of vaporization for a liquid by measuring P_{vap} at several temperatures and then evaluating the slope of a plot of $\ln(P_{vap})$ versus $1/T$. On the other hand, if we know the values of ΔH_{vap} and P_{vap} at one temperature, we can use Equation (16.4) to calculate P_{vap} at another temperature. This can be done by recognizing that the constant C does not depend on temperature. Thus, at two temperatures, T_1 and T_2, we can solve Equation (16.4) for C and then write the equality

$$\ln(P_{vap}^{T_1}) + \frac{\Delta H_{vap}}{RT_1} = C = \ln(P_{vap}^{T_2}) + \frac{\Delta H_{vap}}{RT_2}$$

which can be rearranged to

$$\ln(P_{vap}^{T_1}) - \ln(P_{vap}^{T_2}) = \frac{\Delta H_{vap}}{R}\left(\frac{1}{T_2} - \frac{1}{T_1}\right)$$

or

$$\ln\left(\frac{P_{vap}^{T_1}}{P_{vap}^{T_2}}\right) = \frac{\Delta H_{vap}}{R}\left(\frac{1}{T_2} - \frac{1}{T_1}\right) \tag{16.5}$$

Figure 16.49
Solid iodine sublimes when heated and then recrystallizes when in contact with a cold surface.

Equation (16.5) is called the Clausius–Clapeyron equation.

Like liquids, solids have vapor pressures. Figure 16.49 shows iodine vapor in equilibrium with solid iodine. At 25°C and 1 atm, iodine *sublimes*; that is, it goes directly from the solid to the gaseous state without passing through the liquid state. **Sublimation** also occurs with dry ice (solid carbon dioxide) under these conditions.

Figure 16.50
The heating curve for a given quantity of water where energy is added at a constant rate. The plateau at the boiling point is longer than the plateau at the melting point because it takes almost seven times more energy (and thus seven times the heating time) to vaporize liquid water than to melt ice. The slopes of the other lines are different because the different states of water have different molar heat capacities (the energy required to raise the temperature of 1 mole of a substance by 1°C).

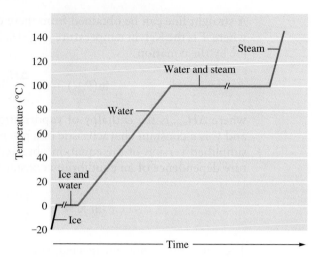

Ionic solids such as NaCl and NaF have very high melting points and very high enthalpies of fusion because of the strong ionic forces in these solids. At the other extreme is $O_2(s)$, a molecular solid containing nonpolar molecules with weak intermolecular forces.

Changes of State

What happens when a solid is heated? Typically, it melts to form a liquid. If the heating continues, the liquid at some point boils and forms the vapor phase. This process can be represented by a **heating curve:** a plot of temperature versus time for a process where energy is added at a constant rate.

The heating curve for water is given in Fig. 16.50. As energy flows into the ice, the random vibrations of the water molecules increase as the temperature rises. Eventually, the molecules become so energetic that they break loose from their lattice positions, and the change from solid to liquid occurs. This is indicated by a plateau at 0°C on the heating curve. At this temperature, called the **melting point,** all the added energy is used to disrupt the ice structure by breaking the hydrogen bonds, thus increasing the potential energy of the water molecules. The enthalpy change that occurs at the melting point when a solid melts is called the **heat of fusion** (or more accurately, the **enthalpy of fusion**) ΔH_{fus}. The melting points and enthalpies of fusion for several representative solids are listed in Table 16.8.

The temperature remains constant until all the solid has changed to liquid; then it begins to increase again. At 100°C the liquid water reaches its *boiling point,* and the temperature again remains constant as the added energy is used to vaporize the liquid. When all the liquid is changed to vapor, the temperature again begins to rise. Note that changes of state are physical changes; although intermolecular forces have been overcome, no chemical bonds have been broken. If the water vapor were heated to much higher temperatures, the water mole-

Table 16.8

Melting Points and Enthalpies of Fusion for Several Representative Solids

Compound	Melting Point (°C)	Enthalpy of Fusion (kJ/mol)
O_2	−218	0.45
HCl	−114	1.99
HI	−51	2.87
CCl_4	−23	2.51
$CHCl_3$	−64	9.20
H_2O	0	6.01
NaF	992	29.3
NaCl	801	30.2

cules would break down into the individual atoms. This is a chemical change, since covalent bonds are broken. We no longer have water after it occurs.

The melting and boiling points for a substance are determined by the vapor pressures of the solid and liquid states. Figure 16.51 shows the vapor pressures of solid and liquid water as functions of temperature near 0°C. Note that below 0°C the vapor pressure of ice is less than the vapor pressure of liquid water. Also note that the vapor pressure of ice has a larger temperature dependence than that of the liquid. That is, the vapor pressure of ice increases more rapidly for a given rise in temperature than does the vapor pressure of water. Thus, as the temperature of the solid is increased, a point is eventually reached where the *liquid and solid have identical vapor pressures*. This is the melting point.

These concepts can be demonstrated experimentally using the apparatus illustrated in Fig. 16.52, where ice occupies one compartment and liquid water the other. Consider the following cases.

Case 1: *A temperature at which the vapor pressure of the solid is greater than that of the liquid.* At this temperature the solid requires a higher pressure of vapor than the liquid to be in equilibrium with the vapor. Thus, as vapor is released from the solid to try to achieve equilibrium, the liquid absorbs vapor in an attempt to reduce the vapor pressure to its equilibrium value. The net effect is a conversion from solid to liquid through the vapor phase. In fact, no solid can exist under these conditions. The amount of solid steadily decreases and the volume of liquid increases. Finally, there is only liquid in the right compartment, which comes to equilibrium with the water vapor, and no further changes occur in the system. The temperature for Case 1 must be *above the melting point* of ice, since only the liquid state can exist.

Case 2: *A temperature at which the vapor pressure of the solid is less than that of the liquid.* This is the opposite of the situation in Case 1. In this case the liquid requires a higher pressure of vapor than the solid to be in equilibrium with the vapor. So the liquid gradually disappears, and the amount of ice increases. Finally, only the solid remains, which achieves equilibrium with the vapor. This temperature must be *below the melting point* of ice, since only the solid state can exist.

Case 3: *A temperature at which the vapor pressures of the solid and liquid are identical.* In this case the solid and liquid states have the same vapor pressure, so they can coexist in the apparatus at equilibrium simultaneously with the vapor. This temperature represents the *melting point*, where both the solid and liquid states can exist.

The melting and boiling points will be defined more precisely later in this section.

Figure 16.51

The vapor pressures of solid and liquid water as a function of temperature. The data for liquid water below 0°C are obtained from supercooled water. The data for solid water above 0°C are estimated by extrapolation of vapor pressure from below 0°C.

Figure 16.52

An apparatus that allows solid and liquid water to interact only through the vapor state.

Constant pressure of 1 atmosphere

— Movable piston

— Liquid water

Figure 16.53

Water in a closed system with a pressure of 1 atm exerted on the piston. No bubbles can form within the liquid as long as the vapor pressure is less than 1 atm.

Charles D. Winters

A boiling chip releasing air bubbles acts as a nucleating agent for the large bubbles that form when water boils.

Figure 16.54

The supercooling of water. The extent of supercooling is given by S.

We can now describe the melting point of a substance more precisely. The **normal melting point** is defined as *the temperature at which the solid and liquid states have the same vapor pressure under conditions where the total pressure is 1 atm.*

Boiling occurs when the vapor pressure of a liquid becomes equal to the pressure of its environment. The **normal boiling point** of a liquid is *the temperature at which the vapor pressure of the liquid is exactly 1 atm.* This concept can be understood by considering Fig. 16.53. At temperatures where the vapor pressure of the liquid is less than 1 atm, no bubbles of vapor can form because the pressure on the surface of the liquid is greater than the pressure in any spaces in the liquid where bubbles are trying to form. Only when the liquid reaches a temperature at which the pressure of vapor in the spaces in the liquid is 1 atm can bubbles form and boiling occur.*

However, observed changes of state do not always occur exactly at the boiling point or melting point. For example, water can be readily **supercooled;** that is, it can be cooled below 0°C at 1 atm pressure and still remain in the liquid state. Supercooling occurs because, as it is cooled, the water may not achieve the degree of organization necessary to form ice at 0°C; thus it continues to exist as the liquid. At some point the correct ordering occurs and ice rapidly forms, releasing energy in the exothermic process and bringing the temperature back up to the melting point, where the remainder of the water freezes (Fig. 16.54).

A liquid can also be **superheated,** or raised to temperatures above its boiling point, especially if it is heated rapidly. Superheating can occur because bubble formation in the interior of the liquid requires that many high-energy molecules gather in the same vicinity. This may not happen at the boiling point, especially if the liquid is heated rapidly. If the liquid becomes superheated, the vapor pressure in the liquid is greater than the atmospheric pressure. Once a bubble does form, since its internal pressure is greater than that of the atmosphere, it can burst before rising to the surface, blowing the surrounding liquid out of the container. This phenomenon is called *bumping* and has ruined many experiments. It can be avoided by adding boiling chips to the flask containing the liquid. Boiling chips are bits of porous ceramic material containing trapped air that escapes on heating, forming tiny bubbles that act as "starters" for vapor bubble formation. These starter bubbles allow a smooth onset of boiling as the boiling point is reached.

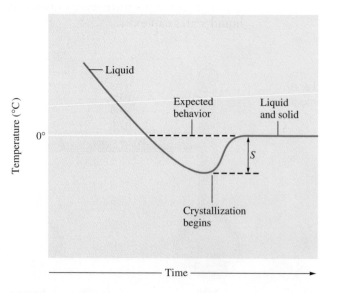

Temperature (°C)

Liquid

Expected behavior

Liquid and solid

0°

S

Crystallization begins

Time

---

*Note that in real life the bubbles seen forming in water as it is being heated to boiling arise from the expulsion of dissolved air.

16.11 | Phase Diagrams

A **phase diagram** is a convenient way of representing the phases of a substance as a function of temperature and pressure. For example, the phase diagram for water (Fig. 16.55) shows which state exists at a given temperature and pressure. It is important to recognize that a phase diagram describes conditions and events for a pure substance in a *closed* system of the type represented in Fig. 16.53, where no material can escape into the surroundings and no air is present.

To show how to interpret the phase diagram for water, we will consider heating experiments at several pressures, shown by the dashed lines in Fig. 16.56.

Experiment 1: *Pressure is 1 atm.* This experiment begins with the cylinder shown in Fig. 16.53 completely filled with ice at a temperature of −20°C and with the piston exerting a pressure of 1 atm directly on the ice (there is no air space). Since at temperatures below 0°C the vapor pressure of ice is less than 1 atm—which is the constant external pressure on the piston—no vapor is present in the cylinder. As the cylinder is heated, ice remains the only component until the temperature reaches 0°C, where the ice changes to liquid water as energy is added. This is the normal melting point of water. When all the solid has changed to liquid, the temperature again rises. At this point the cylinder contains only liquid water. *No vapor is present* because the vapor pressure of liquid water under these conditions is less than 1 atm, the constant external pressure on the piston. Heating continues until the temperature of the liquid

Below the critical temperature and pressure, the gaseous state of a substance is often referred to as a vapor.

Figure 16.55
The phase diagram for water. T_m represents the normal melting point; T_3 and P_3 denote the triple point; T_b represents the normal boiling point; T_c represents the critical temperature; P_c represents the critical pressure. The negative slope of the solid/liquid line reflects the fact that the density of ice is less than that of liquid water. Note that the solid/liquid phase line continues indefinitely.

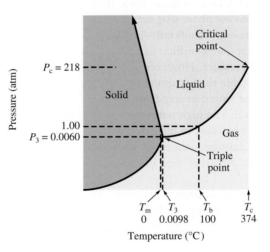

Figure 16.56
Diagrams of various heating experiments on samples of water in closed systems.

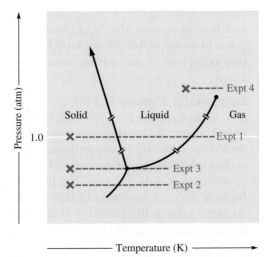

Chemical Insights   Making Diamonds at Low Pressures: Fooling Mother Nature

In 1955 Robert H. Wentorf, Jr., accomplished something that borders on alchemy—he turned peanut butter into diamonds. He and his coworkers at the General Electric Research and Development Center also changed roofing pitch, wood, coal, and many other carbon-containing materials into diamonds using a process involving temperatures of approximately 2000°C and pressures of about 100,000 atm. Although the first diamonds made by this process looked like black sand because of the impurities present, the process has now been developed to a point such that beautiful, clear, gem-quality diamonds can be produced. General Electric now has the capacity to produce 150 million carats (30,000 kg) of diamonds, virtually all of which is "diamond grit" used for industrial purposes such as abrasive coatings on cutting tools.

The high temperatures and pressures used in the GE process for making diamonds make sense if one looks at the accompanying phase diagram for carbon. Note that graphite—not diamond—is the most stable form of carbon under ordinary conditions of temperature and pressure. However, diamond becomes more stable than graphite at very high pressures (as one would expect from the greater density of diamond). The high temperature used in the GE process is necessary to disrupt the bonds in graphite so that diamond (the most stable form of carbon at the high pressures used in the process) can form.

This brings us again to the difference between kinetic and thermodynamic stability. Under normal conditions of temperature and pressure, graphite has a lower free energy than diamond (by about 2 kJ/mol). However, to get from diamond to graphite requires a large expenditure of energy. This is the energy of activation that determines the rate of a reaction at a particular temperature. As a result of this high activation energy, diamonds formed at the high pressures found deep in the earth's crust can be brought to the earth's surface by natural geological processes and continue to exist for millions of years. Although these diamonds are thermodynamically unstable (relative to graphite), they are kinetically stable. That is, the reaction to change diamond to graphite is favored by thermodynamics but is disfavored by kinetics—it is so slow that diamonds *almost* last forever.* Diamond is said to be metastable (thermodynamically unstable but kinetically stable) under normal conditions of temperature and pressure.

We have seen that diamond formed at high pressures is "trapped" in this form by slow kinetics, but this process is very expensive. Can diamond be formed at low pressures? The phase diagram for carbon says "no." However, researchers have found that under the right conditions diamonds can be "grown" at low pressures. The process used is called chemical vapor deposition (CVD). CVD uses an energy source to release carbon atoms from a compound such as methane into a steady flow of hydrogen gas (some of which is catalytically dissociated to produce hydrogen atoms). The carbon atoms then deposit as a

water reaches 100°C. At this point the vapor pressure of liquid water is 1 atm, and boiling occurs; the liquid changes to vapor. This is the normal boiling point of water. After all the liquid has been converted to steam, the temperature again rises as the heating continues. The cylinder now contains only water vapor.

Experiment 2: *Pressure is 2.0 torr.* Again we start with ice as the only component in the cylinder at −20°C. The pressure exerted by the piston in this case is only 2.0 torr. As heating proceeds the temperature rises to −10°C, where the ice changes directly to vapor through the process of sublimation. Sublimation occurs when the vapor pressure of ice is equal to the external pressure, which in this case is only 2.0 torr. No liquid water appears under these conditions because the vapor pressure of liquid water is always greater than 2.0 torr; thus it cannot exist at this pressure. If liquid water were placed in a cylinder at such a low pressure, it would vaporize immediately.

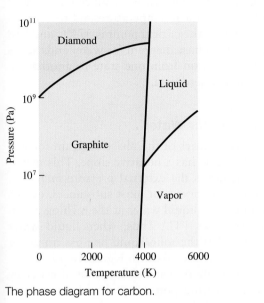

The phase diagram for carbon.

of course, diamond is kinetically trapped. The major advantage of CVD is that there is no need for the extraordinarily high pressures used in the traditional process for synthesizing diamonds.

The first products with diamond films are already on the market. Audiophiles can buy tweeters that have diaphragms coated with a thin diamond film that limits sound distortion. Watches with diamond-coated crystals are planned, as are diamond-coated windows in infrared scanning devices used in analytical instruments and missile guidance systems. These applications represent only the beginning for diamond-coated products.

In addition, the CVD process is now being used to synthesize gem-quality diamonds. Companies have now been formed that can grow gem-quality diamonds as large as several carats. These synthetic diamonds are virtually indistinguishable from diamonds formed by natural processes. This has tremendous implications for the natural diamond industry, which is worth more than $60 billion per year.

diamond film on a surface maintained at a temperature between 600°C and 900°C. Why does diamond form on this surface rather than the thermodynamically favored graphite? Nobody is sure, but it has been suggested that at these relatively high temperatures the diamond structure grows faster than the graphite structure, and so diamond is favored kinetically under these conditions. It has also been suggested that the hydrogen atoms present react much faster with graphite fragments than with diamond fragments, effectively removing any graphite from the growing film. Once it forms,

---

*In Morocco, a 50-km-long slab called Beni Bousera contains chunks of graphite that were probably once diamonds formed in the deposit when it was buried 150 km underground. As this slab slowly rose to the surface over millions of years, the very slow reaction changing diamond to graphite had time to occur. That is, on this time scale thermodynamic control could exert itself. In the diamond-rich kimberlite deposits in South Africa, which rise to the surface much faster, kinetic control exists.

Experiment 3: *Pressure is 4.588 torr.* Again we start with ice as the only component in the cylinder at −20°C. In this case the pressure exerted on the ice by the piston is 4.588 torr. As the cylinder is heated, no new phase appears until the temperature reaches 0.0098°C. At this point, called the **triple point,** solid and liquid water have identical vapor pressures of 4.588 torr. Thus *at 0.0098°C and 4.588 torr all three states of water are present.* In fact, *only* under these conditions can all three states of water coexist.

Experiment 4: *Pressure is 225 atm.* In this experiment we start with liquid water in the cylinder at 300°C; the pressure exerted by the piston on the water is 225 atm. Liquid water can be present at this temperature because of the high external pressure. As the temperature increases, something happens that we did not observe in the first three experiments: The liquid gradually changes into a vapor but goes through an intermediate "fluid" region, which is neither true liquid nor vapor. This is quite unlike the behavior at lower temperatures and pressures, say, at 100°C and 1 atm, where the temperature remains constant while a definite phase change from liquid to vapor occurs. The unusual behavior at 300°C and 225 atm occurs because the conditions are beyond the critical point for water. The **critical temperature** can be defined as the temperature above which the vapor cannot be liquefied no matter what pressure is applied. The **critical pressure** is the pressure required to produce liquefaction *at* the critical temperature. Together, the critical temperature and the critical pressure define the **critical point**. For water, the critical point is 374°C and 218 atm. Note that the liquid/vapor line on the phase diagram for water ends at the critical point. Beyond this point the transition from one state to another involves the intermediate "fluid" region just described.

Applications of the Phase Diagram for Water

There are several additional interesting features of the phase diagram for water. Note that the solid/liquid boundary line has a negative slope. This means that the melting point of water *decreases* as the external pressure *increases*. This behavior, which is opposite to that observed for most substances, occurs because the density of ice is *less* than that of liquid water at the melting point. (The maximum density of water occurs at 4°C.) Thus, when liquid water freezes, its volume increases. Also note that the solid/liquid line has no upper limit. It extends indefinitely, as indicated by the arrow in Figure 16.55.

We can account for the effect of pressure on the melting point of water by using the following reasoning. At the melting point, liquid and solid water coexist—they are in dynamic equilibrium. What happens if we apply pressure to this system? When subjected to increased pressure, matter reduces its volume. This behavior is most dramatic for gases but it also occurs for condensed states. Since a given mass of ice at 0°C has a larger volume than the same mass of liquid water, the system can reduce its volume in response to the increased pressure by changing to liquid. Thus, at 0°C and an external pressure greater than 1 atm, water is liquid. In other words, the freezing point of water is less than 0°C when the pressure is greater than 1 atm.

Figure 16.57 illustrates the effect of pressure on ice. At the point × on the phase diagram, ice is subjected to increased pressure at constant temperature. Note that as the pressure is increased, the solid/liquid line is crossed, indicating that the ice melts. It has long been suggested that this is what happens in ice skating. The narrow blade of the skate exerts a large pressure, since the skater's weight is supported by the tiny area of the blade. If the pressure is high enough, this would cause the ice to melt, providing liquid water to lubricate the passing skate. However, there is now doubt that this is what happens. Recent experiments suggest that the pressure of an ice skate is not sufficient to melt the ice. In fact, new research on the structure of ice indicates that even at temperatures far below freezing the water molecules on the surface of ice vibrate faster than expected, forming a quasi-liquid with a structure intermediate between that of liquid and solid. This would make the surface of the ice slippery enough to aid in ice skating.

Ice's lower density has other implications. When water freezes in a pipe or an engine block, it expands and breaks the container. For this reason water pipes are insulated in cold climates and antifreeze is used in water-cooled engines. The lower density of ice also means that ice formed on rivers and lakes floats, providing a layer of insulation that helps prevent bodies of water from freezing solid in the winter. Aquatic life can therefore continue to live through periods of freezing temperatures.

A liquid boils at the temperature where the vapor pressure of the liquid equals the external pressure. Thus the boiling point of a substance, like the melt-

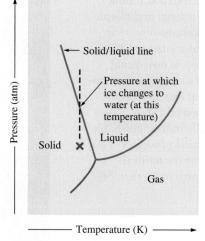

Figure 16.57
The phase diagram for water. At point × on the phase diagram, water is a solid. However, as the external pressure is increased while the temperature remains constant (indicated by the vertical dashed line), the solid/liquid line is crossed and the ice melts.

The motion of an ice skate blade over ice is a complex phenomenon, and other factors, such as frictional heating, may be important.

Table 16.9

Boiling Point of Water at Various Locations

Location	Feet Above Sea Level	P_{atm} (torr)	Boiling Point (°C)
Top of Mt. Everest, Tibet	29,028	240	70
Top of Mt. McKinley, Alaska	20,320	340	79
Top of Mt. Whitney, Calif.	14,494	430	85
Leadville, Colo.	10,150	510	89
Top of Mt. Washington, N.H.	6,293	590	93
Boulder, Colo.	5,430	610	94
Madison, Wis.	900	730	99
New York City, N.Y.	10	760	100
Death Valley, Calif.	−282	770	100.3

ing point, depends on the external pressure. This is why water boils at different temperatures at different elevations (Table 16.9), and any cooking carried out in boiling water will be affected by this variation. For example, it takes longer to hard-boil an egg in Leadville, Colorado (elevation 10,150 ft), than in San Diego (sea level), since water boils at a lower temperature, 89°C, in Leadville.

As we mentioned earlier, the phase diagram for water describes a closed system. Therefore, we must be very cautious in using the phase diagram to explain the behavior of water in a natural setting, such as on the earth's surface. For example, in dry climates (low humidity), snow and ice seem to sublime—a minimum amount of slush is produced. Wet clothes put on an outside line at temperatures below 0°C freeze and then dry while frozen. However, the phase diagram (Fig. 16.55) shows that ice should *not* be able to sublime at normal atmospheric pressures. What is happening in these cases? Ice in the natural environment is not in a closed system. The pressure is provided by the atmosphere rather than by a solid piston. This means that the vapor produced over the ice can escape from the immediate region as soon as it is formed. The vapor does not come to equilibrium with the solid, and the ice slowly disappears. Sublimation, which seems forbidden by the phase diagram, does seem to occur under these conditions, but it is not sublimation under equilibrium conditions.

The Phase Diagram for Carbon Dioxide

The phase diagram for carbon dioxide (Fig. 16.58) differs significantly from that for water. The solid/liquid line has a positive slope, since solid carbon dioxide is more dense than liquid carbon dioxide. The triple point for carbon dioxide occurs at 5.1 atm and −56.6°C, and the critical point occurs at 72.8 atm and 31°C. At a pressure of 1 atm, solid carbon dioxide sublimes at −78°C, a property that leads to its common name, *dry ice*. No liquid phase occurs under normal atmospheric conditions, making dry ice a convenient coolant.

Carbon dioxide is often used in fire extinguishers, where it exists as a liquid at 25°C under high pressures. Liquid carbon dioxide released from the extinguisher into the environment at 1 atm immediately changes to a vapor. Being heavier than air, this vapor smothers the fire by keeping oxygen away from the flame. The liquid/vapor transition is highly endothermic, so cooling also results, which helps to put out the fire. The "fog" produced by a carbon dioxide extinguisher is a mixture of solid carbon dioxide and moisture frozen from the air.

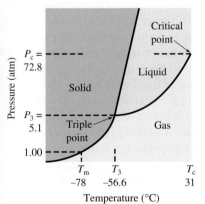

Figure 16.58

The phase diagram for carbon dioxide. The liquid state does not exist at a pressure of 1 atm. The solid/liquid line has a positive slope, since the density of solid carbon dioxide is greater than that of liquid carbon dioxide.

Chemical Insights | Smaller Can Be Better

Because of the emphasis on crystalline materials in introductory chemistry courses, there is a tendency for students to think that most materials are single crystals—that is, that the regular array of the crystal is found without interruption throughout the entire material. But this is not true. There are some materials that are essentially single crystals—the silicon used for integrated circuits and the diamond in an engagement ring are two examples. However, most materials are polycrystalline. They contain multitudes of tiny crystalline fragments called *grains*. For example, if you examine ordinary copper metal under a 100-power microscope, you will see a patchwork quilt of grains, with no two grains the same size or shape. Each of these grains is a single crystal in which the copper atoms are arranged in a regular array. The metal is composed of grains rather than being a large single crystal because when a typical solid forms there are many nucleation sites—many single crystals start growing at about the same time. However, these microcrystals are not oriented identically in space, so when they grow large enough to contact each other, they form grain boundaries (see the figure).

Thus the solid is polycrystalline—it is composed of many grains (single crystals) of various sizes oriented in all different directions. The properties of a piece of copper, such as its hardness, color, electrical conductivity, and so on, depend on both the properties of the individual grains and the relationships and interactions among the grains. Copper is such a good electrical conductor, for example, because electrons can move easily within each grain and can jump readily from one grain to another.

Because the behavior of polycrystalline materials is so sensitive to the way the grains are packed together, the properties of these materials can be dramatically changed by altering the sizes and shapes of the grains. One person who is studying these effects is Dick Siegel of Rennselaer Polytechnic Institute in Troy, New York. Siegel has found that he can make copper that is five times harder than normal copper by lowering the grain size by a factor of 10,000—a change in size proportional to going

Grains of nanophase palladium magnified 200,000 times by an electron microscope.

from a boulder the size of a car to a grain of sand. Siegel has also been able to change the properties of ceramics from their characteristic brittle nature to being flexible and deformable by reducing the grain sizes. In addition, some ceramic materials that are opaque with normal grain sizes become transparent when the grain sizes are reduced.

Because the grain sizes in these substances are on the order of 10 to 100 nm (10^{-9} m), they are usually called "nanocrystalline" materials. The formation of nanocrystalline materials can be accomplished by mechanical grinding of the normal materials in high-speed ball mills for many hours or by controlling the growth of the grains as the solid forms. The latter technique usually works best. For example, to form nanocrystalline copper, Dick Siegel heats a bar of regular pure copper with an electric current to "boil off" individual copper atoms into a chamber filled with helium gas. As clusters containing a few atoms form, they are carried to a liquid nitrogen–cooled "cold finger" by the helium flow. A Teflon blade scrapes off the nanosized clusters and they fall into a compactor to be shaped into pellets of nanograined copper.

Siegel has formed a company called Nanophase Technologies Corporation to commercialize his work. The opportunities look bright for nanocrystalline materials. Sometimes smaller is definitely better.

16.12 | Nanotechnology

A nanometer is so small that it is difficult to imagine. For example, the period at the end of this sentence has a diameter of approximately 500,000 nm. As another example, a man's beard typically grows about a nanometer in the time it takes to raise a razor to his face.

The field of nanotechnology is typically defined as dealing with particles approximately 1 to 100 nm in size. Because of the tiny size of nanoscale particles, they behave quite differently from normal-sized particles, even though the two types of particles may contain the same types of atoms. An important reason for these different behaviors is the incredible surface area present in a sample of nanosized particles. For example, about one gram of nanobeads used in a device to filter water contains an amazing 1000 square meters of surface area. This extremely high surface area of nanoparticles is very useful for catalyzing the decomposition of soil contaminants. For instance, several studies have shown that nanosized metallic particles are very efficient catalysts for the breakdown of the chlorinated solvents often found in contaminated soil.*

Another reason for the unusual properties of nanoparticles is that their tiny size allows them to penetrate into very small spaces. For example, one application of this characteristic developed at Rice University involves using gold nanoparticles (~120 nm in diameter) to penetrate the tangle of capillaries supplying blood to a cancerous tumor. The gold particles (called nanoshells) are then heated with infrared radiation, which kills the surrounding cancer cells.

The field of nanotechnology is virtually exploding today. The number of scientists involved in the field and the amount of money spent on nanoscience are increasing at an incredible rate. Although it is a multidisciplinary field, nanotechnology has its basis in chemistry, and many chemists are now working in this area.

Carbon Nanotubes

The roots of the science of nanotechnology can be traced back to the discovery in 1985 of C_{60} molecules (buckminsterfullerene) by Richard Smalley and his coworkers at Rice University. Although "bucky balls" have not found many practical uses, a close relative, the carbon nanotube, has proved to have great practical potential. Carbon nanotubes contain networks of carbon atoms in interconnected six-membered rings (like "chicken wire") organized into slender tubes (Fig. 16.59). The main attraction of nanotubes is that they are over 50 times stronger than steel wire at one-sixth the weight and can carry a thousand times more electrical current than copper wire. The problem with carbon nanotubes is that when they are formed, they occur as a hodgepodge of tubes of different diameters. Sorting the tubes by size has proved to be a difficult task. However, a new technique pioneered by Michael S. Arnold and his coworkers at Northwestern University appears very promising. In this method, surfactants are added to the jumble of raw nanotubes, which makes the nanotubes water soluble. The solution of nanotubes is then added to a solution whose density increases with depth, and the mixture is centrifuged at high speeds. This treatment causes the tubes to sort themselves into bands (Fig. 16.60). So far only small amounts of sorted nanotubes have been produced, but the method appears capable of being scaled up.

Carbon nanotubes are now used in a variety of consumer products. They strengthen high-end sporting equipment such as tennis rackets, bicycle handle-

Figure 16.59
Forest of nanotubes.

*"Special Treatment," *Sci. News* **167** (2005): 266.

Chemical Insights | Nanogenerators: Power from Motion

Many groups of researchers are working on ways to convert motions involved in everyday life into energy to power electronic devices. This new technology is based on the properties of piezoelectric nanowires and nanocrystals. Piezoelectric materials produce an electric current when they are stressed in some way, usually by bending.

One strategy being pursued is the inclusion of piezoelectric fibers into clothes to convert motions such as walking into electric currents that could power MP3 players or cell phones. One researcher working on this problem is Liwei Lin, a mechanical engineer at the University of California at Berkeley. Lin's goal is to weave long, thin fibers of piezoelectric polyvinylidene fluoride (PVDF) into clothes. Lin calculates that if a million PVDF fibers are included in a single garment, enough energy could be harvested to power an iPod or to keep a smart phone charged.

Other researchers hope to use piezoelectric nanomaterials inside the body to power sensors or even pacemakers. A group led by Zhong Lin Wang, Director of the Center for Nanostructure Characterization at the Georgia Institute of Technology, uses piezoelectric zinc oxide nanowires on a gold-coated surface, which are then attached to a platinum-coated silicon wafer. By placing these nanowires in the artery of a rat, an alternating current can be produced as the heart beats, creating a fluctuating flow of blood that moves the piezoelectric wires. Wang has also been able to boost the power of this device by connecting it to an enzyme-based "biofuel" cell that collects energy from the oxidation of glucose in the blood.

Although current power levels are much smaller than those needed to power an iPod, much work is being done to ramp up the efficiency of these nanopiezoelectric devices.

bars and frames, and golf club shafts. One of the major potential uses for nanotubes is in various electrical devices. Although carbon nanotubes can conduct prodigious amounts of current with very little production of heat, scientists have not yet figured out how to make them into practical devices. As of now, the longest electricity-conducting nanotube in existence measures only a fraction of a centimeter. Research is proceeding to find ways to make practical nanotubes.

Figure 16.60
Graphic illustrating the process of sorting nanotubes.

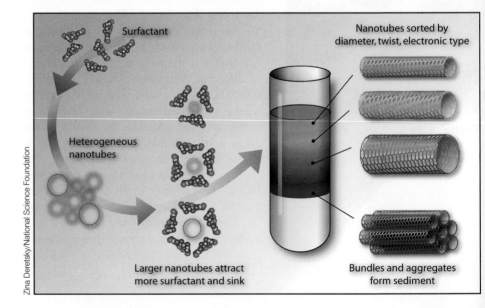

Zina Deretsky/National Science Foundation

Medical Applications of Nanotechnology

Nanoscale species are ideal for biomedical operations because they are comparable in size to many biological entities. A biomedical species smaller than about 50 nm can easily enter most cells (10,000–20,000 nm in diameter), and those smaller than 20 nm can exit blood vessels. As a result, nanoscale biomedical devices can easily interact with biomolecules inside and outside cells.

One rapidly expanding use of nanotechnology involves the transportation via nanoparticles of molecules that improve the spectroscopic detection of disease-causing cells such as cancer cells. Examples include nanosized "quantum dots" composed of cadmium selenide, zinc sulfide, and an organic polymer that can be attached to molecules. These labeled molecules then can be tracked by fluorescence techniques. Another example involves the attachment of magnetic resonance imaging (MRI) contrast agents to tiny cancer cells, making tumor cells as small as 2 mm detectable by MRI.

A further medical use of nanoscale devices is for targeting cancer cells. In this application the "nanocapsule" contains molecules lethal to tumors. The nanodevice is linked to a molecule that has a specific affinity for the receptors on the surfaces of cancer cells. Once at the site of the cancer, the nanocapsule dumps its lethal contents into the cancer cell. One method for releasing the contents of the nanocapsule is through a tiny valve developed at UCLA by Jeffrey I. Zink and his coworkers. The valves consist of dumbbell-like molecules that can be rotated by the energy from a single electron.

Nanotoxicology

The explosive growth of nanotechnology has brought with it some safety concerns about these materials.* The unique properties of nanoparticles raise the possibility of unique types of toxicity. One of the problems with studying the toxicity of nanoparticles is their almost infinite variety. For example, dozens of types of samples of carbon nanotubes are available containing different sized particles and different contaminating substances depending on how they were made. Researchers are now trying to decide how to design a systematic approach to the very complex problem of testing the possible toxicity of the great variety of nanoparticles. Some early results indicate that caution is in order as we continue to develop this technology.

*"Particular Problems," *Sci. News* **169** (2006): 280.

Key Terms

Section 16.1
condensed states of matter
intermolecular forces
dipole–dipole attraction
hydrogen bonding
London dispersion forces

Section 16.2
surface tension
capillary action
viscosity

Section 16.3
crystalline solid
amorphous solid

For Review

 WL and Chemistry
Sign in at **www.cengage.com/owl** to:
• View tutorials and simulations, develop problem-solving skills, and complete online homework assigned by your professor.
• Download Go Chemistry mini lecture modules for quick review and exam prep from OWL (or purchase them at **www.cengagebrain.com**)

Condensed states of matter: liquids and solids
■ Held together by forces among the component molecules, atoms, or ions
■ Liquids exhibit properties such as surface tension, capillary action, and viscosity that depend on the forces among the components

lattice
unit cell
X-ray diffraction
Bragg equation
ionic solid
molecular solid
atomic solid

Section 16.4
closest packing
hexagonal closest packed (hcp)
   structure
cubic closest packed (ccp)
   structure
body-centered cubic (bcc) unit
   cell
electron sea model
band model
bands
conduction band
alloy
substitutional alloy
interstitial alloy

Section 16.5
network solid
silica
silicate
glass
ceramic
aluminosilicate
semiconductor
n-type semiconductor
p-type semiconductor
p–n junction

Section 16.10
vaporization
heat of vaporization
enthalpy of vaporization (ΔH_{vap})
condensation
vapor pressure
sublimation
heating curve
melting point
heat of fusion
enthalpy of fusion (ΔH_{fus})
normal melting point
normal boiling point
supercooled
superheated

Section 16.11
phase diagram
triple point
critical temperature
critical pressure
critical point

Dipole–dipole forces
- Attractions among molecules with dipole moments
- Hydrogen bonding is a particularly strong form of dipole–dipole attraction
  - Occurs in molecules containing hydrogen bonded to a highly electronegative element such as nitrogen, oxygen, or fluorine
  - Produces unusually high boiling points

London dispersion forces
- Caused by instantaneous dipoles that form in atoms or nonpolar molecules

Crystalline solids
- Have a regular arrangement of components often represented as a lattice; the smallest repeating unit of the lattice is called the unit cell
- Classified by the types of components:
  - Atomic solids (atoms)
  - Ionic solids (ions)
  - Molecular solids (molecules)
- Arrangement of the components can be determined by X-ray analysis

Metals
- Structure is modeled by assuming atoms to be uniform spheres
  - Closest packing
    - Hexagonal
    - Cubic
- Metallic bonding can be described in terms of two models
  - Electron sea model: valence electrons circulate freely among the metal cations
  - Band model: electrons are assumed to occupy molecular orbitals
    - Conduction bands: closely spaced molecular orbitals with empty electron spaces
- Alloys: mixtures with metallic properties
  - Substitutional
  - Interstitial

Network solids
- Contain giant networks of atoms covalently bound together
- Examples are diamond and graphite
- Silicates are network solids containing Si—O—Si bridges that form the basis for many rocks, clays, and ceramics

Semiconductors
- Very pure silicon is "doped" with other elements
  - n-type: doping atoms typically contain five valence electrons (one more than silicon)
  - p-type: doping elements typically contain three valence electrons
- Modern electronics are based on devices with p–n junctions

Molecular solids
- Components are discrete molecules
- Intermolecular forces are typically weak, leading to relatively low boiling and melting points

Ionic solids
- Components are ions
- Interionic forces are relatively strong, leading to solids with high melting and boiling points

- Many structures consist of closest packing of the larger ions with the smaller ions in tetrahedral or octahedral holes

Phase changes
- The change from liquid to gas (vapor) is called vaporization or evaporation
- Condensation is the reverse of vaporization
- Equilibrium vapor pressure: the pressure that occurs over a liquid or solid in a closed system when the rate of evaporation equals the rate of condensation
  - Liquids whose components have high intermolecular forces have relatively low vapor pressures
  - Normal boiling point: the temperature at which the vapor pressure of a liquid equals one atmosphere
  - Normal melting point: the temperature at which a solid and its liquid have the same vapor pressure (at 1 atm external pressure)
- Phase diagram
  - Shows what state exists at a given temperature and pressure in a closed system
  - Triple point: temperature at which all three phases exist simultaneously
  - Critical point: defined by the critical temperature and pressure
    - Critical temperature: the temperature above which the vapor cannot be liquefied no matter the applied pressure
    - Critical pressure: the pressure required to produce liquefaction at the critical temperature

Discussion Questions

These questions are designed to be considered by groups of students in class. Often these questions work well for introducing a particular topic in class.

1. It is possible to balance a paper clip on the surface of water in a beaker. If you add a bit of soap to the water, however, the paper clip will sink. Explain how the paper clip can float and why it sinks when soap is added.

2. Consider a sealed container half-filled with water. Which statement best describes what occurs in the container?
   a. Water evaporates until the air is saturated with water vapor; at this point, no more water evaporates.
   b. Water evaporates until the air is overly saturated (supersaturated) with water, and most of this water recondenses; this cycle continues until a certain amount of water vapor is present, and then the cycle ceases.
   c. The water does not evaporate, because the container is sealed.
   d. Water evaporates, and then water evaporates and recondenses simultaneously and continuously.
   e. Water evaporates until it is eventually all in vapor form.
   Explain each choice, and justify the best choice. For those you did not choose, explain why they are incorrect.

3. Explain the following: You add 100 mL of water to a 500-mL round-bottom flask and heat the water until it is boiling. You remove the heat, stopper the flask, and the boiling stops. You then run cool water over the neck of the flask, and the boiling begins again. It seems as though you are boiling water by cooling it.

4. Is it possible for the dispersion forces in a particular substance to be stronger than hydrogen bonding forces in another substance? Explain your answer.

5. Does the nature of intermolecular forces change when a substance goes from a solid to a liquid or from a liquid to a gas? What causes a substance to undergo a phase change?

6. Generally, the vapor pressure of a liquid is related to (there may be more than one answer)
   a. amount of the liquid   c. temperature
   b. atmospheric pressure   d. intermolecular forces
   Explain.

7. What is meant by the term *vapor pressure*? Why do liquids have a vapor pressure? Do all liquids have a vapor pressure? What about solids? How does vapor pressure change with changing temperature? Why? What happens, if anything, when the vapor pressure of a liquid is equal to atmospheric pressure?

8. Consider an open beaker of water. Over time, the water evaporates. As the water is evaporating, is the vapor pressure increasing, decreasing, or staying the same? Why? What is the vapor pressure of water at 100°C? How do you know?

9. How do the following physical properties depend on the strength of intermolecular forces? Explain.
   a. surface tension
   b. viscosity
   c. melting point
   d. boiling point
   e. vapor pressure

10. Use the kinetic molecular theory to explain why a liquid in an insulated vessel gets cooler as it evaporates.

Exercises

A blue exercise number indicates that the answer to that exercise appears at the back of this book and a solution appears in the *Solutions Guide*.

Intermolecular Forces and Physical Properties

11. What are intermolecular forces? How do they differ from intramolecular forces? What are dipole–dipole forces? How do typical dipole–dipole forces differ from hydrogen-bonding interactions? In what ways are they similar? What are London dispersion forces? How do typical London dispersion forces differ from dipole–dipole forces? In what ways are they similar?

12. List the major types of intermolecular forces in order of increasing strength. Is there some overlap? That is, can the strongest London dispersion forces be greater than some dipole–dipole forces? Give examples of such instances.

13. Why is ΔH_{vap} for water much greater than ΔH_{fus}? What does this reveal concerning changes in intermolecular forces in going from solid to liquid to vapor?

14. Rationalize why chalk (calcium carbonate) has a higher melting point than motor oil (large compounds made from carbon and hydrogen), which has a higher melting point than water, which engages in relatively strong hydrogen-bonding interactions.

15. Identify the most important types of interparticle forces present in the solids of each of the following substances.
   a. Ar
   b. HCl
   c. HF
   d. $CaCl_2$
   e. CH_4
   f. CO
   g. $NaNO_3$
   h. NH_4Cl
   i. Teflon, $CF_3(CF_2CF_2)_nCF_3$
   j. polyethylene, $CH_3(CH_2CH_2)_nCH_3$
   k. $CHCl_3$
   l. NH_3
   m. NO
   n. BF_3

16. Predict which substance in each of the following pairs would have the greater intermolecular forces.
   a. CO_2 or OCS
   b. SeO_2 or SO_2
   c. $CH_3CH_2CH_2NH_2$ or $H_2NCH_2CH_2NH_2$
   d. CH_3CH_3 or H_2CO
   e. CH_3OH or H_2CO

17. In each of the following groups of substances, pick the one that has the given property. Justify your answer.
   a. highest boiling point: HBr, Kr, or Cl_2
   b. highest freezing point: H_2O, NaCl, or HF
   c. lowest vapor pressure at 25°C: Cl_2, Br_2, or I_2
   d. lowest freezing point: N_2, CO, or CO_2

   e. lowest boiling point: CH_4, CH_3CH_3, or $CH_3CH_2CH_3$
   f. highest boiling point: HF, HCl, or HBr
   g. lowest vapor pressure at 25°C: $CH_3CH_2CH_3$,

   $$\underset{\text{O}}{\overset{\text{O}}{\underset{\|}{}}}$$

   CH_3CCH_3, or $CH_3CH_2CH_2OH$

18. In each of the following groups of substances, pick the one that has the given property. Justify each answer.
   a. highest boiling point: CCl_4, CF_4, CBr_4
   b. lowest freezing point: LiF, F_2, HCl
   c. lowest vapor pressure at 25°C: CH_3OCH_3, CH_3CH_2OH, $CH_3CH_2CH_3$
   d. greatest viscosity: H_2S, HF, or H_2O_2
   e. greatest heat of vaporization: H_2CO, CH_3CH_3, CH_4
   f. smallest enthalpy of fusion: I_2, CsBr, or CaO

19. Rationalize the difference in boiling points for each of the following pairs of substances:
   a. *n*-pentane $CH_3CH_2CH_2CH_2CH_3$ 36.2°C

   $$\text{neopentane} \quad H_3C-\underset{\underset{\text{CH}_3}{|}}{\overset{\overset{\text{CH}_3}{|}}{C}}-CH_3 \quad 9.5°C$$

   b. HF   20°C
      HCl   −85°C
   c. HCl   −85°C
      LiCl   1360°C
   d. *n*-pentane $CH_3CH_2CH_2CH_2CH_3$ 36.2°C
      n-hexane $CH_3CH_2CH_2CH_2CH_2CH_3$ 69°C

20. Rationalize the following differences in physical properties in terms of intermolecular forces. Compare the first three substances with each other, compare the last three with each other, and then compare all six. Can you account for any anomalies?

Substance	bp (°C)	mp (°C)	ΔH_{vap} (kJ/mol)
Benzene, C_6H_6	80	6	33.9
Naphthalene, $C_{10}H_8$	218	80	51.5
Carbon tetrachloride	76	−23	31.8
Acetone, CH_3COCH_3	56	−95	31.8
Acetic acid, CH_3CO_2H	118	17	39.7
Benzoic acid, $C_6H_5CO_2H$	249	122	68.2

21. Consider the compounds Cl_2, HCl, F_2, NaF, and HF. Which compound has a boiling point closest to that of argon? Explain.

22. Consider the following melting point data:

Compound	NaCl	MgCl₂	AlCl₃	SiCl₄	PCl₃	SCl₂	Cl₂
mp (°C)	801	708	190	−70	−91	−78	−101
Compound	NaF	MgF₂	AlF₃	SiF₄	PF₅	SF₆	F₂
mp (°C)	997	1396	1040	−90	−94	−56	−220

Account for the trends in melting points for the two series of compounds in terms of interparticle forces.

23. Consider the following electrostatic potential diagrams:

Ethanol   Propane

Acetone

Rank the compounds from lowest to highest boiling point, and explain your answer.

24. Consider the following enthalpy changes:

$$F^-(g) + HF(g) \longrightarrow FHF^-(g) \qquad \Delta H = -155 \text{ kJ/mol}$$

$$(CH_3)_2C=O(g) + HF(g) \longrightarrow (CH_3)_2C=O\text{---}HF(g)$$
$$\Delta H = -46 \text{ kJ/mol}$$

$$H_2O(g) + HOH(g) \longrightarrow H_2O\text{---}HOH \quad \text{(in ice)}$$
$$\Delta H = -21 \text{ kJ/mol}$$

How do the strengths of hydrogen bonds vary with the electronegativity of the element to which hydrogen is bonded? Where in the preceding series would you expect hydrogen bonds of the following type to fall?

—N---H—O—   and   —N---H—N⟨

25. Using the heats of fusion and vaporization for water, calculate the change in enthalpy for the sublimation of water:

$$H_2O(s) \longrightarrow H_2O(g)$$

Using the ΔH value given in Exercise 24 and the number of hydrogen bonds formed to each water molecule, estimate what portion of the intermolecular forces in ice can be accounted for by hydrogen bonding.

Properties of Liquids

26. List some physical characteristics that distinguish solids from liquids from gases.

27. Define the following terms, and describe how each depends on the strength of the intermolecular forces.
    a. surface tension   d. boiling point
    b. viscosity   e. vapor pressure
    c. melting point

28. The shape of the meniscus of water in a glass tube is different from that of mercury in a glass tube. Why?

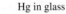

H₂O in glass   Hg in glass

29. Explain why water forms into beads on a waxed car finish.

30. Some of the physical properties of H₂O and D₂O are as follows:

Property	H₂O	D₂O
Density at 20°C (g/mL)	0.997	1.108
Boiling point (°C)	100.00	101.41
Melting point (°C)	0.00	3.79
ΔH°_{vap} (kJ/mol)	40.7	41.61
ΔH°_{fus} (kJ/mol)	6.01	6.3

Account for the differences. (*Note:* D is a symbol often used for ^2H, the deuterium isotope of hydrogen.)

31. Hydrogen peroxide (H_2O_2) is a syrupy liquid with a relatively low vapor pressure and a normal boiling point of 152.2°C. Rationalize the differences between these physical properties and those of water.

32. Carbon diselenide (CSe_2) is a liquid at room temperature. The normal boiling point is 125°C, and the melting point is −45.5°C. Carbon disulfide (CS_2) is also a liquid at room temperature, with normal boiling and melting points of 46.5°C and −111.6°C, respectively. How do the strengths of the intermolecular forces vary from CO_2 to CS_2 to CSe_2? Explain your answer.

Structures and Properties of Solids

33. Distinguish between the solids in the following pairs.
    a. crystalline solid and amorphous solid
    b. ionic solid and molecular solid
    c. molecular solid and network solid
    d. metallic solid and network solid

34. What is closest packing? What is the difference between hexagonal closest packing and cubic closest packing? What is the unit cell for each closest packing arrangement?

35. Compare and contrast the structures of the following solids.
    a. diamond and graphite
    b. silica, silicates, and glass

36. Compare and contrast the structures of the following solids.
    a. $CO_2(s)$ and $H_2O(s)$
    b. $NaCl(s)$ and $CsCl(s)$

37. Will a crystalline solid or an amorphous solid give a simpler X-ray diffraction pattern? Why?

38. What type of solid will each of the following substances form?
    a. CO_2 e. Ru i. NaOH m. GaAs
    b. SiO_2 f. I_2 j. U n. BaO
    c. Si g. KBr k. $CaCO_3$ o. NO
    d. CH_4 h. H_2O l. PH_3 p. GeO_2

39. A topaz crystal has an interplanar spacing (d) of 1.36 Å (1 Å $= 1 \times 10^{-10}$ m). Calculate the wavelength of the X ray that should be used if $\theta = 15.0°$ (assume $n = 1$).

40. X rays of wavelength 2.63 Å were used to analyze a crystal. The angle of first-order diffraction ($n = 1$ in the Bragg equation) was 15.55°. What is the spacing between crystal planes, and what would be the angle for second-order diffraction ($n = 2$)?

41. X rays from a copper X-ray tube ($\lambda = 1.54$ Å) were diffracted at an angle of 14.22° by a crystal of silicon. Assuming first-order diffraction ($n = 1$ in the Bragg equation), what is the interplanar spacing in silicon?

42. In what array (simple cubic, body-centered cubic, and face-centered cubic) do atoms pack most efficiently (greatest percent of space occupied by spheres)? Support your answer mathematically.

43. Calcium has a cubic closest packed structure as a solid. Assuming that calcium has an atomic radius of 197 pm, calculate the density of solid calcium.

44. A certain form of lead has a cubic closest packed structure with an edge length of 492 pm. Calculate the value of the atomic radius and the density of lead.

45. Nickel has a face-centered cubic unit cell. The density of nickel is 6.84 g/cm³. Calculate a value for the atomic radius of nickel.

46. You are given a small bar of an unknown metal X. You find the density of the metal to be 10.5 g/cm³. An X-ray diffraction experiment measures the edge of the face-centered cubic unit cell as 4.09 Å (1 Å $= 10^{-10}$ m). Identify X.

47. Titanium metal has a body-centered cubic unit cell. The density of titanium is 4.50 g/cm³. Calculate the edge length of the unit cell and a value for the atomic radius of titanium. (*Hint:* In a body-centered arrangement of spheres, the spheres touch along the body diagonal.)

48. Barium has a body-centered cubic structure. If the atomic radius of barium is 222 pm, calculate the density of solid barium.

49. The radius of gold is 144 pm and the density is 19.32 g/cm³. Does elemental gold have a face-centered cubic structure or a body-centered cubic structure?

50. The radius of tungsten is 137 pm and the density is 19.3 g/cm³. Does elemental tungsten have a face-centered cubic structure or a body-centered cubic structure?

51. Use the band model to describe differences among insulators, conductors, and semiconductors. Also use the band model to explain why each of the following increases the conductivity of a semiconductor.
    a. increasing the temperature
    b. irradiating with light
    c. adding an impurity

    How do conductors and semiconductors differ as to the effect of temperature on electrical conductivity?

52. How can an n-type semiconductor be produced from pure germanium? How can a p-type semiconductor be produced from pure germanium? Explain how n-type and p-type semiconductors increase electrical conductivity over that of pure germanium.

53. Explain how a p–n junction makes an excellent rectifier.

54. What is an alloy? Explain the differences in structure between substitutional and interstitial alloys. Give an example of each type.

55. Selenium is a semiconductor used in photocopying machines. What type of semiconductor would be formed if a small amount of indium impurity were added to pure selenium?

56. The Group 3A/Group 5A semiconductors are composed of equal amounts of atoms from Group 3A and Group 5A—for example, InP and GaAs. These types of semiconductors are used in light-emitting diodes and solid-state lasers. What would you add to make a p-type semiconductor from pure GaAs? How would you dope pure GaAs to make an n-type semiconductor?

57. The band gap in aluminum phosphide (AlP) is 2.5 electron-volts (1 eV $= 1.6 \times 10^{-19}$ J). What wavelength of light is emitted by an AlP diode?

58. An aluminum antimonide solid-state laser emits light with a wavelength of 730. nm. Calculate the band gap in joules.

59. The structures of some common crystalline substances follow. Show that the net composition of each unit cell corresponds to the correct formula of each substance.

Cl Na   Cl Cs

S   Zn   O   Ti

60. The unit cell for nickel arsenide is shown below. What is the formula of this compound?

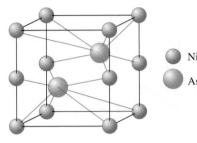

Ni

As

61. Describe, in general, the structures of ionic solids. Compare and contrast the structures of sodium chloride and zinc sulfide. How many tetrahedral holes and octahedral holes are there per closest packed anion? In zinc sulfide, why are only one-half of the tetrahedral holes filled with cations?

62. Assume the two-dimensional structure of an ionic compound M_xA_y is

What is the empirical formula of this ionic compound?

63. Cobalt fluoride crystallizes in a closest packed array of fluoride ions, with the cobalt ions filling one-half of the octahedral holes. What is the formula of this compound?

64. The compounds Na_2O, CdS, and ZrI_4 all can be described as cubic closest packed anions with the cations in tetrahedral holes. What fraction of the tetrahedral holes is occupied for each case?

65. The structure of manganese fluoride can be described as a simple cubic array of manganese ions with fluoride ions at the center of each edge of the cubic unit cell. What is the charge of the manganese ions in this compound?

66. The unit cell of MgO is shown below.

Does MgO have a structure like that of NaCl or ZnS? If the density of MgO is 3.58 g/cm³, estimate the radius (in centimeters) of the O^{2-} anions and the Mg^{2+} cations.

67. From the density of cesium chloride (3.97 g/cm³), calculate the distance between the centers of adjacent Cs^+ and Cl^- ions in the solid. Compare this value with the expected distance based on the sizes of the ions (Fig. 13.8). The ionic radius of Cs^+ is 169 pm.

68. A given sample of wüstite has the formula $Fe_{0.950}O_{1.00}$. Calculate the fraction of iron ions present as Fe^{3+}. What fraction of the sites normally occupied by Fe^{2+} must be vacant in this solid?

69. Use the relative ionic radii in Fig. 13.8 to predict the structures expected for CsBr and KF. Do these predictions agree with observed structures? The ionic radius of Cs^+ is 169 pm.

70. MnO has either the NaCl type structure or the CsCl type structure. The edge length of the MnO unit cell is 4.47×10^{-8} cm, and the density of MnO is 5.28 g/cm³.
    a. Does MnO crystallize in the NaCl type or the CsCl type structure?
    b. Assuming that the ionic radius of oxygen is 140. pm, estimate the ionic radius of manganese.
    c. Does the calculated cation-to-anion radius ratio for MnO substantiate your answer in part a? Explain.

71. Superalloys have been made of nickel and aluminum. The alloy owes its strength to the formation of an ordered phase, called the *gamma-prime phase*, in which Al atoms are at the corners of a cubic unit cell and Ni atoms are at the face centers. What is the composition (relative numbers of atoms) for this phase of the nickel–aluminum superalloy?

72. The memory metal, nitinol, is an alloy of nickel and titanium. It is called a memory metal because after being deformed, a piece of nitinol wire will return to its original shape. (See *Chem. Matters*, October 1993, pp. 4–7.) The structure of nitinol consists of a simple cubic array of Ni atoms and an inner penetrating simple cubic array of Ti atoms. In the extended lattice, a Ti atom is found at the center of a cube of Ni atoms; the reverse is also true.
    a. Describe the unit cell for nitinol.
    b. What is the empirical formula of nitinol?
    c. What are the coordination numbers (number of nearest neighbors) of Ni and Ti in nitinol?

73. A mineral crystallizes in a cubic closest packed array of oxygen ions with aluminum ions in some of the octahedral holes and magnesium ions in some of the tetrahedral holes. Deduce the formula of this mineral, and predict the fraction of octahedral holes and tetrahedral holes that are filled by the various cations.

74. Perovskite is a mineral containing calcium, titanium, and oxygen. The following diagrams represent the unit cell.

Titanium

Calcium

Oxygen

a. What is the formula of perovskite?

b. An alternative way of drawing the unit cell of perovskite has calcium at the center of each cubic unit cell. What are the positions of the titanium and oxygen atoms in this representation of the unit cell? Show that the formula for perovskite is the same for both unit cell representations.

c. How many oxygen atoms surround a given Ti atom in each representation of the unit cell?

75. Materials containing the elements Y, Ba, Cu, and O that are superconductors (electrical resistance equals zero) at temperatures above that of liquid nitrogen were recently discovered. The structures of these materials are based on the perovskite structure. Were they to have the ideal perovskite structure, the superconductors would have the structure shown in part (a) of the accompanying figure.

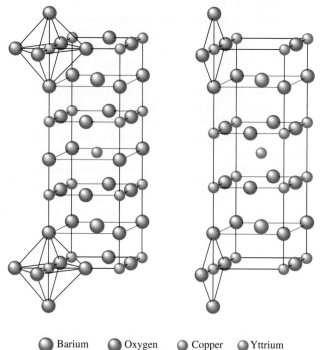

● Barium ● Oxygen ● Copper ● Yttrium

(a) Ideal perovskite structure   (b) Actual structure of superconductor

a. What is the formula of this ideal perovskite material?

b. How is this structure related to the perovskite structure discussed in Exercise 74?

These materials, however, do not act as superconductors unless they are deficient in oxygen. The structure of the actual superconducting phase appears to be that shown in part (b) of the figure.

c. What is the formula of this material?

Phase Changes and Phase Diagrams

76. Define each of the following.
    a. evaporation   e. melting
    b. condensation   f. enthalpy of vaporization
    c. sublimation   g. enthalpy of fusion
    d. boiling   h. heating curve

77. What do we mean when we say that a liquid is *volatile?* Do volatile liquids have large or small vapor pressures at room temperature? What strengths of intermolecular forces occur in highly volatile liquids?

78. Describe what is meant by dynamic equilibrium in terms of the vapor pressure of a liquid.

79. How does each of the following affect the rate of evaporation of a liquid in an open dish?
    a. intermolecular forces
    b. temperature
    c. surface area

80. Consider the following vapor pressure versus temperature plot for three different substances A, B, and C.

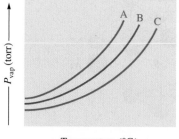

If the three substances are CH_4, SiH_4, and NH_3, match each curve to the correct substance.

81. When a person has a high fever, one therapy used to reduce the fever is an "alcohol rub." Explain how the evaporation of alcohol from a person's skin removes heat energy from the body.

82. Why is a burn from steam typically much more severe than a burn from boiling water?

83. A plot of $\ln(P_{vap})$ versus $1/T$ (K) is linear with a negative slope. Why is this the case?

84. In Breckenridge, Colorado, the typical atmospheric pressure is 520. torr. What is the boiling point of water ($\Delta H_{vap} = 40.7$ kJ/mol) in Breckenridge? What pressure would have to be applied to steam at 350.°C to condense the steam to liquid water?

85. Carbon tetrachloride (CCl_4) has a vapor pressure of 213 torr at 40.°C and 836 torr at 80.°C. What is the normal boiling point of CCl_4?

86. The normal boiling point for acetone is 56.5°C. At an elevation of 5300 ft, the atmospheric pressure is 630. torr. What would be the boiling point of acetone ($\Delta H_{vap} = 32.0$ kJ/mol) at this elevation? What would be the vapor pressure of acetone at 25.0°C at this elevation?

87. Plot the following data, and from the graph determine ΔH_{vap} for magnesium and lithium. In which metal is the bonding stronger?

Vapor Pressure (mm Hg)	Temperature (°C)	
	Li	Mg
1.	750.	620.
10.	890.	740.
100.	1080.	900.
400.	1240.	1040.
760.	1310.	1110.

88. From the following data for liquid nitric acid, determine its heat of vaporization and normal boiling point.

Temperature (°C)	Vapor Pressure (mm Hg)
0	14.4
10.	26.6
20.	47.9
30.	81.3
40.	133
50.	208
80.	670.

89. A substance has the following properties:

			Specific Heat Capacities
ΔH_{vap}	20 kJ/mol	$C_{(s)}$	3.0 J g^{-1} °C^{-1}
ΔH_{fus}	5.0 kJ/mol	$C_{(l)}$	2.5 J g^{-1} °C^{-1}
bp	75°C	$C_{(g)}$	1.0 J g^{-1} °C^{-1}
mp	−15°C		

Sketch a heating curve for the substance, starting at −50°C.

90. Use the heating–cooling curve below to answer the following questions.

Heat added at a constant rate

a. What is the freezing point of the liquid?
b. What is the boiling point of the liquid?
c. Which is greater, the heat of fusion or the heat of vaporization? Explain each term, and explain how the heating–cooling curve above helps you to answer the question.

91. How much energy does it take to convert 0.500 kg of ice at −20.°C to steam at 250.°C? Specific heat capacities: ice, 2.1 J g^{-1} °C^{-1}; liquid, 4.2 J g^{-1} °C^{-1}; steam, 2.0 J g^{-1} °C^{-1}; ΔH_{vap} = 40.7 kJ/mol; ΔH_{fus} = 6.01 kJ/mol.

92. Consider a 75.0-g sample of $H_2O(g)$ at 125°C. What phase or phases are present when 215 kJ of energy is removed from this sample? (See Exercise 91.)

93. A 0.250-g chunk of sodium metal is cautiously dropped into a mixture of 50.0 g of water and 50.0 g of ice, both at 0°C. The reaction is

$$2Na(s) + 2H_2O(l) \longrightarrow 2NaOH(aq) + H_2(g)$$
$$\Delta H = -368 \text{ kJ}$$

Will the ice melt? Assuming the final mixture has a specific heat capacity of 4.18 J g^{-1} °C^{-1}, calculate the final temperature.

94. A 20.0-g sample of ice at −10.0°C is mixed with 100.0 g of water at 80.0°C. Calculate the final temperature of the mixture assuming no heat loss to the surroundings. The heat capacities of $H_2O(s)$ and $H_2O(l)$ are 2.08 J g^{-1} °C^{-1} and 4.18 J g^{-1} °C^{-1}, respectively, and the enthalpy of fusion for ice is 6.01 kJ/mol.

95. An ice cube tray contains enough water at 22.0°C to make 18 ice cubes, each of which has a mass of 30.0 g. The tray is placed in a freezer that uses CF_2Cl_2 as a refrigerant. The heat of vaporization of CF_2Cl_2 is 158 J/g. What mass of CF_2Cl_2 must be vaporized in the refrigeration cycle to convert all the water at 22.0°C to ice at −5.0°C? The heat capacities for $H_2O(s)$ and $H_2O(l)$ are 2.08 J g^{-1} °C^{-1} and 4.18 J g^{-1} °C^{-1}, respectively, and the enthalpy of fusion for ice is 6.01 kJ/mol.

96. In regions with dry climates, evaporative coolers are used to cool air. A typical electric air conditioner is rated at 1.00×10^4 Btu/h (1 Btu, or British thermal unit, equals the amount of energy needed to raise the temperature of 1 lb of water by 1°F). How much water must be evaporated each hour to dissipate as much heat as a typical electric air conditioner?

97. Compare and contrast the phase diagrams of water and carbon dioxide. Why doesn't CO_2 have a normal melting point and a normal boiling point, whereas water does? The slopes of the solid/liquid lines in the phase diagrams of H_2O and CO_2 are different. What do the slopes of the solid/liquid lines indicate in terms of the relative densities of the solid and liquid states for each substance? How do the melting points of H_2O and CO_2 depend on pressure? How do the boiling points of H_2O and CO_2 depend on pressure? Rationalize why the critical temperature for H_2O is greater than that for CO_2.

98. Define *critical temperature* and *critical pressure*. In terms of the kinetic molecular theory, why is it impossible for a substance to exist as a liquid above its critical temperature?

99. The critical point of NH_3 is 132°C and 111 atm, and the critical point of N_2 is −147°C and 34 atm. Which of these substances cannot be liquefied at room temperature no matter how much pressure is applied? Explain.

100. Like most substances, bromine exists in one of the three typical phases. Br_2 has a normal melting point of −7.2°C and a normal boiling point of 59°C. The triple point for Br_2 is −7.3°C and 40 torr, and the critical point is 320°C and 100 atm. Using this information, sketch a phase diagram for bromine indicating the points described above. Based on your phase diagram, order the three phases from least dense to most dense. What is the stable phase of Br_2 at room temperature and 1 atm? Under what temperature conditions can liquid bromine never exist? What phase changes occur as the temperature of a sample of bromine at 0.10 atm is increased from −50°C to 200°C?

101. Consider the following phase diagram. What phases are present at points *A* through *H*? Identify the triple point, normal boiling point, normal freezing point, and critical point. Which phase is denser, solid or liquid?

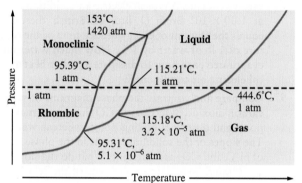

102. Use the accompanying phase diagram for sulfur to answer the following questions. (The phase diagram is not to scale.)

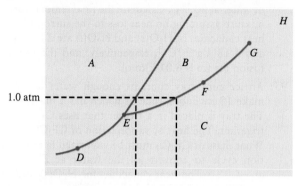

a. How many triple points are in the phase diagram?
b. What phases are in equilibrium at each of the triple points?
c. What phase is stable at room temperature and 1.0 atm pressure?
d. Can monoclinic sulfur exist in equilibrium with sulfur vapor?
e. What are the normal melting point and normal boiling point of sulfur?
f. Which is the denser solid phase, monoclinic or rhombic sulfur?

103. Use the accompanying phase diagram for carbon to answer the following questions.
a. How many triple points are in the phase diagram?
b. What phases can coexist at each triple point?
c. What happens if graphite is subjected to very high pressures at room temperature?

d. If we assume that the density increases with an increase in pressure, which is more dense, graphite or diamond?

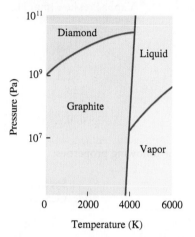

104. Iodine, like most substances, exhibits only three phases: solid, liquid, and vapor. The triple point of iodine is at 90 torr and 115°C. Which of the following statements concerning liquid I_2 must be true? Explain your answer.
a. $I_2(l)$ is more dense than $I_2(g)$.
b. $I_2(l)$ cannot exist above 115°C.
c. $I_2(l)$ cannot exist at 1 atmosphere pressure.
d. $I_2(l)$ cannot have a vapor pressure greater than 90 torr.
e. $I_2(l)$ cannot exist at a pressure of 10 torr.

105. The melting point of a fictional substance X is 225°C at 10.0 atm. If the density of the solid phase of X is 2.67 g/cm³ and the density of the liquid phase is 2.78 g/cm³ at 10.0 atm, predict whether the normal melting point of X will be less than, equal to, or greater than 225°C. Explain.

106. Consider the following data for xenon:

Triple point:	−121°C, 280 torr
Normal melting point:	−112°C
Normal boiling point:	−107°C

Which is more dense, Xe(s) or Xe(l)? How do the melting point and boiling point of xenon depend on pressure?

107. Some water is placed in a sealed glass container connected to a vacuum pump (a device used to pump gases from a container), and the pump is turned on. The water appears to boil and then freezes. Explain these changes by using the phase diagram for water. What would happen to the ice if the vacuum pump was left on indefinitely?

Additional Exercises

108. Oil of wintergreen, or methyl salicylate, has the following structure:

mp = −8°C

Methyl 4-hydroxybenzoate is another molecule with exactly the same molecular formula; it has the following structure:

mp = 127°C

Account for the large difference in the melting points of the two substances.

109. You have three covalent compounds with three very different boiling points. All of the compounds have similar molar mass and relative shape. Explain how these three compounds could have very different boiling points.

110. Boron nitride (BN) exists in two forms. The first is a slippery solid formed from the reaction of BCl_3 with NH_3, followed by heating in an ammonia atmosphere at 750°C. Subjecting the first form of BN to a pressure of 85,000 atm at 1800°C produces a second form that is the second hardest substance known. Both forms of BN remain solids to 3000°C. Suggest structures for the two forms of BN.

111. How could you experimentally determine whether TiO_2 is an ionic solid or a network solid?

112. When wet laundry is hung on a clothesline on a cold winter day, it freezes but eventually dries. Explain.

113. Consider the following data concerning four different substances.

Compound	Conducts Electricity as a Solid	Other Properties
B_2H_6	No	Gas at 25°C
SiO_2	No	High mp
CsI	No	Aqueous solution Conducts electricity
W	Yes	High mp

Label the four substances as either ionic, network, metallic, or molecular solids.

114. A special vessel (see Fig. 16.52) contains ice and supercooled water (both at −10°C) connected by vapor space. Describe what happens to the amounts of ice and water as time passes.

115. Consider a cation in a trigonal hole. What size ion will just fit in the hole if the packed spheres have radius R?

116. Use the diagram of the unit cell for the hexagonal closest packed structure in Fig. 16.14 to determine the net number of atoms in the hcp unit cell.

117. Argon has a cubic closest packed structure as a solid. Assuming that argon has a radius of 190. pm, calculate the density of solid argon.

118. Rubidium chloride has the sodium chloride structure at normal pressures but assumes the cesium chloride structure at high pressures. What ratio of densities is expected for these two forms? Does this change in structure make sense on the basis of simple models?

119. A certain oxide of titanium is 28.31% oxygen by mass and contains a mixture of Ti^{2+} and Ti^{3+} ions. Determine the formula of the compound and the relative numbers of Ti^{2+} and Ti^{3+} ions.

120. Spinel is a mineral that contains 37.9% aluminum, 17.1% magnesium, and 45.0% oxygen, by mass, and has a density of 3.57 g/cm³. The edge of the cubic unit cell measures 809 pm. How many of each type of atom are present in the unit cell?

121. A metallic solid with atoms in a face-centered cubic unit cell with an edge length of 392 pm has a density of 21.45 g/cm³. Calculate the atomic mass and the atomic radius of the metal. Identify the metal.

122. The unit cell for a pure xenon fluoride compound is shown below. What is the formula of the compound?

Xenon

Fluorine

123. In solid KCl the smallest distance between the centers of a potassium ion and a chloride ion is 314 pm. Calculate the length of the edge of the unit cell and the density of KCl, assuming it has the same structure as sodium chloride.

124. The temperature inside a pressure cooker is 115°C. Calculate the vapor pressure of water inside the pressure cooker. What would be the temperature inside the pressure cooker if the vapor pressure of water was 3.50 atm?

125. Dry nitrogen gas is bubbled through liquid benzene (C_6H_6) at 20.0°C. From 100.0 L of the gaseous mixture of nitrogen and benzene, 24.7 g of benzene is condensed by passing the mixture through a trap at a temperature

where nitrogen is gaseous and the vapor pressure of benzene is negligible. What is the vapor pressure of benzene at 20.0°C?

126. A sample of dry nitrogen gas weighing 100.0 g is bubbled through liquid water at 25.0°C. The gaseous mixture of nitrogen and water vapor escapes at a total pressure of 700. torr. What mass of water has vaporized? (The vapor pressure of water at 25°C is 23.8 torr.)

127. The molar enthalpy of vaporization of water at 373 K is 41.16 kJ/mol. What fraction of this energy is used to change the internal energy of the water, and what fraction is used to do work against the atmosphere? (Assume that water vapor is an ideal gas.)

128. You are asked to help set up a historical display in the park by stacking some cannonballs next to a Revolutionary War cannon. You are told to stack them by starting with a triangle in which each side is composed of four touching cannonballs. You are to continue stacking them until you have a single ball on the top centered over the middle of the triangular base.
    a. How many cannonballs do you need?
    b. What type of closest packing arrangement is displayed by the cannonballs?

c. The four corners of the pyramid of cannonballs form the corners of what type of regular geometric solid?

129. Consider the ionic solid A_xB_y, which has the unit cell below. The B ions are packed in a cubic arrangement, where each face has this structure:

There is one B in the center of the cube. The structure can also be described in terms of three parallel planes of B's of the type shown above. The resulting structure thus contains eight intersecting cubes of B's. The A ions are found in the centers of alternate intersecting cubes (that is, four of every eight cubes have A's in the center). What is the formula of A_xB_y? In the extended structure, how many B's surround each A? What structure do the B's form?

130. Mn crystallizes in the same type of cubic unit cell as Cu. Assuming that the radius of Mn is 5.6% larger than the radius of Cu and the density of Cu is 8.96 g/cm³, calculate the density of Mn.

Challenge Problems

131. An electron is trapped in an octahedral hole in a closest packed array of aluminum atoms (assume they behave as uniform hard spheres). In this situation the energy of the electron is quantized and the lowest-energy transition corresponds to a wavelength of 9.50 nm. Assuming that the hole can be approximated as a cube, what is the radius of a sphere that will just fit in the octahedral hole? Reference Exercise 148 in Chapter 12 for the energy equation for a particle in a cube.

132. You and a friend each synthesize a compound with the formula $XeCl_2F_2$. Your compound is a liquid, and your friend's compound is a gas (at the same conditions of temperature and pressure). Explain how the two compounds with the same formulas can exist in different phases at the same conditions of pressure and temperature.

133. A metal burns in air at 600°C under high pressure to form an oxide with formula MO_2. This compound is 23.72% oxygen by mass. The distance between the centers of touching atoms in a cubic closest packed crystal of this metal is 269.0 pm. What is this metal? What is its density?

134. Consider a perfectly insulated and sealed container. Determine the minimum volume of a container such that a gallon of water at 25°C will evaporate completely. If the container is a cube, determine the dimensions in feet. Assume the density of water is 0.998 g/cm³.

135. The vapor pressure of water at 30.0°C is 31.824 torr; at this temperature the density of liquid water is 0.99567 g/cm³. What is the ratio of the average distance between water molecules in the liquid and in the saturated vapor at this temperature?

136. For a simple cubic array, solve for the volume of an interior sphere (cubic hole) in terms of the radius of a sphere in the array.

137. The structures of another class of high-temperature ceramic superconductors are shown below.

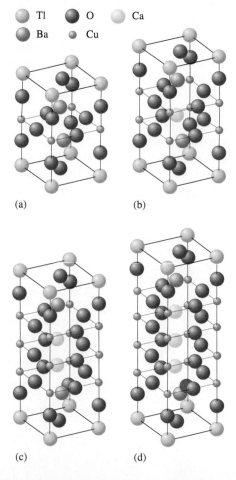

(a)

(b)

(c)

(d)

a. Determine the formula of each of these four superconductors.

b. One of the structural features that appears to be essential for high-temperature superconductivity is the presence of planar sheets of copper and oxygen atoms. As the number of sheets in each unit cell increases, the temperature for the onset of superconductivity increases. Order the four structures from the lowest to highest superconducting temperature.

c. Assign oxidation states to Cu in each structure assuming that Tl exists as Tl^{3+}. The oxidation states of Ca, Ba, and O are assumed to be $+2$, $+2$, and -2, respectively.

d. It also appears that copper must display a mixture of oxidation states for a material to exhibit superconductivity. Explain how this occurs in these materials as well as in the superconductor in Exercise 75.

138. Consider two different compounds, each with the formula C_2H_6O. One of these compounds is a liquid at room conditions and the other is a gas. Write Lewis structures consistent with this observation, and explain your answer.

139. The edge of the LiCl unit cell is 514 pm in length. Assuming that the Li^+ ions just fit in the octahedral holes of the closest packed Cl^- ions, calculate the ionic radii for the Li^+ and Cl^- ions. Compare them with the radii given in Fig. 13.8, and discuss the significance of any discrepancies.

Marathon Problem

140. The table below lists the ionic radii for the cations and anions in three different ionic compounds.

Formula	r_{cation}	r_{anion}
SnO_2	71 pm	140. pm
AlP	50. pm	212. pm
BaO	135 pm	140. pm

Each compound has either the NaCl, CsCl, or ZnS type cubic structure. Predict the type of structure formed (NaCl, CsCl, or ZnS) and the type and fraction of holes filled by the cations, and estimate the density of each compound.

Properties of Solutions

17

chapter

Water and oil are immiscible.

Most of the substances we encounter in daily life are mixtures: Wood, milk, gasoline, shampoo, steel, and air are all well-known examples. When the components of a mixture are uniformly intermingled—that is, when a mixture is homogeneous—it is called a *solution*. Solutions can be gases, liquids, or solids, as shown in Table 17.1. However, we will be concerned in this chapter with the properties of liquid solutions, particularly those containing water. Many essential chemical reactions occur in aqueous solutions, since water is capable of dissolving so many substances.

17.1 | Solution Composition

Because a mixture, unlike a chemical compound, has a variable composition, the relative amounts of substances in a solution must be specified. The qualitative terms *dilute* (relatively little solute present) and *concentrated* (relatively large amount of solute) are often used to describe solution content. However, we need to define solution composition more precisely to perform calculations. For example, in dealing with the stoichiometry of solution reactions in Chapter 4, we found it useful to describe solution composition in terms of **molarity**, or the number of moles of solute per liter of solution.

Other ways of describing solution composition are also useful. **Mass percent** (sometimes called *weight percent*) is the percent solute by mass in the solution:

A solute is the substance being dissolved. The solvent is the dissolving medium.

$$\text{Mass percent} = \left(\frac{\text{grams of solute}}{\text{grams of solution}} \right) \times 100$$

Another way of describing solution composition is the **mole fraction** (symbolized by the Greek letter chi, χ), the ratio of the number of moles of a given component to the total number of moles of solution. For a two-component solution, where n_A and n_B represent the number of moles of the two components,

When liquids are mixed, the liquid present in the largest amount is called the solvent.

$$\text{Mole fraction of component A} = \chi_A = \frac{n_A}{n_A + n_B}$$

Still another way of describing solution composition is **molality** (symbolized by m), the number of moles of solute per *kilogram of solvent*:

In very dilute aqueous solutions, the molality and the molarity are nearly the same.

$$\text{Molality} = \frac{\text{moles of solute}}{\text{kilograms of solvent}}$$

Since molarity depends on the volume of the solution, it changes slightly with temperature. Molality is independent of temperature, since it depends on mass.

Table 17.1

Various Types of Solutions

Example	State of Solution	State of Solute	State of Solvent
Air, natural gas	Gas	Gas	Gas
Vodka in water, antifreeze	Liquid	Liquid	Liquid
Brass, steel	Solid	Solid	Solid
Carbonated water (soda)	Liquid	Gas	Liquid
Seawater, sugar solution	Liquid	Solid	Liquid
Hydrogen in platinum	Solid	Gas	Solid

17.2 | The Thermodynamics of Solution Formation

Dissolving solutes in liquids is very common. We dissolve salt in the water used to cook vegetables, sugar in iced tea, stains in cleaning fluid, gaseous carbon dioxide in water to make soda water, ethanol in gasoline to make gasohol, and so on.

Solubility is important in other ways as well. For example, because the pesticide DDT is fat-soluble, it is retained and concentrated in animal tissues, where it causes detrimental effects. This is why DDT, even though it is effective for killing mosquitos, has been banned in the United States. Also, the solubilities of various vitamins are important in determining correct dosages. The insolubility of barium sulfate means it can be safely used to improve X-ray images of the gastrointestinal tract, even though Ba^{2+} ions are quite toxic.

What factors affect solubility? The cardinal rule of solubility is *like dissolves like*. We find that we must use a polar solvent to dissolve a polar or ionic solute and a nonpolar solvent to dissolve a nonpolar solute. Now we will attempt to see why this behavior occurs from a thermodynamic point of view. As we will see, solubility is an extraordinarily complex phenomenon, especially when water is the solvent. However, it is useful to explore some of the fundamental aspects of solubility because it has such important consequences. To simplify the discussion, we will assume that the formation of a liquid solution takes place in three distinct steps.

Polar solvents dissolve polar solutes; nonpolar solvents dissolve nonpolar solutes.

Step 1
Breaking up the solute into individual components (expanding the solute).

Step 2
Overcoming intermolecular forces in the solvent to make room for the solute (expanding the solvent).

Step 3
Allowing the solute and solvent to interact to form the solution.

These steps are illustrated in Fig. 17.1. Steps 1 and 2 require energy, since forces must be overcome to expand the solute and the solvent. Step 3 usually releases energy. In other words, steps 1 and 2 are endothermic, whereas step 3 is usually exothermic. The overall enthalpy change associated with the forma-

Figure 17.1
The formation of a liquid solution can be divided into three steps: (1) expanding the solute, (2) expanding the solvent, and (3) combining the expanded solute and solvent to form the solution.

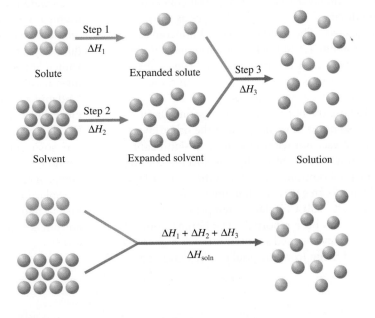

Solute   Step 1 ΔH_1 Expanded solute   Step 3 ΔH_3

Solvent   Step 2 ΔH_2 Expanded solvent   Solution

$\Delta H_1 + \Delta H_2 + \Delta H_3$

ΔH_{soln}

Chemical Insights | An Energy Solution

In today's society we face many serious problems related to energy: turmoil in the Middle East, the greenhouse effect, and polluted city air. Clearly the search for readily available, economical, and clean energy sources is of crucial importance. The solution may be in our backyards—literally.

When the sun shines on a swimming pool, the water is warmed by the solar energy. Because water is colorless (does not absorb visible light), the visible light from the sun passes through the water and strikes the bottom of the pool, where some of the light is absorbed and transformed into heat energy. This energy causes the water near the pool bottom to become warmer than the water above it. This warmer water, which has a lower density than the cooler water above it, then tends to rise toward the surface. This sets up convection currents, which circulate the warmer water to the surface, where it is cooled (mainly by evaporation). The convection currents keep the temperature of the water in the pool relatively uniform throughout.

How can this convective cooling process be stopped, thus allowing a pool of water to be an effective heat sink? The answer lies in adding common salt (NaCl). When sufficient salt is added to a pool of water 2 to 3 m deep, a salinity gradient is established. That is, the salt concentration is not uniform in the pool. In fact, three distinct layers can be identified. The top layer, called the convective layer, has a salt concentration of about 2% by mass and is only about half a meter thick. The bottom layer has a very high salt concentration (about 27% by mass) and serves as the heat storage layer. The middle, so-called nonconvective layer is about 1.5 m thick. Being intermediate in density between the top and bottom layers, the nonconvective layer is trapped between these layers and acts as an insulator.

Because the bottom layer of the solution in the pool is so much more dense than the other layers, it can get very hot without setting up significant convection. With a black, light-absorbing coating on the pool bottom, the water in the deepest layer of the pool can easily reach temperatures in the range of 90–100°C. In fact, a temperature as high as 107°C has been reported. (The boiling point of this very concentrated solution is much higher than 100°C.) Energy from the pool can be extracted if

Richard Nowitz

The solar pond in En Bokek, Israel, near the Dead Sea.

the hot brine from the storage layer is pumped through a heat exchanger to heat water or some other fluid.

A solar pond can be used to generate electricity by employing special turbines that use a working fluid other than water. Typical steam turbines cannot be used because the solar pond cannot produce temperatures high enough to generate steam efficiently. However, lower-boiling liquids can be used.

Solar ponds are now in use. A 52-acre pond at En Bokek near the Dead Sea produces 2.5 MW of electricity at peak power and could produce as much as 5 MW if more heat exchangers and turbines were installed in the powerhouse. This is a useful amount of electricity, but 200 such ponds would be required to provide the electricity produced by a typical conventional power plant. In the United States such installations probably would be most feasible in the Southwest, with its abundant land and sunshine. However, the concept may be more widely applicable. A study financed by the U.S. Department of Energy indicates that a 27,000-acre solar pond producing 600 MW of electricity would be competitive with conventional power plants in all states except Alaska.

Solar ponds are relatively inexpensive to build, easy to maintain, and nonpolluting if the pond bottom is sealed to prevent any leakage of the salt water.

Figure 17.2
(a) The enthalpy of solution ΔH_{soln} has a negative sign (the process is exothermic) if step 3 releases more energy than is required by steps 1 and 2. (b) ΔH_{soln} has a positive sign (the process is endothermic) if steps 1 and 2 require more energy than is released in step 3. (If the energy changes for steps 1 and 2 equal that for step 3, then ΔH_{soln} is zero.)

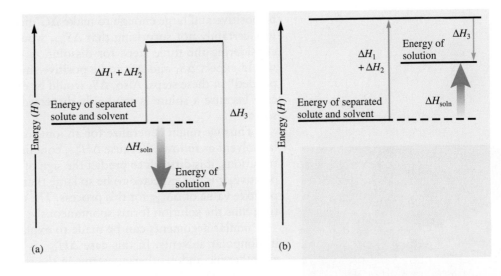

The enthalpy of solution is the sum of energies used in expanding both the solvent and solute and the energy of solvent–solute interaction.

tion of the solution, called the **enthalpy (heat) of solution** (ΔH_{soln}), can be viewed as the sum of the ΔH values for the steps:

$$\Delta H_{soln} = \Delta H_1 + \Delta H_2 + \Delta H_3$$

where ΔH_{soln} may have a positive sign (energy absorbed) or a negative sign (energy released), as shown in Fig. 17.2.

To illustrate the importance of the various energy terms in the equation for ΔH_{soln}, we will consider a familiar case: the solubility of sodium chloride in water. It is clear that for $NaCl(s)$ the term ΔH_1 is large and positive because of the strong ionic forces in the crystal that must be overcome. Also, ΔH_2 is expected to be large and positive because of the hydrogen bonds that must be broken in water. Finally, ΔH_3 is expected to be large and negative because of the strong interactions between the ions and the water molecules. In fact, the exothermic and endothermic terms essentially cancel in this case, as shown from the known values:

$$NaCl(s) \longrightarrow Na^+(g) + Cl^-(g) \qquad \Delta H_1^\circ = 786 \text{ kJ/mol}$$

$$H_2O(l) + Na^+(g) + Cl^-(g) \longrightarrow Na^+(aq) + Cl^-(aq)$$

$$\Delta H_{hyd}^\circ = \Delta H_2^\circ + \Delta H_3^\circ = -783 \text{ kJ/mol}$$

The second step shown here combines the terms ΔH_2 (for expanding the solvent) and ΔH_3 (for solvent–solute interactions) and is called the **enthalpy (heat) of hydration** (ΔH_{hyd}). This term represents the enthalpy change associated with the dispersal of a gaseous solute in water. Thus the standard enthalpy of solution for dissolving sodium chloride is the sum of ΔH_1° and ΔH_{hyd}°:

$$\Delta H_{soln}^\circ = 786 \text{ kJ/mol} - 783 \text{ kJ/mol} = 3 \text{ kJ/mol}$$

Note that ΔH_{soln}° is small but positive; the dissolving process requires a small amount of energy. Then why is NaCl so soluble in water? The answer to this question must involve the entropy change for the dissolving process. Recall from Chapter 10 that to predict whether a given process (at constant temperature and pressure) is spontaneous, we must consider the change in free energy:

$$\Delta G = \Delta H - T\Delta S$$

It is an experimental fact that $NaCl(s)$ dissolves in water to form 1.0 M NaCl. Thus ΔG° for this process must be negative. However, the preceding calculations show that ΔH_{soln}° is positive and thus unfavorable. Therefore, ΔS_{soln}° must be positive and large enough to make $\Delta G°$ negative (through the $-T\Delta S°$ term). It is certainly not surprising that $\Delta S°_{soln}$ would be positive for this process. In considering the three steps for dissolution of a solute mentioned earlier, we would expect ΔS_1 and ΔS_2 to be positive since the solute and solvent are "expanded" in these steps. Also, ΔS_3 would be expected to be positive in a general case because a solute is randomly dispersed in the relatively large volume of solvent.

Thus we might generalize for an ionic (or polar) solute dissolving in a polar solvent as follows: Because $\Delta H°_{soln}$ contains large positive and negative contributions, it is difficult to predict the sign of $\Delta H°_{soln}$. However, even if $\Delta H°_{soln}$ is positive, it is not expected to be so large that it would overwhelm the expected positive value of $\Delta S°_{soln}$ for this process. The overall effect is to make $\Delta G°$ negative; thus the solution forms spontaneously.

Similar arguments can be made to explain why nonpolar solutes dissolve in nonpolar solvents. In this case $\Delta H°_{soln}$ is expected to be small because the endothermic and exothermic terms in the solution process are expected to be similar in size. Thus the expected positive value of $\Delta S°_{soln}$ again would furnish the driving force for the solution process. These arguments suggest that $\Delta S°_{soln}$ provides the principal driving force for the behavior summarized by the rule "like dissolves like."

Now let's consider a process that is not spontaneous: A nonpolar solute does not dissolve in large quantities in a polar solvent. The floating oil slick that results whenever a major oil spill occurs in the ocean provides graphic evidence of this. What causes $\Delta G°$ to be positive for the dispersal of a material containing large nonpolar molecules in a polar solvent such as water? For this case $\Delta H°_{soln}$ is expected to be positive (unfavorable) because $\Delta H°_3$, the only exothermic component of $\Delta H°_{soln}$, is not expected to have a very large magnitude. On the other hand, for reasons given earlier, we expect $\Delta S°_{soln}$ to be positive (favorable). Thus we can explain the incompatibility of nonpolar and polar substances on the basis of the expected large, positive heat of solution that overwhelms the positive entropy change, thus giving a positive value for $\Delta G°$. Therefore, the solution does not form in this case.

Water as a Solvent

Because water is the most significant solvent in our world, it is especially important that we understand the solvent properties of water. As we noted in Chapter 16, water is not a typical liquid, with most of its unusual properties arising from the extensive hydrogen bonding present among the molecules. Because of water's unique nature, we must be very cautious in using simple arguments to account for the solvent properties of water.

To illustrate the unusual nature of water as a solvent, consider the values of $\Delta S°_{soln}$ listed in Table 17.2 for KCl(s), LiF(s), and CaS(s) forming aqueous solutions. Note that when KCl(s) is dissolved in water to form a 1.0 M solution, the value of $\Delta S°_{soln}$ is positive, as expected from the previous discussion. However, note that $\Delta S°_{soln}$ is *negative* for the other two salts. Why? How could the random dispersal in water of ions formerly present in a highly ordered solid produce a negative entropy change?

Obviously something must be occurring in the solution process that leads to increased order, which in some cases is large enough to dominate $\Delta S°_{soln}$. There is little doubt that this ordering effect arises from the hydration of the ions. In describing aqueous solutions containing ionic solutes in Chapter 4, we discussed the fact that the polar water molecules are attracted to the ions to form hydrated species. The assembling of a group of water molecules around the ions is an order-producing phenomenon and would be expected to make a negative contribution to $\Delta S°_{soln}$. Studies show that the more charge density an

A satellite image of the 2010 oil spill in the Gulf of Mexico.

Digital Globe/Getty Images

Table 17.2

Values of $\Delta S°_{soln}$ for Several Salts Dissolving in Water

Process	$\Delta S°$ (J K^{-1} mol^{-1})
KCl(s) $\rightarrow$ K$^+$(aq) + Cl$^-$(aq)	75
LiF(s) $\rightarrow$ Li$^+$(aq) + F$^-$(aq)	-36
CaS(s) $\rightarrow$ Ca^{2+}(aq) + S^{2-}(aq)	-138

Miracle Solvents

When a substance is heated beyond its critical temperature (T_c) and then placed under extremely high pressure, it forms a **supercritical fluid.** Although such fluids resemble liquids, they technically are not liquids. A liquid cannot exist above the critical temperature for a substance. For example, if a gaseous substance is maintained above T_c and pressure is gradually applied, there is no distinct point where the gas changes to a liquid, as would occur below T_c, but the supercritical fluid gradually forms as the pressure is increased.

In experiments at the Agriculture Department's Northern Regional Research Center in Peoria, Illinois, scientists have found that supercritical carbon dioxide behaves as a very useful nonpolar solvent for removing fat from meat. At temperatures above 31°C (T_c for CO_2) and several hundred atmospheres of pressure, the carbon dioxide fluid can dissolve virtually all the fat from samples of meat. Even more important, the fluid also will dissolve any pesticide or drug residues that may be present in the meat. When the carbon dioxide fluid is returned to normal pressures, it immediately vaporizes, and the fat, drug, and pesticide molecules come "raining" out to allow easy analysis of the types and amounts of contaminants present in the meat. Therefore, this method provides an efficient way to test meat for trace pesticide and drug residues.

Like supercritical carbon dioxide, supercritical water is a very interesting substance that has strikingly different properties from those of liquid water. For example, recent experiments have shown that supercritical (superfluid) water can behave simultaneously as both a polar and a nonpolar solvent. While the reasons for this unusual behavior remain unclear, the practical value of this behavior is very clear: It makes superfluid water a very useful reaction medium for a wide variety of substances. One extremely important application of this idea involves the environmentally sound

A scientist examines corn bran oil processed by supercritical fluid extraction.

destruction of industrial wastes. Most hazardous organic (nonpolar) substances can be dissolved in supercritical water and oxidized by dissolved O_2 in a matter of minutes. The products of these reactions are water, carbon dioxide, and possibly simple acids (which result when halogen-containing compounds are reacted). Therefore, the aqueous mixture that results from the reaction often can be disposed of with little further treatment. In contrast to the incinerators used to destroy organic waste products, a supercritical water reactor is a closed system (has no emissions).

Supercritical water has strange and wonderful properties, one of the most astonishing being that a flame can burn within the supercritical fluid during the reaction of O_2 with an organic substance. These properties promise to make supercritical water a versatile medium for chemical reactions.

ion possesses, the greater this hydration effect will be. This idea is borne out by the data in Table 17.2. For example, note that $\Delta S°_{soln}$ for KCl(s) is positive, but the value for LiF(s) is negative. This probably results from the smaller sizes (and thus larger charge densities) of Li$^+$ and F$^-$ as compared with K$^+$ and Cl$^-$. The smaller ions presumably are able to bind the hydrating water molecules more firmly and thus show a more negative value for $\Delta S°_{soln}$. The charges on the ions are also important. Note that CaS(s) exhibits a value of $\Delta S^{\circ}_{\text{soln}}$ that is more negative than that for LiF(s), as might be expected for the more highly charged Ca^{2+} and S^{2-} ions.

We have seen that ionic solutes dissolving in water can lead to negative values of $\Delta S^{\circ}_{\text{soln}}$ presumably because of ion hydration effects. In certain cases the dispersal of nonpolar solute particles in water can also produce negative values of $\Delta S^{\circ}_{\text{soln}}$. For example, for benzene [a nonpolar liquid containing C_6H_6 molecules (see Section 14.5)] dissolving in water, $\Delta S^{\circ}_{\text{soln}}$ has been estimated to be -58 J K^{-1} mol^{-1}. This very negative value for $\Delta S^{\circ}_{\text{soln}}$ suggests that a great deal of ordering occurs when benzene is dispersed in water. This is a surprising result. What is the origin of this ordering? Clearly, the situation here is quite different from that for ionic solutes. The polar water molecules will not strongly hydrate the nonpolar benzene molecules, as they do ions.

What could cause $\Delta S^{\circ}_{\text{soln}}$ to be negative for this nonpolar solute? The negative value for $\Delta S^{\circ}_{\text{soln}}$ in this case seems to arise not from the hydration of the solute but from the opposite behavior. Instead of hydrating the nonpolar molecule, water seems to form a cage to isolate the nonpolar solute from the bulk water structure. This cage formation probably occurs as follows: So that a nonpolar molecule can be introduced into the water structure, a "hole" must be formed, which requires the breaking of some water–water hydrogen bonds. In response, in an effort to recover the lost hydrogen bonding, the water molecules around the edge of the hole apparently form even more hydrogen bonds than are normally found in bulk water. That is, a highly ordered cage of hydrogen-bonded water molecules forms around the nonpolar solute molecule. This ordering of the water structure makes a negative contribution to the entropy of solution and in certain cases leads to a negative value of $\Delta S^{\circ}_{\text{soln}}$. In fact, this unfavorable entropy contribution resulting from cage formation could be an important reason why nonpolar solutes are insoluble in water.

Summary

The point of this discussion has been to consider some of the thermodynamic aspects of the process that occurs when a solute is dispersed in a solvent to form a solution. Our observations tell us that "like dissolves like." However, the dissolution process is so complex that predicting whether a particular solute will dissolve in a given solvent is risky. Solubility is difficult to explain and even more difficult to predict, especially when water is the solvent. The only way to be certain about the compatibility of a given solute and solvent is to do the experiment.

> Benzene does not dissolve in water to the extent that a 1 M solution is possible. The value of $\Delta S^{\circ}_{\text{soln}}$ given here is extrapolated from values measured at much lower concentrations.

17.3 | Factors Affecting Solubility

Structure Effects

In the preceding section, we saw that solubility is favored if the solute and solvent have similar polarities. Since it is the molecular structure that determines polarity, there should be a definite connection between structure and solubility. Vitamins provide an excellent example of the relationship among molecular structure, polarity, and solubility.

For the last several years, there has been considerable publicity about the pros and cons of consuming large quantities of vitamins. For example, large doses of vitamin C have been advocated to combat various illnesses, including the common cold. Vitamin E has been extolled as a youth-preserving elixir and a protector against the carcinogenic (cancer-causing) effects of certain chemicals. However, there are possible detrimental effects from taking large amounts of some vitamins, depending on their solubilities.

Vitamin A

Vitamin C

Figure 17.3

The molecular structures of vitamin A (nonpolar, fat-soluble) and vitamin C (polar, watersoluble). The circles in the structural formulas indicate polar bonds. Note that vitamin C contains far more polar bonds than vitamin A.

Carbonation in a bottle of soda.

Henry's law is often expressed in the form $P = kC$, where C is the concentration of the gas in mol/L. In this case k has the units L atm/mol.

Vitamins can be divided into two classes: *fat-soluble* (vitamins A, D, E, and K) and *water-soluble* (vitamins B and C). The reason for the differing solubility characteristics can be seen by comparing the structures of vitamins A and C (Fig. 17.3). Vitamin A, composed mostly of carbon and hydrogen atoms that have similar electronegativities, is virtually nonpolar. This causes it to be soluble in nonpolar materials such as body fat, which is also largely composed of carbon and hydrogen, but not soluble in polar solvents such as water. On the other hand, vitamin C has many polar O—H and C—O bonds, making the molecule polar and thus water-soluble. We often describe nonpolar materials like vitamin A as *hydrophobic* (water-fearing) and polar substances like vitamin C as *hydrophilic* (water-loving).

Because of their solubility characteristics, the fat-soluble vitamins can build up in the fatty tissues of the body. This buildup has both positive and negative effects. Since these vitamins can be stored, the body can temporarily tolerate a diet deficient in vitamins A, D, E, and K. Conversely, if excessive amounts of these vitamins are consumed, their buildup can lead to the illness *hypervitaminosis*.

In contrast, the water-soluble vitamins are excreted by the body and therefore must be consumed regularly. This fact was first recognized when the British navy discovered that scurvy, a disease often suffered by sailors, could be prevented if the sailors regularly ate fresh limes (which are a good source of vitamin C) when aboard ship (hence the name "limey" for the British sailor).

Pressure Effects

Although pressure has little effect on the solubilities of solids or liquids, it does significantly increase the solubility of a gas. Carbonated beverages, for example, are always bottled at high pressure of carbon dioxide to ensure a high concentration of carbon dioxide in the liquid. The fizzing that occurs when you open a bottle of soda results from the escape of gaseous carbon dioxide because the atmospheric pressure of CO_2 is much lower than that used in the bottling process.

The increase in gas solubility with pressure can be understood from Fig. 17.4. Figure 17.4(a) shows a gas in equilibrium with a solution; that is, the gas molecules are entering and leaving the solution at the same rate. If the pressure is suddenly increased [Fig. 17.4(b)], the number of gas molecules per unit vol-

Figure 17.4

(a) A gaseous solute in equilibrium with a solution. (b) The piston is pushed in, which increases the pressure of the gas and the number of gas molecules per unit volume. This causes an increase in the rate at which the gas enters the solution, so the concentration of dissolved gas increases. (c) The greater gas concentration in the solution causes an increase in the rate of escape. A new equilibrium is reached.

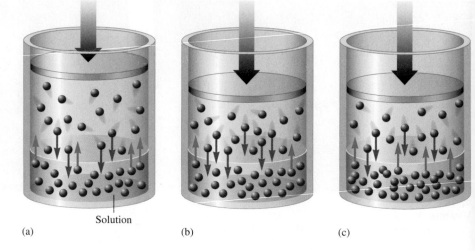

Solution

(a)   (b)   (c)

ume increases; thus the gas enters the solution at a higher rate than it leaves. As the concentration of dissolved gas increases, the rate of escape of the gas also increases until a new equilibrium is reached [Fig. 17.4(c)]. At this point the solution contains more dissolved gas than before.

The relationship between gas pressure and the concentration of a dissolved gas is given by **Henry's law:**

$$P = k_H \chi$$

William Henry (1774–1836), a close friend of John Dalton, formulated his law in 1801.

Henry's law holds only when there is no chemical reaction between solute and solvent.

where P represents the partial pressure of the gaseous solute above the solution, χ represents the mole fraction of the dissolved gas, and k_H is a constant (the Henry's law constant) characteristic of a particular solution. Henry's law states that *the amount of gas dissolved in a solution is directly proportional to the pressure of the gas above the solution.*

Henry's law is obeyed most accurately for dilute solutions of gases that do not dissociate in or react with the solvent. For example, Henry's law is obeyed by oxygen gas in water, but it does *not* correctly represent the behavior of gaseous hydrogen chloride in water because of the dissociation reaction:

$$HCl(g) \xrightarrow{H_2O} H^+(aq) + Cl^-(aq)$$

The Henry's law constants for the aqueous solutions of several gases are given in Table 17.3.

Table 17.3

The Values of Henry's Law Constants for Several Gases Dissolved in Water at 298 K

Gas	k_H (atm)
CH_4	4.13×10^2
CO_2	1.64×10^3
O_2	4.34×10^4
CO	5.71×10^4
H_2	7.03×10^4
N_2	8.57×10^4

Temperature Effects for Aqueous Solutions

Everyday experiences of dissolving substances such as sugar may lead you to think that solubility always increases with temperature. This is not the case. The dissolving of a solid occurs *more rapidly* at higher temperatures, but the amount of solid that can be dissolved may increase or decrease with increasing temperature. The effect of temperature on the solubility in water of several common solids is shown in Fig. 17.5. Note that although the solubility of most solids increases with temperature, the solubilities of some substances (such as sodium sulfate and cerium sulfate) decrease with increasing temperature.

Predicting the temperature dependence of solubility is very difficult. For example, although there is some correlation between the sign of ΔH°_{soln} and the variation of solubility with temperature, important exceptions exist.* The only sure way to determine the temperature dependence of a solid's solubility is by experiment.

Because ΔH°_{soln} refers to dissolving a small amount of solute in a large amount of a 1.0 M ideal solution, it is not necessarily relevant to the process of dissolving a solid in a saturated solution. Thus ΔH°_{soln} is of limited use in predicting the variation of solubility with temperature.

---

*For more information, see R. S. Treptow, "Le Châtelier's Principle Applied to the Temperature Dependence of Solubility," *J. Chem. Ed.* **61** (1984): 499.

Ionic Liquids?

So far in this text you have seen that ionic substances are stable solids with high melting points. For example, sodium chloride has a melting point near 800°C. One of the "hottest" areas of current chemical research is ionic liquids—substances composed of ions that are liquids at normal temperatures and pressures. This unusual behavior results from the differences in the sizes of the anions and cations in the ionic liquids. Dozens of small anions, such as BF_4^- (tetrafluoroborate) or PF_6^- (hexafluorophosphate), can be paired with thousands of large cations, such as 1-hexyl-3-methylimidazolium or 1-butyl-3-methylimidazolium (a and b, respectively, in the accompanying figure). These substances remain liquids because the bulky, asymmetrical cations do not pack together efficiently with the smaller, symmetrical anions. In contrast, in sodium chloride the ions can pack very efficiently to form a compact, orderly arrangement, leading to maximum cation–anion attractions and thus a high melting point.

The excitement being generated by these ionic liquids arises from many factors. For one thing, almost an infinite variety of ionic liquids is possible due to the large variety of bulky cations and small anions available. According to Kenneth R. Seddon, Director of QUILL (Queen's University Ionic Liquid Laboratory) in Northern Ireland, a *trillion* ionic liquids are possible. Another great advantage of these liquids is their long liquid range, typically from $-100°C$ to 200°C.

In addition, the cations in the liquids can be designed to perform specific functions. For example, chemist James H. Davis, of the University

(a)   (b)

of South Alabama in Mobile, has designed various cations that will attract potentially harmful ions such as mercury, cadmium, uranium, and americium (the latter two are commonly found in nuclear waste materials) and leach them out of contaminated solutions. Davis has also developed cations that will remove H_2S (which produces SO_2 when the gas is burned) and CO_2 (which does not burn) from natural gas. Potentially, these ionic solutions might also be used to remove CO_2 from the exhaust gases of fossil-fuel–burning power plants to lessen the "greenhouse effect."

The biggest obstacle to the widespread use of ionic liquids is their cost. Normal organic solvents used in industry typically cost a few cents per liter, but ionic liquids can cost hundreds of times that amount. However, the environmentally friendly nature of ionic liquids (they produce no vapors because the ions are not volatile) and the flexibility of these substances as reaction media make them very attractive. As a consequence, efforts are under way to make their use economically feasible.

The term *ionic liquid* may have seemed like an oxymoron in the past, but these substances have a very promising future.

In contrast to the behavior of gases in water, gases typically become more soluble in most nonaqueous solvents as temperature increases.

The behavior of gases dissolving in water appears to be less complex. The solubility of a gas in water typically decreases with increasing temperature, as shown for several cases in Fig. 17.6. This temperature effect has important environmental implications because of the widespread use of water from lakes and rivers for industrial cooling. After being used as a coolant, the water is returned to its natural source at a higher-than-ambient temperature (**thermal pollution** has occurred). Because it is warmer, this water contains less than the normal concentration of oxygen and is also less dense; it tends to "float" on the colder water below, thus blocking normal oxygen absorption. This effect can be especially important in deep lakes. The warm upper layer can seriously decrease the amount of oxygen available to aquatic life in the deeper layers of the lake.

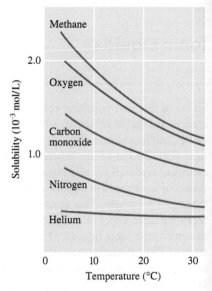

Figure 17.5
The solubilities of several solids as a function of temperature. Note that although most substances become more soluble in water with increasing temperature, sodium sulfate and cerium sulfate become less soluble.

Figure 17.6
The solubilities of several gases in water as a function of temperature at a constant pressure of 1 atm of gas above the solution.

The decreasing water solubility of gases with increased temperature is also responsible for the formation of *boiler scale.* As we discussed in Chapter 7, the bicarbonate ion is formed when carbon dioxide is dissolved in water containing the carbonate ion:

$$CO_3{}^{2-}(aq) + CO_2(aq) + H_2O(l) \longrightarrow 2HCO_3{}^-(aq)$$

When the water also contains Ca^{2+} ions, this reaction is especially important—calcium bicarbonate is soluble in water, but calcium carbonate is insoluble. When the water is heated, the carbon dioxide is driven off. For the system to replace the lost carbon dioxide, the reverse reaction must occur:

$$2HCO_3{}^-(aq) \longrightarrow H_2O(l) + CO_2(aq) + CO_3{}^{2-}(aq)$$

This reaction, however, also increases the concentration of carbonate ions, causing solid calcium carbonate to form. This solid is the boiler scale that coats the walls of containers such as industrial boilers and tea kettles. Boiler scale reduces the efficiency of heat transfer and can lead to blockage of pipes (Fig. 17.7).

Figure 17.7
A pipe with accumulated mineral deposits.

Jim Roger Webb

The Lake Nyos Tragedy

On August 21, 1986, a cloud of gas suddenly boiled from Lake Nyos in Cameroon, killing nearly 2000 people. Although at first it was speculated that the gas was hydrogen sulfide, it now seems clear it was carbon dioxide. What would cause Lake Nyos to emit this huge, suffocating cloud of CO_2? Although the answer may never be known for certain, many scientists believe that the lake suddenly "turned over," bringing to the surface water that contained huge quantities of dissolved carbon dioxide. Lake Nyos is a deep lake that is thermally stratified: Layers of warm, less dense water near the surface float on the colder, denser water layers near the lake's bottom. Under normal conditions the lake stays this way; there is little mixing among the different layers. Scientists believe that over hundreds or thousands of years, carbon dioxide gas had seeped into the cold water at the lake's bottom and dissolved in great amounts because of the large pressure of CO_2 present (in accordance with Henry's law). For some reason, on August 21, 1986, the lake apparently suffered an overturn, possibly due to wind or to unusual cooling of the lake's surface by monsoon clouds. This caused water that was greatly supersaturated with CO_2 to reach the surface and release tremendous quantities of gaseous CO_2 that suffocated thousands of humans

Lake Nyos in Cameroon.

and animals before they knew what hit them—a tragic, monumental illustration of Henry's law.

Since 1986, the scientists studying Lake Nyos and nearby Lake Monoun have observed a rapid recharging of the CO_2 levels in the deep waters of these lakes, causing concern that another deadly gas release could occur at any time. Apparently the only way to prevent such a disaster is to pump away the CO_2-charged deep water in the two lakes. Scientists at a conference to study this problem in 1994 recommended such a solution, but it has not yet been funded by Cameroon.

17.4 | The Vapor Pressures of Solutions

Liquid solutions have physical properties significantly different from those of the pure solvent, a fact that has great practical importance. For example, we add antifreeze to the water in a car's cooling system to prevent freezing in winter and boiling in summer. We also melt ice on sidewalks and streets by spreading salt. These preventive measures work because of the solute's effect on the solvent's properties.

To explore how a nonvolatile solute affects a solvent, we will consider the experiment represented in Fig. 17.8, in which a sealed container encloses a beaker containing an aqueous sugar solution and a beaker containing pure water. Gradually, the volume of the sugar solution increases and the volume of the pure water decreases. Why? We can explain this observation if the vapor pressure of the pure solvent is greater than that of the solution. Under these conditions, the pressure of vapor necessary to achieve equilibrium with the pure solvent is greater than that required to reach equilibrium with the solution. Thus, as the pure solvent emits vapor in an attempt to reach equilibrium, the solution absorbs vapor to try to lower the vapor pressure toward its equi-

A nonvolatile solute has no tendency to escape from solution into the vapor phase.

Figure 17.8
An aqueous solution and pure water in
a closed environment. (a) Initial stage.
(b) After a period of time, the water is
transferred to the solution.

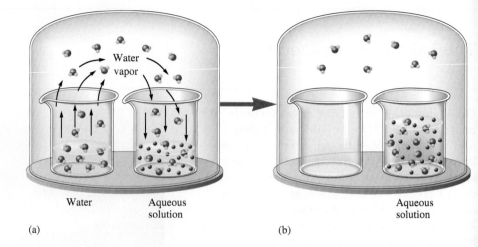

Water   Aqueous   Aqueous
                     solution   solution

(a)   (b)

The presence of a nonvolatile solute
reduces the tendency of solvent molecules to escape.

librium value. This process results in a net transfer of water from the pure
liquid through the vapor phase to the solution. The system can reach an equilibrium vapor pressure only when all the water has been transferred to the solution. This experiment is just one of many observations indicating that the
presence of a *nonvolatile solute lowers the vapor pressure of a solvent.*

We can account for this behavior in terms of the simple model shown in
Fig. 17.9. The dissolved nonvolatile solute decreases the number of solvent
molecules per unit volume. Thus it lowers the number of solvent molecules at
the surface, which proportionately lowers the escaping tendency of the solvent
molecules. For example, in a solution consisting of half nonvolatile solute molecules and half solvent molecules, we expect the observed vapor pressure to be
half that of the pure solvent, since only half as many molecules can escape. In
fact, this agrees with our observations.

Detailed studies of the vapor pressures of solutions containing nonvolatile
solutes were carried out by François M. Raoult. His results are described by
the equation known as **Raoult's law:**

$$P_{soln} = X_{solvent}P^{\circ}_{solvent}$$

where P_{soln} is the observed vapor pressure of the solution, $X_{solvent}$ is the mole
fraction of solvent, and $P^{\circ}_{solvent}$ is the vapor pressure of the pure solvent. Note
that for a solution containing half solute and half solvent molecules, $X_{solvent}$ is

Figure 17.9
The presence of a nonvolatile solute
inhibits the escape of solvent molecules from the liquid and so lowers the
vapor pressure of the solvent.

Pure solvent   Solution with a
                               nonvolatile solute

0.5, so the vapor pressure of the solution is half that of the pure solvent. On the other hand, for a solution where three-fourths of the solution molecules are solvent, $X_{solvent} = \frac{3}{4} = 0.75$, and $P_{soln} = 0.75P°_{solvent}$. The idea is that the non-volatile solute lowers the vapor pressure simply by diluting the solvent.

Raoult's law is a linear equation of the form $y = mx + b$, where $y = P_{soln}$, $x = X_{solvent}$, $m = P°_{solvent}$, and $b = 0$. Thus a plot of P_{soln} versus $X_{solvent}$ gives a straight line with a slope equal to $P°_{solvent}$, as shown in Fig. 17.10.

The effect of the solute on the vapor pressure of a solution gives us a convenient way to "count" molecules and thus provides a means for experimentally determining molar masses. Suppose a certain mass of a compound is dissolved in a solvent, and the vapor pressure of the resulting solution is measured. Using Raoult's law, we can determine the number of moles of solute present. Since the mass of this number of moles is known, we can calculate the molar mass.

Raoult's law states that the vapor pressure of a solution is directly proportional to the mole fraction of solvent present.

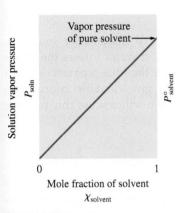

Figure 17.10
For a solution that obeys Raoult's law, a plot of P_{soln} versus $X_{solvent}$ yields a straight line.

⬣WL INTERACTIVE EXAMPLE 17.1

A solution was prepared by adding 20.0 g of urea to 125 g of water at 25°C, a temperature at which pure water has a vapor pressure of 23.76 torr. The observed vapor pressure of the solution was found to be 22.67 torr. Calculate the molar mass of urea.

Solution

■ What are we trying to solve?

We are trying to determine the molar mass of urea. Molar mass has the formula $\dfrac{mass}{mole}$, so we need to know the mass and number of moles. We have the mass as 20.0 g, so we need to determine the number of moles. We can do this by first using Raoult's law.

Raoult's law can be rearranged to give

$$X_{H_2O} = \frac{P_{soln}}{P°_{H_2O}}$$

This form allows us to determine the mole fraction of water in the solution:

$$X_{H_2O} = \frac{22.67 \text{ torr}}{23.76 \text{ torr}} = 0.9541$$

However, we are interested in the urea. To find its molar mass, we must find the number of moles represented by 20.0 g. We can calculate the number of moles of urea from the definition of X_{H_2O}:

$$X_{H_2O} = \frac{\text{mol } H_2O}{\text{mol } H_2O + \text{mol urea}} = \frac{n_{H_2O}}{n_{H_2O} + n_{urea}}$$

From the mass of water used to prepare the solution, we have

$$n_{H_2O} = 125 \text{ g } H_2O \times \frac{1 \text{ mol } H_2O}{18.0 \text{ g } H_2O} = 6.94 \text{ mol } H_2O$$

Since $X_{H_2O} = 0.9541$,

$$X_{H_2O} = 0.9541 = \frac{n_{H_2O}}{n_{H_2O} + n_{urea}} = \frac{6.94}{6.94 + n_{urea}}$$

or

$$0.9541(6.94 + n_{urea}) = 6.94$$

Solving for the number of moles of urea gives

$$n_{urea} = \frac{6.94 - 6.62}{0.9541} = 0.335 \text{ mol}$$

Since 20.0 g of urea was originally dissolved, 0.335 mole of urea weighs 20.0 g. Thus

$$\frac{20.0 \text{ g}}{0.335 \text{ mol}} = 59.7 \text{ g/mol}$$

The value for the molar mass of urea determined in this experiment is thus 59.7 g/mol. Urea has the formula $(NH_2)_2CO$ and a molar mass of 60.0, so the result obtained in this experiment agrees fairly well with the known value.

> The lowering of vapor pressure depends on the number of solute particles present in the solution.

We can also use vapor pressure measurements to characterize solutions. For example, 1 mole of sodium chloride dissolved in water lowers the vapor pressure about twice as much as expected because the ions separate when it dissolves. Thus vapor pressure measurements can give valuable information about the nature of the solute after it dissolves. We will discuss this in more detail in Section 17.7.

Nonideal Solutions

Any solution that obeys Raoult's law is called an **ideal solution.** One might say that Raoult's law is to solutions what the ideal gas law is to gases. As with gases, ideal behavior for solutions is never perfectly achieved but is sometimes closely approached. Nearly ideal behavior is often observed when the solute–solute, solvent–solvent, and solute–solvent interactions are very similar. That is, in solutions where the solute and solvent are very much alike, the solute simply acts to dilute the solvent. However, if the solvent has a special affinity for the solute, such as if hydrogen bonding occurs, the tendency of the solvent molecules to escape will be lowered more than expected. In such cases the observed vapor pressure will be *lower* than the value predicted by Raoult's law; there is a *negative deviation from Raoult's law.*

> Strong solute–solvent interaction gives a vapor pressure lower than that predicted by Raoult's law.

As mentioned, for a solution to behave ideally, the solute–solute, solvent–solvent, and solute–solvent interactions would have to be identical. This would correspond to a situation where $\Delta H_{soln} = 0$. On the other hand, when a solute and solvent release large quantities of energy in the formation of a solution— that is, when ΔH_{soln} is large and negative—we can assume that strong interactions exist between the solute and the solvent. In this case we expect a negative deviation from Raoult's law.

So far we have assumed that the solute is nonvolatile and so does not contribute to the vapor pressure over the solution. However, for liquid–liquid solutions where both components are volatile, a modified form of Raoult's law applies:

$$P_{Total} = P_A + P_B = \chi_A P_A^\circ + \chi_B P_B^\circ$$

where P_{Total} represents the total vapor pressure of a solution containing A and B, χ_A and χ_B are the mole fractions of A and B, P_A° and P_B° are the vapor pressures of pure A and pure B, and P_A and P_B are the partial pressures resulting from molecules of A and B in the vapor above the solution.

Liquid–liquid solutions obeying this form of Raoult's law are said to be *ideal.* However, as with solutions containing nonvolatile solutes, deviations from Raoult's law are often observed. These can be positive or negative, as shown in Fig. 17.11.

Again, large negative heats of solution indicate especially strong solute– solvent interactions, and such solutions are expected to show *negative* devia-

(a)

(b)

(c)

Figure 17.11

Vapor pressure for a solution of two volatile liquids. (a) The behavior predicted for an ideal liquid–liquid solution by Raoult's law. (b) A solution for which P_{Total} is larger than the value calculated from Raoult's law. This solution shows a positive deviation from Raoult's law. (c) A solution for which P_{Total} is smaller than the value calculated from Raoult's law. This solution shows a negative deviation from Raoult's law.

tions from Raoult's law. Both components have a lower escaping tendency in the solution than in the pure liquids. This behavior is illustrated by an acetone–water solution where the molecules can hydrogen-bond effectively:

In contrast, if two liquids mix endothermically, this indicates that the solute–solvent interactions are weaker than the interactions among the molecules in the pure liquids. More energy is required to expand the liquids than is released when the liquids are mixed. In this case the molecules in the solution have a higher tendency to escape than expected, and *positive* deviations from Raoult's law are observed. An example of this case is provided by a solution of ethanol and hexane, whose Lewis structures are as follows:

Ethanol   Hexane

The polar ethanol and the nonpolar hexane molecules are not able to interact effectively. Thus the enthalpy of solution is positive, as is the deviation from Raoult's law.

Finally, for a solution of very similar liquids, such as benzene and toluene,

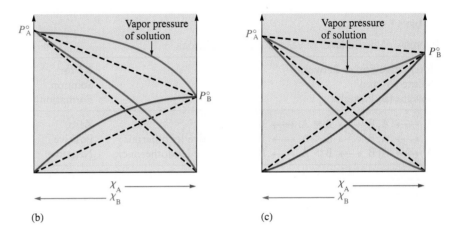

Benzene   Toluene

the enthalpy of solution is very close to zero; thus the solution closely obeys Raoult's law (ideal behavior).

A summary of the behavior of various types of solutions is given in Table 17.4.

Table 17.4

Summary of the Behavior of Various Types of Solutions

Interactive Forces Between Solute (A) and Solvent (B) Particles	ΔH_{soln}	ΔT for Solution Formation	Deviation from Raoult's Law	Example
A $\longleftrightarrow$ A, B $\longleftrightarrow$ B $\equiv$ A $\longleftrightarrow$ B	Zero	Zero	None (ideal solution)	Benzene–toluene
A $\longleftrightarrow$ A, B $\longleftrightarrow$ B < A $\longleftrightarrow$ B	Negative (exothermic)	Positive	Negative	Acetone–water
A $\longleftrightarrow$ A, B $\longleftrightarrow$ B > A $\longleftrightarrow$ B	Positive (endothermic)	Negative	Positive	Ethanol–hexane

17.5 | Boiling-Point Elevation and Freezing-Point Depression

The relationships between vapor pressure and changes of state were discussed in Section 16.10.

In the preceding section, we saw how a nonvolatile solute affects the vapor pressure of a liquid solvent. Because changes of state depend on vapor pressure, the presence of a solute also affects the freezing point and boiling point of a solvent. Freezing-point depression, boiling-point elevation, and osmotic pressure (discussed in Section 17.6) are called **colligative properties.** As we will see, they are grouped together because they depend only on the number, and not on the identity, of the solute particles in an ideal solution. Because of their direct relationship to the number of solute particles, the colligative properties are very useful for characterizing the nature of a solute after it is dissolved in a solvent and for determining the molar masses of substances.

Boiling-Point Elevation

Normal boiling point was defined in Section 16.10.

The normal boiling point of a liquid is the temperature at which the vapor pressure is equal to 1 atm. We have seen that a nonvolatile solute lowers the vapor pressure of the solvent. Therefore, such a solution must be heated to a higher temperature than the boiling point of the pure solvent to reach a vapor pressure of 1 atm. This means that *a nonvolatile solute elevates the boiling point of the solvent.* Figure 17.12 shows the phase diagram for an aqueous solution containing a nonvolatile solute. Note that the liquid/vapor line for this solution is shifted to higher temperatures than that for pure water.

As you might expect, the magnitude of the boiling-point elevation depends on the concentration of the solute. The change in boiling point can be represented by the equation

$$\Delta T = K_b m_{solute}$$

Figure 17.12
Phase diagrams for pure water (red lines) and for an aqueous solution containing a nonvolatile solute (blue lines). Note that the boiling point of the solution is higher than that of pure water. Conversely, the freezing point of the solution is lower than that of pure water. The effect of a nonvolatile solute is to extend the liquid range of a solvent.

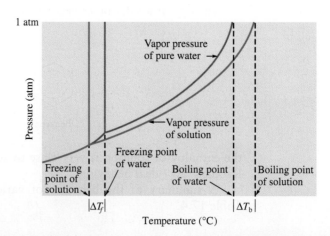

Table 17.5

Molal Boiling-Point Elevation Constants (K_b) and Freezing-Point Depression Constants (K_f) for Several Solvents

Solvent	Boiling Point (°C)	K_b (°C kg/mol)	Freezing Point (°C)	K_f (°C kg/mol)
Water (H_2O)	100.0	0.51	0.	1.86
Carbon tetrachloride (CCl_4)	76.5	5.03	−22.99	30.
Chloroform ($CHCl_3$)	61.2	3.63	−63.5	4.70
Benzene (C_6H_6)	80.1	2.53	5.5	5.12
Carbon disulfide (CS_2)	46.2	2.34	−111.5	3.83
Ethyl ether ($C_4H_{10}O$)	34.5	2.02	−116.29	1.79
Camphor ($C_{10}H_{16}O$)	208.0	5.95	179.8	40.

where ΔT is the boiling-point elevation, or the difference between the boiling point of the solution and that of the pure solvent, K_b is a constant that is characteristic of the solvent and is called the **molal boiling-point elevation constant,** and m_{solute} is the *molality* of the solute in the solution. Values of K_b for some common solvents are given in Table 17.5.

The molar mass of a solute can be determined from the observed boiling-point elevation, as shown in Example 17.2.

⦿WL INTERACTIVE EXAMPLE 17.2

A solution was prepared by dissolving 18.00 g of glucose in 150.0 g of water. The resulting solution was found to have a boiling point of 100.34°C at 1 atm. Calculate the molar mass of glucose. Glucose is a molecular solid that is present as individual molecules in solution.

Solution

■ What are we trying to solve?

We are trying to determine the molar mass of glucose. Molar mass has the formula $\dfrac{\text{mass}}{\text{mole}}$, so we need to know the mass and number of moles. We have the mass as 18.0 g, so we need to determine the number of moles. We are given the boiling point of the solution, so we make use of the equation

$$\Delta T = K_b m_{solute}$$

where $$\Delta T = 100.34°C - 100.00°C = 0.34°C$$

From Table 17.5, $K_b = 0.51$ for water. The molality of this solution can be calculated by rearranging the boiling-point elevation equation to give

$$m_{solute} = \frac{\Delta T}{K_b} = \frac{0.34°C}{0.51\dfrac{°C\ kg}{mol}} = 0.67\ mol/kg$$

The solution was prepared using 0.1500 kg of water. Using the definition of molality, we can find the number of moles of glucose in the solution.

$$m_{solute} = 0.67\ mol/kg = \frac{mol\ solute}{kg\ solvent} = \frac{n_{glucose}}{0.1500\ kg}$$

$$n_{glucose} = (0.67\ mol/kg)(0.1500\ kg) = 0.10\ mol$$

Thus 0.10 mole of glucose weighs 18.00 g, and 1.0 mole of glucose weighs 180 g (10 × 18.00 g). The molar mass of glucose is 180 g/mol.

Melting point and freezing point both refer to the temperature at which the solid and liquid coexist.

Freezing-Point Depression

When a solute is dissolved in a solvent, the freezing point of the solution is lower than that of the pure solvent. Why? Recall that the vapor pressures of ice and liquid water are the same at 0°C. Suppose a solute is dissolved in water. The resulting solution does not freeze at 0°C because *the water in the solution has a lower vapor pressure than that of pure ice.* No ice forms under these conditions. However, the vapor pressure of ice decreases more rapidly than that of liquid water as the temperature decreases. Therefore, as the solution is cooled, the vapor pressure of the ice and that of the liquid water in the solution will eventually become equal. The temperature at which this occurs is the new freezing point of the solution and is below 0°C. The freezing point has been *depressed.*

We can account for this behavior in terms of the simple model shown in Fig. 17.13. The presence of the solute lowers the rate at which molecules in the liquid return to the solid state. Thus for an aqueous solution only the liquid state is found at 0°C. As the solution is cooled, the rate at which water molecules leave the solid ice decreases until this rate and the rate of formation of ice become equal and equilibrium is reached. This is the freezing point of the water in the solution.

Because a solute lowers the freezing point of water, compounds such as sodium chloride and calcium chloride are often spread on streets and sidewalks to prevent ice from forming in freezing weather. Of course, if the outside temperature is lower than the freezing point of the resulting salt solution, ice forms anyway. So this procedure is not effective at extremely cold temperatures.

The solid/liquid line for an aqueous solution is shown in the phase diagram for water in Fig. 17.12. Since the presence of a solute elevates the boiling point and depresses the freezing point of the solvent, adding a solute has the effect of extending the liquid range.

The equation for freezing-point depression is analogous to that for boiling-point elevation:

$$\Delta T = K_f m_{solute}$$

(a)   (b)

Figure 17.13
(a) Ice in equilibrium with liquid water.
(b) Ice in equilibrium with liquid water containing a dissolved solute (shown in pink).

where ΔT is the freezing-point depression, or the difference between the freezing point of the pure solvent and that of the solution, and K_f is a constant that is characteristic of a particular solvent and is called the **molal freezing-point depression constant.** Values of K_f for common solvents are listed in Table 17.5.

♨WL INTERACTIVE EXAMPLE 17.3

What mass of ethylene glycol ($C_2H_6O_2$), the main component of antifreeze, must be added to 10.0 L of water to produce a solution for use in a car's radiator that freezes at $-10.0°F$ ($-23.3°C$)? Assume that the density of water is exactly 1 g/mL.

Solution The freezing point must be lowered from 0°C to $-23.3°C$. To determine the molality of ethylene glycol needed to accomplish this, we can use the equation

$$\Delta T = K_f m_{solute}$$

where $\Delta T = 23.3°C$ and $K_f = 1.86$ (from Table 17.5). Solving for the molality gives

$$m_{solute} = \frac{\Delta T}{K_f} = \frac{23.3°C}{1.86\dfrac{°C\ kg}{mol}} = 12.5\ mol/kg$$

This means that 12.5 moles of ethylene glycol must be added per kilogram of water. We have 10.0 L, or 10.0 kg, of water. Therefore, the total number of moles of ethylene glycol needed is

$$\frac{12.5 \text{ mol}}{\text{kg}} \times 10.0 \text{ kg} = 1.25 \times 10^2 \text{ mol}$$

The mass of ethylene glycol needed is

$$1.25 \times 10^2 \text{ mol} \times \frac{62.1 \text{ g}}{\text{mol}} = 7.76 \times 10^3 \text{ g (or 7.76 kg)}$$

Like the boiling-point elevation, the observed freezing-point depression can be used to determine molar masses and to characterize solutions.

17.6 | Osmotic Pressure

Osmotic pressure, another of the colligative properties, can be understood from Fig. 17.14. A solution and pure solvent are separated by a **semipermeable membrane,** which allows *solvent but not solute* molecules to pass through. As time passes, the volume of the solution increases, whereas that of the solvent decreases. This flow of solvent into the solution through the semipermeable membrane is called **osmosis.** Eventually the liquid levels stop changing, indicating that the system has reached equilibrium. Because the liquid levels are different at this point, there is a greater hydrostatic pressure on the solution than on the pure solvent. This excess pressure is called the **osmotic pressure.** We can take another view of this phenomenon, as illustrated in Fig. 17.15. Osmosis can be prevented by applying a pressure to the solution. *The pressure that just stops the osmosis is equal to the osmotic pressure of the solution.*

A simple model to explain osmotic pressure can be constructed as shown in Fig. 17.16. The membrane allows only solvent molecules to pass through. However, the initial rates of solvent transfer to and from the solution are not the same. The solute particles interfere with the passage of solvent from the solution, so the rate of transfer is slower from the solution to the solvent than in the reverse direction. Thus there is a net transfer of solvent molecules into the solution, causing the solution volume to increase. As the solution level rises in the tube, the resulting pressure exerts an extra "push" on the solvent mole-

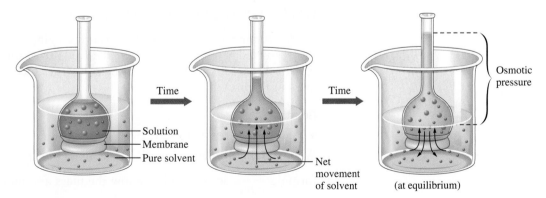

Figure 17.14

A tube with a bulb on the end is covered by a semipermeable membrane. The solution inside the tube is bathed in the pure solvent. There is a net transfer of solvent molecules into the solution until the hydrostatic pressure equalizes the solvent flow in both directions. The solvent level shows little change, because the narrow stem of the bulb has a very small volume.

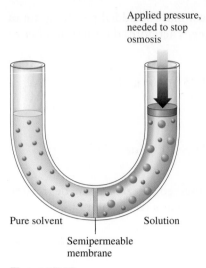

Figure 17.15
The normal flow of solvent into the solution (osmosis) can be prevented by applying an external pressure to the solution. The minimum pressure required to stop the osmosis is equal to the osmotic pressure of the solution.

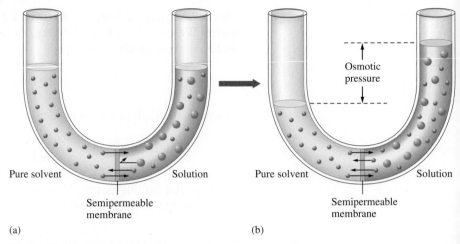

Figure 17.16
(a) A pure solvent and its solution (containing a nonvolatile solute) are separated by a semipermeable membrane through which solvent molecules (blue) can pass but solute molecules (green) cannot. The rate of solvent transfer is greater from solvent to solution than from solution to solvent. (b) The system at equilibrium, where the rate of solvent transfer is the same in both directions.

cules in the solution, forcing them back through the membrane. Eventually, enough pressure develops so that the solvent transfer becomes equal in both directions. At this point, equilibrium is achieved and the levels stop changing.

Osmotic pressure can be used to characterize solutions and to determine molar masses just as the other colligative properties can; however, osmotic pressure is particularly useful because a small concentration of solute produces a relatively large osmotic pressure.

Experiments show that the dependence of the osmotic pressure on solution concentration is represented by the equation

$$\pi = MRT$$

where π is the osmotic pressure in atmospheres, M is the molarity of the solute, R is the gas law constant, and T is the Kelvin temperature.

A molar mass determination using osmotic pressure is illustrated in Example 17.4.

⭕WL INTERACTIVE EXAMPLE 17.4

To determine the molar mass of a certain protein, 1.00×10^{-3} g of the protein was dissolved in enough water to make 1.00 mL of solution. The osmotic pressure of this solution was found to be 1.12 torr at 25.0°C. Calculate the molar mass of the protein.

Solution

■ What are we trying to solve?

We are trying to determine the molar mass of a protein. Molar mass has the formula $\frac{\text{mass}}{\text{mole}}$, so we need to know the mass and number of moles. We have the mass as 1.00×10^{-3} g, so we need to determine the number of moles. We are given the osmotic pressure of the solution, so we use the equation

$$\pi = MRT$$

In this case

$$\pi = 1.12 \text{ torr} \times \frac{1 \text{ atm}}{760 \text{ torr}} = 1.47 \times 10^{-3} \text{ atm}$$

$$R = 0.08206 \text{ L atm K}^{-1} \text{ mol}^{-1}$$

$$T = 25.0 + 273 = 298 \text{ K}$$

Note that the osmotic pressure must be converted to atmospheres because of the units of R.

Solving for M gives

$$M = \frac{1.47 \times 10^{-3} \text{ atm}}{(0.08206 \text{ L atm K}^{-1} \text{ mol}^{-1})(298 \text{ K})} = 6.01 \times 10^{-5} \text{ mol/L}$$

Since 1.00×10^{-3} g of protein was dissolved in 1.00 mL of solution, the mass of protein per liter of solution is 1.00 g. The solution's concentration is 6.01×10^{-5} mol/L. This concentration is produced from 1.00×10^{-3} g of protein per milliliter, or 1.00 g/L. Thus 6.01×10^{-5} mole of protein has a mass of 1.00 g, and

$$\frac{1.00 \text{ g}}{6.01 \times 10^{-5} \text{ mol}} = \frac{x \text{ g}}{1.00 \text{ mol}}$$

$$x = 1.66 \times 10^4 \text{ g/mol}$$

The molar mass of the protein is 1.66×10^4. This molar mass may seem very large, but it is relatively small for a protein.

Measurements of osmotic pressure generally give much more accurate molar mass values than those from freezing-point or boiling-point changes.

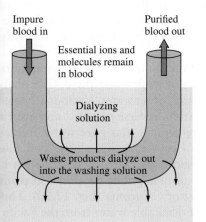

Figure 17.17
Representation of the functioning of an artificial kidney.

In osmosis a semipermeable membrane prevents transfer of *all* solute particles. A similar phenomenon called **dialysis** occurs at the walls of most plant and animal cells. However, in this case the membrane allows transfer of both solvent molecules and *small* solute molecules and ions. One of the most important applications of dialysis is the use of artificial kidney machines to purify the blood. The blood is passed through a cellophane tube, which acts as the semipermeable membrane. The tube is immersed in a dialyzing solution (Fig. 17.17). This "washing" solution contains the same concentrations of ions and small molecules as blood but has none of the waste products normally removed by the kidneys. The resulting dialysis of waste products cleanses the blood.

Solutions that have identical osmotic pressures are said to be **isotonic solutions.** Fluids administered intravenously must be isotonic with body fluids. For example, if cells are bathed in a hypertonic solution, which is a solution having an osmotic pressure higher than that of the cell fluids, the cells will shrivel because of a net transfer of water out of the cells. This phenomenon is called *crenation.* The opposite phenomenon, called *lysis,* occurs when cells are bathed in a hypotonic solution, a solution with an osmotic pressure lower than that of the cell fluids. In this case the cells rupture because of the flow of water into the cells.

We can use the phenomenon of crenation to our advantage. Food can be preserved by treating its surface with a solute that forms a solution hypertonic to bacteria cells. Bacteria on the food then tend to shrivel and die. This is why salt can be used to protect meat and sugar can be used to protect fruit.

❂WL INTERACTIVE EXAMPLE 17.5

What concentration of sodium chloride in water is needed to produce an aqueous solution isotonic with blood ($\pi = 7.70$ atm at 25°C)?

Solution We can calculate the molarity of the solute from the equation

$$\pi = MRT \qquad \text{or} \qquad M = \frac{\pi}{RT}$$

$$M = \frac{7.70 \text{ atm}}{(0.08206 \text{ L atm K}^{-1} \text{ mol}^{-1})(298 \text{ K})} = 0.315 \text{ mol/L}$$

This represents the total molarity of solute particles. But NaCl gives two ions per formula unit. Therefore, the concentration of NaCl needed is 0.315/2, or 0.158 M. That is,

$$\underset{0.1575\ M}{\text{NaCl}} \longrightarrow \underset{0.1575\ M}{\text{Na}^+} + \underset{0.1575\ M}{\text{Cl}^-}$$
$$\underbrace{\qquad\qquad\qquad}_{0.315\ M}$$

Reverse Osmosis

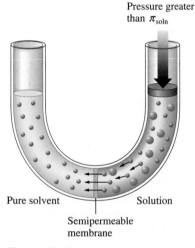

Pressure greater than π_{soln}

Pure solvent   Solution

Semipermeable membrane

Figure 17.18
Reverse osmosis. A pressure greater than the osmotic pressure of the solution is applied, which causes a net flow of solvent molecules (blue) from the solution to the pure solvent. The solute molecules (green) remain behind.

If a solution in contact with pure solvent across a semipermeable membrane is subjected to an external pressure larger than its osmotic pressure, **reverse osmosis** occurs. The pressure will cause a net flow of solvent from the solution to the solvent, as shown in Fig. 17.18. In reverse osmosis, the semipermeable membrane acts as a "molecular filter" to remove solute particles. This fact is potentially applicable to the **desalination** (removal of dissolved salts) of seawater, which is highly hypertonic to body fluids and thus is not drinkable.

A small-scale, manually operated reverse osmosis desalinator has been developed by the U.S. Navy to provide fresh water on life rafts (Fig. 17.19). Potable water can be supplied by this desalinator at the rate of 1.25 gallons of water per hour—enough to keep 25 people alive. This compact desalinator, which weighs only 10 pounds, replaces the bulky cases of fresh water formerly stored on Navy life rafts.

As the population of the Sunbelt areas of the United States increases, more demand will be placed on the limited supplies of fresh water there. One obvious source of fresh water is from the desalination of seawater. Various schemes have been suggested, including solar evaporation, reverse osmosis, and even a plan for towing icebergs from Antarctica (remember that pure water freezes out of an aqueous solution). The problem, of course, is that all the available processes are expensive. However, as water shortages increase, desalination is becoming necessary. For example, the first full-time public desalination plant is found on Catalina Island, just off the coast of California (Fig. 17.20). This plant, which can produce 132,000 gallons of drinkable water from the Pacific

Figure 17.19
A commercially available desalinator, similar to those developed by the Navy for life rafts. The essential part of these desalinators is a cellophane-like membrane wrapped around a tube with holes in it. Seawater is forced through the tube by a hand-operated pump at pressures of about 70 atm to produce water with a salt content only 40% higher than that from a typical tap.

Courtesy, Katadyn North America

Figure 17.20
Residents of Catalina Island off the coast of southern California are benefiting from a desalination plant that can supply 132,000 gallons of drinkable water per day, one-third of the island's daily needs.

5. Brine is pumped into ocean.

1. Salt water pumped from underground wells.

2. Salt water is forced through 20-micron and 5-micron filters at a pressure of 800 pounds per square inch.

3. Fresh water is forced through additional filters.

4. Fresh water is pumped into water supply.

Ocean every day, operates by reverse osmosis. Powerful pumps, developing over 800 lb/in^2 of pressure, are used to force seawater through synthetic semipermeable membranes.

Catalina Island's plant may be just the beginning. The city of Santa Barbara opened a $40 million desalination plant in 1992 that can produce 8 million gallons of drinkable water per day, and the Southern California town of Carlsbad opened a plant in 2012 that can produce 50 million gallons of drinking water from seawater each day. This $320 million project is the largest desalination plant in the Western Hemisphere. Desalination plants are also in the works for Huntington Beach, California, and Camp Pendleton, a military base just north of Carlsbad.

17.7 | Colligative Properties of Electrolyte Solutions

As we have seen, the colligative properties of solutions depend on the total concentration of solute particles. For example, a 0.10 m glucose solution shows a freezing-point depression of 0.186°C:

$$\Delta T = K_f m = (1.86°C \text{ kg/mol})(0.10 \text{ mol/kg}) = 0.186°C$$

On the other hand, a 0.10 m sodium chloride solution should show a freezing-point depression of 0.37°C, since the solution is 0.10 m Na$^+$ ions and 0.10 m Cl$^-$ ions. Therefore, because the solution is 0.20 m in solute particles, $\Delta T = (1.86°C \text{ kg/mol})(0.20 \text{ mol/kg}) = 0.37°C$.

The relationship between the moles of solute dissolved and the moles of particles in solution is usually expressed by the **van't Hoff factor** (i):

Dutch chemist J. H. van't Hoff (1852–1911) received the first Nobel Prize in chemistry in 1901.

$$i = \frac{\text{moles of particles in solution}}{\text{moles of solute dissolved}}$$

Figure 17.21
In an aqueous solution, a few ions aggregate, forming ion pairs that behave as a unit.

Table 17.6

Expected and Observed Values of the van't Hoff Factor for 0.05 m Solutions of Several Electrolytes

Electrolyte	i (expected)	i (observed)
NaCl	2.0	1.9
MgCl$_2$	3.0	2.7
MgSO$_4$	2.0	1.3
FeCl$_3$	4.0	3.4
HCl	2.0	1.9
Glucose*	1.0	1.0

*A nonelectrolyte shown for comparison.

The *expected* value for i can be calculated for a salt by noting the number of ions per formula unit. For example, for NaCl, i is 2; for K$_2$SO$_4$, i is 3; and for Fe$_3$(PO$_4$)$_2$, i is 5. These calculated values assume that when a salt dissolves, it completely dissociates into its component ions, which then move around independently. However, this assumption is not always true. For example, the freezing-point depression observed for 0.10 m NaCl is 1.87 times that observed for 0.10 m glucose rather than twice as great. That is, for a 0.10 m NaCl solution, the observed value for i is 1.87 rather than 2. Why? The best explanation is that **ion pairing** occurs in solution (Fig. 17.21). At a given instant, a small percentage of the sodium and chloride ions are paired and thus count as a single particle. In general, ion pairing is most important in concentrated solutions. As the solution becomes more dilute, the ions are farther apart and less ion pairing occurs. For example, in a 0.0010 m NaCl solution, the observed value of i is 1.97, which is very close to the expected value.

Ion pairing occurs to some extent in all electrolyte solutions. Table 17.6 shows expected and observed values of i for a given concentration of various electrolytes. Note that the deviation of i from the expected value tends to be greatest when the ions have multiple charges. This is expected because ion pairing ought to be most important for highly charged ions.

The colligative properties of electrolyte solutions are described by including the van't Hoff factor in the appropriate equation. For example, for changes in freezing and boiling points, the modified equation is

$$\Delta T = imK$$

where K represents the freezing-point depression constant or the boiling-point elevation constant for the solvent.

For the osmotic pressure of electrolyte solutions, the equation is

$$\pi = iMRT$$

⬛WL INTERACTIVE EXAMPLE 17.6

The observed osmotic pressure for a 0.10 M solution of Fe(NH$_4$)$_2$(SO$_4$)$_2$ at 25°C is 10.8 atm. Compare the expected and experimental values for i.

Solution The ionic solid Fe(NH$_4$)$_2$(SO$_4$)$_2$ dissociates in water to produce 5 ions:

$$\text{Fe(NH}_4)_2(\text{SO}_4)_2 \xrightarrow{\text{H}_2\text{O}} \text{Fe}^{2+} + 2\text{NH}_4^+ + 2\text{SO}_4^{2-}$$

Thus the expected value for i is 5. We can obtain the experimental value for i by using the equation for osmotic pressure:

$$\pi = iMRT \quad \text{or} \quad i = \frac{\pi}{MRT}$$

where $\pi = 10.8$ atm, $M = 0.10$ mol/L, $R = 0.08206$ L atm K^{-1} mol^{-1}, and $T = 25 + 273 = 298$ K. Substituting these values into the equation gives

$$i = \frac{\pi}{MRT} = \frac{10.8 \text{ atm}}{\left(0.10\frac{\text{mol}}{\text{L}}\right)\left(0.08206\frac{\text{L atm}}{\text{K mol}}\right)(298 \text{ K})} = 4.42$$

The experimental value for i is less than the expected value, presumably because of ion pairing.

17.8 | Colloids

Mud can be suspended in water by vigorous stirring. When the stirring stops, most of the particles rapidly settle out, but even after several days some of the smallest particles remain suspended. Although undetected in normal lighting, their presence can be demonstrated by shining a beam of intense light through the suspension. The beam is visible from the side because the light is scattered by the suspended particles. In a true solution, on the other hand, the beam is invisible from the side because the individual ions and molecules dispersed in the solution are too small to scatter visible light.

The scattering of light by particles is called the **Tyndall effect** (Fig. 17.22) and is often used to distinguish between a suspension and a true solution.

A suspension of tiny particles in some medium is called a **colloidal dispersion,** or a **colloid.** The suspended particles can be single, large molecules or aggregates of molecules or ions ranging in size from 1 to 1000 nanometers. Colloids are classified according to the states of the dispersed phase and the dispersing medium. Table 17.7 summarizes various types of colloids.

What stabilizes a colloid? Why do the particles remain suspended rather than forming larger aggregates and precipitating out? The answer is compli-

Figure 17.22
The Tyndall effect. The solution on the left does not show the path of the light beam, whereas the suspension on the right clearly shows the light path.

Table 17.7

Types of Colloids

Examples	Dispersing Medium	Dispersed Substance	Colloid Type
Fog, aerosol sprays	Gas	Liquid	Aerosol
Smoke, airborne bacteria	Gas	Solid	Aerosol
Whipped cream, soap suds	Liquid	Gas	Foam
Milk, mayonnaise	Liquid	Liquid	Emulsion
Paint, clays, gelatin	Liquid	Solid	Sol
Marshmallow, polystyrene foam	Solid	Gas	Solid foam
Butter, cheese	Solid	Liquid	Solid emulsion
Ruby glass	Solid	Solid	Solid sol

Chemical Insights

Organisms and Ice Formation

The ice-cold waters of the polar oceans are teeming with fish that seem immune to freezing. One might think that these fish have some kind of antifreeze in their blood. However, studies show that they are protected from freezing in a way that is very different from the way antifreeze protects our cars. As we have seen in this chapter, solutes such as sugars, salts, and ethylene glycol lower the temperature at which the solid and liquid phases of water can coexist. However, the fish could not tolerate high concentrations of solutes in their blood because of the osmotic pressure effects. Instead, they are protected by proteins in their blood. These proteins allow the water in the bloodstream to be supercooled—exist below 0°C—without forming ice. The proteins apparently coat the surface of each tiny ice crystal as soon as it begins to form, thus preventing it from growing to a size that would cause biological damage. Similar "antifreeze" proteins have been found in other organisms, including the springtail snow flea, beetles, moths, and various bacteria and plants.

Recently, teams of researchers at the University of Notre Dame and the University of Alaska–Fairbanks discovered a new type of antifreeze molecule in the Upis beetle. Instead of a protein-based antifreeze, the Upis antifreeze is a complex sugar called *xylomannan,* which appears to be equally as effective as the proteins at preventing freezing. The Upis beetle freezes at −19°F but remarkably can

survive exposure to temperatures as low as about −100°F.

Although it might at first seem surprising, this research on antifreeze molecules has attracted the attention of ice cream manufacturers. Premium-quality ice cream is smooth; it does not have large ice crystals in it. The makers of ice cream would like to incorporate natural antifreeze molecules, or at least molecules that behave similarly, into ice cream to prevent growth of ice crystals during storage.

Fruit and vegetable growers have a similar interest: They also want to prevent ice formation that could damage their crops during an unusual cold wave. However, this is a very different kind of problem than keeping polar fish from freezing. Many types of fruits and vegetables are colonized by bacteria that manufacture a protein that *encourages* freezing by acting as a nucleating agent for an ice crystal. Chemists have identified the offending protein in the bacteria as well as the gene that is responsible for making it. They have learned to modify the genetic material of these bacteria in such a way that removes their ability to make the protein that encourages ice crystal formation. If testing shows that these modified bacteria have no harmful effects on the crop or the environment, the original bacteria strain will be replaced with the new form so that ice crystals will not form so readily when a cold snap occurs.

Figure 17.23

A representation of two colloidal particles. In each the center particle is surrounded by a layer of positive ions, with negative ions in the outer layer. Thus, although the particles are electrically neutral, they still repel each other because of their outer negative layer of ions.

cated, but the main effect that stabilizes the colloid seems to be *electrostatic repulsion.* A colloid, like all other macroscopic substances, is electrically neutral. However, when a colloid is placed in an electric field, the dispersed particles all migrate to the same electrode; thus they must all have the same charge. How is this possible? The center of a colloidal particle (a tiny ionic crystal, a group of molecules, or a single large molecule) attracts from the medium a layer of ions, all of the same charge. This group of ions in turn attracts another layer of oppositely charged ions, as shown in Fig. 17.23. Because the colloidal particles all have an outer layer of ions with the same charge, they repel each other; thus they do not easily aggregate to form particles that are large enough to precipitate.

The destruction of a colloid, called **coagulation,** can usually be accomplished either by heating or by adding an electrolyte. Heating increases the velocities of the colloidal particles, causing them to collide with enough energy so that the ion barriers are penetrated. This allows the particles to aggregate.

Figure 17.24

The Cottrell precipitator installed in a smokestack. The charged plates attract the colloidal particles because of their ion layers and thus remove them from the smoke.

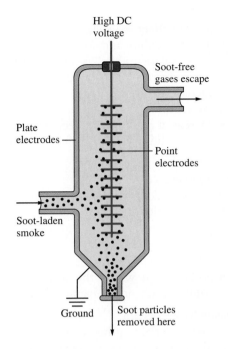

As this is repeated many times, the particle grows to a point where it settles out. Adding an electrolyte neutralizes the adsorbed ion layers. This is why clay suspended in rivers is deposited where the river reaches the ocean, forming the deltas characteristic of large rivers like the Mississippi. The high salt content of the seawater causes the colloidal clay particles to coagulate.

The removal of soot from smoke is another example of the coagulation of a colloid. When smoke is passed through an electrostatic precipitator (Fig. 17.24), the suspended solids are removed. The use of precipitators has produced an immense improvement in the air quality of heavily industrialized cities.

Key Terms

Section 17.1
molarity
mass percent
mole fraction
molality

Section 17.2
enthalpy (heat) of solution
enthalpy (heat) of hydration
supercritical fluid

Section 17.3
Henry's law
thermal pollution

Section 17.4
Raoult's law
ideal solution

Section 17.5
colligative properties
molal boiling-point elevation
    constant

For Review

⦿WL and **go Chemistry**

Sign in at **www.cengage.com/owl** to:
- View tutorials and simulations, develop problem-solving skills, and complete online homework assigned by your professor.
- Download Go Chemistry mini lecture modules for quick review and exam prep from OWL (or purchase them at **www.cengagebrain.com**)

Solution composition
- Molarity (M): moles solute per liter of solution
- Mass percent: ratio of mass of solute to mass of solution times 100%
- Mole fraction (χ): ratio of moles of a given component to total moles of all components
- Molality (m): moles solute per mass of solvent (in kg)
- Normality (N): number of equivalents per liter of solution

Enthalpy of solution (ΔH_{soln})
- The enthalpy change accompanying solution formation
- Can be partitioned into
  - The energy required to overcome the solute–solute interactions
  - The energy required to "make holes" in the solvent
  - The energy associated with solute–solvent interactions

molal freezing-point depression constant

Section 17.6

semipermeable membrane
osmosis
osmotic pressure
dialysis
isotonic solution
reverse osmosis
desalination

Section 17.7

van't Hoff factor
ion pairing

Section 17.8

Tyndall effect
colloid (colloidal dispersion)
coagulation

Factors that affect solubility

- Polarity of solute and solvent
  - "Like dissolves like" is a useful generalization
- Pressure increases the solubility of gases in a solvent
  - Henry's law: $C = kP$
- Temperature effects
  - Increased temperature decreases the solubility of a gas in water
  - Most solids are more soluble at higher temperatures but important exceptions exist

Vapor pressure of solutions

- A solution containing a nonvolatile solute has a lower vapor pressure than a solution of the pure solvent
- Raoult's law defines an ideal solution

$$P_{vapor}^{soln} = \chi_{solvent} P_{vapor}^{solvent}$$

- Solutions in which the solute–solvent attractions differ from the solute–solute and solvent–solvent attractions violate Raoult's law

Colligative properties

- Depend on the number of solute particles present
- Boiling-point elevation: $\Delta T = K_b m_{solute}$
- Freezing-point lowering: $\Delta T = K_f m_{solute}$
- Osmotic pressure: $\Pi = MRT$
  - Osmosis occurs when a solution and pure solvent are separated by a semipermeable membrane that allows solvent molecules to pass but not solute particles
  - Reverse osmosis occurs when the applied pressure is greater than the osmotic pressure of the solution
- Because colligative properties depend on the number of particles, solutes that break into several ions when they dissolve have an effect proportional to the number of ions produced
  - The van't Hoff factor i represents the number of ions produced by each formula unit of solute

Colloids

- A suspension of tiny particles stabilized by electrostatic repulsion among the ion layers surrounding the individual particles
- Can be coagulated (destroyed) by heating or adding an electrolyte

Discussion Questions

These questions are designed to be considered by groups of students in class. Often these questions work well for introducing a particular topic in class.

1. Consider Fig. 17.8. According to the caption and picture, water is transferred from one beaker to another.
   a. Explain why this occurs.
   b. The explanation in the text uses terms such as *vapor pressure* and *equilibrium*. Explain what these terms have to do with the phenomenon. For example, what does the equilibrium involve?
   c. Does all the water end up in the second beaker?

   d. Is the water in the beaker containing the solute evaporating? If so, is the rate of evaporation increasing, decreasing, or staying constant?

   Draw pictures to illustrate your explanations.

2. Consider Fig. 17.8. Suppose that instead of having a nonvolatile solute in the solvent in one beaker, the two beakers have different volatile liquids. That is, suppose one beaker contains liquid A ($P_{vap} = 50$ torr) and the other beaker contains liquid B ($P_{vap} = 100$ torr). Explain what happens as time passes. How is this similar to the first case shown in the figure? How is it different?

3. Assume that you place a freshwater plant into a saltwater solution and examine it under a microscope. What happens to the plant cells? What if you placed a saltwater plant in pure water? Explain. Draw pictures to illustrate your explanations.

4. How does ΔH_{soln} relate to deviations from Raoult's law? Explain.

5. You have read that adding NaCl to water can both increase its boiling point and decrease its freezing point. A friend of yours explains it to you like this: "The ions prevent freezing by blocking the water molecules from joining together. The hydration of the ions also makes the water boil at a higher temperature." What do you say to your friend?

6. You drop an ice cube (made from pure water) into a saltwater solution at 0°C. Explain what happens and why.

7. Using the phase diagram for water and Raoult's law, explain why salt is spread on the roads in winter (even when the temperature is below freezing).

8. You and your friend are each drinking cola from separate 2-L bottles. Both colas are equally carbonated. You are able to drink 1 L of cola, but your friend can drink only about half a liter. You each close the bottles, and place them in the refrigerator. The next day when you each go to get the colas, whose will be more carbonated and why?

9. Is molality or molarity dependent on temperature? Explain your answer. Why is molality, and not molarity, used in the equations describing freezing-point depression and boiling-point elevation?

10. If a solution shows positive deviations from Raoult's law, would you expect it to have a higher or lower boiling point than if it were ideal? Explain.

11. Consider a beaker of salt water sitting open in a room. Over time does the vapor pressure increase, decrease, or stay the same? Explain.

Exercises

A blue exercise number indicates that the answer to that exercise appears at the back of this book and a solution appears in the *Solutions Guide.*

Solution Composition

12. The four most common ways to describe solution composition are mass percent, mole fraction, molarity, and molality. Define each of these solution composition terms. Why is molarity temperature-dependent, whereas the other three solution composition terms are temperature-independent?

13. Write equations showing the ions present after the following strong electrolytes are dissolved in water.
    a. HNO_3 d. $SrBr_2$ g. NH_4NO_3
    b. Na_2SO_4 e. $KClO_4$ h. $CuSO_4$
    c. $Al(NO_3)_3$ f. NH_4Br i. $NaOH$

14. Calculate the sodium ion concentration when 70.0 mL of 3.0 *M* sodium carbonate is added to 30.0 mL of 1.0 *M* sodium bicarbonate.

15. An aqueous antifreeze solution is 40.0% ethylene glycol ($C_2H_6O_2$) by mass. The density of the solution is 1.05 g/cm^3. Calculate the molality, molarity, and mole fraction of the ethylene glycol.

16. Common commercial acids and bases are aqueous solutions with the following properties:

	Density (g/cm^3)	Mass Percent of Solute
Hydrochloric acid	1.19	38
Nitric acid	1.42	70.
Sulfuric acid	1.84	95
Acetic acid	1.05	99
Ammonia	0.90	28

Calculate the molarity, molality, and mole fraction of each of these reagents.

17. A solution is prepared by mixing 50.0 mL of toluene ($C_6H_5CH_3$, $d = 0.867$ g/cm^3) with 125 mL of benzene (C_6H_6, $d = 0.874$ g/cm^3). Assuming that the volumes add on mixing, calculate the mass percent, mole fraction, molality, and molarity of the toluene.

18. A bottle of wine contains 12.5% ethanol by volume. The density of ethanol (C_2H_5OH) is 0.789 g/cm^3. Calculate the concentration of ethanol in wine in terms of mass percent and molality.

19. A 1.37 *M* aqueous solution of citric acid ($H_3C_6H_5O_7$) has a density of 1.10 g/cm^3. What are the mass percent, molality, and mole fraction of the citric acid?

20. Determine the molarity and mole fraction of a 1.00 *m* solution of acetone (CH_3COCH_3) dissolved in ethanol (C_2H_5OH). (Density of acetone = 0.788 g/cm^3; density of ethanol = 0.789 g/cm^3.) Assume that the final volume equals the sum of the volumes of acetone and ethanol.

21. A solution of phosphoric acid was made by dissolving 10.0 g of H_3PO_4 in 100.00 mL of water. The resulting volume was 104 mL. Calculate the density, mole fraction, molarity, and molality of the solution. Assume water has a density of 1.00 g/cm^3.

22. In a lab you need at least 100 mL of each of the following solutions. Explain how you would proceed by using the given information.
    a. 2.0 *m* KCl in water (density of H_2O = 1.00 g/cm^3)
    b. 15% NaOH by mass in water
    c. 25% NaOH by mass in CH_3OH ($d = 0.79$ g/cm^3)
    d. 0.10 mole fraction of $C_6H_{12}O_6$ in water

Thermodynamics of Solutions and Solubility

23. What does the axiom "like dissolves like" mean? There are four types of solute–solvent combinations: polar sol-

utes in polar solvents, nonpolar solutes in polar solvents, and so on. For each type of solution, discuss the magnitude of ΔH_{soln}.

24. For each of the following solute–solvent combinations, state the sign and relative magnitudes for ΔH_1, ΔH_2, ΔH_3, and ΔH_{soln} (as defined in Fig. 17.1 of the text). Explain your answers.

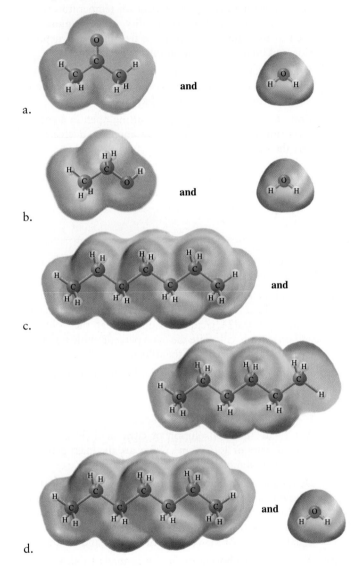

a.

b.

c.

d.

25. In order for sodium chloride to dissolve in water, a small amount of energy must be added during solution formation. This is not energetically favorable. Why is NaCl so soluble in water?

26. The high melting points of ionic solids indicate that a lot of energy must be supplied to separate the ions from one another. How is it possible that the ions can separate from one another when soluble ionic compounds are dis-

solved in water, often with essentially no temperature change?

27. The lattice energy* of NaI is -686 kJ/mol, and the enthalpy of hydration is -694 kJ/mol. Calculate the enthalpy of solution per mole of solid NaI. Describe the process to which this enthalpy change applies.

28. a. Use the following data to calculate the enthalpy of hydration for calcium chloride and calcium iodide.

	Lattice Energy*	ΔH_{soln}
$CaCl_2(s)$	-2247 kJ/mol	-46 kJ/mol
$CaI_2(s)$	-2059 kJ/mol	-104 kJ/mol

b. Based on your answers to part a, which ion, Cl^- or I^-, is more strongly attracted to water?

29. Although $Al(OH)_3$ is insoluble in water, NaOH is very soluble. Explain this difference in terms of lattice energies.

30. Which ion in each of the following pairs would you expect to be more strongly hydrated? Why?
    a. Na^+ or Mg^{2+} d. F^- or Br^-
    b. Mg^{2+} or Be^{2+} e. Cl^- or ClO_4^-
    c. Fe^{2+} or Fe^{3+} f. ClO_4^- or SO_4^{2-}

31. For each of the following pairs, predict which substance would be more soluble in water.

a. NH_3 or PH_3

b. CH_3CN or CH_3CH_3

c. $CH_3C{-}OH$ or $CH_3{-}C{-}OCH_3$
         $\underset{O}{\|}$ $\underset{O}{\|}$

32. Which solvent, water or carbon tetrachloride, would you choose to dissolve each of the following?
    a. KrF_2 e. MgF_2
    b. SF_2 f. CH_2O
    c. SO_2 g. $CH_2{=}CH_2$
    d. CO_2

---

*Lattice energy was defined in Chapter 13 as the energy change for the process $M^+(g) + X^-(g) \rightarrow MX(s)$.

33. Rationalize the trend in water solubility for the following simple alcohols.

Alcohol	Solubility (g/100 g H_2O at 20°C)
Methanol, CH_3OH	Soluble in all proportions
Ethanol, CH_3CH_2OH	Soluble in all proportions
Propanol, $CH_3CH_2CH_2OH$	Soluble in all proportions
Butanol, $CH_3(CH_2)_2CH_2OH$	8.14
Pentanol, $CH_3(CH_2)_3CH_2OH$	2.62
Hexanol, $CH_3(CH_2)_4CH_2OH$	0.59
Heptanol, $CH_3(CH_2)_5CH_2OH$	0.09

34. In the flushing and cleaning of columns used in liquid chromatography, a series of solvents is used. Hexane (C_6H_{14}), chloroform ($CHCl_3$), methanol (CH_3OH), and water are passed through the column in that order. Rationalize the order in terms of intermolecular forces and the mutual solubility (miscibility) of the solvents.

35. Structure, pressure, and temperature all have an effect on solubility. Discuss each of their effects. What is Henry's law? Why does Henry's law not work for $HCl(g)$? What do the terms *hydrophobic* and *hydrophilic* mean?

36. $O_2(g)$ obeys Henry's law in water but not in blood (an aqueous solution). Why?

37. The solubility of nitrogen in water is 8.21×10^{-4} mol/L at 0°C when the N_2 pressure above water is 0.790 atm. Calculate the Henry's law constant for N_2 in units of L atm/mol for Henry's law in the form $P = kC$, where C is the gas concentration in mol/L. Calculate the solubility of N_2 in water when the partial pressure of nitrogen above water is 1.10 atm at 0°C.

38. In Exercise 112 in Chapter 5, the pressure of CO_2 in a bottle of sparkling wine was calculated assuming that the CO_2 was insoluble in water. This was an incorrect assumption. Redo this problem by assuming that CO_2 obeys Henry's law. Use the data given in that problem to calculate the partial pressure of CO_2 in the gas phase and the solubility of CO_2 in the wine at 25°C. The Henry's law constant for CO_2 is 32 L atm/mol at 25°C with Henry's law in the form $P = kC$, where C is the concentration of the gas in mol/L.

39. Rationalize the temperature dependence of the solubility of a gas in terms of the kinetic molecular theory.

Vapor Pressures of Solutions

40. Glycerin ($C_3H_8O_3$) is a nonvolatile liquid. What is the vapor pressure of a solution made by adding 164 g of glycerin to 338 mL of H_2O at 39.8°C? The vapor pressure of pure water at 39.8°C is 54.74 torr and its density is 0.992 g/cm^3.

41. The vapor pressure of a solution containing 53.6 g glycerin ($C_3H_8O_3$) in 133.7 g ethanol (C_2H_5OH) is 113 torr at 40°C. Calculate the vapor pressure of pure ethanol at 40°C assuming that glycerin is a nonvolatile, nonelectrolyte solute in ethanol.

42. Which of the following will have the lowest total vapor pressure at 25°C? Which has the highest vapor pressure at 25°C? At 25°C, the vapor pressure of pure water is 23.8 torr.
   a. pure water
   b. a solution of glucose in water with $X_{glucose} = 0.01$
   c. a solution of sodium chloride in water with $X_{NaCl} = 0.01$
   d. a solution of methanol in water with $X_{CH_3OH} = 0.2$
   (At 25°C, the vapor pressure of pure methanol is 143 torr.)

43. The normal boiling point of methanol is 64.7°C. A solution containing a nonvolatile solute dissolved in methanol has a vapor pressure of 710.0 torr at 64.7°C. What is the mole fraction of methanol in this solution?

44. A solution is prepared by mixing 0.0300 mole of CH_2Cl_2 and 0.0500 mole of CH_2Br_2 at 25°C. Assuming the solution is ideal, calculate the composition of the vapor (in terms of mole fractions) at 25°C. At 25°C the vapor pressures of pure CH_2Cl_2 and pure CH_2Br_2 are 133 and 11.4 torr, respectively.

45. At a certain temperature, the vapor pressure of pure benzene (C_6H_6) is 0.930 atm. A solution was prepared by dissolving 10.0 g of a nondissociating, nonvolatile solute in 78.11 g of benzene at that temperature. The vapor pressure of the solution was found to be 0.900 atm. Assuming that the solution behaves ideally, determine the molar mass of the solute.

46. At 25°C the vapor in equilibrium with a solution containing carbon disulfide and acetonitrile has a total pressure of 263 torr and is 85.5 mole percent carbon disulfide. What is the mole fraction of carbon disulfide in the solution? At 25°C the vapor pressure of carbon disulfide is 375 torr. Assume that the solution and the vapor exhibit ideal behavior.

47. Pentane (C_5H_{12}) and hexane (C_6H_{14}) combine to form an ideal solution. At 25°C the vapor pressures of pentane and hexane are 511 and 150. torr, respectively. A solution is prepared by mixing 25 mL of pentane (density = 0.63 g/mL) with 45 mL of hexane (density = 0.66 g/mL).
   a. What is the vapor pressure of this solution?
   b. What is the mole fraction of pentane in the vapor that is in equilibrium with this solution?

48. Benzene and toluene form ideal solutions. Consider a solution of benzene and toluene prepared at 25°C. Assuming that the mole fractions of benzene and toluene in the vapor phase are equal, calculate the composition of the solution. At 25°C the vapor pressures of benzene and toluene are 95 and 28 torr, respectively.

49. What is the composition of a methanol (CH₃OH)–propanol (CH₃CH₂CH₂OH) solution that has a vapor pressure of 174 torr at 40°C? At 40°C the vapor pressures of pure methanol and pure propanol are 303 and 44.6 torr, respectively. Assume that the solution exhibits ideal behavior.

50. Match the vapor pressure diagrams with the solute–solvent combinations and explain your answers.

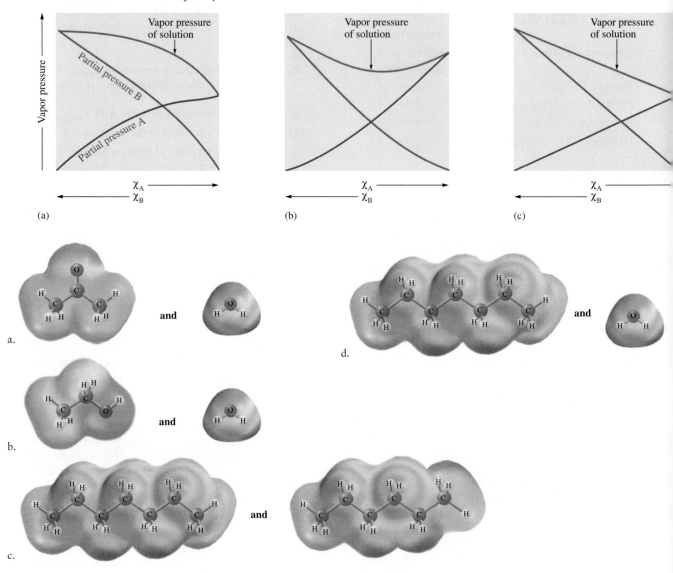

(a)   (b)   (c)

a.   and

b.   and

c.   and

d.   and

51. A solution is made by mixing 50.0 g of acetone (CH₃COCH₃) and 50.0 g of methanol (CH₃OH). What is the vapor pressure of this solution at 25°C? What is the composition of the vapor expressed as a mole fraction? Assume ideal solution and gas behavior. (At 25°C the vapor pressures of pure acetone and pure methanol are 271 and 143 torr, respectively.) The actual vapor pressure of this solution is 161 torr. Explain any discrepancies.

52. The vapor pressures of several solutions of water–propanol (CH₃CH₂CH₂OH) were determined at various compositions, with the following data collected at 45°C:

X_{H_2O}	Vapor Pressure (torr)
0	74.0
0.15	77.3
0.37	80.2
0.54	81.6
0.69	80.6
0.83	78.2
1.00	71.9

a. Are solutions of water and propanol ideal? Explain.
b. Predict the sign of ΔH_{soln} for water–propanol solutions.
c. Are the interactive forces between propanol and water molecules weaker than, stronger than, or equal to the interactive forces between the pure substances? Explain.
d. Which of the solutions in the table would have the lowest normal boiling point?

53. When pure methanol is mixed with water, the solution gets warmer to the touch. Would you expect this solution to be ideal? Explain.

54. The two beakers in the sealed container illustrated below contain pure water and an aqueous solution of a volatile solute.

Water   Aqueous
              solution

If the solute is less volatile than water, explain what will happen to the volumes in the two containers as time passes.

55. The following plot shows the vapor pressure of various solutions of components A and B at some temperature.

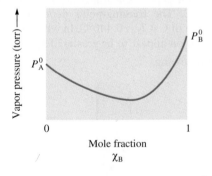

Which of the following statements is false concerning solutions of A and B?
a. The solutions exhibit negative deviations from Raoult's law.
b. ΔH_{soln} for the solutions should be exothermic.
c. The intermolecular forces are stronger in solution than in either pure A or pure B.
d. Pure liquid B is more volatile than pure liquid A.
e. The solution with $X_B = 0.6$ will have a lower boiling point than either pure A or pure B.

Colligative Properties

56. Vapor-pressure lowering is a colligative property, as are freezing-point depression and boiling-point elevation. What is a colligative property? Why is the freezing point depressed for a solution as compared to the pure solvent? Why is the boiling point elevated for a solution as compared to the pure solvent?

57. How would you prepare 1.0 L of an aqueous solution of sucrose ($C_{12}H_{22}O_{11}$) having an osmotic pressure of 15 atm at a temperature of 22°C? Sucrose is a nonelectrolyte.

58. Is the following statement true or false? Explain your answer. When determining the molar mass of a solute using boiling-point or freezing-point data, camphor would be the best solvent choice of all of the solvents listed in Table 17.5.

59. A solution is prepared by dissolving 27.0 g of urea [$(NH_2)_2CO$], in 150.0 g of water. Calculate the boiling point of the solution. Urea is a nonelectrolyte.

60. What mass of glycerin ($C_3H_8O_3$), a nonelectrolyte, must be dissolved in 200.0 g of water to give a solution with a freezing point of $-1.50°C$?

61. Calculate the freezing point and boiling point of an anti-freeze solution that is 50.0% by mass ethylene glycol ($HOCH_2CH_2OH$) in water. Ethylene glycol is a non-electrolyte.

62. The freezing point of t-butanol is 25.50°C and K_f is 9.1°C kg/mol. Usually t-butanol absorbs water on exposure to air. If the freezing point of a 10.0-g sample of t-butanol is 24.59°C, how many grams of water are present in the sample?

63. The molar mass of a nonelectrolyte is 58.0 g/mol. Calculate the boiling point of a solution containing 24.0 g of this compound and 600. g of water if the barometric pressure is such that pure water boils at 99.725°C.

64. If the human eye has an osmotic pressure of 8.00 atm at 25°C, what concentration of solute particles in water will provide an isotonic eyedrop solution (a solution with equal osmotic pressure)?

65. A 2.00-g sample of a large biomolecule was dissolved in 15.0 g of carbon tetrachloride. The boiling point of this solution was determined to be 77.85°C. Calculate the molar mass of the biomolecule. For carbon tetrachloride, the boiling-point constant is 5.03°C kg/mol, and the boiling point of pure carbon tetrachloride is 76.50°C.

66. An aqueous solution of 10.00 g of catalase, an enzyme found in the liver, has a volume of 1.00 L at 27°C. The solution's osmotic pressure at 27°C is found to be 0.745 torr. Calculate the molar mass of catalase.

67. Thyroxine, an important hormone that controls the rate of metabolism in the body, can be isolated from the thyroid gland. When 0.455 g of thyroxine is dissolved in 10.0 g of benzene, the freezing point of the solution is depressed by 0.300°C. What is the molar mass of thyroxine? See Table 17.5.

68. What volume of ethylene glycol ($C_2H_6O_2$), a nonelectrolyte, must be added to 15.0 L of water to produce an antifreeze solution with a freezing point of $-30.0°C$? What is the boiling point of this solution? (The density of ethylene glycol is 1.11 g/cm³, and the density of water is 1.00 g/cm³.)

69. Calculate the freezing-point depression and osmotic pressure in torr at 25°C for an aqueous solution of 1.0 g/L of a protein (molar mass = 9.0×10^4 g/mol) if the density of the solution is 1.0 g/cm³.

70. Considering your answer to Exercise 69, which colligative property, freezing-point depression or osmotic pressure, would be better for determining the molar masses of large molecules? Explain your answer.

71. If the fluid inside a tree is about 0.1 M more concentrated in solute than the groundwater that bathes the roots, how high will a column of fluid rise in the tree at 25°C? Assume that the density of the fluid is 1.0 g/cm³. (The density of mercury is 13.6 g/cm³.)

72. A 1.60-g sample of a mixture of naphthalene ($C_{10}H_8$) and anthracene ($C_{14}H_{10}$) is dissolved in 20.0 g of benzene (C_6H_6). The freezing point of the solution is 2.81°C. What is the composition of the sample mixture in terms of mass percent? The freezing point of benzene is 5.51°C, and K_f is 5.12°C kg/mol.

73. Before refrigeration became common, many foods were preserved by salting them heavily. Fruits were preserved by mixing them with a large amount of sugar (fruit preserves). How do salt and sugar act as preservatives?

Properties of Electrolyte Solutions

74. Calculate the freezing point and the boiling point of each of the following solutions. (Assume complete dissociation.)
    a. 5.0 g NaCl in 25 g H_2O
    b. 2.0 g $Al(NO_3)_3$ in 15 g H_2O

75. A solution of sodium chloride in water has a vapor pressure of 19.6 torr at 25°C. What is the mole fraction of NaCl in this solution? What would be the vapor pressure of this solution at 45°C? The vapor pressure of pure water is 23.8 torr at 25°C and 71.9 torr at 45°C.

76. Consider an aqueous solution containing sodium chloride that has a density of 1.01 g/mL. Assume that the solution behaves ideally. The freezing point of this solution at 1.00 atm is −1.28°C. Calculate the percent composition of this solution (by mass).

77. Consider the following solutions:

    0.010 m Na_3PO_4 in water
    0.020 m $CaBr_2$ in water
    0.020 m KCl in water
    0.020 m HF in water (HF is a weak acid.)

    a. Assuming complete dissociation of the soluble salts, which solution(s) would have the same boiling point as 0.040 m $C_6H_{12}O_6$ in water? ($C_6H_{12}O_6$ is a nonelectrolyte.)
    b. Which solution would have the highest vapor pressure at 28°C?
    c. Which solution would have the largest freezing-point depression?

78. From the following:

    pure water
    solution of $C_6H_{12}O_6$ ($X = 0.01$) in water
    solution of NaCl ($X = 0.01$) in water
    solution of $CaCl_2$ ($X = 0.01$) in water

choose the one with the following:
    a. highest freezing point
    b. lowest freezing point
    c. highest boiling point
    d. lowest boiling point
    e. highest osmotic pressure

79. Determine the van't Hoff factor for the following ionic solute dissolved in water.

80. Consider the following representations of an ionic solute in water. Which flask contains $MgSO_4$, and which flask contains NaCl? How can you tell?

81. The freezing-point depression of a 0.091 m solution of CsCl is 0.320°C. The freezing-point depression of a 0.091 m solution of $CaCl_2$ is 0.440°C. In which solution does ion association appear to be greater? Explain.

82. Consider the following:

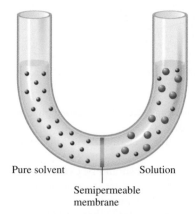

Pure solvent   Solution

Semipermeable membrane

What would happen to the level of liquid in the two arms if the semipermeable membrane separating the two liquids were permeable to
    a. H_2O (the solvent) only?
    b. H_2O and solute?

83. A water desalination plant is set up near a salt marsh containing water that is 0.10 M NaCl. Calculate the

minimum pressure that must be applied at 20.°C to purify the water by reverse osmosis. Assume that NaCl is completely dissociated.

84. Calculate the freezing point and the boiling point of each of the following aqueous solutions. (Assume complete dissociation.)
   a. 0.050 m MgCl$_2$ b. 0.050 m FeCl$_3$

85. Calculate the freezing point and the boiling point of each of the following solutions using the observed van't Hoff factors in Table 17.6.
   a. 0.050 m MgCl$_2$ b. 0.050 m FeCl$_3$

86. Use the data in the following table for three different aqueous solutions of CaCl$_2$ to calculate the apparent value of the van't Hoff factor.

Molality	Freezing-Point Depression (°C)
0.0225	0.110
0.0910	0.440
0.278	1.330

87. A 0.500-g sample of a compound is dissolved in enough water to form 100.0 mL of solution. This solution has an osmotic pressure of 2.50 atm at 25°C. If each molecule of the solute dissociates into two particles (in this solvent), what is the molar mass of this solute?

88. In the winter of 1994, record low temperatures were registered throughout the United States. For example, in Champaign, Illinois, a record low of −29°F was registered. At this temperature can salting icy roads with CaCl$_2$ be effective in melting the ice?
   a. Assume that $i = 3.00$ for CaCl$_2$.
   b. Assume the average value of i from Exercise 86.
   (The solubility of CaCl$_2$ in cold water is 74.5 g per 100.0 g of water.)

Additional Exercises

89. The Tyndall effect is often used to distinguish between a colloidal suspension and a true solution. Explain.

90. Detergent molecules can stabilize the emulsion of oil in water as well as remove dirt from soiled clothes. A typical detergent is sodium dodecylsulfate (SDS), which has a formula of CH$_3$(CH$_2$)$_{10}$CH$_2$SO$_4^-$Na$^+$. In aqueous solution, SDS suspends oil or dirt by forming small aggregates of detergent anions called micelles. Propose a structure for micelles.

91. The destruction of a colloid is done through a process called *coagulation*. What is coagulation?

92. What stabilizes a colloidal suspension? Explain why adding heat or adding an electrolyte can cause the suspended particles to settle out.

93. The term *proof* is defined as twice the percent by volume of pure ethanol in solution. Thus a solution that is 95% (by volume) ethanol is 190 proof. What is the molarity of ethanol in a 92-proof ethanol–water solution? Assume the density of ethanol (C$_2$H$_5$OH) is 0.79 g/cm^3 and the density of water is 1.0 g/cm^3.

94. Patients undergoing an upper gastrointestinal tract laboratory test are typically given an X-ray contrast agent that aids with the radiologic imaging of the anatomy. One such contrast agent is sodium diatrizoate, a nonvolatile water-soluble compound. A 0.378-m solution is prepared by dissolving 38.4 g of sodium diatrizoate (NaDTZ) in 1.60 × 10^2 mL of water at 31.2°C (the density of water at 31.2°C is 0.995 g/mL). What is the molar mass of sodium diatrizoate? What is the vapor pressure of this solution if the vapor pressure of pure water at 31.2°C is 34.1 torr?

95. The freezing point of an aqueous solution is −2.79°C.
   a. Determine the boiling point of this solution.
   b. Determine the vapor pressure (in mm Hg) of this solution at 25°C (the vapor pressure of pure water at 25°C is 23.76 mm Hg).
   c. Explain any assumptions you make in solving parts a and b.

96. An aqueous solution containing 0.250 mole of Q, a strong electrolyte, in 5.00 × 10^2 g of water freezes at −2.79°C. What is the van't Hoff factor for Q? The molal freezing-point depression constant for water is 1.86°C kg/mol. What is the formula of Q if it is 38.68% chlorine by mass and there are twice as many anions as cations in one formula unit of Q?

97. The solubility of benzoic acid,

is 0.34 g/100 mL in water at 25°C and 10.0 g/100 mL in benzene (C$_6$H$_6$) at 25°C. Rationalize this solubility behavior. For a 1.0-m solution of benzoic acid in benzene, would the measured freezing-point depression be equal to, greater than, or less than 5.12°C? ($K_f = 5.12$°C kg/mol for benzene.)

98. Would benzoic acid be more or less soluble in a 0.1-M NaOH solution than it is in water?

99. In a coffee-cup calorimeter, 1.60 g of NH$_4$NO$_3$ was mixed with 75.0 g of water at an initial temperature of 25.00°C. After dissolution of the salt, the final temperature of the calorimeter contents was 23.34°C.

a. Assuming the solution has a heat capacity of $4.18 \text{ J °C}^{-1} \text{ g}^{-1}$, and assuming no heat loss to the calorimeter, calculate the enthalpy of solution (ΔH_{soln}) for the dissolution of NH_4NO_3 in units of kJ/mol.

b. If the enthalpy of hydration for NH_4NO_3 is $-630.$ kJ/mol, calculate the lattice energy of NH_4NO_3.

100. Specifications for lactated Ringer's solution, which is used for intravenous (IV) injections, are as follows for each 100. mL of solution:

   285–315 mg Na^+
   14.1–17.3 mg K^+
   4.9–6.0 mg Ca^{2+}
   368–408 mg Cl^-
   231–261 mg lactate, $C_3H_5O_3^-$

   a. Specify the amounts of NaCl, KCl, $CaCl_2 \cdot 2H_2O$, and $NaC_3H_5O_3$ needed to prepare 100. mL of lactated Ringer's solution.

   b. What is the range of the osmotic pressure of the solution at 37°C, given the above specifications?

101. In the vapor over a pentane–hexane solution at 25°C, the mole fraction of pentane is equal to 0.15. What is the mole fraction of pentane in the solution? (See Exercise 47 for the vapor pressures of the pure liquids.)

102. Explain the following on the basis of the behavior of atoms and/or ions.

   a. Cooking with hot water is faster in a pressure cooker than in an open pan.

   b. Salt is used on icy roads.

   c. Melted sea ice from the Arctic Ocean produces fresh water.

   d. $CO_2(s)$ (dry ice) does not have a normal boiling point under normal atmospheric conditions, even though CO_2 is a liquid in fire extinguishers.

103. Anthraquinone contains only carbon, hydrogen, and oxygen. When 4.80 mg of anthraquinone is burned, 14.2 mg of CO_2 and 1.65 mg of H_2O are produced. The freezing point of camphor is lowered by 22.3°C when 1.32 g of anthraquinone is dissolved in 11.4 g of camphor. Determine the empirical and molecular formulas of anthraquinone.

104. An unknown compound contains only carbon, hydrogen, and oxygen. Combustion analysis of the compound gives mass percents of 31.57% C and 5.30% H. The molar mass is determined by measuring the freezing-point depression of an aqueous solution. A freezing point of −5.20°C is recorded for a solution made by dissolving 10.56 g of the compound in 25.0 g of water. Determine the empirical formula, molar mass, and molecular formula of the compound. Assume that the compound is a nonelectrolyte.

105. A forensic chemist is given a white solid that is suspected of being pure cocaine ($C_{17}H_{21}NO_4$, molar mass =

303.36 g/mol). She dissolves 1.22 ± 0.01 g of the solid in 15.60 ± 0.01 g of benzene. The freezing point is lowered by 1.32 ± 0.04°C.

   a. What is the molar mass of the substance? Assuming that the percentage of uncertainty in the calculated molar mass is the same as the percentage of uncertainty in the temperature change, calculate the uncertainty in the molar mass.

   b. Could the chemist unequivocally state that the substance is cocaine? For example, is the uncertainty small enough to distinguish cocaine from codeine ($C_{18}H_{21}NO_3$, molar mass = 299.37)?

   c. Assuming that the absolute uncertainties in the measurements of temperature and mass remain unchanged, how could the chemist improve the precision of her results?

106. You add an excess of solid MX in 250 g of water. You measure the freezing point and find it to be −0.028°C. What is the K_{sp} of the solid?

107. A solution saturated with a salt of the type M_3X_2 has an osmotic pressure of 2.64×10^{-2} atm at 25°C. Calculate the K_{sp} value for the salt, assuming ideal behavior.

108. You take 20.0 g of a sucrose ($C_{12}H_{22}O_{11}$) and NaCl mixture and dissolve it in 1.00 L of water. The freezing point of this solution is found to be −0.426°C. Assuming ideal behavior, calculate the mass percent composition of the original mixture and the mole fraction of sucrose in the original mixture.

109. A 0.100-g sample of the weak acid HA (molar mass = 100.0 g/mol) is dissolved in 500.0 g of water. The freezing point of the resulting solution is −0.0056°C. Calculate the value of K_a for this acid. Assume molarity equals molality in this solution.

110. A solid consists of a mixture of $NaNO_3$ and $Mg(NO_3)_2$. When 6.50 g of this solid is dissolved in 50.0 g of water, the freezing point is lowered by 5.40°C. What is the composition of the solid (by mass)? Assume ideal behavior.

111. A solid mixture contains $MgCl_2$ (molar mass = 95.218 g/mol) and NaCl (molar mass = 58.443 g/mol). When 0.5000 g of this solid is dissolved in enough water to form 1.000 L of solution, the osmotic pressure at 25.0°C is observed to be 0.3950 atm. What is the mass percent of $MgCl_2$ in the solid? (Assume ideal behavior for the solution.)

112. Some nonelectrolyte solute (molar mass = 142 g/mol) was dissolved in 150. mL of a solvent (density = 0.879 g/cm³). The elevated boiling point of the solution was 355.4 K. What mass of solute was dissolved in the solvent? For the solvent, the enthalpy of vaporization is 33.90 kJ/mol, the entropy of vaporization is $95.95 \text{ J K}^{-1} \text{ mol}^{-1}$, and the boiling-point elevation constant is 2.5 K kg/mol.

Challenge Problems

113. Carbon tetrachloride (CCl_4) and benzene (C_6H_6) form ideal solutions. Consider an equimolar solution of CCl_4 and C_6H_6 at 25°C. The vapor above the solution is collected and condensed. Using the following data, determine the composition in mole fraction of the condensed vapor.

Substance	ΔG_f°
$C_6H_6(l)$	124.50 kJ/mol
$C_6H_6(g)$	129.66 kJ/mol
$CCl_4(l)$	−65.21 kJ/mol
$CCl_4(g)$	−60.59 kJ/mol

114. You have a solution of two volatile liquids, A and B (assume ideal behavior). Pure liquid A has a vapor pressure of 350.0 torr and pure liquid B has a vapor pressure of 100.0 torr at the temperature of the solution. The vapor at equilibrium above the solution has double the mole fraction of substance A as the solution does. What is the mole fraction of liquid A in the solution?

115. The vapor pressure of pure benzene is 750.0 torr and the vapor pressure of toluene is 300.0 torr at a certain temperature. You make a solution by pouring "some" benzene with "some" toluene. You then place this solution in a closed container and wait for the vapor to come into equilibrium with the solution. Next, you condense the vapor. You put this liquid (the condensed vapor) in a closed container and wait for the vapor to come into equilibrium with the solution. You then condense this vapor and find the mole fraction of benzene in this vapor to be 0.714. Determine the mole fraction of benzene in the original solution, assuming the solution behaves ideally.

116. Plants that thrive in salt water must have internal solutions (inside the plant cells) that are isotonic (same osmotic pressure) with the surrounding solution. A leaf of a saltwater plant is able to thrive in an aqueous salt solution (at 25°C) that has a freezing point equal to −0.621°C. You would like to use this information to calculate the osmotic pressure of the solution in the cell.
    a. In order to use the freezing-point depression to calculate osmotic pressure, what assumption must you make (in addition to ideal behavior of the solutions, which we will assume)?
    b. Under what conditions is the assumption in part a reasonable?
    c. Solve for the osmotic pressure (at 25°C) of the solution in the plant cell.
    d. The plant leaf is placed in an aqueous salt solution (at 25°C) that has a boiling point of 102.0°C. What will happen to the plant cells in the leaf?

117. In some regions of the southwest United States, the water is very hard. For example, in Las Cruces, New Mexico, the tap water contains about 560 μg of dissolved solids per milliliter. Reverse osmosis units are marketed in this area to soften water. A typical unit exerts a pressure of 8.0 atm and can produce 45 L of water per day.
    a. Assuming that all the dissolved solids are $MgCO_3$, and assuming a temperature of 27°C, what total volume of water must be processed to produce 45 L of pure water?
    b. Would the same system work for purifying seawater? (Assume that seawater is 0.60 M NaCl.)

118. Erythrocytes are red blood cells containing hemoglobin. In a saline solution, they shrivel when the salt concentration is high and swell when the salt concentration is low. In a 25°C aqueous solution of NaCl, whose freezing point is −0.406°C, erythrocytes neither swell nor shrink. If we want to calculate the osmotic pressure of the solution inside the erythrocytes under these conditions, what do we need to assume? Why? Estimate how good (or poor) of an assumption it is. Make this assumption and calculate the osmotic pressure of the solution inside the erythrocytes.

119. A sample containing 0.0500 mole of $Fe_2(SO_4)_3$ is dissolved in enough water to make 1.00 L of solution. This solution contains hydrated SO_4^{2-} and $Fe(H_2O)_6^{3+}$ ions. The latter behave as an acid:

    $$Fe(H_2O)_6^{3+} \rightleftharpoons Fe(OH)(H_2O)_5^{2+} + H^+$$

    a. Calculate the expected osmotic pressure of this solution at 25°C if the above dissociation is negligible.
    b. The actual osmotic pressure of the solution is 6.73 atm at 25°C. Calculate K_a for the dissociation reaction of $Fe(H_2O)_6^{3+}$. (To do this calculation, you must assume that none of the ions goes through the semipermeable membrane. Actually, this is not a good assumption for the tiny H^+ ion.)

120. In a solution with carbon tetrachloride as the solvent, the compound VCl_4 undergoes dimerization:

    $$2VCl_4 \rightleftharpoons V_2Cl_8$$

    When 6.6834 g of VCl_4 is dissolved in 100.0 g of carbon tetrachloride, the freezing point is lowered by 5.97°C. Calculate the value of the equilibrium constant for the dimerization of VCl_4 at this temperature. (The density of the equilibrium mixture is 1.696 g/cm³, and $K_f = 29.8$°C kg/mol for CCl_4.)

121. An aqueous solution is 1.00% NaCl by mass and has a density of 1.071 g/cm³ at 25°C. The observed osmotic pressure of this solution is 7.83 atm at 25°C.
    a. What fraction of the moles of NaCl in this solution exist as ion pairs?
    b. Calculate the freezing point that would be observed for this solution.

122. Liquid A has vapor pressure x, and liquid B has vapor pressure y. What is the mole fraction of the liquid mixture if the vapor above the solution is 30.% A by moles? 50.% A? 80.% A? (Calculate in terms of x and y.) What is the mole fraction of the vapor above the solution if the liquid mixture is 30.% A by moles? 50.% A? 80.% A? (Calculate in terms of x and y.)

Marathon Problem

123.* Using the following information, identify the strong electrolyte whose general formula is

$$M_x(A)_y \cdot zH_2O$$

Ignore the effect of interionic attractions in the solution.
a. A^{n-} is a common oxyanion. When 30.0 mg of the anhydrous sodium salt containing this oxyanion

(Na$_n$A, where $n = 1, 2,$ or 3) is reduced, 15.26 mL of 0.02313 M reducing agent is required to react completely with the Na$_n$A present. Assume a 1 : 1 mole ratio in the reaction.
b. The cation is derived from a silvery white metal that is relatively expensive. The metal itself crystallizes in a body-centered cubic unit cell and has an atomic radius of 198.4 pm. The solid, pure metal has a density of 5.243 g/cm^3. The oxidation state of M in the strong electrolyte general formula is +3.
c. When 33.45 mg of the compound is present (dissolved) in 10.0 mL of aqueous solution at 25°C, the solution has an osmotic pressure of 558 torr.

*From James H. Burness, "The Use of "Marathon" Problems as Effective Vehicles for the Presentation of General Chemistry Lectures," Journal of Chemical Education, 68(11). Copyright © 1991 American Chemical Society. Reprinted by permission.

The Representative Elements

18

SEM of bismuth crystal.

S o far in this book we have covered the major principles and explored the most important models of chemistry. In particular, we have seen that the chemical properties of the elements can be explained very successfully by the quantum mechanical model of the atom. In fact, the most convincing evidence of that model's validity is its ability to relate the observed periodic properties of the elements to the number of valence electrons in their atoms.

We have learned many properties of the elements and their compounds, but we have not discussed extensively the relationship between the chemical properties of a specific element and its position on the periodic table. In this chapter we will explore the chemical similarities and differences among the elements in the several groups of the periodic table and will try to interpret these data using the wave mechanical model of the atom. In the process we will illustrate a great variety of chemical properties and further demonstrate the practical importance of chemistry.

18.1 │ A Survey of the Representative Elements

The traditional form of the periodic table is shown in Fig. 18.1. Recall that the **representative elements,** whose chemical properties are determined by the valence-level s and p electrons, are designated Groups 1A through 8A. The **transition metals,** in the center of the table, result from the filling of d orbitals. The elements that correspond to the filling of the $4f$ and $5f$ orbitals are listed separately as the **lanthanides** and **actinides,** respectively.

The heavy black line in Fig. 18.1 separates the metals from the nonmetals, except for one case. Hydrogen, which appears on the metal side, is a nonmetal. Some elements just on either side of this line, such as silicon and germanium, exhibit both metallic and nonmetallic properties. These elements are often called **metalloids,** or **semimetals.** The fundamental chemical difference between metals and nonmetals is that metals tend to lose their valence electrons to form *cations,* which usually have the valence electron configuration of the noble gas from the preceding period. On the other hand, nonmetals tend to gain electrons to form *anions* that exhibit the electron configuration of the noble gas in the same period. Metallic character is observed to increase in going down a given group, which is consistent with the trends in ionization energy, electron affinity, and electronegativity discussed earlier (see Sections 12.15 and 13.2).

Metallic character increases going down a group in the periodic table.

Figure 18.1
The periodic table. The elements in the A groups are the representative elements. The elements shown in pink are called transition metals. The heavy black line approximately separates the nonmetals from the metals. The elements that have both metallic and nonmetallic properties (semimetals) are shaded in blue.

1A																	8A
H	2A											3A	4A	5A	6A	7A	He
Li	Be											B	C	N	O	F	Ne
Na	Mg											Al	Si	P	S	Cl	Ar
K	Ca	Sc	Ti	V	Cr	Mn	Fe	Co	Ni	Cu	Zn	Ga	Ge	As	Se	Br	Kr
Rb	Sr	Y	Zr	Nb	Mo	Tc	Ru	Rh	Pd	Ag	Cd	In	Sn	Sb	Te	I	Xe
Cs	Ba	La	Hf	Ta	W	Re	Os	Ir	Pt	Au	Hg	Tl	Pb	Bi	Po	At	Rn
Fr	Ra	Ac	Rf	Ha	Unh	Uns	Uno	Une	Ds	Rg	Cn	Uut	Uuq	Uup		Uus	Uuo

Lanthanides	Ce	Pr	Nd	Pm	Sm	Eu	Gd	Tb	Dy	Ho	Er	Tm	Yb	Lu
Actinides	Th	Pa	U	Np	Pu	Am	Cm	Bk	Cf	Es	Fm	Md	No	Lr

Atomic Size and Group Anomalies

Although the chemical properties of the members of a group have many similarities, there are also important differences. The most dramatic differences usually occur between the first and second member. For example, hydrogen in Group 1A is a nonmetal, whereas lithium is a very active metal. This extreme difference results primarily from the very large difference in the atomic radii of hydrogen and lithium, as shown in Fig. 18.2. Since the small hydrogen atom has a much greater attraction for electrons than do the larger members of Group 1A, it forms covalent bonds with nonmetals. In contrast, the other members of Group 1A lose their valence electrons to nonmetals to form 1+ cations in ionic compounds.

The effect of size is also evident in other groups. For example, the oxides of the metals in Group 2A are all quite basic except for the first member of the series; beryllium oxide (BeO) is amphoteric. The basicity of an oxide depends on its ionic character. Ionic oxides contain the O^{2-} ion, which reacts with water to form two OH^- ions. All the oxides of the Group 2A metals are highly ionic except for beryllium oxide, which has considerable covalent character. The small Be^{2+} ion can effectively polarize the electron "cloud" of the O^{2-} ion, thereby producing significant electron sharing. We see the same pattern in

Figure 18.2

Some atomic radii (in picometers).

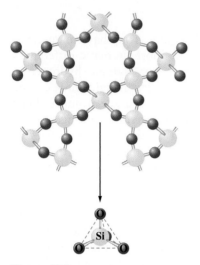

Figure 18.3
The structure of quartz, which has the empirical formula SiO_2. Note that the structure is based on interlocking SiO_4 tetrahedra, in which each oxygen atom is shared by two silicon atoms.

Group 3A, where only the small boron atom behaves as a nonmetal, or sometimes as a semimetal, whereas aluminum and the other members are active metals.

In Group 4A the effect of size is reflected in the dramatic differences between the chemical properties of carbon and silicon. The chemistry of carbon is dominated by molecules containing chains of C—C bonds, but silicon compounds mainly contain Si—O bonds rather than Si—Si bonds. Silicon does form compounds with chains of Si—Si bonds, but these compounds are much more reactive than the corresponding carbon compounds. The reasons for the difference in reactivity between the carbon and silicon compounds are quite complex but are likely related to the differences in the sizes of the carbon and silicon atoms.

Carbon and silicon also differ markedly in their abilities to form π bonds. As we discussed in Section 14.1, carbon dioxide is composed of discrete CO_2 molecules with the Lewis structure

$$\ddot{O}\!=\!C\!=\!\ddot{O}$$

where the carbon and oxygen atoms achieve the [Ne] configuration by forming π bonds. In contrast, the structure of silica (empirical formula SiO_2) is based on SiO_4 tetrahedra with Si—O—Si bridges, as shown in Fig. 18.3. The silicon $3p$ valence orbitals do not overlap very effectively with the smaller oxygen $2p$ orbitals to form π bonds; therefore, discrete SiO_2 molecules with the Lewis structure

$$\ddot{O}\!=\!Si\!=\!\ddot{O}$$

are not stable. Instead, the silicon atoms achieve a noble gas configuration by forming four Si—O single bonds.

The importance of π bonding for the relatively small elements of the second period also explains the different elemental forms of the members of Groups 5A and 6A. For example, elemental nitrogen exists as very stable N_2 molecules with the Lewis structure $:N\!\equiv\!N:$. Elemental phosphorus forms larger aggregates of atoms, the simplest being the tetrahedral P_4 molecules found in white phosphorus (see Fig. 18.18). Like silicon atoms, the relatively large phosphorus atoms do not form strong π bonds but prefer to achieve a noble gas configuration by forming single bonds to several other phosphorus atoms. In contrast, its very strong π bonds make the N_2 molecule the most stable form of elemental nitrogen. Similarly, in Group 6A the most stable form of elemental oxygen is the O_2 molecule with a double bond. However, the larger sulfur atom forms bigger aggregates, such as the cyclic S_8 molecule (see Fig. 18.22), which contain only single bonds.

The relatively large change in size in going from the first to the second member of a group also has important consequences for the Group 7A elements. For example, fluorine has a smaller electron affinity than chlorine. This violation of the expected trend can be attributed to the fact that the small size of the fluorine $2p$ orbitals causes unusually large electron–electron repulsions. The relative weakness of the bond in the F_2 molecule can be explained in terms of the repulsions among the lone pairs, shown in the Lewis structure:

$$:\!\ddot{F}\!-\!\ddot{F}\!:$$

The small size of the fluorine atoms allows close approach of the lone pairs, which leads to much greater repulsions than those found in the Cl_2 molecule with its much larger atoms.

Table 18.1

Distribution (Mass Percent) of the 18 Most Abundant Elements in the Earth's Crust, Oceans, and Atmosphere

Element	Mass Percent	Element	Mass Percent
Oxygen	49.2	Chlorine	0.19
Silicon	25.7	Phosphorus	0.11
Aluminum	7.50	Manganese	0.09
Iron	4.71	Carbon	0.08
Calcium	3.39	Sulfur	0.06
Sodium	2.63	Barium	0.04
Potassium	2.40	Nitrogen	0.03
Magnesium	1.93	Fluorine	0.03
Hydrogen	0.87	All others	0.49
Titanium	0.58		

Thus the relatively large increase in atomic radius in going from the first to the second member of a group causes the first element to exhibit properties quite different from the others.

Abundance and Preparation

Table 18.1 shows the distribution of elements in the earth's crust, oceans, and atmosphere. The major element is, of course, oxygen, which is found in the atmosphere as O_2, in the oceans as H_2O, and in the earth's crust primarily in silicate and carbonate minerals. The second most abundant element, silicon, is found throughout the earth's crust in the silica and silicate minerals that form the basis of most sand, rocks, and soil. The most abundant metals, aluminum and iron, are found in ores, in which they are combined with nonmetals, most commonly oxygen. One notable fact revealed by Table 18.1 is the small incidence of most transition metals. Since many of these relatively rare elements are assuming increasing importance in our high-technology society, it is possible that the control of transition metal ores may ultimately have more significance in world politics than will control of petroleum supplies.

The distribution of elements in living materials is very different from that found in the earth's crust. Table 18.2 shows the distribution of elements in the

Table 18.2

Abundance of Elements in the Human Body

Major Elements	Mass Percent	Trace Elements (in alphabetical order)
Oxygen	65.0	Arsenic
Carbon	18.0	Chromium
Hydrogen	10.0	Cobalt
Nitrogen	3.0	Copper
Calcium	1.4	Fluorine
Phosphorus	1.0	Iodine
Magnesium	0.50	Manganese
Potassium	0.34	Molybdenum
Sulfur	0.26	Nickel
Sodium	0.14	Selenium
Chlorine	0.14	Silicon
Iron	0.004	Vanadium
Zinc	0.003	

Sand, such as that found in the massive sand dunes bordering the desert plain near Namib, Namibia, is composed of silicon and oxygen.

Frank Krahmer/Radium Images/Masterfile

human body. Oxygen, carbon, hydrogen, and nitrogen form the basis for all biologically important molecules. The other elements, even though they are found in relatively small amounts, are often crucial for life. For example, zinc is found in over 150 different biomolecules in the human body.

Only about one-fourth of the elements occur naturally in the free state. Most are found in a combined state. The *process of obtaining a metal from its ore* is called **metallurgy**. Since the metals in ores are found in the form of cations, the chemistry of *metallurgy always involves reduction of the ions to the elemental metal (with an oxidation state of zero)*. A variety of reducing agents can be used, but carbon is the usual choice because of its wide availability and relatively low cost.

Carbon is the cheapest and most readily available industrial reducing agent for metallic ions.

Electrolysis is often used to reduce the most active metals. In Chapter 11 we considered the electrolytic production of aluminum metal. The alkali metals are also produced by electrolysis, usually of their molten halide salts.

The preparation of nonmetals varies widely. Elemental nitrogen and oxygen are usually obtained from the **liquefaction** of air, which is based on the principle that a gas cools as it expands. After each expansion, part of the cooler gas is compressed, whereas the rest is used to carry away the heat of the compression. The compressed gas is then allowed to expand again. This cycle is repeated many times. Eventually, the remaining gas becomes cold enough to form the liquid state. Because liquid nitrogen and liquid oxygen have different boiling points, they can be separated by the distillation of liquid air. Both substances are important industrial chemicals, with nitrogen ranking second in terms of amount manufactured in the United States (approximately 60 billion pounds per year) and oxygen ranking third (over 40 billion pounds per year). Hydrogen can be obtained from the electrolysis of water, but more commonly it is obtained from the decomposition of the methane in natural gas. Sulfur is found underground in its elemental form and is recovered by the Frasch process (see Section 18.12). The halogens are obtained by oxidation of the anions from halide salts (see Section 18.13).

The preparation of sulfur and the halogens is discussed later in this chapter.

18.2 | The Group 1A Metals

1A
H
Li
Na
K
Rb
Cs
Fr

The Group 1A elements with their ns^1 valence electron configurations are all very active metals (they lose their valence electrons very readily), except for hydrogen, which behaves as a nonmetal. We will discuss the chemistry of hydrogen in the next section. Many of the properties of the **alkali metals** have been given previously (see Section 12.16). The sources and methods of preparation of pure alkali metals are given in Table 18.3. The ionization energies, standard reduction potentials, ionic radii, and melting points for the alkali metals are listed in Table 18.4.

In Section 12.16 we saw that the alkali metals all react vigorously with water to release hydrogen gas:

$$2M(s) + 2H_2O(l) \longrightarrow 2M^+(aq) + 2OH^-(aq) + H_2(g)$$

Figure 18.4
Lepidolite is mainly composed of lithium, aluminum, silicon, and oxygen, but it also contains significant amounts of rubidium and cesium.

Several properties of the alkali metals are given in Table 12.9.

Table 18.3

Sources and Methods of Preparation of the Pure Alkali Metals

Element	Source	Method of Preparation
Lithium	Silicate minerals such as spodumene, $LiAl(Si_2O_6)$	Electrolysis of molten LiCl
Sodium	NaCl	Electrolysis of molten NaCl
Potassium	KCl	Electrolysis of molten KCl
Rubidium	Impurity in lepidolite, $Li_2(F,OH)_2Al_2(SiO_3)_3$	Reduction of RbOH with Mg and H_2
Cesium	Pollucite ($Cs_4Al_4Si_9O_{26} \cdot H_2O$) and an impurity in lepidolite (Fig. 18.4)	Reduction of CsOH with Mg and H_2

We will reconsider this process briefly because it illustrates several important concepts. From the ionization energies, we might expect lithium to be the weakest of the alkali metals as a reducing agent in water. However, the standard reduction potentials indicate that it is the strongest. This reversal results mainly from the very large energy of hydration of the small Li^+ ion. Because of its relatively high charge density, the Li^+ ion very effectively attracts water molecules. A large quantity of energy is released in the process, favoring the formation of the Li^+ ion and making lithium a strong reducing agent in aqueous solution.

We also saw in Section 12.16 that lithium, although it is the strongest reducing agent, reacts more slowly with water than sodium or potassium. From the discussions in Chapters 10 and 15, we know that the *equilibrium position* for a reaction (in this case indicated by the $\mathscr{E}°$ values) is controlled by thermodynamic factors but that the *rate* of a reaction is controlled by kinetic factors. There is *no* direct connection between these factors. Lithium reacts more slowly with water than sodium or potassium because as a solid lithium has a higher melting point than either of the other elements. Since lithium does not become molten from the heat of reaction with water as sodium and potassium do, it has a smaller area of contact with the water.

Table 18.5 summarizes some important reactions of the alkali metals.

The alkali metal ions are very important for the proper functioning of biological systems such as nerves and muscles; Na^+ and K^+ ions are present in all body cells and fluids. In human blood plasma, the concentrations are

$$[Na^+] \approx 0.15 \ M \qquad \text{and} \qquad [K^+] \approx 0.005 \ M$$

In the fluids *inside* the cells, the concentrations are reversed:

$$[Na^+] \approx 0.005 \ M \qquad \text{and} \qquad [K^+] \approx 0.16 \ M$$

Sodium reacts violently with water.

Table 18.4

Selected Physical Properties of the Alkali Metals

Element	Ionization Energy (kJ/mol)	Standard Reduction Potential (V) for $M^+ + e^- \rightarrow M$	Radius of M^+ (pm)	Melting Point (°C)
Lithium	520	−3.05	60	180
Sodium	495	−2.71	95	98
Potassium	419	−2.92	133	64
Rubidium	409	−2.99	148	39
Cesium	382	−3.02	169	29

Table 18.5

Selected Reactions of the Alkali Metals

Reaction	Comment
$2M + X_2 \longrightarrow 2MX$	X_2 = any halogen molecule
$4Li + O_2 \longrightarrow 2Li_2O$	Excess oxygen
$2Na + O_2 \longrightarrow Na_2O_2$	
$M + O_2 \longrightarrow MO_2$	M = K, Rb, or Cs
$2M + S \longrightarrow M_2S$	
$6Li + N_2 \longrightarrow 2Li_3N$	Li only
$12M + P_4 \longrightarrow 4M_3P$	
$2M + H_2 \longrightarrow 2MH$	
$2M + 2H_2O \longrightarrow 2MOH + H_2$	
$2M + 2H^+ \longrightarrow 2M^+ + H_2$	Violent reaction!

Since the concentrations are so different inside and outside the cells, an elaborate mechanism involving selective ligands is needed to transport Na^+ and K^+ ions through the cell membranes.

18.3 | The Chemistry of Hydrogen

Under ordinary conditions of temperature and pressure, hydrogen is a colorless, odorless gas composed of H_2 molecules. Because of its low molar mass and nonpolarity, hydrogen has a very low boiling point ($-253°C$) and melting point ($-260°C$). Hydrogen gas is highly flammable; mixtures of air containing from 18% to 60% hydrogen by volume are explosive. In a common lecture demonstration, hydrogen and oxygen gases are bubbled into soapy water. The resulting bubbles are then ignited with a candle on a long stick, producing a loud explosion.

The major industrial source of hydrogen gas is the reaction of methane with water at high temperatures (800–1000°C) and pressures (10–50 atm) in the presence of a metallic catalyst (often nickel):

$$CH_4(g) + H_2O(g) \xrightarrow[\text{Catalyst}]{\text{Heat, pressure}} CO(g) + 3H_2(g)$$

Large quantities of hydrogen are also formed as a by-product of gasoline production, when hydrocarbons with high molecular masses are broken down (or *cracked*) to produce smaller molecules more suitable for use as a motor fuel.

Very pure hydrogen can be produced by the electrolysis of water (see Section 11.7), but this method is currently not economically feasible for large-scale production because of the relatively high cost of electricity.

The major industrial use of hydrogen is in the production of ammonia by the Haber process. Large quantities of hydrogen are also used for hydrogenating unsaturated vegetable oils (those containing carbon–carbon double bonds) to produce solid shortenings that are saturated (containing carbon–carbon single bonds):

The catalysis of this process was discussed in Section 15.9.

(left) Hydrogen gas being used to blow soap bubbles. (right) As the bubbles float upward, they are lighted by using a candle on a long stick. The orange flame results from the heat of the reaction between hydrogen and oxygen, which excites sodium atoms in the soap bubbles.

Chemically, hydrogen behaves as a typical nonmetal, forming covalent compounds with other nonmetals and forming salts with very active metals. Binary compounds containing hydrogen are called **hydrides,** of which there are three classes. The **ionic** (or saltlike) **hydrides** are formed when hydrogen combines with the most active metals, those from Groups 1A and 2A. Examples are LiH and CaH_2, which can best be characterized as containing hydride ions (H^-) and metal cations. Because the presence of two electrons in the small $1s$ orbital produces large electron–electron repulsions and because the nucleus has only a 1+ charge, the hydride ion is a strong reducing agent. For example, when ionic hydrides are placed in water, a violent reaction takes place. This reaction results in the formation of hydrogen gas, as seen in the equation

$$LiH(s) + H_2O(l) \longrightarrow H_2(g) + Li^+(aq) + OH^-(aq)$$

Boiling points of covalent hydrides were discussed in Section 16.1.

Covalent hydrides are formed when hydrogen combines with other nonmetals. We have encountered many of these compounds already: HCl, CH_4, NH_3, H_2O, and so on. The most important covalent hydride is water. The polarity of the H_2O molecule leads to many of water's unusual properties. Water has a much higher boiling point than is expected from its molar mass. It has a large heat of vaporization and a large heat capacity, both of which make it a very useful coolant. Water has a higher density as a liquid than as a solid because of the open structure of ice, which results from maximizing the hydrogen bonding (Fig. 18.5). Because water is an excellent solvent for ionic and polar substances, it provides an effective medium for life processes. In fact, water is one of the few covalent hydrides that is nontoxic to organisms.

The third class of hydrides is the **metallic,** or **interstitial, hydrides,** which are formed when transition metal crystals are treated with hydrogen gas. The hydrogen molecules dissociate at the metal's surface, and the small hydrogen atoms migrate into the crystal structure to occupy holes, or *interstices.* These metal–hydrogen mixtures are more like solid solutions than true compounds. Palladium can absorb about *900 times* its own volume of hydrogen gas. In fact, hydrogen can be purified by placing it under slight pressure in a vessel containing a thin wall of palladium. The hydrogen diffuses into and through the metal wall, leaving the impurities behind.

Although hydrogen can react with transition metals to form compounds such as UH_3 and FeH_6, most of the interstitial hydrides have variable compositions (often called *nonstoichiometric* compositions) with formulas such as

Figure 18.5
The structure of ice, showing the hydrogen bonding.

H_2O

Ice

LaH$_{2.76}$ and VH$_{0.56}$. The compositions of the nonstoichiometric hydrides vary with the length of exposure of the metal to hydrogen gas.

When interstitial hydrides are heated, much of the absorbed hydrogen is lost as hydrogen gas. Because of this behavior, these materials offer possibilities for storing hydrogen for use as a portable fuel. The internal combustion engines in current automobiles can burn hydrogen gas with little modification, but storage of enough hydrogen to provide an acceptable mileage range remains a problem. One possible solution might be to use a fuel tank containing a porous solid that includes a transition metal. The hydrogen gas could be pumped into the solid to form the interstitial hydride. The hydrogen gas could then be released when the engine requires additional energy. This system is now being tested by several automobile companies.

See Section 9.8 for a discussion of the feasibility of using hydrogen gas as a fuel.

18.4 | The Group 2A Elements

2A
Be
Mg
Ca
Sr
Ba
Ra

The Group 2A elements (with the valence electron configuration ns^2) are very reactive, losing their two valence electrons to form ionic compounds that contain M^{2+} cations. These elements are commonly called the **alkaline earth metals** because of the basicity of their oxides:

$$MO(s) + H_2O(l) \longrightarrow M^{2+}(aq) + 2OH^-(aq)$$

Only the amphoteric beryllium oxide (BeO) also shows some acidic properties, such as dissolving in aqueous solutions containing hydroxide ions:

$$BeO(s) + 2OH^-(aq) + H_2O(l) \longrightarrow Be(OH)_4{}^{2-}(aq)$$

The more active alkaline earth metals react with water as the alkali metals do, producing hydrogen gas:

$$M(s) + 2H_2O(l) \longrightarrow M^{2+}(aq) + 2OH^-(aq) + H_2(g)$$

An amphoteric oxide displays both acidic and basic properties.

Calcium, strontium, and barium react vigorously at 25°C. The less easily oxidized beryllium and magnesium show no observable reaction with water at 25°C, although magnesium reacts with boiling water. Table 18.6 summarizes various properties, sources, and methods of preparation of the alkaline earth metals.

The alkaline earth metals have great practical importance. Calcium and magnesium ions are essential for human life. Calcium is found primarily in the

Table 18.6

Selected Physical Properties, Sources, and Methods of Preparation of the Group 2A Elements

Element	Radius of M^{2+} (pm)	Ionization Energy (kJ/mol)		$\mathscr{E}°$ (V) for $M^{2+} + 2e^- \longrightarrow M$	Source	Method of Preparation
		First	Second			
Beryllium	≈ 300	900	1760	-1.70	Beryl $(Be_3Al_2Si_6O_{18})$	Electrolysis of molten $BeCl_2$
Magnesium	65	735	1445	-2.37	Magnesite $(MgCO_3)$, dolomite $(MgCO_3 \cdot CaCO_3)$, carnallite $(MgCl_2 \cdot KCl \cdot 6H_2O)$	Electrolysis of molten $MgCl_2$
Calcium	99	590	1146	-2.76	Various minerals containing $CaCO_3$	Electrolysis of molten $CaCl_2$
Strontium	113	549	1064	-2.89	Celestite $(SrSO_4)$, strontianite $(SrCO_3)$	Electrolysis of molten $SrCl_2$
Barium	135	503	965	-2.90	Baryte $(BaSO_4)$, witherite $(BaCO_3)$	Electrolysis of molten $BaCl_2$
Radium	140	509	979	-2.92	Pitchblende (1 g of Ra/7 tons of ore)	Electrolysis of molten $RaCl_2$

Calcium metal reacting with water to form bubbles of hydrogen gas.

structural minerals composing bones and teeth. Magnesium (as the Mg^{2+} ion) plays a vital role in metabolism and in muscle functions. Because magnesium metal has a relatively low density and displays moderate strength, it is a useful structural material, especially if alloyed with aluminum.

Table 18.7 summarizes some important reactions involving the alkaline earth metals.

Relatively large concentrations of Ca^{2+} and Mg^{2+} ions are often found in natural water supplies. These ions in this so-called **hard water** interfere with the action of detergents and form precipitates with soap. In Section 7.6 we saw that Ca^{2+} is often removed by precipitation as $CaCO_3$ in large-scale water softening. In individual homes Ca^{2+}, Mg^{2+}, and other cations are removed by **ion exchange**. An **ion exchange resin** consists of large molecules (polymers) that have many ionic sites. A cation exchange resin is represented schemati-

Table 18.7

Selected Reactions of the Group 2A Elements

Reaction	Comment
$M + X_2 \longrightarrow MX_2$	X_2 = any halogen molecule
$2M + O_2 \longrightarrow 2MO$	Ba gives BaO_2 as well
$M + S \longrightarrow MS$	
$3M + N_2 \longrightarrow M_3N_2$	High temperatures
$6M + P_4 \longrightarrow 2M_3P_2$	High temperatures
$M + H_2 \longrightarrow MH_2$	M = Ca, Sr, or Ba; high temperatures; Mg at high pressure
$M + 2H_2O \longrightarrow M(OH)_2 + H_2$	M = Ca, Sr, or Ba
$M + 2H^+ \longrightarrow M^{2+} + H_2$	
$Be + 2OH^- + 2H_2O \longrightarrow Be(OH)_4^{2-} + H_2$	

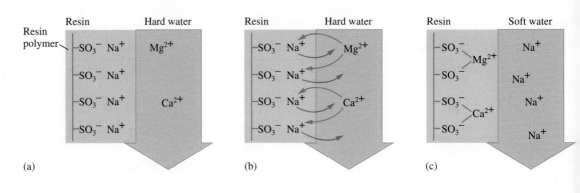

Figure 18.6
(a) A schematic representation of a typical cation exchange resin.
(b) and (c) When hard water is passed over the cation exchange resin, the Ca^{2+} and Mg^{2+} bind to the resin.

cally in Fig. 18.6(a), showing Na^+ ions bound ionically to the SO_3^- groups that are covalently attached to the resin polymer. When hard water is passed over the resin, Ca^{2+} and Mg^{2+} bind to the resin in place of Na^+, which is released into the solution [Fig. 18.6(b)]. Replacing Mg^{2+} and Ca^{2+} by Na^+ [Fig. 18.6(c)] "softens" the water because the sodium salts of soap are soluble.

18.5 | The Group 3A Elements

The Group 3A elements (valence electron configuration ns^2np^1) generally show the increase in metallic character in going down the group that is characteristic of the representative elements. Some physical properties, sources, and methods of preparation of the Group 3A elements are summarized in Table 18.8.

Boron is a typical nonmetal, and most of its compounds are covalent. The most interesting compounds of boron are the covalent hydrides called **boranes.** We might expect BH_3 to be the simplest hydride, since boron has three valence electrons to share with three hydrogen atoms. However, this compound is unstable, and the simplest known member of the series is diborane (B_2H_6), with the structure shown in Fig. 18.7(a). In this molecule the terminal B—H bonds are normal covalent bonds, each involving one electron pair. The bridging bonds are three-center bonds similar to those in solid BeH_2. Another interesting borane contains the square pyramidal B_5H_9 molecule [Fig. 18.7(b)], which

Table 18.8

Selected Physical Properties, Sources, and Methods of Preparation of the Group 3A Elements

Element	Radius of M^{3+} (pm)	Ionization Energy (kJ/mol)	$\mathscr{E}°$ (V) for $M^{3+} + 3e^- \longrightarrow M$	Source	Method of Preparation
Boron	20	798	—	Kernite, a form of borax ($Na_2B_4O_7 \cdot 4H_2O$)	Reduction by Mg or H_2
Aluminum	50	581	−1.66	Bauxite (Al_2O_3)	Electrolysis of Al_2O_3 in molten Na_3AlF_6
Gallium	62	577	−0.53	Traces in various minerals	Reduction with H_2 or electrolysis
Indium	81	556	−0.34	Traces in various minerals	Reduction with H_2 or electrolysis
Thallium	95	589	0.72	Traces in various minerals	Electrolysis

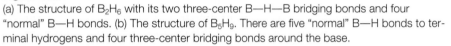

(a)   (b)

Figure 18.7
(a) The structure of B_2H_6 with its two three-center B—H—B bridging bonds and four "normal" B—H bonds. (b) The structure of B_5H_9. There are five "normal" B—H bonds to terminal hydrogens and four three-center bridging bonds around the base.

An old ad from *The Saturday Evening Post* for Boraxo, a hand-cleaning product containing sodium tetraborate (NaB_4O_7). Extensive natural deposits of borax ($Na_2B_4O_7 \cdot 10H_2O$) found in saline lakes near Death Valley, California, were hauled to a factory in wagons pulled by teams of 20 mules—hence the name 20 Mule Team Borax.

Gallium melts in the hand.

has four three-center bonds situated around the base of the pyramid. Because the boranes are extremely electron-deficient, they are highly reactive. The boranes react very exothermically with oxygen and were once evaluated as potential fuels for rockets in the U.S. space program.

Aluminum, the most abundant metal on earth, has metallic physical properties, such as high thermal and electrical conductivities and a lustrous appearance; however, its bonds to nonmetals are significantly covalent. This covalency is responsible for the amphoteric nature of Al_2O_3, which dissolves in acidic or basic solution, and for the acidity of $Al(H_2O)_6^{3+}$ (see Section 7.8):

$$Al(H_2O)_6^{3+}(aq) \rightleftharpoons Al(OH)(H_2O)_5^{2+}(aq) + H^+(aq)$$

One especially interesting property of *gallium* is its unusually low melting point of 29.8°C, which is in contrast to the 660°C melting point of aluminum. Also, since gallium's boiling point is about 2400°C, it has the largest liquid range of any metal. This makes it useful for thermometers, especially to measure high temperatures. Gallium, like water, expands when it freezes. The chemistry of gallium is quite similar to that of aluminum. For example, Ga_2O_3 is amphoteric.

The chemistry of *indium* is similar to that of aluminum and gallium except that compounds containing the 1+ ion are known, such as InCl and In_2O, in addition to those with the more common 3+ ion. The chemistry of *thallium* is completely metallic.

Table 18.9 summarizes some important reactions of the Group 3A elements.

Table 18.9

Selected Reactions of the Group 3A Elements

Reaction	Comment
$2M + 3X_2 \longrightarrow 2MX_3$	X_2 = any halogen molecule; Tl gives TlX as well, but no TlI_3
$4M + 3O_2 \longrightarrow 2M_2O_3$	High temperatures; Tl gives Tl_2O as well
$2M + 3S \longrightarrow M_2S_3$	High temperatures; Tl gives Tl_2S as well
$2M + N_2 \longrightarrow 2MN$	M = Al only
$2M + 6H^+ \longrightarrow 2M^{3+} + 3H_2$	M = Al, Ga, or In; Tl gives Tl^+
$2M + 2OH^- + 6H_2O \longrightarrow 2M(OH)_4^- + 3H_2$	M = Al or Ga

18.6 | The Group 4A Elements

4A
C
Si
Ge
Sn
Pb

Group 4A (with the valence electron configuration ns^2np^2) contains two of the most important elements on earth: carbon, the fundamental constituent of the molecules necessary for life, and silicon, which forms the basis of the geological world. The change from nonmetallic to metallic properties seen in Group 3A is also apparent in going down Group 4A from carbon, a typical nonmetal, to silicon and germanium, usually considered semimetals, to the metals tin and lead. Table 18.10 summarizes some physical properties, sources, and methods of preparation of the elements in this group.

All the Group 4A elements can form four covalent bonds to nonmetals—for example, CH_4, SiF_4, $GeBr_4$, $SnCl_4$, and $PbCl_4$. In each of these tetrahedral molecules, the central atom is described as sp^3 hybridized by the localized electron model.

We have seen that carbon also differs markedly from the other members of Group 4A in its ability to form π bonds. This accounts for the completely different structures and properties of CO_2 and SiO_2. Note from Table 18.11 that C—C bonds and Si—O bonds are stronger than Si—Si bonds. This partly explains why the chemistry of carbon is dominated by C—C bonds, whereas that of silicon is dominated by Si—O bonds.

Carbon occurs in the allotropic forms graphite, diamond, and fullerenes, whose structures were given in Section 16.5. The most important chemistry of carbon is organic chemistry, which is described in detail in Chapter 21.

Silicon, the second most abundant element in the earth's crust, is a semimetal found widely distributed in silica and silicates (see Section 16.5). About 85% of the earth's crust is composed of these substances. Although silicon is found in some steel and aluminum alloys, its major use is in semiconductors for electronic devices (see Chapter 16).

Germanium, a relatively rare element, is a semimetal used mainly in the manufacture of semiconductors for transistors and similar electronic devices.

Tin is a soft, silvery metal that can be rolled into thin sheets (tin foil) and has been used for centuries in various alloys such as bronze (20% Sn and 80% Cu), solder (33% Sn and 67% Pb), and pewter (85% Sn, 7% Cu, 6% Bi, and 2% Sb). Tin exists as three allotropes: *white tin*, stable at normal temperatures; *gray tin*, stable at temperatures below 13.2°C; and *brittle tin*, found at temperatures above 161°C. When tin is exposed to low temperatures, it gradually changes to powdery gray tin and crumbles away; this is known as *tin disease*.

A new form of elemental carbon, the fullerenes, was discussed in Chapter 2.

Table 18.10

Selected Physical Properties, Sources, and Methods of Preparation of the Group 4A Elements

Element	Electronegativity	Melting Point (°C)	Boiling Point (°C)	Source	Method of Preparation
Carbon	2.6	3727 (sublimes)	—	Graphite, diamond, petroleum, coal	—
Silicon	1.9	1410	2355	Silicate minerals, silica	Reduction of K_2SiF_6 with Al, or reduction of SiO_2 with Mg
Germanium	2.0	937	2830	Germinate (mixture of copper, iron, and germanium sulfides)	Reduction of GeO_2 with H_2 or C
Tin	2.0	232	2270	Cassiterite (SnO_2)	Reduction of SnO_2 with C
Lead	2.3	327	1740	Galena (PbS)	Roasting of PbS with O_2 to form PbO_2 and then reduction with C

Beethoven: Hair Is the Story

Ludwig van Beethoven, arguably the greatest composer who ever lived, led a troubled life fraught with sickness, deafness, and personality aberrations. Now we may know the source of these difficulties: lead poisoning. Scientists have recently reached this conclusion through analysis of Beethoven's hair. When Beethoven died in 1827 at age 56, many mourners took samples of the great man's hair. In fact, it was said at the time that he was practically bald by the time he was buried. The hair that was recently analyzed consisted of 582 strands—3 to 6 inches long—bought for the Center of Beethoven Studies for $7300 in 1994 from Sotheby's auction house in London.

According to William Walsh of the Health Research Institute (HRI) in suburban Chicago, Beethoven's hair showed a lead concentration 100 times the normal levels. The scientists concluded that Beethoven's exposure to lead came as an adult, possibly from the mineral water he drank and swam in when he visited spas.

The lead poisoning may well explain Beethoven's volatile temper—the composer was subject to towering rages and sometimes had the look of a wild animal. In rare cases lead poisoning has been known to cause deafness, but the researchers remain unsure if this problem led to Beethoven's hearing loss.

According to Walsh, the scientists at HRI were originally looking for mercury, a common treatment for syphilis in the early nineteenth century, in

The Granger Collection

Portrait of Beethoven by Josef Karl Stieler.

Beethoven's hair. The absence of mercury supports the consensus of scholars that Beethoven did not have this disease. Not surprisingly, Beethoven himself wanted to know what made him so ill. In a letter to his brothers in 1802, he asked them to have doctors find the cause of his frequent abdominal pain after his death.

Table 18.11	
Strengths of C—C, Si—Si, and Si—O Bonds	

Bond	Bond Energy (kJ/mol)
C—C	347
Si—Si	340
Si—O	368

Currently, tin is used mainly as a protective coating for steel, especially for cans used as food containers. The thin layer of tin, applied electrolytically, forms a protective oxide coating that prevents further corrosion.

Lead is easily obtained from its ore, galena (PbS). Because lead melts at such a low temperature, it may have been the first pure metal obtained from its ore. We know that lead was used as early as 3000 B.C. by the Egyptians. It was later used by the Romans to make eating utensils, glazes on pottery, and even intricate plumbing systems. The Romans also prepared a sweetener called *sapa* by boiling down grape juice in lead-lined vessels. The sweetness of this syrup was partly caused by the formation of lead(II) acetate (formerly called sugar of lead), a very sweet-tasting compound. The problem with these practices is that lead is very toxic. In fact, the Romans had so much contact with lead that it may have contributed to the demise of their civilization. Analysis of bones from that era shows significant levels of lead.

Although lead poisoning has been known since at least the second century B.C., lead continues to be a problem. For example, many children have been

Table 18.12

Selected Reactions of the Group 4A Elements

Reaction	Comment
$M + 2X_2 \longrightarrow MX_4$	X_2 = any halogen molecule; M = Ge or Sn; Pb gives PbX_2
$M + O_2 \longrightarrow MO_2$	M = Ge or Sn; high temperatures; Pb gives PbO or Pb_3O_4
$M + 2H^+ \longrightarrow M^{2+} + H_2$	M = Sn or Pb

exposed to lead by eating chips of lead-based paint. Because of this problem, lead-based paints are no longer used for children's furniture, and many states have banned lead-based paint for interior use. Lead poisoning can also occur when acidic foods and drinks leach the lead from lead-glazed pottery dishes that were improperly fired and when liquor is stored in leaded crystal decanters, producing toxic levels of lead in the drink in a relatively short time. In addition, the widespread use of tetraethyl lead $[(C_2H_5)_4Pb]$ as an antiknock agent in gasoline has increased the lead levels in our environment. Concern about the effects of this lead pollution has caused the U.S. government to require the gradual replacement of the lead in gasoline with other antiknock agents. The largest commercial use of lead (over one million tons annually) is for electrodes in the lead storage batteries used in automobiles (see Section 11.5).

Table 18.12 summarizes some important reactions of the Group 4A elements.

18.7 | The Group 5A Elements

The Group 5A elements (with the valence electron configuration ns^2np^3), which are prepared as shown in Table 18.13, exhibit remarkably varied chemical properties. As usual, metallic character increases going down the group, as is apparent from the electronegativity values (Table 18.13). Nitrogen and

Table 18.13

Selected Physical Properties, Sources, and Methods of Preparation of the Group 5A Elements

Element	Electronegativity	Source	Method of Preparation
Nitrogen	3.0	Air	Liquefaction of air
Phosphorus	2.2	Phosphate rock $[Ca_3(PO_4)_2]$, fluorapatite $[Ca_5(PO_4)_3F]$	$2Ca_3(PO_4)_2 + 6SiO_2 \longrightarrow 6CaSiO_3 + P_4O_{10}$ $P_4O_{10} + 10C \longrightarrow 4P + 10CO$
Arsenic	2.2	Arsenopyrite (Fe_3As_2, FeS)	Heating arsenopyrite in the absence of air
Antimony	2.1	Stibnite (Sb_2S_3)	Roasting Sb_2S_3 in air to form Sb_2O_3 and then reduction with carbon
Bismuth	2.0	Bismite (Bi_2O_3), bismuth glance (Bi_2S_3)	Roasting Bi_2S_3 in air to form Bi_2O_3 and then reduction with carbon

Figure 18.8
The pyramidal shape of the Group 5A MX_3 molecules.

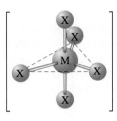

Figure 18.9
The trigonal bipyramidal shape of the MX_5 molecules.

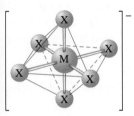

Figure 18.10
The structures of the tetrahedral MX_4^+ and the octahedral MX_6^- ions.

phosphorus are nonmetals that can gain three electrons to form 3− anions in salts with active metals; examples are magnesium nitride (Mg_3N_2) and beryllium phosphide (Be_3P_2). The chemistry of these two important elements is discussed in the next two sections.

Bismuth and *antimony* tend to be metallic, readily losing electrons to form cations. Although these elements have five valence electrons, so much energy is required to remove all five that no ionic compounds containing Bi^{5+} or Sb^{5+} ions are known.

The Group 5A elements can form molecules or ions that involve three, five, or six covalent bonds to the Group 5A atom. Examples involving three single bonds are NH_3, PH_3, NF_3, and $AsCl_3$. Each of these molecules has a lone pair of electrons (and thus can behave as a Lewis base) and a pyramidal shape as predicted by the VSEPR model (Fig. 18.8).

All the Group 5A elements except nitrogen can form molecules with five covalent bonds (of general formula MX_5). Nitrogen cannot form such molecules because of its small size. The MX_5 molecules have a trigonal bipyramidal shape (Fig. 18.9) as predicted by the VSEPR model, and the central atom can be described as dsp^3 hybridized.

Although the MX_5 molecules have a trigonal bipyramidal structure in the gas phase, the solids of many of these compounds contain a 1:1 mixture of the ions MX_4^+ and MX_6^- (Fig. 18.10). The MX_4^+ cation is tetrahedral (the atom represented by M is sp^3 hybridized), and the MX_6^- anion is octahedral (the atom represented by M is d^2sp^3 hybridized). Examples are PCl_5 (which in the solid state contains PCl_4^+ and PCl_6^-) and AsF_3Cl_2 (which in the solid state contains $AsCl_4^+$ and AsF_6^-).

As discussed in Section 18.1, the ability of the Group 5A elements to form π bonds decreases dramatically after nitrogen. This explains why elemental nitrogen exists as N_2 molecules containing two π bonds, whereas the other elements in the group exist as larger aggregates containing single bonds. For example, in the gas phase the elements phosphorus, arsenic, and antimony consist of P_4, As_4, and Sb_4 molecules, respectively.

18.8 | The Chemistry of Nitrogen

At the earth's surface, virtually all elemental nitrogen exists as the N_2 molecule with its very strong triple bond (941 kJ/mol). Because of this large bond strength, the N_2 molecule is so unreactive that it can coexist with most other elements under normal conditions without undergoing any appreciable reaction. This property makes nitrogen gas very useful as a medium for experiments involving substances that react with oxygen or water. Such experiments can be done using an inert atmosphere box of the type shown in Fig. 18.11.

The strength of the triple bond in the N_2 molecule is important both thermodynamically and kinetically. Thermodynamically, the great stability of the

Figure 18.11

An inert atmosphere box used when working with oxygen- or water-sensitive materials. The box is filled with an inert gas such as nitrogen, and work is done through the ports fitted with large rubber gloves.

Paul Ridgway/Lawrence Livermore National

N≡N bond means that most binary compounds containing nitrogen decompose exothermically to the elements, for example:

$$N_2O(g) \longrightarrow N_2(g) + \tfrac{1}{2}O_2(g) \qquad \Delta H° = -82 \text{ kJ}$$

$$NO(g) \longrightarrow \tfrac{1}{2}N_2(g) + \tfrac{1}{2}O_2(g) \qquad \Delta H° = -90 \text{ kJ}$$

$$NO_2(g) \longrightarrow \tfrac{1}{2}N_2(g) + O_2(g) \qquad \Delta H° = -34 \text{ kJ}$$

$$N_2H_4(g) \longrightarrow N_2(g) + 2H_2(g) \qquad \Delta H° = -95 \text{ kJ}$$

$$NH_3(g) \longrightarrow \tfrac{1}{2}N_2(g) + \tfrac{3}{2}H_2(g) \qquad \Delta H° = +46 \text{ kJ}$$

Of these compounds, only ammonia is thermodynamically more stable than its component elements. That is, only for ammonia is energy required to decompose the molecule to its elements. For the remaining molecules, energy is released when decomposition to the elements occurs, as a result of the great stability of N_2.

The importance of the thermodynamic stability of N_2 can be clearly seen in the power of nitrogen-based explosives, such as nitroglycerin ($C_3H_5N_3O_9$), which has the following structure:

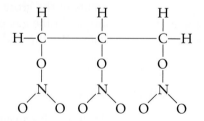

When ignited or subjected to sudden impact, nitroglycerin decomposes very rapidly and exothermically:

$$4C_3H_5N_3O_9(l) \longrightarrow 6N_2(g) + 12CO_2(g) + 10H_2O(g) + O_2(g) + \text{energy}$$

An explosion occurs; that is, large volumes of gas are produced in a fast, highly exothermic reaction. Note that 4 moles of liquid nitroglycerin produce 29 (6 + 12 + 10 + 1) moles of gaseous products. This alone produces a large increase in volume. However, also note that the products, which include N_2, are very stable molecules with strong bonds. Their formation is therefore accompanied by the release of large quantities of energy as heat, which increases the gaseous volume. The hot, rapidly expanding gases produce a pressure surge and damaging shock wave.

Most high explosives are organic compounds that, like nitroglycerin, contain nitro ($-NO_2$) groups and produce nitrogen and other gases as products. Another example is *trinitrotoluene* (TNT), a solid at normal temperatures, which decomposes as follows:

$$2C_7H_5N_3O_6(s) \longrightarrow 12CO(g) + 5H_2(g) + 3N_2(g) + 2C(s) + \text{energy}$$

Note that 2 moles of solid TNT produce 20 moles of gaseous products plus energy.

The effect of bond strength on the kinetics of reactions involving the N_2 molecule is illustrated by the synthesis of ammonia from nitrogen and hydrogen, a reaction we have discussed many times before. Because a large quantity of energy is required to disrupt the $N \equiv N$ bond, the ammonia synthesis reaction occurs at a negligible rate at room temperature, even though the equilibrium constant is very large ($K \approx 10^8$). Of course, the most direct way to increase the rate of a reaction is to raise the temperature. However, since this reaction is very exothermic,

$$N_2(g) + 3H_2(g) \longrightarrow 2NH_3(g) \qquad \Delta H° = -92 \text{ kJ}$$

the value of K decreases significantly with a temperature increase (at $500°C$, $K \approx 10^{-2}$).

Obviously, the kinetics and the thermodynamics of this reaction are in opposition. A compromise must be reached, involving high pressure to force the equilibrium to the right and high temperature to produce a reasonable rate. The **Haber process** for manufacturing ammonia represents such a compromise (Fig. 18.12). The process is carried out at a pressure of about 250 atm and a temperature of approximately $400°C$. Even higher temperatures would be required if a catalyst consisting of a solid iron oxide mixed with small amounts of potassium oxide and aluminum oxide were not used to facilitate the reaction.

Nitrogen is essential to living systems. The problem with nitrogen is not one of supply—we are surrounded by it—but rather one of changing it from the inert N_2 molecule to a form usable by plants and animals. The process of transforming N_2 to other nitrogen-containing compounds is called **nitrogen fixation**. The Haber process is one example of nitrogen fixation. The ammonia produced can be applied to the soil as a fertilizer, since plants can readily use the nitrogen in ammonia to make the nitrogen-containing biomolecules essential for their growth.

Nitrogen fixation also results from the high-temperature combustion process in automobile engines. The nitrogen in the air is drawn into the engine and reacts at a significant rate with oxygen to form nitric oxide (NO), which further reacts with oxygen from the air to form nitrogen dioxide (NO_2). This nitrogen dioxide, which contributes to photochemical smog in many urban areas (see Section 15.9), reacts with moisture in the air and eventually reaches the soil to form nitrate salts, which are plant nutrients.

Nitrogen fixation also occurs naturally. For example, lightning provides the energy to disrupt N_2 and O_2 molecules in the air, producing highly reactive nitrogen and oxygen atoms. These atoms in turn attack other N_2 and O_2 molecules to form nitrogen oxides that eventually become nitrates. Although lightning has traditionally been credited with forming about 10% of the total fixed nitrogen, recent studies indicate that lightning may account for as much as half of the fixed nitrogen available on earth. Another natural nitrogen fixation process involves bacteria that reside in the root nodules of plants such as beans, peas, and alfalfa. These **nitrogen-fixing bacteria** readily allow the conversion of nitrogen to ammonia and to other nitrogen-containing compounds useful to

TNT

Figure 18.12
A schematic diagram of the Haber process for the manufacture of ammonia.

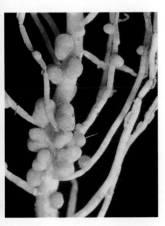

Nodules on the roots of pea plants contain nitrogen-fixing bacteria.

Chemical Insights   An Explosive Discovery

For the first time in more than 100 years, a new species containing only nitrogen atoms has been discovered. In 1999 chemists Karl O. Christe and William W. Wilson, working at Edwards Air Force Base in California, reported a compound containing the N_5^+ cation. The only other all-nitrogen species known are molecular nitrogen (N_2), isolated in 1772, and the azide ion (N_3^-), first synthesized in 1890.

The Edwards scientists synthesized the compound N_5AsF_6, which contains the N_5^+ and AsF_6^- ions, by reacting N_2FAsF_6 with hydrazoic acid (HN_3) in liquid hydrogen fluoride at $-78°C$. The resulting N_5AsF_6 is a white, powdery substance that is extremely explosive. The compound has an enthalpy of formation of $+1460$ kJ/mol, an extraordinarily large value. Because the compound is so explosive, it is treacherous to handle. Indeed, its synthesis and characterization can be carried out only using special facilities that are available at a few laboratories in the world.

The N_5^+ ion is one of the most powerful oxidizing agents ever discovered. It reacts explosively with both water and organic materials. Calculations indicate that the N_5^+ ion is V-shaped and can be represented by the Lewis structure

and its accompanying resonance structures.

Christe, Wilson, and their colleagues are working to prepare other compounds containing N_5^+, including N_5SbF_6 and N_5N_3 (containing N_5^+ and N_3^-). This should be an exciting (and hazardous) search.

plants. The efficiency of these bacteria is intriguing: They produce ammonia at soil temperatures and 1 atm pressure, whereas the Haber process requires severe conditions of 400°C and 250 atm. For obvious reasons, researchers are studying these bacteria intensively.

When plants and animals die and decompose, the elements they consist of are returned to the environment. In the case of nitrogen, the return of the element to the atmosphere as nitrogen gas, called **denitrification,** is carried out by bacteria that change nitrates to nitrogen. The complex **nitrogen cycle** is summarized in Fig. 18.13. It has been estimated that as much as 10 million tons more nitrogen per year is currently being fixed by natural and human processes than is being returned to the atmosphere. This fixed nitrogen is accumulating in soil, lakes, rivers, and oceans, where it promotes the growth of algae and other undesirable organisms.

Figure 18.13

The nitrogen cycle. To be used by plants and animals, nitrogen must be converted from N_2 to nitrogen-containing compounds, such as nitrates, ammonia, and proteins. The nitrogen is returned to the atmosphere by natural decay processes.

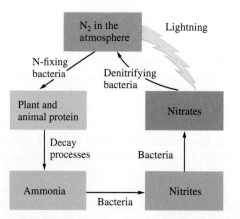

Nitrogen Hydrides

By far the most important hydride of nitrogen is **ammonia.** A toxic, colorless gas with a pungent odor, ammonia is manufactured in huge quantities (approximately 40 billion pounds per year), mainly for use in fertilizers.

The pyramidal ammonia molecule has a lone pair of electrons on its nitrogen atom (see Fig. 18.8) and polar N—H bonds. This structure leads to a high degree of intermolecular interaction by hydrogen bonding in the liquid state, thereby producing an unusually high boiling point ($-33.4°C$) for a substance with such a low molar mass. Note, however, that the hydrogen bonding in liquid ammonia is clearly not as important as that in liquid water, which has about the same molar mass but a much higher boiling point. The water molecule has two polar bonds involving hydrogen and two lone pairs—the right combination for optimum hydrogen bonding—in contrast to the one lone pair and three polar bonds of the ammonia molecule.

As we saw in Chapter 7, ammonia behaves as a base, reacting with acids to produce ammonium salts. For example,

$$NH_3(g) + HCl(g) \longrightarrow NH_4Cl(s)$$

A second nitrogen hydride of major importance is **hydrazine** (N_2H_4). The Lewis structure of hydrazine

indicates that each nitrogen atom should be sp^3 hybridized with bond angles close to 109.5° (the tetrahedral angle), since the nitrogen atom is surrounded by four electron pairs. The observed structure with bond angles of 112° (Fig. 18.14) agrees reasonably well with these predictions. Hydrazine, a colorless liquid with an ammoniacal odor, freezes at 2°C and boils at 113.5°C. This boiling point is quite high for a compound with a molar mass of 32; this suggests that considerable hydrogen bonding occurs among the polar hydrazine molecules.

Hydrazine is a powerful reducing agent and has been widely used as a rocket propellant. For example, its reaction with oxygen is highly exothermic:

$$N_2H_4(l) + O_2(g) \longrightarrow N_2(g) + 2H_2O(g) \qquad \Delta H° = -622 \text{ kJ}$$

Since hydrazine also reacts vigorously with the halogens, fluorine is often used instead of oxygen as the oxidizer in rocket engines. Substituted hydrazines, where one or more of the hydrogen atoms are replaced by other groups, are also useful rocket fuels. For example, monomethylhydrazine,

is used with the oxidizer dinitrogen tetroxide (N_2O_4) to power the U.S. space shuttle orbiter. The reaction is

$$5N_2O_4(l) + 4N_2H_3(CH_3)(l) \longrightarrow 12H_2O(g) + 9N_2(g) + 4CO_2(g)$$

Because of the large number of gaseous molecules produced and the exothermic nature of this reaction, a very high thrust per mass of fuel is achieved. The reaction is also self-starting—it begins immediately when the fuels are mixed—which is a useful property for rocket engines that must be started and stopped frequently.

The use of hydrazine as a rocket propellant is a rather specialized application. The main industrial use of hydrazine is as a "blowing" agent in the manu-

Figure 18.14
The molecular structure of hydrazine (N_2H_4). This arrangement minimizes the repulsion between the lone pairs on the nitrogen atoms by placing them on opposite sides.

Blowing agents—such as hydrazine, which forms nitrogen gas on decomposition—are used to produce porous plastics like these polystyrene products.

facture of plastics. Hydrazine decomposes to form nitrogen gas, which causes foaming in the liquid plastic and results in a porous texture. Another major use of hydrazine is in the production of agricultural pesticides. Of the many hundreds of hydrazine derivatives (substituted hydrazines) that have been tested, 40 are used as fungicides, herbicides, insecticides, or plant growth regulators.

Nitrogen Oxides

Nitrogen forms a series of oxides in which its oxidation state ranges from $+1$ to $+5$, as shown in Table 18.14.

Dinitrogen monoxide (N_2O), more commonly called *nitrous oxide* or laughing gas, has an inebriating effect and has been used as a mild anesthetic by dentists. Because of its high solubility in fats, nitrous oxide is widely used as a propellant in aerosol cans of whipped cream. It is dissolved in the liquid inside the can at high pressure and forms bubbles that produce foaming as the liquid is released from the can. A significant amount of N_2O exists in the atmosphere, mostly produced by soil microorganisms, and its concentration appears to be gradually increasing. Because it can strongly absorb infrared radiation, nitrous oxide plays a small but probably significant role in controlling the earth's temperature in the same way that atmospheric carbon dioxide and water vapor do (see the discussion of the greenhouse effect in Section 9.7). Some scientists fear that the rapid decrease of tropical rain forests resulting from the development of countries such as Brazil will significantly affect the rate of pro-

A copper penny reacts with nitric acid to produce NO gas, which is immediately oxidized in air to give reddish brown NO_2.

Table 18.14

Some Common Nitrogen Compounds

Oxidation State of Nitrogen	Compound	Formula	Lewis Structure*
-3	Ammonia	NH_3	H—N—N with H below
-2	Hydrazine	N_2H_4	H—N—N—H with H H below
-1	Hydroxylamine	NH_2OH	H—N—O—H with H below
0	Nitrogen	N_2	$:N{\equiv}N:$
$+1$	Dinitrogen monoxide (nitrous oxide)	N_2O	$N{=}N{=}O$
$+2$	Nitrogen monoxide (nitric oxide)	NO	$:N{=}O$
$+3$	Dinitrogen trioxide	N_2O_3	O, N—N=O, O
$+4$	Nitrogen dioxide	NO_2	$O{-}N{=}O$
$+5$	Nitric acid	HNO_3	O—N—O—H, O

*In some cases additional resonance structures are needed to fully describe the electron distribution.

Figure 18.15
The molecular orbital energy-level diagram for nitric oxide (NO). The bond order is 2.5, or (8 − 3)/2.

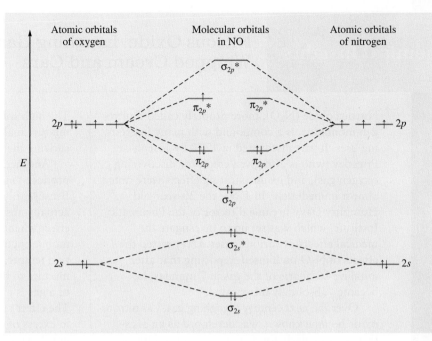

duction of N_2O by soil organisms and thus will have important effects on the earth's temperature.

Nitrogen monoxide (NO), commonly called *nitric oxide*, has been found to be an important regulator in biological systems. Nitric oxide is a colorless gas under normal conditions and can be produced in the laboratory by reacting 6 *M* nitric acid with copper metal:

$$8H^+(aq) + 2NO_3^-(aq) + 3Cu(s) \longrightarrow 3Cu^{2+}(aq) + 4H_2O(l) + 2NO(g)$$

When this reaction is carried out in the air, the nitric oxide is immediately oxidized by O_2 to reddish brown nitrogen dioxide (NO_2).

Since the NO molecule has an odd number of electrons, it is most conveniently described in terms of the molecular orbital model. The molecular orbital energy-level diagram is shown in Fig. 18.15. Note that the NO molecule should be paramagnetic and have a bond order of 2.5, predictions that are supported by experimental observations. Since the NO molecule has one high-energy electron, it is not surprising that it can be rather easily oxidized to form NO^+, the *nitrosyl ion*. Because an antibonding electron is removed in going from NO to NO^+, the resulting ion should have a stronger bond (the predicted bond order is 3) than the molecule. This is borne out by experiment. The bond lengths and bond energies for nitric oxide and the nitrosyl ion are shown in Table 18.15.

Nitric oxide is thermodynamically unstable and decomposes to nitrous oxide and nitrogen dioxide:

$$3NO(g) \longrightarrow N_2O(g) + NO_2(g)$$

Nitrogen dioxide (NO_2), which is also an odd-electron molecule, has a V-shaped structure. The reddish brown, paramagnetic NO_2 molecule readily dimerizes to form dinitrogen tetroxide,

$$2NO_2(g) \rightleftharpoons N_2O_4(g)$$

which is diamagnetic and colorless. The value of the equilibrium constant is approximately 1 for this process at 55°C, and since the dimerization is exothermic, *K* decreases as the temperature increases.

Table 18.15

Comparison of the Bond Lengths and Bond Energies for Nitric Oxide and the Nitrosyl Ion

	NO	NO⁺
Bond length (Å)	1.15	1.09
Bond energy (kJ/mol)	630	1020
Bond order (predicted by MO model)	2.5	3

Chemical Insights

Nitrous Oxide: Laughing Gas That Propels Whipped Cream and Cars

Nitrous oxide (N_2O), more properly called dinitrogen monoxide, is a compound with many interesting uses. It was discovered in 1772 by Joseph Priestley (who is also given credit for discovering oxygen gas), and its intoxicating effects were noted almost immediately. In 1798, the 20-year-old Humphry Davy became director of the Pneumatic Institute, which was set up to investigate the medical effects of various gases. Davy tested the effects of N_2O on himself, reporting that after inhaling 16 quarts of the gas in 7 minutes, he became "absolutely intoxicated."

Over the next century "laughing gas," as nitrous oxide became known, was developed as an anesthetic, particularly for dental procedures. Nitrous oxide is still used as an anesthetic, although it has been primarily replaced by more modern drugs.

One major use of nitrous oxide today is as the propellant in cans of "instant" whipped cream.

The high solubility of N_2O in the whipped cream mixture makes it an excellent candidate for pressurizing the cans of whipping cream.

Another current use of nitrous oxide is to produce "instant horsepower" for street racers. Because the reaction of N_2O with O_2 to form NO actually absorbs heat, this reaction has a cooling effect when placed in the fuel mixture in an automobile engine. This cooling effect lowers combustion temperatures, thus allowing the fuel–air mixture to be significantly more dense (the density of a gas is inversely proportional to temperature). The effect can produce a burst of additional power in excess of 200 horsepower. Because engines are not designed to run steadily at such high power levels, the nitrous oxide is injected from a tank when extra power is desired.

The least common of the nitrogen oxides are *dinitrogen trioxide* (N_2O_3), a blue liquid that readily dissociates to gaseous nitric oxide and nitrogen dioxide, and *dinitrogen pentoxide* (N_2O_5), which under normal conditions is a solid that is best viewed as a mixture of NO_2^+ and NO_3^- ions. Although N_2O_5 molecules can exist in the gas phase, they readily dissociate to nitrogen dioxide and oxygen:

$$2N_2O_5(g) \rightleftharpoons 4NO_2(g) + O_2(g)$$

This reaction follows first-order kinetics, as discussed in Section 15.4.

Oxyacids of Nitrogen

Nitric acid is an important industrial chemical (approximately 8 million tons produced annually) used in the manufacture of many products, such as nitrogen-based explosives and ammonium nitrate for use as a fertilizer.

Nitric acid is produced commercially by the oxidation of ammonia in the **Ostwald process** (Fig. 18.16). In the first step of this process, ammonia is oxidized to nitric oxide:

$$4NH_3(g) + 5O_2(g) \longrightarrow 4NO(g) + 6H_2O(g) \qquad \Delta H^\circ = -905 \text{ kJ}$$

Although this reaction is highly exothermic, it is very slow at 25°C. A side reaction occurs between nitric oxide and ammonia:

$$4NH_3(g) + 6NO(g) \longrightarrow 5N_2(g) + 6H_2O(g)$$

which is particularly undesirable because it traps the nitrogen in the very unreactive N_2 molecules. The desired reaction can be accelerated and the effects of the competing reaction can be minimized if the ammonia oxidation is carried out by using a catalyst of a platinum–rhodium alloy heated to 900°C. Under these conditions, there is a 97% conversion of the ammonia to nitric oxide.

Figure 18.16
The Ostwald process.

Figure 18.17
(a) The molecular structure of HNO₃.
(b) The resonance structures of HNO₃.

(a)

(b)

In the second step, nitric oxide is reacted with oxygen to produce nitrogen dioxide:

$$2NO(g) + O_2(g) \longrightarrow 2NO_2(g) \qquad \Delta H° = -113 \text{ kJ}$$

This oxidation reaction has a rate that *decreases* with increasing temperature. Because of this very unusual behavior, the reaction is carried out at approximately 25°C and is kept at this temperature by cooling with water.

The third step in the Ostwald process is the absorption of nitrogen dioxide by water:

$$3NO_2(g) + H_2O(l) \longrightarrow 2HNO_3(aq) + NO(g) \qquad \Delta H° = -139 \text{ kJ}$$

The gaseous NO produced in the reaction is recycled so that it can be oxidized to NO_2. The aqueous nitric acid from this process is about 50% HNO_3 by mass, which can be increased to 68% by distillation to remove some of the water. The maximum concentration attainable by this method is 68% because nitric acid and water form an *azeotrope* at this concentration. The solution can be further concentrated to 95% HNO_3 by treatment with concentrated sulfuric acid, which strongly absorbs water; H_2SO_4 is often used as a *dehydrating (water-removing) agent*.

Nitric acid is a colorless, fuming liquid (bp = 83°C) with a pungent odor; it decomposes in sunlight by the following reaction:

$$4HNO_3(l) \xrightarrow{hv} 4NO_2(g) + 2H_2O(l) + O_2(g)$$

As a result, nitric acid turns yellow as it ages because of the dissolved nitrogen dioxide. The common laboratory reagent called *concentrated nitric acid* is 15.9 *M* HNO_3 (70.4% HNO_3 by mass) and is a very strong oxidizing agent. The resonance structures and molecular structure of HNO_3 are shown in Fig. 18.17. Note that the hydrogen is bound to an oxygen atom rather than to nitrogen as the formula might suggest.

Nitrous acid (HNO_2) is a weak acid,

$$HNO_2(aq) \rightleftharpoons H^+(aq) + NO_2^-(aq) \qquad K_a = 4.0 \times 10^{-4}$$

that forms pale yellow nitrite (NO_2^-) salts. In contrast to nitrates, which are often used as explosives, nitrites are quite stable even at high temperatures.

An *azeotrope* is a solution that, like a pure liquid, distills at a constant temperature without a change in composition.

18.9 │ The Chemistry of Phosphorus

Although phosphorus lies directly below nitrogen in Group 5A of the periodic table, its chemical properties are significantly different from those of nitrogen. The differences arise mainly from four factors: nitrogen's ability to form much stronger π bonds, the greater electronegativity of nitrogen, the larger size of phosphorus atoms, and the potential availability of empty valence *d* orbitals on phosphorus.

White phosphorus reacts vigorously with the oxygen in air and must be stored under water. Red phosphorus is stable in air.

(a) (b) (c)

Figure 18.18

(a) The P_4 molecule found in white phosphorus. (b) The crystalline network structure of black phosphorus. (c) The chain structure of red phosphorus.

The chemical differences between nitrogen and phosphorus are apparent in their elemental forms. In contrast to the diatomic form of elemental nitrogen, which is stabilized by strong π bonds, there are several solid forms of phosphorus that all contain aggregates of atoms. *White phosphorus,* which contains discrete tetrahedral P_4 molecules [Fig. 18.18(a)], is very reactive; it bursts into flames on contact with air (it is said to be *pyrophoric*). Consequently, white phosphorus is commonly stored under water. White phosphorus is quite toxic; the P_4 molecules are very damaging to tissue, particularly the cartilage and bones of the nose and jaw. The much less reactive forms, called *black phosphorus* and *red phosphorus,* are network solids (see Section 16.5). Black phosphorus has a regular crystalline structure [Fig. 18.18(b)], but red phosphorus is amorphous and is thought to consist of chains of P_4 units [Fig. 18.18(c)]. Red phosphorus can be obtained by heating white phosphorus in the absence of air at 1 atm. Black phosphorus is obtained from either white or red phosphorus by heating at high pressures.

Even though phosphorus has a lower electronegativity than nitrogen, it will form phosphides (ionic substances containing the P^{3-} anion) such as Na_3P and Ca_3P_2. Phosphide salts react vigorously with water to produce *phosphine* (PH_3), a toxic, colorless gas:

$$2Na_3P(s) + 6H_2O(l) \longrightarrow 2PH_3(g) + 6Na^+(aq) + 6OH^-(aq)$$

Phosphine is analogous to ammonia, although it is a much weaker base ($K_b \approx 10^{-26}$) and is much less soluble in water.

Phosphine has the Lewis structure

and a pyramidal molecular structure, as we would predict from the VSEPR model. However, it has bond angles of 94° rather than 107°, as found in the ammonia molecule. The reasons for this are complex; therefore, we will simply regard phosphine as an exception to the simple version of the VSEPR model that we use.

Phosphorus Oxides and Oxyacids

The terminal oxygens are the nonbridging oxygen atoms.

Phosphorus reacts with oxygen to form oxides in which its oxidation states are +5 and +3. The oxide P_4O_6 is formed when elemental phosphorus is burned in a limited supply of oxygen, and P_4O_{10} is produced when the oxygen is in excess. Picture these oxides (shown in Fig. 18.19) as being constructed by adding oxygen atoms to the fundamental P_4 structure. The intermediate states, P_4O_7, P_4O_8, and P_4O_9, which contain one, two, and three terminal oxygen atoms, respectively, are also known.

Figure 18.19
The structures of P_4O_6 and P_4O_{10}.

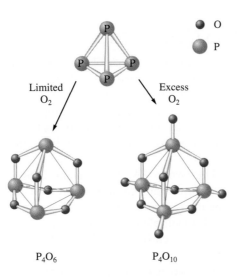

P_4O_6 P_4O_{10}

Tetraphosphorus decoxide (P_4O_{10}), which was formerly represented as P_2O_5 and called phosphorus pentoxide, has a great affinity for water and thus is a powerful dehydrating agent. For example, it can be used to convert HNO_3 and H_2SO_4 to their parent oxides, N_2O_5 and SO_3, respectively.

When tetraphosphorus decoxide dissolves in water, **phosphoric acid** (H_3PO_4), also called **orthophosphoric acid**, is produced:

$$P_4O_{10}(s) + 6H_2O(l) \longrightarrow 4H_3PO_4(aq)$$

Pure phosphoric acid is a white solid that melts at 42°C. Aqueous phosphoric acid is a much weaker acid ($K_{a_1} \approx 10^{-2}$) than nitric acid or sulfuric acid and is a poor oxidizing agent.

When the oxide P_4O_6 is placed in water, **phosphorous acid** (H_3PO_3) is formed [Fig. 18.20(a)]. Although the formula suggests a triprotic acid, phosphorous acid is a *diprotic* acid. The hydrogen atom bonded directly to the phosphorus atom is not acidic in aqueous solution; only those hydrogen atoms bonded to the oxygen atoms in H_3PO_3 can be released as protons.

A third oxyacid of phosphorus is *hypophosphorous acid* (H_3PO_2) [Fig. 18.20(b)], which is a monoprotic acid.

Phosphorus in Fertilizers

Phosphorus is essential for plant growth. Although most soil contains large amounts of phosphorus, it is often present in insoluble minerals, making it inaccessible to the plants. Soluble phosphate fertilizers are manufactured by treating phosphate rock with sulfuric acid to make **superphosphate of lime,** a mixture of $CaSO_4 \cdot 2H_2O$ and $Ca(H_2PO_4)_2 \cdot H_2O$. If phosphate rock is treated with phosphoric acid, $Ca(H_2PO_4)_2$, known as *triple phosphate,* is produced. The reaction of ammonia with phosphoric acid gives *ammonium dihydrogenphosphate* ($NH_4H_2PO_4$), a very efficient fertilizer that furnishes both phosphorus and nitrogen.

Figure 18.20
(a) The structure of phosphorous acid (H_3PO_3). (b) The structure of hypophosphorous acid (H_3PO_2).

(a)   (b)

18.10 | The Group 6A Elements

6A
O
S
Se
Te
Po

Although in Group 6A (Table 18.16) there is the usual tendency for metallic properties to increase going down the group, none of the Group 6A elements behaves as a typical metal. The most common chemical behavior of a Group 6A element involves reacting with a metal to achieve a noble gas electron configuration by adding two electrons to become a 2− anion in ionic compounds. In fact, for most metals, the oxides and sulfides constitute the most common minerals.

The Group 6A elements can form covalent bonds with other nonmetals. For example, they combine with hydrogen to form a series of covalent hydrides of the general formula H_2X. Those members of the group that have valence d orbitals available (all except oxygen) commonly form molecules in which they are surrounded by more than eight electrons. Examples are SF_4, SF_6, TeI_4, and $SeBr_4$.

The two heaviest members of Group 6A can lose electrons to form cations. Although they do not lose all six valence electrons because of the high energies that would be required, tellurium and polonium appear to exhibit some chemistry involving their 4+ cations. However, the chemistry of these Group 6A cations is much more limited than that of the Group 5A elements bismuth and antimony.

In recent years there has been a growing interest in the chemistry of selenium, an element found throughout the environment in trace amounts. Selenium's toxicity has long been known, but some medical studies have shown an *inverse* relationship between the incidence of cancer and the selenium levels in soil. It has been suggested that the greater dietary intake of selenium by people living in areas with relatively high selenium levels somehow furnishes protection from cancer. These studies are only preliminary, but selenium is definitely known to be physiologically important (it is involved in the activity of vitamin E and certain enzymes). Selenium (as well as tellurium) is also a semiconductor and therefore finds some application in the electronics industry.

Polonium was discovered in 1898 by Marie and Pierre Curie in their search for the sources of radioactivity in pitchblende. Polonium has 27 isotopes and is highly toxic and very radioactive. It has been suggested that the isotope ^{210}Po, a natural contaminant of tobacco and an α-particle producer (see Section 20.1), might be at least partly responsible for the incidence of cancer in smokers.

Eyebyte/Royalty Free Image/Alamy Images

Walnuts contain trace amounts of selenium.

Table 18.16

Selected Physical Properties, Sources, and Methods of Preparation of the Group 6A Elements

Element	Electronegativity	Radius of X^{2-} (pm)	Source	Method of Preparation
Oxygen	3.4	140	Air	Distillation from liquid air
Sulfur	2.6	184	Sulfur deposits	Melted with hot water and pumped to the surface
Selenium	2.6	198	Impurity in sulfide ores	Reduction of H_2SeO_4 with SO_2
Tellurium	2.1	221	Nagyagite (mixed sulfide and telluride)	Reduction of ore with SO_2
Polonium	2.0	230	Pitchblende	

A U.S. Navy test pilot in an F-14 jet using an oxygen mask.

18.11 | The Chemistry of Oxygen

It is hard to overstate the importance of oxygen, the most abundant element in and near the earth's crust. Oxygen is present in the atmosphere as oxygen gas and ozone; in soil and rocks in oxide, silicate, and carbonate minerals; in the oceans in water; and in our bodies in water and a myriad of other molecules. In addition, most of the energy we need to live and run our civilization comes from the exothermic reactions of oxygen with carbon-containing molecules.

The most common elemental form of oxygen (O_2) constitutes 21% of the volume of the earth's atmosphere. Since nitrogen has a lower boiling point than oxygen, nitrogen can be boiled away from liquid air, leaving oxygen and small amounts of argon, another component of air. Liquid oxygen is a pale blue liquid that freezes at $-219°C$ and boils at $-183°C$. The paramagnetism of the O_2 molecule can be demonstrated by pouring liquid oxygen between the poles of a strong magnet, where it "sticks" until it boils away (see Fig. 14.42). The paramagnetism of the O_2 molecule can be accounted for by the molecular orbital model (Fig. 14.41), which also explains its bond strength.

The other form of elemental oxygen is **ozone** (O_3), a molecule that can be represented by the resonance structures

The bond angle in the O_3 molecule is 117°, in reasonable agreement with the prediction of the VSEPR model (three effective pairs require a trigonal planar arrangement). That the bond angle is slightly less than 120° can be explained by concluding that more space is required for the lone pair than for the bonding pairs.

Ozone can be prepared by passing an electrical discharge through pure oxygen gas. The electrical energy disrupts the bonds in some O_2 molecules, thereby producing oxygen atoms, which react with other O_2 molecules to form O_3. Ozone is much less stable than oxygen at 25°C and 1 atm. For example, $K \approx 10^{-56}$ for the equilibrium

$$3O_2(g) \rightleftharpoons 2O_3(g)$$

A pale blue, highly toxic gas, ozone is a much more powerful oxidizing agent than oxygen. The strong oxidizing power of ozone makes it useful for killing bacteria in swimming pools, hot tubs, and aquariums. It is also increasingly being used in municipal water treatment and for washing produce after it comes out of the fields. One of the main advantages of using ozone for water purification is that it does not leave potentially toxic residues behind. On the other hand, chlorine, which is widely used for water purification, leaves residues of chloro compounds, such as chloroform ($CHCl_3$), which may cause cancer after long-term exposure. Although ozone effectively kills the bacteria in water, one problem with **ozonolysis** is that the water supply is not protected against recontamination, since virtually no ozone remains after the initial treatment. In contrast, for chlorination, significant residual chlorine remains after treatment.

The oxidizing ability of ozone can be detrimental, especially when it is present in the pollution from automobile exhausts (see Section 5.11).

Ozone exists naturally in the upper atmosphere of the earth. The *ozone layer* is especially important because it absorbs ultraviolet light and thus acts as a screen to prevent this radiation, which can cause skin cancer, from pene-

Scientists have become concerned that Freons and nitrogen dioxide are promoting the destruction of the ozone layer (see Section 15.9).

trating to the earth's surface. When an ozone molecule absorbs this energy, it splits into an oxygen molecule and an oxygen atom:

$$O_3 \xrightarrow{h\nu} O_2 + O$$

If the oxygen molecule and atom collide, they will not stay together as ozone unless a "third body," such as a nitrogen molecule, is present to help absorb the energy released by bond formation. The third body absorbs this energy as kinetic energy; its temperature is increased. Therefore, the energy originally absorbed as ultraviolet radiation is eventually changed to thermal energy. Thus the ozone prevents the harmful high-energy ultraviolet light from reaching the earth.

18.12 | The Chemistry of Sulfur

Sulfur is found in nature both in large deposits of the free element and in widely distributed ores, such as galena (PbS), cinnabar (HgS), pyrite (FeS_2), gypsum ($CaSO_4 \cdot 2H_2O$), epsomite ($MgSO_4 \cdot 7H_2O$), and glauberite ($Na_2SO_4 \cdot CaSO_4$).

About 60% of the sulfur produced in the United States comes from the underground deposits of elemental sulfur found in Texas and Louisiana. This sulfur is recovered by using the **Frasch process** developed by Herman Frasch in the 1890s. Superheated water is pumped into the deposit to melt the sulfur (mp = 113°C), which is then forced to the surface by air pressure (Fig. 18.21). The remaining 40% of sulfur produced in the United States either is a by-product of the purification of fossil fuels before combustion to prevent pollution or comes from the sulfur dioxide (SO_2) scrubbed from the exhaust gases when sulfur-containing fuels are burned.

In contrast to oxygen, elemental sulfur exists as S_2 molecules only in the gas phase at high temperatures. Because sulfur atoms form much stronger σ bonds than π bonds, S_2 is less stable at 25°C than larger aggregates such as S_6 and S_8 rings and S_n chains (Fig. 18.22). The most stable form of sulfur at 25°C and 1 atm is called *rhombic sulfur* [Fig. 18.23(a)], which contains stacked S_8 rings. If rhombic sulfur is melted and heated to 120°C, it forms *monoclinic sulfur* as it slowly cools [Fig. 18.23(b)]. The monoclinic form also contains S_8 rings, but the rings are stacked differently than in rhombic sulfur.

Charles D. Winters

Cinnabar from New Almaden, California.

Figure 18.21

The Frasch method for recovering sulfur from underground deposits.

Sulfur piles in Vancouver, British Columbia.

Sulfur Oxides

From its position below oxygen in the periodic table, we might expect the simplest stable oxide of sulfur to have the formula SO. However, *sulfur monoxide*, which can be produced in small amounts when gaseous sulfur dioxide (SO_2) is subjected to an electrical discharge, is very unstable. The difference in the stabilities of the O_2 and SO molecules probably reflects the much stronger π bonding between oxygen atoms than between a sulfur and an oxygen atom.

The scrubbing of sulfur dioxide from exhaust gases was discussed in Section 5.11.

Sulfur burns in air with a bright blue flame to give *sulfur dioxide* (SO_2), a colorless gas with a pungent odor, which condenses to a liquid at $-10°C$ and 1 atm. Sulfur dioxide is a trigonal planar molecule, which is a very effective antibacterial agent often used to preserve stored fruit.

Figure 18.22

(a) The S_8 molecule. (b) Chains of sulfur atoms in viscous liquid sulfur. The chains may contain as many as 10,000 atoms.

(a)

(b)

(a)

Figure 18.23

(a) Crystals of rhombic sulfur. (b) Crystals of monoclinic sulfur.

(b)

Sulfur dioxide reacts with oxygen to produce *sulfur trioxide* (SO_3):

$$2SO_2(g) + O_2(g) \longrightarrow 2SO_3(g)$$

However, this reaction is very slow in the absence of a catalyst. One of the mysteries during early research on air pollution was how the sulfur dioxide produced from the combustion of sulfur-containing fuels is so rapidly converted to sulfur trioxide in the atmosphere. It is now known that dust and other particles can act as heterogeneous catalysts for this process (see Section 15.9).

Oxyacids of Sulfur

Sulfur dioxide dissolves in water to form an acidic solution. The reaction is often represented as

$$SO_2(g) + H_2O(l) \longrightarrow H_2SO_3(aq)$$

where H_2SO_3 is called *sulfurous acid*. However, very little H_2SO_3 actually exists in the solution. The major form of sulfur dioxide in water is SO_2, and the acid dissociation equilibria are best represented as

$$SO_2(aq) + H_2O(l) \rightleftharpoons H^+(aq) + HSO_3^-(aq) \qquad K_{a_1} = 1.5 \times 10^{-2}$$

$$HSO_3^-(aq) \rightleftharpoons H^+(aq) + SO_3^{2-}(aq) \qquad K_{a_2} = 1.0 \times 10^{-7}$$

This situation is analogous to the behavior of carbon dioxide in water (see Section 7.7). Although H_2SO_3 cannot be isolated, salts of SO_3^{2-} (*sulfites*) and HSO_3^- (*hydrogen sulfites*) are well known.

Sulfur trioxide reacts violently with water to produce the diprotic acid **sulfuric acid**:

$$SO_3(g) + H_2O(l) \longrightarrow H_2SO_4(aq)$$

Manufactured in greater amounts than any other chemical, sulfuric acid is usually produced by the *contact process*. About 60% of the sulfuric acid manufactured in the United States is used to produce fertilizers from phosphate rock. The other 40% is used in lead storage batteries, in petroleum refining, in steel manufacturing, and for various other purposes in the chemical industry.

Because sulfuric acid has a high affinity for water, it is often used as a dehydrating agent. Gases that do not react with sulfuric acid, such as oxygen, nitrogen, and carbon dioxide, are often dried by bubbling them through concentrated solutions of the acid. Sulfuric acid is such a powerful dehydrating agent that it will remove hydrogen and oxygen from a substance in a 2:1 ratio even when the substance contains no molecular water. For example, concentrated sulfuric acid reacts vigorously with common table sugar (sucrose), leaving a charred mass of carbon (Fig. 18.24):

$$\underset{\text{Sucrose}}{C_{12}H_{22}O_{11}(s)} + 11H_2SO_4(conc) \longrightarrow 12C(s) + 11H_2SO_4 \cdot H_2O(l)$$

Figure 18.24
The reaction of H_2SO_4 with sucrose (on the left) to produce a blackened column of carbon (on the right).

18.13 | The Group 7A Elements

7A
F
Cl
Br
I
At

In our coverage of the representative elements, we have progressed from the groups of metallic elements (Groups 1A and 2A), through groups in which the lighter members are nonmetals and the heavier members are metals (Groups 3A, 4A, and 5A), to a group containing all nonmetals (Group 6A—although some might prefer to call polonium a metal). The Group 7A elements, the **halogens** (with the valence electron configuration ns^2np^5), are all nonmetals whose properties generally vary smoothly going down the group. The only notable exceptions are the unexpectedly low value for the electron affinity of fluorine and the unexpectedly small bond energy of the F_2 molecule (see Sec-

Samples of chlorine gas, liquid bromine, and solid iodine.

Table 18.17

Trends in Selected Physical Properties of the Group 7A Elements

Element	Electronegativity	Radius of X^- (pm)	$\mathscr{E}°$ (V) for $X_2 + 2e \rightarrow 2X^-$	Bond Energy of X_2 (kJ/mol)
Fluorine	4.0	136	2.87	154
Chlorine	3.2	181	1.36	239
Bromine	3.0	195	1.09	193
Iodine	2.7	216	0.54	149
Astatine	2.2	—	—	—

tion 18.1). Table 18.17 summarizes the trends in some physical properties of the halogens.

Because of their high reactivities, the halogens are not found as free elements in nature. Instead, they are found as halide ions (X^-) in various minerals and in seawater (Table 18.18).

Although astatine is a member of Group 7A, its chemistry is of no practical importance because all its known isotopes are radioactive. The longest-lived isotope, ^{210}At, has a half-life of only 8.3 hours.

The halogens, particularly fluorine, have very high electronegativity values (Table 18.17). They tend to form polar covalent bonds with other nonmetals and ionic bonds with metals in their lower oxidation states. When a metal ion is in a higher oxidation state, such as +3 or +4, the metal–halogen bonds are polar and covalent. For example, $TiCl_4$ and $SnCl_4$ are both covalent compounds that are liquids under normal conditions.

Hydrogen Halides

The hydrogen halides can be prepared by a reaction of the elements

$$H_2(g) + X_2(g) \longrightarrow 2HX(g)$$

This reaction occurs with explosive vigor when fluorine and hydrogen are mixed. On the other hand, hydrogen and chlorine can coexist with little apparent reaction for relatively long periods in the dark. However, ultraviolet light causes an explosively fast reaction, and this is the basis of a popular lecture demonstration, the "hydrogen–chlorine cannon." Bromine and iodine also react with hydrogen, but more slowly.

Table 18.18

Some Physical Properties, Sources, and Methods of Preparation of the Group 7A Elements

Element	Color and State	Percentage of Earth's Crust	Melting Point (°C)	Boiling Point (°C)	Source	Method of Preparation
Fluorine	Pale yellow gas	0.07	−220	−188	Fluorospar (CaF_2), cryolite (Na_3AlF_6), fluorapatite [$Ca_5(PO_4)_3F$]	Electrolysis of molten KHF_2
Chlorine	Yellow-green gas	0.14	−101	−34	Rock salt (NaCl), halite (NaCl), sylvite (KCl)	Electrolysis of aqueous NaCl
Bromine	Red-brown liquid	2.5×10^{-4}	−7.3	59	Seawater, brine wells	Oxidation of Br^- by Cl_2
Iodine	Violet-black solid	3×10^{-5}	113	184	Seaweed, brine wells	Oxidation of I^- by electrolysis or MnO_2

A candle burning in an atmosphere of $Cl_2(g)$. The exothermic reaction, which involves breaking C—C and C—H bonds in the wax and forming C—Cl bonds in their places, produces enough heat to make the gases in the region incandescent (a flame results).

Figure 18.25
The hydrogen bonding among HF molecules in liquid hydrogen fluoride.

Table 18.19

Some Physical Properties of the Hydrogen Halides

HX	Melting Point (°C)	Boiling Point (°C)	H—X Bond Energy (kJ/mol)
HF	−83	20	565
HCl	−114	−85	427
HBr	−87	−67	363
HI	−51	−35	295

Some physical properties of the hydrogen halides are listed in Table 18.19. Note the very high boiling point for hydrogen fluoride, which results from extensive hydrogen bonding among the very polar HF molecules (Fig. 18.25). Fluoride ion has such a high affinity for protons that in concentrated aqueous solutions of hydrogen fluoride, the ion $[F\text{-}\text{-}\text{-}H\text{-}\text{-}\text{-}F]^-$ exists, in which an H^+ ion is centered between two F^- ions.

When dissolved in water, the hydrogen halides behave as acids, and all except hydrogen fluoride are completely dissociated. Because water is a much stronger base than Cl^-, Br^-, or I^- ion, the acid strengths of HCl, HBr, and HI cannot be differentiated in water. However, in a less basic solvent, such as glacial (pure) acetic acid, the acids show different strengths:

$$H—I > H—Br > H—Cl \gg H—F$$

Strongest   Weakest
acid   acid

To see why hydrogen fluoride is the only weak acid in water among the HX molecules, let's consider the dissociation equilibrium,

$$HX(aq) \rightleftharpoons H^+(aq) + X^-(aq) \qquad \text{where} \qquad K_a = \frac{[H^+][X^-]}{[HX]}$$

from a thermodynamic point of view. Recall that acid strength is reflected by the magnitude of K_a—a small K_a value means a weak acid. Also recall that the value of an equilibrium constant is related to the standard free energy change for the reaction,

$$\Delta G° = -RT \ln(K)$$

As $\Delta G°$ becomes more negative, K becomes larger; a *decrease* in free energy favors a given reaction. As we saw in Chapter 10, free energy depends on enthalpy, entropy, and temperature. For a process at constant temperature,

$$\Delta G° = \Delta H° - T\Delta S°$$

Thus, to explain the various acid strengths of the hydrogen halides, we must focus on the factors that determine $\Delta H°$ and $\Delta S°$ for the acid dissociation reaction.

What energy terms are important in determining $\Delta H°$ for the dissociation of HX in water? (Keep in mind that large, positive contributions to the value of $\Delta H°$ will tend to make $\Delta G°$ more highly positive, K_a smaller, and the acid weaker.) One important factor is certainly the H—X bond strength. Note from Table 18.19 that the H—F bond is much stronger than the other H—X bonds. This factor tends to make HF a weaker acid than the others.

Another important contribution to $\Delta H°$ is the enthalpy of hydration (see Section 17.2) of X^- (Table 18.20). As we would expect, the smallest of the halide ions, F^-, has the most negative value—its hydration is the most exother-

Table 18.20

The Enthalpies and Entropies of Hydration for the Halide Ions

$X^-(g) \xrightarrow{H_2O} X^-(aq)$		
X^-	$\Delta H°$ (kJ/mol)	$\Delta S°$ (J/K mol)
F^-	−510	−159
Cl^-	−366	−96
Br^-	−334	−81
I^-	−291	−64

mic. This term favors the dissociation of HF into its ions more so than it does for the other HX molecules.

So far we have two conflicting factors: The large HF bond energy tends to make HF a weaker acid than the other hydrogen halides, but the enthalpy of hydration favors the dissociation of HF more than that of the others. When we compare data for HF and HCl, the difference in bond energy (138 kJ/mol) is slightly smaller than the difference in the enthalpies of hydration for the anions (144 kJ/mol). If these were the *only* important factors, HF should be a stronger acid than HCl because the large enthalpy of hydration of F^- more than compensates for the large HF bond strength.

As it turns out, the *deciding factor appears to be entropy.* Note from Table 18.20 that the entropy of hydration for F^- is much more negative than the entropy of hydration for the other halides because of the high degree of ordering that occurs as the water molecules associate with the small F^- ion. Remember that a negative change in entropy is unfavorable. Thus, although the enthalpy of hydration favors dissociation of HF, the *entropy* of hydration strongly opposes it.

When all these factors are taken into account, ΔG° for the dissociation of HF in water is positive; that is, K_a is small. In contrast, ΔG° for dissociation of the other HX molecules in water is negative (K_a is large). This example illustrates the complexity of the processes that occur in aqueous solutions and the importance of entropy effects in that medium.

In practical terms, **hydrochloric acid** is the most important of the **hydrohalic acids,** the aqueous solutions of the hydrogen halides. About 3 million tons of hydrochloric acid are produced annually for use in cleaning steel before galvanizing and in the manufacture of many other chemicals.

Hydrofluoric acid is used to etch glass by reacting with the silica in glass to form the volatile gas SiF_4:

$$SiO_2(s) + 4HF(aq) \longrightarrow SiF_4(g) + 2H_2O(l)$$

Oxyacids and Oxyanions

All the halogens except fluorine combine with various numbers of oxygen atoms to form a series of oxyacids, as shown in Table 18.21. The strengths of these acids vary in direct proportion to the number of oxygen atoms attached to the halogen, with the acid strength increasing as more oxygens are added.

The only member of the chlorine series that has been obtained in the pure state is *perchloric acid* ($HOClO_3$), a strong acid and a powerful oxidizing agent. Because perchloric acid reacts explosively with many organic materials, it must be handled with great caution. The other oxyacids of chlorine are

Table 18.21

The Known Oxyacids of the Halogens

Oxidation State of Halogen	Fluorine	Chlorine	Bromine	Iodine*	General Name of Acids	General Name of Salts
+1	HOF†	HOCl	HOBr	HOI	Hypohalous acid	Hypohalites, MOX
+3	‡	HOClO	‡	‡	Halous acid	Halites, MXO_2
+5	‡	$HOClO_2$	$HOBrO_2$	$HOIO_2$	Halic acid	Halates, MXO_3
+7	‡	$HOClO_3$	$HOBrO_3$	$HOIO_3$	Perhalic acid	Perhalates, MXO_4

*Iodine also forms $H_4I_2O_9$ (mesodiperiodic acid) and H_5IO_6 (paraperiodic acid).

†HOF oxidation state is best represented as -1.

‡Compound is unknown.

Figure 18.26
The structures of the oxychloro anions.

| Hypochlorite ion, OCl^- Linear | Chlorite ion, ClO_2^- Bent | Chlorate ion, ClO_3^- Pyramidal | Perchlorate ion, ClO_4^- Tetrahedral |

known only in solution, although salts containing their anions are well known (Fig. 18.26).

Hypochlorous acid (HOCl) is formed when chlorine gas is dissolved in cold water:

$$Cl_2(aq) + H_2O(l) \rightleftharpoons HOCl(aq) + H^+(aq) + Cl^-(aq)$$

Note that in this reaction chlorine is both oxidized (from 0 in Cl_2 to +1 in HOCl) and reduced (from 0 in Cl_2 to −1 in Cl^-). Such a reaction, *in which a given element is both oxidized and reduced,* is called a **disproportionation reaction.** Hypochlorous acid and its salts are strong oxidizing agents; their solutions are widely used as household bleaches and disinfectants.

Chlorate salts, such as $KClO_3$, are also strong oxidizing agents and are used as weed killers and as oxidizers in fireworks (see Chapter 12) and explosives.

Fluorine forms only one oxyacid, hypofluorous acid (HOF), but it forms at least two oxides. When fluorine gas is bubbled into a dilute solution of sodium hydroxide, the compound *oxygen difluoride* (OF_2) is formed:

The name for OF_2 is oxygen difluoride rather than difluorine oxide because fluorine has a higher electronegativity than oxygen and thus is named as the anion.

$$4F_2(g) + 3H_2O(l) \longrightarrow 6HF(aq) + OF_2(g) + O_2(g)$$

Oxygen difluoride is a pale yellow gas (bp = −145°C) that is a strong oxidizing agent. The oxide *dioxygen difluoride* (O_2F_2) is an orange solid that can be prepared by an electric discharge in an equimolar mixture of fluorine and oxygen gases:

$$F_2(g) + O_2(g) \xrightarrow[\text{discharge}]{\text{Electric}} O_2F_2(s)$$

18.14 | The Group 8A Elements

The Group 8A elements, the **noble gases,** are characterized by filled s and p valence orbitals (electron configurations of $2s^2$ for helium and ns^2np^6 for the others). Because of their completed valence shells, these elements are very unreactive. In fact, no noble gas compounds were known 50 years ago. Selected properties of the Group 8A elements are summarized in Table 18.22.

Helium was identified by its characteristic emission spectrum as a component of the sun before it was found on earth. The major sources of helium on earth are natural gas deposits, where helium was formed from the α-particle decay of radioactive elements. The α particle is a helium nucleus that can easily pick up electrons from the environment to form a helium atom. Although he-

Automatic Sunglasses

Sunglasses can be troublesome. It seems they are always getting lost or sat on. One solution to this problem for people who wear glasses is photochromic glass—glass that darkens in response to intense light. Recall that glass is a complex, noncrystalline material that is composed of polymeric silicates (see Chapter 16). Of course, glass transmits visible light—its transparency is its most useful property.

Glass can be made photochromic by adding tiny silver chloride crystals, which get trapped in the glass matrix as the glass solidifies. Silver chloride has the unusual property of darkening when struck by light—the property that makes the silver halide salts so useful for photographic films. This darkening occurs because light causes an electron transfer from Cl^- to Ag^+ in the silver chloride crystal, forming a silver atom and a chlorine atom. The silver atoms formed in this way tend to migrate to the surface of the silver chloride crystal, where they aggregate to form a tiny crystal of silver metal, which is opaque to light.

In photography the image defined by the grains of silver is fixed by chemical treatment so that it remains permanent. However, in photochromic glass this process must be reversible—the glass must become fully transparent again when the person goes back indoors. The secret to the reversibility of photochromic glass is the presence of Cu^+ ions. The added Cu^+ ions serve two important functions. First, they reduce the Cl atoms formed in the light-induced reaction. This prevents them from escaping from the crystal:

$$Ag^+ + Cl^- \xrightarrow{h\nu} Ag + Cl$$
$$Cl + Cu^+ \longrightarrow Cu^{2+} + Cl^-$$

Second, when the exposure to intense light ends (the person goes indoors), the Cu^{2+} ions migrate to the surface of the silver chloride crystal, where they accept electrons from silver atoms as the tiny crystal of silver atoms disintegrates:

$$Cu^{2+} + Ag \longrightarrow Cu^+ + Ag^+$$

The Ag^+ ions that are re-formed in this way then return to their places in the silver chloride crystal, making the glass transparent once again.

Although these glass lenses still are produced, the market for glass has decreased significantly since the development of plastic photochromic lenses in the 1990s.

The chemistry of plastic photochromic lenses is completely different from that of glass lenses. The photochromic process in plastic uses organic dyes that change structure when they absorb light. For example, the dye naphthopyran rearranges as follows when it absorbs UV light:

Absorbs UV light

Absorbs UV and visible light

Note that the bond shown in red breaks when the molecule absorbs UV light, causing rearrangement to a molecule that absorbs visible light, which in turn causes the lens to darken. Although the dyes are central to the reversible darkening process, they do not work unless they are incorporated in special ways in the plastic lenses. For example, for lenses composed of polycarbonate, the dye is sandwiched between layers of polyurethane on the surface of the lens.

One drawback of self-darkening lenses is that they do not work well inside automobiles because automotive windshields are constructed with materials that are very effective UV light absorbers. Research is underway to find dyes that will cause darkening by absorbing more into the visible region of the spectrum to solve this problem. Until then, old-fashioned sunglasses will be required for driving.

Table 18.22

Selected Properties of Group 8A Elements

Element	Melting Point (°C)	Boiling Point (°C)	Atmospheric Abundance (% by volume)	Examples of Compounds
Helium	−270	−269	5×10^{-4}	None
Neon	−249	−246	1×10^{-3}	None
Argon	−189	−186	9×10^{-1}	HArF
Krypton	−157	−153	1×10^{-4}	KrF_2
Xenon	−112	−107	9×10^{-6}	XeF_4, XeO_3, XeF_6

Neon signmaker and artist Jess Baird shows off a few of the items he has made in his Weatherford, Texas, shop.

lium forms no compounds, it is an important substance that is used as a coolant, as a pressurizing gas for rocket fuels, as a diluent in the gases used for deep-sea diving and spaceship atmospheres, and as the gas in lighter-than-air airships (blimps).

Like helium, *neon* forms no compounds, but it is a very useful element. For example, neon is widely used in luminescent lighting (neon signs). *Argon,* which recently has been shown to form chemical bonds under special circumstances, is used to provide the noncorrosive atmosphere in incandescent light bulbs, which prolongs the life of the tungsten filament.

Krypton and *xenon* have been observed to form many stable chemical compounds. The first of these was prepared in 1962 by Neil Bartlett, an English chemist who made an ionic compound that he thought had the formula $XePtF_6$. Subsequent studies indicated that the compound might be better represented as $XeFPtF_6$ and contains the XeF^+ and PtF_6^- ions.

Less than a year after Bartlett's report, a group at Argonne National Laboratory near Chicago prepared xenon tetrafluoride by reacting xenon and fluorine gases in a nickel reaction vessel at 400°C and 6 atm:

$$Xe(g) + 2F_2(g) \longrightarrow XeF_4(s)$$

Figure 18.27
The structures of several known xenon compounds.

XeF₂ Linear   XeO₂F₂ Distorted tetrahedron   XeO₃ Pyramidal   XeO₄ Tetrahedral

XeF₄ Square planar   XeO₃F₂ Trigonal bipyramid   XeO₂F₄ Octahedral

Xenon tetrafluoride forms stable colorless crystals. Two other xenon fluorides, XeF_2 and XeF_6, were synthesized by the group at Argonne, and a highly explosive xenon oxide (XeO_3) was also found. The xenon fluorides react with water to form hydrogen fluoride and oxycompounds. For example:

$$XeF_6(s) + 3H_2O(l) \longrightarrow XeO_3(aq) + 6HF(aq)$$

$$XeF_6(s) + H_2O(l) \longrightarrow XeOF_4(aq) + 2HF(g)$$

In the past 35 years, other xenon compounds have been prepared. Examples are XeO_4 (explosive), $XeOF_4$, $XeOF_2$, and XeO_3F_2. These compounds contain discrete molecules with covalent bonds between the xenon atom and the other atoms. A few compounds of krypton, such as KrF_2 and KrF_4, have also been observed. The structures of several known xenon compounds are shown in Fig. 18.27. Radon also has been shown to form compounds similar to those of xenon and krypton.

Key Terms

Section 18.1
representative elements
transition metals
lanthanides
actinides
metalloids (semimetals)
metallurgy
liquefaction

Section 18.2
alkali metals

Section 18.3
hydride
ionic (saltlike) hydride
covalent hydride
metallic (interstitial) hydride

Section 18.4
alkaline earth metals
hard water
ion exchange
ion exchange resin

Section 18.5
boranes

Section 18.8
Haber process
nitrogen fixation
nitrogen-fixing bacteria
denitrification
nitrogen cycle
ammonia
hydrazine
nitric acid
Ostwald process

Section 18.9
phosphoric (orthophosphoric)
    acid
phosphorous acid
superphosphate of lime

For Review

⊙WL and **go Chemistry**
Sign in at **www.cengage.com/owl** to:
• View tutorials and simulations, develop problem-solving skills, and complete online homework assigned by your professor.
• Download Go Chemistry mini lecture modules for quick review and exam prep from OWL (or purchase them at **www.cengagebrain.com**)

Representative elements
■ Chemical properties are determined by their s and p valence-electron configurations
■ Metallic character increases going down the group
■ The properties of the first element in a group usually differ most from the properties of the other elements in the group due to a significant difference in size
   ■ In Group 1A, hydrogen is a nonmetal and the other members of the group are active metals
   ■ The first member of a group forms the strongest π bonds, causing nitrogen and oxygen to exist as N_2 and O_2 molecules

Elemental abundances on earth
■ Oxygen is the most abundant element, followed by silicon
■ The most abundant metals are aluminum and iron, which are found as ores

Group 1A elements (alkali metals)
■ Have valence configuration ns^1
■ Except for hydrogen, readily lose one electron to form M^+ ions in their compounds with nonmetals
■ React vigorously with water to form M^+ and OH^- ions and hydrogen gas
■ Form a series of oxides of the types M_2O (oxide), M_2O_2 (peroxide), and MO_2 (superoxide)
   ■ Not all metals form all types of oxide compounds
■ Hydrogen forms covalent compounds with nonmetals
■ With very active metals, hydrogen forms hydrides that contain the H^- ion

Group 2A (alkaline earth metals)
■ Have valence configuration ns^2
■ React less violently with water than alkali metals

- The heavier alkaline earth metals form nitrides and hydrides
- Hard water contains Ca^{2+} and Mg^{2+} ions
  - Form precipitates with soap
  - Usually removed by ion-exchange resins that replace the Ca^{2+} and Mg^{2+} ions with Na^+

Group 3A
- Have valence configuration ns^2np^1
- Show increasing metallic character going down the group
- Boron is a nonmetal that forms many types of covalent compounds, including boranes, which are highly electron-deficient and thus are very reactive
- The metals aluminum, gallium, and indium show some covalent tendencies

Group 4A
- Have valence configuration ns^2np^2
- Lighter members are nonmetals; heavier members are metals
  - All group members can form covalent bonds to nonmetals
- Carbon forms a huge variety of compounds, most of which are classified as organic compounds

Group 5A
- Elements show a wide variety of chemical properties
  - Nitrogen and phosphorus are nonmetals
  - Antimony and bismuth tend to be metallic, although no ionic compounds containing Sb^{5+} and Bi^{5+} are known; the compounds containing Sb(V) and Bi(V) are molecular rather than ionic
  - All group members except N form molecules with five covalent bonds
  - The ability to form π bonds decreases dramatically after N
- Chemistry of nitrogen
  - Most nitrogen-containing compounds decompose exothermically, forming the very stable N_2 molecule, which explains the power of nitrogen-based explosives
  - The nitrogen cycle, which consists of a series of steps, shows how nitrogen is cycled in the natural environment
  - Nitrogen fixation changes the N_2 in air into compounds useful to plants
    - The Haber process is a synthetic method of nitrogen fixation
    - In the natural world, nitrogen fixation occurs through nitrogen-fixing bacteria in the root nodules of certain plants and through lightning in the atmosphere
  - Ammonia is the most important hydride of nitrogen
    - Contains pyramidal NH_3 molecules
    - Widely used as a fertilizer
  - Hydrazine (N_2H_4) is a powerful reducing agent
  - Nitrogen forms a series of oxides including N_2O, NO, NO_2, and N_2O_5
  - Nitric acid (HNO_3) is a very important strong acid manufactured by the Ostwald process
- Chemistry of phosphorus
  - Exists in three elemental forms: white (contains P_4 molecules), red, and black
  - Phosphine (PH_3) has bond angles close to 90 degrees
  - Phosphorus forms oxides including P_4O_6 and P_4O_{10} (which dissolves in water to form phosphoric acid, H_3PO_4)

Group 6A
- Metallic character increases going down the group but no element behaves as a typical metal
- The lighter members tend to gain two electrons to form X^{2-} ions in compounds with metals
- Chemistry of oxygen
  - Elemental forms are O_2 and O_3
  - Oxygen forms a wide variety of oxides
  - O_2 and especially O_3 are powerful oxidizing agents
- Chemistry of sulfur
  - The elemental forms are called rhombic and monoclinic sulfur, both of which contain S_8 molecules
  - The most important oxides are SO_2 (which forms H_2SO_3 in water) and SO_3 (which forms H_2SO_4 in water)
  - Sulfur forms a wide variety of compounds in which it shows the oxidation states $+6, +4, +2, 0,$ and -2

Group 7A (halogens)
- All nonmetals
- Form hydrides of the type HX that behave as strong acids in water except for HF, which is a weak acid
- The oxyacids of the halogens become stronger as more oxygen atoms are present
- The interhalogens contain two or more different halogens

Group 8A (noble gases)
- All elements are monatomic gases and are generally very unreactive
- The heavier elements form compounds with electronegative elements such as fluorine and oxygen

Exercises

OWL Interactive versions of these problems may be assigned in OWL.

A blue exercise number indicates that the answer to that exercise appears at the back of this book and a solution appears in the *Solutions Guide*.

Group 1A Elements

1. Although the earth was formed from the same interstellar material as the sun, there is little hydrogen in the earth's atmosphere. How can you explain this?

2. Hydrogen is produced commercially by the reaction of methane with steam:

$$CH_4(g) + H_2O(g) \rightleftharpoons CO(g) + 3H_2(g)$$

   a. Calculate $\Delta H°$ and $\Delta S°$ for this reaction (use the data in Appendix 4).
   b. What temperatures will favor product formation assuming standard conditions and assuming that $\Delta H°$ and $\Delta S°$ do not depend on temperature?

3. The major industrial use of hydrogen is in the production of ammonia by the Haber process:

$$3H_2(g) + N_2(g) \longrightarrow 2NH_3(g)$$

   a. Using data from Appendix 4, calculate $\Delta H°$, $\Delta S°$, and $\Delta G°$ for the Haber process reaction.
   b. Is this reaction spontaneous at standard conditions?
   c. At what temperatures is the reaction spontaneous at standard conditions? Assume that $\Delta H°$ and $\Delta S°$ do not depend on temperature.

4. List two major industrial uses of hydrogen.

5. Label the following hydrides as ionic, covalent, or interstitial, and support your answer. Note: The light blue atoms are hydrogen atoms.

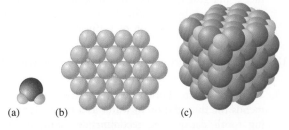

(a)   (b)   (c)

6. Many lithium salts are hygroscopic (absorb water), but the corresponding salts of the other alkali metals are not. Why are lithium salts different from the others?

7. What is the valence electron configuration for the alkali metals? List some common properties of alkali metals. How are the pure metals prepared?

8. What will be the atomic number of the next alkali metal to be discovered? How would you expect the physical properties of the next alkali metal to compare with the properties of the other alkali metals summarized in Table 18.4?

9. What evidence supports putting hydrogen in Group 1A of the periodic table? In some periodic tables hydrogen is listed separately from all of the groups. In what ways is hydrogen unlike a Group 1A element?

10. The electrolysis of aqueous sodium chloride (brine) is an important industrial process for the production of chlorine and sodium hydroxide. In fact, this process is the second largest consumer of electricity in the United States, after the production of aluminum. Write a balanced equation for the electrolysis of aqueous sodium chloride (hydrogen gas is also produced).

11. Write balanced equations describing the reaction of lithium metal with each of the following: O_2, S_8, Cl_2, P_4, H_2, H_2O, and HCl.

Group 2A Elements

12. What is the valence electron configuration for alkaline earth metals? List some common properties of alkaline earth metals. How are alkaline earth metals prepared?

13. How long will it take to produce 1.00×10^3 kg of magnesium metal by the electrolysis of molten magnesium chloride using a current of 5.00×10^4 A?

14. Suppose 10.00 g of an alkaline earth metal reacts with 10.0 L of water to produce 6.10 L of hydrogen gas at 1.00 atm and 25°C. Identify the metal, and determine the pH of the solution.

15. What ions are found in hard water? What happens when water is "softened"?

16. Write balanced equations describing the reaction of Sr with each of the following: O_2, S_8, Cl_2, P_4, H_2, H_2O, and HCl.

17. One harmful effect of acid rain is the deterioration of structures and statues made of marble or limestone, both of which are essentially calcium carbonate. The reaction of calcium carbonate with sulfuric acid yields carbon dioxide, water, and calcium sulfate. Because calcium sulfate is marginally soluble in water, part of the object is washed away by the rain. Write a balanced chemical equation for the reaction of sulfuric acid with calcium carbonate.

18. What mass of barium is produced when molten $BaCl_2$ is electrolyzed by a current of 2.50×10^5 A for 6.00 h?

19. The United States Public Health Service (USPHS) recommends the fluoridation of water as a means for preventing tooth decay. The recommended concentration is 1 mg F^-/L. The presence of calcium ions in hard water can precipitate the added fluoride. What is the maximum molarity of calcium ions in hard water if the fluoride concentration is at the USPHS recommended level? (K_{sp} for $CaF_2 = 4.0 \times 10^{-11}$.)

20. Slaked lime [$Ca(OH)_2$] is used to soften hard water by removing calcium ions from hard water through the reaction

$$Ca(OH)_2(aq) + Ca^{2+}(aq) + 2HCO_3^-(aq) \longrightarrow 2CaCO_3(s) + 2H_2O(l)$$

Although $CaCO_3(s)$ is considered insoluble, some of it does dissolve in aqueous solutions. Calculate the molar solubility of $CaCO_3$ in water ($K_{sp} = 8.7 \times 10^{-9}$).

Group 3A Elements

21. What is the valence electron configuration for the Group 3A elements? How does metallic character change as one goes down this group? How are boron and aluminum different?

22. What are three-centered bonds?

23. Boron hydrides were once evaluated for possible use as rocket fuels. Complete and balance the following equation:

$$B_2H_6 + O_2 \longrightarrow B(OH)_3$$

24. Consider element 113. What is the expected electron configuration for element 113? What oxidation states would be exhibited by element 113 in its compounds?

25. Write equations describing the reactions of Ga with each of the following: F_2, O_2, S_8, and HCl.

26. Thallium and indium form +1 and +3 oxidation states when in compounds. Predict the formulas of the possible compounds between thallium and oxygen and between indium and chlorine. Name the compounds.

Group 4A Elements

27. What is the valence electron configuration for Group 4A elements? Group 4A contains two of the most important elements on earth. What are they, and why are they so important? How does metallic character change as one goes down Group 4A?

28. Discuss the importance of the C—C and Si—Si bond strengths and of π bonding to the properties of carbon and silicon.

29. The following illustration shows the orbitals used to form the bonds in carbon dioxide.

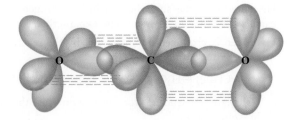

Each color represents a different orbital. Label each orbital, draw the Lewis structure for carbon dioxide, and explain how the localized electron model describes the bonding in CO_2.

30. In addition to CO_2, two additional stable oxides of carbon form. The space filling models for CO_2 and the other two stable oxides are:

What are the formulas for the two additional stable oxides of carbon? Explain the bonding in each of these forms using the localized electron model.

31. From the information on the temperature stability of white and gray tin given in this chapter, which form would you expect to have the more ordered structure (have the smaller positional probability)?

32. Silicon is produced for the chemical and electronics industries by the following reactions. Give the balanced equation for each reaction.
    a. $SiO_2(s) + C(s) \longrightarrow Si(s) + CO(g)$
    b. Silicon tetrachloride is reacted with very pure magnesium, producing silicon and magnesium chloride.
    c. $Na_2SiF_6(s) + Na(s) \longrightarrow Si(s) + NaF(s)$

33. Tin forms compounds in the +2 and +4 oxidation states. Therefore, when tin reacts with fluorine, two products are possible. Write balanced equations for the production of the two tin halide compounds and name them.

34. Write equations describing the reactions of Sn with each of the following: Cl_2, O_2, and HCl.

35. The compound Pb_3O_4 (red lead) contains a mixture of lead(II) and lead(IV) oxidation states. What is the mole ratio of lead(II) to lead(IV) in Pb_3O_4?

36. The resistivity (a measure of electrical resistance) of graphite is $(0.4 \text{ to } 5.0) \times 10^{-4}$ ohm · cm in the basal plane. (The basal plane is the plane of the six-membered rings of carbon atoms.) The resistivity is 0.2 to 1.0 ohm · cm along the axis perpendicular to the plane. The resistivity of diamond is 10^{14} to 10^{16} ohm · cm and is independent of direction. How can you account for this behavior in terms of the structures of graphite and diamond?

Group 5A Elements

37. The oxyanion of nitrogen in which it has the highest oxidation state is the nitrate ion (NO_3^-). The corresponding oxyanion of phosphorus is PO_4^{3-}. The NO_4^{3-} ion is known but is not very stable. The PO_3^- ion is not known. Account for these differences in terms of the bonding in the four anions.

38. Using data from Appendix 4, calculate $\Delta H°$, $\Delta S°$, and $\Delta G°$ for the reaction

    $$N_2(g) + O_2(g) \longrightarrow 2NO(g)$$

    Why does the NO formed in an automobile engine not readily decompose back to N_2 and O_2 in the atmosphere?

39. Table 18.14 lists some common nitrogen compounds having oxidation states ranging from −3 to +5. Rationalize this spread in oxidation states.

40. What is nitrogen fixation? Give some examples of nitrogen fixation.

41. Elemental nitrogen exists as N_2, whereas in the gas phase the elements phosphorus, arsenic, and antimony consist of P_4, As_4, and Sb_4 molecules, respectively. Give a possible reason for this difference between N_2 and the other Group 5A elements.

42. The compound NF_3 is quite stable, but NCl_3 is very unstable (NCl_3 was first synthesized in 1811 by P. L. Dulong, who lost three fingers and an eye studying its properties). The compounds NBr_3 and NI_3 are unknown, although the explosive $NI_3 \cdot NH_3$ is known. How do you account for the instability of these halides of nitrogen?

43. Lewis structures can be used to understand why some molecules react in certain ways. Write the Lewis structure for the reactants and products in the following reactions.
    a. Nitrogen dioxide dimerizes to produce dinitrogen tetroxide.
    b. Boron trifluoride accepts a pair of electrons from ammonia, forming BF_3NH_3.

    Give a possible explanation for why these two reactions occur.

44. Use bond energies (Table 13.6) to show that the preferred products for the decomposition of N_2O_3 are NO_2 and NO rather than O_2 and N_2O. (The N—O single-bond energy is 201 kJ/mol.) (*Hint:* Consider the reaction kinetics.)

45. Ammonia is produced by the Haber process, in which nitrogen and hydrogen are reacted directly using an iron mesh impregnated with oxides as a catalyst. For the reaction

    $$N_2(g) + 3H_2(g) \rightleftharpoons 2NH_3(g)$$

    equilibrium constants (K_p values) as a function of temperature are

300°C,	4.34×10^{-3}
500°C,	1.45×10^{-5}
600°C,	2.25×10^{-6}

    Is the reaction exothermic or endothermic?

46. The synthesis of ammonia gas from nitrogen gas and hydrogen gas represents a classic case in which a knowledge of kinetics and equilibrium was used to make a desired chemical reaction economically feasible. Explain how each of the following conditions helps to maximize the yield of ammonia.
    a. running the reaction at an elevated temperature
    b. removing the ammonia from the reaction mixture as it forms
    c. using a catalyst
    d. running the reaction at high pressure

47. Write an equation for the reaction of hydrazine with fluorine gas to produce nitrogen gas and hydrogen fluoride gas. Estimate ΔH for this reaction, using bond energies from Table 13.6.

48. In each of the following pairs of substances, one is stable and known, whereas the other is unstable. For each pair, choose the stable substance, and explain why the other compound is unstable.
    a. NF_5 or PF_5 b. AsF_5 or AsI_5 c. NF_3 or NBr_3

49. Write balanced equations for the reactions described in Table 18.13 for the production of Bi and Sb.

50. Phosphoric acid (H_3PO_4) is a triprotic acid, phosphorous acid (H_3PO_3) is a diprotic acid, and hypophosphorous acid (H_3PO_2) is a monoprotic acid. Explain this phenomenon.

51. Trisodium phosphate (TSP) is an effective grease remover. Like many cleaners, TSP acts as a base in water. Write a balanced equation to account for this basic behavior.

52. White phosphorus is much more reactive than black or red phosphorus. Explain.

53. Arsenic reacts with oxygen to form oxides analogous to the phosphorus oxides. These arsenic oxides react with water similarly to the phosphorus oxides. Write balanced chemical equations describing the reaction of arsenic with oxygen and the reaction of the oxides with water.

54. Compare the description of the localized electron model (Lewis structure) with that of the molecular orbital model for the bonding in NO, NO^+, and NO^-. Account for any discrepancies between the two models.

55. Many oxides of nitrogen have positive values for the standard free energy of formation. Using NO as an example, explain why this is the case.

56. Draw Lewis structures for the $AsCl_4^+$ and $AsCl_6^-$ ions. What type of reaction (acid–base, oxidation–reduction, or the like) is the following?

$$2AsCl_5(g) \longrightarrow AsCl_4AsCl_6(s)$$

57. In many natural waters, nitrogen and phosphorus are the least abundant nutrients available for plant life. Some waters that become polluted from agricultural runoff or municipal sewage become infested with algae. The algae flourish, and fish life dies off as a result. Describe how these events are chemically related.

58. Nitric acid is produced commercially by the Ostwald process, represented by the following equations:

$$4NH_3(g) + 5O_2(g) \longrightarrow 4NO(g) + 6H_2O(g)$$

$$2NO(g) + O_2(g) \longrightarrow 2NO_2(g)$$

$$3NO_2(g) + H_2O(l) \longrightarrow 2HNO_3(aq) + NO(g)$$

What mass of NH_3 must be used to produce 1.0×10^6 kg HNO_3 by the Ostwald process? Assume 100% yield in each reaction, and assume that the NO produced in the third step is not recycled.

59. The space shuttle orbiter utilizes the oxidation of methylhydrazine by dinitrogen tetroxide for propulsion:

$$4N_2H_3CH_3(l) + 5N_2O_4(l) \longrightarrow$$
$$12H_2O(g) + 9N_2(g) + 4CO_2(g)$$

Calculate $\Delta H°$ for this reaction using data in Appendix 4.

60. How is phosphine's (PH_3) structure different from that of ammonia?

61. Ammonia forms hydrogen-bonding intermolecular forces resulting in an unusually high boiling point for a substance with the small size of NH_3. Can hydrazine (N_2H_4) also form hydrogen-bonding interactions?

Group 6A Elements

62. What is the valence electron configuration of Group 6A elements? What are some property differences between oxygen and polonium?

63. What are the Lewis structures for the two allotropic forms of oxygen? How can the paramagnetism of O_2 be explained using the molecular orbital model? What are the molecular structure and the bond angles in ozone?

64. Use bond energies to estimate the maximum wavelength of light that will cause the reaction

$$O_3 \xrightarrow{h\nu} O_2 + O$$

65. Ozone is desirable in the upper atmosphere but undesirable in the lower atmosphere. A dictionary states that ozone has the scent of a spring thunderstorm. How can these seemingly conflicting statements be reconciled in terms of the chemical properties of ozone?

66. Ozone is a possible replacement for chlorine in municipal water purification. Unlike chlorine, virtually no ozone remains after treatment. This has good and bad consequences. Explain.

67. Sulfur forms a wide variety of compounds in which it has +6, +4, +2, 0, and −2 oxidation states. Give examples of sulfur compounds having each of these oxidation states.

68. In large doses, selenium is toxic. However, in moderate intake, selenium is a physiologically important element. How is selenium physiologically important?

69. Write a balanced equation describing the reduction of H_2SeO_4 by SO_2 to produce selenium.

Group 7A Elements

70. What is the valence electron configuration of the halogens? Why do the boiling points and melting points of the halogens increase steadily from F_2 to I_2?

71. Draw the Lewis structure of O_2F_2. Assign oxidation states and formal charges to the atoms in O_2F_2. The compound O_2F_2 is a vigorous and potent oxidizing and fluorinating agent. Are oxidation states or formal charges more useful in accounting for these properties of O_2F_2?

72. The oxidation states of the halogens vary from −1 to +7. Identify compounds of chlorine that have −1, +1, +3, +5, and +7 oxidation states. How does the oxyacid strength of the halogens vary as the number of oxygens in the formula increases?

73. Give two reasons why F_2 is the most reactive of the halogens.

74. Explain why HF is a weak acid, whereas HCl, HBr, and HI are all strong acids.

75. Hydrazine is somewhat toxic. Use the following half-reactions to explain why household bleach (highly alkaline solutions of sodium hypochlorite) should not be

mixed with household ammonia or glass cleansers that contain ammonia.

$$ClO^- + H_2O + 2e^- \longrightarrow 2OH^- + Cl^-$$
$$\mathscr{E}° = 0.90 \text{ V}$$

$$N_2H_4 + 2H_2O + 2e^- \longrightarrow 2NH_3 + 2OH^-$$
$$\mathscr{E}° = -0.10 \text{ V}$$

76. What is a disproportionation reaction? Use the following reduction potentials,

$$ClO_3^- + 3H^+ + 2e^- \longrightarrow HClO_2 + H_2O$$
$$\mathscr{E}° = 1.21 \text{ V}$$

$$HClO_2 + 2H^+ + 2e^- \longrightarrow HClO + H_2O$$
$$\mathscr{E}° = 1.65 \text{ V}$$

to predict whether $HClO_2$ will disproportionate.

77. Photogray lenses contain small embedded crystals of solid silver chloride. Silver chloride is light-sensitive because of the reaction

$$AgCl(s) \xrightarrow{h\nu} Ag(s) + Cl(s)$$

Small particles of metallic silver cause the lenses to darken. In the lenses this process is reversible. When the light is removed, the reverse reaction occurs. However, when pure white silver chloride is exposed to sunlight, it darkens; the reverse reaction does not occur in the dark.
   a. How do you explain this difference?
   b. Photogray lenses do become permanently dark in time. How do you account for this?

Group 8A Elements

78. What special property of the noble gases makes them unreactive? The boiling points and melting points of the noble gases increase steadily from He to Xe. Explain.

79. Although He is the second most abundant element in the universe, it is very rare on earth. Why?

80. The noble gases were among the latest elements discovered; their existence was not predicted by Mendeleev when he published his first periodic table. Explain. In chemistry textbooks written before 1962, the noble gases were referred to as the inert gases. Why do we no longer use the term *inert gases*?

81. Using the data in Table 18.22, calculate the mass of argon at 25°C and 1.0 atm in a room 10.0 m × 10.0 m × 10.0 m. How many Ar atoms are in this room? How many Ar atoms do you inhale in one breath (approximately 2 L) of air at 25°C and 1.0 atm? Argon gas is inert, so it poses no serious health risks. However, if significant amounts of radon are inhaled into the lungs, lung cancer is a possible result. Explain the health risk differences between argon gas and radon gas.

82. For the structures of the xenon compounds in Fig. 18.27, give the bond angles exhibited and the hybridization of the central atom in each compound.

83. There is evidence that radon reacts with fluorine to form compounds similar to those formed by xenon and fluorine. Predict the formulas of these RnF_x compounds. Why is the chemistry of radon difficult to study?

Additional Exercises

84. What are the two most abundant elements by mass in the earth's crust, oceans, and atmosphere? Does this make sense? Why? What are the four most abundant elements by mass in the human body? Does this make sense? Why?

85. In most compounds the solid phase is denser than the liquid phase. Why isn't this true for water?

86. Diagonal relationships in the periodic table exist in addition to the vertical relationships. For example, Be and Al are similar in some of their properties, as are B and Si. Rationalize why these diagonal relationships hold for properties such as size, ionization energy, and electron affinity.

87. In the 1950s and 1960s, several nations conducted tests of nuclear warheads in the atmosphere. It was customary, following each test, to monitor the concentration of strontium-90 (a radioactive isotope of strontium) in milk. Why would strontium-90 tend to accumulate in milk?

88. Calculate the pH of a 0.050 *M* $Al(NO_3)_3$ solution. The K_a value for $Al(H_2O)_6^{3+}$ is 1.4×10^{-5}.

89. The compound with the formula TlI_3 is a black solid. Given the following standard reduction potentials,

$$Tl^{3+} + 2e^- \longrightarrow Tl^+ \quad \mathscr{E}° = +1.25 \text{ V}$$
$$I_3^- + 2e^- \longrightarrow 3I^- \quad \mathscr{E}° = +0.55 \text{ V}$$

would you formulate this compound as thallium(III) iodide or thallium(I) triiodide?

90. Atomic size seems to play an important role in explaining some of the differences between the first element in a group and the subsequent group elements. Explain.

91. The inert pair effect is sometimes used to explain the tendency of heavier members of Group 3A to exhibit +1 and +3 oxidation states. What does the inert pair effect reference? (*Hint:* Consider the valence electron configuration for Group 3A elements.)

92. How could you determine experimentally whether the compound Ga_2Cl_4 contains two gallium(II) ions or one gallium(I) ion and one gallium(III) ion? (*Hint:* Consider the electron configurations of the three possible ions.)

93. It takes 15 kWh (kilowatt-hours) of electrical energy to produce 1.0 kg of aluminum metal from aluminum oxide by the Hall–Heroult process. Compare this to the amount of energy necessary to melt 1.0 kg of aluminum metal. Why is it economically feasible to recycle aluminum cans? [The enthalpy of fusion for aluminum metal is 10.7 kJ/mol (1 W = 1 J/s).]

94. Reference Table 18.5, and give examples of the three types of alkali metal oxides that form. How do they differ?

95. Why are the tin(IV) halides more volatile than the tin(II) halides?

96. Beryllium shows some covalent characteristics in some of its compounds, unlike the other alkaline earth halides. Give a possible explanation for this phenomenon.

97. One reason suggested for the instability of long chains of silicon atoms is that the decomposition involves the transition state shown below:

$$
\begin{array}{cc}
H & H \\
| & | \\
H-Si-Si-H & \longrightarrow \\
| & | \\
H & H
\end{array}
$$

$$\longrightarrow \quad SiH_4 + \;:SiH_2$$

The activation energy for such a process is 210 kJ/mol, which is less than either the Si—Si or the Si—H bond energy. Why would a similar mechanism not be expected to be very important in the decomposition of long carbon chains?

98. Many structures of phosphorus- and sulfur-containing compounds are drawn with some P=O and P=S bonds. These bonds are not the typical π bonds we've considered, which involve the overlap of two *p* orbitals. They result instead from the overlap of a *d* orbital on the phosphorus or sulfur atom with a *p* orbital on oxygen. This type of π bonding is sometimes used as an explanation for why H_3PO_3 has the first structure below rather than the second:

$$
\begin{array}{cc}
O & OH \\
\parallel & | \\
H-P-OH & HO-P: \\
| & | \\
OH & OH
\end{array}
$$

Draw a picture showing how a *d* orbital and a *p* orbital overlap to form a π bond.

99. The N_2O molecule is linear and polar.
   a. On the basis of this experimental evidence, which arrangement, NNO or NON, is correct? Explain your answer.
   b. On the basis of your answer in part a, write the Lewis structure of N_2O (including resonance forms). Give the formal charge on each atom and the hybridization of the central atom.
   c. How would the multiple bonding in

   $$:N\equiv N-\ddot{O}:$$

   be described in terms of orbitals?

100. Bacterial digestion is an economical method of sewage treatment. The reaction

   $$5CO_2(g) + 55NH_4^+(aq) + 76O_2(g) \xrightarrow{\text{Bacteria}}$$

   $$C_5H_7O_2N(s) + 54NO_2^-(aq) + 52H_2O(l) + 109H^+(aq)$$
   Bacterial tissue

   is an intermediate step in the conversion of the nitrogen in organic compounds into nitrate ions. What mass of bacterial tissue is produced in a treatment plant for every 1.0×10^4 kg of wastewater containing 3.0% NH_4^+ ions by mass? Assume that 95% of the ammonium ions are consumed by the bacteria.

101. Phosphate buffers are important in regulating the pH of intracellular fluids. If the concentration ratio of $H_2PO_4^-$ to HPO_4^{2-} in a sample of intracellular fluid is 1.1:1, what is the pH of this sample of intracellular fluid?

   $$H_2PO_4^-(aq) \rightleftharpoons HPO_4^{2-}(aq) + H^+(aq)$$
   $$K_a = 6.2 \times 10^{-8}$$

102. The unit cell for a pure xenon fluoride compound is shown below. What is the formula of the compound?

Challenge Problems

103. Indium(III) phosphide is a semiconducting material that has been frequently used in lasers, light-emitting diodes (LED), and fiberoptic devices. This material can be synthesized at 900. K according to the following reaction:

   $$In(CH_3)_3(g) + PH_3(g) \longrightarrow InP(s) + 3CH_4(g)$$

   a. If 2.56 L $In(CH_3)_3$ at 2.00 atm is allowed to react with 1.38 L PH_3 at 3.00 atm, what mass of InP(s) will be produced assuming the reaction is 87% efficient?

   b. When an electric current is passed through an optoelectronic device containing InP, the light emitted has an energy of 2.03×10^{-19} J. What is the wavelength of this light, and is it visible to the human eye?

   c. The semiconducting properties of InP can be altered by doping. If a small number of phosphorus atoms are replaced by atoms with an electron configuration of $[Kr]5s^24d^{10}5p^4$, is this n-type or p-type doping?

104. While selenic acid has the formula H_2SeO_4 and thus is directly related to sulfuric acid, telluric acid is best visualized as H_6TeO_6 or $Te(OH)_6$.
   a. What is the oxidation state of tellurium in $Te(OH)_6$?
   b. Despite its structural differences with sulfuric and selenic acid, telluric acid is a diprotic acid with $pK_{a_1} = 7.68$ and $pK_{a_2} = 11.29$. Telluric acid can be prepared by hydrolysis of tellurium hexafluoride according to the equation

$$TeF_6(g) + 6H_2O(l) \longrightarrow Te(OH)_6(aq) + 6HF(aq)$$

   Tellurium hexafluoride can be prepared by the reaction of elemental tellurium with fluorine gas:

$$Te(s) + 3F_2(g) \longrightarrow TeF_6(g)$$

   If a cubic block of tellurium (density = 6.240 g/cm^3) measuring 0.545 cm on edge is allowed to react with 2.34 L fluorine gas at 1.06 atm and 25°C, what is the pH of a solution of $Te(OH)_6$ formed by dissolving the isolated $TeF_6(g)$ in 115 mL solution? Assume 100% yield in all reactions.

105. Sodium tripolyphosphate ($Na_5P_3O_{10}$) is used in many synthetic detergents. Its major effect is to soften the water by complexing Mg^{2+} and Ca^{2+} ions. It also increases the efficiency of surfactants, or wetting agents that lower a liquid's surface tension. The pK value for the formation of $MgP_3O_{10}{}^{3-}$ is −8.60. The reaction is $Mg^{2+} + P_3O_{10}{}^{5-} \rightleftharpoons MgP_3O_{10}{}^{3-}$. Calculate the concentration of Mg^{2+} in a solution that was originally 50. ppm Mg^{2+} (50. mg/L of solution) after 40. g of $Na_5P_3O_{10}$ is added to 1.0 L of the solution.

106. Nitrogen gas reacts with hydrogen gas to form ammonia gas (NH_3). Consider the following illustration representing the original reaction mixture (the numbers of each molecule shown are relative numbers):

1.00 atm

15.0 L

N_2

H_2

Assume this reaction mixture goes to completion. The piston apparatus allows the container volume to change in order to keep the pressure constant at 1.00 atm. Assume ideal behavior and constant temperature.
   a. What is the partial pressure of ammonia in the container when the reaction is complete?
   b. What is the mole fraction of ammonia in the container when the reaction is complete?

c. What is the volume of the container when the reaction is complete?

107. Using data from Appendix 4, calculate $\Delta H°$, $\Delta G°$, and K_p (at 298 K) for the production of ozone from oxygen:

$$3O_2(g) \rightleftharpoons 2O_3(g)$$

At 30 km above the surface of the earth, the temperature is about 230. K and the partial pressure of oxygen is about 1.0×10^{-3} atm. Estimate the partial pressure of ozone in equilibrium with oxygen at 30 km above the earth's surface. Is it reasonable to assume that the equilibrium between oxygen and ozone is maintained under these conditions? Explain.

108. You travel to a distant, cold planet where the ammonia flows like water. In fact, the inhabitants of this planet use ammonia (an abundant liquid on their planet) much as earthlings use water. Ammonia is also similar to water in that it is amphoteric and undergoes autoionization. The K value for the autoionization of ammonia is 1.8×10^{-12} at the standard temperature of the planet. What is the pH of ammonia at this temperature?

109. A proposed two-step mechanism for the destruction of ozone in the upper atmosphere is

N

O

   a. What is the overall balanced equation for the ozone destruction reaction?
   b. Which species is a catalyst?
   c. Which species is an intermediate?
   d. What is the rate law derived from this mechanism if the first step in the mechanism is slow and the second step is fast?
   e. One of the concerns about the use of Freons is that they will migrate to the upper atmosphere, where chlorine atoms can be generated by the reaction

$$CCl_2F_2 \xrightarrow{h\nu} CF_2Cl + Cl$$

Freon-12

   Chlorine atoms also can act as a catalyst for the destruction of ozone. The first step of a proposed mechanism for chlorine-catalyzed ozone destruction is

$$Cl(g) + O_3(g) \longrightarrow ClO(g) + O_2(g) \quad \text{Slow}$$

   Assuming a two-step mechanism, propose the second step in the mechanism and give the overall balanced equation.

110. Provide a reasonable estimate for the number of atoms in a 150-lb adult human. Use the information given in Table 18.2.

111. EDTA is used as a complexing agent in chemical analysis. Solutions of EDTA, usually containing the disodium salt Na_2H_2EDTA, are also used to treat heavy metal poisoning. The equilibrium constant for the following reaction is 6.7×10^{21}:

$$Pb^{2+}(aq) + H_2EDTA^{2-}(aq) \rightleftharpoons PbEDTA^{2-}(aq) + 2H^+(aq)$$

$$EDTA^{4-} = \begin{array}{c} {}^{-}O_2C{-}CH_2 \\ \diagdown \\ {}^{-}O_2C{-}CH_2 \end{array} N{-}CH_2{-}CH_2{-}N \begin{array}{c} CH_2{-}CO_2{}^{-} \\ \diagup \\ CH_2{-}CO_2{}^{-} \end{array}$$

Ethylenediaminetetraacetate

Calculate $[Pb^{2+}]$ at equilibrium in a solution originally 0.0050 M in Pb^{2+}, 0.075 M in H_2EDTA^{2-}, and buffered at pH = 7.00.

112. Lead forms compounds in the +2 and +4 oxidation states. All lead(II) halides are known (and are known to be ionic). Only PbF_4 and $PbCl_4$ are known among the possible lead(IV) halides. Presumably lead (IV) oxidizes bromide and iodide ions, producing the lead(II) halide and the free halogen:

$$PbX_4 \longrightarrow PbX_2 + X_2$$

Suppose 25.00 g of a lead(IV) halide reacts to form 16.12 g of a lead(II) halide and the free halogen. Identify the halogen.

113. a. Many biochemical reactions that occur in cells require relatively high concentrations of potassium ion (K^+). The concentration of K^+ in muscle cells is about 0.15 M. The concentration of K^+ in blood plasma is about 0.0050 M. The high internal concentration in cells is maintained by pumping K^+ from the plasma. How much work must be done to transport 1.0 mole of K^+ from the blood to the inside of a muscle cell at 37°C (normal body temperature)?

b. When 1.0 mole of K^+ is transferred from blood to the cells, do any other ions have to be transported? Why or why not?

c. Cells use the hydrolysis of adenosine triphosphate, abbreviated ATP, as a source of energy. Symbolically, this reaction can be represented as

$$ATP(aq) + H_2O(l) \longrightarrow ADP(aq) + H_2PO_4{}^{-}(aq)$$

where ADP represents adenosine diphosphate. For this reaction at 37°C, $K = 1.7 \times 10^5$. How many moles of ATP must be hydrolyzed to provide the energy for the transport of 1.0 mole of K^+? Assume standard conditions for the ATP hydrolysis reaction.

Transition Metals and Coordination Chemistry

19

chapter

SEM of palladium crystal.

Eye of Science/Photo Researchers, Inc.

Transition metals have many uses in our society. Iron is used for steel; copper for electrical wiring and water pipes; titanium for paint; silver for photographic paper; manganese, chromium, vanadium, and cobalt as additives to steel; platinum for industrial and automotive catalysts; and so on.

One indication of the importance of transition metals is the great concern shown by the U.S. government for continuing the supply of these elements. The United States is a net importer of more than 60 "strategic and critical" minerals, including cobalt, manganese, platinum, palladium, and chromium. All these metals play a vital role in the U.S. economy and defense, but about 90% of the required amounts must be imported (Table 19.1).

In addition to being important in industry, transition metal ions play a vital role in living organisms. For example, complexes of iron provide for the transport and storage of oxygen, molybdenum and iron compounds are catalysts in nitrogen fixation, zinc is found in more than 150 biomolecules in humans, copper and iron play a crucial role in the respiratory cycle, and cobalt is found in essential biomolecules such as vitamin B_{12}.

In this chapter we explore the general properties of transition metals, paying particular attention to the bonding, structure, and properties of the complex ions of these metals.

19.1 | The Transition Metals: A Survey

General Properties

One striking characteristic of the representative elements is that their chemistry changes markedly across a given period as the number of valence electrons changes. The chemical similarities occur mainly within the vertical groups. In contrast, *the transition metals show great similarities within a given period as well as within a given vertical group*. This difference occurs because the last electrons added to the transition metal elements are inner electrons: *d* electrons for the *d*-block transition metals and *f* electrons for the lanthanides and actinides. These inner *d* and *f* electrons cannot participate in bonding as readily as the valence *s* and *p* electrons can. Thus the chemistry of the transition elements is not as greatly affected by the gradual change in the number of electrons as is the chemistry of the representative elements.

Group designations are traditionally given on the periodic table for the *d*-block transition metals (Fig. 19.1). However, these designations do not relate as directly to the chemical behavior of these elements as do the designations for the representative elements (the A groups), so we will not use them.

Table 19.1

Some Transition Metals Important to the U.S. Economy and Defense

Metal	Uses	Percentage Imported
Chromium	Stainless steel (especially for parts exposed to corrosive gases and high temperatures)	~91%
Cobalt	High-temperature alloys in jet engines, magnets, catalysts, drill bits	~93%
Manganese	Steelmaking	~97%
Platinum and palladium	Catalysts	~87%

The Lanthanides: Critical Elements

The lanthanide elements are traditionally known as rare earths, but this name is misleading. Many of these elements are, in fact, quite abundant, and many of them are crucial to modern life. For example, typical hybrid cars contain about 10 kg of lanthanum in their nickel-metal hydride batteries and smaller amounts of neodymium, praseodymium, dysprosium, and terbium in their electric motors and generators. In addition, the electricity-producing windmills that seem to be springing up everywhere depend on magnets that weigh about 1 ton and contain hundreds of pounds of neodymium in the form of the neodymium-iron-boron compound $Nd_2Fe_{14}B$. These neodymium-iron-boron–based magnets are also found in today's computer disk drives.

Because these elements are so important to modern technology, they play a key role in global economics. Although China possesses only about 52% of the world's known rare-earth reserves, in 2010 nearly 100% of the world's rare-earth metals and more than 94% of rare-earth oxides came from China. China has gained this status because it produces the rare earths at a much lower cost than the rest of the world. Although the United States has rare-earth reserves estimated at 13% of the world's supply, it produces little, if any, rare earths. A plant in Mountain Pass, California, owned by Molycorp, produced ore composed of 49% cerium, 33% lanthanum, 13% praseodymium, 4% samarium, and 1% heavier rare-earth elements, but the plant was shut down in 2002 because it could not compete price-wise with China. However, China recently has begun to reduce its rare-earth exports, which has caused concern about supplies of these critical elements for the United States and other nations. As a result, Molycorp is searching for less expensive ways to produce rare earths at the Mountain Pass mine. The current plan is to reopen the Mountain Pass operation in 2012.

Although the rare-earth elements are not as economically important to the global economy as petroleum, they will become increasingly important to the global economy and world politics in the coming years.

As a class, the transition metals behave as typical metals, exhibiting metallic luster and relatively high electrical and thermal conductivities. Silver is the best conductor of heat and electrical current. However, copper is a close second, which explains copper's wide use in the electrical systems of homes and factories.

In spite of their many similarities, the properties of the transition metals do vary considerably. For example, tungsten with a melting point of 3400°C is

Figure 19.1

The position of the transition elements on the periodic table. The *d*-block elements correspond to filling the 3*d*, 4*d*, 5*d*, or 6*d* orbitals. The inner transition metals correspond to filling the 4*f* (lanthanides) or 5*f* (actinides) orbitals.

(clockwise from upper left) Calcite stalactites colored by traces of iron. Quartz is often colored by the presence of transition metals such as Mn, Fe, and Ni. Wulfenite contains $PbMoO_4$. Rhodochrosite is a mineral containing $MnCO_3$.

(from left to right) Aqueous solutions containing the metal ions Co^{2+}, Mn^{2+}, Cr^{3+}, Fe^{3+}, and Ni^{2+}.

used for filaments in light bulbs; in contrast, mercury is a liquid at 25°C. Some transition metals such as iron and titanium are hard and strong and therefore make very useful structural materials; others such as copper, gold, and silver are relatively soft. The chemical reactivity of the transition metals also varies significantly. Some react readily with oxygen to form oxides. Of these metals, some, such as chromium, nickel, and cobalt, form oxides that adhere tightly to the metallic surface, thereby protecting the metal from further oxidation. Others, such as iron, form oxides that scale off, constantly exposing new metal to the corrosion process. On the other hand, the noble metals—primarily gold, silver, platinum, and palladium—do not readily form oxides.

In forming ionic compounds with nonmetals, the transition metals exhibit several typical characteristics:

More than one oxidation state is often found. For example, iron combines with chlorine to form $FeCl_2$ and $FeCl_3$.

The cations are often **complex ions,** species in which *the transition metal ion is surrounded by a certain number of ligands* (molecules or ions that behave as Lewis bases). For example, the compound $[Co(NH_3)_6]Cl_3$ contains $Co(NH_3)_6^{3+}$ cations and Cl^- anions:

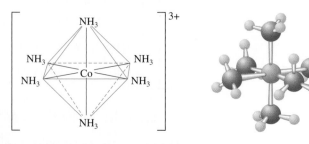

The $Co(NH_3)_6^{3+}$ ion

Table 19.2

Selected Properties of the First-Row Transition Metals

Property	Scandium	Titanium	Vanadium	Chromium	Manganese	Iron	Cobalt	Nickel	Copper	Zinc
Atomic number	21	22	23	24	25	26	27	28	29	30
Electron configuration*	$4s^2 3d^1$	$4s^2 3d^2$	$4s^2 3d^3$	$4s^1 3d^5$	$4s^2 3d^5$	$4s^2 3d^6$	$4s^2 3d^7$	$4s^2 3d^8$	$4s^1 3d^{10}$	$4s^2 3d^{10}$
Atomic radius† (pm)	162	147	134	130	135	126	125	124	128	138
Ionization energies (eV/atom)										
First	6.54	6.82	6.74	6.77	7.44	7.87	7.86	7.64	7.73	9.39
Second	12.80	13.58	14.65	16.50	15.64	16.18	17.06	18.17	20.29	17.96
Third	24.76	27.49	29.31	30.96	33.67	30.65	33.50	35.17	36.83	39.72
Reduction potential‡ (V)	−2.08	−1.63	−1.2	−0.91	−1.18	−0.44	−0.28	−0.23	+0.34	−0.76
Common oxidation states	+3	+2,+3, +4	+2,+3, +4,+5	+2,+3, +6	+2,+3, +4,+7	+2,+3	+2,+3	+2	+1,+2	+2
Melting point (°C)	1397	1672	1710	1900	1244	1530	1495	1455	1083	419
Density (g/cm³)	2.99	4.49	5.96	7.20	7.43	7.86	8.9	8.90	8.92	7.14
Electrical conductivity§	—	2	3	10	2	17	24	24	97	27

*Each atom has an argon inner-core configuration.
†Covalent atomic radii.
‡For the reduction process $M^{2+} + 2e^- \longrightarrow M$ (except for scandium, where the ion is Sc^{3+}).
§Compared with an arbitrarily assigned value of 100 for silver.

Most compounds are colored because the typical transition metal ion in a complex ion can absorb visible light of specific wavelengths.

Many compounds are paramagnetic (they contain unpaired electrons).

In this chapter we will concentrate on the **first-row transition metals** (scandium through zinc) because they are representative of the other transition series and because they have great practical significance. Some important properties of these elements are summarized in Table 19.2 and are discussed below.

Electron Configurations

> Chromium has the electron configuration $[Ar]4s^1 3d^5$.

The electron configurations of the first-row transition metals were discussed in Section 12.13. The $3d$ orbitals begin to fill after the $4s$ orbital is complete—that is, after calcium ($[Ar]4s^2$). The first transition metal, *scandium*, has one electron in the $3d$ orbitals; the second, *titanium*, has two; and the third, *vanadium*, has three. We would expect *chromium*, the fourth transition metal, to have the electron configuration $[Ar]4s^2 3d^4$. However, the actual configuration is $[Ar]4s^1 3d^5$; it has a half-filled $4s$ orbital and a half-filled set of $3d$ orbitals (one electron in each of the five $3d$ orbitals). It is tempting to say that the configuration results because half-filled "shells" are especially stable. Although there are some reasons to think that this explanation might be valid, it is an oversimplification. For instance, tungsten, which is in the same vertical group as chromium, has the configuration $[Xe]6s^2 4f^{14} 5d^4$, where half-filled s and d shells are not found. There are several similar cases that dispute the importance of half-filled shells.

The rigorous explanation of the electron configuration of chromium, which requires knowledge that is beyond the scope of an introductory course, involves the details of the electron interactions. It turns out that orbital energies are not constant for a given atom but depend on the way that the other orbitals in the atom are occupied. Thus there is no simple explanation for why chromium has the $4s^1 3d^5$ configuration rather than the $4s^2 3d^4$ configuration. Suffice it to say that for all the first-row transition metals, because the $4s$ and $3d$ orbitals have similar energies, the $4s^2 3d^n$ and the $4s^1 3d^{n+1}$ configurations have similar energies. For most elements, $4s^2 3d^n$ is lower in energy, but for chromium and for copper ($[Ar]4s^1 3d^{10}$), the $4s^1 3d^{n+1}$ configuration is more stable.

In contrast to the neutral transition metals, where the $3d$ and $4s$ orbitals have very similar energies, the *energy of the $3d$ orbitals in transition metal ions is significantly less than that of the $4s$ orbital.* This means that the electrons remaining after the ion is formed occupy the $3d$ orbitals, since they are lower in energy. *First-row transition metal ions do not have $4s$ electrons.* For example, manganese has the configuration $[Ar]4s^2 3d^5$, but that of Mn^{2+} is $[Ar]3d^5$. The neutral titanium atom has the configuration $[Ar]4s^2 3d^2$, but that of Ti^{3+} is $[Ar]3d^1$.

Oxidation States and Ionization Energies

The transition metals can form a variety of ions by losing one or more electrons. The common oxidation states of these elements are shown in Table 19.2. Note that for the first five metals the maximum possible oxidation state corresponds to the loss of all the $4s$ and $3d$ electrons. For example, the maximum oxidation state of chromium ($[Ar]4s^1 3d^5$) is $+6$. Toward the right end of the period, the maximum oxidation states are not observed; in fact, the $2+$ ions are the most common. The higher oxidation states are not seen for these metals because the $3d$ orbitals become lower in energy as the nuclear charge increases, making the electrons increasingly difficult to remove. From Table 19.2 we see that ionization energy increases gradually from left to right across the period. However, the third ionization energy (corresponding to the removal of an electron from a $3d$ orbital) increases faster than the first ionization energy, clear evidence of the significant decrease in the energy of the $3d$ orbitals in going across the period (Fig. 19.2).

Standard Reduction Potentials

When a metal acts as a *reducing agent,* the half-reaction is

$$M \longrightarrow M^{n+} + ne^-$$

Figure 19.2

Plots of the first (red dots) and third (blue dots) ionization energies for the first-row transition metals.

Table 19.3

Relative Reducing Abilities of the First-Row
Transition Metals in Aqueous Solution

Reaction	Potential (V)
$Sc \rightarrow Sc^{3+} + 3e^-$	2.08
$Ti \rightarrow Ti^{2+} + 2e^-$	1.63
$V \rightarrow V^{2+} + 2e^-$	1.2
$Mn \rightarrow Mn^{2+} + 2e^-$	1.18
$Cr \rightarrow Cr^{2+} + 2e^-$	0.91
$Zn \rightarrow Zn^{2+} + 2e^-$	0.76
$Fe \rightarrow Fe^{2+} + 2e^-$	0.44
$Co \rightarrow Co^{2+} + 2e^-$	0.28
$Ni \rightarrow Ni^{2+} + 2e^-$	0.23
$Cu \rightarrow Cu^{2+} + 2e^-$	−0.34

Reducing ability ↑

This is the reverse of the conventional listing of half-reactions in tables. Thus, when we rank the transition metals in order of reducing ability, it is most convenient to reverse the reactions and the signs given in Table 19.2. The metal with the most positive potential is thus the best reducing agent. The transition metals are listed in order of reducing ability in Table 19.3.

Recall that $\mathscr{E}°$ is zero by definition for the process

$$2H^+ + 2e^- \longrightarrow H_2$$

Therefore, all the metals except copper can reduce H^+ ions in 1 M aqueous solutions of strong acid to hydrogen gas:

$$M(s) + 2H^+(aq) \longrightarrow H_2(g) + M^{2+}(aq)$$

As Table 19.3 shows, the reducing abilities of the first-row transition metals generally decrease going from left to right across the period. Only chromium and zinc do not follow this trend.

The 4d and 5d Transition Series

In comparing the $3d$, $4d$, and $5d$ transition series, it is instructive to consider the atomic radii of these elements (Fig. 19.3). Note that there is a general, although not regular, decrease in size going from left to right across each of the series. Also note that although there is a significant increase in radius in going from the $3d$ to the $4d$ metals, the $4d$ and $5d$ metals are remarkably similar in size. This

Figure 19.3

Atomic radii of the $3d$, $4d$, and $5d$ transition series.

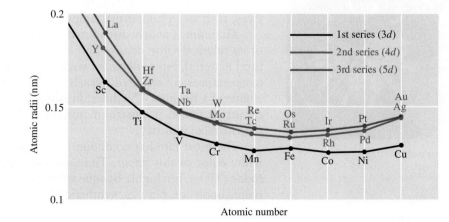

latter phenomenon is the result of the **lanthanide contraction. In the lanthanide series,** which consists of the elements between lanthanum and hafnium (Fig. 19.1), electrons are filling the $4f$ orbitals. Since the $4f$ orbitals are buried in the interior of these atoms, the additional electrons do not add to the atomic size. In fact, the increasing nuclear charge (remember that a proton is added to the nucleus with the addition of each electron) causes the radii of the lanthanide elements to decrease significantly going from left to right. This lanthanide contraction just offsets the normal increase in size due to changing from one principal quantum level to another. Thus the $5d$ elements, instead of being significantly larger than the $4d$ elements, are almost identical to them in size. This leads to a great similarity in the chemistry of the $4d$ and $5d$ elements in a given vertical group. For example, the chemical properties of hafnium and zirconium are remarkably similar, and they always occur together in nature. Their separation, which is probably more difficult than the separation of any other pair of elements, often requires fractional distillation of their compounds.

In general, the differences between the $4d$ and $5d$ elements in a group increase gradually going from left to right. For example, niobium and tantalum are also quite similar, but less so than zirconium and hafnium.

Although generally less well known than the $3d$ elements, the $4d$ and $5d$ transition metals have certain very useful properties. For example, zirconium and zirconium oxide (ZrO_2) are quite resistant to high temperatures and are used, along with niobium and molybdenum alloys, for space vehicle parts that are exposed to high temperatures during reentry into the earth's atmosphere. Niobium and molybdenum are also important alloying materials for certain types of steel. Tantalum, which has a high resistance to attack by body fluids, is often used for surgical clips. The *platinum group metals*—ruthenium, osmium, rhodium, iridium, palladium, and platinum—are all quite similar and are widely used as catalysts for many types of industrial processes.

Niobium was originally called columbium and is still occasionally referred to by that name.

19.2 The First-Row Transition Metals

We have seen that while the transition metals are similar in many ways, they also show important differences. We will now explore some of the specific properties of each of the $3d$ transition metals.

Scandium is a rare element that exists in compounds mainly in the $+3$ oxidation state—for example, in $ScCl_3$, Sc_2O_3, and $Sc_2(SO_4)_3$. The chemistry of scandium strongly resembles that of the lanthanides, with most of its compounds being colorless and diamagnetic. This is not surprising, since Sc^{3+} has no d electrons. As we will see in Section 19.6, the color and magnetism of transition metal compounds usually arise from the d electrons on the metal ion. Scandium metal, which can be prepared by electrolysis of molten $ScCl_3$, is not widely used because of its rarity. However, it is found in some electronic devices, such as high-intensity lamps.

Titanium is widely distributed in the earth's crust (0.6% by mass). Because of its relatively low density and high strength, titanium is an excellent structural material, especially in jet engines, where light weight and stability at high temperatures are required. Nearly 5000 kg of titanium alloys are used in each engine of a Boeing 747 jetliner. In addition, the resistance of titanium to chemical attack makes it a useful material for pipes, pumps, and reaction vessels in the chemical industry.

The most familiar compound of titanium is no doubt responsible for the white color of this paper. Titanium dioxide, or more correctly, *titanium(IV) oxide* (TiO_2), is a highly opaque substance used as the white pigment in paper, paint, linoleum, plastics, synthetic fibers, whitewall tires, and cosmetics (sun-

A titanium watch.

Bobby Ray Strange/Shutterstock.com

Liquid titanium(IV) chloride being added to water, forming a cloud of solid titanium oxide and hydrochloric acid.

The manufacture of sulfuric acid was discussed in Section 3.8.

The most common oxidation state for vanadium is +5.

screens, for example). About 700,000 tons of TiO_2 are used annually in these and similar products. Titanium(IV) oxide is widely dispersed in nature, but the main ores are rutile (impure TiO_2) and ilmenite ($FeTiO_3$). Rutile is processed by treatment with chlorine to form volatile $TiCl_4$, which is then separated from the impurities and burned to form TiO_2:

$$TiCl_4(g) + O_2(g) \longrightarrow TiO_2(s) + 2Cl_2(g)$$

Ilmenite is treated with sulfuric acid to form a soluble sulfate,

$$FeTiO_3(s) + 2H_2SO_4(aq) \longrightarrow$$
$$Fe^{2+}(aq) + TiO^{2+}(aq) + 2SO_4{}^{2-}(aq) + 2H_2O(l)$$

When this aqueous mixture is allowed to stand under vacuum, solid $FeSO_4 \cdot 7H_2O$ forms and is removed. The mixture remaining is then heated, and the insoluble titanium(IV) oxide hydrate ($TiO_2 \cdot H_2O$) forms. The water of hydration is driven off by heating to form pure TiO_2:

$$TiO_2 \cdot H_2O(s) \xrightarrow{\text{Heat}} TiO_2(s) + H_2O(g)$$

In its compounds titanium most often exists in the $+4$ oxidation state. Examples are TiO_2 and $TiCl_4$, the latter a colorless liquid (bp = 137°C) that fumes in moist air to produce TiO_2:

$$TiCl_4(l) + 2H_2O(l) \longrightarrow TiO_2(s) + 4HCl(g)$$

Titanium(III) compounds can be produced by reduction of compounds containing titanium in the $+4$ state. In aqueous solution Ti^{3+} exists as the purple $Ti(H_2O)_6{}^{3+}$ ion, which is slowly oxidized to titanium(IV) by air. Titanium(II) is not stable in aqueous solution but does exist in the solid state in compounds such as TiO and dihalides of the type TiX_2.

Vanadium is widely dispersed throughout the earth's crust (0.02% by mass). It is used mostly in alloys with other metals such as iron (80% of vanadium is used in steel) and titanium. Vanadium(V) oxide (V_2O_5) is used as an industrial catalyst in the production of materials such as sulfuric acid.

Pure vanadium can be obtained from the electrolytic reduction of fused salts, such as VCl_2, to produce a metal similar to titanium that is steel gray, hard, and corrosion-resistant. Often the pure element is not required for alloying. For example, *ferrovanadium*, produced by reducing a mixture of V_2O_5 and Fe_2O_3 with aluminum, is added to iron to form *vanadium steel*, a hard steel used for engine parts and axles.

The principal oxidation state of vanadium is $+5$, found in compounds such as the orange V_2O_5 (mp = 650°C) and the colorless VF_5 (mp = 19.5°C). The oxidation states ranging from $+5$ to $+2$ all exist in aqueous solution (Table 19.4). The higher oxidation states, $+5$ and $+4$, do not exist as hydrated ions of the type $V^{n+}(aq)$ because these highly charged ions cause the attached water molecules to be very acidic. The H^+ ions are lost to give the oxycations $VO_2{}^+$ and VO^{2+}. The hydrated V^{3+} and V^{2+} ions are easily oxidized and thus can function as reducing agents in aqueous solution.

Although *chromium* is relatively rare, it is a very important industrial material. The chief ore of chromium, chromite ($FeCr_2O_4$), can be reduced by carbon to give *ferrochrome*,

$$FeCr_2O_4(s) + 4C(s) \longrightarrow \underbrace{Fe(s) + 2Cr(s)}_{\text{Ferrochrome}} + 4CO(g)$$

which can be added directly to iron in the steelmaking process. Chromium metal, which is often used to plate steel, is hard and brittle. It maintains a bright surface by developing a tough, invisible oxide coating.

Table 19.4

Oxidation States and Species for Vanadium in Aqueous Solution

Oxidation State of Vanadium	Species in Aqueous Solution
+5	$VO_2{}^+$ (yellow)
+4	VO^{2+} (blue)
+3	$V^{3+}(aq)$ (blue-green)
+2	$V^{2+}(aq)$ (violet)

Chemical Insights | Titanium Makes Great Bicycles

One of the most interesting characteristics of the world of bicycling is the competition among various frame materials. Bicycle frames are now built from steel, aluminum, carbon fiber composites, and titanium, with each material having advantages and disadvantages. Steel is strong, economical, adaptable, and (unfortunately) "rustable." Aluminum is light and stiff but has relatively low fatigue limits (resistance to repeated stresses). Carbon fiber composites have amazing strength-to-mass ratios and have shock- and vibration-dampening properties superior to any metal; however, they are very expensive. Titanium has a density approximately 43% less than that of steel, a yield strength (when alloyed with metals such as aluminum and tin) that is 30% greater than that of steel, an extraordinary resistance to fatigue, and a high resistance to corrosion but is expensive and difficult to work.

Of all these materials, titanium gives the bicycle that fanatics seem to love the most (Fig. 19.4). After their first ride on a bicycle with a titanium frame, most experienced cyclists find themselves shaking their heads and searching hard for the right words to describe the experience. Typically, the word *magic* is used a great deal in the ensuing description.

Figure 19.4
A bicycle with a titanium frame.

The magic of titanium results from its combination of toughness, stretchability, and resilience. A bicycle that is built stiff to resist pedaling loads usually responds by giving a harsh, uncomfortable ride. A titanium bike is very stiff against high pedaling torques, but it seems to transmit much less road shock than bikes made of competitive materials. Why titanium excels in dampening vibrations is not entirely clear. Despite titanium's significantly lower density than steel, shock waves travel more slowly in titanium than steel. Whatever the explanation for its shock-absorbing abilities, titanium provides three things that cyclists find crucial: light weight, stiffness, and a smooth ride—magic.

Titanium is quite abundant in the earth's crust, ranking ninth of all the elements and second among the transition elements. The metallurgy of titanium presents special challenges. Carbon, the reducing agent most commonly used to obtain metals from their oxide ores, cannot be used because it forms intractable interstitial carbides with titanium. These carbides are extraordinarily hard and have melting points above 3000°C. However, if chlorine gas is used in conjunction with carbon to treat the ore, volatile $TiCl_4$ is formed, which can be distilled off and then reduced with magnesium or sodium at approximately 1000°C to form a titanium "sponge." This sponge is then ground up, cleaned with aqua regia (a 1:3 mixture of concentrated HNO_3 and concentrated HCl), melted under a blanket of inert gas (to prevent reaction with oxygen), and cast into ingots. Titanium, a lustrous, silvery metal with a high melting point (1667°C), crystallizes in a hexagonal closest packed structure. Because titanium tends to become quite brittle when trace impurities such as C, N, and O are present, it must be fabricated with great care.

Titanium's unusual ability to stretch makes it hard to machine. It tends to push away even from a very sharp cutting blade, giving a rather unpredictable final dimension. Also, because titanium is embrittled by reaction with oxygen, all welding operations must be carried out under a shielding gas such as argon.

However, the bicycle that results is worth all these difficulties. One woman described a titanium bicycle as "the one God rides on Sunday."

Jodi Jacobson/Peter Arnold, Inc./PhotoLibrary

Table 19.5

Typical Chromium Compounds

Oxidation State of Chromium	Examples of Compounds (X = halogen)
+2	CrX_2
+3	CrX_3
	Cr_2O_3 (green)
	$Cr(OH)_3$ (blue-green)
+6	$K_2Cr_2O_7$ (orange)
	Na_2CrO_4 (yellow)
	CrO_3 (red)

Chromium commonly forms compounds in which it has an oxidation state of +2, +3, or +6, as shown in Table 19.5. The Cr^{2+} (chromous) ion is a powerful reducing agent in aqueous solution. In fact, traces of O_2 in other gases can be removed from those gases by bubbling the gaseous mixture through a Cr^{2+} solution:

$$4Cr^{2+}(aq) + O_2(g) + 4H^+(aq) \longrightarrow 4Cr^{3+}(aq) + 2H_2O(l)$$

The chromium(VI) species are excellent oxidizing agents, especially in acidic solution, where chromium(VI) as the dichromate ion ($Cr_2O_7^{2-}$) is reduced to the Cr^{3+} ion:

$$Cr_2O_7^{2-}(aq) + 14H^+(aq) + 6e^- \longrightarrow 2Cr^{3+}(aq) + 7H_2O(l) \qquad \mathscr{E}° = 1.33 \text{ V}$$

The oxidizing ability of the dichromate ion is strongly pH-dependent; it increases as [H$^+$] increases, as predicted by Le Châtelier's principle. In basic solution chromium(VI) exists as the chromate ion, a much less powerful oxidizing agent:

$$CrO_4^{2-}(aq) + 4H_2O(l) + 3e^- \longrightarrow Cr(OH)_3(s) + 5OH^-(aq)$$
$$\mathscr{E}° = -0.13 \text{ V}$$

The structures of the $Cr_2O_7^{2-}$ and CrO_4^{2-} ions are shown in Fig. 19.5.

Red chromium(VI) oxide (CrO_3) dissolves in water to give a strongly acidic, red-orange solution:

$$2CrO_3(s) + H_2O(l) \longrightarrow 2H^+(aq) + Cr_2O_7^{2-}(aq)$$

It is possible to precipitate bright orange dichromate salts, such as $K_2Cr_2O_7$, from these solutions. When made basic, the solution turns yellow and chromate salts such as Na_2CrO_4 can be obtained. A mixture of chromium(VI) oxide and concentrated sulfuric acid, commonly called *cleaning solution*, is a powerful oxidizing medium that can remove organic materials from analytical glassware, yielding a very clean surface.

Manganese is relatively abundant (0.1% of the earth's crust), although no significant sources are found in the United States. The most common use of manganese is in the production of an especially hard steel used for rock crushers, bank vaults, and armor plate. One interesting source of manganese is *manganese nodules* found on the ocean floor. These roughly spherical "rocks" contain mixtures of manganese and iron oxides as well as smaller amounts of other metals such as cobalt, nickel, and copper. Apparently, the nodules were formed at least partly by the action of marine organisms. Because of the abundance of these nodules, there is much interest in developing economical methods for their recovery and processing.

Manganese can exist in all oxidation states from +2 to +7, although +2 and +7 are the most common. Manganese(II) forms an extensive series of salts

Manganese nodules on the sea floor.

Figure 19.5
The structures of the chromium(VI) anions: (a) $Cr_2O_7^{2-}$, which exists in acidic solution; and (b) CrO_4^{2-}, which exists in basic solution.

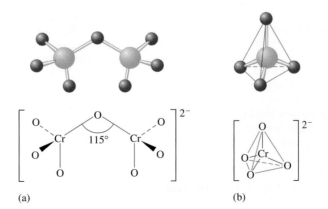

(a)   (b)

Table 19.6

Some Compounds of Manganese in Its Most Common Oxidation States

Oxidation State of Manganese	Examples of Compounds
+2	$Mn(OH)_2$ (pink)
	MnS (salmon)
	$MnSO_4$ (reddish)
	$MnCl_2$ (pink)
+4	MnO_2 (dark brown)
+7	$KMnO_4$ (purple)

with all the common anions. In aqueous solution Mn^{2+} forms $Mn(H_2O)_6^{2+}$, which has a light pink color. Manganese(VII) is found in the intensely purple permanganate ion (MnO_4^-). Widely used as an analytical reagent in acidic solution, the MnO_4^- ion behaves as a strong oxidizing agent, producing Mn^{2+}:

$$MnO_4^-(aq) + 8H^+(aq) + 5e^- \longrightarrow Mn^{2+}(aq) + 4H_2O(l) \qquad \mathscr{E}° = 1.51 \text{ V}$$

Several typical compounds of manganese are listed in Table 19.6.

Iron is the most abundant heavy metal (constituting 4.7% of the earth's crust) and the most important to our civilization. It is a white, lustrous, not particularly hard metal that is very reactive toward oxidizing agents. For example, in moist air it is rapidly oxidized by oxygen to form rust, a mixture of iron oxides.

The chemistry of iron mainly involves its +2 and +3 oxidation states. Typical compounds are shown in Table 19.7. In aqueous solutions, iron(II) salts are generally light green because of the presence of $Fe(H_2O)_6^{2+}$. Although the $Fe(H_2O)_6^{3+}$ ion is colorless, aqueous solutions of iron(III) salts are usually yellow to brown in color because of the presence of $Fe(OH)(H_2O)_5^{2+}$. This latter ion results from the acidity of $Fe(H_2O)_6^{3+}$ ($K_a = 6 \times 10^{-3}$):

$$Fe(H_2O)_6^{3+}(aq) \rightleftharpoons Fe(OH)(H_2O)_5^{2+}(aq) + H^+(aq)$$

Although *cobalt* is relatively rare, it is found in ores such as smaltite ($CoAs_2$) and cobaltite (CoAsS) in large enough concentrations to make its production economically feasible. Cobalt is a hard, bluish white metal mainly used in alloys such as stainless steel and stellite, which is an alloy of iron, copper, and tungsten used in surgical instruments.

The chemistry of cobalt involves mainly its +2 and +3 oxidation states, although compounds containing cobalt in the 0, +1, and +4 oxidation states are known. Aqueous solutions of cobalt(II) salts contain the $Co(H_2O)_6^{2+}$ ion, which has a characteristic rose color. Cobalt forms a wide variety of coordination compounds, many of which will be discussed in later sections of this chapter. Some typical cobalt compounds are listed in Table 19.8.

Nickel ranks twenty-fourth in elemental abundance in the earth's crust. It is found in ores, where it is combined mainly with arsenic, antimony, and sulfur. Nickel metal, a silver-white substance with high electrical and thermal conductivities, is quite resistant to corrosion and is often used for plating more active metals. Nickel is also widely used in the production of alloys such as steel.

Nickel is found almost exclusively in the +2 oxidation state in its compounds. Aqueous solutions of nickel(II) salts contain the $Ni(H_2O)_6^{2+}$ ion,

Table 19.7

Typical Compounds of Iron

Oxidation State of Iron	Examples of Compounds
+2	FeO (black)
	FeS (brownish black)
	$FeSO_4 \cdot 7H_2O$ (green)
	$K_4Fe(CN)_6$ (yellow)
+3	$FeCl_3$ (brownish black)
	Fe_2O_3 (reddish brown)
	$K_3Fe(CN)_6$ (red)
	$Fe(SCN)_3$ (red)
+2, +3 (mixture)	Fe_3O_4 (black)
	$KFe[Fe(CN)_6]$ (deep blue, Prussian blue)

Table 19.8

Typical Compounds of Cobalt

Oxidation State of Cobalt	Examples of Compounds
+2	$CoSO_4$ (dark blue)
	$[Co(H_2O)_6]Cl_2$ (pink)
	$[Co(H_2O)_6](NO_3)_2$ (red)
	CoS (black)
	CoO (greenish brown)
+3	CoF_3 (brown)
	Co_2O_3 (charcoal)
	$K_3[Co(CN)_6]$ (yellow)
	$[Co(NH_3)_6]Cl_3$ (yellow)

An aqueous solution containing the Ni^{2+} ion.

Copper roofs and bronze statues, such as the Statue of Liberty, turn green in air because $Cu_3(OH)_4SO_4$ and $Cu_4(OH)_6SO_4$ form.

Table 19.9

Typical Compounds of Nickel

Oxidation State of Nickel	Examples of Compounds
+2	$NiCl_2$ (yellow)
	$[Ni(H_2O)_6]Cl_2$ (green)
	NiO (greenish black)
	NiS (black)
	$[Ni(H_2O)_6]SO_4$ (green)
	$[Ni(NH_3)_6](NO_3)_2$ (blue)

which has a characteristic emerald green color. Coordination compounds of nickel(II) will be discussed later in this chapter. Some typical nickel compounds are shown in Table 19.9.

Copper, widely distributed in nature in ores containing sulfides, arsenides, chlorides, and carbonates, is valued for its high electrical conductivity and its resistance to corrosion. It is widely used for plumbing, and 50% of all copper produced annually is used for electrical applications. Copper is a major constituent in several well-known alloys (Table 19.10).

Although copper is not highly reactive (it will not reduce H^+ to H_2, for example), this reddish colored metal does slowly corrode in air, producing the characteristic green *patina* consisting of basic copper sulfate,

$$3Cu(s) + 2H_2O(l) + SO_2(g) + 2O_2(g) \longrightarrow Cu_3(OH)_4SO_4(s)$$

Basic copper sulfate

and other similar compounds.

The chemistry of copper principally involves the +2 oxidation state, but many compounds containing copper(I) are also known. Aqueous solutions of copper(II) salts are a characteristic bright blue color because of the presence of the $Cu(H_2O)_6^{2+}$ ion. Table 19.11 lists some typical copper compounds.

Although trace amounts of copper are essential for life, this substance is quite toxic in large amounts; copper salts are used to kill bacteria, fungi, and algae. For example, paints containing copper are used on ship hulls to prevent fouling by marine organisms.

Widely dispersed in the earth's crust, *zinc* is mainly refined from sphalerite $[(ZnFe)S]$, which often occurs with galena (PbS). Zinc is a white, lustrous, very active metal that behaves as an excellent reducing agent and that tarnishes

Table 19.10

Alloys Containing Copper

Alloy	Composition (% by mass in parentheses)
Brass	Cu (20–97), Zn (2–80), Sn (0–14), Pb (0–12), Mn (0–25)
Bronze	Cu (50–98), Sn (0–35), Zn (0–29), Pb (0–50), P (0–3)
Sterling silver	Cu (7.5), Ag (92.5)
Gold (18-karat)	Cu (5–14), Au (75), Ag (10–20)
Gold (14-karat)	Cu (12–28), Au (58), Ag (4–30)

Table 19.11

Typical Compounds of Copper

Oxidation State of Copper	Examples of Compounds
+1	Cu_2O (red)
	Cu_2S (black)
	$CuCl$ (white)
+2	CuO (black)
	$CuSO_4 \cdot 5H_2O$ (blue)
	$CuCl_2 \cdot 2H_2O$ (green)
	$[Cu(H_2O)_6](NO_3)_2$ (blue)

rapidly. About 90% of the zinc produced is used for galvanizing steel. Zinc forms colorless salts containing Zn^{2+} ions.

Keith Weller/USDA Photo

Alpine pennycress thrives on soils containing zinc and cadmium. The metals can be harvested by extracting them from the plant's shoots.

19.3 | Coordination Compounds

Transition metal ions characteristically form **coordination compounds,** which are usually colored and often paramagnetic. A coordination compound typically consists of a *complex ion,* a transition metal ion with its attached ligands (see Section 8.10), and **counter ions,** anions or cations needed to produce a compound with no net charge. The substance $[Co(NH_3)_5Cl]Cl_2$ is a typical coordination compound. The square brackets indicate the composition of the complex ion—in this case $Co(NH_3)_5Cl^{2+}$—and the two Cl^- counter ions are shown outside the brackets. Note that in this compound one Cl^- acts as a ligand along with the five NH_3 molecules. In the solid state, this compound consists of the large $Co(NH_3)_5Cl^{2+}$ cations with twice as many Cl^- anions, all packed together as efficiently as possible. When dissolved in water, the solid behaves like any ionic solid; the cations and anions are assumed to separate and move about independently:

$$[Co(NH_3)_5Cl]Cl_2(s) \xrightarrow{H_2O} Co(NH_3)_5Cl^{2+}(aq) + 2Cl^-(aq)$$

Coordination compounds have been known since about 1700, but their true nature was not understood until the 1890s when a young Swiss chemist named Alfred Werner proposed that transition metal ions have two types of valence (combining ability). One type of valence, which Werner called the secondary valence, refers to the ability of a metal ion to bind to Lewis bases (ligands) to form complex ions. The other type, the primary valence, refers to the ability of the metal ion to form ionic bonds with oppositely charged ions. Thus Werner explained that the compound originally written as $CoCl_3 \cdot 5NH_3$ is actually $[Co(NH_3)_5Cl]Cl_2$, in which the Co^{3+} ion has a primary valence of 3, satisfied by the three Cl^- ions, and a secondary valence of 6, satisfied by the six ligands (five NH_3 and one Cl^-). We now call the primary valence the **oxidation state** and the secondary valence the **coordination number.** The latter reflects the number of bonds formed between the metal ion and the ligands in the complex ion.

Coordination Number

The number of bonds formed by metal ions to ligands in complex ions varies from two to eight, depending on the size, charge, and electron configuration of the transition metal ion. As shown in Table 19.12, 6 is the most common co-

---

Table 19.12

Typical Coordination Numbers for Some Common Metal Ions

M^+	Coordination Numbers	M^{2+}	Coordination Numbers	M^{3+}	Coordination Numbers
Cu^+	2, 4	Mn^{2+}	4, 6	Sc^{3+}	6
Ag^+	2	Fe^{2+}	6	Cr^{3+}	6
Au^+	2, 4	Co^{2+}	4, 6	Co^{3+}	6
		Ni^{2+}	4, 6	Au^{3+}	4
		Cu^{2+}	4, 6		
		Zn^{2+}	4, 6		

ordination number, followed closely by 4, with a few metal ions showing a coordination number of 2. Many metal ions show more than one coordination number, and there is really no simple way to predict what the coordination number will be in a particular case. The typical geometries for the various common coordination numbers are shown in Fig. 19.6. Note that six ligands produce an octahedral arrangement around the metal ion. Four ligands can form either a tetrahedral or a square planar arrangement, and two ligands give a linear structure.

Ligands

A **ligand** is a *neutral molecule or ion having a lone pair that can be used to form a bond to a metal ion*. In the 1920s G. N. Lewis suggested a general definition for acid–base behavior in terms of electron pairs. Lewis defined an **acid** as an **electron-pair acceptor** and a **base** as an **electron-pair donor**. Because a ligand donates an electron pair to an empty orbital on a metal ion, the formation of a metal–ligand bond can be described as the interaction between a Lewis base (the ligand) and a Lewis acid (the metal ion). This is often called a **coordinate covalent bond.**

A *ligand that can form one bond to a metal ion* is called a **monodentate ligand,** or a **unidentate ligand** (from root words meaning "one tooth"). Examples of unidentate ligands are shown in Table 19.13.

The Lewis definition of acids and bases also encompasses the Brønsted–Lowry definition. For example,

$$H^+ + :NH_3 \longrightarrow NH_4^+$$

Table 19.13

Some Common Ligands

Type	Examples	
Unidentate/monodentate	H_2O NH_3 CN^- NO_2^- (nitrite)	SCN^- (thiocyanate) OH^- X^- (halides)
Bidentate	Oxalate	Ethylenediamine (en)
Polydentate	Diethylenetriamine (dien) Ethylenediaminetetraacetate (EDTA)	

Coordination number	Geometry
2	Linear
4	Tetrahedral Square planar
6	Octahedral

Figure 19.6
The ligand arrangements for coordination numbers 2, 4, and 6.

(a)

(b)

Figure 19.7
(a) The bidentate ligand ethylenediamine can bond to the metal ion through the lone pair on each nitrogen atom, thus forming two coordinate covalent bonds. (b) Ammonia is a monodentate ligand.

Figure 19.8
The coordination of EDTA with a 2+ metal ion.

Some ligands have more than one atom with a lone pair that can be used to bond to a metal ion. Such ligands are said to be **chelating ligands,** or **chelates** (from the Greek word *chela,* meaning "claw"). A ligand that can form two bonds to a metal ion is called a **bidentate ligand.** A very common bidentate ligand is ethylenediamine (abbreviated en), which is shown coordinating to a metal ion in Fig. 19.7(a). Note the relationship between this ligand and the unidentate ligand ammonia [Fig. 19.7(b)]. Oxalate, another typical bidentate ligand, is shown in Table 19.13.

Ligands that can form more than two bonds to a metal ion are called **polydentate ligands.** Some ligands can form as many as six bonds to a metal ion. The best-known example of such a ligand is ethylenediaminetetraacetate (abbreviated EDTA), which is shown in Table 19.13. This ligand virtually surrounds the metal ion (Fig. 19.8), coordinating through six atoms (a *hexadentate ligand*). As might be expected from the large number of coordination sites, EDTA forms very stable complex ions with most metal ions. It is therefore useful as a "scavenger" to remove toxic heavy metals such as lead from the human body. It is also used as a reagent to analyze solutions for their metal ion content. EDTA is found in countless consumer products, including soda, beer, salad dressings, bar soaps, and most cleaners. In these products EDTA ties up trace metal ions that would otherwise catalyze decomposition and produce unwanted precipitates.

Even more complicated ligands are found in biological systems, where metal ions play crucial roles in catalyzing reactions, transferring electrons, and transporting and storing oxygen. A discussion of these complex ligands will follow in Section 19.8.

Nomenclature

In Werner's lifetime no system was used to name coordination compounds. Names of the compounds were commonly based on colors and names of discoverers. As the field expanded and more coordination compounds were identified, an orderly system of nomenclature became necessary. A simplified version of this system is summarized by the following rules.

Rules for Naming Coordination Compounds

1. As with any ionic compound, *the cation is named before the anion.*
2. In naming a complex ion, *the ligands are named before the metal ion.*
3. In naming ligands, *an o is added to the root name of an anion.* For example, the halides as ligands are called fluoro, chloro, bromo, and iodo; hydroxide is hydroxo; and cyanide is cyano. *For a neutral ligand, the name of the molecule is used,* with the exception of H_2O, NH_3, CO, and NO, as illustrated in Table 19.14.
4. *The prefixes* mono-, di-, tri-, tetra-, penta-, *and* hexa- *are used to denote the number of simple ligands.* The prefixes *bis-, tris-, tetrakis-,* and so on are also used, especially for more complicated ligands or ones that already contain *di-, tri-,* and so on.
5. *The oxidation state of the central metal ion is designated by a Roman numeral in parentheses.*
6. *When more than one type of ligand is present, ligands are named in alphabetical order.** Prefixes do not affect the order.
7. *If the complex ion has a negative charge, the suffix* -ate *is added to the name of the metal.* Sometimes the Latin name is used to identify the metal (Table 19.15).

---

*In an older system, the negatively charged ligands were named first, followed by neutral ligands, with positively charged ligands named last. We will follow the newer convention in this text.

Table 19.14

Names of Some Common Unidentate Ligands

Neutral Molecules		Anions	
Aqua	H_2O	Fluoro	F^-
Ammine	NH_3	Chloro	Cl^-
Methylamine	CH_3NH_2	Bromo	Br^-
Carbonyl	CO	Iodo	I^-
Nitrosyl	NO	Hydroxo	OH^-
		Cyano	CN^-

Table 19.15

Latin Names Used for Some Metal Ions in Anionic Complex Ions

Metal	Anionic Complex Base Name
Iron	Ferrate
Copper	Cuprate
Lead	Plumbate
Silver	Argentate
Gold	Aurate
Tin	Stannate

These rules are applied in Example 19.1.

◉WL INTERACTIVE EXAMPLE 19.1

Give the systematic name for each of the following coordination compounds.

a. $[Co(NH_3)_5Cl]Cl_2$ **b.** $K_3Fe(CN)_6$ **c.** $[Fe(en)_2(NO_2)_2]_2SO_4$

Solution

a. To determine the oxidation state of the metal ion, we examine the charges of all ligands and counter ions. The ammonia molecules are neutral and each chloride ion has a $1-$ charge, so the cobalt ion must have a $3+$ charge to produce a neutral compound. Since cobalt has the oxidation state $+3$, we use cobalt(III) in the name.

   The ligands include one Cl^- ion and five NH_3 molecules. The chloride ion is designated as *chloro,* and each ammonia molecule is designated *ammine.* The prefix *penta-* indicates that there are five NH_3 ligands present. The name of the complex cation is therefore pentaamminechlorocobalt(III). Note that the ligands are named alphabetically, disregarding the prefix. Since the counter ions are chloride ions, the compound is named as a chloride salt:

$$\underbrace{\text{pentaamminechlorocobalt(III)}}_{\text{Cation}} \underbrace{\text{chloride}}_{\text{Anion}}$$

b. First, we determine the oxidation state of the iron by considering the other charged species. The compound contains three K^+ ions and six CN^- ions. Therefore, the iron must carry a charge of $3+$, giving a total of six positive charges to balance the six negative charges. Thus the complex ion present is $Fe(CN)_6^{3-}$. The cyanide ligands are each designated *cyano,* and the prefix *hexa-* indicates that six are present. Since the complex ion is an anion, we use the Latin name *ferrate.* The oxidation state is indicated by ferrate(III) in the name. The anion name is therefore hexacyanoferrate(III). The cations are K^+ ions, which are simply named potassium. Combining all this gives the name

$$\underbrace{\text{potassium}}_{\text{Cation}} \underbrace{\text{hexacyanoferrate(III)}}_{\text{Anion}}$$

(The common name of this compound is potassium ferricyanide.)

c. We first determine the oxidation state of the iron by looking at the other charged species: four NO_2^- ions and one SO_4^{2-} ion. The ethylenediamine is neutral. Thus the two iron ions must carry a total of six positive charges to

(top) An aqueous solution of $[Co(NH_3)_5Cl]Cl_2$.
(bottom) Solid $K_3Fe(CN)_6$.

balance the six negative charges. This means that each iron has a $+3$ oxidation state and is designated as iron(III).

Since the name ethylenediamine already contains *di*, we use *bis-* instead of *di-* to indicate the presence of two en ligands. The name for NO_2^- as a ligand is *nitro*, and the prefix *di-* indicates the presence of two NO_2^- ligands. The anion is sulfate. Therefore, the compound's name is

$$\underbrace{\text{bis(ethylenediamine)dinitroiron(III)}}_{\text{Cation}} \underbrace{\text{sulfate}}_{\text{Anion}}$$

Since the complex ion is a cation in this case, the Latin name for iron is not used.

⬢WL INTERACTIVE EXAMPLE 19.2

Given the following systematic names, predict the formula of each coordination compound.

a. triamminebromoplatinum(II) chloride

b. potassium hexafluorocobaltate(III)

Solution

a. *Triammine* signifies three ammonia ligands, and *bromo* indicates one bromide ion as a ligand. The oxidation state of platinum is $+2$, as indicated by the Roman numeral II. Thus the complex ion is $[Pt(NH_3)_3Br]^+$. One chloride ion is needed to balance the $1+$ charge of this cation. The formula of the compound is $[Pt(NH_3)_3Br]Cl$. Note that square brackets enclose the complex ion.

b. The complex ion contains six fluoride ligands attached to a Co^{3+} ion to give CoF_6^{3-}. Note the *-ate* ending that indicates that the complex ion is an anion. Three K^+ cations are required to balance the $3-$ charge on the complex ion. Thus the formula is $K_3[CoF_6]$.

19.4 | Isomerism

When two or more species have the same formula but exhibit different properties, they are said to be **isomers**. Although isomers contain exactly the same types and numbers of atoms, the arrangements of their atoms differ, and this leads to different properties. We will consider two main types of isomerism: **structural isomerism**, in which the isomers contain the same atoms but one or more bonds differ, and **stereoisomerism**, in which all of the bonds in the isomers are the same but the spatial arrangements of the atoms are different. Each of these classes also has subclasses (Fig. 19.9), which we will now consider.

Structural Isomerism

The first type of structural isomerism we will consider is **coordination isomerism**, in which the composition of the complex ion varies. For example, $[Cr(NH_3)_5SO_4]Br$ and $[Cr(NH_3)_5Br]SO_4$ are coordination isomers. In the first case, SO_4^{2-} is coordinated to Cr^{3+}, whereas Br^- acts as the counter ion; in the second case, the roles of these ions are reversed.

Another example of coordination isomerism involves the $[Co(en)_3]$ $[Cr(ox)_3]$ and $[Cr(en)_3][Co(ox)_3]$ pair, where ox represents the oxalate ion, a bidentate ligand shown in Table 19.13.

In a second type of structural isomerism, **linkage isomerism**, the composition of the complex ion is the same, but the point of attachment of at least one

Figure 19.9
Some classes of isomers.

(a)

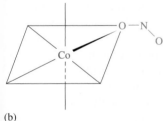

(b)

Figure 19.10
As a ligand, NO_2^- can bond to a metal ion (a) through a lone pair on the nitrogen atom or (b) through a lone pair on one of the oxygen atoms.

of the ligands differs. Two ligands that can attach to metal ions in different ways are thiocyanate, SCN^- (which can bond through lone pairs on the nitrogen or the sulfur atom), and the nitrite ion, NO_2^- (which can bond through lone pairs on the nitrogen or the oxygen atom). For example, the following two compounds are linkage isomers:

$$[Co(NH_3)_4(NO_2)Cl]Cl$$
Tetraamminechloronitrocobalt(III) chloride
(yellow)

$$[Co(NH_3)_4(ONO)Cl]Cl$$
Tetraamminechloronitritocobalt(III) chloride
(red)

In the first case, the NO_2^- ligand is called *nitro* and is attached to Co^{3+} through the nitrogen atom; in the second case, the NO_2^- ligand is called *nitrito* and is attached to Co^{3+} through an oxygen atom (Fig. 19.10).

Stereoisomerism

Stereoisomers have the same bonds, but they exhibit different spatial arrangements of their atoms. One type, **geometrical isomerism,** or ***cis–trans*** **isomerism,** occurs when atoms or groups of atoms can assume different positions around a rigid ring or bond. An important example is the compound $Pt(NH_3)_2Cl_2$, which has a square planar structure. The two possible arrangements of the ligands are shown in Fig. 19.11. In the *cis* isomer, the ammonia molecules are next (*cis*) to each other. In the *trans* isomer, the ammonia molecules are across (*trans*) from each other.

Geometrical isomerism also occurs in octahedral complex ions. For example, the compound $[Co(NH_3)_4Cl_2]Cl$ has *cis* and *trans* isomers (Fig. 19.12).

A second type of stereoisomerism is called **optical isomerism** because the isomers have opposite effects on plane-polarized light. When light is emitted from a source such as a glowing filament, the oscillating electric fields of the

Figure 19.11
(a) The *cis* isomer of $Pt(NH_3)_2Cl_2$ (yellow).
(b) The *trans* isomer of $Pt(NH_3)_2Cl_2$ (pale yellow).

(a)

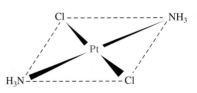

(b)

Chemical Insights — Alfred Werner: Coordination Chemist

During the early and middle parts of the nineteenth century, chemists prepared a large number of colored compounds containing transition metals and other substances such as ammonia, chloride ion, cyanide ion, and water. These compounds were very interesting to chemists who were trying to understand the nature of bonding (Dalton's atomic theory of 1808 was very new at this time), and many theories were suggested to explain these substances. The most widely accepted early theory was the *chain theory,* championed by Sophus Mads Jorgensen (1837–1914), professor of chemistry at the University of Copenhagen. The chain theory got its name from the postulate that metal–ammine* complexes contain chains of NH_3 molecules. For example, Jorgensen proposed the structure

$$Co \begin{matrix} NH_3-Cl \\ -NH_3-NH_3-NH_3-NH_3-Cl \\ NH_3-Cl \end{matrix}$$

for the compound $Co(NH_3)_6Cl_3$. In the late nineteenth century, this theory was used in classrooms around the world to explain the nature of metal–ammine compounds.

However, in 1890 a young Swiss chemist named Alfred Werner, who had just obtained a Ph.D. in the field of organic chemistry, became so interested in these compounds that he apparently even dreamed about them. In the middle of one night, Werner awoke realizing that he had discovered the correct explanation for the constitution of these compounds. Writing furiously the rest of that night and into the late afternoon of the following day, he constructed a scientific paper containing his now famous *coordination theory.* This model postulates an octahedral arrangement of ligands around the Co^{3+} ion, leading to the $Co(NH_3)_6^{3+}$ complex ion with three Cl^- ions as counter ions. Thus Werner's picture of $Co(NH_3)_6Cl_3$ differed greatly from the chain theory.

In his paper on the coordination theory, Werner explained not only the metal–ammine compounds but also most of the other known transition metal compounds, and the importance of his contribution was recognized immediately. He was appointed professor at the University of Zurich, where he spent the rest of his life studying coordination compounds and refining his theory. Alfred Werner was a confident, impulsive man of seemingly boundless energy who was known for his inspiring lectures, his intolerance of incompetence (he once threw a chair at a student who performed poorly on an oral exam), and his intuitive scientific brilliance. For example, he was the first to show that stereochemistry is a general phenomenon, not one exhibited only by carbon, as was previously thought. He also recognized and named many types of isomerism.

For his work on coordination chemistry and stereochemistry, Werner became the fourteenth Nobel Prize winner in chemistry and the first Swiss chemist to be so honored. Werner's work is even more remarkable when one realizes that his ideas preceded any real understanding of the nature of covalent bonds by many years.

---

*Ammine is the name for NH_3 as a ligand.

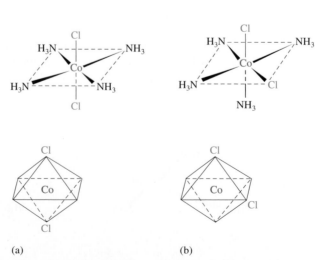

Figure 19.12
(a) The *trans* isomer of $[Co(NH_3)_4Cl_2]^+$. The chloride ligands are directly across from each other. (b) The *cis* isomer of $[Co(NH_3)_4Cl_2]^+$. The chloride ligands in this case share an edge of the octahedron. Because of their different structures, the *trans* isomer of $[Co(NH_3)_4Cl_2]$Cl is green and the *cis* isomer is violet.

(a)   (b)

photons in the beam are oriented randomly, as shown in Fig. 19.13. If this light is passed through a polarizer, only the photons with electric fields oscillating in a single plane remain, constituting *plane-polarized light*.

In 1815 French physicist Jean Biot discovered that certain crystals could rotate the plane of polarization of light. Later, scientists found that solutions of certain compounds could do the same thing (Fig. 19.14). Louis Pasteur was the first to understand this behavior. In 1848 he noted that solid sodium ammonium tartrate ($NaNH_4C_4H_4O_6$) existed as a mixture of two types of crystals, which he painstakingly separated with tweezers. Separate solutions of these two types of crystals rotated plane-polarized light in exactly opposite directions. This led to a connection between optical activity and molecular structure.

We now realize that optical activity is exhibited by molecules that have *nonsuperimposable mirror images*. Your hands are nonsuperimposable mirror images (Fig. 19.15). That is, human hands are related like an object and its

Figure 19.13
Unpolarized light consists of waves vibrating in many different planes (indicated by the arrows). The polarizing filter blocks all waves except those vibrating in a given plane.

Figure 19.14
The rotation of the plane of polarized light by an optically active substance. The angle of rotation is called theta (θ).

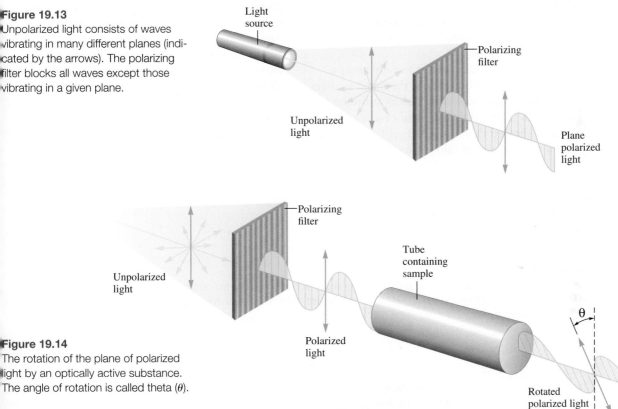

Figure 19.15
A human hand has a nonsuperimposable mirror image. Note that the mirror image of the right hand (while identical to the left hand) cannot be turned in any way to make it identical to (superimposable on) the actual right hand.

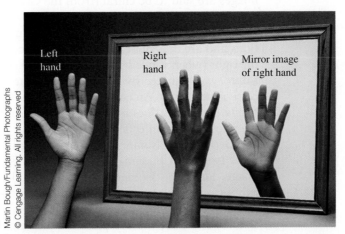

Chemical Insights

The Importance of Being *cis*

Some of the most important advancements of science are the results of accidental discoveries—for example, penicillin, Teflon, and the sugar substitutes cyclamate and aspartame. Another important chance discovery occurred in 1964, when a group of scientists using platinum electrodes to apply an electric field to a colony of *E. coli* bacteria noticed that the bacteria failed to divide but continued to grow, forming long, fibrous cells. Further study revealed that cell division was inhibited by small concentrations of the compounds *cis*-Pt(NH$_3$)$_2$Cl$_2$ and *cis*-Pt(NH$_3$)$_2$Cl$_4$ formed electrolytically in the solution.

Cancerous cells multiply very rapidly because cell division is uncontrolled. Thus these and similar platinum complexes were evaluated as antitumor agents, which inhibit the division of cancer cells. The results showed that *cis*-Pt(NH$_3$)$_2$Cl$_2$ was active against a wide variety of tumors, including testicu-

lar and ovarian tumors, which are very resistant to treatment by more traditional methods. However, although the *cis* complex showed significant antitumor activity, the corresponding *trans* complex had no effect on tumors. This illustrates the importance of isomerism in biological systems. When drugs are synthesized, great care must be taken to obtain the correct isomer.

Unfortunately, although *cis*-Pt(NH$_3$)$_2$Cl$_2$ has proved to be a valuable drug, it has some troublesome side effects, the most serious being kidney damage. As a result, the search continues for even more effective antitumor agents. Promising candidates are shown in Fig. 19.16. Note that they are all *cis* complexes.

Suggested Reading
Ann M. Thayer, "Platinum Drugs Take Their Toll," *C&EN*, June 28 (2010): 24

Figure 19.16
Some *cis* complexes of platinum and palladium that show significant antitumor activity. It is thought that the *cis* complexes work by losing two adjacent ligands and then forming coordinate covalent bonds to adjacent bases on a DNA molecule.

mirror image, and one hand cannot be turned to make it identical to the other. Many molecules show this same feature—for example, the complex ion [Co(en)$_3$]$^{3+}$ shown in Fig. 19.17. Objects that have nonsuperimposable mirror images are said to be **chiral** (from the Greek word for hand, *cheir*).

The isomers of [Co(en)$_3$]$^{3+}$ (Fig. 19.17) are nonsuperimposable mirror images called **enantiomers;** they rotate plane-polarized light in opposite directions and are thus optical isomers. The isomer that rotates the plane of light to the right (when viewed down the beam of oncoming light) is said to be *dextrorotatory,* designated by *d*. The isomer that rotates the plane of light to the left is *levorotatory* (*l*). An equal mixture of the *d* and *l* isomers in solution, called a *racemic mixture,* does not rotate the plane of the polarized light at all because the two opposite effects cancel.

Geometrical isomers are not necessarily optical isomers. For instance, the *trans* isomer of [Co(en)$_2$Cl$_2$]$^+$ shown in Fig. 19.18 is identical to its mirror image. Since this isomer is superimposable on its mirror image, it does not exhibit optical isomerism and is therefore not chiral. On the other hand, *cis*-[Co(en)$_2$Cl$_2$]$^+$ is *not* superimposable on its mirror image; thus a pair of enantiomers exists for the complex ion, making the *cis* isomer chiral.

Figure 19.17
Isomers I and II of [Co(en)₃]³⁺ are mirror images (the mirror image of I is identical to II) that cannot be superimposed. That is, there is no way that I can be turned in space so that it is the same as II.

Mirror image of Isomer I

Isomer I   Isomer II

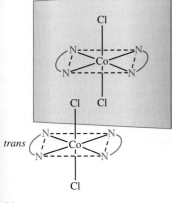

The *trans* isomer and its mirror image are identical. They are not isomers of each other.

Isomer II cannot be superimposed exactly on isomer I. They are not identical structures.

Isomer II has the same structure as the mirror image of isomer I.

trans

cis   Isomer I   Isomer II

(a)   (b)

Figure 19.18
(a) The *trans* isomer of [Co(en)₂Cl₂]⁺ and its mirror image are identical (superimposable). (b) The *cis* isomer of [Co(en)₂Cl₂]⁺ and its mirror image are not superimposable and are thus a pair of optical isomers.

EXAMPLE 19.3

Does the complex ion [Co(NH₃)Br(en)₂] exhibit geometrical isomerism? Does it exhibit optical isomerism?

Solution The complex ion exhibits geometrical isomerism, since the ethylenediamine ligands can be across from or next to each other:

Chemical Insights

Chirality: Why Is It Important?

A molecule is said to be chiral if it can exist as isomers (called enantiomers) that are nonsuperimposable mirror images of each other. We often say these molecules exhibit "handedness," after our nonsuperimposable mirror image left and right hands. Enantiomers rotate plane-polarized light by the same angle but in opposite directions; however, the importance of this type of isomerism goes far beyond this rather curious behavior. In fact, many of the molecules produced by organisms exhibit a specific handedness. This is important because the response of an organism to a particular molecule often depends on how that molecule fits a particular site on a receptor molecule in the organism. Just as a left hand requires a left-handed glove, a left-handed receptor requires a particular enantiomer for a correct fit. Therefore, in designing pharmaceuticals, chemists must be concerned about which enantiomer is the active one—the one that fits the intended receptor.

Ideally, the pharmaceutical should consist of the pure active isomer. One way to obtain the compound as a pure active isomer is to produce the chemical by using organisms, because the production of biomolecules in organisms is stereospecific (yields a specific stereoisomer). For example, amino acids, vitamins, and hormones are naturally produced by yeast in the fermentation of sugar and can be harvested from the ferment. Biotechnology, in which the gene for a particular molecule is inserted into the DNA of a bacterium, provides another approach. Insulin is now produced in this way.

In contrast to the synthesis of biomolecules by organisms where a specific isomer is produced, when chiral molecules are made by "normal" chemical procedures (reactants are mixed and allowed to react), a mixture of the enantiomers is obtained. For example, when one chiral center is present in a molecule, normal chemical synthesis gives an equal mixture of the two mirror image isomers—called a racemic mixture. How does one deal with a pharmaceutical produced as a racemic mixture? One possibility is to administer the drug in its racemic form, assuming that the inactive form (50% of the mixture) will have no effect, positive or negative. In fact, this procedure is being followed for many drugs now on the market. However, it is a procedure that is growing increasingly controversial as evidence mounts that the "inactive" form of the drug may actually produce detrimental effects often totally unrelated to the effect of the active isomer. In effect, a drug administered as a racemic mixture contains a 50% impurity, the effects of which are not well understood.

The alternative to using racemic mixtures is to find a way to produce the substance as a pure isomer or a way to separate the isomers from the racemic mixtures. Both of these options are difficult and thus expensive. However, it is becoming increasingly clear that many pharmaceuticals must be administered as pure isomers to produce the desired results with no side effects. Therefore, a great deal of effort is now being directed toward the synthesis and separation of chiral compounds.

The *cis* isomer of the complex ion also exhibits optical isomerism since its mirror images,

cannot be turned in any way to make them superimposable. Thus these two *cis* isomers are shown to be enantiomers that will rotate plane-polarized light in opposite directions.

Most important, since biomolecules are chiral, their reactions are highly structure-dependent. For example, a drug might have a particular effect because its molecules can bind to chiral molecules in the body. For the binding to be correct, the correct optical isomer of the drug must be administered. Just as the right hand of one person requires the right hand of another to perform a handshake, a given isomer in the body requires a specific isomer of the drug for an interaction to occur. Consequently, the syntheses of drugs, which are usually very complicated molecules, must be carried out in a way that produces the correct "handedness," a requirement that greatly adds to the difficulties in bringing these substances to market.

19.5 | Bonding in Complex Ions: The Localized Electron Model

By this point in your study of chemistry, you no doubt recognize that the localized electron model, although very simple, is a very useful model for describing the bonding in molecules. Recall that a central feature of the model is the formation of hybrid atomic orbitals that are used for sharing electron pairs to form σ bonds between atoms. This same model can be used to account for the bonding in complex ions, but there are two important points to keep in mind.

1. The VSEPR model for predicting structure *does not work for complex ions*. However, we can safely assume that a complex ion with a coordination number of 6 has an octahedral arrangement of ligands and that complexes with two ligands are linear. On the other hand, complex ions with a coordination number of 4 can be either tetrahedral or square planar; there is no reliable way to predict which will occur in a particular case.

2. The interaction between a metal ion and a ligand can be viewed as a Lewis acid–base reaction, with the ligand donating a lone pair of electrons to an *empty* orbital on the metal ion to form a coordinate covalent bond:

Empty metal ion hybrid atomic orbital

Lone pair on the ligand in a hybrid atomic orbital

Coordinate covalent bond

The hybrid orbitals used by the metal ion depend on the number and arrangement of the ligands. For example, accommodating the lone pair from each ammonia molecule in the octahedral $Co(NH_3)_6^{3+}$ ion requires a set of six empty hybrid atomic orbitals with an octahedral arrangement. Recall that an octahedral set of orbitals is formed by the hybridization of two d, one s, and three p orbitals to give six d^2sp^3 orbitals (Fig. 19.19).

The hybrid orbitals predicted for the metal ion in four-coordinate complexes depend on whether the structure is tetrahedral or square planar. For a tetrahedral arrangement of ligands, an sp^3 hybrid set is required (Fig. 19.20). For example, in the tetrahedral $CoCl_4^{2-}$ ion, the Co^{2+} is described as sp^3 hybridized. A square planar arrangement of ligands requires a dsp^2 hybrid orbital set on the metal ion (Fig. 19.20). For example, in square planar $Ni(CN)_4^{2-}$, the Ni^{2+} is described as dsp^2 hybridized.

A linear complex requires two hybrid orbitals 180° from each other. This arrangement is given by an sp hybrid set (Fig. 19.20). Thus in the linear $Ag(NH_3)_2^+$ ion, the Ag^+ is described as sp hybridized.

Although the localized electron model can account in a general way for metal–ligand bonds, it is rarely used today because it cannot predict important properties of complex ions, such as magnetism and color. Thus we will not pursue the model any further.

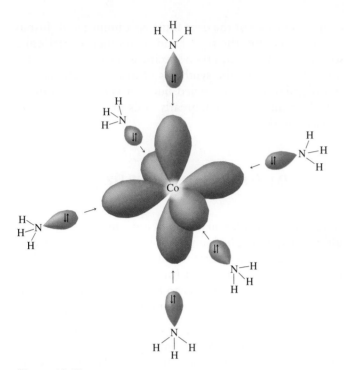

Figure 19.19
A set of six d^2sp^3 hybrid orbitals on Co^{3+} can accept an electron pair from each of six NH_3 ligands to form the $Co(NH_3)_6^{3+}$ ion.

Tetrahedral ligand arrangement; sp^3 hybridization

Square planar ligand arrangement; dsp^2 hybridization

Linear ligand arrangement; sp hybridization

Figure 19.20
The hybrid orbitals required for tetrahedral, square planar, and linear complex ions. The metal ion hybrid orbitals are empty, so the metal ion bonds to the ligands by accepting lone pairs.

19.6 | The Crystal Field Model

The main reason that the localized electron model cannot fully account for the properties of complex ions is that in its simplest form it gives no information about how the energies of the d orbitals are affected by complex ion formation. This is critical because, as we will see, the color and magnetism of complex ions result from changes in the energies of the metal ion d orbitals caused by the metal–ligand interactions.

The **crystal field model** focuses on the energies of the d orbitals. In fact, this model is not so much a bonding model as it is an attempt to account for the colors and magnetic properties of complex ions. In its simplest form, the crystal field model assumes that the ligands can be approximated by *negative point charges* and that metal–ligand bonding is *entirely ionic*.

Octahedral Complexes

We will illustrate the fundamental principles of the crystal field model by applying it to an octahedral complex. Figure 19.21 shows the orientation of the $3d$ orbitals relative to an octahedral arrangement of point-charge ligands. The

Figure 19.21

An octahedral arrangement of point-charge ligands and the orientation of the 3d orbitals.

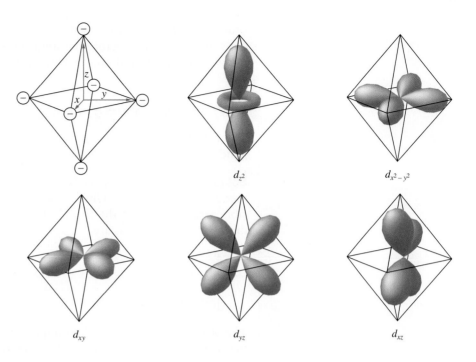

d_{z^2}

$d_{x^2-y^2}$

d_{xy}

d_{yz}

d_{xz}

Figure 19.22

The energies of the 3d orbitals for a metal ion in an octahedral complex. The 3d orbitals are degenerate (all have the same energy) in the free metal ion. In the octahedral complex, the orbitals are split into two sets as shown. The difference in energy between the two sets is designated as Δ (delta).

important thing to note is that two of the orbitals, d_{z^2} and $d_{x^2-y^2}$, point their lobes *directly at* the point-charge ligands, whereas three of the orbitals, d_{xz}, d_{yz}, and d_{xy}, point their lobes *between* the point charges.

To understand the effect of this difference, we need to consider which type of orbital is lower in energy. Because the negative point-charge ligands repel negatively charged electrons, the electrons will prefer the d orbitals farthest from the ligands. In other words, the d_{xz}, d_{yz}, and d_{xy} orbitals (called the t_{2g} set) are at a *lower energy* in the octahedral complex than are the d_{z^2} and $d_{x^2-y^2}$ orbitals (the e_g set). This is shown in Fig. 19.22. The negative point-charge ligands increase the energies of all the d orbitals. However, the orbitals that point at the ligands are raised in energy more than those that point between the ligands.

It is this **splitting of the 3d orbital energies** (symbolized by Δ) that explains the color and magnetism of complex ions of the first-row transition metal ions. For example, in an octahedral complex of Co^{3+} (a metal ion with six 3d electrons), there are two possible ways to place the electrons in the split 3d orbitals (Fig. 19.23). If the splitting produced by the ligands is very large, a situation called the **strong-field case,** the electrons will pair in the lower-energy t_{2g} orbitals. This gives a *diamagnetic* complex in which all electrons are paired. On the

Figure 19.23

Possible electron arrangements in the split 3d orbitals of an octahedral complex of Co^{3+} (electron configuration $3d^6$). (a) In a strong field (large Δ value), the electrons fill the t_{2g} set first, giving a diamagnetic complex. (b) In a weak field (small Δ value), the electrons occupy all five orbitals before any pairing occurs.

other hand, if the splitting is small (the **weak-field case**), the electrons will occupy all five orbitals before pairing occurs. In this case the complex has four unpaired electrons and thus is *paramagnetic*.

◯WL INTERACTIVE EXAMPLE 19.4

The $Fe(CN)_6^{3-}$ ion is known to have one unpaired electron. Does the CN^- ligand produce a strong or weak field?

Solution Since the ligand is CN^- and the overall complex ion charge is $3-$, the metal ion must be Fe^{3+}, which has a $3d^5$ electron configuration. The two possible arrangements of the five electrons in the d orbitals split by the octahedrally arranged ligands are

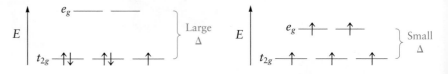

The strong-field case gives one unpaired electron, which agrees with the experimental observation. The CN^- ion is a strong-field ligand toward the Fe^{3+} ion.

The crystal field model allows us to account for the differences in the magnetic properties of $Co(NH_3)_6^{3+}$ and CoF_6^{3-}. The $Co(NH_3)_6^{3+}$ ion is known to be diamagnetic and thus corresponds to the strong-field case, also called the **low-spin case**, since it yields the *minimum* number of unpaired electrons. In contrast, the CoF_6^{3-} ion, which is known to have four unpaired electrons, corresponds to the weak-field case, also known as the **high-spin case**, since it gives the *maximum* number of unpaired electrons.

From studies of many octahedral complexes, we can arrange ligands in order of their ability to produce d-orbital splitting. A partial listing of ligands in this so-called **spectrochemical series** is

$$CN^- > NO_2^- > en > NH_3 > H_2O > OH^- > F^- > Cl^- > Br^- > I^-$$

Strong-field	Weak-field
ligands	ligands
(large Δ)	(small Δ)

The ligands are arranged in order of decreasing Δ values toward a given metal ion.

It has also been observed that *the magnitude of Δ for a given ligand increases as the charge on the metal ion increases*. For example, NH_3 is a weak-field ligand toward Co^{2+} but acts as a strong-field ligand toward Co^{3+}. This makes sense; as the metal ion charge increases, the ligands are drawn closer to the metal ion because of its increased charge density. As the ligands move closer, they cause greater splitting of the d orbitals, thereby producing a larger Δ value.

◯WL INTERACTIVE EXAMPLE 19.5

Predict the number of unpaired electrons in the complex ion $[Cr(CN)_6]^{4-}$.

Solution The net charge of $4-$ means that the metal ion present must be Cr^{2+} $(-6 + 2 = -4)$, which has a $3d^4$ electron configuration. Since CN^- is a strong-

Figure 19.24
The visible spectrum.

Figure 19.25
(a) When white light shines on a filter that absorbs wavelengths in the yellow-green region, the emerging light is violet. (b) Because the complex ion $Ti(H_2O)_6^{3+}$ absorbs yellow-green light, a solution of it is violet.

Filter absorbs yellow-green light

(a)

$Ti(H_2O)_6^{3+}$

(b)

field ligand (see the spectrochemical series), the correct crystal field diagram for $[Cr(CN)_6]^{4-}$ is

The complex ion will have two unpaired electrons. Note that the CN^- ligand produces such a large splitting that two of the electrons will be paired in the same orbital rather than forcing one electron up through the large energy gap Δ.

We have seen how the crystal field model accounts for the magnetic properties of octahedral complexes. The same model also explains the colors of these complex ions. For example, consider $Ti(H_2O)_6^{3+}$, an octahedral complex of Ti^{3+}, which has a $3d^1$ electron configuration. This complex ion is violet because it absorbs light in the middle of the visible region of the spectrum (Fig. 19.24). When a substance absorbs certain wavelengths of light in the visible region, the color of that substance is determined by the wavelengths of visible light that remain. We say that the substance exhibits the color *complementary* to those absorbed. The $Ti(H_2O)_6^{3+}$ ion is violet because it absorbs light in the yellow-green region, thus allowing red light and blue light to pass. The red and blue colors not absorbed produce the observed violet color. This effect is shown schematically in Fig. 19.25. Table 19.16 shows the general relationship between the wavelengths of visible light absorbed and the approximate color observed.

The reason that the $Ti(H_2O)_6^{3+}$ ion absorbs specific wavelengths of visible light can be traced to the transfer of the lone d electron between the split

Table 19.16

Approximate Relationship of Wavelength of Visible Light Absorbed to Color Observed

Absorbed Wavelength in nm (color)	Observed Color
400 (violet)	Greenish yellow
450 (blue)	Yellow
490 (blue-green)	Red
570 (yellow-green)	Violet
580 (yellow)	Dark blue
600 (orange)	Blue
650 (red)	Green

Figure 19.26
The complex ion Ti(H$_2$O)$_6^{3+}$ can absorb visible light in the yellow-green region to transfer the lone d electron from the t_{2g} to the e_g set.

Table 19.17

Several Octahedral Complexes of Cr^{3+} and Their Colors

Isomer	Color
[Cr(H$_2$O)$_6$]Cl$_3$	Violet
[Cr(H$_2$O)$_5$Cl]Cl$_2$	Blue-green
[Cr(H$_2$O)$_4$Cl$_2$]Cl	Green
[Cr(NH$_3$)$_6$]Cl$_3$	Yellow
[Cr(NH$_3$)$_5$Cl]Cl$_2$	Purple
[Cr(NH$_3$)$_4$Cl$_2$]Cl	Violet

d orbitals (Fig. 19.26). A given photon of light can be absorbed by a molecule only if the wavelength of the light provides the exact amount of energy needed by the molecule. In other words, whether a wavelength is absorbed is determined by the relationship

$$\Delta E = \frac{hc}{\lambda}$$

where ΔE represents the energy spacing in the molecule (we have used simply Δ in this chapter) and λ represents the wavelength of light needed to provide exactly that amount of energy. Because the d-orbital splitting in most octahedral complexes corresponds to the energies of photons in the visible region, octahedral complex ions are usually colored.

Since the ligands coordinated to a given metal ion determine the size of the d-orbital splitting, the color changes as the ligands are changed. This occurs because a change in Δ means a change in the wavelength of light is needed to transfer electrons between the t_{2g} and e_g orbitals. Several octahedral complexes of Cr^{3+} and their colors are listed in Table 19.17.

Other Coordination Geometries

Using the same principles developed for octahedral complexes, we will now consider complexes with other geometries. For example, Fig. 19.27 shows a tetrahedral arrangement of point charges in relation to the $3d$ orbitals of a metal ion. There are two important facts to note.

1. None of the $3d$ orbitals "points at the ligands" in the tetrahedral arrangement, as the $d_{x^2-y^2}$ and d_{z^2} orbitals do in the octahedral case. Thus the tetrahedrally arranged ligands do not differentiate the d orbitals as much in the tetrahedral case as in the octahedral case. That is, the difference in energy between the split d orbitals is significantly less in tetrahedral com-

Figure 19.27
(a) Tetrahedral and octahedral arrangements of ligands shown inscribed in cubes. Note that in the two types of arrangements, the point charges occupy opposite parts of the cube: The octahedral point charges are at the centers of the cube faces, whereas the tetrahedral point charges occupy opposite corners of the cube. (b) The orientations of the $3d$ orbitals relative to the tetrahedral set of point charges.

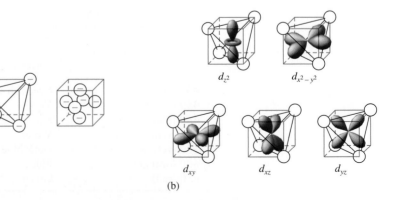

Figure 19.28
The crystal field diagrams for octahedral and tetrahedral complexes. The relative energies of the sets of d orbitals are reversed. For a given type of ligand, the splitting is much larger for the octahedral complex ($\Delta_{oct} > \Delta_{tet}$). This occurs because in the octahedral arrangement the d_{z^2} and $d_{x^2-y^2}$ orbitals point their lobes directly at the point charges and are thus relatively high in energy.

plexes. Although we will not derive it here, the tetrahedral splitting is $\frac{4}{9}$ that of the octahedral splitting for a given ligand and metal ion:

$$\Delta_{tet} = \tfrac{4}{9}\Delta_{oct}$$

2. Although not exactly pointing at the ligands, the d_{xy}, d_{xz}, and d_{yz} orbitals are closer to the point charges than are the d_{z^2} and $d_{x^2-y^2}$ orbitals. This means that the d-orbital splitting is opposite to that for the octahedral arrangement. The two arrangements are contrasted in Fig. 19.28. Because the d-orbital splitting is relatively small for the tetrahedral case, the weak-field case (high-spin case) *always* applies. There are no known ligands powerful enough to produce the strong-field case in a tetrahedral complex.

⬤WL INTERACTIVE EXAMPLE 19.6

Give the crystal field diagram for the tetrahedral complex ion $CoCl_4^{2-}$.

Solution The complex ion contains Co^{2+}, which has a $3d^7$ electron configuration. The splitting of the d orbitals will be small since this is a tetrahedral complex, giving the high-spin case with three unpaired electrons.

The crystal field model also applies to square planar and linear complexes. The crystal field diagrams for these cases are shown in Fig. 19.29. The ranking of orbitals in these diagrams can be explained by considering the relative orientations of the point charges and the orbitals. The diagram in Fig. 19.28 for the octahedral arrangement can be used to obtain these orientations. We can obtain the square planar complex by starting with an octahedral arrangement of six point charges and then removing the two point charges along the z axis. Removal of the two point charges on the z axis greatly lowers the energy of d_{z^2}. Now only the four lobes of the $d_{x^2-y^2}$ orbital point directly at the four remaining point charges. Therefore, $d_{x^2-y^2}$ is the highest-energy orbital for the square planar case. The relative energies of the remaining orbitals depend on how close their lobes are to the four point charges. The ordering of d_{z^2} and d_{xy} is not entirely obvious because d_{z^2} has a significant band of electron density centered in the xy plane. We will not deal with this issue here. We can obtain the linear complex from the octahedral arrangement by arbitrarily leaving the two li-

Figure 19.29
(a) The crystal field diagram for a square planar complex oriented in the xy plane with ligands along the x and y axes. The position of the d_{z^2} orbital is higher than those of the d_{xz} and d_{yz} orbitals because of the "doughnut" of electron density in the xy plane. The actual position of d_{z^2} is somewhat uncertain and varies in different square planar complexes. (b) The crystal field diagram for a linear complex where the ligands lie along the z axis.

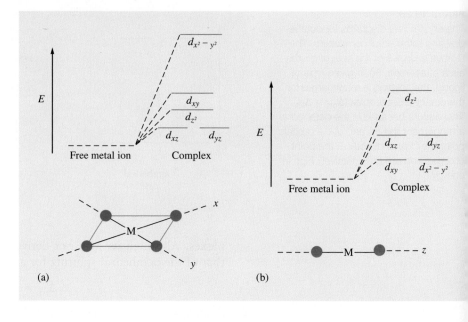

(a) (b)

gands along the z axis and removing the four in the xy plane. This means that only the d_{z^2} orbital points at the ligands and is highest in energy.

19.7 | The Molecular Orbital Model

Although quite successful in accounting for the magnetic and spectral (light absorption) properties of complex ions, the crystal field model has limited use other than explaining those properties dependent on the d-orbital splitting. For example, the model gives a very crude and misleading view of the nature of the metal–ligand bonding.

Of the various models in their simplest forms, the molecular orbital (MO) model gives the most realistic view of the bonding in complex ions. Recall from our discussions in Chapter 14 that the MO model postulates that a new set of orbitals characteristic of the molecule is formed from the atomic orbitals of the component atoms. To illustrate how this model can be applied to complex ions, we will describe the MOs in an octahedral complex of general formula ML_6^{n+}. To keep things as simple as possible, we will focus only on those ligand orbitals having lone pairs that interact with the metal ion valence orbitals ($3d$, $4s$, and $4p$). There are two important considerations in predicting how atomic orbitals will interact to form MOs:

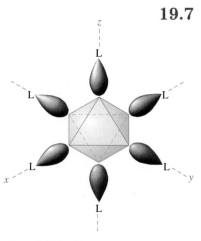

Figure 19.30
An octahedral arrangement of ligands showing their lone pair orbitals.

1. *Extent of orbital overlap.* Atomic orbitals must have a net overlap in space to form MOs. Figure 19.30 shows an octahedral arrangement of ligands with lone pair orbitals. Recall from our previous discussion that two of the metal ion's $3d$ orbitals (d_{z^2} and $d_{x^2-y^2}$) point at the ligands and thus will form MOs with the ligand lone pair orbitals. On the other hand, the d_{xy}, d_{xz}, and d_{yz} orbitals point *between* the ligands and thus will not be involved in the σ bonding with the ligands. The spherical $4s$ orbital of the metal ion overlaps with all the ligand lone pair orbitals, and each of the $4p$ orbitals overlaps with pairs of ligand lone pair orbitals on the three coordinate axes. Thus the d_{z^2}, $d_{x^2-y^2}$, $4s$, $4p_x$, $4p_y$, and $4p_z$ orbitals will be involved in the σ MOs in the complex ion.

2. *Relative orbital energies.* Atomic orbitals that are close in energy will interact more strongly than those widely separated in energy.

Figure 19.31

The MO energy-level diagram for an octahedral complex ion ML_6^{n+}. The e_g^* MOs are essentially pure d_{z^2} and $d_{x^2-y^2}$ orbitals of the metal ion. Little mixing with the ligand orbitals occurs because of the large energy difference between the $3d$ and ligand orbitals.

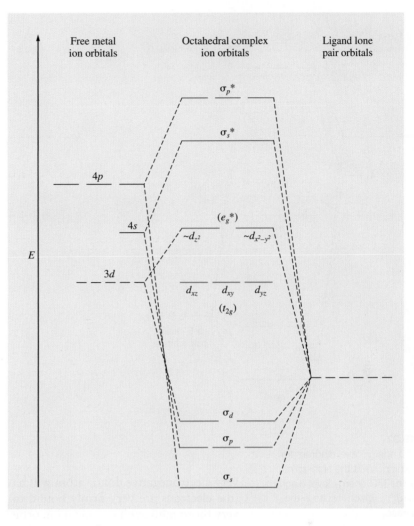

The MO model was introduced in Section 14.2.

When we apply these principles to the general complex ML_6^{n+}, we obtain the energy-level diagram shown in Fig. 19.31. Note that the σ_s, σ_p, and σ_d MOs are bonding MOs; they are *lower* in energy than the ligand orbitals and metal ion orbitals that mix to form them. Electrons in these MOs have lower energies than they do in either the isolated metal ion or the ligands. These bonding electrons are mainly responsible for the stability of the complex ion.

Because the d_{xz}, d_{yz}, and d_{xy} orbitals (the t_{2g} set) of the metal ion do not overlap with the ligand orbitals, they remain unchanged. Thus they have the same energy in the complex ion as they had in the free metal ion and make no contribution to the stability of the complex. They are called *nonbonding orbitals*.

The e_g^* MOs are antibonding orbitals, since they are higher in energy than the atomic orbitals that mix to form them. Since electrons in these orbitals have higher energies than they do in the free metal ion, they destabilize the complex ion relative to the separated metal ion and ligands. However, *the most important characteristic of the e_g^* orbitals is that they are primarily composed of d_{z^2} and $d_{x^2-y^2}$ atomic orbitals*, with relatively little contribution from ligand orbitals. This lack of mixing is caused by the large energy difference between the ligand orbitals and the metal ion $3d$ orbitals. Thus we can see that the MO model predicts the same type of d-orbital splitting as the crystal field model, with the added advantage of giving a much more realistic picture of both the metal–ligand bonding interaction and the origin of the splitting. Because it is a more realistic physical model, we can use the MO model to explain why different ligands produce different magnitudes of splitting. In particular, a ligand with a

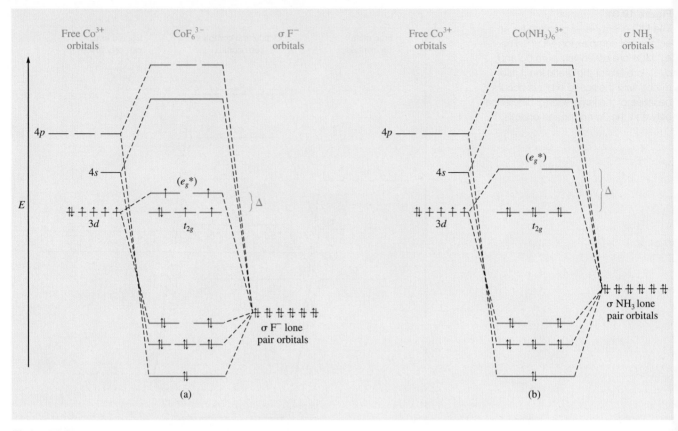

Figure 19.32
(a) The MO energy-level diagram for CoF_6^{3-}, which yields the high-spin case. (b) The MO energy-level diagram for $Co(NH_3)_6^{3+}$, which results in the low-spin case.

very electronegative donor atom will have lone pair orbitals of very low energy (the electrons are very firmly bound to the ligand); these orbitals do not mix very thoroughly with the metal ion orbitals. This will result in a small difference between the t_{2g} (nonbonding) and e_g^* (antibonding) orbitals. In other words, in this case the e_g orbitals are not much perturbed by the small amount of mixing that occurs. This means that the e_g orbital energies are not changed much by complex ion formation. For example, in CoF_6^{3-} [Fig. 19.32(a)] the low-energy orbitals of the very electronegative fluoride ion ligands mix only to a small extent with the cobalt ion orbitals. A small amount of d-orbital splitting results, giving the high-spin case.

On the other hand, in $Co(NH_3)_6^{3+}$ the ammonia lone pair orbitals are closer in energy to the metal ion orbitals, a situation that produces a larger degree of mixing between the two sets of orbitals. This in turn gives a relatively large amount of d-orbital splitting, and the low-spin case results [Fig. 19.32(b)].

We have seen that the MO model correctly predicts the d-orbital splitting in octahedral complexes, thereby accounting for the magnetic and spectral properties of these species. Moreover, it has a major advantage in that it accounts in a realistic way for metal–ligand bonding. However, it suffers from the disadvantage of being much more complicated to apply than the crystal field model. To take advantage of the relative strengths of the MO and crystal field models, the two have been combined to give the **ligand field model.** We will not consider the details of this model here.

The MO model can be applied to all types of complex ions, although we will not extend the model to other cases here. In addition, note that in our use of the MO model to describe octahedral complexes, we considered only σ bonding effects to keep the model as simple as possible. For a complete treatment of complex ions, π bonding interactions also would have to be considered.

Transition Metal Ions Lend Color to Gems

The beautiful pure color of gems, so valued by cultures everywhere, arises from trace transition metal ion impurities in minerals that would otherwise be colorless. For example, the stunning red of a ruby, the most valuable of all gemstones, is caused by Cr^{3+} ions, which replace about 1% of the Al^{3+} ions in the mineral corundum, which is a form of aluminum oxide (Al_2O_3) that is nearly as hard as diamond. In the corundum structure, the Cr^{3+} ions are surrounded by six oxide ions at the vertices of an octahedron. This leads to the characteristic octahedral splitting of chromium's $3d$ orbitals, such that the Cr^{3+} ions absorb strongly in the blue-violet and yellow-green regions of the visible spectrum but transmit red light to give the characteristic ruby color. (On the other hand, if some of the Al^{3+} ions in corundum are replaced by a mixture of Fe^{2+}, Fe^{3+}, and Ti^{4+} ions, the gem is a sapphire with its brilliant blue color, or if some of the Al^{3+} ions are replaced by Fe^{3+} ions, the stone is a yellow topaz.)

Emeralds are derived from the mineral beryl, which is a beryllium aluminum silicate (empirical formula $3BeO \cdot Al_2O_3 \cdot 6SiO_2$). When some of the Al^{3+} ions in beryl are replaced by Cr^{3+} ions, the characteristic green color of emerald results. In this environment the splitting of the Cr^{3+} $3d$ orbitals causes it to strongly absorb yellow and blue-violet light and to transmit green light.

A gem closely related to ruby and emerald is alexandrite, named after Alexander II of Russia. This gem is based on the mineral chrysoberyl, a beryllium aluminate with the empirical formula $BeO \cdot Al_2O_3$ in which approximately 1% of the Al^{3+} ions are replaced by Cr^{3+} ions. In the chrysoberyl environment, Cr^{3+} absorbs strongly in the yellow region of the spectrum. Alexandrite has the interesting property of changing colors depending

Photos Courtesy, International Colored Gemstone Association

Alexandrite is a bluish color in sunlight and changes to red in incandescent light.

on the light source. When the first alexandrite stone was discovered deep in a mine in the Russian Ural Mountains in 1831, it appeared to be a deep red color in the firelight of the miners' lamps. However, when the stone was brought to the surface, its color was blue. This seemingly magical color change occurs because the firelight of a miner's helmet is rich in the yellow and red wavelengths of the visible spectrum but does not contain much blue. Absorption of the yellow by the stone produces a reddish color. However, daylight has much more intensity in the blue region than firelight. Thus the extra blue in the light transmitted by the stone gives it a bluish color in daylight.

Once the structure of a natural gem is known, it is usually not very difficult to make the gem artificially. For example, rubies and sapphires are made on a large scale by fusing $Al(OH)_3$ with the appropriate transition metal salts at about 1200°C to make the "doped" corundum. With these techniques gems of astonishing size can be manufactured. Rubies as large as 10 lb and sapphires up to 100 lb have been synthesized. Smaller synthetic stones produced for jewelry are virtually identical to the corresponding natural stones, and it takes great skill for a gemologist to tell the difference.

19.8 | The Biological Importance of Coordination Complexes

The ability of metal ions to coordinate with and then release ligands and to easily undergo oxidation and reduction makes them ideal for use in biological systems. For example, metal ion complexes are used in humans for the transport and storage of oxygen, as electron transfer agents, as catalysts, and as drugs. Most of the first-row transition metals are essential for human health, as is summarized in Table 19.18. We will concentrate on iron's role in biological systems, since several of its coordination complexes have been studied extensively.

Iron plays a central role in almost all living cells. In mammals the principal source of energy comes from the oxidation of carbohydrates, proteins, and fats. Although oxygen is the oxidizing agent for these processes, it does not react directly with the nutrient molecules. Instead, the electrons from the breakdown of these nutrients are passed along a complex chain of molecules, called the *respiratory chain,* eventually reaching the O_2 molecule. The principal electron transfer molecules in the respiratory chain are iron-containing species called **cytochromes,** consisting of two main parts: an iron complex called **heme** and a protein. The structure of the heme complex is shown in Fig. 19.33. Note that it contains an iron ion (it can be either Fe^{2+} or Fe^{3+}) coordinated to a rather complicated planar ligand called a **porphyrin.** As a class, porphyrins all contain the same central ring structure but have different substituent groups at the edges of the rings. The various porphyrin molecules act as tetradentate ligands for many metal ions, including iron, cobalt, and magnesium. In fact, *chlorophyll,* a substance essential to the process of photosynthesis, is a magnesium–porphyrin complex of the type shown in Fig. 19.34.

In addition to participating in the transfer of electrons from nutrients to oxygen, iron plays a principal role in the transport and storage of oxygen in mammalian blood and tissues. Oxygen is stored using a molecule called **myoglobin,** which consists of a heme complex and a protein in a structure very

A protein is a large molecule assembled from α-amino acids, which have the general structure

$$\text{H}_2\text{N}-\overset{\overset{\text{R}}{|}}{\underset{\underset{\text{H}}{|}}{\text{C}}}-\text{COOH}$$

where R varies.

Table 19.18

The First-Row Transition Metals and Their Biological Significance

First-Row Transition Metal	Biological Function(s)
Scandium	None known
Titanium	None known
Vanadium	None known in humans
Chromium	Assists insulin in the control of blood sugar; may also be involved in the control of cholesterol
Manganese	Necessary for a number of enzymatic reactions
Iron	Component of hemoglobin and myoglobin; involved in the electron transport chain
Cobalt	Component of vitamin B_{12}, which is essential for the metabolism of carbohydrates, fats, and proteins
Nickel	Component of the enzymes urease and hydrogenase
Copper	Component of several enzymes; assists in iron storage; involved in the production of color pigments of hair, skin, and eyes
Zinc	Component of insulin and many enzymes

Figure 19.33
The heme complex, in which an Fe^{2+} ion is coordinated to four nitrogen atoms of a planar porphyrin ligand.

similar to that of the cytochromes. In myoglobin the Fe^{2+} ion is coordinated to four nitrogen atoms of the porphyrin ring and to one nitrogen atom of the protein chain, as shown in Fig. 19.35. Since Fe^{2+} is normally six-coordinate, this leaves one position open for attachment of an O_2 molecule.

One especially interesting feature of myoglobin is that it involves an O_2 molecule attaching directly to Fe^{2+}. However, if gaseous O_2 is bubbled into an aqueous solution containing "bare" heme (no protein attached), the Fe^{2+} is immediately oxidized to Fe^{3+}. This oxidation of the Fe^{2+} in heme does not happen in myoglobin. This fact is of crucial importance because Fe^{3+} does not form a coordinate covalent bond with O_2. Therefore, myoglobin would not function if the bound Fe^{2+} could be oxidized. Since Fe^{2+} in the "bare" heme complex can be oxidized, it must be the protein that somehow prevents the oxidation. How?

Figure 19.34
Chlorophyll is a porphyrin complex of Mg^{2+}. There are two similar forms of chlorophyll, one of which is shown here.

Figure 19.35

A representation of the myoglobin molecule. The Fe^{2+} ion is coordinated to four nitrogen atoms in the porphyrin of the heme (represented by the disk) and one nitrogen in the protein chain. This leaves a sixth coordination position (indicated by the W) available for an oxygen molecule.

Research results indicate that the oxidation of Fe^{2+} to Fe^{3+} involves an oxygen bridge between two iron ions (the circles indicate the ligands):

The bulky protein around the heme group in myoglobin prevents two myoglobin molecules from getting close enough to form the oxygen bridge; therefore, oxidation of the Fe^{2+} is prevented.

The transport of O_2 in the blood is carried out by **hemoglobin,** a molecule consisting of four myoglobin-like units, as shown in Fig. 19.36. Each hemoglobin can therefore bind four O_2 molecules to form a bright red diamagnetic complex. The diamagnetism indicates that oxygen is a strong-field ligand toward Fe^{2+}, which has a $3d^6$ electron configuration. When the oxygen molecule is released, a water molecule occupies the sixth coordination position around each Fe^{2+}, yielding a bluish paramagnetic complex (H_2O is a weak-field ligand toward Fe^{2+}) that gives venous blood its characteristic bluish tint.

Hemoglobin dramatically demonstrates how sensitive the function of a biomolecule is to its structure. In certain people, in the synthesis of the proteins needed for hemoglobin, an improper amino acid is inserted into the protein in two places. This may not seem very serious, since several hundred amino acids are present. However, because the incorrectly inserted amino acid has a non-polar substituent instead of the polar one found on the proper amino acid, the hemoglobin drastically changes its shape. The red blood cells are then sickle-shaped rather than disk-shaped, as shown in Fig. 19.37. The misshapen cells can aggregate, causing clogging of tiny capillaries. This condition, known as *sickle cell anemia,* is the subject of intense research.

Our knowledge of the workings of hemoglobin allows us to understand the effects of high altitudes on humans. The reaction between hemoglobin and oxygen can be represented by the following equilibrium:

$$Hb(aq) + 4O_2(g) \rightleftharpoons Hb(O_2)_4(aq)$$

Hemoglobin   Oxyhemoglobin

Figure 19.36

A representation of the hemoglobin structure. There are two slightly different types of protein chains (α and β). Each hemoglobin has two α chains and two β chains, each with a heme complex near the center. Thus each hemoglobin molecule can complex with four O_2 molecules.

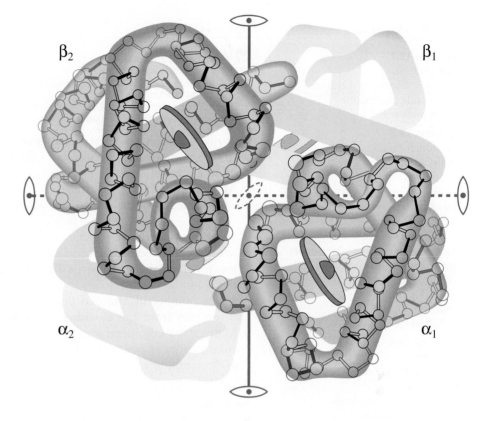

Figure 19.37

A normal red blood cell (left) and a sickle cell, both magnified 18,000 times.

At high altitudes, where the oxygen content of the air is lower than at sea level, the position of this equilibrium will shift to the left, according to Le Châtelier's principle. Because less oxyhemoglobin is formed, fatigue, dizziness, and even a serious illness called *high-altitude sickness* can result. One way to combat this problem is to use supplemental oxygen, as most high-altitude mountain climbers do. However, this is impractical for people who live at high elevations. In fact, the human body adapts to the lower oxygen concentrations by making more hemoglobin, causing the equilibrium to shift back to the right. Someone moving from Chicago to Boulder, Colorado (elevation 5300 feet), would notice the effects of the new altitude for a couple of weeks, but as the hemoglobin level increases, the effects disappear. This change is called *high-altitude acclimatization*, which explains why athletes who want to compete at high elevations should practice under such conditions for several weeks prior to the event.

Our understanding of the biological role of iron also enables us to explain the toxicities of substances such as carbon monoxide and the cyanide ion. Both CO and CN^- are very good ligands toward iron and so can interfere with the normal workings of the iron complexes in the body. For example, carbon monoxide has about 200 times the affinity for the Fe^{2+} in hemoglobin as oxygen does. The resulting stable complex, **carboxyhemoglobin**, prevents the normal uptake of O_2, thus depriving the body of needed oxygen. Asphyxiation can result if enough carbon monoxide is present in the air. The mechanism for the toxicity of the cyanide ion is somewhat different. Cyanide coordinates strongly to cytochrome oxidase, an iron-containing cytochrome enzyme that catalyzes the oxidation–reduction reactions of certain cytochromes. The coordinated cyanide thus prevents the electron transfer process, causing rapid death. Because of its behavior, cyanide is called a *respiratory inhibitor.*

Key Terms

Section 19.1
complex ion
first-row transition metals
lanthanide contraction
lanthanide series

Section 19.3
coordination compound
counter ion
oxidation state
coordination number
ligand
Lewis acid (electron-pair
acceptor)
Lewis base (electron-pair donor)
coordinate covalent bond
monodentate (unidentate) ligand
chelating ligand (chelate)
bidentate ligand
polydentate ligand

Section 19.4
isomers
structural isomerism
stereoisomerism
coordination isomerism
linkage isomerism
geometrical (*cis–trans*) isomerism
cis isomer
trans isomer
optical isomerism
chiral
enantiomers

Section 19.6
crystal field model
d-orbital splitting
strong-field (low-spin) case
weak-field (high-spin) case
spectrochemical series

Section 19.7
ligand field model

Section 19.8
cytochromes
heme
porphyrin
myoglobin
hemoglobin
carboxyhemoglobin

For Review

OWL and **go Chemistry**
Sign in at **www.cengage.com/owl** to:
- View tutorials and simulations, develop problem-solving skills, and complete online homework assigned by your professor.
- Download Go Chemistry mini lecture modules for quick review and exam prep from OWL (or purchase them at **www.cengagebrain.com**)

First-row transition metals (scandium–zinc)
- All have one or more electrons in the $4s$ orbital and various numbers of $3d$ electrons
- All exhibit metallic properties
  - A particular element often shows more than one oxidation state in its compounds
- Most compounds are colored, and many are paramagnetic
- Most commonly form coordination compounds containing a complex ion involving ligands (Lewis bases) attached to a central transition metal ion
  - The number of attached ligands (called the coordination number) can vary from 2 to 8, with 4 and 6 being most common
- Many transition metal ions have major biologic importance in molecules such as enzymes and those that transport and store oxygen
  - Chelating ligands form more than one bond to the transition metal ion

Isomerism
- Isomers: two or more compounds with the same formula but different properties
  - Coordination isomerism: the composition of the coordination sphere varies
  - Linkage isomerism: the point of attachment of one or more ligands varies
  - Stereoisomerism: isomers have identical bonds but different spatial arrangements
    - Geometric isomerism: ligands assume different relative positions in the coordination sphere; examples are *cis* and *trans* isomers
    - Optical isomerism: molecules with nonsuperimposable mirror images rotate plane-polarized light in opposite directions

Spectral and magnetic properties
- Usually explained in terms of the crystal field model
- Model assumes the ligands are point charges that split the energies of the $3d$ orbitals
- Color and magnetism are explained in terms of how the $3d$ electrons occupy the split $3d$ energy levels
  - Strong-field case: relatively large orbital splitting
  - Weak-field case: relatively small orbital splitting

Metallurgy
- The processes connected with separating a metal from its ore
  - The minerals in ores are often converted to oxides (roasting) before being reduced to the metal (smelting)
- The metallurgy of iron: most common method for reduction uses a blast furnace; process involves iron ore, coke, and limestone
  - Impure product (~90% iron) is called pig iron
- Steel is manufactured by oxidizing the impurities in pig iron

Discussion Questions

These questions are designed to be considered by groups of students in class. Often these questions work well for introducing a particular topic in class.

1. You isolate a compound with the formula $PtCl_4 \cdot 2KCl$. From electrical conductance tests of an aqueous solution of the compound, you find that three ions are present, and you also notice that the addition of $AgNO_3$ does not cause a precipitate. Give the formula for this compound that shows the complex ion present. Explain your findings, and name this compound.

2. Both $Ni(NH_3)_4{}^{2+}$ and $Ni(CN)_4{}^{2-}$ have four ligands. The first is paramagnetic and the second is diamagnetic. Are the complex ions tetrahedral or square planar? Explain.

3. Which is more likely to be paramagnetic, $Fe(CN)_6{}^{4-}$ or $Fe(H_2O)_6{}^{2+}$? Explain.

4. A metal ion in a high-spin octahedral complex has two more unpaired electrons than the same ion does in a low-spin octahedral complex. Name some possible metal ions for which this arrangement would apply.

5. Discuss the advantages and disadvantages of the molecular orbital model and the crystal field model. Under which circumstances is it more useful to use the MO model? The crystal field model?

Exercises

OWL Interactive versions of these problems may be assigned in OWL.

A blue exercise number indicates that the answer to that exercise appears at the back of this book and a solution appears in the *Solutions Guide*.

Transition Metals

6. Write electron configurations for each of the following.
   a. Ti, Ti^{2+}, Ti^{4+}
   b. Re, Re^{2+}, Re^{3+}
   c. Ir, Ir^{2+}, Ir^{3+}

7. Write electron configurations for each of the following.
   a. Cr, Cr^{2+}, Cr^{3+}
   b. Cu, Cu^+, Cu^{2+}
   c. V, V^{2+}, V^{3+}

8. What two first-row transition metals have unexpected electron configurations? A statement in the text says that first-row transition metal ions do not have $4s$ electrons. Why not? Why do transition metal ions often have several oxidation states, whereas representative metals generally have only one?

9. What is the lanthanide contraction? How does the lanthanide contraction affect the properties of the $4d$ and $5d$ transition metals?

10. We expect the atomic radius to increase down a group in the periodic table. Can you suggest why the atomic radius of hafnium breaks this rule? (See the following data.)

Element	Atomic Radius (Å)	Element	Atomic Radius (Å)
Sc	1.57	Ti	1.477
Y	1.693	Zr	1.593
La	1.915	Hf	1.476

11. Molybdenum is obtained as a by-product of copper mining or is mined directly (primary deposits are in the Rocky Mountains in Colorado). In both cases it is obtained as MoS_2, which is then converted to MoO_3. The MoO_3 can be used directly in the production of stainless steel for high-speed tools (which accounts for about 85% of the molybdenum used). Molybdenum can be purified by dissolving MoO_3 in aqueous ammonia and crystallizing ammonium molybdate. Depending on conditions, either $(NH_4)_2Mo_2O_7$ or $(NH_4)_6Mo_7O_{24} \cdot 4H_2O$ is obtained.
   a. Give names for MoS_2 and MoO_3.
   b. What is the oxidation state of Mo in each of the compounds mentioned above?

12. Titanium dioxide, the most widely used white pigment, occurs naturally but is often colored by the presence of impurities. The chloride process is often used in purifying rutile, a mineral form of titanium dioxide.
   a. Show that the unit cell for rutile, illustrated below, conforms to the formula TiO_2. (*Hint:* Recall the discussion in Section 16.4.)

● O   ◔ Ti

   b. The reactions for the chloride process are

$$2TiO_2(s) + 3C(s) + 4Cl_2(g) \xrightarrow{950°C} 2TiCl_4(g) + CO_2(g) + 2CO(g)$$

$$TiCl_4(g) + O_2(g) \xrightarrow{1000-1400°C} TiO_2(s) + 2Cl_2(g)$$

   Assign oxidation states to the elements in both reactions. Which elements are being reduced, and which are being oxidized? Identify the oxidizing agent and the reducing agent in each reaction.

13. The melting and boiling points of the titanium tetrahalides are given below.

	bp (°C)	mp (°C)
TiF_4	284	—
$TiCl_4$	−24	136.5
$TiBr_4$	38	233.5
TiI_4	155	377

Rationalize these data in terms of the bonding in and the intermolecular forces among these compounds.

14. Iron is present in the earth's crust in many types of minerals. The iron oxide minerals are hematite (Fe_2O_3) and magnetite (Fe_3O_4). What is the oxidation state of iron in each mineral? The iron ions in magnetite are a mixture of Fe^{2+} and Fe^{3+} ions. What is the ratio of Fe^{3+} to Fe^{2+} ions in magnetite? The formula for magnetite is usually written as $FeO \cdot Fe_2O_3$. Does this make sense? Explain.

15. Chromium(VI) forms two different oxyanions, the orange dichromate ion ($Cr_2O_7^{2-}$) and the yellow chromate ion (CrO_4^{2-}). The equilibrium reaction between the two ions is

$$Cr_2O_7^{2-}(aq) + H_2O(l) \rightleftharpoons 2CrO_4^{2-}(aq) + 2H^+(aq)$$

The following pictures show what happens when sodium hydroxide is added to a dichromate solution.

Explain what happened.

Coordination Compounds

16. Define each of the following terms.
    a. coordination compound
    b. complex ion
    c. counter ions
    d. coordination number
    e. ligand
    f. chelate
    g. bidentate

17. How would transition metal ions be classified using the Lewis definition of acids and bases? What must a ligand have to bond to a metal? What do we mean when we say that a bond is a "coordinate covalent bond"?

18. When a metal ion has a coordination number of 2, 4, or 6, what are the observed geometries and associated bond angles? For each of the following, give the correct formulas for the complex ions.
    a. linear Ag^+ complex ions having CN^- ligands
    b. tetrahedral Cu^+ complex ions having H_2O ligands
    c. tetrahedral Mn^{2+} complex ions having oxalate ligands
    d. square planar Pt^{2+} complex ions having NH_3 ligands
    e. octahedral Fe^{3+} complex ions having EDTA ligands
    f. octahedral Co^{2+} complex ions having Cl^- ligands
    g. octahedral Cr^{3+} complex ions having ethylenediamine ligands

19. The compound cisplatin, $Pt(NH_3)_2Cl_2$, has been studied extensively as an antitumor agent. The reaction for the synthesis of cisplatin is:

$$K_2PtCl_4(aq) + 2NH_3(aq) \longrightarrow Pt(NH_3)_2Cl_2(s) + 2KCl(aq)$$

Write the electron configuration for platinum ion in cisplatin. Most d^8 transition metal ions exhibit square planar geometry. With this and the name in mind, draw the structure of cisplatin.

20. What is the electron configuration for the transition metal ion(s) in each of the following compounds?
    a. $(NH_4)_2[Fe(H_2O)_2Cl_4]$
    b. $[Co(NH_3)_2(NH_2CH_2CH_2NH_2)_2]I_2$
    c. $Na_2[TaF_7]$
    d. $[Pt(NH_3)_4I_2][PtI_4]$
    Pt forms +2 and +4 oxidation states in compounds.

21. Name the following complex ions:

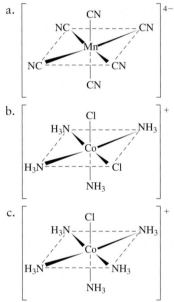

22. Name the following coordination compounds.
    a. $[Co(NH_3)_6]Cl_2$
    b. $[Co(H_2O)_6]I_3$
    c. $K_2[PtCl_4]$
    d. $K_4[PtCl_6]$
    e. $[Co(NH_3)_5Cl]Cl_2$
    f. $[Co(NH_3)_3(NO_2)_3]$

23. Name the following complex ions.
    a. $Ru(NH_3)_5Cl^{2+}$
    b. $Fe(CN)_6^{4-}$
    c. $Mn(NH_2CH_2CH_2NH_2)_3^{2+}$
    d. $Co(NH_3)_5NO_2^{2+}$

24. Name the following coordination compounds.
    a. $[Cr(H_2O)_5Br]Br_2$
    b. $Na_3[Co(CN)_6]$
    c. $[Fe(NH_2CH_2CH_2NH_2)_2(NO_2)_2]Cl$
    d. $[Pt(NH_3)_4I_2][PtI_4]$

25. Give formulas for the following.
    a. potassium tetrachlorocobaltate(II)
    b. aquatricarbonylplatinum(II) bromide
    c. sodium dicyanobis(oxalato)ferrate(III)
    d. triamminechloroethylenediaminechromium(III) iodide

26. Give formulas for the following complex ions.
    a. tetrachloroferrate(III) ion
    b. pentaammineaquaruthenium(III) ion
    c. tetracarbonyldihydroxochromium(III) ion
    d. amminetrichloroplatinate(II) ion

27. A coordination compound of cobalt(III) contains four ammonia molecules, one sulfate ion, and one chloride ion. Addition of aqueous BaCl₂ solution to an aqueous solution of the compound gives no precipitate. Addition of aqueous AgNO₃ to an aqueous solution of the compound produces a white precipitate. Propose a structure for this coordination compound.

28. When an aqueous solution of KCN is added to a solution containing Ni²⁺ ions, a precipitate forms, which redissolves upon addition of more KCN solution. No precipitate forms when H₂S is bubbled into this solution. Write reactions describing what happens in this solution. [*Hint:* CN⁻ is a Brønsted–Lowry base ($K_b \approx 10^{-5}$) and a Lewis base.]

29. Consider aqueous solutions of the following coordination compounds: Co(NH₃)₆I₃, Pt(NH₃)₄I₄, Na₂PtI₆, and Cr(NH₃)₄I₃. If aqueous AgNO₃ is added to separate beakers containing solutions of each coordination compound, how many moles of AgI will precipitate per mole of transition metal present? Assume that each transition metal ion forms an octahedral complex.

30. A series of chemicals was added to some AgNO₃(*aq*). NaCl(*aq*) was added first to the silver nitrate solution with the end result shown below in test tube 1, NH₃(*aq*) was then added with the end result shown in test tube 2, and HNO₃(*aq*) was added last with the end result shown in test tube 3.

    Explain the results shown in each test tube. Include a balanced equation for the reaction(s) taking place.

31. Define each of the following, and give examples.
    a. isomers   e. linkage isomers
    b. structural isomers   f. geometric isomers
    c. stereoisomers   g. optical isomers
    d. coordination isomers

32. How many bonds could each of the following chelating ligands form with a metal ion?
    a. acetylacetone (acacH)

$$CH_3-\overset{\overset{\textstyle O}{\|}}{C}-CH_2-\overset{\overset{\textstyle O}{\|}}{C}-CH_3$$

    b. diethylenetriamine

$$NH_2-CH_2-CH_2-NH-CH_2-CH_2-NH_2$$

    c. salen

    d. porphine

33. Draw geometrical isomers of each of the following complex ions.
    a. [Co(C₂O₄)₂(H₂O)₂]⁻   c. [Ir(NH₃)₃Cl₃]
    b. [Pt(NH₃)₄I₂]²⁺   d. [Cr(en)(NH₃)₂I₂]⁺

34. Draw structures for each of the following.
    a. *cis*-dichloroethylenediamineplatinum(II)
    b. *trans*-dichlorobis(ethylenediamine)cobalt(II)
    c. *cis*-tetraamminechloronitrocobalt(III) ion
    d. *trans*-tetraamminechloronitritocobalt(III) ion
    e. *trans*-diaquabis(ethylenediamine)copper(II) ion

35. Figure 19.18 shows that the *cis* isomer of Co(en)₂Cl₂⁺ is optically active, whereas the *trans* isomer is not optically active. Is the same true for Co(NH₃)₄Cl₂⁺? Explain.

36. For the process

$$Co(NH_3)_5Cl^{2+} + Cl^- \longrightarrow Co(NH_3)_4Cl_2^+ + NH_3$$

    What would be the expected ratio of *cis* to *trans* isomers in the product?

37. Amino acids can act as ligands toward transition metal ions. The simplest amino acid is glycine (NH₂CH₂CO₂H). Draw a structure of the glycinate anion (NH₂CH₂CO₂⁻), acting as a bidentate ligand. Draw the structural isomers of the square planar complex Cu(NH₂CH₂CO₂)₂.

38. The carbonate ion (CO₃²⁻) can act as either a monodentate or a bidentate ligand. Draw a picture of CO₃²⁻ coordinating to a metal ion as a bidentate and as a monodentate ligand. The carbonate ion can also act as a bridge between two metal ions. Draw a picture of a CO₃²⁻ ion bridging between two metal ions.

39. Which of the following ligands are capable of linkage isomerism? Explain your answer.

$$SCN^-, \ N_3^-, \ NO_2^-, \ NH_2CH_2CH_2NH_2, \ OCN^-, \ I^-$$

40. Draw all geometrical and linkage isomers of Co(NH₃)₄(NO₂)₂.

41. Acetylacetone, abbreviated acacH, is a bidentate ligand. It loses a proton and coordinates as acac⁻, as shown below, where M is a transition metal:

Which of the following complexes are optically active: *cis*-Cr(acac)₂(H₂O)₂, *trans*-Cr(acac)₂(H₂O)₂, and Cr(acac)₃?

42. Draw all geometrical isomers of Pt(CN)₂Br₂(H₂O)₂. Which of these isomers have an optical isomer? Draw the various optical isomers.

43. Draw all the geometrical isomers of [Cr(en)(NH₃)₂BrCl]⁺. Which of these isomers also have an optical isomer? Draw the various isomers.

Bonding, Color, and Magnetism in Coordination Compounds

44. For the following crystal field diagrams, label each as low spin, high spin, or cannot tell. Explain your answers.

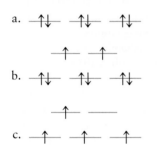

45. Define each of the following.
    a. weak-field ligand   c. low-spin complex
    b. strong-field ligand   d. high-spin complex

46. Compounds of copper(II) are generally colored, but compounds of copper(I) are not. Explain. Would you expect Cd(NH₃)₄Cl₂ to be colored? Explain.

47. Compounds of Sc³⁺ are not colored, but those of Ti³⁺ and V³⁺ are. Why?

48. Match the crystal field diagrams given below with the following complex ions.

    [Cr(NH₃)₅Cl]²⁺   [Co(NH₃)₄Br₂]⁺   [Fe(H₂O)₆]³⁺
                    (assume strong field) (assume weak field)

49. Match the crystal field diagrams given below with the following complex ions.

    [Fe(CN)₆]³⁻   [Mn(H₂O)₆]²⁺

    a.

    b.

50. Consider the complex ions Co(NH₃)₆³⁺, Co(CN)₆³⁻, and CoF₆³⁻. The wavelengths of absorbed electromagnetic radiation for these compounds are (in no specific order) 770 nm, 440 nm, and 290 nm. Match the complex ion to the wavelength of absorbed electromagnetic radiation.

51. Draw the *d*-orbital splitting diagrams for the octahedral complex ions of each of the following.
    a. Fe²⁺ (high and low spin)
    b. Fe³⁺ (high spin)
    c. Ni²⁺
    d. Zn²⁺
    e. Co²⁺ (high and low spin)

52. The Co(NH₃)₆³⁺ ion is diamagnetic, but Fe(H₂O)₆²⁺ is paramagnetic. Explain.

53. How many unpaired electrons are in the following complex ions?
    a. Ru(NH₃)₆²⁺ (low-spin case)
    b. Ni(H₂O)₆²⁺
    c. V(en)₃³⁺

54. Rank the following complex ions in order of increasing wavelength of light absorbed.

    Co(H₂O)₆³⁺, Co(CN)₆³⁻, CoI₆³⁻, Co(en)₃³⁺

55. The complex ion [Cu(H₂O)₆]²⁺ has an absorption maximum at around 800 nm. When four ammonias replace water, [Cu(NH₃)₄(H₂O)₂]²⁺, the absorption maximum shifts to around 600 nm. What do these results signify in terms of the relative field splittings of NH₃ and H₂O? Explain.

56. The complex ion Fe(CN)₆³⁻ is paramagnetic with one unpaired electron. The complex ion Fe(SCN)₆³⁻ has five unpaired electrons. Where does SCN⁻ lie in the spectrochemical series with respect to CN⁻?

57. The following test tubes each contain a different chromium complex ion.

For each compound, predict the predominant color of light absorbed. If the complex ions are $Cr(NH_3)_6^{3+}$, $Cr(H_2O)_6^{3+}$, and $Cr(H_2O)_4Cl_2^+$, what is the identity of the complex ion in each test tube? (*Hint:* Reference the spectrochemical series.)

58. Would it be better to use octahedral Ni^{2+} complexes or octahedral Cr^{2+} complexes to determine whether a ligand is a strong-field or a weak-field ligand by determining experimentally the number of unpaired electrons? How else could the relative ligand field strengths be determined?

59. The complex ion $Ru(phen)_3^{2+}$ has been used as a probe for the structure of DNA. (Phen is a bidentate ligand.)
    a. What type of isomerism is found in $Ru(phen)_3^{2+}$?
    b. $Ru(phen)_3^{2+}$ is diamagnetic (as are all complex ions of Ru^{2+}). Draw the crystal field diagram for the d orbitals in this complex ion.

    phen = 1,10-phenanthroline =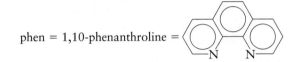

60. Tetrahedral complexes of Co^{2+} are quite common. Use a d-orbital splitting diagram to rationalize the stability of Co^{2+} tetrahedral complex ions.

61. Why do tetrahedral complex ions have a different crystal field diagram than octahedral complex ions? Why are virtually all tetrahedral complex ions "high spin"?

62. When concentrated hydrochloric acid is added to a red solution containing the $Co(H_2O)_6^{2+}$ complex ion, the solution turns blue as the tetrahedral $CoCl_4^{2-}$ complex ion forms. Explain this color change.

63. The wavelength of absorbed electromagnetic radiation for $CoBr_4^{2-}$ is 3.4×10^{-6} m. Will the complex ion $CoBr_6^{4-}$ absorb electromagnetic radiation having a wavelength longer or shorter than 3.4×10^{-6} m? Explain.

64. The complex ion $PdCl_4^{2-}$ is diamagnetic. Propose a structure for $PdCl_4^{2-}$.

Additional Exercises

65. When aqueous KI is added gradually to mercury(II) nitrate, an orange precipitate forms. Continued addition of KI causes the precipitate to dissolve. Write balanced equations to explain these observations. (*Hint:* Hg^{2+} reacts with I^- to form HgI_4^{2-}.) Would you expect HgI_4^{2-} to form colored solutions? Explain.

66. A certain first-row transition metal ion forms many different colored solutions. When four coordination compounds of this metal, each having the same coordination number, are dissolved in water, the colors of the solutions are red, yellow, green, and blue. Further experiments reveal that two of the complex ions are paramagnetic with four unpaired electrons and the other two are diamagnetic. What can be deduced from this information about the four coordination compounds?

67. Nickel can be purified by producing the volatile compound nickel tetracarbonyl [$Ni(CO)_4$]. Nickel is the only metal that reacts directly with CO at room temperature. What is the oxidation state of nickel in $Ni(CO)_4$?

68. Why are CN^- and CO toxic to humans?

69. What causes high-altitude sickness, and what is high-altitude acclimatization?

70. Acetylacetone (see Exercise 32, part a), abbreviated acacH, is a bidentate ligand. It loses a proton and coordinates as $acac^-$, as shown below:

Acetylacetone reacts with an ethanol solution containing a salt of europium to give a compound that is 40.1% C and 4.71% H by mass. Combustion of 0.286 g of the compound gives 0.112 g Eu_2O_3. Assuming the compound contains only C, H, O, and Eu, determine the formula of the compound formed from the reaction of acetylacetone and the europium salt. (Assume that the compound contains one europium ion.)

71. Ammonia and potassium iodide solutions were added to an aqueous solution of $Cr(NO_3)_3$. A solid was isolated (compound A), and the following data were collected:
    i. When 0.105 g of compound A was strongly heated in excess O_2, 0.0203 g of CrO_3 was formed.
    ii. In a second experiment, it took 32.93 mL of 0.100 M HCl to titrate completely the NH_3 present in 0.341 g of compound A.
    iii. Compound A was found to contain 73.53% iodine by mass.
    iv. The freezing point of water was lowered by 0.64°C when 0.601 g of compound A was dissolved in 10.00 g of H_2O ($K_f = 1.86°C$ kg/mol).

    What is the formula of the compound? What is the structure of the complex ion present? [*Hints:* Cr^{3+} is expected to be six-coordinate with NH_3 and (possibly) I^- acting as ligands. The I^- ions will be the counter ions if needed.]

72. In the production of printed circuit boards for the electronics industry, a 0.60-mm layer of copper is laminated onto an insulating plastic board. Next, a circuit pattern made of a chemically resistant polymer is printed on the board. The unwanted copper is removed by chemical etching, and the protective polymer is finally removed by solvents. One etching reaction is

    $[Cu(NH_3)_4]Cl_2(aq) + 4NH_3(aq) + Cu(s) \longrightarrow$
    $2[Cu(NH_3)_4]Cl(aq)$

a. Is this reaction an oxidation–reduction process? Explain.

b. A plant needs to manufacture 10,000 printed circuit boards, each 8.0 cm × 16.0 cm in area. An average of 80.% of the copper is removed from each board (density of copper = 8.96 g/cm³). What masses of [Cu(NH₃)₄]Cl₂ and NH₃ are needed to accomplish this task? Assume 100% yield.

73. BAL is a chelating agent used in treating heavy metal poisoning. It acts as a bidentate ligand. What types of linkage isomers are possible when BAL coordinates to a metal ion?

$$CH_2-SH$$
$$CH-SH$$
$$CH_2-OH$$

BAL

74. Until the discoveries of Werner, it was thought that the presence of carbon in a compound was required for it to be optically active. Werner prepared the following compound containing OH⁻ ions as bridging groups and then separated the optical isomers.

a. Draw structures of the two optically active isomers of this compound.

b. What are the oxidation states of the cobalt ions?

c. How many unpaired electrons are present if the complex is the low-spin case?

75. Chelating ligands often form more stable complex ions than the corresponding monodentate ligands form with the same donor atoms. For example,

$$Ni^{2+}(aq) + 6NH_3(aq) \rightleftharpoons Ni(NH_3)_6^{2+}(aq)$$
$$K_f = 3.2 \times 10^8$$

$$Ni^{2+}(aq) + 3en(aq) \rightleftharpoons Ni(en)_3^{2+}(aq)$$
$$K_f = 1.6 \times 10^{18}$$

$$Ni^{2+}(aq) + penten(aq) \rightleftharpoons Ni(penten)^{2+}(aq)$$
$$K_f = 2.0 \times 10^{19}$$

where en is ethylenediamine and penten is

$$NH_2CH_2CH_2 \quad\quad CH_2CH_2NH_2$$
$$N-CH_2-CH_2-N$$
$$NH_2CH_2CH_2 \quad\quad CH_2CH_2NH_2$$

The increased stability that results is called the chelate effect. From the bond energies, would you expect the enthalpy changes for the preceding reactions to be very different? What is the order (from least favorable to most favorable) of the entropy changes for the preceding reactions? How do the values of the formation constants correlate with $\Delta S°$? How can this be used to explain the chelate effect?

76. There are three salts that contain octahedral complex ions of chromium and have the molecular formula CrCl₃ · 6H₂O. Treating 0.27 g of the first salt with a strong dehydrating agent resulted in a mass loss of 0.036 g. Treating 270 mg of the second salt with the same dehydrating agent resulted in a mass loss of 18 mg. The third salt did not lose any mass when treated with the same dehydrating agent. Addition of excess aqueous silver nitrate to 100.0-mL portions of 0.100 M solutions of each salt resulted in the formation of different masses of silver chloride; one solution yielded 1430 mg AgCl; another, 2870 mg AgCl; the third, 4300 mg AgCl. Two of the salts are green and one is violet. Suggest probable structural formulas for these salts, defending your answer on the basis of the preceding observations. State which salt is most likely to be violet.

77. Henry Taube, the 1983 Nobel Prize winner in chemistry, has studied the mechanisms of oxidation–reduction reactions involving transition metal complexes. In one experiment he and his students studied the following reaction:

$$Cr(H_2O)_6^{2+}(aq) + Co(NH_3)_5Cl^{2+}(aq) \longrightarrow$$
$$Cr(III) \text{ complexes} + Co(II) \text{ complexes}$$

Chromium(III) and cobalt(III) complexes are substitutionally inert (no exchange of ligands) under conditions of the experiment. However, chromium(II) and cobalt(II) complexes can exchange ligands very rapidly. One of the products of the reaction is $Cr(H_2O)_5Cl^{2+}$. Is this consistent with the reaction proceeding through formation of $(H_2O)_5Cr-Cl-Co(NH_3)_5$ as an intermediate? Explain your answer.

78. A compound related to acetylacetone is 1,1,1-trifluoroacetylacetone (abbreviated Htfa):

$$\begin{matrix} O & & O \\ \| & & \| \end{matrix}$$
$$CF_3CCH_2CCH_3$$

Htfa forms complexes in a manner similar to acetylacetone. (See Exercise 41.) Both Be²⁺ and Cu²⁺ form complexes with tfa⁻ having the formula M(tfa)₂. Two isomers are formed for each metal complex.

a. The Be²⁺ complexes are tetrahedral. Draw the two isomers of Be(tfa)₂. What type of isomerism is exhibited by Be(tfa)₂?

b. The Cu²⁺ complexes are square planar. Draw the two isomers of Cu(tfa)₂. What type of isomerism is exhibited by Cu(tfa)₂?

79. The equilibrium constant K_a for the reaction

$$Fe(H_2O)_6^{3+}(aq) + H_2O(l) \rightleftharpoons$$
$$Fe(H_2O)_5(OH)^{2+}(aq) + H_3O^+(aq)$$

is 6.0×10^{-3}.

a. Calculate the pH of a 0.10 M solution of $Fe(H_2O)_6^{3+}$.

b. Will a 1.0 M solution of iron(II) nitrate have a higher or lower pH than a 1.0 M solution of iron(III) nitrate? Explain.

80. Ethylenediaminetetraacetate (EDTA⁴⁻) is used as a complexing agent in chemical analysis with the structure shown in Fig. 19.8. Solutions of EDTA⁴⁻ are used to treat

heavy metal poisoning by removing the heavy metal in the form of a soluble complex ion. The complex ion virtually prevents the heavy metal ions from reacting with biochemical systems. The reaction of $EDTA^{4-}$ with Pb^{2+} is

$$Pb^{2+}(aq) + EDTA^{4-}(aq) \rightleftharpoons PbEDTA^{2-}(aq)$$
$$K = 1.1 \times 10^{18}$$

Consider a solution with 0.010 mole of $Pb(NO_3)_2$ added to 1.0 L of an aqueous solution buffered at pH = 13.00 and containing 0.050 M Na_4EDTA. Does $Pb(OH)_2$ precipitate from this solution? [K_{sp} for $Pb(OH)_2 = 1.2 \times 10^{-15}$.]

81. Hemoglobin (abbreviated Hb) is a protein that is responsible for the transport of oxygen in the blood of mammals. Each hemoglobin molecule contains four iron atoms that serve as the binding sites for O_2 molecules. The oxygen binding is pH dependent. The relevant equilibrium reaction is

$$HbH_4^{4+}(aq) + 4O_2(g) \rightleftharpoons Hb(O_2)_4(aq) + 4H^+(aq)$$

Use Le Châtelier's principle to answer the following.
a. What form of hemoglobin, HbH_4^{4+} or $Hb(O_2)_4$, is favored in the lungs? What form is favored in the cells?

b. When a person hyperventilates, the concentration of CO_2 in the blood decreases. How does this affect the oxygen-binding equilibrium? How does breathing into a paper bag help to counteract this effect? (*Hint:* CO_2 reacts with water to produce carbonic acid.)
c. When a person has suffered a cardiac arrest, an injection of a sodium bicarbonate solution is given. Why is this step necessary? (*Hint:* CO_2 blood levels increase during cardiac arrest.)

82. Carbon monoxide is toxic because it binds more strongly to iron in hemoglobin (Hb) than does O_2. Consider the following reactions and approximate standard free energy changes:

$$Hb + O_2 \longrightarrow HbO_2 \qquad \Delta G° = -70 \text{ kJ}$$
$$Hb + CO \longrightarrow HbCO \qquad \Delta G° = -80 \text{ kJ}$$

Using these data, estimate the equilibrium constant value at 25°C for the following reaction:

$$HbO_2 + CO \rightleftharpoons HbCO + O_2$$

Challenge Problems

83. Qualitatively draw the crystal field splitting of the *d* orbitals in a trigonal planar complex ion. (Let the *z* axis be perpendicular to the plane of the complex.)

84. Consider the following complex ion, where A and B represent ligands.

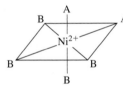

The complex is known to be diamagnetic. Do A and B produce very similar or very different crystal fields? Explain.

85. Qualitatively draw the crystal field splitting for a trigonal bipyramidal complex ion. (Let the *z* axis be perpendicular to the trigonal plane.)

86. Sketch and explain the most likely crystal field diagram for the following complex ion:

Note: The CN^- ligand produces a *much* stronger crystal field than NH_3. Assume the NH_3 ligands lie on the *z* axis.

87. Consider the following data:

$$Co^{3+} + e^- \longrightarrow Co^{2+} \qquad \mathscr{E}° = 1.82 \text{ V}$$
$$Co(en)_3^{2+} \qquad K_f = 1.5 \times 10^{12}$$
$$Co(en)_3^{3+} \qquad K_f = 2.0 \times 10^{47}$$

where en = ethylenediamine.
a. Calculate $\mathscr{E}°$ for the half-reaction

$$Co(en)_3^{3+} + e^- \longrightarrow Co(en)_3^{2+}$$

b. Based on your answer to part a, which is the stronger oxidizing agent, Co^{3+} or $Co(en)_3^{3+}$?
c. Use the crystal field model to rationalize the result in part b.

88. Consider the following complex ion where A and B represent neutral ligands, and A produces a stronger crystal field than B.

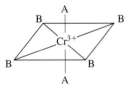

a. Draw an appropriate crystal field diagram for this complex ion (include the electrons). Assume the A ligands lie on the *z* axis.
b. Draw an approximate molecular orbital diagram for this complex ion, assuming only sigma bonding.
c. The two diagrams (parts a and b) should be slightly different with respect to *d*-orbital energies. How

could the assumptions used in constructing the diagrams be modified to achieve agreement between the two?

89. a. Calculate the molar solubility of AgBr in pure water. K_{sp} for AgBr is 5.0×10^{-13}.
    b. Calculate the molar solubility of AgBr in 3.0 M NH$_3$. The overall formation constant for Ag(NH$_3$)$_2{}^+$ is 1.7×10^7.
    c. Compare the calculated solubilities from parts a and b. Explain any differences.

d. What mass of AgBr will dissolve in 250.0 mL of 3.0 M NH$_3$?
e. What effect does adding HNO$_3$ have on the solubilities calculated in parts a and b?

90. Sketch a d-orbital energy diagram for the following:
    a. a linear complex ion with ligands on the x axis
    b. a linear complex ion with ligands on the y axis

The Nucleus:
A Chemist's View

20

chapter

Solar prominence eruption.

Since the chemistry of an atom is determined by the number and arrangement of its electrons, the properties of the nucleus are not of primary importance to chemists. In the simplest view, the nucleus provides the positive charge to bind the electrons in atoms and molecules. However, a quick reading of any daily newspaper will show you that the nucleus and its properties have an important impact on our society. This chapter considers those aspects of the nucleus about which everyone should have some knowledge.

Several aspects of the nucleus are immediately impressive: its very small size, its very large density, and the magnitude of the energy that holds it together. The radius of a typical nucleus appears to be about 10^{-13} cm. This can be compared with the radius of a typical atom, which is on the order of 10^{-8} cm. A visualization will help you appreciate the small size of the nucleus: If the nucleus of the hydrogen atom were the size of a Ping-Pong ball, the electron in the 1s orbital would be, on average, 0.5 kilometer (0.3 mile) away. The density of the nucleus is equally impressive—about 1.6×10^{14} g/cm^3. A sphere of nuclear material the size of a Ping-Pong ball would have a mass of 2.5 *billion tons!* In addition, the energies involved in nuclear processes are typically millions of times larger than those associated with normal chemical reactions. This fact makes nuclear processes very attractive for feeding the voracious energy appetite for our civilization.

Atomos, the Greek root of the word *atom,* means "indivisible." It was originally believed that the atom was the ultimate indivisible particle of which all matter was composed. However, as we discussed in Chapter 2, Lord Rutherford showed in 1911 that the atom is not homogeneous but instead has a dense, positively charged center surrounded by electrons. Subsequently, scientists learned that the nucleus of the atom can be described as containing neutrons and protons. In fact, in the past three decades, it has become widely accepted that even the protons and neutrons are composed of smaller particles called *quarks.*

For most purposes, the nucleus can be regarded as a collection of nucleons (neutrons and protons), and the internal structures of these particles can be ignored. Recall that the number of protons in a particular nucleus is the atomic number (Z) and that the sum of the neutrons and protons is the mass number (A). Atoms that have identical atomic numbers but different mass number values are called isotopes. The general term *nuclide* is applied to each unique atom and is represented by $^A_Z X$, where X represents the symbol for a particular element.

20.1 | Nuclear Stability and Radioactive Decay

Nuclear stability is the central topic of this chapter and forms the basis for all the important applications related to nuclear processes. Nuclear stability can be considered from both a kinetic and a thermodynamic point of view. Thermodynamic stability, as we use the term here, refers to the potential energy of a particular nucleus as compared with the sum of the potential energies of its component protons and neutrons. We will use the term *kinetic stability* to describe the probability that a nucleus will undergo decomposition to form a different nucleus—a process called radioactive decay. We will consider radioactivity in this section.

Many nuclei are radioactive; that is, they decompose, forming another nucleus and producing one or more particles. An example is carbon-14, which decays as follows:

$$^{14}_{6}C \longrightarrow {}^{14}_{7}N + {}^{0}_{-1}e$$

Figure 20.1

The known nuclides. The red dots indicate the nuclides that *do not* undergo radioactive decay. Note that as the number of protons (Z) in a nuclide increases, the neutron/proton ratio required for stability also increases.

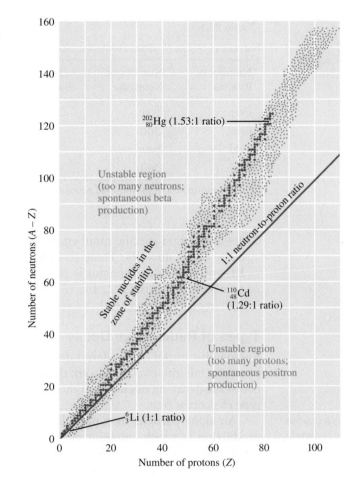

where $_{-1}^{0}$e represents an electron, which is called a **beta particle, or β particle,** in nuclear terminology. This equation is typical of those representing radioactive decay in that both A and Z must be conserved. That is, the Z values must give the same sum on both sides of the equation ($6 = 7 - 1$), as must the A values ($14 = 14 + 0$).

Of the approximately 2000 known nuclides, only 279 are stable with respect to radioactive decay. Tin has the largest number of stable isotopes—10.

It is instructive to examine how the numbers of neutrons and protons in a nucleus are related to its stability with respect to radioactive decay. Figure 20.1 shows a plot of the positions of the known nuclides as a function of the number of protons (Z) and the number of neutrons ($A - Z$). The stable nuclides are said to reside in the **zone of stability**.

The following are some important observations concerning radioactive decay:

All nuclides with 84 or more protons are unstable with respect to radioactive decay.

Light nuclides are stable when Z equals $A - Z$, that is, when the neutron/proton ratio is 1. However, for heavier elements, the neutron/proton ratio required for stability is greater than 1 and increases with Z.

Certain combinations of protons and neutrons seem to confer special stability. For example, nuclides with even numbers of protons and neutrons are more often stable than those with odd numbers, as shown by the data in Table 20.1.

Table 20.1

Number of Stable Nuclides Related to Numbers of Protons and Neutrons

Number of Protons	Number of Neutrons	Number of Stable Nuclides	Examples
Even	Even	168	$^{12}_{6}C$, $^{16}_{8}O$
Even	Odd	57	$^{13}_{6}C$, $^{47}_{22}Ti$
Odd	Even	50	$^{19}_{9}F$, $^{23}_{11}Na$
Odd	Odd	4	$^{2}_{1}H$, $^{6}_{3}Li$

Note: Even numbers of protons and neutrons seem to favor stability.

There are certain specific numbers of protons or neutrons that produce especially stable nuclides. These so-called **magic numbers** are 2, 8, 20, 28, 50, 82, and 126. This behavior is reminiscent of that for atoms, where certain numbers of electrons (2, 10, 18, 36, 54, and 86) produce special chemical stability (the noble gases).

Types of Radioactive Decay

Radioactive nuclei can undergo decomposition in various ways. These decay processes fall into two categories: those that involve a change in the mass number of the decaying nucleus and those that do not. We will consider the former type of process first.

An **alpha particle**, or **α particle**, is a helium nucleus ($^{4}_{2}He$). **Alpha-particle production** is a very common mode of decay for heavy radioactive nuclides. For example, $^{238}_{92}U$, the predominant isotope of natural uranium (99.3%), decays by α-particle production:

$$^{238}_{92}U \longrightarrow {}^{4}_{2}He + {}^{234}_{90}Th$$

α-Particle production involves a change in A for the decaying nucleus; β-particle production has no effect on A.

Another α-particle producer is $^{230}_{90}Th$:

$$^{230}_{90}Th \longrightarrow {}^{4}_{2}He + {}^{226}_{88}Ra$$

Another decay process in which the mass number of the decaying nucleus changes is **spontaneous fission,** the splitting of a heavy nuclide into two lighter nuclides with similar mass numbers. Although this process occurs at an extremely slow rate for most nuclides, it is important in some cases. For instance, spontaneous fission is the predominant mode of decay for $^{254}_{98}Cf$.

The most common decay process in which the mass number of the decaying nucleus remains constant is **beta-particle production.** For example, the thorium-234 nuclide produces a β particle and is converted to protactinium-234:

$$^{234}_{90}Th \longrightarrow {}^{234}_{91}Pa + {}^{0}_{-1}e$$

Iodine-131 is also a β-particle producer:

$$^{131}_{53}I \longrightarrow {}^{0}_{-1}e + {}^{131}_{54}Xe$$

The β particle is assigned the mass number 0, since its mass is tiny compared with that of a proton or neutron. Because the value of Z is −1 for the β particle, the atomic number for the new nuclide is greater by 1 than for the original nuclide. Thus *the net effect of β-particle production is to change a neutron to a proton.* We therefore expect nuclides that lie above the zone of stability (those nuclides whose neutron/proton ratios are too high) to be β-particle producers.

Although the β particle is an electron, the emitting nucleus does not contain electrons. As we shall see later in this chapter, a given quantity of energy (which is best regarded as a form of matter) can become a particle (another form of matter) under certain circumstances. The unstable nuclide creates an electron as it releases energy in the decay process. The electron thus results from the decay process rather than being present before the decay occurs. Think of this process as being analogous to talking: Words are not stored inside us but are formed as we speak. Later in this chapter we will discuss in more detail this very interesting phenomenon in which matter in the form of particles and matter in the form of energy can interchange.

A **gamma ray**, or **γ ray**, refers to a high-energy photon. Frequently, gamma-ray production accompanies nuclear decays and particle reactions, such as in the α-particle decay of $^{238}_{92}U$:

$$^{238}_{92}U \longrightarrow {}^{4}_{2}He + {}^{234}_{90}Th + 2{}^{0}_{0}\gamma$$

in which two γ rays of different energies are sometimes produced in addition to the α particle. The emission of γ rays is one way a nucleus with excess energy (in an excited nuclear state) can relax to its ground state.

Positron production occurs for nuclides below the zone of stability (those nuclides whose neutron/proton ratios are too small). The positron is a particle with the same mass as the electron but opposite charge. An example of a nuclide that decays by positron production is sodium-22:

$$^{22}_{11}Na \longrightarrow {}^{0}_{1}e + {}^{22}_{10}Ne$$

Note that *the net effect of this process is to change a proton to a neutron,* causing the product nuclide to have a higher neutron/proton ratio than the original nuclide.

Besides being oppositely charged, the positron shows an even more fundamental difference from the electron: It is the **antiparticle** of the electron. When a positron collides with an electron, the particulate matter is changed to electromagnetic radiation in the form of high-energy photons:

$$_{-1}^{0}e + {}^{0}_{1}e \longrightarrow 2{}^{0}_{0}\gamma$$

This process, which is characteristic of matter–antimatter collisions, is called *annihilation* and is another example of the interchange of the forms of matter.

Electron capture is a process in which one of the inner-orbital electrons is captured by the nucleus, as illustrated by the process

$$^{201}_{80}Hg + {}_{-1}^{0}e \longrightarrow {}^{201}_{79}Au + {}^{0}_{0}\gamma$$

Inner-orbital electron

This reaction would have been of great interest to the alchemists, but unfortunately, it does not occur at a rate that would make it a practical means for changing mercury to gold. The various types of radioactive decay are summarized in Table 20.2.

Table 20.2

Various Types of Radioactive Processes Showing the Changes That Take Place in the Nuclides

Process	Change in A	Change in Z	Change in Neutron/Proton Ratio	Example
β-Particle (electron) production	0	+1	Decrease	$^{227}_{89}Ac \longrightarrow {}^{227}_{90}Th + {}_{-1}^{0}e$
Positron production	0	−1	Increase	$^{13}_{7}N \longrightarrow {}^{13}_{6}C + {}^{0}_{1}e$
Electron capture	0	−1	Increase	$^{73}_{33}As + {}_{-1}^{0}e \longrightarrow {}^{73}_{32}Ge$
α-Particle production	−4	−2	Increase	$^{210}_{84}Po \longrightarrow {}^{206}_{82}Pb + {}^{4}_{2}He$
γ-Ray production	0	0	—	Excited nucleus $\longrightarrow$ ground-state nucleus $+ {}^{0}_{0}\gamma$
Spontaneous fission	—	—	—	$^{254}_{98}Cf \longrightarrow$ lighter nuclides $+$ neutrons

Chemical Insights | Does Antimatter Matter?

Ever since its discovery in the early twentieth century scientists have been fascinated by antimatter, the "inverse" of matter. Individual antimatter particles are well known and have been studied extensively in particle accelerators. For example, the positron, the antiparticle for the electron, has the same mass as the electron but a positive charge, and the antiproton has the same mass as the proton but a negative charge. Antiparticles are tricky to study because they undergo immediate annihilation, releasing large quantities of energy, when they meet their corresponding matter particles.

Although both the antiparticles for antihydrogen (the antiproton and the positron) can be stored for a certain time in accelerators, no one had been able to create antihydrogen until recently. In September 1995 at the European Laboratory for Particle Physics (CERN) in Geneva, a team of researchers led by Walter Oelert observed antihydrogen for the first time. Using the Low Energy Antiproton Ring (LEAR), the scientists sent a beam of antiprotons at nearly the speed of light into a stream of xenon gas. Occasionally an antiproton interacted with a xenon atom to produce a positron and an electron. In the very rare cases in which the created positron had a velocity similar to that of the antiproton beam, the positron would be captured by an antiproton to form antihydrogen.

Physicists are very interested in comparing the properties of antihydrogen with those of hydrogen,

CERN, the world's largest particle accelerator, lies at the foot of the Jura Mountains near Geneva, Switzerland. This is a view of the CMS (compact muon solenoid).

especially to determine antimatter's response to gravity. However, these antiatoms, created in flight in the accelerator, lasted for a fleeting 40-billionths of a second, too short a time for the scientists to observe their properties. Physicists are now trying to find ways to make low-energy antihydrogen so that it can be stored long enough to study it more thoroughly. They hope that these experiments will provide answers to questions such as why there is so little antimatter in the universe relative to matter—present theory indicates that equal amounts of matter and antimatter would have been created in the early universe.

Often a radioactive nucleus cannot reach a stable state through a single decay process. In such a case, a **decay series** occurs until a stable nuclide is formed. A well-known example is the decay series that starts with $^{238}_{92}U$ and ends with $^{206}_{82}Pb$, as shown in Fig. 20.2. Similar series exist for $^{235}_{92}U$:

$$^{235}_{92}U \xrightarrow[\text{decays}]{\text{Series of}} \,^{207}_{82}Pb$$

and for $^{232}_{90}Th$:

$$^{232}_{90}Th \xrightarrow[\text{decays}]{\text{Series of}} \,^{208}_{82}Pb$$

20.2 | The Kinetics of Radioactive Decay

In a sample consisting of radioactive nuclides of a given type, each nuclide has a certain probability of undergoing decay. Suppose that a sample containing 1000 atoms of a certain nuclide produces 10 decay events per hour. This means

Figure 20.2
The decay series from $^{238}_{92}U$ to $^{206}_{82}Pb$. Each nuclide in the series except $^{206}_{82}Pb$ is unstable, and the successive transformations (shown by the arrows) continue until $^{206}_{82}Pb$ is finally formed. Note that horizontal arrows indicate processes where A is unchanged, whereas diagonal arrows signify that both A and Z change.

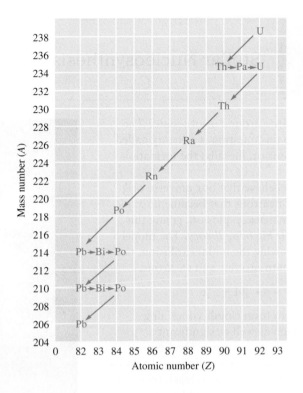

Rates of reaction are discussed in Chapter 15.

that over the span of an hour, 1 out of every 100 nuclides will decay. Assuming that this probability of decay is characteristic for this type of nuclide, we could predict that a 2000-atom sample would give 20 decay events per hour. Thus, for radioactive nuclides, the **rate of decay,** which is the negative of the change in the number of nuclides per unit time $(-\Delta N/\Delta t)$, is directly proportional to the number of **nuclides** (N) in a given sample:

$$\text{Rate} = -\frac{\Delta N}{\Delta t} \propto N$$

The negative sign is included because the number of nuclides is decreasing. We now insert a proportionality constant k to give

$$\text{Rate} = -\frac{\Delta N}{\Delta t} = -\frac{dN}{dt} = kN$$

Recall from Chapter 15 that this is the rate law for a first-order process. The integrated first-order rate law is

$$\ln\left(\frac{N}{N_0}\right) = -kt$$

where N_0 represents the original number of nuclides (at $t = 0$) and N represents the number of nuclides *remaining* at time t.

Half-Life

The **half-life** $(t_{1/2})$ of a radioactive sample is defined as the time required for the number of nuclides to reach half of the original value $(N_0/2)$. We can use this definition in connection with the integrated first-order rate law (see Section 15.4) to produce the following expression for $t_{1/2}$:

$$t_{1/2} = \frac{\ln(2)}{k} = \frac{0.693}{k}$$

Chemical Insights   Stellar Nucleosynthesis

How did all the matter around us originate? The scientific answer to this question is a theory called *stellar nucleosynthesis* or, literally, the formation of nuclei in the stars.

Many scientists believe that our universe originated as a cloud of neutrons that became unstable and produced an immense explosion, giving this model its name—*the big bang theory*. The model postulates that following the initial explosion, neutrons decomposed into protons and electrons,

$$\,^1_0\text{n} \longrightarrow \,^1_1\text{H} + \,^0_{-1}\text{e}$$

which recombined to form clouds containing hydrogen and helium as well as significant amounts of lithium and deuterium. Over eons, gravitational forces caused many of these clouds to contract and heat up sufficiently to reach temperatures where proton fusion was possible, releasing large quantities of energy. When the tendency to expand because of the heat from fusion and the tendency to contract because of the forces of gravity are balanced, a stable young star such as our sun can be formed.

Eventually, when the supply of hydrogen is exhausted, the core of the star again contracts with further heating until temperatures are reached where fusion of helium nuclei can occur. This leads to the formation of $\,^{12}_6\text{C}$ and $\,^{16}_8\text{O}$ nuclei. In turn, when the supply of helium nuclei is depleted, further contraction and heating occur, until the fusion of heavier nuclei takes place. This process occurs repeatedly, forming heavier and heavier nuclei until iron nuclei are formed. Because the iron nucleus is the most stable of all, energy is required to fuse iron nuclei. This endothermic fusion process cannot furnish energy to sustain the star; therefore, it cools to a small, dense *white dwarf*.

The evolution just described is characteristic of small and medium-sized stars. Much larger stars, however, become unstable during their evolution and undergo a *supernova explosion*. In the latter stages in this explosion, which is actually an extreme implosion that occurs when the fusion

Image of a portion of the Cygnus Loop supernova remnant, taken by the Hubble space telescope.

Jeff Hester/Arizona State University/NASA

heat source is exhausted, some medium-mass nuclei are fused to form heavy elements. Also, some light nuclei capture neutrons. These neutron-rich nuclei then produce β particles, increasing their atomic number with each event. This eventually leads to nuclei with large atomic numbers. In fact, almost all nuclei beyond iron are thought to originate from supernova explosions. The debris of a supernova explosion thus contains a large variety of elements that are spread widely and become part of hydrogen clouds that eventually become stars, which in turn form solar systems. For example, our sun and solar system probably formed from materials that had been through two previous supernova explosions.

Although other theories for the origin of matter have been suggested, there is much evidence to support the big bang theory. It continues to be widely accepted, although the details continue to be modified.

Figure 20.3
The decay of a 10.0-g sample of strontium-90 over time. Note that the half-life is a constant 28.8 years.

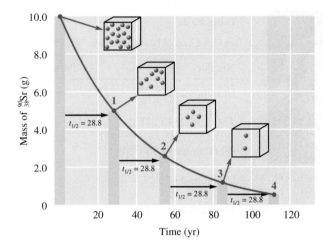

The harmful effects of radiation will be discussed in Section 20.7.

Thus, if the half-life of a radioactive nuclide is known, the rate constant can be easily calculated, and vice versa.

As we saw in Section 15.4, the half-life for a first-order process is constant. This is illustrated for the β-particle decay of strontium-90 in Fig. 20.3; it takes 28.8 years for each halving of the amount of $^{90}_{38}Sr$. Contamination of the environment with $^{90}_{38}Sr$ poses serious health hazards because of the similar chemistry of strontium and calcium (both are in Group 2A). Strontium-90 in grass and hay is incorporated into cow's milk along with calcium and is then passed on to humans, where it lodges in the bones. Because of its relatively long half-life, ^{90}Sr persists for years in humans, causing radiation damage that may lead to cancer.

EXAMPLE 20.1

The half-life of molybdenum-99 is 67.0 h. How much of a 1.000-mg sample of $^{99}_{42}Mo$ remains after 335 h?

Solution The easiest way to solve this problem is to recognize that 335 h represents five half-lives for $^{99}_{42}Mo$:

$$335 = 5 \times 67.0$$

We can sketch the change that occurs, as shown in Fig. 20.4. Thus, after 335 h, 0.031 mg of $^{99}_{42}Mo$ remains.

Figure 20.4
The change in the amount of $^{99}_{42}Mo$ with time ($t_{1/2} = 67$ h).

A uranium "button" for use as a fuel in a nuclear reactor.

Table 20.3

The Half-Lives of Nuclides in the $^{238}_{92}$U Decay Series

Nuclide	Particle Produced	Half-Life
Uranium-238 ($^{238}_{92}$U)	α	4.51×10^9 years
Thorium-234 ($^{234}_{90}$Th)	β	24.1 days
Protactinium-234 ($^{234}_{91}$Pa)	β	6.75 hours
Uranium-234 ($^{234}_{92}$U)	α	2.48×10^5 years
Thorium-230 ($^{230}_{90}$Th)	α	8.0×10^4 years
Radium-226 ($^{226}_{88}$Ra)	α	1.62×10^3 years
Radon-222 ($^{222}_{86}$Rn)	α	3.82 days
Polonium-218 ($^{218}_{84}$Po)	α	3.1 minutes
Lead-214 ($^{214}_{82}$Pb)	β	26.8 minutes
Bismuth-214 ($^{214}_{83}$Bi)	β	19.7 minutes
Polonium-214 ($^{214}_{84}$Po)	α	1.6×10^{-4} second
Lead-210 ($^{210}_{82}$Pb)	β	20.4 years
Bismuth-210 ($^{210}_{83}$Bi)	β	5.0 days
Polonium-210 ($^{210}_{84}$Po)	α	138.4 days
Lead-206 ($^{206}_{82}$Pb)	—	Stable

The half-lives of radioactive nuclides vary over a tremendous range. For example, $^{144}_{60}$Nd has a half-life of 5×10^{15} years, whereas $^{214}_{84}$Po has a half-life of 2×10^{-4} second. To give perspective on this, the half-lives of the nuclides in the $^{238}_{92}$U decay series are given in Table 20.3.

20.3 | Nuclear Transformations

In 1919 Lord Rutherford observed the first **nuclear transformation,** *the conversion of one element into another.* He found that by bombarding $^{14}_{7}$N with α particles, the $^{17}_{8}$O nuclide could be produced:

$$^{14}_{7}\text{N} + ^{4}_{2}\text{He} \longrightarrow ^{17}_{8}\text{O} + ^{1}_{1}\text{H}$$

Fourteen years later Irene Curie and her husband Frederick Joliot observed a similar transformation from aluminum to phosphorus,

$$^{27}_{13}\text{Al} + ^{4}_{2}\text{He} \longrightarrow ^{30}_{15}\text{P} + ^{1}_{0}\text{n}$$

where $^{1}_{0}$n represents a neutron.

Over the years, many other nuclear transformations have been achieved, mostly using **particle accelerators,** which, as the name reveals, are devices used to give particles very high velocities. Because of the electrostatic repulsion between the target nucleus and a positive ion, accelerators are needed when posi-

A cyclotron at TRIUMF, Canada's national laboratory of particle and nuclear physics.

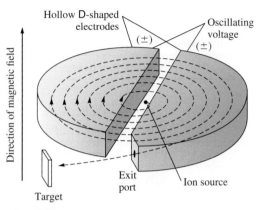

Hollow D-shaped electrodes

Oscillating voltage

Direction of magnetic field

Exit port

Target

Ion source

Figure 20.5

A schematic diagram of a cyclotron. The ion is introduced in the center and is then pulled back and forth between the hollow D-shaped electrodes by constant reversals of the electric field. Magnets above and below these electrodes produce a spiral path that expands as the particle velocity increases. When the particle has sufficient speed, it exits the accelerator and is directed at the target nucleus.

tive ions are used as bombarding particles. The particle, accelerated to a very high velocity, can overcome the repulsion and penetrate the target nucleus, thus effecting the transformation. A schematic diagram of one type of particle accelerator, the **cyclotron,** is shown in Fig. 20.5. The ion is introduced at the center of the cyclotron and is accelerated in an expanding spiral path by use of alternating electric fields in the presence of a magnetic field. The **linear accelerator** illustrated in Fig. 20.6 uses changing electric fields to achieve high velocities along a linear pathway.

In addition to positive ions, neutrons are often used as bombarding particles to effect nuclear transformations. Because neutrons are uncharged and thus not repelled electrostatically by a target nucleus, they are readily absorbed by many nuclei, leading to the formation of new nuclides. The most common source of neutrons for this purpose is a fission reactor (see Section 20.6).

By using neutron and positive-ion bombardment, scientists have been able to extend the periodic table. Prior to 1940, the heaviest known element was uranium ($Z = 92$). However, in 1940 neptunium ($Z = 93$) was produced by neutron bombardment of $^{238}_{92}U$. The process initially gives $^{239}_{92}U$, which then decays to $^{239}_{93}Np$ by β-particle production:

$$^{238}_{92}U + {}^{1}_{0}n \longrightarrow {}^{239}_{92}U \xrightarrow[t_{1/2} = 23 \text{ min}]{} {}^{239}_{93}Np + {}^{0}_{-1}e$$

Ion source

Target

Figure 20.6

Schematic diagram of a linear accelerator, which uses a changing electric field to accelerate a positive ion along a linear path. As the ion leaves the source, the odd-numbered tubes are negatively charged, and the even-numbered tubes are positively charged. The positive ion is thus attracted into tube 1. As the ion leaves tube 1, the tube polarities are reversed. Now tube 1 is positive, repelling the positive ion, and tube 2 is negative, attracting the positive ion. This process continues, eventually producing high particle velocity.

Table 20.4

Syntheses of Some of the Transuranium Elements

Element	Neutron Bombardment	Half-Life
Neptunium ($Z = 93$)	$^{238}_{92}U + ^{1}_{0}n \longrightarrow ^{239}_{92}U \longrightarrow ^{239}_{93}Np + ^{0}_{-1}e$	2.35 days ($^{239}_{93}Np$)
Plutonium ($Z = 94$)	$^{239}_{93}Np \longrightarrow ^{239}_{94}Pu + ^{0}_{-1}e$	24,400 years ($^{239}_{94}Pu$)
Americium ($Z = 95$)	$^{239}_{94}Pu + 2^{1}_{0}n \longrightarrow ^{241}_{94}Pu \longrightarrow ^{241}_{95}Am + ^{0}_{-1}e$	458 years ($^{241}_{95}Am$)

Element	Positive-Ion Bombardment	Half-Life
Curium ($Z = 96$)	$^{239}_{94}Pu + ^{4}_{2}He \longrightarrow ^{242}_{96}Cm + ^{1}_{0}n$	163 days ($^{242}_{96}Cm$)
Californium ($Z = 98$)	$^{242}_{96}Cm + ^{4}_{2}He \longrightarrow ^{245}_{98}Cf + ^{1}_{0}n$ or $^{238}_{92}U + ^{12}_{6}C \longrightarrow ^{246}_{98}Cf + 4^{1}_{0}n$	44 minutes ($^{245}_{98}Cf$)
Rutherfordium ($Z = 104$)	$^{249}_{98}Cf + ^{12}_{6}C \longrightarrow ^{257}_{104}Rf + 4^{1}_{0}n$	
Dubnium ($Z = 105$)	$^{249}_{98}Cf + ^{15}_{7}N \longrightarrow ^{260}_{105}Db + 4^{1}_{0}n$	
Seaborgium ($Z = 106$)	$^{249}_{98}Cf + ^{18}_{8}O \longrightarrow ^{263}_{106}Sg + 4^{1}_{0}n$	

In the years since 1940, the elements with atomic numbers 93 through 112 and 114, 116, and 118, called the **transuranium elements,*** have been synthesized. Many of these elements have very short half-lives, as shown in Table 20.4. As a result, only a few atoms of some of the transuranium elements have ever been formed. This, of course, makes the chemical characterization of these elements extremely difficult.

20.4 | **Detection and Uses of Radioactivity**

Geiger counters are often called survey meters in industry.

Various instruments measure radioactivity levels, the most familiar being the **Geiger-Müller counter,** or **Geiger counter** (Fig. 20.7). This instrument takes advantage of the fact that the high-energy particles from radioactive decay processes produce ions when they travel through matter. The probe of the Geiger counter is filled with argon gas, which can be ionized by a rapidly moving particle:

$$Ar(g) \xrightarrow[\text{particle}]{\text{High-energy}} Ar^{+}(g) + e^{-}$$

Normally, a sample of argon gas does not conduct a current when an electrical potential is applied. However, the formation of ions and electrons produced by the passage of the high-energy particle allows a momentary current to flow.

Figure 20.7
A schematic representation of a Geiger-Müller counter. The high-energy radioactive particle enters the window and ionizes argon atoms along its path. The resulting ions and electrons produce a momentary current pulse, which is amplified and counted.

*For an excellent article on the history of these elements, see G. B. Kauffman, "Beyond Uranium," *Chem. Eng. News,* November 19, 1990, p. 18.

Electronic devices detect this current flow, so the number of these events can be counted. Thus the decay rate of the radioactive sample can be determined.

Another instrument often used to detect levels of radioactivity is a **scintillation counter,** which takes advantage of the fact that certain substances, such as zinc sulfide, give off light when they are struck by high-energy radiation. A photocell senses the flashes of light that occur as the radiation strikes and thus measures the number of decay events per unit time.

Dating by Radioactivity

Carbon-14 radioactivity is often used to date human skeletons found at archaeological sites.

Archaeologists, geologists, and others involved in reconstructing the ancient history of the earth rely heavily on radioactivity to provide accurate dates for artifacts and rocks. A method that has been very important for dating ancient articles made from wood or cloth is **radiocarbon dating, or carbon-14 dating.** This technique was originated in the 1940s by Willard Libby, an American chemist who received a Nobel Prize for his efforts in this field.

Radiocarbon dating is based on the radioactivity of the nuclide $^{14}_{6}C$, which decays via β-particle production:

$$^{14}_{6}C \longrightarrow {}^{0}_{-1}e + {}^{14}_{7}N$$

Carbon-14 is produced in the atmosphere when high-energy neutrons from space collide with nitrogen-14:

$$^{14}_{7}N + {}^{1}_{0}n \longrightarrow {}^{14}_{6}C + {}^{1}_{1}H$$

Carbon-14 is continuously produced by this process, and it continuously decomposes through β-particle production. Over the years, the rates for these two processes have become equal. Like a participant in a chemical reaction at equilibrium, the amount of $^{14}_{6}C$ that is present in the atmosphere remains about constant.

Carbon-14 can be used to date wood and cloth artifacts because the $^{14}_{6}C$, along with the other carbon isotopes in the atmosphere, reacts with oxygen to form carbon dioxide. A living plant consumes carbon dioxide in the photosynthesis process and incorporates the carbon, including $^{14}_{6}C$, into its molecules. As long as the plant lives, the $^{14}_{6}C/^{12}_{6}C$ ratio in its molecules remains the same as that in the atmosphere because of the continuous uptake of carbon. However, as soon as a tree is cut to make a wooden bowl or a flax plant is harvested to make linen, the $^{14}_{6}C/^{12}_{6}C$ ratio begins to decrease because of the radioactive decay of $^{14}_{6}C$ (the $^{12}_{6}C$ nuclide is stable). Since the half-life of $^{14}_{6}C$ is 5730 years, a wooden bowl found in an archaeological dig showing a $^{14}_{6}C/^{12}_{6}C$ ratio half that found in currently living trees must be about 5730 years old. This reasoning assumes that the current $^{14}_{6}C/^{12}_{6}C$ ratio is the same as that found in ancient times.

The $^{14}_{6}C/^{12}_{6}C$ ratio is the basis for carbon-14 dating.

Dendrochronologists—scientists who date trees from annual growth rings—have used data collected from long-lived species of trees, such as bristlecone pines and sequoias, to show that the $^{14}_{6}C$ content of the atmosphere has changed significantly over the ages. These data have been used to derive correction factors that allow very accurate dates to be determined from the observed $^{14}_{6}C/^{12}_{6}C$ ratio in an artifact, especially for artifacts up to 10,000 years old. Recent measurements of uranium/thorium ratios in ancient coral have raised questions about the accuracy of ^{14}C dates extending back 20,000 to 30,000 years, suggesting that errors up to 3000 years may have occurred. Efforts are now being made to recalibrate the ^{14}C dates over this period.

One drawback of radiocarbon dating is that a fairly large piece of the object (up to several grams) must be burned to form carbon dioxide, which is then analyzed for radioactivity. Another method for counting $^{14}_{6}C$ nuclides avoids destruction of a significant portion of a valuable artifact. This technique, requiring only about 10^{-3} gram, uses a mass spectrometer (Chapter 3), in which the carbon atoms are ionized and accelerated through a magnetic field that deflects their paths. Because of their different masses, the various ions are deflected by different amounts and can be counted separately. This allows a very accurate determination of the $^{14}_{6}C/^{12}_{6}C$ ratio in the sample.

In their attempts to establish the geological history of the earth, geologists have made extensive use of radioactivity. For example, since $^{238}_{92}U$ decays to the stable $^{206}_{82}Pb$ nuclide, the ratio of $^{206}_{82}Pb$ to $^{238}_{92}U$ in a rock can, under favorable circumstances, be used to estimate the age of the rock.

Because the half-life of $^{238}_{92}U$ is very long compared with those of the other members of the decay series (Table 20.3) to reach $^{206}_{82}Pb$, the number of nuclides in intermediate stages of decay is negligible. That is, once a $^{238}_{92}U$ nuclide starts to decay, it reaches $^{206}_{82}Pb$ relatively fast.

EXAMPLE 20.2

A rock containing $^{238}_{92}U$ and $^{206}_{82}Pb$ was examined to determine its approximate age. Analysis showed the ratio of $^{206}_{82}Pb$ atoms to $^{238}_{92}U$ atoms to be 0.115. Assuming that no lead was originally present, that all the $^{206}_{82}Pb$ formed over the years has remained in the rock, and that the number of nuclides in the intermediate stages of decay between $^{238}_{92}U$ and $^{206}_{82}Pb$ is negligible, calculate the age of the rock. The half-life of $^{238}_{92}U$ is 4.5×10^9 yr.

Solution The problem can be solved using the integrated first-order rate law:

$$\ln\left(\frac{N}{N_0}\right) = -kt = -\left(\frac{0.693}{4.5 \times 10^9 \text{ yr}}\right)t$$

where N/N_0 represents the ratio of $^{238}_{92}U$ atoms now found in the rock to the number present when the rock was formed. We are assuming that each $^{206}_{82}Pb$ nuclide present must have come from decay of a $^{238}_{92}U$ atom:

$$^{238}_{92}U \longrightarrow \,^{206}_{82}Pb$$

Thus

Number of $^{238}_{92}U$ atoms originally present	=	number of $^{206}_{82}Pb$ atoms now present	+	number of $^{238}_{92}U$ atoms now present

$$\frac{\text{Atoms of } ^{206}_{82}Pb \text{ now present}}{\text{Atoms of } ^{238}_{92}U \text{ now present}} = 0.115 = \frac{0.115}{1.000} = \frac{115}{1000}$$

Think carefully about what this means. For every 1115 $^{238}_{92}U$ atoms originally present in the rock, 115 have been changed to $^{206}_{82}Pb$ and 1000 remain as $^{238}_{92}U$. Thus

$$\frac{N}{N_0} = \frac{\overset{\text{Now present}}{\overset{\downarrow}{^{238}_{92}U}}}{\underbrace{^{206}_{82}Pb + \,^{238}_{92}U}_{^{238}_{92}U \text{ originally present}}} = \frac{1000}{1115} = 0.8969$$

$$\ln\left(\frac{N}{N_0}\right) = \ln(0.8969) = -\left(\frac{0.693}{4.5 \times 10^9 \text{ yr}}\right)t$$

$$t = 7.1 \times 10^8 \text{ yr}$$

This is the approximate age of the rock. It was formed sometime during the Cambrian Period.

Medical Applications of Radioactivity

Although the rapid advances of the medical sciences in recent decades are the result of many causes, one of the most important has been the discovery and use of **radiotracers**, which are radioactive nuclides that can be introduced into

Figure 20.8
After consumption of Na^{131}I, the patient's thyroid is scanned for radioactivity levels to determine the efficiency of iodine absorption. (top) A normal thyroid. (bottom) An enlarged thyroid.

The *m* in technetium-99m designates an excited nuclear state of ^{99}Tc that decays to the ground state by γ production:

$$^{99m}\text{Tc} \longrightarrow\ ^{99}\text{Tc} + \gamma$$

organisms through food or drugs and whose pathways can be *traced* by monitoring their radioactivity (Fig. 20.8). For example, the incorporation of nuclides such as $^{14}_{6}$C and $^{32}_{15}$P into nutrients has produced important information about metabolic pathways.

Iodine-131 has proved very useful in the diagnosis and treatment of illnesses of the thyroid gland. Patients drink a solution containing small amounts of Na^{131}I, and the uptake of the iodine by the thyroid gland is monitored with a scanner.

Thallium-201 can be used to assess the damage to the heart muscle in a person who has suffered a heart attack because thallium is concentrated in healthy muscle tissue. Technetium-99m is also taken up by normal heart tissue and is used for damage assessment in a similar way.

A relatively new technique that uses radioactivity to study body processes and diagnose malfunctions is commonly called *positron emission tomography* (PET). In this technique radionuclides that decay by positron emission are incorporated into compounds. For example, brain function can be studied by incorporating $^{11}_{6}$C into glucose, which is the main source of energy for the brain. By studying how this labeled glucose is metabolized in the brain, doctors can discover abnormalities caused by diseases such as cancer, Parkinson's disease, and epilepsy.

Radiotracers provide sensitive and noninvasive methods for learning about biological systems, for detection of disease, for monitoring the action and effectiveness of drugs, and for early detection of pregnancy; their usefulness should continue to grow. Some useful radiotracers are listed in Table 20.5.

In contrast to the use of radiotracers, where the patient is exposed to only very small quantities of radiation, **radiation therapy** uses larger radiation doses to kill cancer cells. Typically the radioactive nuclides used in radiation therapy emit high-energy γ rays. The radiation can be administered external to the body or implanted in the cancerous tissue, depending on the location and nature of the cancer. For example, $^{192}_{77}$Ir pellets (covered by a platinum shell that stops α and β particles from entering the body but is easily penetrated by γ rays) are placed directly in the tumor to be destroyed. When implants are not practical, $^{60}_{27}$Co is often used externally to direct γ rays at the target tissue. Because virtually all the iodine that enters the body ends up in the thyroid gland, large doses of ^{131}I can be ingested to treat thyroid cancer. Because γ radiation is so highly penetrating, it is impossible to confine it to cancerous tissue in radiation therapy, and patients usually suffer nausea, hair loss, fatigue, and a weakened immune system. Despite its dangers and unpleasant side effects, however, radiation therapy is a potent tool to fight many forms of cancer.

Table 20.5

Some Radioactive Nuclides, with Half-Lives and Medical Applications as Radiotracers

Nuclide	Half-Life	Area of the Body Studied
^{131}I	8.1 days	Thyroid
^{59}Fe	45.1 days	Red blood cells
^{99}Mo	67 hours	Metabolism
^{32}P	14.3 days	Eyes, liver, tumors
^{51}Cr	27.8 days	Red blood cells
^{87}Sr	2.8 hours	Bones
^{99}Tc	6.0 hours	Heart, bones, liver, lungs
^{133}Xe	5.3 days	Lungs
^{24}Na	14.8 hours	Circulatory system

20.5 | Thermodynamic Stability of the Nucleus

We can determine the thermodynamic stability of a nucleus by calculating the change in potential energy that would occur if that nucleus were formed from its constituent protons and neutrons. As an example, let's consider the hypothetical process of forming a $^{16}_{8}O$ nucleus from eight neutrons and eight protons:

$$8^1_0n + 8^1_1H \longrightarrow {}^{16}_{8}O$$

The energy change associated with this process can be calculated by comparing the sum of the masses of eight protons and eight neutrons with the mass of the oxygen nucleus:

$$\text{Mass of } (8^1_0n + 8^1_1H) = 8(1.67493 \times 10^{-24} \text{ g}) + 8(1.67262 \times 10^{-24} \text{ g})$$

Mass of ^1_0n Mass of ^1_1H

$$= 2.67804 \times 10^{-23} \text{ g}$$

$$\text{Mass of } {}^{16}_{8}O \text{ nucleus} = 2.65535 \times 10^{-23} \text{ g}$$

The difference in mass for one nucleus is

$$\text{Mass of } {}^{16}_{8}O - \text{mass of } (8^1_0n + 8^1_1H) = -2.269 \times 10^{-25} \text{ g}$$

The difference in mass for the formation of 1 mole of $^{16}_{8}O$ nuclei is therefore

$$(-2.269 \times 10^{-25} \text{ g/nucleus})(6.022 \times 10^{23} \text{ nuclei/mol}) = -0.1366 \text{ g/mol}$$

Thus 0.1366 gram of mass would be lost if 1 mole of oxygen-16 were formed from the constituent protons and neutrons. Why does the mass change, and how can this information be used to calculate the energy change that accompanies this process?

The answers to these questions can be found in the work of Albert Einstein. As we discussed in Section 12.2, Einstein's theory of relativity showed that energy should be considered a form of matter. His famous equation,

Energy is a form of matter.

$$E = mc^2$$

where c is the speed of light, gives the relationship between a quantity of energy and its mass. When a system gains or loses energy, it also gains or loses a quantity of mass, given by E/c^2. Thus the mass of a nucleus is less than that of its component nucleons because the process is so exothermic.

Einstein's equation in the form

The energy changes associated with normal chemical reactions are small enough that the corresponding mass changes are not detectable.

$$\text{Energy change} = \Delta E = \Delta mc^2$$

where Δm, the change in mass (the **mass defect**), can be used to calculate ΔE for the formation of a nucleus from its component nucleons.

The thermodynamic stability of a particular nucleus is normally represented as energy released per nucleon. To illustrate how this quantity is obtained, we will continue to consider $^{16}_{8}O$. First, we calculate ΔE for 1 mole of $^{16}_{8}O$ nuclei from the equation

$$\Delta E = \Delta mc^2$$

where $c = 3.00 \times 10^8 \text{ m/s}$

and $\Delta m = -0.1366 \text{ g/mol} = -1.366 \times 10^{-4} \text{ kg/mol}$

as calculated above. Thus

$$\Delta E = (-1.366 \times 10^{-4} \text{ kg/mol})(3.00 \times 10^8 \text{ m/s})^2 = -1.23 \times 10^{13} \text{ J/mol}$$

Next, we calculate ΔE per nucleus by dividing the molar value by Avogadro's number:

$$\Delta E \text{ per } {}^{16}_{8}\text{O nucleus} = \frac{-1.23 \times 10^{13} \text{ J/mol}}{6.022 \times 10^{23} \text{ nuclei/mol}} = -2.04 \times 10^{-11} \text{ J/nucleus}$$

In terms of a more convenient energy unit, the MeV (million electron-volts), where

$$1 \text{ MeV} = 1.60 \times 10^{-13} \text{ J}$$

we have

$$\Delta E \text{ per } {}^{16}_{8}\text{O nucleus} = \left(-2.04 \times 10^{-11} \frac{\text{J}}{\text{nucleus}}\right)\left(\frac{1 \text{ MeV}}{1.60 \times 10^{-13} \text{ J}}\right)$$

$$= -1.28 \times 10^{2} \text{ MeV/nucleus}$$

Next, we can calculate the value of ΔE per nucleon by dividing by A, the sum of the numbers of neutrons and protons:

$$\Delta E \text{ per nucleon for } {}^{16}_{8}\text{O} = \frac{-1.28 \times 10^{2} \text{ MeV/nucleus}}{16 \text{ nucleons/nucleus}}$$

$$= -8.00 \text{ MeV/nucleon}$$

This means that 8.00 MeV of energy per nucleon would be *released* if ${}^{16}_{8}\text{O}$ were formed from free neutrons and protons. The energy required to *decompose* this nucleus into its components has the same numeric value but is positive. This is called the **binding energy** per nucleon for ${}^{16}_{8}\text{O}$.

The values of the binding energy per nucleon for the various nuclides are shown in Fig. 20.9. Note that the most stable nuclei (those requiring the largest energy per nucleon to decompose the nucleus) occur at the top of the curve. The most stable nucleus known is ${}^{56}_{26}\text{Fe}$, which has a binding energy per nucleon of 8.79 MeV.

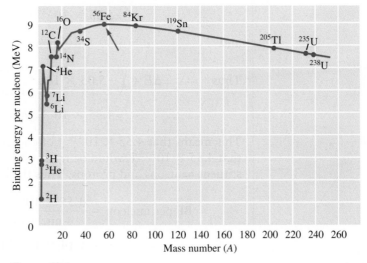

Figure 20.9
The binding energy per nucleon as a function of mass number. The most stable nuclei are at the top of the curve. The most stable nucleus is ${}^{56}_{26}\text{Fe}$.

⬮WL INTERACTIVE EXAMPLE 20.3

Calculate the binding energy per nucleon for the ^4_2He nucleus (atomic masses: $^4_2\text{He} = 4.0026$ amu, $^1_1\text{H} = 1.0078$ amu).

Solution First, we must calculate the mass defect (Δm) for ^4_2He. Since atomic masses (which include the electrons) are given, we must decide how to account for the electron mass:

$$4.0026 = \text{mass of } ^4_2\text{He atom} = \text{mass of } ^4_2\text{He nucleus} + 2m_e$$

Electron mass

$$1.0078 = \text{mass of } ^1_1\text{H atom} = \text{mass of } ^1_1\text{H nucleus} + m_e$$

Thus, since a ^4_2He nucleus is "synthesized" from two protons and two neutrons, we see that

$$\Delta m = \underbrace{(4.0026 - 2m_e)}_{\substack{\text{Mass of} \\ ^4_2\text{He nucleus}}} - [\underbrace{2(1.0078 - m_e)}_{\substack{\text{Mass of } ^1_1\text{H} \\ \text{nucleus (proton)}}} + \underbrace{2(1.0087)}_{\substack{\text{Mass of} \\ \text{neutron}}}]$$

$$= 4.0026 - 2m_e - 2(1.0078) + 2m_e - 2(1.0087)$$

$$= 4.0026 - 2(1.0078) - 2(1.0087)$$

$$= -0.0304 \text{ amu}$$

Note that in this case the electron mass cancels in taking the difference. This will always happen in this type of calculation if the atomic masses are used both for the nuclide of interest and for the ^1_1H. Thus 0.0304 amu of mass is *lost* per ^4_2He nucleus formed.

The corresponding energy change can be calculated from

$$\Delta E = \Delta mc^2$$

where

$$\Delta m = -0.0304 \frac{\text{amu}}{\text{nucleus}}$$

$$= \left(-0.0304 \frac{\text{amu}}{\text{nucleus}}\right)\left(1.66 \times 10^{-27} \frac{\text{kg}}{\text{amu}}\right)$$

$$= -5.05 \times 10^{-29} \text{ kg/nucleus}$$

and

$$c = 3.00 \times 10^8 \text{ m/s}$$

Thus

$$\Delta E = \left(-5.05 \times 10^{-29} \frac{\text{kg}}{\text{nucleus}}\right)\left(3.00 \times 10^8 \frac{\text{m}}{\text{s}}\right)^2$$

$$= -4.55 \times 10^{-12} \text{ J/nucleus}$$

This means that 4.55×10^{-12} J of energy is *released* per nucleus formed and that 4.55×10^{-12} J would be required to decompose the nucleus into the constituent neutrons and protons. Thus the binding energy (BE) per nucleon is

$$\text{BE per nucleon} = \frac{4.55 \times 10^{-12} \text{ J/nucleus}}{4 \text{ nucleons/nucleus}}$$

$$= 1.14 \times 10^{-12} \text{ J/nucleon}$$

$$= \left(1.14 \times 10^{-12} \frac{\text{J}}{\text{nucleon}}\right)\left(\frac{1 \text{ MeV}}{1.60 \times 10^{-13} \text{ J}}\right)$$

$$= 7.13 \text{ MeV/nucleon}$$

Figure 20.10

Both fission and fusion produce more stable nuclides and are thus exothermic.

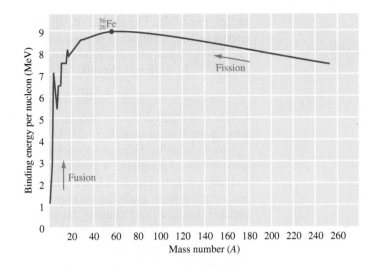

20.6 | Nuclear Fission and Nuclear Fusion

The graph shown in Fig. 20.9 has very important implications for the use of nuclear processes as sources of energy. Recall that energy is released—that is, ΔE is negative—when a process goes from a less stable to a more stable state. The higher a nuclide is on the curve, the more stable it is. This means that two types of nuclear processes are exothermic (Fig. 20.10):

1. Combining two light nuclei to form a heavier, more stable nucleus. This process is called **fusion.**

2. Splitting a heavy nucleus into two nuclei with smaller mass numbers. This process is called **fission.**

Because of the large binding energies involved in holding the nucleus together, both of these processes involve energy changes more than a million times larger than those associated with chemical reactions.

Nuclear Fission

Nuclear fission was discovered in the late 1930s when $^{235}_{92}U$ nuclides bombarded with neutrons were observed to split into lighter elements:

$$^{1}_{0}n + {}^{235}_{92}U \longrightarrow {}^{141}_{56}Ba + {}^{92}_{36}Kr + 3{}^{1}_{0}n$$

This process shown schematically in Fig. 20.11, releases 3.5×10^{-11} J of energy per event, which translates to 2.1×10^{13} J per mole of $^{235}_{92}U$. Compare this figure with that for the combustion of methane, which releases only 8.0×10^{5} J of

Figure 20.11

Upon capturing a neutron, the $^{235}_{92}U$ nucleus undergoes fission to produce two lighter nuclides, free neutrons (typically three), and a large amount of energy.

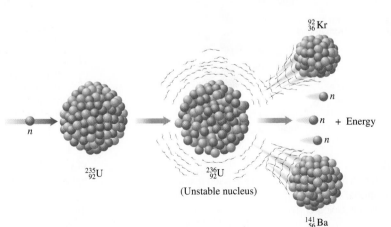

energy per mole. The fission of $^{235}_{92}U$ produces about 26 million times as much energy as the combustion of methane.

The process previously shown is only one of the many fission processes that $^{235}_{92}U$ can undergo. Another is

$$^1_0n + {}^{235}_{92}U \longrightarrow {}^{137}_{52}Te + {}^{97}_{40}Zn + 2{}^1_0n$$

In fact, over 200 different isotopes of 35 different elements have been observed among the fission products of $^{235}_{92}U$.

In addition to the product nuclides, neutrons are produced in the fission reactions of $^{235}_{92}U$. This makes it possible to produce a self-sustaining fission process—a **chain reaction** (Fig. 20.12). For the fission process to be self-sustaining, at least one neutron from each fission event must go on to split another nucleus. If, on average, *less than one* neutron causes another fission event, the process dies out; the reaction is said to be **subcritical**. If *exactly one* neutron from each fission event causes another fission event, the process sustains itself at the same level and is said to be **critical**. If *more than one* neutron from each fission event causes another fission event, the process rapidly escalates, and the heat buildup causes a violent explosion. This situation is described as **supercritical.**

The critical state requires a certain mass of fissionable material, called the **critical mass.** If the sample is too small, too many neutrons escape before they have a chance to cause a fission event; thus the process stops. This is illustrated in Fig. 20.13.

During World War II an intense research effort (the Manhattan Project) was carried out by the United States to build a bomb based on the principles of nuclear fission. This program produced the fission bombs that were used with devastating effects on the cities of Hiroshima and Nagasaki in 1945. Basically, a fission bomb operates by suddenly combining two subcritical masses of fissionable material to form a supercritical mass, thereby producing an explosion of incredible intensity.

Nuclear Reactors

Because of the tremendous energies involved, it seemed desirable after World War II to develop the fission process as an energy source for producing electricity. Therefore, reactors were designed in which controlled fission can occur.

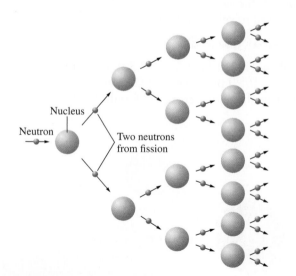

Figure 20.12

Representation of a fission process in which each event produces two neutrons, which can go on to split other nuclei, leading to a self-sustaining chain reaction.

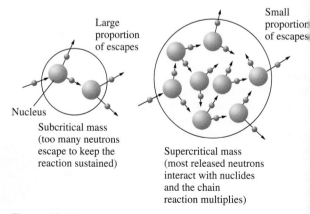

Figure 20.13

If the mass of fissionable material is too small, most of the neutrons escape before causing another fission event; thus the process dies out.

Figure 20.14

A schematic diagram of a nuclear power plant.

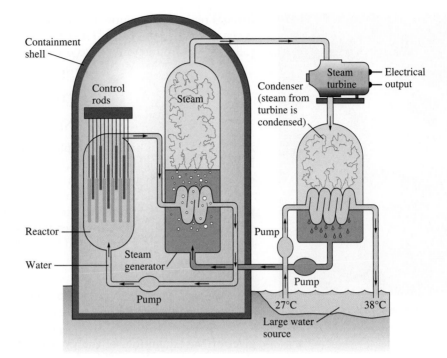

The resulting energy is used to heat water to produce steam to run turbine generators, in much the same way that a coal-burning power plant generates energy. A schematic diagram of a nuclear power plant is shown in Fig. 20.14.

In the **reactor core,** shown in Fig. 20.15, uranium that has been enriched to approximately 3% $^{235}_{92}U$ (natural uranium contains only 0.7% $^{235}_{92}U$) is housed in cylinders. A **moderator** surrounds the cylinders to slow down the neutrons so that the uranium fuel can capture them more efficiently. **Control rods,** composed of substances that absorb neutrons, are used to regulate the power level of the reactor. The reactor is designed so that should a malfunction occur, the control rods are automatically inserted into the core to stop the reaction. A liquid (usually water) is circulated through the core to extract the heat generated by the energy of fission; the energy is then passed on via a heat exchanger to water in the turbine system.

^{235}U enrichment is described in Section 5.7.

Although the concentration of $^{235}_{92}U$ in the fuel elements is not great enough to allow a supercritical mass to develop in the core, a failure of the cooling system can lead to temperatures high enough to melt the core. As a result, the building housing the core must be designed to contain the core even if a meltdown occurs. A great deal of controversy now exists about the efficiency of the safety systems in nuclear power plants. Accidents such as the one at the Three Mile Island facility in Pennsylvania in 1979 and the one in Chernobyl,* USSR, in 1986 have led many people to question the wisdom of continuing to build fission-based power plants.

Breeder Reactors

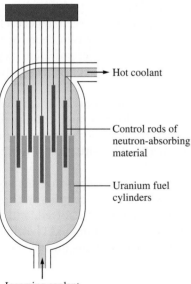

One potential problem facing the nuclear power industry is the supply of $^{235}_{92}U$. Some scientists have suggested that we have nearly depleted those uranium deposits rich enough in $^{235}_{92}U$ to make production of fissionable fuel economically feasible. Because of this possibility, **breeder reactors** have been developed, in which fissionable fuel is actually produced while the reactor runs. In a

- Hot coolant

- Control rods of neutron-absorbing material

- Uranium fuel cylinders

Incoming coolant

Figure 20.15

A schematic of a reactor core. The position of the control rods determines the level of energy production by regulating the amount of fission taking place.

*For a detailed account of this incident, see C. A. Atwood, "Chernobyl—What Happened?" *J. Chem. Ed.* **65** (1988): 1037.

A core of a nuclear reactor.

breeder reactor, the major component of natural uranium, nonfissionable $^{238}_{92}$U, is changed to fissionable $^{239}_{94}$Pu. The reaction involves absorption of a neutron, followed by production of two β particles:

$$^{1}_{0}\text{n} + {}^{238}_{92}\text{U} \longrightarrow {}^{239}_{92}\text{U}$$

$$^{239}_{92}\text{U} \longrightarrow {}^{239}_{93}\text{Np} + {}^{0}_{-1}\text{e}$$

$$^{239}_{93}\text{Np} \longrightarrow {}^{239}_{94}\text{Pu} + {}^{0}_{-1}\text{e}$$

As the reactor runs and $^{235}_{92}$U is split, some of the excess neutrons are absorbed by $^{238}_{92}$U to produce $^{239}_{94}$Pu. The $^{239}_{94}$Pu is then separated out and used to fuel another reactor. Such a reactor thus "breeds" nuclear fuel as it operates.

Although breeder reactors are now used in France, the United States is proceeding slowly with the reactors' development because of their controversial nature. One problem involves the hazards in handling plutonium, which flames upon contact with air and is very toxic.

Fusion

Large quantities of energy are also produced by the fusion of two light nuclei. In fact, stars produce their energy through nuclear fusion. Our sun, which presently consists of 73% hydrogen, 26% helium, and 1% other elements, gives off vast quantities of energy from the fusion of protons to form helium:

$$^{1}_{1}\text{H} + {}^{1}_{1}\text{H} \longrightarrow {}^{2}_{1}\text{H} + {}^{0}_{1}\text{e}$$

$$^{1}_{1}\text{H} + {}^{2}_{1}\text{H} \longrightarrow {}^{3}_{2}\text{He}$$

$$^{3}_{2}\text{He} + {}^{3}_{2}\text{He} \longrightarrow {}^{4}_{2}\text{He} + 2{}^{1}_{1}\text{H}$$

$$^{3}_{2}\text{He} + {}^{1}_{1}\text{H} \longrightarrow {}^{4}_{2}\text{He} + {}^{0}_{1}\text{e}$$

Intense research is under way to develop a feasible fusion process because of the ready availability of many light nuclides (deuterium, $^{2}_{1}$H, in seawater, for example) that can serve as fuel in fusion reactors. The major stumbling block is the high temperatures required to initiate fusion. The forces that bind nucleons together to form a nucleus are effective only at *very small* distances ($\approx 10^{-13}$ cm). Thus, for two protons to bind together and thereby release energy, they must get very close together. But protons, because they are identically charged, repel each other electrostatically. This means that to get two protons (or two deuterons) close enough to bind together (the nuclear binding force is *not* electrostatic), they must be "shot" at each other at speeds high enough to overcome the electrostatic repulsion.

The electrostatic repulsion forces between two $^{2}_{1}$H nuclei are so great that a temperature of 4×10^{7} K is required to give them velocities large enough to cause them to collide with sufficient energy that the nuclear forces can bind the particles together and thus release the binding energy. This situation is represented in Fig. 20.16.

Currently, scientists are studying two types of systems to produce the extremely high temperatures required: high-powered lasers and heating by electric currents. At present, many technical problems remain to be solved, and it is not clear which method will prove more useful or when fusion might become a practical energy source. However, there is still hope that fusion will be a major energy source in the twenty-first century.

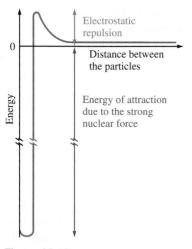

Figure 20.16

A plot of energy versus the separation distance for two $^{2}_{1}$H nuclei. The nuclei must have sufficient velocities to get over the electrostatic repulsion "hill" and get close enough for the nuclear binding forces to become effective, thus "fusing" the particles into a new nucleus and releasing large quantities of energy. The binding force is at least 100 times the electrostatic repulsion.

20.7 | Effects of Radiation

Everyone knows that being hit by a train is very serious. The problem is the energy transfer involved. In fact, any source of energy is potentially harmful to organisms. Energy transferred to cells can break chemical bonds and cause

Nuclear Physics: An Introduction

Nuclear physics is concerned with the fundamental nature of matter. The central focuses of this area of study are the relationship between a quantity of energy and its mass, given by $E = mc^2$, and the fact that matter can be converted from one form (energy) to another (particulate) in particle accelerators. Collisions between high-speed particles have produced a dazzling array of new particles—hundreds of them. These events can best be seen as conversions of kinetic energy into particles. For example, a collision of sufficient energy between a proton and a neutron can produce four particles: two protons, one antiproton, and a neutron:

$$\,^1_1\text{H} + \,^1_0\text{n} \longrightarrow 2\,^1_1\text{H} + \,^1_{-1}\text{H} + \,^1_0\text{n}$$

where $\,^1_{-1}\text{H}$ is the symbol for an *antiproton*, which has the same mass as a proton but the opposite charge. This process is a little like throwing one baseball at a very high speed into another and having the collision produce four baseballs.

The results of such accelerator experiments have led scientists to postulate the existence of three types of forces important in the nucleus: the *strong force,* the *weak force,* and the *electromagnetic force.* Along with the *gravitational force,* these forces are thought to account for all types of interactions found in matter. These forces are believed to be generated by the exchange of particles between the interacting pieces of matter. For example, gravitational force is thought to be carried by particles called *gravitons.* The electromagnetic force (the classical electrostatic force between charged particles) is assumed to be exerted through the exchange of *photons.* The strong force, not charge-related and effective only at very short distances ($\approx 10^{-13}$ cm), is postulated to involve the exchange of particles called *gluons.* The weak force is 100 times weaker than the strong force and seems to be exerted by the exchange of two types of large particles, the W (has a mass 70 times the proton mass) and the Z (has a mass 90 times the proton mass).

The particles discovered have been classified into several categories. Three of the most important classes are as follows:

1. *Hadrons* are particles that respond to the strong force and have internal structure.

2. *Leptons* are particles that do not respond to the strong force and have no internal structure.

3. *Quarks* are particles with no internal structure that are thought to be the fundamental constitu-

Courtesy, Fermilab Visual Media/Batavia, IL.

The accelerator tunnel at Fermilab, a high-energy particle accelerator in Batavia, Illinois.

ents of hadrons. Neutrons and protons are hadrons that are thought to be composed of three quarks each.

The world of particle physics appears mysterious and complicated. For example, particle physicists have discovered new properties of matter they call "color," "charm," and "strangeness" and have postulated conservation laws involving these properties. This area of science is extremely important because it should help us to understand the interactions of matter in a more elegant and unified way. For example, the classification of forces into four categories is probably necessary only because we do not understand the true nature of forces. All forces may be special cases of a single, all-pervading force field that governs all of nature. In fact, Einstein spent the last 30 years of his life looking for a way to unify gravitational and electromagnetic forces—without success. Physicists may now be on the verge of accomplishing what Einstein failed to do.

Although the practical aspects of much of the work in nuclear physics are not yet totally apparent, a more fundamental understanding of the way nature operates could lead to presently undreamed-of devices for energy production, communication, and so on, which could revolutionize our lives.

malfunctioning of the cell systems. This fact is behind the concern about the ozone layer in the earth's upper atmosphere, which screens out high-energy ultraviolet radiation from the sun. Radioactive elements, which are sources of high-energy particles, are also potentially hazardous, although the effects are usually quite subtle. The reason for the subtlety of radiation damage is that even though high-energy particles are involved, the quantity of energy actually deposited in tissues *per event* is quite small. However, the resulting damage is no less real, although the effects may not be apparent for years.

The α particles, β particles, and γ rays produced by radioactive nuclei have energies far greater than the bond energies and the ionization energies of biological molecules. Therefore, nuclear radiation fragments and ionizes biomolecules, generating reactive species that can cause further damage. For example, γ rays can knock an electron from a water molecule to form H_2O^+ ions, which can react with another water molecule as follows:

$$H_2O^+ + H_2O \longrightarrow H_3O^+ + OH$$

The OH fragment produced in this reaction is a *free radical,* a species with one or more unpaired electrons. Because it has an unpaired electron, the OH molecule readily attacks other molecules, forming more free radicals that in turn can react with additional molecules. Thus the formation of a single OH radical by a γ ray can lead to extensive damage in a cell.

Radiation damage to organisms can be classified as somatic or genetic damage. **Somatic damage** is damage to the organism itself, resulting in sickness or death. The effects may appear almost immediately if a massive dose of radiation is received; for smaller doses, damage may appear years later, usually in the form of cancer. **Genetic damage** is damage to the genetic machinery, which produces malfunctions in the offspring of the organism.

The biological effects of a particular source of radiation depend on several factors:

1. *The energy of the radiation.* The higher the energy content of the radiation, the more damage it can cause by formation of free radicals and ions. The official SI unit for radiation doses is the *Gray* (1 J of energy deposited per kg of tissue), although the **rad** (10^{-2} J/kg tissue) is still commonly used.

2. *The penetrating ability of the radiation.* The particles and rays produced in radioactive processes vary in their abilities to penetrate human tissue: γ rays are highly penetrating; β particles can penetrate about 1 cm; and α particles are stopped by the skin.

3. *The chemical properties of the radiation source.* When a radioactive nuclide is ingested into the body, its effectiveness in causing damage depends on its residence time. For example, $^{85}_{36}Kr$ and $^{90}_{38}Sr$ are both β-particle producers. However, since krypton is chemically inert, it passes through the body quickly and does not have much time to do damage. Strontium, being chemically similar to calcium, can collect in bones, where it may cause leukemia and bone cancer.

Because of the differences in the behavior of the particles and rays produced by radioactive decay, both the energy dose of the radiation and its effectiveness in causing biological damage must be taken into account. The **rem** (which is short for *r*oentgen *e*quivalent for *m*an) is defined as follows:

$$\text{Number of rems} = (\text{number of rads}) \times \text{RBE}$$

where RBE represents the relative effectiveness of the radiation in causing biological damage.

Table 20.6 shows the physical effects of short-term exposure to various doses of radiation, and Table 20.7 gives the sources and amounts of radiation

Table 20.6

Effects of Short-Term Exposures to Radiation

Dose (rem)	Clinical Effect
0–25	Nondetectable
25–50	Temporary decrease in white blood cell counts
100–200	Strong decrease in white blood cell counts
500	Death of half the exposed population within 30 days after exposure

Table 20.7

Typical Radiation Exposures for a Person Living in the United States (1 millirem = 10^{-3} rem)

Source	Exposure (millirems/year)
Radon	200
Cosmic radiation	27
From the earth	28
From building materials	3
In human tissues	39
Inhalation of air	5
Total from natural sources	302
X-ray diagnosis	50
Radiotherapy	10
Internal diagnosis/ therapy	1
Nuclear power industry	0.2
TV tubes, industrial wastes, etc.	2
Radioactive fallout	4
Total from human activities	67
Total	369

exposure for a typical person in the United States. Note that natural sources contribute four to five times as much as human activities to the total exposure. However, although the nuclear industry contributes only a small percentage of the total exposure, the major controversy associated with nuclear power plants is the *potential* for radiation hazards. These arise mainly from two sources: accidents allowing the release of radioactive materials and improper disposal of the radioactive products in spent fuel elements. The radioactive products of the fission of $^{235}_{92}U$, although constituting only a small percentage of the total products, have half-lives of several hundred years and remain dangerous for a long time. Various schemes have been advanced for the disposal of these wastes. The one that seems to hold the most promise is the incorporation of the wastes into ceramic blocks and the burial of these blocks in geologically stable formations. At present, however, no disposal method has been accepted, and nuclear wastes continue to accumulate in temporary storage facilities.

Note from Table 20.7 that exposure to radon is by far the most significant source of natural radiation. $^{222}_{86}Rn$, a decay product of $^{238}_{92}U$ (Table 20.3), is continuously generated in the earth's crust. This gaseous radon emerges from the ground and is trapped in the basements of houses and other buildings, where it is circulated by heating and cooling systems. Because radon is an α-particle producer,

$$^{222}_{86}Rn \longrightarrow {}^{218}_{84}Po + {}^4_2He$$

with a short half-life of 3.82 days, it causes biological damage when inhaled. In addition, the $^{218}_{84}Po$ formed, a solid that can be trapped in lung tissue, is an even more potent α-particle producer ($t_{1/2} = 3.11$ min). Because α particles have a high RBE (because of their ability to produce a very high concentration of ions in affected tissue), radon is particularly dangerous and there is great concern that this exposure can lead to a significant incidence of lung cancer.

Key Terms

Section 20.1
beta (β) particle
zone of stability
magic numbers
alpha (α) particle
alpha-particle production
spontaneous fission
beta-particle production
gamma (γ) ray
positron production
antiparticle

For Review

OWL and **go Chemistry**

Sign in at **www.cengage.com/owl** to:
- View tutorials and simulations, develop problem-solving skills, and complete online homework assigned by your professor.
- Download Go Chemistry mini lecture modules for quick review and exam prep from OWL (or purchase them at **www.cengagebrain.com**)

Radioactivity
- Certain nuclei decay spontaneously into more stable nuclei
- Types of radioactive decay:
  - α-particle (^4_2He) production
  - β-particle ($^0_{-1}e$) production

- Positron ($_{1}^{0}$e) production
- γ rays are usually produced in a radioactive decay event
- A decay series involves several radioactive decays to finally reach a stable nuclide
- Radioactive decay follows first-order kinetics
  - Half-life of a radioactive sample: the time required for half of the nuclides to decay
- The transuranium elements (those beyond uranium in the periodic table) can be synthesized by particle bombardment of uranium or heavier elements
- Radiocarbon dating employs the $_{6}^{14}$C/$_{6}^{12}$C ratio in an object to establish its date of origin

Thermodynamic stability of a nucleus

- Compares the mass of a nucleus to the sum of the masses of its component nucleons
- When a system gains or loses energy, it also gains or loses mass as described by the relationship $E = mc^2$
- The difference between the sum of the masses of the component nucleons and the actual mass of a nucleus (called the mass defect) can be used to calculate the nuclear binding energy

Nuclear energy production

- Fusion: the process of combining two light nuclei to form a heavier, more stable nucleus
- Fission: the process of splitting a heavy nucleus into two lighter, more stable nuclei
  - Current nuclear power reactors employ controlled fission to produce energy

Radiation damage

- Radiation can cause direct (somatic) damage to a living organism or genetic damage to the organism's offspring
- The biologic effects of radiation depend on the energy, the penetrating ability, the ionizing ability of the radiation, and the chemical properties of the nuclide producing the radiation

Exercises

OWL Interactive versions of these problems may be assigned in OWL.

A blue exercise number indicates that the answer to that exercise appears at the back of this book and a solution appears in the *Solutions Guide.*

Radioactive Decay and Nuclear Transformations

1. Define or illustrate the following terms.
   a. thermodynamic stability
   b. kinetic stability
   c. radioactive decay
   d. β-particle production
   e. α-particle production
   f. positron production
   g. electron capture
   h. γ-ray emissions

2. Which type of radioactive decay has the net effect of changing a neutron into a proton? Which type of decay has the net effect of turning a proton into a neutron?

3. Supply the missing particle, and state the type of decay for each of the following nuclear processes.
   a.

$_{92}^{238}$U

b.

$^{234}_{90}$Th → $^{234}_{91}$Pa + ?

4. Write an equation describing the radioactive decay of each of the following nuclides. (The particle produced is shown in parentheses, except for electron capture, where an electron is a reactant.)
   a. $^3_1$H (β)
   b. $^8_3$Li (β followed by α)
   c. $^7_4$Be (electron capture)
   d. $^8_5$B (positron)

5. Write balanced equations for each of the following processes.
   a. Chromium-51, which targets the spleen and is used as a tracer in studies of red blood cells, decays by electron capture.
   b. Iodine-131, used to treat hyperactive thyroid glands, decays by producing a β particle.
   c. Phosphorus-32, which accumulates in the liver, decays by β-particle production.

6. In each of the following radioactive decay processes, supply the missing particle.
   a. ^{73}Ga → ^{73}Ge + ?
   b. ^{192}Pt → ^{188}Os + ?
   c. ^{205}Bi → ^{205}Pb + ?
   d. ^{241}Cm + ? → ^{241}Am
   e. ^{60}Co → ^{60}Ni + ?
   f. ^{97}Tc + ? → ^{97}Mo
   g. ^{99}Tc → ^{99}Ru + ?
   h. ^{239}Pu → ^{235}U + ?

7. Write an equation describing the radioactive decay of each of the following nuclides. (The particle produced is shown in parentheses, except for electron capture, where an electron is a reactant.)
   a. ^{68}Ga (electron capture)
   b. ^{62}Cu (positron)
   c. ^{212}Fr (α)
   d. ^{129}Sb (β)

8. One type of commercial smoke detector contains a minute amount of radioactive americium-241 (^{241}Am), which decays by α-particle production. The α particles ionize molecules in the air, allowing it to conduct an electric current. When smoke particles enter, the conductivity of the air changes, and the alarm buzzes.
   a. Write the equation for the decay of $^{241}_{95}$Am by α-particle production.
   b. The complete decay of ^{241}Am involves successively α, α, β, α, α, β, α, α, α, β, α, and β production. What is the final stable nucleus produced in this decay series?
   c. Identify the 11 intermediate nuclides.

9. The radioactive isotope ^{247}Bk decays by a series of α-particle and β-particle productions, taking ^{247}Bk through many transformations to end up as ^{207}Pb. In the complete decay series, how many α particles and β particles are produced?

10. There are four stable isotopes of iron with mass numbers 54, 56, 57, and 58. There are also two radioactive isotopes: iron-53 and iron-59. Predict modes of decay for these two isotopes, and write a nuclear reaction for each. (See Table 20.2.)

11. The only stable isotope of fluorine is fluorine-19. Predict possible modes of decay for fluorine-21, fluorine-18, and fluorine-17.

12. Predict whether each of the following nuclides is stable or unstable (radioactive). If the nuclide is unstable, predict the type of radioactivity you would expect it to exhibit.
    a. $^{45}_{19}$K
    b. $^{56}_{26}$Fe
    c. $^{20}_{11}$Na
    d. $^{194}_{81}$Tl

13. In 1994 it was proposed (and eventually accepted) that element 106 be named seaborgium (Sg) in honor of Glenn T. Seaborg, discoverer of the transuranium elements.
    a. ^{263}Sg was produced by the bombardment of ^{249}Cf with a beam of ^{18}O nuclei. Complete and balance an equation for this reaction.
    b. ^{263}Sg decays by α-particle emission. What is the other product resulting from the α decay of ^{263}Sg?

14. Many elements have been synthesized by bombarding relatively heavy atoms with high-energy particles in particle accelerators. Complete the following nuclear reactions, which have been used to synthesize elements.
    a. _____ + $^4_2$He → $^{243}_{97}$Bk + $^1_0$n
    b. $^{238}_{92}$U + $^{12}_6$C → _____ + 6$^1_0$n
    c. $^{249}_{98}$Cf + _____ → $^{260}_{105}$Db + 4$^1_0$n
    d. $^{249}_{98}$Cf + $^{10}_5$B → $^{257}_{103}$Lr + _____

Kinetics of Radioactive Decay

15. Americium-241 is widely used in smoke detectors. The radiation released by this element ionizes particles that are then detected by a charged-particle collector. The half-life of ^{241}Am is 433 years, and it decays by emitting alpha particles. How many alpha particles are emitted each second by a 5.00-g sample of ^{241}Am?

16. Krypton consists of several radioactive isotopes, some of which are listed in the following table.

Isotope	Half-life
Kr-73	27 s
Kr-74	11.5 min
Kr-76	14.8 h
Kr-81	2.1×10^5 yr

Which of these isotopes is most stable, and which isotope is "hottest"? How long does it take for 87.5% of each isotope to decay?

17. Radioactive copper-64 decays with a half-life of 12.8 days.
    a. What is the value of k in s^{-1}?
    b. A sample contains 28.0 mg ^{64}Cu. How many decay events will be produced in the first second? Assume that the atomic mass of ^{64}Cu is 64.0.
    c. A chemist obtains a fresh sample of ^{64}Cu and measures its radioactivity. She then determines that to do an experiment, the radioactivity cannot fall below 25% of the initial measured value. How long does she have to perform the experiment?

18. The curie (Ci) is a commonly used unit for measuring nuclear radioactivity: 1 curie of radiation is equal to 3.7 ×

10^{10} decay events per second (the number of decay events from 1 g of radium in 1 s).

a. What mass of $Na_2{}^{38}SO_4$ has an activity of 10.0 mCi? Sulfur-38 has an atomic mass of 38.0 and a half-life of 2.87 h.

b. How long does it take for 99.99% of a sample of sulfur-38 to decay?

19. The first atomic explosion was detonated in the desert north of Alamogordo, New Mexico, on July 16, 1945. What percentage of the strontium-90 ($t_{1/2}$ = 28.9 yr) originally produced by that explosion still remains as of July 16, 2012?

20. Iodine-131 is used in the diagnosis and treatment of thyroid disease and has a half-life of 8.0 days. If a patient with thyroid disease consumes a sample of $Na^{131}I$ containing 10. μg of ^{131}I, how long will it take for the amount of ^{131}I to decrease to 1/100 of the original amount?

21. Phosphorus-32 is a commonly used radioactive nuclide in biochemical research, particularly in studies of nucleic acids. The half-life of phosphorus-32 is 14.3 days. What mass of phosphorus-32 is left from an original sample of 175 mg of $Na_3{}^{32}PO_4$ after 35.0 days? Assume that the atomic mass of ^{32}P is 32.0.

22. A chemist wishing to do an experiment requiring $^{47}Ca^{2+}$ (half-life = 4.5 days) needs 5.0 μg of the nuclide. What mass of $^{47}CaCO_3$ must be ordered if it takes 48 h for delivery from the supplier? Assume that the atomic mass of ^{47}Ca is 47.0.

23. Explain the theory behind carbon-14 dating. What assumptions must be made and what problems arise when using carbon-14 dating?

24. The decay of uranium-238 to lead-206 is also used to estimate the age of objects. Specifically, ^{206}Pb-to-^{238}U ratios allow dating of rocks. Why is the ^{238}U decay to ^{206}Pb useful for dating rocks but useless for dating objects 10,000 years old or younger? Similarly, why is carbon-14 dating useful for dating objects 10,000 years old or younger but useless for dating rocks?

25. At a flea market you've found a very interesting painting done in the style of Rembrandt's "Dark Period" (1642–1672). You suspect that you really do not have a genuine Rembrandt, so you take it to the local university for testing. Living wood shows a carbon-14 activity of 15.3 counts per minute per gram. Your painting showed a carbon-14 activity of 15.1 counts per minute per gram. Could it be a genuine Rembrandt? (For ^{14}C, $t_{1/2}$ = 5730 years.)

26. A living plant contains about the same fraction of carbon-14 as atmospheric carbon dioxide. The observed rate of decay of carbon-14 from a living plant is 15.3 counts per minute per gram of carbon. How many counts per minute per gram of carbon will be measured from a 15,000-year-old sample? Will radiocarbon dating work well for small samples of 10 mg or less? (For ^{14}C, $t_{1/2}$ = 5730 years.)

27. During World War II, tritium (^3H) was a component of fluorescent watch dials and hands. Assume you have such a watch that was made in January 1944. If 17% or more of the original tritium was needed to read the dial in dark

places, until what year could you read the time at night? (For ^3H, $t_{1/2}$ = 12.3 years.)

28. A proposed system for storing nuclear wastes involves storing the radioactive material in caves or deep mine shafts. One of the most toxic nuclides that must be disposed of is plutonium-239, which is produced in breeder reactors and has a half-life of 24,100 years. A suitable storage place must be geologically stable long enough for the activity of plutonium-239 to decrease to 0.1% of its original value. How long is this period for plutonium-239?

29. A rock contains 0.688 mg of ^{206}Pb for every 1.000 mg of ^{238}U present. Assuming that no lead was originally present, that all the ^{206}Pb formed over the years has remained in the rock, and that the number of nuclides in intermediate stages of decay between ^{238}U and ^{206}Pb is negligible, calculate the age of the rock. (For ^{238}U, $t_{1/2}$ = 4.5×10^9 years.)

30. The mass ratios of ^{40}Ar to ^{40}K can also be used to date geological materials. Potassium-40 decays by two processes:

$$^{40}_{19}K + {}^{0}_{-1}e \longrightarrow {}^{40}_{18}Ar \ (10.7\%)$$

$$t_{1/2} = 1.27 \times 10^9 \text{ yr}$$

$$^{40}_{19}K \longrightarrow {}^{40}_{20}Ca + {}^{0}_{-1}e \ (89.3\%)$$

a. Why are $^{40}Ar/^{40}K$ ratios rather than $^{40}Ca/^{40}K$ ratios used to date materials?

b. What assumptions must be made in using this technique?

c. A sedimentary rock has a $^{40}Ar/^{40}K$ ratio of 0.95. Calculate the age of the rock.

d. How will the measured age of a rock compare with the actual age if some ^{40}Ar has escaped from the sample?

Energy Changes in Nuclear Reactions

31. The sun radiates 3.9×10^{23} J of energy into space every second. What is the rate at which mass is lost from the sun?

32. The earth receives 1.8×10^{14} kJ/s of solar energy. What mass of solar material is converted to energy over a 24-h period to provide the daily amount of solar energy to the earth? What mass of coal would have to be burned to provide the same amount of energy? Coal releases 32 kJ of energy per gram when burned.

33. The most stable nucleus in terms of binding energy per nucleon is ^{56}Fe. If the atomic mass of ^{56}Fe is 55.9349 amu, calculate the binding energy per nucleon for ^{56}Fe.

34. Calculate the binding energy per nucleon for ^2_1H and ^3_1H. The atomic masses are ^2_1H, 2.01410 amu, and ^3_1H, 3.01605 amu.

35. Calculate the binding energy in J/nucleon for carbon-12 (atomic mass 12.00000) and uranium-235 (atomic mass 235.0439). The atomic mass of ^1_1H is 1.00782 amu, and the mass of a neutron is 1.00866 amu. The most stable nucleus known is ^{56}Fe (see Exercise 33). Would the binding energy per nucleon for ^{56}Fe be larger or smaller than that for ^{12}C or ^{235}U? Explain.

36. The mass defect for a lithium-6 nucleus is −0.03434 g/mol. Calculate the atomic mass of lithium-6.

37. The binding energy per nucleon for magnesium-27 is 1.326×10^{-12} J/nucleon. Calculate the atomic mass of magnesium-27.

38. A positron and an electron annihilate each other upon colliding, thereby producing energy:

$$_{-1}^{0}e + _{+1}^{0}e \longrightarrow 2\,_{0}^{0}\gamma$$

Assuming that both γ rays have the same energy, calculate the wavelength of the electromagnetic radiation produced.

39. The easiest fusion reaction to initiate is

$$_{1}^{2}H + _{1}^{3}H \longrightarrow _{2}^{4}He + _{0}^{1}n$$

Calculate the energy released per nucleus of $_{2}^{4}He$ produced and per mole of $_{2}^{4}He$ produced. The atomic masses are as follows: $_{1}^{2}H$, 2.01410 amu; $_{1}^{3}H$, 3.01605 amu; and $_{2}^{4}He$, 4.00260 amu. The masses of the electron and neutron are 5.4858×10^{-4} amu and 1.00866 amu, respectively.

40. Calculate the amount of energy released per gram of hydrogen nuclei reacted for the following reaction. The atomic masses are $_{1}^{1}H$, 1.00782 amu, and $_{1}^{2}H$, 2.01410 amu. (*Hint:* Think carefully about how to account for the electron mass.)

$$_{1}^{1}H + _{1}^{1}H \longrightarrow _{1}^{2}H + _{+1}^{0}e$$

Detection, Uses, and Health Effects of Radiation

41. The typical response of a Geiger-Müller tube is shown below. Explain the shape of this curve.

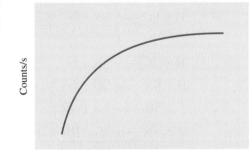

Disintegrations/s from sample

42. When using a Geiger-Müller counter to measure radioactivity, one must maintain the same geometrical orientation between the sample and the Geiger-Müller tube to compare different measurements. Why?

43. Define *fission* and *fusion*. Fusion processes are more likely to occur for lighter elements, whereas fission processes are more likely to occur for heavier elements. Explain.

44. Why are elevated temperatures necessary to initiate fusion reactions but not fission reactions?

45. What are the purposes of the moderator and control rods in a fission reactor?

46. Much of the research on controlled fusion focuses on the problem of how to contain the reacting material. Magnetic fields appear to be the most promising mode of containment. Why is containment such a problem? Why must one resort to magnetic fields for containment?

47. During the research that led to production of the two atomic bombs used against Japan in World War II, different mechanisms for obtaining a supercritical mass of fissionable material were investigated. In one type of bomb, a "gun" shot one piece of fissionable material into a cavity containing another piece of fissionable material. In the second type of bomb, the fissionable material was surrounded with a high explosive that, when detonated, compressed the fissionable material into a smaller volume. Discuss what is meant by critical mass, and explain why the ability to achieve a critical mass is essential to sustaining a nuclear reaction.

48. There is a trend in the United States toward using coal-fired power plants to generate electricity rather than building new nuclear fission power plants. Is the use of coal-fired power plants without risk? Make a list of the risks to society from the use of each type of power plant.

49. How could a radioactive nuclide be used to demonstrate that chemical equilibrium is a dynamic process?

50. Consider the following reaction to produce methyl acetate:

$$CH_3OH + CH_3\overset{\displaystyle O}{\overset{\displaystyle \|}{C}}OH \longrightarrow CH_3\overset{\displaystyle O}{\overset{\displaystyle \|}{C}}OCH_3 + H_2O$$

Methyl acetate

When this reaction is carried out with CH_3OH containing radioactive oxygen-18, the water produced is not radioactive. Explain.

51. Photosynthesis in plants can be represented by the following overall reaction:

$$6CO_2(g) + 6H_2O(l) \xrightarrow{\text{Light}} C_6H_{12}O_6(s) + 6O_2(g)$$

Algae grown in water containing some radioactive ^{18}O (in $H_2^{18}O$) evolve oxygen gas with the same isotopic composition as the oxygen in the water. When algae growing in water containing only ^{16}O were furnished with carbon dioxide containing ^{18}O, no ^{18}O was found to be evolved from the oxygen gas produced. What conclusions about photosynthesis can be drawn from these experiments?

52. Radiotracers are used in the medical sciences to learn about metabolic pathways. What are radiotracers? Explain why ^{14}C and ^{32}P radioactive nuclides would be very helpful in learning about metabolic pathways.

53. The biological effects of a particular source of radiation depend on several factors. List some of these factors. Even though ^{85}Kr and ^{90}Sr are both β-particle emitters, the dangers associated with the decay of ^{90}Sr are much greater than those linked to ^{85}Kr. Why?

54. Although γ rays are far more penetrating than α particles, the latter are more likely to cause damage to an organism. Why? Which type of radiation is more effective at promoting the ionization of biomolecules?

55. Consider the following information:
    i. The layer of dead skin on our bodies is sufficient to protect us from most α-particle radiation.
    ii. Plutonium is an α-particle producer.
    iii. The chemistry of Pu^{4+} is similar to that of Fe^{3+}.
    iv. Pu oxidizes readily to Pu^{4+}.

    Why is plutonium one of the most toxic substances known?

Additional Exercises

56. Consider the following graph of binding energy per nucleon as a function of mass number.

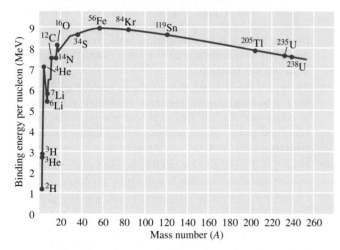

a. What does this graph tell us about the relative half-lives of the nuclides? Explain your answer.

b. Which nuclide shown is the most thermodynamically stable? Which is the least thermodynamically stable?

c. What does this graph tell us about which nuclides undergo fusion and which undergo fission to become more stable? Support your answer.

57. The mass percent of carbon in a typical human is 18%, and the mass percent of ^{14}C in natural carbon is $1.6 \times 10^{-10}\%$. Assuming a 180-lb person, how many decay events per second occur in this person due exclusively to the β-particle decay of ^{14}C? (For ^{14}C, $t_{1/2} = 5730$ years.)

58. Using the kinetic molecular theory (Section 5.6), calculate the root mean square velocity and the average kinetic energy of $^{2}_{1}H$ nuclei at a temperature of 4×10^{7} K. (See Exercise 39 for the appropriate mass values.)

59. A small atomic bomb releases energy equivalent to the detonation of 20,000 tons of TNT; a ton of TNT releases 4×10^{9} J of energy when exploded. Using 2×10^{13} J/mol as the energy released by fission of ^{235}U, about what mass of ^{235}U undergoes fission in this atomic bomb?

60. When nuclei undergo nuclear transformations, γ rays of characteristic frequencies are observed. How does this fact, along with other information in the chapter on nuclear stability, suggest that a model similar to the quantum mechanics used for atoms may apply to the nucleus?

61. A chemist studied the reaction mechanism for the reaction

$$2NO(g) + O_2(g) \longrightarrow 2NO_2(g)$$

by reacting $N^{16}O$ with $^{18}O_2$. If the reaction mechanism is

$$NO + O_2 \rightleftharpoons NO_3 \text{ (fast equilibrium)}$$

$$NO_3 + NO \longrightarrow 2NO_2 \text{ (slow)}$$

what distribution of ^{18}O would you expect in the NO_2? Assume that N is the central atom in NO_3, assume only $N^{16}O^{18}O_2$ forms, and assume stoichiometric amounts of reactants are combined.

62. Define "third-life" in a similar way to "half-life," and determine the "third-life" for a nuclide that has a half-life of 31.4 years.

63. A 0.10-cm^3 sample of a solution containing a radioactive nuclide (5.0×10^3 counts per minute per milliliter) is injected into a rat. Several minutes later, 1.0 cm^3 of blood is removed. The blood shows 48 counts of radioactivity per minute. What is the volume of blood in the rat? What assumptions must be made in performing this calculation?

64. In addition to the process described in the text, a second process called the carbon–nitrogen cycle occurs in the sun:

$$^{1}_{1}H + ^{12}_{6}C \longrightarrow ^{13}_{7}N + ^{0}_{0}\gamma$$

$$^{13}_{7}N \longrightarrow ^{13}_{6}C + ^{0}_{+1}e$$

$$^{1}_{1}H + ^{13}_{6}C \longrightarrow ^{14}_{7}N + ^{0}_{0}\gamma$$

$$^{1}_{1}H + ^{14}_{7}N \longrightarrow ^{15}_{8}O + ^{0}_{0}\gamma$$

$$^{15}_{8}O \longrightarrow ^{15}_{7}N + ^{0}_{+1}e$$

$$^{1}_{1}H + ^{15}_{7}N \longrightarrow ^{12}_{6}C + ^{4}_{2}He + ^{0}_{0}\gamma$$

Overall reaction: $4\,^{1}_{1}H \longrightarrow ^{4}_{2}He + 2\,^{0}_{+1}e$

a. What is the catalyst in the above scheme?

b. What nucleons are intermediates?

c. How much energy is released per mole of hydrogen nuclei reacted in the overall reaction? (See Exercises 39 and 40 for the appropriate mass values.)

Challenge Problems

65. Naturally occurring uranium is composed mostly of ^{238}U and ^{235}U, with relative abundances of 99.28% and 0.72%, respectively. The half-life for ^{238}U is 4.5×10^9 years, and the half-life for ^{235}U is 7.1×10^8 years. Assuming that the earth was formed 4.5 billion years ago, calculate the relative abundances of the ^{238}U and ^{235}U isotopes when the earth was formed.

66. The curie (Ci) is a commonly used unit for measuring nuclear radioactivity: 1 curie of radiation is equal to 3.7×10^{10} decay events per second (the number of decay events from 1 g radium in 1 s). A 1.7-mL sample of water containing tritium was injected into a 150-lb person. The total activity of radiation injected was 86.5 mCi. After some time to allow the tritium activity to equally distribute throughout the body, a sample of blood plasma containing 2.0 mL water at an activity of 3.6 μCi was removed. From these data, calculate the mass percent of water in this 150-lb person.

67. Estimate the temperature needed to achieve the fusion of deuterium to make an α particle. The energy required can be estimated from Coulomb's law [use the form $E = 9.0 \times 10^9 (Q_1Q_2/r)$, using $Q = 1.6 \times 10^{-19}$ C for a proton and $r = 2 \times 10^{-15}$ m for the helium nucleus; the unit for the proportionality constant in Coloumb's law is $J \cdot m/C^2$].

68. Radioactive cobalt-60 is used to study defects in vitamin B_{12} absorption because cobalt is the metallic atom at the center of the vitamin B_{12} molecule. The nuclear synthesis of this cobalt isotope involves a three-step process. The overall reaction is iron-58 reacting with two neutrons to produce cobalt-60 along with the emission of another particle. What particle is emitted in this nuclear synthesis? What is the binding energy in J per nucleon for the cobalt-60 nucleus (atomic masses $^{60}Co = 59.9338$ amu, $^1H = 1.00782$ amu)? What is the de Broglie wavelength of the emitted particle if it has a velocity equal to $0.90c$, where c is the speed of light?

69. To determine the K_{sp} value of Hg_2I_2, a chemist obtained a solid sample of Hg_2I_2 in which some of the iodine is present as radioactive ^{131}I. The count rate of the Hg_2I_2 sample is 5.0×10^{11} counts per minute per mole of I. An excess amount of $Hg_2I_2(s)$ is placed in some water, and the solid is allowed to come to equilibrium with its respective ions. A 150.0-mL sample of the saturated solution is withdrawn and the radioactivity measured at 33 counts per minute. From this information, calculate the K_{sp} value for Hg_2I_2.

$$Hg_2I_2(s) \rightleftharpoons Hg_2^{2+}(aq) + 2I^-(aq) \qquad K_{sp} = [Hg_2^{2+}][I^-]^2$$

70. The most significant source of natural radiation is radon-222. ^{222}Rn, a decay product of ^{238}U, is continuously generated in the earth's crust allowing gaseous Rn to seep into the basements of buildings. Because ^{222}Rn is an α-particle producer with a relatively short half-life of 3.82 days, it can cause biological damage when inhaled.
   a. How many α particles and β particles are produced when ^{238}U decays to ^{222}Rn? What nuclei is produced when ^{222}Rn decays?
   b. Radon is a noble gas so one would expect it to pass through the body quickly. Why is there a concern over inhaling ^{222}Rn?
   c. Another problem associated with ^{222}Rn is that the decay of ^{222}Rn produces a more potent α-particle producer ($t_{1/2} = 3.11$ min) that is a solid. What is the identity of the solid? Give the balanced equation of this species decaying by α-particle production. Why is the solid a more potent α-particle producer?
   d. The U.S. Environmental Protection Agency (EPA) recommends that ^{222}Rn levels not exceed 4 pCi per liter of air (1 Ci = 1 curie = 3.7×10^{10} decay events per second; 1 pCi = 1×10^{-12} Ci). Convert 4.0 pCi per liter of air into concentration units of ^{222}Rn atoms per liter of air and mole of ^{222}Rn per liter of air.

71. For uranium to be useful as a nuclear fuel, the relative amount of ^{235}U to ^{238}U must be increased from about 0.7% ^{235}U in naturally occurring uranium to about 3%. The process of gas diffusion enrichment utilizes the velocity differences between $^{238}UF_6$ and $^{235}UF_6$ to accomplish the desired enrichment. Since the mass differences between $^{238}UF_6$ and $^{235}UF_6$ are relatively small, several steps are required in the diffusion process to enrich a natural uranium sample to the desired 3% ^{235}U. (For a complete discussion of this process, see Section 5.7.)
   a. Which molecule, $^{238}UF_6$ or $^{235}UF_6$, has the greater average velocity at a certain temperature? Explain.
   b. In theory, how many steps are required to enrich a uranium sample from 0.700% ^{235}U to 3.00% ^{235}U using the UF_6 multistage diffusion process? The molar masses of $^{235}UF_6$ and $^{238}UF_6$ are 349.03 g/mol and 352.05 g/mol, respectively.
   c. A certain sample of uranium is reacted with fluorine to form a mixture of $^{235}UF_6(g)$ and $^{238}UF_6(g)$. After 100 diffusion steps, the gas contains 1526 $^{235}UF_6$ molecules per 1.000×10^5 total number of molecules in the gas ($^{235}UF_6 + {}^{238}UF_6$). What is the ratio of ^{235}U to ^{238}U atoms in the original sample of uranium?

72. Zirconium is one of the few metals that retains its structural integrity upon exposure to radiation. The fuel rods in most nuclear reactors therefore are often made of zirconium. Answer the following questions about the redox properties of zirconium based on the half-reaction

$$ZrO_2 \cdot H_2O + H_2O + 4e^- \longrightarrow Zr + 4OH^-$$
$$\mathscr{E}° = -2.36 \text{ V}$$

   a. Is zirconium metal capable of reducing water to form hydrogen gas at standard conditions?
   b. Write a balanced equation for the reduction of water by zirconium.
   c. Calculate $\mathscr{E}°$, $\Delta G°$, and K for the reduction of water by zirconium metal.
   d. The reduction of water by zirconium occurred during the accident at Three Mile Island in 1979. The hydrogen produced was successfully vented and no chemical explosion occurred. If 1.00×10^3 kg of Zr reacts, what mass of H_2 is produced? What volume of H_2 at 1.0 atm and 1000.°C is produced?
   e. At Chernobyl in 1986, hydrogen was produced by the reaction of superheated steam with the graphite reactor core:

$$C(s) + H_2O(g) \longrightarrow CO(g) + H_2(g)$$

   It was not possible to prevent a chemical explosion at Chernobyl. In light of this, do you think it was a correct decision to vent the hydrogen and other radioactive gases into the atmosphere at Three Mile Island? Explain.

Organic and Biochemical Molecules

A rainbow eucalyptus tree in Maui, Hawaii.

Two Group 4A elements, carbon and silicon, form the basis of most natural substances. Silicon, with its great affinity for oxygen, forms chains and rings containing Si—O—Si bridges to produce the silica and silicates that form the basis for most rocks, sands, and soils. What silicon is to the geological world, carbon is to the biological world. Carbon has the unusual ability of bonding strongly to itself to form long chains or rings of carbon atoms. In addition, carbon forms strong bonds to other nonmetals such as hydrogen, nitrogen, oxygen, sulfur, and the halogens. Because of these bonding properties, there are a myriad of carbon compounds; several million are now known, and the number continues to grow rapidly. Among these many compounds are the **biomolecules,** those responsible for maintaining and reproducing life.

The study of carbon-containing compounds and their properties is called **organic chemistry.** Although a few compounds involving carbon, such as its oxides and carbonates, are considered to be inorganic substances, the vast majority are organic compounds that typically contain chains or rings of carbon atoms.

Originally, the distinction between inorganic and organic substances was based on whether a compound was produced by living systems. For example, until the early nineteenth century, it was believed that organic compounds had some sort of "life force" and could be synthesized only by living organisms. This view was dispelled in 1828 when German chemist Friedrich Wöhler (1800–1882) prepared urea from the inorganic salt ammonium cyanate by simple heating:

$$NH_4OCN \xrightarrow{\text{Heat}} H_2N-\overset{\displaystyle O}{\underset{\displaystyle \|}{C}}-NH_2$$

Ammonium cyanate   Urea

Urea is a component of urine, so it is clearly an organic material, yet here was clear evidence that it could be produced in the laboratory as well as by living things.

Organic chemistry plays a vital role in our quest to understand living systems. Beyond that, the synthetic fibers, plastics, artificial sweeteners, and drugs that are such an accepted part of modern life are products of industrial organic chemistry. In addition, the energy on which we rely so heavily to power our civilization is based mostly on the organic materials found in coal and petroleum.

Because organic chemistry is such a vast subject, we can provide only a brief introduction to it in this book. We will begin with the simplest class of organic compounds, the hydrocarbons, and then show how most other organic compounds can be considered to be derivatives of hydrocarbons.

21.1 | Alkanes: Saturated Hydrocarbons

As the name indicates, **hydrocarbons** are compounds composed of carbon and hydrogen. Those compounds whose carbon–carbon bonds are all single bonds are said to be **saturated** because each carbon is bound to four atoms, the maximum number. Hydrocarbons containing carbon–carbon multiple bonds are described as being **unsaturated,** since the carbon atoms involved in a multiple

Chemistry in the Garden

As we learn more about the biological world, we are finding that humble plants are often master chemists. For example, certain plants in the Amazon rain forests use chemistry in a very clever way to protect themselves. When attacked by herbivores such as spider mites or caterpillars, these plants produce and release compounds into the air that attract certain mites that are natural enemies of the attacking herbivores. These "bodyguard" mites assist the plant in fending off the attackers.

Although some plants can defend themselves using chemistry to attract "bodyguards," most cannot do this. As a result, scientists are trying to modify important food plants such as tomato plants so that they will emit chemicals to attract protective mites. For example, scientists from the Netherlands and Israel have begun a joint venture to genetically engineer *Arabidopis thaliava* plants that produce mite-attracting chemicals [*Science* **309** (2005): 2070].

Another example of the cooperation of plants and insects occurs in the so-called devil's gardens, in which a single species of tree predominates (*D. hirsute*) in large areas of the Amazon rain forests. Local legend attributes this strange phe-

A "bodyguard" mite (red) attacks a spider mite.

nomenon to an evil forest spirit that prevents other types of trees from growing. However, scientists at the University of Colorado, Denver, have found that colonies of ants that make nests in the stems of the *D. hirsute* trees produce formic acid, which prevents growth of other plants in the area. It is clear that plants and insects can team up to make great chemistry together.

---

bond can react with additional atoms, as shown by the *addition* of hydrogen to ethylene:

$$\underset{\text{Unsaturated}}{\overset{\displaystyle H}{\underset{\displaystyle H}{>}}C=C\overset{\displaystyle H}{\underset{\displaystyle H}{<}} + H_2 \longrightarrow \underset{\text{Saturated}}{H-\overset{\overset{\displaystyle H}{|}}{\underset{\underset{\displaystyle H}{|}}{C}}-\overset{\overset{\displaystyle H}{|}}{\underset{\underset{\displaystyle H}{|}}{C}}-H}$$

Note that each carbon in ethylene is bonded to three atoms (one carbon and two hydrogens) but that each can bond to one additional atom if one bond of the carbon–carbon double bond is broken.

The simplest member of the saturated hydrocarbons, which are also called the **alkanes,** is *methane* (CH_4). As discussed in Section 14.1, methane has a tetrahedral structure and can be described in terms of a carbon atom using an sp^3 hybrid set of orbitals to bond to the four hydrogen atoms (Fig. 21.1). The next alkane, the one containing two carbon atoms, is *ethane* (C_2H_6), as shown in Fig. 21.2. Each carbon in ethane is surrounded by four atoms and thus adopts a tetrahedral arrangement and sp^3 hybridization, as predicted by the localized electron model.

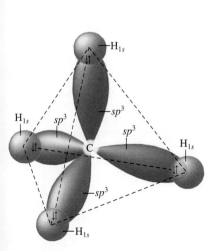

Figure 21.1
The C—H bonds in methane.

(a)

(b)

Figure 21.2
(a) The Lewis structure of ethane (C_2H_6). (b) The molecular structure of ethane represented by space-filling and ball-and-stick models.

(a)   (b)

Figure 21.3
The structures of (a) propane ($CH_3CH_2CH_3$) and (b) butane ($CH_3CH_2CH_2CH_3$). Each angle shown in red is 109.5°.

The next two members of the series are *propane* (C_3H_8) and *butane* (C_4H_{10}), shown in Fig. 21.3. Again, each carbon is bonded to four atoms and is described as sp^3 hybridized.

Alkanes in which the carbon atoms form long "strings" or chains are called **normal, straight-chain,** or **unbranched hydrocarbons.** As can be seen from Fig. 21.3, the chains in normal alkanes are not really straight but zig-zag, since the tetrahedral C—C—C angle is 109.5°. The normal alkanes can be represented by the structure

where n is an integer. Note that each member is obtained from the previous one by inserting a *methylene* (CH_2) group. We can condense the structural formulas by omitting some of the C—H bonds. For example, the general formula for normal alkanes shown on the previous page can be condensed to

$$CH_3—(CH_2)_n—CH_3$$

The first 10 normal alkanes and some of their properties are listed in Table 21.1. Note that all alkanes can be represented by the general formula C_nH_{2n+2}. For example, nonane, which has nine carbon atoms, is represented by $C_9H_{(2\times9)+2}$, or C_9H_{20}. Also note from Table 21.1 that the melting points and boiling points increase as the molar masses increase, as we would expect.

Table 21.1

Selected Properties of the First 10 Normal Alkanes

Name	Formula	Molar Mass	Melting Point (°C)	Boiling Point (°C)	Number of Structural Isomers
Methane	CH_4	16	−182	−162	1
Ethane	C_2H_6	30	−183	−89	1
Propane	C_3H_8	44	−187	−42	1
Butane	C_4H_{10}	58	−138	0	2
Pentane	C_5H_{12}	72	−130	36	3
Hexane	C_6H_{14}	86	−95	68	5
Heptane	C_7H_{16}	100	−91	98	9
Octane	C_8H_{18}	114	−57	126	18
Nonane	C_9H_{20}	128	−54	151	35
Decane	$C_{10}H_{22}$	142	−30	174	75

Figure 21.4
(a) Normal butane (abbreviated *n*-butane).
(b) The branched isomer of butane (called isobutane).

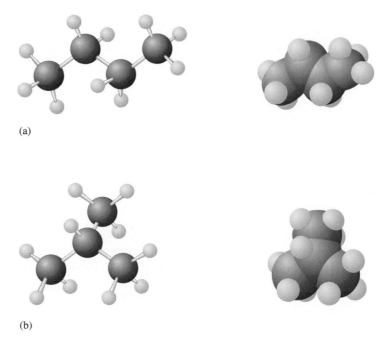

(a)

(b)

Isomerism in Alkanes

Butane and all succeeding members of the alkanes exhibit **structural isomerism.** Recall from Section 19.4 that structural isomerism occurs when two molecules have the same atoms but different bonds. For example, butane can exist as a straight-chain molecule (normal butane, or *n*-butane) or with a branched-chain structure (called isobutane), as shown in Fig. 21.4. Because of their different structures, these molecules exhibit different properties. For example, the boiling point of *n*-butane is $-0.5°C$, whereas that of isobutane is $-12°C$.

EXAMPLE 21.1

Draw the isomers of pentane.

Solution Pentane (C_5H_{12}) has the following isomeric structures:

1. $CH_3—CH_2—CH_2—CH_2—CH_3$

n-Pentane

2.
$$\begin{array}{c} CH_3 \\ | \\ CH_3—CH—CH_2—CH_3 \end{array}$$

Isopentane

3.
$$\begin{array}{c} CH_3 \\ | \\ CH_3—C—CH_3 \\ | \\ CH_3 \end{array}$$

Neopentane

Note that the structures

$$CH_3-CH_2-\overset{\overset{\displaystyle CH_3}{|}}{CH}-CH_3 \qquad CH_3-\overset{\underset{\displaystyle CH_3}{|}}{CH}-CH_2-CH_3$$

$$CH_3-CH_2-\overset{\underset{\displaystyle CH_3}{|}}{CH}-CH_3$$

which might appear to be other isomers, are actually identical to structure 2.

Nomenclature

Because there are literally millions of organic compounds, it would be impossible to remember common names for all of them. We must have a systematic method for naming them. The following rules are used in naming alkanes.

Rules for Naming Alkanes

1. The names of the alkanes beyond butane are obtained by adding the suffix -*ane* to the Greek root for the number of carbon atoms (*pent-* for five, *hex-* for six, and so on). For a branched hydrocarbon, the longest continuous chain of carbon atoms determines the root name for the hydrocarbon. For example, in the alkane

the longest chain contains six carbon atoms, and this compound is named as a hexane.

2. When alkane groups appear as substituents, they are named by dropping the -*ane* and adding -*yl*. For example, —CH_3 is obtained by removing a hydrogen from methane and is called *methyl*, —C_2H_5 is called *ethyl*, —C_3H_7 is called *propyl*, and so on. The compound above is therefore an ethylhexane (Table 21.2).

3. The positions of substituent groups are specified by numbering the longest chain of carbon atoms sequentially, starting at the end closest to the branching. For example, the compound

$$\overset{\overset{\displaystyle CH_3}{|}}{CH_3-CH_2-CH-CH_2-CH_2-CH_3}$$

| 1 | 2 | 3 | 4 | 5 | 6 | Correct numbering |
| 6 | 5 | 4 | 3 | 2 | 1 | Incorrect numbering |

is called 3-methylhexane. Note that the top set of numbers is correct because the left end of the molecule is closest to the branching, and this gives the smallest number for the position of the substituent. Also note that a hyphen is placed between the number and the substituent name.

4. The location and name of each substituent are followed by the root alkane name. The substituents are listed in alphabetical order, and the prefixes *di-*, *tri-*, and so on are used to indicate multiple, identical substituents.

Table 21.2

The Most Common Alkyl Substituents and Their Names

Structure*	Name†
—CH_3	Methyl
—CH_2CH_3	Ethyl
—$CH_2CH_2CH_3$	Propyl
$CH_3\overset{\overset{\displaystyle |}{}}{C}HCH_3$	Isopropyl
—$CH_2CH_2CH_2CH_3$	Butyl
$CH_3\overset{\overset{\displaystyle |}{}}{C}HCH_2CH_3$	*sec*-Butyl
—$CH_2-\overset{\overset{\displaystyle H}{|}}{\underset{\underset{\displaystyle CH_3}{|}}{C}}-CH_3$	Isobutyl
—$\overset{\overset{\displaystyle CH_3}{|}}{\underset{\underset{\displaystyle CH_3}{|}}{C}}-CH_3$	*tert*-Butyl

*The bond with one end open shows the point of attachment of the substituent to the carbon chain.
†For the butyl groups, *sec*- indicates attachment to the chain through a secondary carbon, a carbon atom attached to *two* other carbon atoms. The designation *tert*- signifies attachment through a tertiary carbon, a carbon attached to *three* other carbon atoms.

EXAMPLE 21.2

Draw the structural isomers for the alkane C_6H_{14}, and give the systematic name for each one.

Solution We will proceed systematically, starting with the longest chain and then rearranging the carbons to form the shorter, branched chains.

1. $CH_3CH_2CH_2CH_2CH_2CH_3$ Hexane

    Note that although a structure such as

    may look different, it is still hexane, since the longest carbon chain has six atoms.

2. We now take one carbon out of the chain and make it a methyl substituent.

    Since the longest chain consists of five carbons, this is a substituted pentane: 2-methylpentane. The 2 indicates the position of the methyl group on the chain. Note that if we numbered the chain from the right end, the methyl group would be on carbon 4. Because we want the smallest possible number, the numbering shown is correct.

3. The methyl substituent can also be on carbon 3 to give

    Note that we have now exhausted all possibilities for placing a single methyl group on pentane.

4. Next, we can take two carbons out of the original six-member chain:

    Since the longest chain now has four carbons, the root name is butane. Since there are two methyl groups, we use the prefix *di-*. The numbers denote that the two methyl groups are positioned on the second and third carbons in the butane chain. Note that when two or more numbers are used, they are separated by a comma.

5. The two methyl groups can also be attached to the same carbon atom as shown here:

    $$\overset{1}{CH_3}-\overset{2}{\underset{\underset{CH_3}{|}}{\overset{\overset{CH_3}{|}}{C}}}-\overset{3}{CH_2}\overset{4}{CH_3} \quad \text{2,2-Dimethylbutane}$$

We might also try ethyl-substituted butanes, such as

$$CH_3-\underset{\underset{\underset{CH_3}{|}}{\overset{|}{CH_2}}}{CH}CH_2CH_3$$

Pentane

However, note that this is instead a pentane (3-methylpentane), since the longest chain has five carbon atoms. Thus this is not a new isomer. Trying to reduce the chain to three atoms provides no further isomers either. For example, the structure

$$CH_3-\underset{\underset{\underset{CH_3}{|}}{\overset{|}{CH_2}}}{\overset{\overset{CH_3}{|}}{C}}-CH_3$$

is actually 2,2-dimethylbutane.

Thus there are only five distinct structural isomers of C_6H_{14}: hexane, 2-methylpentane, 3-methylpentane, 2,3-dimethylbutane, and 2,2-dimethylbutane.

EXAMPLE 21.3

Determine the structure for each of the following compounds.

a. 4-ethyl-3,5-dimethylnonane   **b.** 4-*tert*-butylheptane

Solution

a. The root name *nonane* signifies a nine-carbon chain. Thus we have

$$\underset{\underset{\underset{CH_3}{|}}{\overset{\overset{}{|}}{CH_2}}}{\overset{1\quad2\quad3}{CH_3CH_2CH}}-\underset{\overset{|}{CH_3}}{\overset{4}{CH}}-\underset{\overset{|}{CH_3}}{\overset{5}{CH}}\overset{6\quad7\quad8\quad9}{CH_2CH_2CH_2CH_3}$$

b. Heptane signifies a seven-carbon chain, and the *tert*-butyl group is

$$H_3C-\underset{\overset{|}{CH_3}}{\overset{\overset{|}{}}{C}}-CH_3$$

Thus we have

$$\underset{\underset{\overset{|}{CH_3}}{\overset{\overset{|}{C}}{H_3C}}-CH_3}{\overset{1\quad2\quad3\quad4\quad5\quad6\quad7}{CH_3CH_2CH_2CHCH_2CH_2CH_3}}$$

Reactions of Alkanes

Because they are saturated compounds and because the C—C and C—H bonds are relatively strong, the alkanes are fairly unreactive. For example, at 25°C they do not react with acids, bases, or strong oxidizing agents. This chemical inertness makes them valuable as lubricating materials and as the backbone for structural materials such as plastics.

At a sufficiently high temperature, alkanes do react vigorously and exothermically with oxygen, and these **combustion reactions** are the basis for their widespread use as fuels. For example, the reaction of butane with oxygen is

$$2C_4H_{10}(g) + 13O_2(g) \longrightarrow 8CO_2(g) + 10H_2O(g)$$

The alkanes can also undergo **substitution reactions,** primarily where halogen atoms replace hydrogen atoms. For example, methane can be successively chlorinated as follows:

$$CH_4 + Cl_2 \xrightarrow{h\upsilon} \underset{\text{Chloromethane}}{CH_3Cl} + HCl$$

$$CH_3Cl + Cl_2 \xrightarrow{h\upsilon} \underset{\text{Dichloromethane}}{CH_2Cl_2} + HCl$$

$$CH_2Cl_2 + Cl_2 \xrightarrow{h\upsilon} \underset{\substack{\text{Trichloromethane} \\ \text{(chloroform)}}}{CHCl_3} + HCl$$

$$CHCl_3 + Cl_2 \xrightarrow{h\upsilon} \underset{\substack{\text{Tetrachloromethane} \\ \text{(carbon tetrachloride)}}}{CCl_4} + HCl$$

Note that the products of the last two reactions have two names; the systematic name is given first, followed by the common name in parentheses. (This format will be used throughout this chapter for compounds that have common names.) Also note that ultraviolet light ($h\upsilon$) furnishes the energy to break the Cl—Cl bond to produce chlorine atoms:

$$Cl_2 \longrightarrow Cl \cdot + Cl \cdot$$

A chlorine atom has an unpaired electron, as indicated by the dot, which makes it very reactive and able to attack the C—H bond.

As we mentioned before, substituted methanes with the general formula CF_xCl_{4-x} containing both chlorine and fluorine as substituents are called chlorofluorocarbons (CFCs) and are also known as *Freons*. These substances are very unreactive and have been extensively used as coolant fluids in refrigerators and air conditioners. Unfortunately, their chemical inertness allows Freons to remain in the atmosphere so long that they eventually reach altitudes where they are a threat to the protective ozone layer (see Section 15.9), and the use of these compounds is being rapidly phased out.

Alkanes can also undergo **dehydrogenation reactions** in which hydrogen atoms are removed and the product is an unsaturated hydrocarbon. For example, in the presence of chromium(III) oxide at high temperatures, ethane can be dehydrogenated, yielding ethylene:

$$CH_3CH_3 \xrightarrow[500°C]{Cr_2O_3} \underset{\text{Ethylene}}{CH_2{=}CH_2} + H_2$$

Cyclic Alkanes

Besides forming chains, carbon atoms also form rings. The simplest of the **cyclic alkanes** (general formula C_nH_{2n}) is cyclopropane (C_3H_6), shown in Fig. 21.5(a). Since the carbon atoms in cyclopropane form an equilateral triangle with 60° bond angles, their sp^3 hybrid orbitals do not overlap head-on as in normal alkanes [Fig. 21.5(b)]. This results in unusually weak, or *strained*, C—C bonds; thus the cyclopropane molecule is much more reactive than

The $h\upsilon$ above the arrow represents ultraviolet light.

(a)

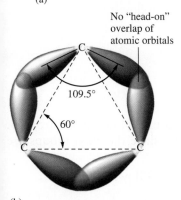

No "head-on" overlap of atomic orbitals

109.5°

60°

(b)

Figure 21.5

(a) The molecular structure of cyclopropane (C_3H_6). (b) The overlap of the sp^3 orbitals that form the C—C bonds in cyclopropane.

Chair

(a)

These two H
atoms repel
each other

Boat

(b)

Figure 21.6
The (a) chair and (b) boat forms of cyclohexane.

straight-chain propane. The carbon atoms in cyclobutane (C_4H_8) form a square with 90° bond angles, and cyclobutane is also quite reactive.

The next two members of the series, cyclopentane (C_5H_{10}) and cyclohexane (C_6H_{12}), are quite stable because their rings have bond angles very close to tetrahedral angles, which allows the sp^3 hybrid orbitals on adjacent carbon atoms to overlap head-on and form normal C—C bonds, which are quite strong. To attain tetrahedral angles, the cyclohexane ring must "pucker"— that is, become nonplanar. Cyclohexane can exist in two forms, the *chair* and the *boat* forms, as shown in Fig. 21.6. The two hydrogen atoms above the ring in the boat form are quite close to each other, and the resulting repulsion between these atoms causes the chair form to be preferred. At 25°C more than 99% of cyclohexane exists in the chair form.

For simplicity, the cyclic alkanes are often represented by the following structures:

Thus the structure

represents methylcyclopropane.

The nomenclature for cycloalkanes follows the same rules as for the other alkanes except that the root name is preceded by the prefix *cyclo-*. The ring is numbered to yield the smallest substituent numbers possible.

🦉WL INTERACTIVE EXAMPLE 21.4

Name each of the following cyclic alkanes.

a. CH_3—CH—CH_3 b. CH_2CH_3

CH_3 $CH_2CH_2CH_3$

Solution

a. The six-carbon cyclohexane ring is numbered as follows:

CH_3—CH—CH_3

CH_3

There is an isopropyl group at carbon 1 and a methyl group at carbon 3. The name is 1-isopropyl-3-methylcyclohexane, since the alkyl groups are named in alphabetical order.

b. This is a cyclobutane ring, which is numbered as follows:

CH_2CH_3

$CH_2CH_2CH_3$

The name is 1-ethyl-2-propylcyclobutane.

21.2 | Alkenes and Alkynes

Multiple carbon–carbon bonds result when hydrogen atoms are removed from alkanes. Hydrocarbons that contain at least one carbon–carbon double bond are called **alkenes** and have the general formula C_nH_{2n}. The simplest alkene (C_2H_4), commonly known as *ethylene*, has the Lewis structure

As discussed in Section 14.1, each carbon in ethylene can be described as sp^2 hybridized. The C—C σ bond is formed by sharing an electron pair between sp^2 orbitals, and the π bond is formed by sharing a pair of electrons between p orbitals (Fig. 21.7).

The systematic nomenclature for alkenes is quite similar to that for alkanes.

1. The root hydrocarbon name ends in *-ene* rather than *-ane*. Thus the systematic name for C_2H_4 is *ethene* and the name for C_3H_6 is *propene*.

2. In alkenes containing more than three carbon atoms, the location of the double bond is indicated by the lowest-numbered carbon atom involved in the bond. Thus CH_2=$CHCH_2CH_3$ is called 1-butene, and CH_3CH=$CHCH_3$ is called 2-butene.

Note from Fig. 21.7 that the p orbitals on the two carbon atoms in ethylene must be lined up (parallel) to allow formation of the π bond. This prevents rotation of the two CH_2 groups relative to each other at ordinary temperatures, in contrast to alkanes, where free rotation is possible (Fig. 21.8). The restricted rotation around doubly bonded carbon atoms means that alkenes exhibit **cis–trans** isomerism. For example, there are two stereoisomers of 2-butene (Fig. 21.9). Identical substituents on the same side of the double bond are designated *cis*, and those on opposite sides are labeled *trans*.

Alkynes are unsaturated hydrocarbons containing at least one triple carbon–carbon bond. The simplest alkyne is C_2H_2 (commonly called *acety-*

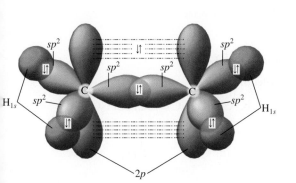

Figure 21.7
The bonding in ethylene.

Figure 21.8
The bonding in ethane.

Figure 21.9
The two stereoisomers of 2-butene: (a) *cis*-2-butene and (b) *trans*-2-butene.

(a)

(b)

Figure 21.10
The bonding in acetylene.

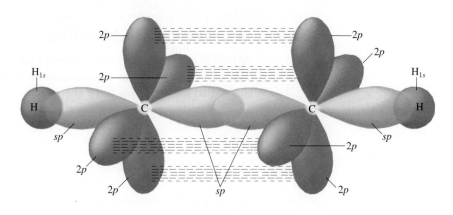

lene), which has the systematic name *ethyne*. As discussed in Section 14.1, the triple bond in acetylene can be described as one σ bond between two sp hybrid orbitals on the two carbon atoms and two π bonds involving two $2p$ orbitals on each carbon atom (Fig. 21.10).

The nomenclature for alkynes involves the use of *-yne* as a suffix to replace the *-ane* of the parent alkane. Thus the molecule $CH_3CH_2C\equiv CCH_3$ has the name 2-pentyne.

Like alkanes, unsaturated hydrocarbons can exist as ringed structures, for example,

For cyclic alkenes, number through the double bond toward the substituent.

Cyclohexene

4-Methyl-cyclopentene

⬤**WL INTERACTIVE EXAMPLE 21.5**

Name each of the following molecules.

a.

b. $CH_3CH_2C\equiv CCHCH_2CH_3$
$\qquad\qquad\qquad\quad |$
$\qquad\qquad\qquad\ CH_2$
$\qquad\qquad\qquad\quad |$
$\qquad\qquad\qquad\ CH_3$

Solution

a. The longest chain, which contains six carbon atoms, is numbered as follows.

Thus the hydrocarbon is a 2-hexene. Since the hydrogen atoms are located on opposite sides of the double bond, this molecule corresponds to the *trans* isomer. The name is 4-methyl-*trans*-2-hexene.

b. The longest chain, consisting of seven carbon atoms, is numbered as shown (giving the triple bond the lowest possible number):

$$\overset{1}{C}H_3\overset{2}{C}H_2\overset{3}{C}\equiv\overset{4\ 5}{C}CH\overset{6}{C}H_2\overset{7}{C}H_3$$
$$\underset{\displaystyle CH_3}{\overset{\displaystyle |}{\underset{\displaystyle |}{CH_2}}}$$

The hydrocarbon is a 3-heptyne. The full name is 5-ethyl-3-heptyne, where the position of the triple bond is indicated by the lower-numbered carbon atom involved in this bond.

Reactions of Alkenes and Alkynes

Because alkenes and alkynes are unsaturated, their most important reactions are **addition reactions.** In these reactions, π bonds, which are weaker than the C—C σ bonds, are broken, and new σ bonds are formed to the atoms being added. For example, **hydrogenation reactions** involve the addition of hydrogen atoms:

$$CH_2{=}CHCH_3 + H_2 \xrightarrow{\text{Catalyst}} CH_3CH_2CH_3$$
$$\text{1-Propene} \qquad\qquad\qquad \text{Propane}$$

For this reaction to proceed rapidly at normal temperatures, a catalyst of platinum, palladium, or nickel is used. The catalyst serves to help break the relatively strong H—H bond, as was discussed in Section 15.9. Hydrogenation of alkenes is an important industrial process, particularly in the manufacture of solid shortenings, where unsaturated fats (fats containing double bonds), which are generally liquid, are converted to solid saturated fats.

Halogenation of unsaturated hydrocarbons involves addition of halogen atoms. For example,

$$CH_2{=}CHCH_2CH_2CH_3 + Br_2 \longrightarrow CH_2BrCHBrCH_2CH_2CH_3$$
$$\text{1-Pentene} \qquad\qquad\qquad\qquad \text{1,2-Dibromopentane}$$

Another important reaction involving certain unsaturated hydrocarbons is **polymerization,** a process in which many small molecules are joined together to form a large molecule. Polymerization will be discussed in Section 21.5.

21.3 | Aromatic Hydrocarbons

A special class of cyclic unsaturated hydrocarbons is known as the **aromatic hydrocarbons.** The simplest of these is benzene (C_6H_6), which has a planar ring structure, as shown in Fig. 21.11(a). In the localized electron model of the bonding in benzene, resonance structures of the type shown in Fig. 21.11(b) are used to account for the known equivalence of all the carbon–carbon bonds. But as we discussed in Section 14.5, the best description of the benzene molecule assumes that sp^2 hybrid orbitals on each carbon are used to form the C—C and C—H σ bonds, whereas the remaining $2p$ orbital on each carbon is used

(a)

(b)

(c)

Figure 21.11
(a) The structure of benzene, a planar ring system in which all bond angles are 120°. (b) Two of the resonance structures of benzene. (c) The usual representation of benzene. The circle represents the electrons in the delocalized π system. All C—C bonds in benzene are equivalent.

to form π molecular orbitals. The delocalization of these π electrons is usually indicated by a circle inside the ring [Fig. 21.11(c)].

The delocalization of the π electrons makes the benzene ring behave quite differently from a typical unsaturated hydrocarbon. As we have seen previously, unsaturated hydrocarbons generally undergo rapid addition reactions. However, benzene does not. Instead, it undergoes substitution reactions in which *hydrogen atoms are replaced by other atoms*. For example,

Chlorobenzene

Nitrobenzene

Toluene

In each case the substance shown over the arrow is needed to catalyze these substitution reactions.

Substitution reactions are characteristic of saturated hydrocarbons, and addition reactions are characteristic of unsaturated ones. The fact that benzene reacts more like a saturated hydrocarbon indicates the great stability of the delocalized π electron system.

The nomenclature of benzene derivatives is similar to the nomenclature for saturated ring systems. If there is more than one substituent present, numbers are used to indicate substituent positions. For example, the compound

is named 1,2-dichlorobenzene. Another nomenclature system uses the prefix *ortho-* (*o*-) for two adjacent substituents, *meta-* (*m*-) for two substituents with one carbon between them, and *para-* (*p*-) for two substituents opposite each other. When benzene is used as a substituent, it is called the **phenyl group**. Examples of some aromatic compounds are shown in Fig. 21.12.

Benzene is the simplest aromatic molecule. More complex aromatic systems can be viewed as consisting of a number of "fused" benzene rings. Some examples are given in Table 21.3.

Figure 21.12
Some selected substituted benzenes and their names. Common names are given in parentheses.

| 1,2-Dibromobenzene (*o*-dibromobenzene) | 1,3-Dibromobenzene (*m*-dibromobenzene) | 1,4-Dibromobenzene (*p*-dibromobenzene) |

Methylbenzene (toluene)

3-Bromonitrobenzene (*m*-bromonitrobenzene)

3-Chlorotoluene (*m*-chlorotoluene)

Phenyl group   4-Chloro-2-phenylhexane

Table 21.3

More Complex Aromatic Systems

Structural Formula	Name	Use or Effect
	Naphthalene	Formerly used in mothballs
	Anthracene	Dyes
	Phenanthrene	Dyes, explosives, and synthesis of drugs
	3,4-Benzpyrene	Active carcinogen found in smoke and smog

21.4 | Hydrocarbon Derivatives

The vast majority of organic molecules contain elements in addition to carbon and hydrogen. However, most of these substances can be viewed as **hydrocarbon derivatives,** molecules that are fundamentally hydrocarbons but that have

Table 21.4

The Common Functional Groups

Class	Functional Group	General Formula*	Example
Halohydrocarbons	—X (F, Cl, Br, I)	R—X	CH_3I Iodomethane (methyl iodide)
Alcohols	—OH	R—OH	CH_3OH Methanol (methyl alcohol)
Ethers	—O—	R—O—R′	CH_3OCH_3 Dimethyl ether
Aldehydes	$\overset{\displaystyle O}{\overset{\|}{-C-H}}$	$\overset{\displaystyle O}{\overset{\|}{R-C-H}}$	CH_2O Methanal (formaldehyde)
Ketones	$\overset{\displaystyle O}{\overset{\|}{-C-}}$	$\overset{\displaystyle O}{\overset{\|}{R-C-R'}}$	CH_3COCH_3 Propanone (dimethyl ketone or acetone)
Carboxylic acids	$\overset{\displaystyle O}{\overset{\|}{-C-OH}}$	$\overset{\displaystyle O}{\overset{\|}{R-C-OH}}$	CH_3COOH Ethanoic acid (acetic acid)
Esters	$\overset{\displaystyle O}{\overset{\|}{-C-O-}}$	$\overset{\displaystyle O}{\overset{\|}{R-C-O-R'}}$	$CH_3COOCH_2CH_3$ Ethyl acetate
Amines	$-NH_2$	$R-NH_2$	CH_3NH_2 Aminomethane (methylamine)

*R and R′ represent hydrocarbon fragments.

Compounds containing aromatic rings are often used in dyes, such as these for sale in a market in Nepal.

additional atoms or groups of atoms called **functional groups.** The common functional groups are listed in Table 21.4. Because each functional group exhibits characteristic chemistry, we will consider the groups separately.

Alcohols

Alcohols are characterized by the presence of the hydroxyl group (—OH). Some common alcohols are shown in Table 21.5. The systematic name for an alcohol is obtained by replacing the final -*e* of the parent hydrocarbon with -*ol.* The position of the —OH group is specified by a number (where necessary) chosen so that it is the smallest of the substituent numbers. Alcohols are classified according to the number of hydrocarbon fragments bonded to the carbon where the —OH group is attached,

R—CH₂OH $\overset{R}{\underset{R'}{\diagdown}}CHOH$ $\overset{R}{\underset{R''}{\overset{\|}{\underset{\|}{R'-COH}}}}$

Primary alcohol   *Secondary* alcohol   *Tertiary* alcohol
(one R group)   (two R groups)   (three R groups)

Table 21.5

Some Common Alcohols

Formula	Systematic Name	Common Name
CH_3OH	Methanol	Methyl alcohol
CH_3CH_2OH	Ethanol	Ethyl alcohol
$CH_3CH_2CH_2OH$	1-Propanol	n-Propyl alcohol
CH_3CHCH_3 | OH	2-Propanol	Isopropyl alcohol

where R, R′, and R″ (which may be the same or different) represent hydrocarbon fragments.

Alcohols usually have much higher boiling points than might be expected from their molar masses. For example, both methanol and ethane have a molar mass of 30, but the boiling point for methanol is 65°C, whereas that for ethane is −89°C. This difference can be understood if we consider the types of intermolecular attractions that occur in these liquids. Ethane molecules are nonpolar and exhibit only weak London dispersion interactions. However, the polar —OH group of methanol produces extensive hydrogen bonding similar to that found in water (see Section 16.1), which results in the relatively high boiling point.

Although there are many important alcohols, the simplest ones, methanol and ethanol, have the greatest commercial value. Methanol, also known as *wood alcohol* because it was formerly obtained by heating wood in the absence of air, is prepared industrially (approximately 4 million tons annually in the United States) by the hydrogenation of carbon monoxide:

$$CO + 2H_2 \xrightarrow[\text{ZnO/Cr}_2\text{O}_3]{400°C} CH_3OH$$

Methanol is used as a starting material for the synthesis of acetic acid and for many types of adhesives, fibers, and plastics. It is also used (and such use may increase) as a motor fuel. Methanol is highly toxic to humans and can lead to blindness and death if ingested.

Ethanol is the alcohol found in beverages such as beer, wine, and whiskey; it is produced by the fermentation of glucose in corn, barley, grapes, and so on:

$$\underset{\text{Glucose}}{C_6H_{12}O_6} \xrightarrow{\text{Yeast}} \underset{\text{Ethanol}}{2CH_3CH_2OH} + 2CO_2$$

The reaction is catalyzed by the enzymes found in yeast. This reaction can proceed only until the alcohol content reaches about 13% (the percentage found in most wines), at which point the yeast can no longer survive. Beverages with higher alcohol content are made by distilling the fermentation mixture.

Ethanol, like methanol, can be burned in the internal combustion engines of automobiles and is now commonly added to gasoline to form gasohol (see Section 9.8). It is also used in industry as a solvent and for the preparation of acetic acid. The commercial production of ethanol (500,000 tons per year in the United States) is carried out by reaction of water with ethylene:

$$CH_2{=}CH_2 + H_2O \xrightarrow[\text{Catalyst}]{\text{Acid}} CH_3CH_2OH$$

A fuel consisting of 85% ethanol and 15% gasoline is now widely available in the United States.

Many polyhydroxyl (more than one —OH group) alcohols are known, the most important being *1,2-ethanediol* (ethylene glycol),

$$H_2C—OH$$
$$|$$
$$H_2C—OH$$

a toxic substance that is the major constituent of most automobile antifreeze solutions.

The simplest aromatic alcohol is

which is commonly called **phenol.** Most of the 1 million tons of phenol produced annually in the United States are used to make polymers for adhesives and plastics.

⏺WL INTERACTIVE EXAMPLE 21.6

For each of the following alcohols, give the systematic name, and specify whether the alcohol is primary, secondary, or tertiary.

a. CH$_3$CHCH$_2$CH$_3$
   |
   OH

b. ClCH$_2$CH$_2$CH$_2$OH

       CH$_3$
       |
c. CH$_3$CCH$_2$CH$_2$CH$_2$CH$_2$Br
       |
       OH

Solution

a. The chain is numbered as follows:

  1 2 3 4
CH$_3$CHCH$_2$CH$_3$
  |
  OH

The compound is called 2-butanol, since the —OH group is located at the number 2 position of a four-carbon chain. Note that the carbon to which the —OH is attached also has —CH$_3$ and —CH$_2$CH$_3$ groups attached:

Therefore, this is a *secondary* alcohol.

b. The chain is numbered as follows:

$$\overset{3}{\text{Cl}}—\overset{}{\text{CH}_2}—\overset{2}{\text{CH}_2}—\overset{1}{\text{CH}_2}—\text{OH}$$

The name is 3-chloro-1-propanol. This is a *primary* alcohol:

One R group attached to the carbon with the —OH group

c. The chain is numbered as follows:

The name is 6-bromo-2-methyl-2-hexanol. This is a *tertiary* alcohol since the carbon where the —OH is attached also has three other R groups attached.

Aldehydes and Ketones

Aldehydes and ketones contain the **carbonyl group,**

In **ketones** this group is bonded to two carbon atoms, as in acetone,

$$\text{CH}_3—\overset{}{\underset{\overset{\|}{\text{O}}}{\text{C}}}—\text{CH}_3$$

In **aldehydes** the carbonyl group is bonded to at least one hydrogen atom, as in formaldehyde,

$$\text{H}—\overset{}{\underset{\overset{\|}{\text{O}}}{\text{C}}}—\text{H}$$

or acetaldehyde,

$$\text{CH}_3—\overset{}{\underset{\overset{\|}{\text{O}}}{\text{C}}}—\text{H}$$

Cinnamaldehyde produces the characteristic odor of cinnamon.

Figure 21.13

Some common ketones and aldehydes. Note that since the aldehyde functional group always appears at the end of a carbon chain, carbon is assigned the number 1 when the compound is named.

Methanal (formaldehyde)

Ethanal (acetaldehyde)

2-Propanone (acetone)

2-Pentanone

3-Chlorobutanal

Benzaldehyde

2-Butanone (methyl ethyl ketone, or MEK)

Methyl phenyl ketone

Vanillin

Cinnamaldehyde

$CH_3CH_2CH_2C$

Butyraldehyde

The systematic name for an aldehyde is obtained from the parent alkane by removing the final *-e* and adding *-al*. For ketones the final *-e* is replaced by *-one*, and a number indicates the position of the carbonyl group where necessary. Examples of common aldehydes and ketones are shown in Fig. 21.13. Note that since the aldehyde functional group always occurs at the end of the carbon chain, the aldehyde carbon is assigned the number 1 when substituent positions are listed in the name.

Ketones often have useful solvent properties (acetone is found in nail polish remover, for example) and are frequently used in industry for this purpose. Aldehydes typically have strong odors. Vanillin is responsible for the pleasant odor in vanilla beans; cinnamaldehyde produces the characteristic odor of cinnamon. On the other hand, the unpleasant odor in rancid butter arises from the presence of butyraldehyde.

Aldehydes and ketones are most often produced commercially by the oxidation of alcohols. For example, oxidation of a *primary* alcohol yields the corresponding aldehyde:

$$CH_3CH_2OH \xrightarrow{\text{Oxidation}} CH_3C \diagup \substack{O \\ H}$$

Oxidation of a *secondary* alcohol results in a ketone:

$$\underset{\underset{OH}{|}}{CH_3CHCH_3} \xrightarrow{\text{Oxidation}} \underset{\underset{O}{\|}}{CH_3CCH_3}$$

Carboxylic Acids and Esters

Carboxylic acids are characterized by the presence of the **carboxyl group**

that gives an acid of the general formula RCOOH. Typically, these molecules are weak acids in aqueous solution (see Section 7.5). Organic acids are named from the parent alkane by dropping the final *-e* and adding *-oic*. Thus CH_3COOH, commonly called acetic acid, has the systematic name ethanoic

$CH_3CH_2CH_2COOH$

Butanoic acid

COOH

Benzoic acid

$CH_3CHCH_2CH_2COOH$

|
Br

4-Bromopentanoic acid

Cl
|
Cl—C—COOH
|
Cl

Trichloroethanoic acid
(trichloroacetic acid)

Figure 21.14
Some carboxylic acids.

acid, since the parent alkane is ethane. Other examples of carboxylic acids are shown in Fig. 21.14.

Many carboxylic acids are synthesized by oxidizing primary alcohols with a strong oxidizing agent. For example, ethanol can be oxidized to acetic acid by using potassium permanganate:

$$CH_3CH_2OH \xrightarrow{\text{KMnO}_4(aq)} CH_3COOH$$

A carboxylic acid reacts with an alcohol to form an **ester** and a water molecule. For example, the reaction of acetic acid with ethanol produces ethyl acetate and water:

React to
form water

Esters often have a sweet, fruity odor that is in contrast to the often pungent odors of the parent carboxylic acids. For example, the odor of bananas is caused by *n*-amyl acetate,

and that of oranges is caused by *n*-octyl acetate,

$$CH_3C—OC_8H_{17}$$
‖
O

The systematic name for an ester is formed by changing the *-oic* ending of the parent acid to *-oate*. The parent alcohol chain is named first with a *-yl* ending. For example, the systematic name for *n*-octyl acetate is *n*-octylethanoate (from ethanoic acid).

A very important ester is formed from the reaction of salicylic acid and acetic acid:

Salicylic acid   Acetic acid   Acetylsalicylic acid

The product is acetylsalicylic acid, commonly known as *aspirin,* which is used in huge quantities as an analgesic (painkiller).

Amines

Amines are probably best viewed as derivatives of ammonia in which one or more N—H bonds are replaced by N—C bonds. The resulting amines are classified as *primary* if one N—C bond is present, *secondary* if two N—C bonds are present, and *tertiary* if all three N—H bonds in NH_3 have been replaced by

Computer-generated space-filling model of acetylsalicylic acid (aspirin).

Table 21.6

Some Common Amines

Formula	Common Name	Type
CH_3NH_2	Methylamine	Primary
$CH_3CH_2NH_2$	Ethylamine	Primary
$(CH_3)_2NH$	Dimethylamine	Secondary
$(CH_3)_3N$	Trimethylamine	Tertiary
	Aniline	Primary
(Diphenylamine structure)	Diphenylamine	Secondary

Primary amine   Secondary amine

Tertiary amine

Figure 21.15
The general formulas for primary, secondary, and tertiary amines. R, R', and R" represent carbon-containing substituents.

N—C bonds (Fig. 21.15). Examples of some common amines are given in Table 21.6.

Common names are often used for simple amines; the systematic nomenclature for more complex molecules uses the name *amino-* for the —NH_2 functional group. For example, the molecule

$$\underset{\underset{NH_2}{|}}{CH_3CHCH_2CH_3}$$

is named 2-aminobutane.

Many amines have unpleasant "fishlike" odors. For example, the odors associated with decaying animal and human tissues are caused by amines such as putrescine ($H_2NCH_2CH_2CH_2NH_2$) and cadaverine ($H_2NCH_2CH_2CH_2CH_2CH_2NH_2$).

Aromatic amines are primarily used to make dyes. Since many of them are carcinogenic, they must be handled with great care.

21.5 | Polymers

Polymers are large, usually chainlike molecules that are built from small molecules called *monomers.* Polymers form the basis for synthetic fibers, rubbers, and plastics and have played a leading role in the revolution that has been brought about in daily life by chemistry during the past 50 years. It has been estimated that about 50% of the industrial chemists in the United States work in some area of polymer chemistry, a fact that illustrates just how important polymers are to our economy and standard of living.

The Development and Properties of Polymers

The development of the polymer industry provides a striking example of the importance of serendipity in the progress of science. Many discoveries in polymer chemistry arose from accidental observations that scientists followed up.

The age of plastics might be traced to a day in 1846 when Christian Schoenbein, a chemistry professor at the University of Basel in Switzerland,

The soybeans on the left are coated with a red acrylic polymer to delay soybean emergence. This allows farmers to plant their crops more efficiently.

AP Photo/Indianapolis Star/Karen Ducey

spilled a flask containing nitric and sulfuric acids. In his hurry to clean up the spill, he grabbed his wife's cotton apron, which he then rinsed out and hung up in front of a hot stove to dry. Instead of drying, the apron flared and burned.

Very interested in this event, Schoenbein repeated the reaction under more controlled conditions and found that the new material, which he correctly concluded to be nitrated cellulose, had some surprising properties. As he had experienced, nitrated cellulose is extremely flammable and, under certain circumstances, highly explosive. In addition, he found that it could be molded at moderate temperatures to give objects that were, upon cooling, tough but elastic. Predictably, the explosive nature of the substance was initially of more interest than its other properties, and cellulose nitrate rapidly became the basis for smokeless gun powder. Although Schoenbein's discovery cannot be described as a truly synthetic polymer (because he simply found a way to modify the natural polymer cellulose), it formed the basis for a large number of industries that grew up to produce photographic films, artificial fibers, and molded objects of all types.

A radio from the 1930s made of Bakelite.

The first synthetic polymers were produced as by-products of various organic reactions and were regarded as unwanted contaminants. Thus the first preparations of many of the polymers now regarded as essential to our modern lifestyle were thrown away in disgust. One chemist who refused to be defeated by the "tarry" products obtained when he reacted phenol with formaldehyde was Belgian-American chemist Leo H. Baekeland (1863–1944). Baekeland's work resulted in the first completely synthetic plastic (called Bakelite), a substance that when molded to a certain shape under high pressure and temperature cannot be softened again or dissolved. Bakelite is a **thermoset polymer.** In contrast, cellulose nitrate is a **thermoplastic polymer;** that is, it can be remelted after it has been molded.

The discovery of Bakelite in 1907 spawned a large plastics industry, producing telephones, billiard balls, and insulators for electrical devices. During the early days of polymer chemistry, there was a great deal of controversy over the nature of these materials. Although the German chemist Hermann Staudinger speculated in 1920 that polymers were very large molecules held together by strong chemical bonds, most chemists of the time assumed that these materials were much like colloids, in which small molecules are aggregated into large units by forces weaker than chemical bonds.

Nylon netting magnified 62 times.

One chemist who contributed greatly to the understanding of polymers as giant molecules was Wallace H. Carothers of the DuPont Chemical Company. Among his accomplishments was the preparation of nylon. The nylon story further illustrates the importance of serendipity in scientific research. When nylon is first prepared, the resulting product is a sticky material with little structural integrity. Because of this, it was initially put aside as having no apparently useful characteristics. However, Julian Hill, a chemist in the Carothers research group, one day put a small ball of this nylon on the end of a stirring rod and drew it away from the remaining sticky mass, forming a string. He noticed the silky appearance and strength of this thread and realized that nylon could be drawn into useful fibers.

The reason for this behavior of nylon is now understood. When nylon is first formed, the individual polymer chains are oriented randomly, like cooked spaghetti, and the substance is highly amorphous. However, when drawn out into a thread, the chains tend to line up (the nylon becomes more crystalline), which leads to increased hydrogen bonding between adjacent chains. This increase in crystallinity, along with the resulting increase in hydrogen-bonding interactions, leads to strong fibers and thus to a highly useful material. Commercially, nylon is produced by forcing the raw material through a *spinneret,* a plate containing small holes, which forces the polymer chains to line up.

Another property that adds strength to polymers is **crosslinking,** the existence of covalent bonds between adjacent chains. The structure of Bakelite is highly crosslinked, which accounts for the strength and toughness of this polymer. Another example of crosslinking occurs in the manufacture of rubber. Raw natural rubber consists of chains of the type

$$\text{\small wwwww}CH_2-CH_2-CH=\underset{\underset{CH_3}{|}}{C}-CH_2-CH_2-CH=\underset{\underset{CH_3}{|}}{C}-CH_2\text{\small wwwww}$$

and is a soft, sticky material unsuitable for tires. However, in 1839 Charles Goodyear (1800–1860), an American chemist, accidentally found that if sulfur is added to rubber and the resulting mixture is heated (a process called **vulcanization**), the resulting rubber is still elastic (reversibly stretchable) but is much stronger. This change in character occurs because sulfur atoms become bonded between carbon atoms on different chains. These sulfur atoms form bridges between the polymer chains, thus linking the chains together.

Colored water drops are shown beading on Kevlar fabric treated with a nanoscale water-resistant coating.

Types of Polymers

The simplest and one of the best-known polymers is *polyethylene,* which is constructed from ethylene monomers:

$$n CH_2{=}CH_2 \xrightarrow{\text{Catalyst}} \left(\!\!\begin{array}{c}\underset{\underset{H}{|}}{\overset{\overset{H}{|}}{C}}-\underset{\underset{H}{|}}{\overset{\overset{H}{|}}{C}}\end{array}\!\!\right)_{\!n}$$

where *n* represents a large number (usually several thousand). Polyethylene is a tough, flexible plastic used for piping, bottles, electrical insulation, packaging films, garbage bags, and many other purposes. Its properties can be varied by using substituted ethylene monomers. For example, when tetrafluoroethylene is the monomer, the polymer Teflon is obtained:

Tetrafluoroethylene   Teflon

The discovery of Teflon, a very important substituted polyethylene, is another illustration of the role of chance in chemical research. In 1938 a DuPont chemist named Roy Plunkett was studying the chemistry of gaseous tetrafluoroethylene. He synthesized about 100 pounds of the chemical and stored it in steel cylinders. When one of the cylinders failed to produce perfluoroethylene gas when the valve was opened, the cylinder was cut open to reveal a white powder. This powder turned out to be a polymer of perfluoroethylene, which was eventually developed into Teflon. Because of the resistance of the strong C—F bonds to chemical attack, Teflon is an inert, tough, and nonflammable material widely used for electrical insulation, nonstick coatings on cooking utensils, and bearings for low-temperature applications.

Other polyethylene-type polymers are made from monomers containing chloro, methyl, cyano, and phenyl substituents, as summarized in Table 21.7. In each case the double carbon–carbon bond in the substituted ethylene monomer becomes a single bond in the polymer. The different substituents lead to a wide variety of properties.

Table 21.7

Some Common Synthetic Polymers, Their Monomers, and Applications

Monomer		Polymer		
Name	Formula	Name	Formula	Uses
Ethylene	$H_2C{=}CH_2$	Polyethylene	$-(CH_2-CH_2)_{\overline{n}}$	Plastic piping, bottles, electrical insulation, toys
Propylene	$H_2C{=}C$ with H and CH_3	Polypropylene	$-(CH-CH_2-CH-CH_2)_{\overline{n}}$ with CH_3 CH_3	Film for packaging, carpets, lab wares, toys
Vinyl chloride	$H_2C{=}C$ with H and Cl	Polyvinyl chloride (PVC)	$-(CH_2-CH)_{\overline{n}}$ with Cl	Piping, siding, floor tile, clothing, toys
Acrylonitrile	$H_2C{=}C$ with H and CN	Polyacrylonitrile (PAN)	$-(CH_2-CH)_{\overline{n}}$ with CN	Carpets, fabrics
Tetrafluoro-ethylene	$F_2C{=}CF_2$	Teflon	$-(CF_2-CF_2)_{\overline{n}}$	Cooking utensils, electrical insulation, bearings
Styrene	$H_2C{=}C$ with H and phenyl	Polystyrene	$-(CH_2CH)_{\overline{n}}$ with phenyl	Containers, thermal insulation, toys
Butadiene	$H_2C{=}C-C{=}CH_2$ with H H	Polybutadiene	$-(CH_2CH{=}CHCH_2)_{\overline{n}}$	Tire tread, coating resin
Butadiene and styrene	(See above.)	Styrene-butadiene rubber	$-(CH-CH_2-CH_2-CH{=}CH-CH_2)_{\overline{n}}$ with phenyl	Synthetic rubber

The polyethylene polymers illustrate one of the major types of polymerization reactions, called **addition polymerization,** in which the monomers simply "add together" to produce the polymer. No other products are formed. The polymerization process is initiated by a **free radical** (a species with an unpaired electron) such as the hydroxyl radical (HO ·). The free radical attacks and breaks the π bond of an ethylene molecule to form a new free radical, which is then available to attack another ethylene molecule:

Repetition of this process thousands of times creates a long-chain polymer. Termination of the growth of the chain occurs when *two radicals* react to form a bond, a process that consumes two radicals without producing any others.

Another common type of polymerization is **condensation polymerization,** in which a small molecule, such as water, is formed for each extension of the polymer chain. The most familiar polymer produced by condensation is *nylon.* Nylon is a **copolymer,** since two different types of monomers combine to form the chain; a **homopolymer** is the result of polymerizing a single type of monomer. One common form of nylon is produced when hexamethylenediamine and adipic acid react by splitting out a water molecule to form a C—N bond:

The molecule formed, called a **dimer** (two monomers joined), can undergo further condensation reactions since it has an amino group at one end and a carboxyl group at the other. Thus both ends are free to react with another monomer. Repetition of this process leads to a long chain of the type

which is the basic structure of nylon. The reaction to form nylon occurs quite readily and is often used as a lecture demonstration (Fig. 21.16). The properties of nylon can be varied by changing the number of carbon atoms in the chain of the acid or amine monomer.

More than 1 million tons of nylon are produced annually in the United States for use in clothing, carpets, rope, and so on. Many other types of condensation polymers are also produced. For example, Dacron is a copolymer formed from the condensation reaction of ethylene glycol (a dialcohol) and *p*-terephthalic acid (a dicarboxylic acid):

Charles D. Winters/Photo Researchers, Inc.

Figure 21.16
The reaction to form nylon can be carried out at the interface of two immiscible liquid layers in a beaker. The bottom layer contains adipoyl chloride,

$$Cl—\overset{O}{\underset{\parallel}{C}}—(CH_2)_4—\overset{O}{\underset{\parallel}{C}}—Cl$$

dissolved in CCl₄, and the top layer contains hexamethylenediamine,

$$H_2N—(CH_2)_6—NH_2$$

dissolved in water. A molecule of HCl is formed as each C—N bond forms.

The repeating unit of Dacron is

Note that this polymerization involves a carboxylic acid and an alcohol forming an ester group:

$$R-O-\overset{\overset{\textstyle O}{\|}}{C}-R_1$$

Thus Dacron is called a **polyester.** By itself or blended with cotton, Dacron is widely used in fibers for the manufacture of clothing.

Polymers Based on Ethylene

A large section of the polymer industry involves the production of macromolecules from ethylene or substituted ethylenes. As discussed previously, ethylene molecules polymerize by addition after the double bond has been broken by some initiator:

$$
\begin{array}{c}
\underset{\underset{\textstyle H}{|}}{\overset{\overset{\textstyle H}{|}}{X-C}}-\underset{\underset{\textstyle H}{|}}{\overset{\overset{\textstyle H}{|}}{C}}\cdot\ \ \underset{\underset{\textstyle H}{|}}{\overset{\overset{\textstyle H}{|}}{C}}=\underset{\underset{\textstyle H}{|}}{\overset{\overset{\textstyle H}{|}}{C}}\ \longrightarrow\ \underset{\underset{\textstyle H}{|}}{\overset{\overset{\textstyle H}{|}}{X-C}}-\underset{\underset{\textstyle H}{|}}{\overset{\overset{\textstyle H}{|}}{C}}-\underset{\underset{\textstyle H}{|}}{\overset{\overset{\textstyle H}{|}}{C}}-\underset{\underset{\textstyle H}{|}}{\overset{\overset{\textstyle H}{|}}{C}}\cdot
\end{array}
$$

This process continues by adding new ethylene molecules to eventually give polyethylene, a thermoplastic material.

There are two forms of polyethylene: low-density polyethylene (LDPE) and high-density polyethylene (HDPE). The chains in LDPE contain many branches and thus do not pack as tightly as those in HDPE, which consist of mostly straight-chain molecules.

> psi is the abbreviation for pounds per square inch: 15 psi ≈ 1 atm.

Traditionally, LDPE has been manufactured under conditions of high pressure (≈20,000 psi) and high temperature (500°C). These severe reaction conditions require specially designed equipment, and for safety reasons, the reaction usually has been run behind a reinforced concrete barrier. More recently, lower reaction pressures and temperatures have become possible through the use of catalysts. One catalytic system using triethylaluminum $[Al(C_2H_5)_3]$ and titanium(IV) chloride was developed by Karl Ziegler in Germany and Giulio Natta in Italy. Although this catalyst is very efficient, it catches fire on contact with air and must be handled very carefully. A safer catalytic system was developed at Phillips Petroleum Company. It uses a chromium(III) oxide (Cr_2O_3) and aluminosilicate catalyst and has mainly taken over in the United States. The product of the catalyzed reaction is highly linear (unbranched) and is often called *linear low-density polyethylene.* It is very similar to HDPE.

The major use of LDPE is in the manufacture of the tough, transparent film that is used in packaging so many consumer goods. Two-thirds of the approximately 10 billion pounds of LDPE produced annually in the United States are used for this purpose. The major use of HDPE is for blow-molded products, such as bottles for consumer products (Fig. 21.17).

> Molecular weight (not molar mass) is the common terminology in the polymer industry.

The useful properties of polyethylene are due primarily to its high molecular weight (molar mass). Although the strengths of the interactions between specific points on the nonpolar chains are quite small, the chains are so long that these small attractions accumulate to a very significant value so that the chains stick together very tenaciously. There is also a great deal of physical tangling of the lengthy chains. The combination of these interactions gives the

Chemical Insights	Wallace Hume Carothers

Wallace H. Carothers, a brilliant organic chemist who was principally responsible for the development of nylon and the first synthetic rubber (Neoprene), was born in 1896 in Burlington, Iowa. As a youth, Carothers was fascinated by tools and mechanical devices and spent many hours experimenting. In 1915 he entered Tarkio College in Missouri. Carothers so excelled in chemistry that even before his graduation he was made a chemistry instructor.

Carothers eventually moved to the University of Illinois at Urbana–Champaign, where he was appointed to the faculty when he completed his Ph.D. in organic chemistry in 1924. He moved to Harvard University in 1926 and then to DuPont in 1928 to participate in a new program in fundamental research. At DuPont, Carothers headed the organic chemistry division, and during his 10 years there he played a prominent role in laying the foundations of polymer chemistry.

By the age of 33, Carothers had become a world-famous chemist whose advice was sought by almost everyone working in polymers. He was the first industrial chemist to be elected to the prestigious National Academy of Sciences.

Carothers was an avid reader of poetry and a lover of classical music. Unfortunately, he also suffered from severe bouts of depression that finally

Wallace H. Carothers

led to his suicide in 1937 in a Philadelphia hotel room, where he drank a cyanide solution. He was 41 years old. Despite the brevity of his career, Carothers was truly one of the finest American chemists of all time. His great intellect, his love of chemistry, and his insistence on perfection produced his special genius.

Figure 21.17

A major use of HDPE is for blow-molded objects such as bottles for soft drinks, shampoos, bleaches, and so on. (a) A tube composed of HDPE is inserted into the mold (die). (b) The die closes, sealing the bottom of the tube. (c) Compressed air is forced into the warm HDPE tube, which then expands to take the shape of the die. (d) The molded bottle is removed from the die.

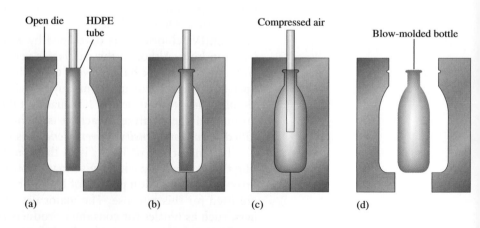

(a) (b) (c) (d)

polymer strength and toughness. However, a material like polyethylene can be melted and formed into a new shape (thermoplastic behavior) because in the melted state the molecules can readily flow past one another.

Since a high molecular weight gives a polymer useful properties, one might think that the goal would be to produce polymers with chains as long as possible. However, this is not the case—polymers become much more difficult to process as the molecular weights increase. Most industrial operations require that the polymer flow through pipes as it is processed. But, as the chain lengths increase, viscosity also increases. In practice, the upper limit of a polymer's molecular weight is set by the flow requirements of the manufacturing process. Thus the final product often reflects a compromise between the optimal properties for the application and those needed for ease of processing.

Although many polymer properties are greatly influenced by molecular weight, some other important properties are not. For example, chain length does not affect a polymer's resistance to chemical attack. Physical properties such as color, refractive index, hardness, density, and electrical conductivity are also not greatly influenced by molecular weight.

We have already seen that one way of altering the strength of a polymeric material is to vary the chain length. Another method for modifying polymer behavior involves varying the substituents. For example, if we use a monomer of the type

the properties of the resulting polymer depend on the identity of X. The simplest example is polypropylene, whose monomer is

and that has the form

The CH$_3$ groups can be arranged on the same side of the chain (called an **isotactic chain**) as shown above, can alternate (called a **syndiotactic chain**) as shown below,

or can be randomly distributed (called an **atactic chain**).

The chain arrangement has a significant effect on the polymer's properties. Most polypropylene is made using the Ziegler-Natta catalyst [Al(C$_2$H$_5$)$_3$ · TiCl$_4$], which produces highly isotactic chains that pack together quite closely. As a result, polypropylene is more crystalline and therefore stronger and harder than polyethylene. The major uses of polypropylene are for molded parts (40%), fibers (35%), and packaging films (10%). Polypropylene fibers are especially useful for athletic wear because they do not absorb water from perspiration, as cotton does. Rather, the moisture is drawn away from the skin to the surface of the polypropylene garment, where it can evaporate. The annual U.S. production of polypropylene is about 7 billion pounds.

Chemical Insights | Heal Thyself

One major problem with structural materials is that they crack and weaken as they age. The human body has mechanisms for healing itself if the skin is cut or a bone is broken. However, inanimate materials have had no such mechanisms—until now. Scientists at the University of Illinois at Urbana–Champaign (UIUC) have invented a plastic that automatically heals microscopic cracks before they can develop into large cracks that would degrade the usefulness of the material. This accomplishment was achieved by an interdisciplinary team of scientists including aeronautical engineering professors Scott White and Philippe Geubelle, applied mechanics professor Nancy Sottos, and chemistry professor Jeffrey Moore.

The self-healing system is based on microcapsules containing liquid dicyclopentadiene

A scanning electron microscope image showing the fractured plane of a self-healing material with a ruptured microcapsule in a thermosetting matrix.

Dicyclopentadiene

that are blended into the plastic. When a microscopic crack develops, it encounters and breaks a microcapsule. The dicyclopentadiene then leaks out, where it encounters a catalyst (blended into the plastic when it was formulated) that mediates a repair polymerization process. This process involves opening the cyclopentadiene rings, which leads to a highly crosslinked repair of the crack.

The trickiest part of the repair mechanism is to get the microcapsules to be the correct size and to have the appropriate wall strength. They must be small enough not to degrade the strength of the plastic. The walls must also be thick enough to survive the molding of the plastic but thin enough to burst as the lengthening crack reaches them.

Self-healing materials should have many applications. The U.S. Air Force, which partially funded the research at UIUC, is interested in using the materials in tanks that hold gases and liquids under pressure. The current materials used for these tanks are subject to microcracks that eventually grow, causing the tanks to leak. Self-healing materials would also be valuable in situations where repair is impossible or impractical, such as electronic circuit boards, components of deep space probes, and implanted medical devices.

Another related polymer, **polystyrene,** is constructed from the monomer styrene,

Pure polystyrene is too brittle for many uses, so most polystyrene-based polymers are actually *copolymers* of styrene and butadiene,

thus incorporating bits of butadiene rubber into the polystyrene matrix. The resulting polymer is very tough and is often used as a substitute for wood in furniture.

Another polystyrene-based product is acrylonitrile-butadiene-styrene (ABS), a tough, hard, and chemically resistant plastic used for pipes and for items such as radio housings, telephone cases, and golf club heads, for which shock resistance is an essential property. Originally, ABS was produced by copolymerization of the three monomers:

| Acrylonitrile | Styrene | Butadiene |

It is now prepared by a special process called *grafting,* in which butadiene is polymerized first, and then the cyanide and phenyl substituents are added chemically.

Another high-volume polymer, **polyvinyl chloride (PVC),** is constructed from the monomer vinyl chloride,

---

21.6 | Natural Polymers

Proteins

We have seen that many useful synthetic materials are polymers. Thus it should not be surprising that a great many natural materials are also polymers: starch, hair, silicate chains in soil and rocks, silk and cotton fibers, and the cellulose in woody plants, to name only a few.

In this section we consider a class of natural polymers, the **proteins,** which make up about 15% of our bodies and have molecular weights (molar masses) that range from about 6000 to over 1,000,000 grams per mole. Proteins perform many functions in the human body. **Fibrous proteins** provide structural integrity and strength for many types of tissue and are the main components of muscle, hair, and cartilage. Other proteins, usually called **globular proteins**

α-Carbon

At the pH in biological fluids, the amino acids shown in Fig. 21.18 exist in a different form, with the proton of the —COOH group transferred to the —NH₂ group. For example, glycine would be in the form $H_3^+NCH_2COO^-$.

because of their roughly spherical shape, are the "worker" molecules of the body. These proteins transport and store oxygen and nutrients, act as catalysts for the thousands of reactions that make life possible, fight invasion by foreign objects, participate in the body's many regulatory systems, and transport electrons in the complex process of metabolizing nutrients.

The building blocks of all proteins are the **α-amino acids,** where R may represent H, CH₃, or a more complex substituent. These molecules are called α-amino acids because the amino group (—NH₂) is always attached to the α-carbon, the one next to the carboxyl group (—CO₂H). The 20 amino acids most commonly found in proteins are shown in Fig. 21.18.

Note from Fig. 21.18 that the amino acids are grouped into polar and nonpolar classes, determined by the R groups, or **side chains.** Nonpolar side chains contain mostly carbon and hydrogen atoms, whereas polar side chains contain large numbers of nitrogen and oxygen atoms. This difference is important because polar side chains are *hydrophilic* (water-loving), but nonpolar side chains are *hydrophobic* (water-fearing), and this characteristic greatly affects the three-dimensional structure of the resulting protein.

The protein polymer is built by condensation reactions between amino acids. For example,

The product shown above is called a **dipeptide.** This name is used because the structure

The peptide linkage is also found in nylon (see Section 21.5).

is called a **peptide linkage** by biochemists. (The same grouping is called an *amide* by organic chemists.) Additional condensation reactions lengthen the chain to produce a **polypeptide,** eventually yielding a protein.

You can imagine that with 20 amino acids, which can be assembled in any order, there is essentially an infinite variety possible in the construction of proteins. This flexibility allows an organism to tailor proteins for the many types of functions that must be carried out.

The order, or sequence, of amino acids in the protein chain is called the **primary structure,** conveniently indicated by using three-letter codes for the amino acids (Fig. 21.18), where it is understood that the terminal carboxyl group is on the right and the terminal amino group is on the left. For example, one possible sequence for a tripeptide containing the amino acids lysine, alanine, and leucine is

which is represented in the shorthand notation by

lys-ala-leu

Figure 21.18
The 20 α-amino acids found in most proteins. The R group is shown in color.

Note from Example 21.7 that six sequences are possible for a polypeptide with three given amino acids. There are three possibilities for the first amino acid (any one of the three given amino acids), there are two possibilities for the second amino acid (one has already been accounted for), but there is only one possibility left for the third amino acid. Thus the number of sequences is $3 \times 2 \times 1 = 6$. The product $3 \times 2 \times 1$ is often written 3! (and is called *3 factorial*). Similar reasoning shows that for a polypeptide with four amino acids, there are 4!, or $4 \times 3 \times 2 \times 1 = 24$, possible sequences.

A tripeptide containing glycine, cysteine, and alanine.

ⓌWL INTERACTIVE EXAMPLE 21.7

Write the sequences of all possible tripeptides composed of the amino acids tyrosine, histidine, and cysteine.

Solution There are six possible sequences:

tyr-his-cys	his-tyr-cys	cys-tyr-his
tyr-cys-his	his-cys-tyr	cys-his-tyr

ⓌWL INTERACTIVE EXAMPLE 21.8

What number of possible sequences exists for a polypeptide composed of 20 different amino acids?

Solution The answer is 20!, or

$$20 \times 19 \times 18 \times 17 \times 16 \times \ldots \times 5 \times 4 \times 3 \times 2 \times 1 = 2.43 \times 10^{18}$$

cys–tyr–ile–gln–asn–cys–pro–leu–gly
(a)

cys–tyr–phe–gln–asn–cys–pro–arg–gly
(b)

Figure 21.19
The amino acid sequences in (a) oxytocin and (b) vasopressin. The differing amino acids are boxed.

A striking example of the importance of the primary structure of polypeptides can be seen in the differences between *oxytocin* and *vasopressin*. Both of these molecules are nine-unit polypeptides that differ by only two amino acids (Fig. 21.19), yet they perform completely different functions in the human body. Oxytocin is a hormone that triggers contraction of the uterus and milk secretion. Vasopressin raises blood pressure levels and regulates kidney function.

A second level of structure in proteins, beyond the sequence of amino acids, is the arrangement of the chain of the long molecule. The **secondary structure** is determined to a large extent by hydrogen bonding between lone pairs on an oxygen in the carbonyl group of an amino acid and a hydrogen atom attached to a nitrogen of another amino acid:

Such interactions can occur *within* the chain coils to form a spiral structure called an **α-helix,** as shown in Figs. 21.20 and 21.21. This type of secondary structure gives the protein elasticity (springiness) and is found in the fibrous proteins in wool, hair, and tendons. Hydrogen bonding can also occur *between different* protein chains, joining them together in an arrangement called a **pleated sheet,** as shown in Fig. 21.22. Silk contains this arrangement of proteins, making its fibers flexible yet very strong and resistant to stretching. The pleated sheet is also found in muscle fibers. The hydrogen bonds in the α-helical protein are called *intrachain* (within a given protein chain), and those in the pleated sheet are said to be *interchain* (between protein chains).

As you might imagine, a molecule as large as a protein has a great deal of flexibility and can assume a variety of overall shapes. The specific shape that a protein assumes depends on its function. For long, thin structures, such as hair,

Figure 21.20
Hydrogen bonding within a protein chain causes it to form a stable helical structure called an α-helix. Only the main atoms in the helical backbone are shown here. The hydrogen bonds are not shown.

Figure 21.21
Ball-and-stick model of a portion of a protein chain in the α-helical arrangement, showing the hydrogen-bonding interactions.

Figure 21.22
When hydrogen bonding occurs between protein chains rather than within them, a stable structure (the pleated sheet) results. This structure contains many protein chains and is found in natural fibers, such as silk, and in muscles.

(a)   (b)

Figure 21.23
(a) Collagen, a protein found in tendons, consists of three protein chains (each with a helical structure) twisted together to form a superhelix. The result is a long, relatively narrow protein. (b) The pleated-sheet arrangement of many proteins bound together to form the elongated protein found in silk fibers.

wool and silk fibers, and tendons, an elongated shape is required. This may involve an α-helical secondary structure, as found in the protein α-keratin in hair and wool or in the collagen found in tendons [Fig. 21.23(a)], or it may involve a pleated-sheet secondary structure, as found in silk [Fig. 21.23(b)]. Many of the proteins in the body having nonstructural functions are globular, such as myoglobin (Fig. 21.24). Note that the secondary structure of myoglo-

Figure 21.24
The protein myoglobin.

bin is basically α-helical. However, in the areas where the chain bends to give the protein its compact globular structure, the α-helix breaks down to give a secondary configuration known as the **random-coil arrangement.**

The overall shape of the protein, long and narrow or globular, is called its **tertiary structure** and is maintained by several different types of interactions: hydrogen bonding, dipole–dipole interactions, ionic bonds, covalent bonds, and London dispersion forces between nonpolar groups. These bonds, which represent all the bonding types discussed in this text, are summarized in Fig. 21.25.

The amino acid *cysteine*

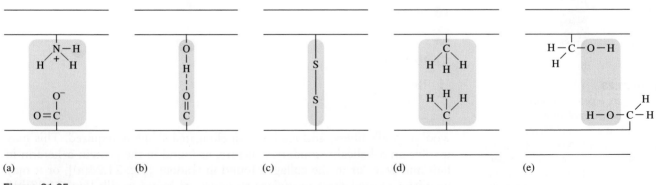

(a)   (b)   (c)   (d)   (e)

Figure 21.25
Summary of the various types of interactions that stabilize the tertiary structure of a protein: (a) ionic, (b) hydrogen bonding, (c) covalent, (d) London dispersion, and (e) dipole–dipole.

plays a special role in stabilizing the tertiary structure of many proteins because the —SH groups on two cysteines can react in the presence of an oxidizing agent to form a S—S bond called a **disulfide linkage:**

$$C-CH_2-S-H + H-S-CH_2-C \longrightarrow C-CH_2-\boxed{S-S}-CH_2-C$$

A practical application of the chemistry of disulfide bonds is permanent waving of hair, as summarized in Fig. 21.26. The S—S linkages in the protein of hair are broken by treatment with a reducing agent. The hair is then set in curlers to change the tertiary protein structure to the desired shape. Then treatment with an oxidizing agent causes new S—S bonds to form, which allow the hair protein to retain the new structure.

The three-dimensional structure of a protein is crucial to its function. The process of breaking down this structure is called **denaturation** (Fig. 21.27). For example, the denaturation of egg proteins occurs when an egg is cooked. Any source of energy can cause denaturation of proteins and is thus potentially dangerous to living organisms. For example, ultraviolet and X-ray radiation or nuclear radioactivity can disrupt protein structure, which may lead to cancer or genetic damage. Protein damage is also caused by chemicals like benzene, trichloroethane, and 1,2-dibromoethane (called EDB). The metals lead and mercury, which have a very high affinity for sulfur, cause protein denaturation by disrupting disulfide bonds between protein chains.

The tremendous flexibility in the various levels of protein structure allows the tailoring of proteins for a wide range of specific functions. Proteins are the "workhorse" molecules of living organisms.

Carbohydrates

Carbohydrates form another class of biologically important molecules. They serve as a food source for most organisms and as a structural material for plants. Because many carbohydrates have the empirical formula CH_2O, it was originally believed that these substances were hydrates of carbon, thus accounting for the name.

Most important carbohydrates, such as starch and cellulose, are polymers composed of monomers called **monosaccharides,** or **simple sugars.** The monosaccharides are polyhydroxy ketones and aldehydes. The most important con-

Natural cysteine linkages in hair

Reduction

SH SH SH SH

SH SH SH SH

Chains shift

HS HS HS HS

HS HS HS HS

Hair set in curlers alters tertiary structures

Oxidation

New cysteine linkages in waved hair

Figure 21.26
The permanent waving of hair.

General Name of Sugar	Number of Carbon Atoms
Triose	3
Tetrose	4
Pentose	5
Hexose	6
Heptose	7
Octose	8
Nonose	9

Figure 21.27
A schematic representation of the thermal denaturation of a protein.

Energy

Chemical Insights Tanning in the Shade

Among today's best-selling cosmetics are self-tanning lotions. Many light-skinned people want to look like they have just spent a vacation in the Caribbean, but they recognize the dangers of too much sun—it causes premature aging and may lead to skin cancer. Chemistry has come to the rescue in the form of lotions that produce an authentic-looking tan. All of these lotions have the same active ingredient: dihydroxyacetone (DHA). DHA, which has the structure

is a nontoxic, simple sugar that occurs as an intermediate in carbohydrate metabolism in higher-order plants and animals. The DHA used in self-tanners is prepared by bacterial fermentation of glycerine,

The tanning effects of DHA were discovered by accident in the 1950s at Children's Hospital at the University of Cincinnati, where DHA was being used to treat children with glycogen storage disease. When the DHA was accidentally spilled on the skin, it produced brown spots.

The mechanism of the browning process involves the Maillard reaction, which was discovered by Louis-Camille Maillard in 1912. In this process amino acids react with sugars to create brown or golden-brown products. The same reaction is responsible for much of the browning that occurs during the manufacture and storage of foods. It is also the reason that beer is golden brown.

The browning of skin occurs in the stratum corneum—the outermost, dead layer—where the DHA reacts with free amino ($-NH_2$) groups of the proteins found there.

DHA is present in most tanning lotions at concentrations between 2% and 5%, although some

Self-tanning products and a close-up of a label showing the contents.

products designed to give a deeper tan are more concentrated. Because the lotions themselves turn brown above pH 7, the tanning lotions are buffered at pH 5.

Thanks to these new products, tanning is now both safe and easy.

Mirror

tain five carbon atoms (**pentoses**) or six carbon atoms (**hexoses**). One important hexose is *fructose,* a sugar found in honey and fruit. Its structure is

$$CH_2OH$$
$$C{=}O$$
$$HO{-}^*C{-}H$$
$$H{-}^*C{-}OH$$
$$H{-}^*C{-}OH$$
$$CH_2OH$$

Fructose

where the asterisks indicate chiral carbon atoms. In Section 19.4 we saw that molecules with nonsuperimposable mirror images exhibit optical isomerism. A carbon atom with four *different* groups bonded to it in a tetrahedral arrangement *always* has a nonsuperimposable mirror image (Fig. 21.28), which gives rise to a pair of optical isomers. For example, the simplest sugar, glyceraldehyde,

which has one chiral carbon, has two optical isomers, as shown in Fig. 21.29.

In fructose each of the three chiral carbon atoms satisfies the requirement of being surrounded by four different groups. This leads to a total of 2^3, or 8, isomers that differ in their ability to rotate polarized light. The particular isomer whose structure is given above is called D-fructose. Generally, monosaccharides have one isomer that is more common in nature than the others. The most important pentoses and hexoses are shown in Table 21.8.

Figure 21.28

When a tetrahedral carbon atom has four different substituents, there is no way that its mirror image can be superimposed. The lower two forms show other possible orientations of the molecule. Compare these with the mirror image and note that they cannot be superimposed.

Figure 21.29

The mirror-image optical isomers of glyceraldehyde. Note that these mirror images cannot be superimposed.

Table 21.8

Some Important Monosaccharides

Pentoses		
D-Ribose	D-Arabinose	D-Ribulose
CHO	CHO	CH$_2$OH
H—C—OH	HO—C—H	C=O
H—C—OH	H—C—OH	H—C—OH
H—C—OH	H—C—OH	H—C—OH
CH$_2$OH	CH$_2$OH	CH$_2$OH

Hexoses			
D-Glucose	D-Mannose	D-Galactose	D-Fructose
CHO	CHO	CHO	CH$_2$OH
H—C—OH	HO—C—H	H—C—OH	C=O
HO—C—H	HO—C—H	HO—C—H	HO—C—H
H—C—OH	H—C—OH	HO—C—H	H—C—OH
H—C—OH	H—C—OH	H—C—OH	H—C—OH
CH$_2$OH	CH$_2$OH	CH$_2$OH	CH$_2$OH

⬤WL INTERACTIVE EXAMPLE 21.9

Determine the number of chiral carbon atoms in the following pentose:

Solution We must look for carbon atoms that have four different substituents. The top carbon has only three substituents and thus cannot be chiral. The three carbon atoms shown in blue each have four different groups attached to them.

Since the fifth carbon atom has only three types of substituents (it has two hydrogen atoms), it is not chiral.

Thus the three chiral carbon atoms in this pentose are those shown in blue:

Note that D-ribose and D-arabinose, shown in Table 21.8, are two of the eight isomers of this pentose.

Although we have so far represented the monosaccharides as straight-chain molecules, they usually cyclize, or form a ring structure, in aqueous solution. Figure 21.30 shows this reaction for fructose. Note that a new bond is formed between the oxygen of the terminal hydroxyl group and the carbon of the ketone group. In the cyclic form, fructose is a five-membered ring containing a C—O—C bond. The same type of reaction can occur between a hydroxyl group and an aldehyde group, as shown for D-glucose in Fig. 21.31. In this case a six-membered ring is formed.

More complex carbohydrates are formed by combining monosaccharides. For example, **sucrose**, common table sugar, is a **disaccharide** formed from glucose and fructose by elimination of water to form a C—O—C bond between the rings, which is called a **glycoside linkage** (Fig. 21.32). When sucrose is consumed in food, the preceding reaction is reversed. An enzyme in saliva catalyzes the breakdown of this disaccharide.

Figure 21.30
The cyclization of D-fructose.

Figure 21.31

The cyclization of glucose. Two different rings are possible; they differ in the orientation of the hydroxyl group and hydrogen on one carbon, as indicated. The two forms are designated α and β and are shown here in two representations.

Figure 21.32

Sucrose is a disaccharide formed from α-D-glucose and fructose.

Large polymers consisting of many monosaccharide units, called polysaccharides, can form when each ring forms two glycoside linkages, as shown in Fig. 21.32. Three of the most important of these polymers are starch, cellulose, and glycogen. All these substances are polymers of glucose, differing from each other in the nature of the glycoside linkage, the amount of branching, and molecular weight (molar mass).

Starch, a polymer of α-D-glucose, consists of two parts: *amylose,* a straight-chain polymer of α-glucose [Fig. 21.33(a)], and *amylopectin,* a highly branched polymer of α-glucose with a molecular weight that is 10 to 20 times that of amylose. Branching occurs when a third glycoside linkage attaches a branch to the main polymer chain.

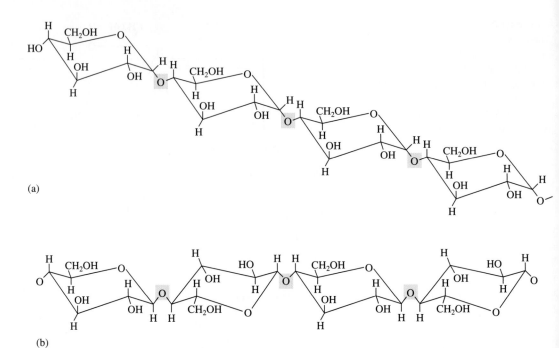

(a)

(b)

Figure 21.33

(a) The polymer amylose is a major component of starch and is made up of α-D-glucose monomers.
(b) The polymer cellulose, which consists of β-D-glucose monomers.

Starch, the carbohydrate reservoir in plants, is the form in which glucose is stored by the plant for later use as cellular fuel. Glucose is stored in this high-molecular-weight form because it results in less stress on the plant's internal structure by osmotic pressure. Recall from Section 17.6 that it is the concentration of solute molecules (or ions) that determines the osmotic pressure. Combining the individual glucose molecules into one large chain keeps the concentration of solute molecules relatively low, minimizing the osmotic pressure.

Cellulose, the major structural component of woody plants and natural fibers (such as cotton), is a polymer of β-D-glucose and has the structure shown in Fig. 21.33(b). Note that the β-glycoside linkages in cellulose give the glucose rings a different relative orientation than is found in starch. Although this difference may seem minor, it has very important consequences. The human digestive system contains α-glycosidases, enzymes that can catalyze breakage of the α-glycoside bonds in starch. These enzymes are not effective on the β-glycoside bonds of cellulose, presumably because the different structure results in a poor fit between the enzyme's active site and the carbohydrate. The enzymes necessary to cleave β-glycoside linkages, the β-glycosidases, are found in bacteria that exist in the digestive tracts of termites, cows, deer, and many other animals. Thus, unlike humans, these animals can derive nutrition from cellulose.

Glycogen, the main carbohydrate reservoir in animals, has a structure similar to that of amylopectin but with more branching. It is this branching that is thought to facilitate the rapid breakdown of glycogen into glucose when energy is required.

Nucleic Acids

Life is possible only because each cell, when it divides, can transmit the vital information about how it works to the next generation. It has been known for a long time that this process involves the chromosomes in the nucleus of the cell. Only since 1953, however, have scientists understood the molecular basis of this intriguing cellular "talent."

The substance that stores and transmits the genetic information is a polymer called **deoxyribonucleic acid (DNA),** a huge molecule with a molecular weight as high as several billion grams per mole. Together with other similar nucleic acids called the **ribonucleic acids (RNA),** DNA is also responsible for

(a)

(b)

Figure 21.34
The structure of the pentoses
(a) deoxyribose and (b) ribose.
Deoxyribose is the sugar molecule
present in DNA; ribose is found in RNA.

Figure 21.35
The organic bases found in DNA and RNA.

the synthesis of the various proteins needed by the cell to carry out its life functions. The RNA molecules, which are found in the cytoplasm outside the nucleus, are much smaller than DNA polymers, with molecular weights of only 20,000 to 40,000 grams per mole.

The monomers of the nucleic acids, called **nucleotides,** are composed of three distinct parts:

1. A *five-carbon sugar,* deoxyribose in DNA and ribose in RNA (Fig. 21.34)
2. A *nitrogen-containing organic base* of the type shown in Fig. 21.35
3. A *phosphoric acid molecule* (H_3PO_4)

The base and the sugar combine as shown in Fig. 21.36(a) to form a unit that in turn reacts with phosphoric acid to create the nucleotide, which is an ester

Figure 21.36
(a) Adenosine is formed by the reaction of adenine with ribose. (b) The reaction of phosphoric acid with adenosine to form the ester adenosine 5-phosphoric acid, a nucleotide. (At biological pH, the phosphoric acid would not be fully protonated as is shown here.)

Figure 21.37
A portion of a typical nucleic acid chain. Note that the backbone consists of sugar–phosphate esters.

[see Fig. 21.36(b)]. The nucleotides become connected through condensation reactions that eliminate water to give a polymer of the type represented in Fig. 21.37; such a polymer can contain a *billion* units.

The key to DNA's functioning is its *double-helical structure with complementary bases on the two strands*. The bases form hydrogen bonds to each other, as shown in Fig. 21.38. Note that the structures of cytosine and guanine make them perfect partners for hydrogen bonding, and they are *always* found as pairs on the two strands of DNA. Thymine and adenine form similar hydrogen-bonding pairs.

There is much evidence to suggest that the two strands of DNA unwind during cell division and that new complementary strands are constructed on the unraveled strands (Fig. 21.39). Because the bases on the strands always pair in the same way—cytosine with guanine and thymine with adenine—each unraveled strand serves as a template for attaching the complementary bases (along with the rest of the nucleotide). This process results in two double-helix DNA structures that are identical to the original one. Each new double strand contains one strand from the original DNA double helix and one newly synthesized strand. This replication of DNA allows for the transmission of genetic information as the cells divide.

The other major function of DNA is **protein synthesis.** A given segment of the DNA, called a **gene,** contains the code for a specific protein. These codes transmit the primary structure of the protein (the sequence of amino acids) to the construction "machinery" of the cell. There is a specific code for each amino acid in the protein, which ensures that the correct amino acid will be inserted as the protein chain grows. A code consists of a set of three bases called a **codon.**

DNA stores the genetic information, whereas RNA molecules are responsible for transmitting this information to the ribosomes, where protein synthesis actually occurs. This complex process involves, first, the construction of a

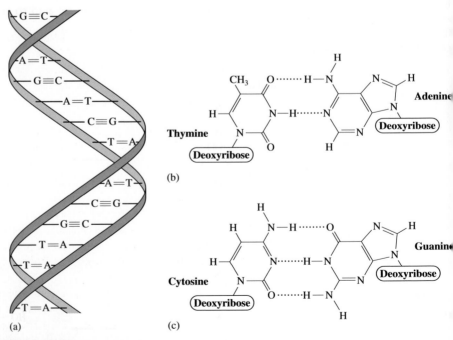

Figure 21.38
(a) The DNA double helix contains two sugar–phosphate backbones, with the bases from the two strands hydrogen-bonded to each other. The complementarity of the (b) thymine-adenine and (c) cytosine-guanine pairs.

Figure 21.39

During cell division, the original DNA double helix unwinds, and new complementary strands are constructed on each original strand.

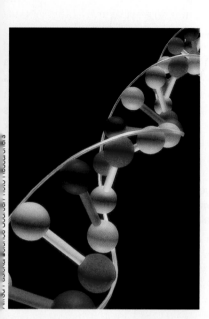

A computer image of the base pairs of DNA. The blue lines represent the sugar–phosphate backbone, and the colored bars represent the hydrogen bonding between the base pairs.

special RNA molecule called **messenger RNA (mRNA)**. The mRNA is built in the cell nucleus on the appropriate section of DNA (the gene); the double helix is "unzipped," and the complementarity of the bases is used in a process similar to that used in DNA replication. The mRNA then migrates into the cytoplasm of the cell, where, with the assistance of the ribosomes, the protein is synthesized.

Small RNA fragments, called **transfer RNA (tRNA),** are tailored to find specific amino acids and then to attach them to the growing protein chain as dictated by the codons in the mRNA. Transfer RNA has a lower molecular weight than messenger RNA. It consists of a chain of 75 to 80 nucleotides, including the bases adenine, cytosine, guanine, and uracil, among others. The chain folds back onto itself in various places as the complementary bases along the chain form hydrogen bonds. The tRNA decodes the genetic message from the mRNA, using a complementary triplet of bases called an **anticodon.** The nature of the anticodon governs which amino acid will be brought to the protein under construction.

The protein is built in several steps. First, a tRNA molecule brings an amino acid to the mRNA [the anticodon of the tRNA must complement the codon of the mRNA (Fig. 21.40)]. Once this amino acid is in place, another tRNA moves to the second codon site of the mRNA with its specific amino acid. The two amino acids link via a peptide bond, and the tRNA on the first codon breaks away. The process is repeated down the chain, always matching the tRNA anticodon with the mRNA codon.

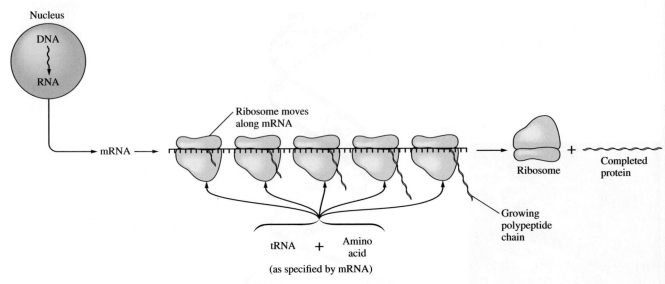

Figure 21.40
The mRNA molecule, constructed from a specific gene on the DNA, is used as the pattern to construct a given protein with the assistance of ribosomes. The tRNA molecules attach to specific amino acids and put them in place as called for by the codons on the mRNA.

Key Terms

biomolecule
organic chemistry

Section 21.1
hydrocarbons
saturated
unsaturated
alkanes
normal (straight-chain or
    unbranched) hydrocarbons
structural isomerism
combustion reaction
substitution reaction
dehydrogenation reaction
cyclic alkanes

Section 22.2
alkenes
cis–trans isomerism
alkynes
addition reaction
hydrogenation reaction
halogenation
polymerization

Section 22.3
aromatic hydrocarbons
phenyl group

Section 22.4
hydrocarbon derivatives
functional group
alcohols
phenol
carbonyl group

For Review

Hydrocarbons
■ Compounds composed of mostly carbon and hydrogen atoms that typically contain chains or rings of carbon atoms
■ Alkanes
  ■ Contain compounds with only C—C single bonds
  ■ Can be represented by the formula C_nH_{2n+2}
  ■ Are said to be saturated because each carbon present is bonded to the maximum number of atoms (4)
  ■ The carbon atoms are described as being sp^3 hybridized
  ■ Their structural isomerism involves the formation of branched chains
  ■ React with O_2 to form CO_2 and H_2O (called a combustion reaction)
  ■ Undergo substitution reactions
■ Alkenes
  ■ Contain one or more C=C double bonds
  ■ Simplest alkene is C_2H_4 (ethylene), which is described as containing sp^2 hybridized carbon atoms
  ■ Restricted rotation about the C=C bonds in alkenes can lead to *cis–trans* isomerism
  ■ Undergo addition reactions
■ Alkynes
  ■ Contain one or more C≡C triple bonds
  ■ Simplest example is C_2H_2 (acetylene), described as containing sp-hybridized carbon atoms
  ■ Undergo addition reactions

ketones
aldehydes
carboxylic acids
carboxyl group
ester
amine

Section 22.5

polymer
thermoset polymer
thermoplastic polymer
crosslinking
vulcanization
addition polymerization
free radical
condensation polymerization
copolymer
homopolymer
dimer
polyester
isotactic chain
syndiotactic chain
atactic chain
polystyrene
polyvinyl chloride (PVC)

Section 22.6

proteins
fibrous proteins
globular proteins
α-amino acids
side chains
dipeptide
peptide linkage
polypeptide
primary structure
secondary structure
α-helix
pleated sheet
random-coil arrangement
tertiary structure
disulfide linkage
denaturation
carbohydrates
monosaccharides (simple sugars)
pentoses
hexoses
sucrose
disaccharide
glycoside linkage
starch
cellulose
glycogen
deoxyribonucleic acid (DNA)
ribonucleic acid (RNA)
nucleotides
protein synthesis
gene
codon
messenger RNA (mRNA)
transfer RNA (tRNA)
anticodon

- Aromatic hydrocarbons
  - Contain rings of carbon atoms with delocalized π electrons
  - Undergo substitution reactions rather than addition reactions

Hydrocarbon derivatives
- Contain one or more functional groups
- Alcohols: contain the —OH group
- Aldehydes: contain a $\overset{\diagdown}{\underset{H}{C}}$=O group
- Ketones: contain the $\overset{\diagdown}{\underset{\diagup}{C}}$=O group
- Carboxylic acids: contain the —$C\overset{\diagup O}{\diagdown OH}$ group

Polymers
- Large molecules formed from many small molecules (called monomers)
  - Addition polymerization: monomers add together by a free radical mechanism
  - Condensation polymerization: monomers connect by splitting out a small molecule, such as water

Proteins
- A class of natural polymers with molar masses ranging from 600 to 1,000,000
- Fibrous proteins form the structural basis of muscle, hair, and cartilage
- Globular proteins perform many biologic functions, including transport and storage of oxygen, catalysis of biologic reactions, and regulation of biologic systems
- Building blocks of proteins (monomers) are α-amino acids, which connect by a condensation reaction to form a peptide linkage
- Protein structure
  - Primary: the order of amino acids in the chain
  - Secondary: the arrangement of the protein chain
    - α-helix
    - pleated sheet
  - Tertiary structure: the overall shape of the protein

Carbohydrates
- Contain carbon, hydrogen, and oxygen
- Serve as food sources for most organisms
- Monosaccharides are most commonly five-carbon and six-carbon polyhydroxy ketones and aldehydes
  - Monosaccharides combine to form more complex carbohydrates, such as sucrose, starch, and cellulose

Genetic processes
- When a cell divides, the genetic information is transmitted via deoxyribonucleic acid (DNA), which has a double helical structure
  - During cell division, the double helix unravels and a new polymer forms along each strand of the original DNA
  - The genetic code is carried by organic bases that hydrogen-bond to each other in specific pairs in the interior of the DNA double helix

Exercises

A blue exercise number indicates that the answer to that exercise appears at the back of this book and a solution appears in the *Solutions Guide*.

Hydrocarbons

1. What is a hydrocarbon? What is the difference between a saturated hydrocarbon and an unsaturated hydrocarbon? Distinguish between normal and branched hydrocarbons.

2. In the shorthand notation for cyclic alkanes, the hydrogens are usually omitted. How do you determine the number of hydrogens bonded to each carbon in a ring structure?

3. Why are cyclopropane and cyclobutane so reactive?

4. What are aromatic hydrocarbons? Give a detailed description of the bonding in benzene. The π electrons in benzene are delocalized, whereas the π electrons in simple alkenes and alkynes are localized. Explain the difference.

5. Draw all the structural isomers for C_8H_{18} that have the following root name (longest carbon chain). Name the structural isomers.
   a. heptane   c. pentane
   b. hexane   d. butane

6. The normal (unbranched) hydrocarbons are often referred to as the straight-chain hydrocarbons. To what does this name refer? Does this mean that all carbon atoms in a straight-chain hydrocarbon actually have a linear arrangement? Explain your answer.

7. A general rule for a group of hydrocarbon isomers is that as the amount of branching increases, the boiling point decreases. Explain why this would be true.

8. Name the five structural isomers of C_6H_{14}.

9. Draw the structural formula for each of the following.
   a. 3-isobutylhexane
   b. 2,2,4-trimethylpentane, also called *isooctane*. This substance is the reference (100 level) for octane ratings.
   c. 2-*tert*-butylpentane
   d. The names given in parts a and c are incorrect. Give the correct names for these hydrocarbons.

10. Draw the structure for 4-ethyl-2,3-diisopropylpentane. This name is incorrect. Give the correct systematic name.

11. Name each of the following.

   a. CH₃—C(CH₃)—CH₂—CH—CH₂—CH₃ with CH₃ above and CH₃ below

   a. $CH_3-\underset{\underset{CH_3}{|}}{\overset{\overset{CH_3}{|}}{C}}-CH_2-\underset{\underset{CH_3}{|}}{CH}-CH_2-CH_3$

   b. $\underset{\underset{CH_3}{|}}{CH_2}-CH_2-CH_2-\underset{\underset{CH_3}{|}}{CH}-CH_2-CH_2-\underset{\underset{CH_3}{|}}{CH_2}$

   c. $CH_3-\underset{\underset{CH_3}{|}}{\overset{\overset{CH_3}{|}}{C}}-CH_2-\underset{\underset{CH_3}{|}}{\overset{\overset{CH_3}{|}}{C}}-CH_3$

   d. $CH_3-\underset{\underset{CH_2-CH_3}{|}}{\overset{\overset{CH_2-CH_3}{|}}{C}}-CH_2-CH_2-CH_2-CH_2-CH_3$

12. Name each of the following cyclic alkanes, and indicate the formula of the compound.

   a. (cyclobutane)—CHCH₃ with CH₃ below

   b. (cyclopentane with CH₃, —CCH₃(CH₃), CH₃ substituents)

   c. (cyclohexane with CH₃, CH₂CH₂CH₃, —CH₃)

13. Name each of the following alkenes or alkynes.
   a. $CH_2{=}CH-CH_2-CH_3$

   b. $\underset{CH_3}{\overset{CH_3}{>}}C{=}CH-CH_3$

   c. $CH_3CH_2CH-CH{=}CH-CH\underset{CH_3}{\overset{CH_3}{<}}$ with CH₃ above the first CH

   d. $CH_2{=}\underset{\underset{CH_3}{|}}{C}-\underset{\underset{CH_2-CH_3}{|}}{CH}-CH_3$

   e. (cyclopentene with CH₃ and CH₂CH₃)

   f. (cyclobutene with CH₃ and —CH₂CH₃)

   g. $C{\equiv}C-\underset{\underset{CH_3}{|}}{CH}-CH_3$ with CH₃ above

14. Give the structure for each of the following.
   a. 3-hexene
   b. 2,4-heptadiene
   c. 2-methyl-3-octene
   d. 4-methyl-1-pentyne

15. Name each of the following.
   a. Cl—CH₂—CH₂—CH—CH₃
                          |
                          Cl

   b. CH₃CH₂CH₂CCl₃

   c.

   d. CH₂FCH₂F

   e. CH₃CHCH=CH₂
              |
              I

   f. CH₃ Br

   g. CH₃ Br

   h. CH₃ Br

16. Give the structure for each of the following aromatic hydrocarbons.
   a. *o*-ethyltoluene
   b. *p*-di-*tert*-butylbenzene
   c. *m*-diethylbenzene
   d. 1-phenyl-2-butene

17. Cumene is the starting material for the industrial production of acetone and phenol. The structure of cumene is

   Give the systematic name for cumene.

Isomerism

18. Distinguish between isomerism and resonance. Distinguish between structural and geometric isomerism.

19. A confused student was doing an isomer problem and listed the following six names as different structural isomers of C₇H₁₆.
   a. 1-*sec*-butylpropane
   b. 4-methylhexane
   c. 2-ethylpentane
   d. 1-ethyl-1-methylbutane
   e. 3-methylhexane
   f. 4-ethylpentane

   How many different structural isomers are actually present in these six names?

20. There is only one compound that is named 1,2-dichloroethane, but there are two distinct compounds that can be named 1,2-dichloroethene. Why?

21. Which of the compounds in Exercise 13 exhibit *cis–trans* isomerism?

22. Which of the compounds in Exercise 14 exhibit *cis–trans* isomerism?

23. Consider the following four structures:

   a. Which of these compounds have the same physical properties (melting point, boiling point, density, and so on)?
   b. Which of these compounds are *trans* isomers?
   c. Which of these compounds do not exhibit *cis–trans* isomerism?

24. Alkenes and cycloalkanes are structural isomers of each other. Give an example of each using C₄H₈. Another common feature of alkenes and cycloalkanes is that both have restricted rotation about one or more bonds in the compound, so both can exhibit *cis–trans* isomerism. What is required for an alkene or cycloalkane to exhibit *cis–trans* isomerism?

25. *Cis–trans* isomerism is also possible in molecules with rings. Draw the *cis* and *trans* isomers of 1,2-dimethylcyclohexane.

26. Draw the following.
   a. *cis*-2-hexene
   b. *trans*-2-butene
   c. *cis*-2,3-dichloro-2-pentene

27. Draw all the structural and geometric (*cis–trans*) isomers of C₃H₅Cl.

28. Draw all the structural and geometric (*cis–trans*) isomers of C₄H₇F. (*Hint:* Refer to Exercise 25.)

29. Draw all the structural isomers of C₅H₁₀. Ignore any cyclic isomers. Which of the structural isomers exhibit *cis–trans* isomerism?

30. Draw all the structural and geometric (*cis–trans*) isomers of bromochloropropene.

31. Name the following compounds.
   a.

c.

32. If one hydrogen in a hydrocarbon is replaced by a halogen atom, the number of isomers that exist for the substituted compound depends on the number of types of hydrogen in the original hydrocarbon. Thus there is only one form of chloroethane (all hydrogens in ethane are equivalent), but there are two isomers of propane that arise from the substitution of a methyl hydrogen or a methylene hydrogen. How many isomers can be obtained when one hydrogen in each of the compounds named below is replaced by a chlorine atom?
   a. *n*-pentane
   b. 2-methylbutane
   c. 2,4-dimethylpentane
   d. methylcyclobutane

33. There are three isomers of dichlorobenzene, one of which has now replaced naphthalene as the main constituent of mothballs.
   a. Identify the *ortho, meta,* and *para* isomers of dichlorobenzene.
   b. Predict the number of isomers for trichlorobenzene.
   c. The presence of one chlorine atom on a benzene ring will cause the next substituent to add *ortho* or *para* to the first chlorine atom on the benzene ring. What does this tell you about the synthesis of *m*-dichlorobenzene?
   d. Which of the isomers of trichlorobenzene will be the hardest to prepare?

34. Polychlorinated dibenzo-*p*-dioxins, or PCDDs, are highly toxic substances that are present in trace amounts as byproducts of some chemical manufacturing processes. They have been implicated in a number of environmental incidents—for example, the chemical contamination at Love Canal and the herbicide spraying in Vietnam. The structure of dibenzo-*p*-dioxin, along with the customary numbering convention, is

The most toxic PCDD is 2,3,7,8-tetrachloro-dibenzo-*p*-dioxin. Draw the structure of this compound. Also draw the structures of two other isomers containing four chlorine atoms.

Functional Groups

35. Carboxylic acids are often written as RCOOH. What does —COOH indicate, and what does R indicate? Aldehydes are sometimes written as RCHO. What does —CHO indicate?

36. Alcohols and ethers are structural isomers of each other, as are aldehydes and ketones. Give an example of each to illustrate. Which functional group in Table 21.4 can be structural isomers of carboxylic acids?

37. Identify each of the following compounds as a carboxylic acid, ester, ketone, aldehyde, or amine.
   a. anthraquinone, an important starting material in the manufacture of dyes:

   b.
   c. HO—C—CH$_2$CHCH$_3$
   d.

38. Identify the functional groups present in the following compounds.

   a.
   Testosterone

   b. Vanillin

   c. Aspartame

39. Mimosine is a natural product found in large quantities in the seeds and foliage of some legume plants. It has been shown to cause inhibition of hair growth as well as hair loss in mice.

Mimosine ($C_8H_{10}N_2O_4$)

a. What functional groups are present in mimosine?
b. Give the hybridization of the eight carbon atoms in mimosine.
c. How many σ and π bonds are found in mimosine?

40. Minoxidil ($C_9H_{15}N_5O$) is a compound produced by the Pharmacia & Upjohn Company that has been approved as a treatment for some types of male pattern baldness.

a. Would minoxidil be more soluble in acidic or basic aqueous solution? Explain.
b. Give the hybridization of the five nitrogen atoms in minoxidil.
c. Give the hybridization of each of the nine carbon atoms in minoxidil.
d. Give approximate values for the bond angles marked $a, b, c, d, e,$ and f.
e. Including all the hydrogen atoms, how many σ bonds exist in minoxidil?
f. How many π bonds exist in minoxidil?

41. For each of the following alcohols, give the systematic name and specify whether the alcohol is primary, secondary, or tertiary.

a. CH₃CHCH₂CH₂
$\quad\quad$ |$\quad\quad\quad\quad$|
$\quad\quad$ Cl (above), OH (below)

Cl
|
a. CH₃CHCH₂CH₂
$\quad\quad\quad\quad\quad$ |
$\quad\quad\quad\quad\quad$ OH

$\quad\quad$ CH₂CH₂CH₃
$\quad\quad\quad$ |
b. CH₃CCH₂CH₃
$\quad\quad\quad$ |
$\quad\quad\quad$ OH

c.

42. Draw structural formulas for each of the following alcohols. Indicate whether the alcohol is primary, secondary, or tertiary.
a. 1-butanol
b. 2-butanol
c. 2-methyl-1-butanol
d. 2-methyl-2-butanol

43. Name all the alcohols that have the formula $C_5H_{12}O$. How many ethers have the formula $C_5H_{12}O$?

44. Name all the aldehydes and ketones that have the formula $C_5H_{10}O$.

45. Name the following compounds.

Cl$\quad$O
|$\quad\quad$||
a. CH₃CHCHCCH₂
$\quad\quad$ |$\quad\quad$|
$\quad\quad$ Cl$\quad$CH₃

O$\quad$CH₂CH₃
||$\quad\quad$|
b. HCCHCHCH₃
$\quad\quad\quad$ |
$\quad\quad\quad$ CH₃

46. Name the following compounds.

$\quad\quad\quad\quad\quad\quad$O
$\quad\quad\quad\quad\quad\quad$||
a. Cl—⟨ ⟩—C—OH

$\quad\quad\quad\quad$ CH₃$\quad$O
$\quad\quad\quad\quad$ |$\quad\quad$||
b. CH₃CH₂CHCH—C—OH
$\quad\quad\quad\quad\quad\quad$ |
$\quad\quad\quad\quad\quad\quad$ CH₂CH₂CH₃

c. HCOOH

47. Draw the structural formula for each of the following.
a. formaldehyde (methanal)
b. 4-heptanone
c. 3-chlorobutanal
d. 5,5-dimethyl-2-hexanone

48. Draw a structural formula for each of the following.
a. 3-methylpentanoic acid
b. ethyl methanoate
c. methyl benzoate
d. 3-chloro-2,4-dimethylhexanoic acid

49. Draw the isomer(s) specified. There may be more than one possible isomer for each part.
a. a cyclic compound that is an isomer of trans-2-butene
b. an ester that is an isomer of propanoic acid
c. a ketone that is an isomer of butanal
d. a secondary amine that is an isomer of butylamine
e. a tertiary amine that is an isomer of butylamine
f. an ether that is an isomer of 2-methyl-2-propanol
g. a secondary alcohol that is an isomer of 2-methyl-2-propanol

50. Which of the following statements is (are) false? Explain why the statement(s) is (are) false.

$\quad\quad\quad\quad\quad\quad\quad\quad$ O
$\quad\quad\quad\quad\quad\quad\quad\quad$ ||
a. CH₃CH₂CH₂COCH₃ is a structural isomer of pentanoic acid.

$\quad\quad\quad$ O$\quad\quad\quad\quad$CH₃
$\quad\quad\quad$ ||$\quad\quad\quad\quad$|
b. HCCH₂CH₂CHCH₃ is a structural isomer of 2-methyl-3-pentanone.

c. CH₃CH₂OCH₂CH₂CH₃ is a structural isomer of 2-pentanol.

d. CH₂=CHCHCH₃ is a structural isomer of 2-butenal.
$\quad\quad\quad\quad\quad$ |
$\quad\quad\quad\quad\quad$ OH

e. Trimethylamine is a structural isomer of CH₃CH₂CH₂NH₂.

51. The following organic compounds cannot exist. Why?
    a. 2-chloro-2-butyne
    b. 2-methyl-2-propanone
    c. 1,1-dimethylbenzene
    d. 2-pentanal
    e. 3-hexanoic acid
    f. 5,5-dibromo-1-cyclobutanol

52. Mycomycin is a naturally occurring antibiotic produced by the fungus *Nocardia acidophilus*. The molecular formula of the substance is $C_{13}H_{10}O_2$, and its systematic name is 3,5,7,8-tridecatetraene-10,12-diynoic acid. Draw the structure of mycomycin.

Reactions of Organic Compounds

53. Distinguish between substitution and addition reactions. Give an example of each type.

54. Alkanes and aromatics are fairly stable compounds. To make them react, a special catalyst must be present. What catalyst must be present when reacting Cl_2 with an alkane or with benzene? Adding Cl_2 to an alkene or alkyne does not require a special catalyst. Why are alkenes and alkynes more reactive than alkanes and aromatic compounds?

55. The following are some other organic reactions covered in Section 21.4. Give an example to illustrate each type of reaction.
    a. Adding H_2O to an alkene (in the presence of H^+) yields an alcohol.
    b. Primary alcohols are oxidized to aldehydes, which can be further oxidized to carboxylic acids.
    c. Secondary alcohols are oxidized to ketones.
    d. Reacting an alcohol with a carboxylic acid (in the presence of H^+) produces an ester.

56. In the presence of light, chlorine can substitute for one (or more) of the hydrogens in an alkane. For the following reactions, draw the possible monochlorination products.
    a. 2,2-dimethylpropane + Cl_2 $\xrightarrow{hv}$
    b. 1,3-dimethylcyclobutane + Cl_2 $\xrightarrow{hv}$
    c. 2,3-dimethylbutane + Cl_2 $\xrightarrow{hv}$

57. Complete the following reactions.
    a. $CH_3CH{=}CHCH_3 + H_2 \xrightarrow{Pt}$
    b. $CH_2{=}CHCHCH{=}CH + 2Cl_2 \longrightarrow$

    with CH₃ and CH₃ substituents below

    c. $+ Cl_2 \xrightarrow{FeCl_3}$

    d. $CH_3C{=}CH_2 + O_2 \xrightarrow{Spark}$

    with CH₃ substituent below

58. Reagents such as HCl, HBr, and HOH (H_2O) can add across carbon–carbon double and triple bonds, with H forming a bond to one of the carbon atoms in the multiple bond and Cl, Br, or OH forming a bond to the other carbon atom in the multiple bond. In some cases,

two products are possible. For the major organic product, the addition occurs so that the hydrogen atom in the reagent attaches to the carbon atom in the multiple bond that already has the greater number of hydrogen atoms bonded to it. With this rule in mind, draw the structure of the major product in each of the following reactions.

a. $CH_3CH_2CH{=}CH_2 + H_2O \xrightarrow{H^+}$
b. $CH_3CH_2CH{=}CH_2 + HBr \longrightarrow$
c. $CH_3CH_2C{\equiv}CH + 2HBr \longrightarrow$
d. (cyclopentene with CH₃) $+ H_2O \xrightarrow{H^+}$
e. (alkene with CH_3CH_2, CH_3, CH_3, H groups) $+ HCl \longrightarrow$

59. Why is it preferable to produce chloroethane by the reaction of HCl(g) with ethene than by the reaction of $Cl_2(g)$ with ethane? (See Exercise 58.)

60. Give an example reaction that would yield the following products. Name the organic reactant and product in each reaction.
    a. alkane
    b. monohalogenated alkane
    c. dihalogenated alkane
    d. tetrahalogenated alkane
    e. monohalogenated benzene
    f. alkene

61. Using appropriate reactants, alcohols can be oxidized into aldehydes, ketones, and/or carboxylic acids. Primary alcohols can be oxidized into aldehydes, which can then be oxidized into carboxylic acids. Secondary alcohols can be oxidized into ketones. Tertiary alcohols do not undergo this type of oxidation. Give the structure of the product(s) resulting from the oxidation of each of the following alcohols.
    a. 3-methyl-1-butanol
    b. 3-methyl-2-butanol
    c. 2-methyl-2-butanol
    d. (benzene ring with CH₂ bearing OH)
    e. (cyclohexane ring with OH and CH₃)
    f. (cyclohexane ring with HO, OH, CH₃, CH₂, OH groups)

62. Oxidation of an aldehyde yields a carboxylic acid:

$$R{-}\overset{O}{\overset{\|}{C}}H \xrightarrow{[ox]} R{-}\overset{O}{\overset{\|}{C}}{-}OH$$

Draw the structures for the products of the following oxidation reactions.

a. propanal $\xrightarrow{[ox]}$

b. 2,3-dimethylpentanal $\xrightarrow{[ox]}$

c. 3-ethylbenzaldehyde $\xrightarrow{[ox]}$

63. Three different organic compounds have the formula C_3H_8O. Only two of these isomers react with $KMnO_4$ (a strong oxidizing agent). What are the names of the products when these isomers react with excess $KMnO_4$?

64. Give an example reaction that would yield the following products as major organic products. See Exercises 58 and 61 for some hints. For oxidation reactions, just write *oxidation* over the arrow and don't worry about the actual reagent.
    a. primary alcohol
    b. secondary alcohol
    c. tertiary alcohol
    d. aldehyde
    e. ketone
    f. carboxylic acid
    g. ester

65. How would you synthesize each of the following?
    a. 1,2-dibromopropane from propene
    b. acetone (2-propanone) from an alcohol
    c. *tert*-butyl alcohol (2-methyl-2-propanol) from an alkene (see Exercise 58)
    d. propanoic acid from an alcohol

66. What tests could you perform to distinguish between the following pairs of compounds?
    a. $CH_3CH_2CH_2CH_3$, $CH_2{=}CHCH_2CH_3$
    b.
    $CH_3CH_2CH_2COOH$, $CH_3CH_2\overset{\overset{\displaystyle O}{\|}}{C}CH_3$
    c.
    $CH_3CH_2CH_2OH$, $CH_3\overset{\overset{\displaystyle O}{\|}}{C}CH_3$
    d. $CH_3CH_2NH_2$, CH_3OCH_3

67. Complete the following reactions.
    a. $CH_3CO_2H + CH_3OH \rightarrow$
    b. $CH_3CH_2CH_2OH + HCOOH \rightarrow$

68. How would you synthesize the following esters?
    a. *n*-octylacetate
    b. $CH_3CH_2CH_2CH_2CH_2CH_2O{-}\overset{\overset{\displaystyle O}{\|}}{C}CH_2CH_3$

Polymers

69. Define and give an example of each of the following.
    a. addition polymer
    b. condensation polymer
    c. copolymer
    d. homopolymer
    e. polyester
    f. polyamide

70. What is polystyrene? The following processes result in a stronger polystyrene polymer. Explain why in each case.
    a. addition of catalyst to form syndiotactic polystyrene
    b. addition of 1,3-butadiene and sulfur
    c. producing long chains of polystyrene
    d. addition of a catalyst to make linear polystyrene

71. Answer the following questions regarding the formation of polymers.
    a. What structural features must be present in a monomer in order to form a homopolymer polyester?
    b. What structural features must be present in the monomers in order to form a copolymer polyamide? (*Hint:* Nylon is an example of a polyamide. When the monomers link together to form nylon, an amide functional group results from each linkage.)
    c. What structural features must be present in a monomer that can form both an addition polymer and a condensation polymer?

72. What monomer(s) must be used to produce the following polymers?

e.

f.

(This polymer is Kodel, used to make fibers of stain-resistant carpeting.)

Classify these polymers as condensation or addition polymers. Which are copolymers?

73. Kel-F is a polymer with the structure

$$\left(\begin{array}{c} \overset{F}{\underset{Cl}{|}}\,\overset{F}{\underset{F}{|}}\,\overset{F}{\underset{Cl}{|}}\,\overset{F}{\underset{F}{|}}\,\overset{F}{\underset{Cl}{|}}\,\overset{F}{\underset{F}{|}} \\ C{-}C{-}C{-}C{-}C{-}C \end{array}\right)_n$$

What is the monomer for Kel-F?

74. The polymer nitrile is a copolymer made from acrylonitrile and butadiene; it is used to make automotive hoses and gaskets. Draw the structure of nitrile. (*Hint:* See Table 21.7.)

75. Polyaramid is a term applied to polyamides containing aromatic groups. These polymers were originally made for use as tire cords but have since found many other uses.
    a. Kevlar is used in bulletproof vests and many high-strength composites. The structure of Kevlar is

    Which monomers are used to make Kevlar?
    b. Nomex is a polyaramid used in fire-resistant clothing. It is a copolymer of

    Draw the structure of the Nomex polymer. How do the structures of Kevlar and Nomex differ?

76. The polyester formed from lactic acid,

    $$CH_3-CH-CO_2H$$
    $$\quad\quad\quad | $$
    $$\quad\quad\quad OH$$

    is used for tissue implants and surgical sutures that will dissolve in the body. Draw the structure of a portion of this polymer.

77. "Super glue" contains methyl cyanoacrylate,

    which readily polymerizes on exposure to traces of water or alcohols on the surfaces to be bonded together. The polymer provides a strong bond between the two surfaces. Draw the structure of the polymer formed by methyl cyanoacrylate.

78. Isoprene is the repeating unit in natural rubber. The structure of isoprene is

    $$\overset{\quad\quad CH_3}{\underset{}{CH_2=C-CH=CH_2}}$$

    a. Give a systematic name for isoprene.
    b. When isoprene is polymerized, two polymers of the form

    $$\left(\overset{\quad CH_3}{\underset{}{CH_2-C=CH-CH_2}}\right)_n$$

    are possible. In natural rubber, the *cis* configuration is found. The polymer with the *trans* configuration around the double bond is called gutta percha and was once used in the manufacture of golf balls. Draw the structure of natural rubber and gutta percha showing three repeating units and the configuration around the carbon–carbon double bonds.

79. Polystyrene can be made more rigid by copolymerizing styrene with divinylbenzene,

    What purpose does the divinylbenzene serve? Why is the copolymer more rigid?

80. Polyimides are polymers that are tough and stable at temperatures up to 400°C. They are used as a protective coating on the quartz fibers in fiber optics. What monomers are used to make the following polyimide?

81. Polycarbonates are a class of thermoplastic polymers that are used in the plastic lenses of eyeglasses and in the shells of bicycle helmets. A polycarbonate is made from the reaction of bisphenol A (BPA) with phosgene ($COCl_2$):

    BPA

    $$\xrightarrow{\text{Catalyst}} \text{polycarbonate} + 2n\text{HCl}$$

    Phenol (C_6H_5OH) is used to terminate the polymer (stop its growth).
    a. Draw the structure of the polycarbonate chain formed in the above reaction.
    b. Is this reaction a condensation or an addition polymerization?

82. In which polymer, polyethylene or polyvinyl chloride, would you expect to find the stronger intermolecular forces, assuming that the average chain lengths are equal?

83. When acrylic polymers are burned, toxic fumes are produced. For example, in many airplane fires, more passenger deaths have been caused by breathing toxic fumes than by the fire itself. Using polyacrylonitrile as an example, what would you expect to be one of the most toxic, gaseous combustion products created in the reaction?

84. Polyesters containing double bonds are often crosslinked by reacting the polymer with styrene. This type of reaction is common in the manufacture of fiberglass.
    a. Draw the structure of the copolymer of
       $$HO—CH_2CH_2—OH \quad \text{and}$$
       $$HO_2C—CH=CH—CO_2H$$
    b. Draw the structure of the crosslinked polymer (after the polyester has been reacted with styrene).

85. Another way of producing highly crosslinked polyesters (see Exercise 84) is to use glycerol. Alkyd resins are a polymer of this type. The polymer forms very tough coatings when baked onto a surface and is used in paints for automobiles and large appliances. Draw the structure of the polymer formed from the condensation of

Glycerol   Phthalic acid

Explain how individual polymer chains could be crosslinked.

Natural Polymers

86. In Section 21.6 three important classes of biologically important natural polymers are discussed. What are the three classes, what are the monomers used to form the polymers, and why are they biologically important?

87. Give the general formula for an amino acid. Some amino acids are labeled hydrophilic and some are labeled hydrophobic. What do these terms refer to?

88. Distinguish between the primary, secondary, and tertiary structures of a protein. Give examples of the types of forces that maintain each type of structure.

89. Describe how denaturation affects the function of a protein.

90. Aqueous solutions of amino acids are buffered solutions. Why?

91. Which of the amino acids in Fig. 21.18 contain the following functional groups in their R group?
    a. alcohol   c. amine
    b. carboxylic acid   d. amide

92. When pure crystalline amino acids are heated, decomposition generally occurs before the solid melts. Account for this observation. (*Hint:* Crystalline amino acids exist as $H_3\overset{+}{N}CRHCOO^-$, called zwitterions.)

93. Aspartame, the artificial sweetener marketed under the name NutraSweet, is a methyl ester of a dipeptide. The structure of aspartame is

    a. What two amino acids are used to prepare aspartame?
    b. There is concern that methanol may be produced by the decomposition of aspartame. From what portion of the molecule can methanol be produced? Write an equation for this reaction.

94. Glutathione, a tripeptide found in virtually all cells, functions as a reducing agent. The structure of glutathione is

What amino acids make up glutathione?

95. Draw the structures of the two dipeptides that can be formed from serine and alanine.

96. Draw the structures of the tripeptides gly-ala-ser and ser-ala-gly. How many other tripeptides are possible using these three amino acids?

97. Write the sequence of all possible tetrapeptides composed of the following amino acids.
    a. two phenylalanines and two glycines
    b. two phenylalanines, glycine, and alanine

98. How many different pentapeptides can be formed using five different amino acids?

99. What types of interactions can occur between the side chains of the following amino acids that would help maintain the tertiary structure of a protein?
    a. cysteine and cysteine
    b. glutamine and serine
    c. glutamic acid and lysine
    d. proline and leucine

100. Give examples of amino acids that could give rise to the interactions pictured in Fig. 21.25 that maintain the tertiary structures of proteins.

101. Oxygen is carried from the lungs to tissues by the protein hemoglobin in red blood cells. Sickle cell anemia is a disease resulting from abnormal hemoglobin molecules in which a valine is substituted for a single glutamic acid in normal hemoglobin. How might this substitution affect the structure of hemoglobin?

102. All amino acids have at least two functional groups with acidic or basic properties. In alanine the carboxylic acid group has $K_a = 4.5 \times 10^{-3}$ and the amino group has $K_b = 7.4 \times 10^{-5}$. Three ions of alanine are possible when alanine is dissolved in water. Which of these ions would predominate in a solution with $[H^+] = 1.0\ M$? in a solution with $[OH^-] = 1.0\ M$?

103. Monosodium glutamate (MSG) is commonly used as a flavoring in foods. Draw the structure of MSG.

104. Over 100 different kinds of mutant hemoglobin molecules have been detected in humans. Unlike sickle cell anemia (see Exercise 101), not all of these mutations are as serious. In one nonlethal mutation, glutamine substitutes for a single glutamic acid in normal hemoglobin. Rationalize why this substitution is nonlethal.

105. Draw cyclic structures for D-ribose and D-mannose.

106. Indicate the chiral carbon atoms found in the monosaccharides D-ribose and D-mannose.

107. In addition to using *numerical* prefixes in the general names of sugars to indicate how many carbon atoms are present, we sometimes use the prefixes *keto-* and *aldo-* to indicate whether the sugar is a ketone or an aldehyde. For example, the monosaccharide fructose is often called a *ketohexose* to emphasize that it contains six carbons as well as the ketone functional group. For each of the monosaccharides shown in Table 21.8, classify the sugars as aldohexoses, aldopentoses, ketohexoses, or ketopentoses.

108. Glucose can occur in three forms: two cyclic forms and one open-chain structure. In aqueous solution, only a tiny fraction of the glucose is in the open-chain form. Yet tests for the presence of glucose depend on reaction with the aldehyde group, which is found only in the open-chain form. Explain why these tests work.

109. What is a *disaccharide*? What monosaccharide units make up the dissacharide sucrose? What is the bond called that forms between the monosaccharide units?

110. Cows can digest cellulose, but humans can't. Why not?

111. What are the structural differences between α- and β-glucose? Each of these two cyclic forms of glucose is the building block to form two different polymers. Explain.

112. What is optical isomerism? What do you look for to determine whether an organic compound exhibits optical isomerism? 1-bromo-1-chloroethane is optically active, whereas 1-bromo-2-chloroethane is not optically active. Explain.

113. Which of the amino acids in Fig. 21.18 contain more than one chiral carbon atom? Draw the structures of these amino acids, and indicate all chiral carbon atoms.

114. Why is glycine not optically active?

115. Which of the noncyclic isomers of bromochloropropene is (are) optically active?

116. How many chiral carbon atoms does the following structure have?

117. The compounds adenine, guanine, cytosine, and thymine are called the nucleic acid bases. What structural features in these compounds make them bases?

118. Describe the structural differences between DNA and RNA. Describe the complementary base pairing between the two individual strands of DNA that forms the overall double-helical structure. How is complementary base pairing involved in the replication of the DNA molecule during cell division?

119. Part of a certain DNA sequence is G-G-T-C-T-A-T-A-C. What is the complementary sequence?

120. The codons (words) in DNA that identify which amino acid should be in a protein are three bases long. How many such three-letter words can be made from the four bases adenine, cytosine, guanine, and thymine?

121. Which base will hydrogen-bond with uracil within an RNA molecule? Draw the structure of this base pair.

122. Tautomers are molecules that differ in the position of a hydrogen atom. A tautomeric form of thymine has the structure

If this tautomer, rather than the stable form of thymine, were present in a strand of DNA during replication, what would be the result?

123. The base sequences in mRNA that code for certain amino acids are
Glu: GAA, GAG
Val: GUU, GUC, GUA, GUG
Met: AUG
Trp: UGG
Phe: UUU, UUC
Asp: GAU, GAC

These sequences are complementary to the sequences in DNA.
a. Give the corresponding sequences in DNA for the amino acids listed above.
b. Give a DNA sequence that would code for the peptide trp-glu-phe-met.
c. How many different DNA sequences can code for the peptide in part b?
d. What is the peptide that is produced from the DNA sequence T-A-C-C-T-G-A-A-G?
e. What other DNA sequences would yield the same tripeptide as in part d?

124. The change of a single base in the DNA sequence for normal hemoglobin can encode for the abnormal hemoglobin, giving rise to sickle cell anemia. Which base in the codon for glu in DNA is replaced to give the codon(s) for val? (See Exercises 101 and 123.)

125. The deletion of a single base from a DNA molecule can be a fatal mutation. Substitution of one base for another is often not as serious a mutation. Why?

126. The average molar mass of one base pair of nucleotides in DNA is approximately 600 g/mol. The spacing between successive base pairs is about 0.34 nm, and a complete turn in the helical structure of DNA occurs about every 3.4 nm. If a DNA molecule has a molar mass of 4.5×10^9 g/mol, approximately how many complete turns exist in the DNA α-helix structure?

Additional Exercises

127. Is octanoic acid more soluble in 1 *M* HCl, 1 *M* NaOH, or pure water? Explain. Drugs such as morphine ($C_{17}H_{19}O_3N$) are often treated with strong acids. The most commonly used form of morphine is morphine hydrochloride ($C_{17}H_{20}O_3NCl$). Why is morphine treated in this way? (*Hint:* Morphine is an amine.)

128. Sorbic acid is used to prevent mold and fungus growth in some food products, especially cheeses. The systematic name for sorbic acid is 2,4-hexadienoic acid. Draw structures for the four geometric isomers of sorbic acid.

129. When toluene ($C_6H_5CH_3$) reacts with chlorine gas in the presence of an iron(III) catalyst, the product is a mixture of the *ortho* and *para* isomers of $C_6H_4ClCH_3$. However, when the reaction is light-catalyzed with no Fe^{3+} catalyst present, the product is $C_6H_5CH_2Cl$. Explain.

130. Consider the reaction to produce the ester methyl acetate:

$$CH_3OH + CH_3\overset{O}{\overset{\|}{C}}OH \longrightarrow CH_3\overset{O}{\overset{\|}{C}}OCH_3 + H_2O$$
Methyl
acetate

When this reaction is carried out with CH_3OH containing radioactive oxygen-18, the water produced does not contain oxygen-18. Explain the results of this radioisotope tracer experiment.

131. A compound containing only carbon and hydrogen is 85.63% C by mass. Reaction of this compound with H_2O produces a secondary alcohol as the major product and a primary alcohol as the minor product (see Exercise 58). If the molar mass of the hydrocarbon is between 50 g/mol and 60 g/mol, name the compound.

132. Poly(lauryl methacrylate) is used as an additive in motor oils to counter the loss of viscosity at high temperature. The structure is

$$\left(\begin{array}{c} CH_3 \\ | \\ +C-CH_2 \\ | \\ C \\ \diagup \diagdown \\ O \quad O-(CH_2)_{11}CH_3 \end{array} \right)_{\!n}$$

The long hydrocarbon chain of poly(lauryl methacrylate) makes the polymer soluble in oil (a mixture of hydrocarbons with mostly 12 or more carbon atoms). At low temperatures the polymer is coiled into balls. At higher temperatures the balls uncoil and the polymer exists as long chains. Explain how this helps control the viscosity of oil.

133. Ethylene oxide, $\quad \overset{\displaystyle CH_2-CH_2}{\diagdown \underset{O}{\diagup}}$

is an important industrial chemical. Although most ethers are unreactive, ethylene oxide is quite reactive. It resembles C_2H_4 in its reactions in that many addition reactions occur across the C—O bond.

a. Why is ethylene oxide so reactive? (*Hint:* Consider the bond angles in ethylene oxide as compared with those predicted by the VSEPR model.)

b. Ethylene oxide undergoes addition polymerization, forming a polymer used in many applications requiring a non-ionic surfactant. Draw the structure of this polymer.

134. The Amoco Chemical Company has successfully raced a car with a plastic engine. Many of the engine parts, including piston skirts, connecting rods, and valve-train components, are made of a polymer called *Torlon*:

What monomers are used to make this polymer?

135. A urethane linkage occurs when an alcohol adds across the carbon–nitrogen double bond in an isocyanate:

$$R-O-H + O=C=N-R' \longrightarrow RO-\overset{O}{\overset{\|}{C}}-\underset{H}{\overset{\displaystyle}{N}}-R'$$

Alcohol   Isocyanate   Urethane

Polyurethanes are formed from the copolymerization of a diol with a diisocyanate. Polyurethanes are used in foamed insulation and a variety of other construction materials. What is the structure of the polyurethane formed by the following reaction?

$$HOCH_2CH_2OH + O=C=N \underset{\diagdown}{} \overset{\displaystyle}{\bigcirc} \underset{\diagup}{} N=C=O \longrightarrow$$

136. Stretch a rubber band while holding it gently to your lips. Then slowly let it relax while still in contact with your lips.

a. What happens to the temperature of the rubber band on stretching?

b. Is the stretching an exothermic or endothermic process?

c. Explain the above result in terms of intermolecular forces.

d. What is the sign of ΔS and ΔG for stretching the rubber band?

e. Give the molecular explanation for the sign of ΔS for stretching.

137. Consider the compounds butanoic acid, pentanal, *n*-hexane, and 1-pentanol. The boiling points of these compounds (in no specific order) are 69°C, 103°C, 137°C, and 164°C. Match the boiling points to the correct compound.

138. Consider the following five compounds.

a. $CH_3CH_2CH_2CH_2CH_3$

b.
$$\underset{CH_3CH_2CH_2CH_2}{\overset{\overset{\displaystyle OH}{|}}{}}$$

c. $CH_3CH_2CH_2CH_2CH_2CH_3$

d.
$$\underset{CH_3CH_2CH_2CH}{\overset{\overset{\displaystyle O}{\|}}{}}$$

e.
$$CH_3\overset{\overset{\displaystyle CH_3}{|}}{\underset{\underset{\displaystyle CH_3}{|}}{C}}CH_3$$

The boiling points of these five compounds are 9.5°C, 36°C, 69°C, 76°C, and 117°C. Which compound boils at 36°C? Explain.

139. Consider the following polymer:

Is this polymer a homopolymer or a copolymer, and is it formed by addition polymerization or condensation polymerization? What is (are) the monomer(s) for this polymer?

140. For the following formulas, what types of isomerism could be exhibited? For each formula, give an example that illustrates the specific type of isomerism. The types of isomerism are structural, geometric, and optical.

a. C_6H_{12} b. $C_5H_{12}O$ c. $C_6H_4Br_2$

141. What is wrong with the following names? Give the correct name for each compound.

a. 2-ethylpropane
b. 5-iodo-5,6-dimethylhexane
c. *cis*-4-methyl-3-pentene
d. 2-bromo-3-butanol

142. a. Use bond energies (Table 13.6) to estimate ΔH for the reaction of two molecules of glycine to form a peptide linkage.
b. Would you predict ΔS to favor the formation of peptide linkages between two molecules of glycine?
c. Would you predict the formation of proteins to be a spontaneous process?

143. The reaction to form a phosphate–ester linkage between two nucleotides can be approximated as follows:

Would you predict the formation of a dinucleotide from two nucleotides to be a spontaneous process?

144. Considering your answers to Exercises 142 and 143, how can you justify the existence of proteins and nucleic acids in light of the second law of thermodynamics?

145. The structure of tartaric acid is

$$HO_2C\overset{\overset{\displaystyle OH}{|}}{-}CH\overset{\overset{\displaystyle OH}{|}}{-}CH-CO_2H$$

a. Is the form of tartaric acid pictured below optically active? Explain.

$$HOOC\overset{\overset{\displaystyle OH\ \ OH}{|\ \ \ |}}{\underset{\underset{\displaystyle H\ \ \ H}{|\ \ \ |}}{C-C}}COOH$$

Note: The dashed lines show groups directed behind the plane of the page. The wedges show groups directed in front of the plane of the page.

b. Draw the optically active forms of tartaric acid.

146. In glycine, the carboxylic acid group has $K_a = 4.3 \times 10^{-3}$ and the amino group has $K_b = 6.0 \times 10^{-5}$. Use these equilibrium constant values to calculate the equilibrium constants for the following.

a. $^+H_3NCH_2CO_2^- + H_2O$
$$\rightleftharpoons H_2NCH_2CO_2^- + H_3O^+$$

b. $H_2NCH_2CO_2^- + H_2O$
$$\rightleftharpoons H_2NCH_2CO_2H + OH^-$$

c. $^+H_3NCH_2CO_2H \rightleftharpoons 2H^+ + H_2NCH_2CO_2^-$

147. The isoelectric point of an amino acid is the pH at which the molecule has no net charge. For glycine, that would be the pH at which virtually all glycine molecules are in the form $^+H_3NCH_2CO_2^-$. If we assume that the principal equilibrium is

$$2^+H_3NCH_2CO_2^-$$
$$\rightleftharpoons H_2NCH_2CO_2^- + {}^+H_3NCH_2CO_2H \qquad (i)$$

then at equilibrium

$$[H_2NCH_2CO_2^-] = [^+H_3NCH_2CO_2H] \qquad (ii)$$

Use this result and your answer to part c of Exercise 146 to calculate the pH at which Equation (ii) is true. This will be the isoelectric point of glycine.

148. Nylon is named according to the number of C atoms between the N atoms in the chain. Nylon-46 has 4 C atoms then 6 C atoms, and this pattern repeats. Nylon-6 always has 6 atoms in a row. Speculate as to why nylon-46 is stronger than nylon-6. (*Hint:* Consider the strengths of interchain forces.)

149. A chemical "breathalyzer" test works because ethyl alcohol in the breath is oxidized by the dichromate ion (orange) to form acetic acid and chromium(III) ion (green). The balanced reaction is

$$3C_2H_5OH(aq) + 2Cr_2O_7^{2-}(aq) + 2H^+(aq) \longrightarrow$$
$$3HC_2H_3O_2(aq) + 4Cr^{3+}(aq) + 11H_2O(l)$$

You analyze a breathalyzer test in which 4.2 mg of $K_2Cr_2O_7$ was reduced. Assuming the volume of the breath was 0.500 L at 30.°C and 750. mm Hg, what was the mole percent alcohol of the breath?

Challenge Problems

150. Alcohols are very useful starting materials for the production of many different compounds. The following conversions, starting with 1-butanol, can be carried out in two or more steps. Show the steps (reactants/catalysts) you would follow to carry out the conversions, drawing the formula for the organic product in each step. For each step, a major product must be produced.

    See Exercise 58. (*Hint:* In the presence of H^+, an alcohol is converted into an alkene and water. This is the exact reverse of the reaction of adding water to an alkene to form an alcohol.)
    a. 1-butanol $\longrightarrow$ butane
    b. 1-butanol $\longrightarrow$ 2-butanone

151. Consider a sample of a hydrocarbon at 0.959 atm and 298 K. Upon combusting the entire sample in oxygen, you collect a mixture of gaseous carbon dioxide and water vapor at 1.51 atm and 375 K. This mixture has a density of 1.391 g/L and occupies a volume four times as large as that of the pure hydrocarbon. Determine the molecular formula of the hydrocarbon and name it.

152. Using one of the Lewis structures for benzene (C_6H_6), estimate ΔH_f° for $C_6H_6(g)$ using bond energies and given that the standard enthalpy of formation of $C(g)$ is 717 kJ/mol. The experimental ΔH_f° value for $C_6H_6(g)$ is 83 kJ/mol. Explain the discrepancy between the experimental value and the calculated ΔH_f° value for $C_6H_6(g)$.

153. Consider the following reactions. For parts b–d, reference Exercise 58.
    a. When C_5H_{12} is reacted with $Cl_2(g)$ in the presence of ultraviolet light, four different monochlorination products form. What is the structure of C_5H_{12} in this reaction?
    b. When C_4H_8 is reacted with H_2O, a tertiary alcohol is produced as the major product. What is the structure of C_4H_8 in this reaction?
    c. When C_7H_{12} is reacted with HCl, 1-chloro-1-methylcyclohexane is produced as the major product. What are the two possible structures for C_7H_{12} in this reaction?
    d. When a hydrocarbon is reacted with H_2O and the major product of this reaction is then oxidized, acetone (2-propanone) is produced. What is the structure of the hydrocarbon in this reaction?
    e. When $C_5H_{12}O$ is oxidized, a carboxylic acid is produced. What are the possible structures for $C_5H_{12}O$ in this reaction?

154. ABS plastic is a tough, hard plastic used in applications requiring shock resistance. (See Section 21.5 of the text.) The polymer consists of three monomer units: acrylonitrile (C_3H_3N), butadiene (C_4H_6), and styrene (C_8H_8).
    a. Draw two repeating units of ABS plastic assuming the three monomer units react in a 1:1:1 mole ratio and react in the same order as the monomers previously listed.
    b. A sample of ABS plastic contains 8.80% N by mass. It took 0.605 g of Br_2 to react completely with a 1.20-g sample of ABS plastic. What is the percent by mass of acrylonitrile, butadiene, and styrene in this polymer sample?
    c. ABS plastic does not react in a 1:1:1 mole ratio between the three monomer units. Using the results from part b, determine the relative numbers of the monomer units in this sample of ABS plastic.

155. Consider the titration of 50.0 mL of 1.0 M glycine hydrochloride [$(H_3NCH_2COOH)Cl$], with 1.0 M NaOH. For $^+H_3NCH_2COOH$, K_a for the carboxylic acid group is 4.3×10^{-3} and K_b for the amino group is 6.0×10^{-5}.
    a. Calculate the pH after 25.0 mL, 50.0 mL, and 75.0 mL of NaOH has been added. *Hint:* Refer to Section 8.7 of the text, and treat the titration of $^+H_3NCH_2COOH$ as a diprotic acid titration.
    b. Sketch the titration curve and indicate the major amino acid species present after 0.0 mL, 25.0 mL, 50.0 mL, 75.0 mL, and 100.0 mL of 1.0 M NaOH have reacted completely. Assume the initial pH is 1.2 and the pH at the second equivalence point is 11.7.
    c. At what pH do the majority of amino acid molecules have a net charge of zero? This pH is called the isoelectric point.
    d. At what pH is the net charge of the major amino acid species present equal to $+\frac{1}{2}$? $-\frac{1}{2}$?

156. In 1994 chemists at Texas A&M University reported the synthesis of a non-naturally occurring amino acid (*C & E News*, April 18, 1994, pp. 26–27):

    a. To which naturally occurring amino acid is this compound most similar?
    b. A tetrapeptide, phe-met-arg-phe—NH_2, is synthesized in the brains of rats addicted to morphine and heroin. (The —NH_2 indicates that the peptide ends
    in $\underset{\|}{\overset{O}{-C-NH_2}}$ instead of —CO_2H.) The TAMU
    scientists synthesized a similar tetrapeptide, with the synthetic amino acid above replacing one of the original amino acids. Draw a structure for the tetrapeptide containing the synthetic amino acid.
    c. Indicate the chiral carbon atoms in the synthetic amino acid.
    d. Draw the geometric isomers for this synthetic amino acid. (*Hint:* Refer to Exercise 25.)

Appendixes

Appendix One | Mathematical Procedures

A1.1 Exponential Notation

The numbers characteristic of scientific measurements are often very large or very small; thus it is convenient to express them by using powers of 10. For example, the number 1,300,000 can be expressed as 1.3×10^6, which means multiply 1.3 by 10 six times:

$$1.3 \times 10^6 = 1.3 \times \underbrace{10 \times 10 \times 10 \times 10 \times 10 \times 10}_{10^6 = 1 \text{ million}}$$

Note that each multiplication by 10 moves the decimal point one place to the right, and the easiest way to interpret the notation 1.3×10^6 is that it means move the decimal point in 1.3 to the right six times.

In this notation the number 1985 can be expressed as 1.985×10^3. Note that the usual convention is to write the number that appears before the power of 10 as a number between 1 and 10. Some other examples are given below.

Number	Exponential Notation
5.6	5.6×10^0 or 5.6×1
39	3.9×10^1
943	9.43×10^2
1126	1.126×10^3

To represent a number smaller than 1 in exponential notation, start with a number between 1 and 10 and *divide* by the appropriate power of 10:

$$0.0034 = \frac{3.4}{10 \times 10 \times 10} = \frac{3.4}{10^3} = 3.4 \times 10^{-3}$$

Division by 10 moves the decimal point one place to the *left*. Thus the number 0.00000014 can be written as 1.4×10^{-7}.

To summarize, we can write any number in the form

$$N \times 10^{\pm n}$$

where N is between 1 and 10 and the exponent n is an integer. If the sign preceding n is positive, it means the decimal point in N should be moved n places to the right. If a negative sign precedes n, the decimal point in N should be moved n places to the left.

Multiplication and Division

When two numbers expressed in exponential notation are multiplied, the initial numbers are multiplied and the exponents of 10 are added:

$$(M \times 10^m)(N \times 10^n) = (MN) \times 10^{m+n}$$

For example,

$$(3.2 \times 10^4)(2.8 \times 10^3) = 9.0 \times 10^7$$

When the numbers are multiplied, if a result greater than 10 is obtained for the initial number, the number is adjusted to conventional notation:

$$(5.8 \times 10^2)(4.3 \times 10^8) = 24.9 \times 10^{10} = 2.49 \times 10^{11} = 2.5 \times 10^{11}$$

Division of two numbers expressed in exponential notation involves normal division of the initial numbers and *subtraction* of the exponent of the divisor from that of the dividend. For example,

$$\underbrace{\frac{4.8 \times 10^8}{2.1 \times 10^3}}_{\text{Divisor}} = \frac{4.8}{2.1} \times 10^{(8-3)} = 2.3 \times 10^5$$

Addition and Subtraction

When we add or subtract numbers expressed in exponential notation, *the exponents of the numbers must be the same*. For example, to add 1.31×10^5 and 4.2×10^4, rewrite one number so that the exponents of both are the same:

$$13.1 \times 10^4$$
$$+ \quad 4.2 \times 10^4$$
$$\overline{17.3 \times 10^4}$$

In correct exponential notation, the result is expressed as 1.73×10^5.

Powers and Roots

When a number expressed in exponential notation is taken to some power, the initial number is taken to the appropriate power and the exponent of 10 is multiplied by that power:

$$(N \times 10^n)^m = N^m \times 10^{m \cdot n}$$

For example,*

$$(7.5 \times 10^2)^3 = 7.5^3 \times 10^{3 \cdot 2} = 422 \times 10^6 = 4.22 \times 10^8$$
$$= 4.2 \times 10^8 \text{ (rounded to 2 significant figures)}$$

When a root is taken of a number expressed in exponential notation, the root of the initial number is taken and the exponent of 10 is divided by the number representing the root:

$$\sqrt{N \times 10^n} = (N \times 10^n)^{1/2} = \sqrt{N} \times 10^{n/2}$$

For example, $(2.9 \times 10^6)^{1/2} = \sqrt{2.9} \times 10^{6/2} = 1.7 \times 10^3$

Because the exponent of the result must be an integer, we may sometimes have to change the form of the number so that the power divided by the root equals an integer; for example,

$$\sqrt{1.9 \times 10^3} = (1.9 \times 10^3)^{1/2} = (0.19 \times 10^4)^{1/2}$$
$$= \sqrt{0.19} \times 10^2 = 0.44 \times 10^2$$
$$= 4.4 \times 10^1$$

---

*Refer to the instruction booklet for your calculator for directions concerning how to take roots and powers of numbers.

The same procedure is followed for roots other than square roots; for example,

$$\sqrt[3]{4.6 \times 10^{10}} = (4.6 \times 10^{10})^{1/3} = (46 \times 10^9)^{1/3}$$

$$= \sqrt[3]{46} \times 10^3 = 3.6 \times 10^3$$

A1.2 Logarithms

A logarithm is an exponent. Any number N can be expressed as follows:

$$N = 10^x$$

For example,

$$1000 = 10^3$$

$$100 = 10^2$$

$$10 = 10^1$$

$$1 = 10^0$$

The common, or base 10, logarithm of a number is the power to which 10 must be taken to yield that number. Thus, since $1000 = 10^3$,

$$\log 1000 = 3$$

Similarly,

$$\log 100 = 2$$

$$\log 10 = 1$$

$$\log 1 = 0$$

For a number between 10 and 100, the required exponent of 10 will be between 1 and 2. For example, $65 = 10^{1.8129}$; that is, $\log 65 = 1.8129$. For a number between 100 and 1000, the exponent of 10 will be between 2 and 3. For example, $650 = 10^{2.8129}$ and $\log 650 = 2.8129$.

A number N greater than 0 and less than 1 can be expressed as follows:

$$N = 10^{-x} = \frac{1}{10^x}$$

For example,

$$0.001 = \frac{1}{1000} = \frac{1}{10^3} = 10^{-3}$$

$$0.01 = \frac{1}{100} = \frac{1}{10^2} = 10^{-2}$$

$$0.1 = \frac{1}{10} = \frac{1}{10^1} = 10^{-1}$$

Thus

$$\log 0.001 = -3$$

$$\log 0.01 = -2$$

$$\log 0.1 = -1$$

Although common logs are often tabulated, the most convenient method for obtaining such logs is to use a calculator.

Since logs are simply exponents, they are manipulated according to the rules for exponents. For example, if $A = 10^x$ and $B = 10^y$, then their product is

$$A \cdot B = 10^x \cdot 10^y = 10^{x+y}$$

and

$$\log AB = x + y = \log A + \log B$$

For division we have

$$\frac{A}{B} = \frac{10^x}{10^y} = 10^{x-y}$$

and
$$\log \frac{A}{B} = x - y = \log A - \log B$$

For a number raised to a power, we have

$$A^n = (10^x)^n = 10^{nx}$$

and
$$\log A^n = nx = n \log A$$

It follows that
$$\log \frac{1}{A^n} = \log A^{-n} = -n \log A$$

or for $n = 1$,
$$\log \frac{1}{A} = -\log A$$

When a common log is given, to find the number it represents, we must carry out the process of exponentiation. For example, if the log is 2.673, then $N = 10^{2.673}$. The process of exponentiation is also called taking the antilog, or the inverse logarithm, and is easily carried out by using a calculator.

A second type of logarithm, the natural logarithm, is based on the number 2.7183, which is referred to as e. In this case a number is represented as $N = e^x = 2.7183^x$. For example,

$$N = 7.15 = e^x$$

$$\ln 7.15 = x = 1.967$$

If a natural logarithm is given, to find the number it represents, we must carry out exponentiation to the base e (2.7183) by using a calculator.

A1.3 Graphing Functions

In the interpretation of the results of a scientific experiment, it is often useful to make a graph. It is usually most convenient to graph the function in a form that gives a straight line. The equation for a straight line (a *linear equation*) can be represented by the general form

$$y = mx + b$$

where y is the *dependent variable*, x is the *independent variable*, m is the *slope*, and b is the *intercept* with the y axis.

As an illustration of the characteristics of a linear equation, the function $y = 3x + 4$ is plotted in Fig. A1.1. For this equation, $m = 3$ and $b = 4$. Note that the y intercept occurs when $x = 0$. In this case the intercept is 4, as can be seen from the equation ($b = 4$).

The slope of a straight line is defined as the ratio of the rate of change in y to that in x:

$$m = \text{slope} = \frac{\Delta y}{\Delta x}$$

For the equation $y = 3x + 4$, y changes three times as fast as x (since x has a coefficient of 3). Thus the slope in this case is 3. This can be verified from the graph. For the triangle shown in Fig. A1.1:

$$\text{Slope} = \frac{\Delta y}{\Delta x} = \frac{24}{8} = 3$$

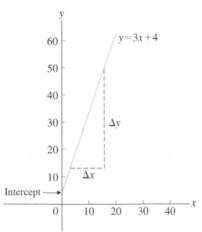

Figure A1.1
Graph of the linear equation
$y = 3x + 4$.

Sometimes an equation that is not in standard form can be changed to the form $y = mx + b$ by rearrangement or mathematical manipulation. An example is the equation $k = Ae^{-E_a/RT}$, where A, E_a, and R are constants, k is the

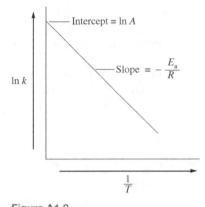

Figure A1.2
Graph of ln k versus $1/T$.

dependent variable, and $1/T$ is the independent variable. This equation can be changed to standard form by taking the natural logarithm of both sides,

$$\ln k = \ln Ae^{-E_a/RT} = \ln A + \ln e^{-E_a/RT} = \ln A - \frac{E_a}{RT}$$

noting that the log of a product is equal to the sum of the logs of the individual terms and that the natural log of $e^{-E_a/RT}$ is simply the exponent $-E_a/RT$. Thus in standard form the equation $k = Ae^{-E_a/RT}$ is written

$$\underbrace{\ln k}_{y} = \underbrace{-\frac{E_a}{R}}_{m} \underbrace{\left(\frac{1}{T}\right)}_{x} + \underbrace{\ln A}_{b}$$

A plot of ln k versus $1/T$ (see Fig. A1.2) gives a straight line with slope $-E_a/R$ and intercept ln A.

Of course, many relationships that arise from the description of natural systems are nonlinear, and the "slope" of a curve is continuously changing. In this case the instantaneous slope is given by the tangent to the curve at that point, which is described by a new function obtained by taking the derivative of the original function. For example, for the function in x, $f = ax^2$, the derivative (df/dx) is $2ax$. Thus the slope at each point on the curve defined by the function ax^2 is given by $2ax$.

A1.4 Solving Quadratic Equations

A *quadratic equation*, a polynomial in which the highest power of x is 2, can be written as

$$ax^2 + bx + c = 0$$

One method for finding the two values of x that satisfy a quadratic equation is to use the *quadratic formula*:

$$x = \frac{-b \pm \sqrt{b^2 - 4ac}}{2a}$$

where a, b, and c represent the coefficients of x^2 and x and the constant, respectively. For example, in the determination of $[H^+]$ in a solution of 1.0×10^{-4} M acetic acid, the following expression arises:

$$1.8 \times 10^{-5} = \frac{x^2}{1.0 \times 10^{-4} - x}$$

which yields $\qquad x^2 + (1.8 \times 10^{-5})x - 1.8 \times 10^{-9} = 0$

where $a = 1$, $b = 1.8 \times 10^{-5}$, and $c = -1.8 \times 10^{-9}$. Using the quadratic formula, we have

$$x = \frac{-b \pm \sqrt{b^2 - 4ac}}{2a}$$

$$= \frac{-1.8 \times 10^{-5} \pm \sqrt{3.24 \times 10^{-10} - (4)(1)(-1.8 \times 10^{-9})}}{2(1)}$$

and $\qquad x = \frac{6.9 \times 10^{-5}}{2} = 3.5 \times 10^{-5}$

or $\qquad x = \frac{-10.5 \times 10^{-5}}{2} = -5.2 \times 10^{-5}$

Note that there are two roots, as there always will be for a polynomial in x^2. In this case x represents a concentration of H^+ (see Section 7.5). Thus the positive root is the one that solves the problem, since a concentration cannot be a negative number.

A second method for solving quadratic equations is by *successive approximations,* a systematic method of trial and error. A value of x is guessed and substituted into the equation everywhere x (or x^2) appears, except for one place. For example, for the equation

$$x^2 + (1.8 \times 10^{-5})x - 1.8 \times 10^{-9} = 0$$

we might guess $x = 2 \times 10^{-5}$. Substituting that value into the equation gives

$$x^2 + (1.8 \times 10^{-5})(2 \times 10^{-5}) - 1.8 \times 10^{-9} = 0$$

or $$x^2 = 1.8 \times 10^{-9} - 3.6 \times 10^{-10} = 1.4 \times 10^{-9}$$

Thus $$x = 3.7 \times 10^{-5}$$

Note that the guessed value of x (2×10^{-5}) is not the same as the value of x that is calculated (3.7×10^{-5}) after inserting the estimated value. This means that $x = 2 \times 10^{-5}$ is not the correct solution, and we must try another guess.

We take the calculated value (3.7×10^{-5}) as our next guess:

$$x^2 + (1.8 \times 10^{-5})(3.7 \times 10^{-5}) - 1.8 \times 10^{-9} = 0$$

$$x^2 = 1.8 \times 10^{-9} - 6.7 \times 10^{-10} = 1.1 \times 10^{-9}$$

Thus $$x = 3.3 \times 10^{-5}$$

Now we compare the two values of x again:

Guessed: $x = 3.7 \times 10^{-5}$

Calculated: $x = 3.3 \times 10^{-5}$

These values are closer but still not identical.

Next, we try 3.3×10^{-5} as our guess:

$$x^2 + (1.8 \times 10^{-5})(3.3 \times 10^{-5}) - 1.8 \times 10^{-9} = 0$$

$$x^2 = 1.8 \times 10^{-9} - 5.9 \times 10^{-10} = 1.2 \times 10^{-9}$$

Thus $$x = 3.5 \times 10^{-5}$$

Compare:

Guessed: $x = 3.3 \times 10^{-5}$

Calculated: $x = 3.5 \times 10^{-5}$

Next, we guess $x = 3.5 \times 10^{-5}$, which leads to

$$x^2 + (1.8 \times 10^{-5})(3.5 \times 10^{-5}) - 1.8 \times 10^{-9} = 0$$

$$x^2 = 1.8 \times 10^{-9} - 6.3 \times 10^{-10} = 1.2 \times 10^{-9}$$

Thus $$x = 3.5 \times 10^{-5}$$

Now the guessed value and the calculated value are the same; we have found the correct solution. Note that this agrees with one of the roots found with the quadratic formula in the first method above.

To further illustrate the method of successive approximations, we will solve Example 7.9 by using this procedure. In solving for $[H^+]$ for 0.010 M H_2SO_4, we obtain the following expression:

$$1.2 \times 10^{-2} = \frac{x(0.010 + x)}{0.010 - x}$$

which can be rearranged to give

$$x = (1.2 \times 10^{-2})\left(\frac{0.010 - x}{0.010 + x}\right)$$

We will guess a value for x, substitute it into the right side of the equation, and then calculate a value for x. In guessing a value for x, we know it must be less than 0.010, since a larger value would make the calculated value for x negative and the guessed and calculated values will never match. We start by guessing $x = 0.005$.

The results of the successive approximations are shown in the following table:

Trial	Guessed Value for x	Calculated Value for x
1	0.0050	0.0040
2	0.0040	0.0051
3	0.00450	0.00455
4	0.00452	0.00453

Note that the first guess was close to the actual value and that there was oscillation between 0.004 and 0.005 for the guessed and calculated values. For trial 3, an average of these values was used as the guess, and this led rapidly to the correct value (0.0045 to the correct number of significant figures). Also note that it is useful to carry extra digits until the correct value is obtained, which is then rounded off to the correct number of significant figures.

The method of successive approximations is especially useful for solving polynomials containing x to a power of 3 or higher. The procedure is the same as for quadratic equations: Substitute a guessed value for x into the equation for every x term but one, and then solve for x. Continue this process until the guessed and calculated values agree.

A1.5 Uncertainties in Measurements

The number associated with a measurement is obtained by using some measuring device. For example, consider the measurement of the volume of a liquid in a buret, as shown in Fig. A1.3, where the scale is greatly magnified. The volume is about 22.15 mL. Note that the last number must be estimated by interpolating between the 0.1-mL marks. Since the last number is estimated, its value may vary depending on who makes the measurement. If five different people read the same volume, the results might be as follows:

Person	Result of Measurement
1	22.15 mL
2	22.14 mL
3	22.16 mL
4	22.17 mL
5	22.16 mL

Note from these results that the first three numbers (22.1) remain the same regardless of who makes the measurement; these are called certain digits. However, the digit to the right of the 1 must be estimated and thus varies; it is called an uncertain digit. We customarily report a measurement by recording all the certain digits plus the *first* uncertain digit. In our example it would not make any sense to try to record the volume to thousandths of a milliliter because the value for hundredths of a milliliter must be estimated when using the buret.

Figure A1.3
Measurement of volume using a buret. The volume is read at the bottom of the liquid curve (called the meniscus).

It is very important to realize that a *measurement always has some degree of uncertainty*. The uncertainty of a measurement depends on the precision of the measuring device. For example, using a bathroom scale, you might estimate that the mass of a grapefruit is about 1.5 pounds. Weighing the same grapefruit on a highly precise balance might produce a result of 1.476 pounds. In the first case the uncertainty occurs in the tenths of a pound place; in the second case the uncertainty occurs in the thousandths of a pound place. Suppose we weigh two similar grapefruit on the two devices and obtain the following results:

	Bathroom Scale	Balance
Grapefruit 1	1.5 lb	1.476 lb
Grapefruit 2	1.5 lb	1.518 lb

Do the two grapefruits have the same mass? The answer depends on which set of results you consider. Thus a conclusion based on a series of measurements depends on the certainty of those measurements. For this reason, it is important to indicate the uncertainty in any measurement. This is done by always recording the certain digits and the first uncertain digit (the estimated number). These numbers are called the **significant figures** of a measurement.

The convention of significant figures automatically gives an indication of the uncertainty in a measurement. The uncertainty in the last number (the estimated number) is usually assumed to be ±1 unless otherwise indicated. For example, the measurement 1.86 kilograms can be interpreted to mean 1.86 ± 0.01 kilograms.

Precision and Accuracy

Two terms often used to describe uncertainty in measurements are *precision* and *accuracy*. Although these words are frequently used interchangeably in everyday life, they have different meanings in the scientific context. **Accuracy** refers to the agreement of a particular value with the true value. **Precision** refers to the degree of agreement among several measurements of the same quantity. Precision reflects the *reproducibility* of a given type of measurement. The difference between these terms is illustrated by the results of three different target practices shown in Fig. A1.4.

Two different types of errors are also introduced in Fig. A1.4. A **random error** (also called an indeterminate error) means that a measurement has an equal probability of being high or low. This type of error occurs in estimating the value of the last digit of a measurement. The second type of error is called **systematic error** (or determinate error). This type of error occurs in the same direction each time; it is either always high or always low. Figure A1.4(a) indicates large random errors (poor technique). Figure A1.4(b) indicates small random errors but a large systematic error, and Fig. A1.4(c) indicates small random errors and no systematic error.

In quantitative work precision is often used as an indication of accuracy; we assume that the *average* of a series of precise measurements (which should "average out" the random errors because of their equal probability of being high or low) is accurate, or close to the "true" value. However, this assumption is valid only if systematic errors are absent. Suppose we weigh a piece of brass five times on a very precise balance and obtain the following results:

(a)

(b)

(c)

Figure A1.4
Shooting targets show the difference between *precise* and *accurate*.
(a) Neither accurate nor precise (large random errors). (b) Precise but not accurate (small random errors, large systematic error). (c) Bull's-eye! Both precise and accurate (small random errors, no systematic error).

Weighing	Result
1	2.486 g
2	2.487 g
3	2.485 g
4	2.484 g
5	2.488 g

Normally, we would assume that the true mass of the piece of brass is very close to 2.486 grams, which is the average of the five results. However, if the balance has a defect causing it to give a result that is consistently 1.000 gram too high (a systematic error of +1.000 gram), then 2.486 grams would be seriously in error. The point here is that high precision among several measurements is an indication of accuracy *only* if you can be sure that systematic errors are absent.

Expression of Experimental Results

The accuracy of a measurement refers to how close it is to the true value. An inaccurate result occurs as a result of some flaw (systematic error) in the measurement: the presence of an interfering substance, incorrect calibration of an instrument, operator error, and so on. The goal of chemical analysis is to eliminate systematic error, but random errors can only be minimized. In practice, an experiment is almost always done in order to find an unknown value (the true value is not known—someone is trying to obtain that value by doing the experiment). In this case the precision of several replicate determinations is used to assess the accuracy of the result. The results of the replicate experiments are expressed as an average (which we assume is close to the true value) with an error limit that gives some indication of how close the average value may be to the true value. The error limit represents the uncertainty of the experimental result.

To illustrate this procedure, consider a situation that might arise in the pharmaceutical industry. Assume that the specification for a commercial 500-mg acetaminophen (the active painkiller in Tylenol) tablet is that each batch of tablets must contain 450 to 550 mg of acetaminophen per tablet. Suppose that chemical analysis gave the following results for a batch of acetaminophen tablets: 428, 479, 442, and 435 mg. How can these results be used to decide whether the batch of tablets meets the specification? Although the details of how to draw such conclusions from measured data are beyond the scope of this discussion, we will consider some aspects of this process. We will focus here on the types of experimental uncertainty, the expression of experimental results, and a simplified method for estimating experimental uncertainty when several types of measurements contribute to the final result.

There are two common ways of expressing an average: the mean and the median. The mean ($\bar{x}$) is the arithmetic average of the results, or

$$\text{Mean} = \bar{x} = \sum_{i=1}^{n} \frac{x_i}{n} = \frac{x_1 + x_2 + \cdots + x_n}{n}$$

where Σ means take the sum of the values. The mean is equal to the sum of all the measurements divided by the number of measurements. For the acetaminophen results given previously, the mean is

$$\bar{x} = \frac{428 + 479 + 442 + 435}{4} = 446 \text{ mg}$$

The median is the value that lies in the middle among the results. Half of the measurements are above the median and half are below the median. For results of 465, 485, and 492 mg, the median is 485 mg. When there is an even number of results, the median is the average of the two middle results. For the acetaminophen results, the median is

$$\frac{442 + 435}{2} = 439 \text{ mg}$$

There are several advantages to using the median. If a small number of measurements is made, one value can greatly affect the mean. Consider the results for the analysis of acetaminophen: 428, 479, 442, and 435 mg. The mean is 446 mg, which is larger than three of the four results. The median is 439 mg, which lies near the three values that are relatively close to one another.

In addition to expressing an average value for a series of results, we must also express the uncertainty. This usually means expressing either the precision of the measurements or the observed range of the measurements. The range of a series of measurements is defined by the smallest value and the largest value. For the analytical results on the acetaminophen tablets, the range is from 428 to 479 mg. Using this range, we can express the results by saying that the true value lies between 428 and 479 mg. That is, we can express the amount of acetaminophen in a typical tablet as 446 ± 33 mg, where the error limit is chosen to give the observed range (approximately).

The most common way to specify precision is by the standard deviation s, which for a small number of measurements is given by the formula

$$s = \left[\frac{\sum\limits_{i=1}^{n} (x_i - \bar{x})^2}{n - 1} \right]^{1/2}$$

where x_i is an individual result, $\bar{x}$ is the average (either mean or median), and n is the total number of measurements. For the acetaminophen example, we have

$$s = \left[\frac{(428 - 446)^2 + (479 - 446)^2 + (442 - 446)^2 + (435 - 446)^2}{4 - 1} \right]^{1/2} = 23$$

Thus we can say that the amount of acetaminophen in a typical tablet in the batch of tablets is 446 mg with a sample standard deviation of 23 mg. Statistically, this means that any additional measurement has a 68% probability (68 chances out of 100) of being between 423 mg $(446 - 23)$ and 469 mg $(446 + 23)$. Thus the standard deviation is a measure of the precision of a given type of measurement.

In scientific calculations it is also useful to be able to estimate the precision of a procedure that involves several measurements by combining the precisions of the individual steps. That is, we want to answer the following question: How do the uncertainties propagate when we combine the results of several different types of measurements? There are many ways to deal with the propagation of uncertainty. We will discuss one simple method below.

Worst-Case Method for Estimating Experimental Uncertainty

To illustrate this method, we will consider the determination of the density of an irregularly shaped solid. In this determination we make three measurements. First, we measure the mass of the object on a balance. Next, we must obtain the volume of the solid. The easiest method for doing this is to partially fill a graduated cylinder with a liquid and record the volume. Then we add the solid and record the volume again. The difference in the measured volumes is the volume of the solid. We can then calculate the density of the solid from the equation

$$D = \frac{M}{V_2 - V_1}$$

where M is the mass of the solid, V_1 is the initial volume of liquid in the graduated cylinder, and V_2 is the volume of liquid plus solid. Suppose we get the following results:

$$M = 23.06 \text{ g}$$

$$V_1 = 10.4 \text{ mL}$$

$$V_2 = 13.5 \text{ mL}$$

The calculated density is

$$\frac{23.06 \text{ g}}{13.5 \text{ mL} - 10.4 \text{ mL}} = 7.44 \text{ g/mL}$$

Now suppose that the precision of the balance used is ± 0.02 g and that the volume measurements are precise to ± 0.05 mL. How do we estimate the uncertainty of the density? We can do this by assuming a worst case. That is, we assume the largest uncertainties in all measurements, and we see what combinations of measurements will give the largest and smallest possible results (the greatest range). Since the density is the mass divided by the volume, the largest value of the density will be that obtained by using the largest possible mass and the smallest possible volume:

Largest possible mass = 23.06 + 0.02

$$D_{max} = \frac{23.08}{13.45 - 10.45} = 7.69 \text{ g/mL}$$

Smallest possible V_2 Largest possible V_1

The smallest value of the density is

Smallest possible mass

$$D_{min} = \frac{23.04}{13.55 - 10.35} = 7.20 \text{ g/mL}$$

Largest possible V_2 Smallest possible V_1

Thus the calculated range is from 7.20 to 7.69, and the average of these values is 7.45. The error limit is the number that gives the high and low range values when added and subtracted from the average. Therefore, we can express the density as 7.45 ± 0.25 g/mL, which is the average value plus or minus the quantity that gives the range calculated by assuming the largest uncertainties.

Analysis of the propagation of uncertainties is useful in drawing qualitative conclusions from the analysis of measurements. For example, suppose that we obtained the preceding results for the density of an unknown alloy and we want to know if it is one of the following alloys:

Alloy A: $D = 7.58$ g/mL

Alloy B: $D = 7.42$ g/mL

Alloy C: $D = 8.56$ g/mL

We can safely conclude that the alloy is not C. But the values of the densities for alloys A and B are both within the inherent uncertainty of our method. To distinguish between A and B, we need to improve the precision of our determination. The obvious choice is to improve the precision of the volume measurement.

The worst-case method is useful for estimating the maximum uncertainty expected when the results of several measurements are combined to obtain a result. We assume the maximum uncertainty in each measurement and then calculate the minimum and maximum possible results. These extreme values describe the range and thus the maximum error limit associated with a particular determination.

	Values of *t* for Confidence Intervals	
n	90%	95%
2	6.31	12.7
3	2.92	4.30
4	2.35	3.18
5	2.13	2.78
6	2.02	2.57
7	1.94	2.45
8	1.90	2.36
9	1.86	2.31
10	1.83	2.26

Confidence Limits

A more sophisticated method for estimating the uncertainty of a particular type of determination involves the use of confidence limits. A confidence limit is defined as

$$\text{Confidence limit} = \pm\frac{ts}{\sqrt{n}}$$

where t = a weighting factor based on statistical analysis

s = the standard deviation

n = the number of experiments carried out

In this context an experiment may refer to a single type of measurement (for example, weighing an object) or to a procedure that requires various types of measurements to obtain a given final result (for example, obtaining the percentage of iron in a particular sample of iron ore). Some representative values of t are listed in Table A1.1.

A 95% confidence level means that the true value (the *average* obtained if the experiment were repeated an *infinite* number of times) will lie within $\pm ts/\sqrt{n}$ of the *observed* average (obtained from n experiments) with a 95% probability (95 of 100 times). Thus the factor $\pm ts/\sqrt{n}$ represents an error limit for a given set of results from a particular type of experiment. Thus we might represent the result of n determinations as

$$\bar{x} \pm \frac{ts}{\sqrt{n}}$$

where $\bar{x}$ is the average of the results from the n experiments. This type of error limit is expected to be considerably smaller than that obtained from a worst-case analysis.

A1.6 Significant Figures

Calculating the final result for an experiment usually involves adding, subtracting, multiplying, or dividing the results of various types of measurements. Thus it is important to be able to estimate the uncertainty in the final result. In the previous section we have considered this process in some detail. A closely related matter concerns the number of digits that should be retained in the result of a given calculation. In other words, how many of the digits in the result are significant (meaningful) relative to the uncertainty expected in the result? From statistical analyses of how uncertainties accumulate when arithmetic operations are carried out, rules have been developed for determining the correct number of significant figures in a final result. First, we must consider how to count the number of significant figures (digits) represented in a particular number.

Rules for Counting Significant Figures (Digits)

1. *Nonzero integers*. Nonzero integers always count as significant figures.
2. *Zeros*. There are three classes of zeros:
    a. *Leading zeros* are zeros that *precede* all the nonzero digits. They do not count as significant figures. In the number 0.0025 the three zeros simply indicate the position of the decimal point. This number has only two significant figures.
    b. *Captive zeros* are zeros *between* nonzero digits. They always count as significant figures. The number 1.008 has four significant figures.

c. *Trailing zeros* are zeros at the *right end* of the number. They are significant only if the number contains a decimal point. The number 100 has only one significant figure, whereas the number 1.00×10^2 has three significant figures. The number one hundred written as 100. also has three significant figures.

3. *Exact numbers.* Many times calculations involve numbers that were not obtained by using measuring devices but were determined by counting: 10 experiments, 3 apples, 8 molecules. Such numbers are called *exact numbers.* They can be assumed to have an infinite number of significant figures. Other examples of exact numbers are the 2 in $2\pi r$ (the circumference of a circle) and the 4 and the 3 in $\frac{4}{3}\pi r^3$ (the volume of a sphere). Exact numbers can also arise from definitions. For example, one inch is defined as exactly 2.54 centimeters. Thus, in the statement 1 in = 2.54 cm, neither the 2.54 nor the 1 limits the number of significant figures when used in a calculation.

The following rules apply for determining the number of significant figures in the result of a calculation.

Rules for Significant Figures in Mathematical Operations*

1. For *multiplication or division* the number of significant figures in the result is the same as the number in the least precise measurement used in the calculation. For example, consider this calculation:

$$4.56 \times 1.4 = 6.38 \xrightarrow{\text{Corrected}} 6.4$$

Limiting term has two significant figures

Two significant figures

The correct product has only two significant figures, since 1.4 has two significant figures.

2. *For addition or subtraction* the result has the same number of decimal places as the least precise measurement used in the calculation. For example, consider the following sum:

$$
\begin{array}{r}
12.11 \\
18.0 \quad \leftarrow \text{Limiting term has one decimal place} \\
1.013 \\
\hline
31.123 \xrightarrow{\text{Corrected}} 31.1
\end{array}
$$

One decimal place

The correct result is 31.1, since 18.0 has only one decimal place.

Note that for multiplication and division significant figures are counted. For addition and subtraction the decimal places are counted.

In most calculations you will need to round off numbers to obtain the correct number of significant figures. The following rules should be applied for rounding.

---

*Although these rules work well for most cases, they can give misleading results in certain cases. For a discussion of this, see L. M. Schwartz, "Propagation of Significant Figures," *J. Chem. Ed.* **62** (1985):693.

Rules for Rounding

1. In a series of calculations, carry the extra digits through to the final result, *then* round off.*
2. If the digit to be removed[†]
   a. is less than 5, the preceding digit stays the same. For example, 1.33 rounds to 1.3.
   b. is equal to or greater than 5, the preceding digit is increased by 1. For example, 1.36 rounds to 1.4.

When rounding, use only the first number to the right of the last significant figure. Do not round off sequentially. For example, the number 4.348 when rounded to two significant figures is 4.3, not 4.4.

Appendix Two | Units of Measurement and Conversions Among Units

A2.1 Measurements

Making observations is fundamental to all science. A quantitative observation, or **measurement,** always consists of two parts: a *number* and a scale (a *unit*). Both parts must be present for the measurement to be meaningful.

The two most widely used systems of units are the *English system* used in the United States and the *metric system* used by most of the rest of the industrialized world. This duality obviously causes a good deal of trouble; for example, parts as simple as bolts are not interchangeable between machines built using the different systems. As a result, the United States has begun to adopt the metric system.

For many years, most scientists worldwide have used the metric system. In 1960 an international agreement established a system of units called the *International System (le Système International* in French), abbreviated SI. This system is based on the metric system and the units derived from the metric system. The fundamental SI units are listed in Table A2.1.

Because the fundamental units are not always convenient (expressing the mass of a pin in kilograms is awkward), the SI system uses prefixes to change the size of the unit. These prefixes are listed in Table A2.2.

Table A2.1

The Fundamental SI Units

Physical Quantity	Name of Unit	Abbreviation
Mass	kilogram	kg
Length	meter	m
Time	second	s
Temperature	Kelvin	K
Electric current	ampere	A
Amount of substance	mole	mol
Luminous intensity	candela	cd

---

*This practice will not usually be followed in the examples in this text because we want to show the correct number of significant figures in each step. However, in the answers to the end-of-chapter exercises, only the final answer is rounded.
†This procedure is consistent with the operation of calculators.

Table A2.2

The Prefixes Used in the SI System

Prefix	Symbol	Meaning	Exponential Notation*
exa	E	1,000,000,000,000,000,000	10^{18}
peta	P	1,000,000,000,000,000	10^{15}
tera	T	1,000,000,000,000	10^{12}
giga	G	1,000,000,000	10^{9}
mega	M	1,000,000	10^{6}
kilo	k	1000	10^{3}
hecto	h	100	10^{2}
deka	da	10	10^{1}
—	—	1	10^{0}
deci	d	0.1	10^{-1}
centi	c	0.01	10^{-2}
milli	m	0.001	10^{-3}
micro	μ	0.000001	10^{-6}
nano	n	0.000000001	10^{-9}
pico	p	0.000000000001	10^{-12}
femto	f	0.000000000000001	10^{-15}
atto	a	0.000000000000000001	10^{-18}

*The most common notations are shown in bold. See Appendix A1.1 if you need a review of exponential notation.

One physical quantity that is very important in chemistry is *volume*, which is not a fundamental SI unit; it is derived from length. A cube with dimensions of 1 m on each edge has a volume of $(1\ m)^3 = 1\ m^3$. Then, recognizing that there are 10 decimeters (dm) in a meter, the volume of the cube is $(10\ dm)^3 = 1000\ dm^3$. A cubic decimeter, dm^3, is commonly called a liter (L), which is a unit of volume slightly larger than a quart. Similarly, since 1 dm equals 10 centimeters (cm), the liter $(1\ dm)^3$ contains 1000 cm^3, or 1000 milliliters (mL).

A2.2 Unit Conversions

It is often necessary to convert results from one system of units to another. The most common way of converting units is by the *unit factor method,* more commonly called **dimensional analysis.** To illustrate the use of this method, we will look at a simple unit conversion.

Consider a pin measuring 2.85 cm in length. What is its length in inches? To solve this problem, we must use the equivalence statement

$$2.54\ cm = 1\ in \quad (exactly)$$

If we divide both sides of this equation by 2.54 cm, we get

$$\frac{2.54\ cm}{2.54\ cm} = 1 = \frac{1\ in}{2.54\ cm}$$

Note that the expression 1 in/2.54 cm equals 1. This expression is called a **unit factor.** Since 1 in and 2.54 cm are exactly equivalent, multiplying any expression by this unit factor will not change its value.

The pin has a length of 2.85 cm. Multiplying this length by the unit factor gives

$$2.85\ \cancel{cm} \times \frac{1\ in}{1.54\ \cancel{cm}} = \frac{2.85}{2.54}\ in = 1.12\ in$$

Note that the centimeter units cancel to give inches for the result. This is exactly what we wanted to accomplish. Note also that the result has three significant figures, as required by the number 2.85. Recall that the 1 and 2.54 in the conversion factor are exact numbers by definition.

| **Converting from One Unit to Another**

1 To convert from one unit to another, use the equivalence statement that relates the two units.
2 Derive the appropriate unit factor by noting the direction of the required change (to cancel the unwanted units).
3 Multiply the quantity to be converted by the unit factor to give the quantity with the desired units.

In dimensional analysis your verification that everything has been done correctly is that the correct units are obtained in the end. *In doing chemistry problems, you should always include the units for the quantities used.* Always check to see that the units cancel to give the correct units for the final result. This provides a very valuable check, especially for complicated problems.

Appendix Three | Spectral Analysis

Although volumetric and gravimetric analyses are still commonly used, spectroscopy is the technique most often used for modern chemical analysis. *Spectroscopy* is the study of electromagnetic radiation emitted or absorbed by a given chemical species. Since the quantity of radiation absorbed or emitted can be related to the quantity of the absorbing or emitting species present, this technique can be used for quantitative analysis. There are many spectroscopic techniques, since electromagnetic radiation spans a wide range of energies to include microwaves, X rays, and ultraviolet, infrared, and visible light, to name a few of its familiar forms. However, we will consider here only one procedure, which is based on the absorption of visible light.

If a liquid is colored, it is because some component of the liquid absorbs visible light. In a solution the greater the concentration of the light-absorbing substance, the more light is absorbed, and the more intense is the color of the solution.

The quantity of light absorbed by a substance can be measured by a *spectrophotometer*, shown schematically in Fig. A3.1. This instrument consists of a source that emits all wavelengths of light in the visible region (wavelengths of $\approx$400–700 nm); a monochromator, which selects a given wavelength of light; a sample holder for the solution being measured; and a detector, which compares the intensity of incident light I_0 with the intensity of light after it has passed through the sample I. The ratio I/I_0, called the *transmittance*, is a measure of the fraction of light that passes through the sample. The amount of light absorbed is given by the *absorbance A*, where

$$A = -\log \frac{I}{I_0}$$

The absorbance can be expressed by the *Beer-Lambert law:*

$$A = \epsilon l c$$

Figure A3.1
A schematic diagram of a simple spectrophotometer. The source emits all wavelengths of visible light, which are dispersed by using a prism or grating and then focused, one wavelength at a time, onto the sample. The detector compares the intensity of the incident light (I_0) with the intensity of the light after it has passed through the sample (I).

Source   Monochromator   Sample   Detector

where ϵ is the molar absorptivity or the molar extinction coefficient (in L mol^{-1} cm^{-1}), l is the distance the light travels through the solution (in cm), and c is the concentration of the absorbing species (in mol/L). The Beer-Lambert law is the basis for using spectroscopy in quantitative analysis. If ϵ and l are known, determining A for a solution allows us to calculate the concentration of the absorbing species in the solution.

Suppose we have a pink solution containing an unknown concentration of $Co^{2+}(aq)$ ions. A sample of this solution is placed in a spectrophotometer, and the absorbance is measured at a wavelength where ϵ for $Co^{2+}(aq)$ is known to be 12 L mol^{-1} cm^{-1}. The absorbance A is found to be 0.60. The width of the sample tube is 1.0 cm. We want to determine the concentration of $Co^{2+}(aq)$ in the solution. This problem can be solved by a straightforward application of the Beer-Lambert law,

$$A = \epsilon l c$$

where

$$A = 0.60$$

$$\epsilon = \frac{12 \text{ L}}{\text{mol cm}}$$

$$l = \text{light path} = 1.0 \text{ cm}$$

Solving for the concentration gives

$$c = \frac{A}{\epsilon l} = \frac{0.60}{\left(12 \dfrac{\text{L}}{\text{mol cm}}\right)(1.0 \text{ cm})} = 5.0 \times 10^{-2} \text{ mol/L}$$

To obtain the unknown concentration of an absorbing species from the measured absorbance, we must know the product ϵl, since

$$c = \frac{A}{\epsilon l}$$

We can obtain the product ϵl by measuring the absorbance of a solution of *known* concentration, since

Measured using a
spectrophotometer

$$\epsilon l = \frac{A}{c}$$

Known from making
up the solution

However, a more accurate value of the product ϵl can be obtained by plotting A versus c for a series of solutions. Note that the equation $A = \epsilon l c$ gives a straight line with slope ϵl when A is plotted against c.

For example, consider the following typical spectroscopic analysis. A sample of steel from a bicycle frame is to be analyzed to determine its manganese content. The procedure involves weighing out a sample of the steel, dissolving it in strong acid, treating the resulting solution with a very strong oxidizing agent to convert all the manganese to permanganate ion (MnO_4^-), and then using spectroscopy to determine the concentration of the intensely purple MnO_4^- ions in the solution. To do this, however, the value of ϵl for MnO_4^- must be determined at an appropriate wavelength. The absorbance values for four solutions with known MnO_4^- concentrations were measured to give the following data:

Solution	Concentration of MnO_4^- (mol/L)	Absorbance
1	7.00×10^{-5}	0.175
2	1.00×10^{-4}	0.250
3	2.00×10^{-4}	0.500
4	3.50×10^{-4}	0.875

A plot of absorbance versus concentration for the solutions of known concentration is shown in Fig. A3.2. The slope of this line (change in A/change in c) is 2.48×10^3 L/mol. This quantity represents the product ϵl.

A sample of the steel weighing 0.1523 g was dissolved, and the unknown amount of manganese was converted to MnO_4^- ions. Water was then added to give a solution with a final volume of 100.0 mL. A portion of this solution was placed in a spectrophotometer, and its absorbance was found to be 0.780. We can use these data to calculate the percent manganese in the steel. The MnO_4^- ions from the manganese in the dissolved steel sample show an absorbance of 0.780. Using the Beer-Lambert law, we calculate the concentration of MnO_4^- in this solution:

$$c = \frac{A}{\epsilon l} = \frac{0.780}{2.48 \times 10^3 \text{ L/mol}} = 3.15 \times 10^{-4} \text{ mol/L}$$

However, there is a more direct way for finding c. Using a graph such as that in Fig. A3.2 (often called a Beer's law plot), we can read the concentration that corresponds to $A = 0.780$. This interpolation is shown by dashed lines on

Figure A3.2
A plot of absorbance versus concentration of MnO_4^- in a series of solutions of known concentration.

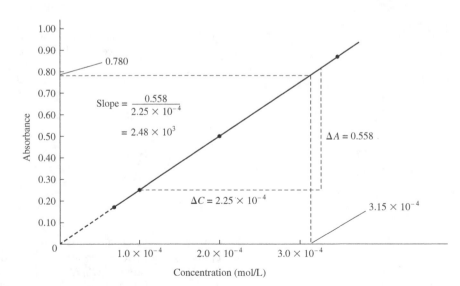

the graph. By this method, $c = 3.15 \times 10^{-4}$ mol/L, which agrees with the value obtained above.

Recall that the original 0.1523-g steel sample was dissolved, the manganese was converted to permanganate, and the volume was adjusted to 100.0 mL. We now know that the $[MnO_4^-]$ in that solution is 3.15×10^{-4} M. Using this concentration, we can calculate the total number of moles of MnO_4^- in that solution:

$$\text{Mol of } MnO_4^- = 100.0 \text{ mL} \times \frac{1 \text{ L}}{1000 \text{ mL}} \times 3.15 \times 10^{-4} \frac{\text{mol}}{\text{L}}$$

$$= 3.15 \times 10^{-5} \text{ mol}$$

Each mole of manganese in the original steel sample yields a mole of MnO_4^-. That is,

$$1 \text{ mol of Mn} \xrightarrow{\text{Oxidation}} 1 \text{ mol of } MnO_4^-$$

so the original steel sample must have contained 3.15×10^{-5} mol of manganese. The mass of manganese present in the sample is

$$3.15 \times 10^{-5} \text{ mol of Mn} \times \frac{54.938 \text{ g of Mn}}{1 \text{ mol of Mn}} = 1.73 \times 10^{-3} \text{ g of Mn}$$

Since the steel sample weighed 0.1523 g, the percent manganese in the steel is

$$\frac{1.73 \times 10^{-3} \text{ g of Mn}}{1.523 \times 10^{-1} \text{ g of sample}} \times 100\% = 1.14\%$$

This example illustrates a typical use of spectroscopy in quantitative analysis. The steps commonly involved are as follows:

1. Preparation of a calibration plot (a Beer's law plot) from the measured absorbance values of a series of solutions with known concentrations.

2. Measurement of the absorbance of the solution of unknown concentration.

3. Use of the calibration plot to determine the unknown concentration.

Appendix Four | Selected Thermodynamic Data*

Substance and State	ΔH_f° (kJ/mol)	ΔG_f° (kJ/mol)	S° (J K^{-1} mol^{-1})	Substance and State	ΔH_f° (kJ/mol)	ΔG_f° (kJ/mol)	S° (J K^{-1} mol^{-1})
Aluminum				Bromine			
Al(s)	0	0	28	Br$_2$(l)	0	0	152
Al$_2$O$_3$(s)	−1676	−1582	51	Br$_2$(g)	31	3	245
Al(OH)$_3$(s)	−1277	—	—	Br$_2$(aq)	−3	4	130
AlCl$_3$(s)	−704	−629	111	Br$^-$(aq)	−121	−104	82
Barium				HBr(g)	−36	−53	199
Ba(s)	0	0	67	Cadmium			
BaCO$_3$(s)	−1219	−1139	112	Cd(s)	0	0	52
BaO(s)	−582	−552	70	CdO(s)	−258	−228	55
Ba(OH)$_2$(s)	−946	—	—	Cd(OH)$_2$(s)	−561	−474	96
BaSO$_4$(s)	−1465	−1353	132	CdS(s)	−162	−156	65
Beryllium				CdSO$_4$(s)	−935	−823	123
Be(s)	0	0	10	Calcium			
BeO(s)	−599	−569	14	Ca(s)	0	0	41
Be(OH)$_2$(s)	−904	−815	47	CaC$_2$(s)	−63	−68	70

*All values are assumed precise to at least ±1.

(continued)

Appendix Four (continued)

Substance and State	ΔH_f° (kJ/mol)	ΔG_f° (kJ/mol)	S° (J K^{-1} mol^{-1})	Substance and State	ΔH_f° (kJ/mol)	ΔG_f° (kJ/mol)	S° (J K^{-1} mol^{-1})
$CaCO_3(s)$	-1207	-1129	93	$H_2O(l)$	-286	-237	70
$CaO(s)$	-635	-604	40	$H_2O(g)$	-242	-229	189
$Ca(OH)_2(s)$	-987	-899	83	Iodine			
$Ca_3(PO_4)_2(s)$	-4126	-3890	241	$I_2(s)$	0	0	116
$CaSO_4(s)$	-1433	-1320	107	$I_2(g)$	62	19	261
$CaSiO_3(s)$	-1630	-1550	84	$I_2(aq)$	23	16	137
Carbon				$I^-(aq)$	-55	-52	106
$C(s)$ (graphite)	0	0	6	Iron			
$C(s)$ (diamond)	2	3	2	$Fe(s)$	0	0	27
$CO(g)$	-110.5	-137	198	$Fe_3C(s)$	21	15	108
$CO_2(g)$	-393.5	-394	214	$Fe_{0.95}O(s)$			
$CH_4(g)$	-75	-51	186	(wustite)	-264	-240	59
$CH_3OH(g)$	-201	-163	240	$FeO(s)$	-272	-255	61
$CH_3OH(l)$	-239	-166	127	$Fe_3O_4(s)$			
$H_2CO(g)$	-116	-110	219	(magnetite)	-1117	-1013	146
$HCOOH(g)$	-363	-351	249	$Fe_2O_3(s)$			
$HCN(g)$	135.1	125	202	(hematite)	-826	-740	90
$C_2H_2(g)$	227	209	201	$FeS(s)$	-95	-97	67
$C_2H_4(g)$	52	68	219	$FeS_2(s)$	-178	-166	53
$CH_3CHO(g)$	-166	-129	250	$FeSO_4(s)$	-929	-825	121
$C_2H_5OH(l)$	-278	-175	161	Lead			
$C_2H_6(g)$	-84.7	-32.9	229.5	$Pb(s)$	0	0	65
$C_3H_6(g)$	20.9	62.7	266.9	$PbO_2(s)$	-277	-217	69
$C_3H_8(g)$	-104	-24	270	$PbS(s)$	-100	-99	91
$C_2H_4O(g)$				$PbSO_4(s)$	-920	-813	149
(ethylene oxide)	-53	-13	242	Magnesium			
$CH_2PCHCN(g)$	185.0	195.4	274	$Mg(s)$	0	0	33
$CH_3COOH(l)$	-484	-389	160	$MgCO_3(s)$	-1113	-1029	66
$C_6H_{12}O_6(s)$	-1275	-911	212	$MgO(s)$	-602	-569	27
$CCl_4(l)$	-135	-65	216	$Mg(OH)_2(s)$	-925	-834	64
Chlorine				Manganese			
$Cl_2(g)$	0	0	223	$Mn(s)$	0	0	32
$Cl_2(aq)$	-23	7	121	$MnO(s)$	-385	-363	60
$Cl^-(aq)$	-167	-131	57	$Mn_3O_4(s)$	-1387	-1280	149
$HCl(g)$	-92	-95	187	$Mn_2O_3(s)$	-971	-893	110
Chromium				$MnO_2(s)$	-521	-466	53
$Cr(s)$	0	0	24	$MnO_4^-(aq)$	-543	-449	190
$Cr_2O_3(s)$	-1128	-1047	81	Mercury			
$CrO_3(s)$	-579	-502	72	$Hg(l)$	0	0	76
Copper				$Hg_2Cl_2(s)$	-265	-211	196
$Cu(s)$	0	0	33	$HgCl_2(s)$	-230	-184	144
$CuCO_3(s)$	-595	-518	88	$HgO(s)$	-90	-59	70
$Cu_2O(s)$	-170	-148	93	$HgS(s)$	-58	-49	78
$CuO(s)$	-156	-128	43	Nickel			
$Cu(OH)_2(s)$	-450	-372	108	$Ni(s)$	0	0	30
$CuS(s)$	-49	-49	67	$NiCl_2(s)$	-316	-272	107
Fluorine				$NiO(s)$	-241	-213	38
$F_2(g)$	0	0	203	$Ni(OH)_2(s)$	-538	-453	79
$F^-(aq)$	-333	-279	-14	$NiS(s)$	-93	-90	53
$HF(g)$	-271	-273	174	Nitrogen			
Hydrogen				$N_2(g)$	0	0	192
$H_2(g)$	0	0	131	$NH_3(g)$	-46	-17	193
$H(g)$	217	203	115	$NH_3(aq)$	-80	-27	111
$H^+(aq)$	0	0	0	$NH_4^+(aq)$	-132	-79	113
$OH^-(aq)$	-230	-157	-11	$NO(g)$	90	87	211

Appendix Four (continued)

Substance and State	ΔH_f° (kJ/mol)	ΔG_f° (kJ/mol)	S° (J K^{-1} mol^{-1})	Substance and State	ΔH_f° (kJ/mol)	ΔG_f° (kJ/mol)	S° (J K^{-1} mol^{-1})
$NO_2(g)$	34	52	240	$NaHCO_3(s)$	−948	−852	102
$N_2O(g)$	82	104	220	$NaCl(s)$	−411	−384	72
$N_2O_4(g)$	10	98	304	$NaH(s)$	−56	−33	40
$N_2O_4(l)$	−20	97	209	$NaI(s)$	−288	−282	91
$N_2O_5(s)$	−42	134	178	$NaNO_2(s)$	−359	—	—
$N_2H_4(l)$	51	149	121	$NaNO_3(s)$	−467	−366	116
$N_2H_3CH_3(l)$	54	180	166	$Na_2O(s)$	−416	−377	73
$HNO_3(aq)$	−207	−111	146	$Na_2O_2(s)$	−515	−451	95
$HNO_3(l)$	−174	−81	156	$NaOH(s)$	−427	−381	64
$NH_4ClO_4(s)$	−295	−89	186	$NaOH(aq)$	−470	−419	50
$NH_4Cl(s)$	−314	−203	96	**Sulfur**			
Oxygen				$S(s)$ (rhombic)	0	0	32
$O_2(g)$	0	0	205	$S(s)$ (monoclinic)	0.3	0.1	33
$O(g)$	249	232	161	$S^{2-}(aq)$	33	86	−15
$O_3(g)$	143	163	239	$S_8(g)$	102	50	431
Phosphorus				$SF_6(g)$	−1209	−1105	292
$P(s)$ (white)	0	0	41	$H_2S(g)$	−21	−34	206
$P(s)$ (red)	−18	−12	23	$SO_2(g)$	−297	−300	248
$P(s)$ (black)	−39	−33	23	$SO_3(g)$	−396	−371	257
$P_4(g)$	59	24	280	$SO_4^{2-}(aq)$	−909	−745	20
$PF_5(g)$	−1578	−1509	296	$H_2SO_4(l)$	−814	−690	157
$PH_3(g)$	5	13	210	$H_2SO_4(aq)$	−909	−745	20
$H_3PO_4(s)$	−1279	−1119	110	**Tin**			
$H_3PO_4(l)$	−1267	—	—	$Sn(s)$ (white)	0	0	52
$H_3PO_4(aq)$	−1288	−1143	158	$Sn(s)$ (gray)	−2	0.1	44
$P_4O_{10}(s)$	−2984	−2698	229	$SnO(s)$	−285	−257	56
Potassium				$SnO_2(s)$	−581	−520	52
$K(s)$	0	0	64	$Sn(OH)_2(s)$	−561	−492	155
$KCl(s)$	−436	−408	83	**Titanium**			
$KClO_3(s)$	−391	−290	143	$TiCl_4(g)$	−763	−727	355
$KClO_4(s)$	−433	−304	151	$TiO_2(s)$	−945	−890	50
$K_2O(s)$	−361	−322	98	**Uranium**			
$K_2O_2(s)$	−496	−430	113	$U(s)$	0	0	50
$KO_2(s)$	−283	−238	117	$UF_6(s)$	−2137	−2008	228
$KOH(s)$	−425	−379	79	$UF_6(g)$	−2113	−2029	380
$KOH(aq)$	−481	−440	9.20	$UO_2(s)$	−1084	−1029	78
Silicon				$U_3O_8(s)$	−3575	−3393	282
$SiO_2(s)$ (quartz)	−911	−856	42	$UO_3(s)$	−1230	−1150	99
$SiCl_4(l)$	−687	−620	240	**Xenon**			
Silver				$Xe(g)$	0	0	170
$Ag(s)$	0	0	43	$XeF_2(g)$	−108	−48	254
$Ag^+(aq)$	105	77	73	$XeF_4(s)$	−251	−121	146
$AgBr(s)$	−100	−97	107	$XeF_6(g)$	−294	—	—
$AgCN(s)$	146	164	84	$XeO_3(s)$	402	—	—
$AgCl(s)$	−127	−110	96	**Zinc**			
$Ag_2CrO_4(s)$	−712	−622	217	$Zn(s)$	0	0	42
$AgI(s)$	−62	−66	115	$ZnO(s)$	−348	−318	44
$Ag_2O(s)$	−31	−11	122	$Zn(OH)_2(s)$	−642	—	—
$Ag_2S(s)$	−32	−40	146	$ZnS(s)$			
Sodium				(wurtzite)	−193	—	—
$Na(s)$	0	0	51	$ZnS(s)$			
$Na^+(aq)$	−240	−262	59	(zinc blende)	−206	−201	58
$NaBr(s)$	−360	−347	84	$ZnSO_4(s)$	−983	−874	120
$Na_2CO_3(s)$	−1131	−1048	136				

Appendix Five | Equilibrium Constants and Reduction Potentials

Table A5.1

K_a for Some Common Monoprotic Acids

Name	Formula	Value of K_a
Hydrogen sulfate ion	HSO_4^-	1.2×10^{-2}
Chlorous acid	$HClO_2$	1.2×10^{-2}
Monochloracetic acid	$HC_2H_2ClO_2$	1.35×10^{-3}
Hydrofluoric acid	HF	7.2×10^{-4}
Nitrous acid	HNO_2	4.0×10^{-4}
Formic acid	HCO_2H	1.8×10^{-4}
Lactic acid	$HC_3H_5O_3$	1.38×10^{-4}
Benzoic acid	$HC_7H_5O_2$	6.4×10^{-5}
Acetic acid	$HC_2H_3O_2$	1.8×10^{-5}
Hydrated aluminum(III) ion	$[Al(H_2O)_6]^{3+}$	1.4×10^{-5}
Propanoic acid	$HC_3H_5O_2$	1.3×10^{-5}
Hypochlorous acid	$HOCl$	3.5×10^{-8}
Hypobromous acid	$HOBr$	2×10^{-9}
Hydrocyanic acid	HCN	6.2×10^{-10}
Boric acid	H_3BO_3	5.8×10^{-10}
Ammonium ion	NH_4^+	5.6×10^{-10}
Phenol	HOC_6H_5	1.6×10^{-10}
Hypoiodous acid	HOI	2×10^{-11}

Table A5.2

Stepwise Dissociation Constants for Several Common Polyprotic Acids

Name	Formula	K_{a_1}	K_{a_2}	K_{a_3}
Phosphoric acid	H_3PO_4	7.5×10^{-3}	6.2×10^{-8}	4.8×10^{-13}
Arsenic acid	H_3AsO_4	5×10^{-3}	8×10^{-8}	6×10^{-10}
Carbonic acid	H_2CO_3	4.3×10^{-7}	4.8×10^{-11}	
Sulfuric acid	H_2SO_4	Large	1.2×10^{-2}	
Sulfurous acid	H_2SO_3	1.5×10^{-2}	1.0×10^{-7}	
Hydrosulfuric acid	H_2S	1.0×10^{-7}	$\sim 10^{-19}$	
Oxalic acid	$H_2C_2O_4$	6.5×10^{-2}	6.1×10^{-5}	
Ascorbic acid (vitamin C)	$H_2C_6H_6O_6$	7.9×10^{-5}	1.6×10^{-12}	
Citric acid	$H_3C_6H_5O_7$	8.4×10^{-4}	1.8×10^{-5}	4.0×10^{-6}

Table A5.3

K_b for Some Common Weak Bases

Name	Formula	Conjugate Acid	K_b
Ammonia	NH_3	NH_4^+	1.8×10^{-5}
Methylamine	CH_3NH_2	$CH_3NH_3^+$	4.38×10^{-4}
Ethylamine	$C_2H_5NH_2$	$C_2H_5NH_3^+$	5.6×10^{-4}
Diethylamine	$(C_2H_5)_2NH$	$(C_2H_5)_2NH_2^+$	1.3×10^{-3}
Triethylamine	$(C_2H_5)_3N$	$(C_2H_5)_3NH^+$	4.0×10^{-4}
Hydroxylamine	$HONH_2$	$HONH_3^+$	1.1×10^{-8}
Hydrazine	H_2NNH_2	$H_2NNH_3^+$	3.0×10^{-6}
Aniline	$C_6H_5NH_2$	$C_6H_5NH_3^+$	3.8×10^{-10}
Pyridine	C_5H_5N	$C_5H_5NH^+$	1.7×10^{-9}

Table A5.4

Values of K_{sp} at 25°C for Common Ionic Solids

Ionic Solid	K_{sp} (at 25°C)	Ionic Solid	K_{sp} (at 25°C)	Ionic Solid	K_{sp} (at 25°C)
Fluorides		**Chromates** (*continued*)		**Hydroxides** (*continued*)	
BaF_2	2.4×10^{-5}	Hg_2CrO_4*	2×10^{-9}	$Co(OH)_3$	2.5×10^{-16}
MgF_2	6.4×10^{-9}	$BaCrO_4$	8.5×10^{-11}	$Ni(OH)_2$	1.6×10^{-16}
PbF_2	4×10^{-8}	Ag_2CrO_4	9.0×10^{-12}	$Zn(OH)_2$	4.5×10^{-17}
SrF_2	7.9×10^{-10}	$PbCrO_4$	2×10^{-16}	$Cu(OH)_2$	1.6×10^{-19}
CaF_2	4.0×10^{-11}			$Hg(OH)_2$	3×10^{-26}
		Carbonates		$Sn(OH)_2$	3×10^{-27}
Chlorides		$NiCO_3$	1.4×10^{-7}	$Cr(OH)_3$	6.7×10^{-31}
$PbCl_2$	1.6×10^{-5}	$CaCO_3$	8.7×10^{-9}	$Al(OH)_3$	2×10^{-32}
$AgCl$	1.6×10^{-10}	$BaCO_3$	1.6×10^{-9}	$Fe(OH)_3$	4×10^{-38}
Hg_2Cl_2*	1.1×10^{-18}	$SrCO_3$	7×10^{-10}	$Co(OH)_3$	2.5×10^{-43}
		$CuCO_3$	2.5×10^{-10}		
Bromides		$ZnCO_3$	2×10^{-10}	**Sulfides**	
$PbBr_2$	4.6×10^{-6}	$MnCO_3$	8.8×10^{-11}	MnS	2.3×10^{-13}
$AgBr$	5.0×10^{-13}	$FeCO_3$	2.1×10^{-11}	FeS	3.7×10^{-19}
Hg_2Br_2*	1.3×10^{-22}	Ag_2CO_3	8.1×10^{-12}	NiS	3×10^{-21}
		$CdCO_3$	5.2×10^{-12}	CoS	5×10^{-22}
Iodides		$PbCO_3$	1.5×10^{-15}	ZnS	2.5×10^{-22}
PbI_2	1.4×10^{-8}	$MgCO_3$	1×10^{-15}	SnS	1×10^{-26}
AgI	1.5×10^{-16}	Hg_2CO_3*	9.0×10^{-15}	CdS	1.0×10^{-28}
Hg_2I_2*	4.5×10^{-29}			PbS	7×10^{-29}
		Hydroxides		CuS	8.5×10^{-45}
Sulfates		$Ba(OH)_2$	5.0×10^{-3}	Ag_2S	1.6×10^{-49}
$CaSO_4$	6.1×10^{-5}	$Sr(OH)_2$	3.2×10^{-4}	HgS	1.6×10^{-54}
Ag_2SO_4	1.2×10^{-5}	$Ca(OH)_2$	1.3×10^{-6}		
$SrSO_4$	3.2×10^{-7}	$AgOH$	2.0×10^{-8}	**Phosphates**	
$PbSO_4$	1.3×10^{-8}	$Mg(OH)_2$	8.9×10^{-12}	Ag_3PO_4	1.8×10^{-18}
$BaSO_4$	1.5×10^{-9}	$Mn(OH)_2$	2×10^{-13}	$Sr_3(PO_4)_2$	1×10^{-31}
		$Cd(OH)_2$	5.9×10^{-15}	$Ca_3(PO_4)_2$	1.3×10^{-32}
Chromates		$Pb(OH)_2$	1.2×10^{-15}	$Ba_3(PO_4)_2$	6×10^{-39}
$SrCrO_4$	3.6×10^{-5}	$Fe(OH)_2$	1.8×10^{-15}	$Pb_3(PO_4)_2$	1×10^{-54}

*Contains Hg_2^{2+} ions. $K_{sp} = [Hg_2^{2+}][X^-]^2$ for Hg_2X_2 salts.

Table A5.5

Standard Reduction Potentials at 25°C (298 K) for Many Common Half-Reactions

Half-Reaction	$\mathscr{E}°$ (V)	Half-Reaction	$\mathscr{E}°$ (V)
$F_2 + 2e^- \longrightarrow 2F^-$	2.87	$O_2 + 2H_2O + 4e^- \longrightarrow 4OH^-$	0.40
$Ag^{2+} + e^- \longrightarrow Ag^+$	1.99	$Cu^{2+} + 2e^- \longrightarrow Cu$	0.34
$Co^{3+} + e^- \longrightarrow Co^{2+}$	1.82	$Hg_2Cl_2 + 2e^- \longrightarrow 2Hg + 2Cl^-$	0.27
$H_2O_2 + 2H^+ + 2e^- \longrightarrow 2H_2O$	1.78	$AgCl + e^- \longrightarrow Ag + Cl^-$	0.22
$Ce^{4+} + e^- \longrightarrow Ce^{3+}$	1.70	$SO_4^{2-} + 4H^+ + 2e^- \longrightarrow H_2SO_3 + H_2O$	0.20
$PbO_2 + 4H^+ + SO_4^{2-} + 2e^- \longrightarrow PbSO_4 + 2H_2O$	1.69	$Cu^{2+} + e^- \longrightarrow Cu^+$	0.16
$MnO_4^+ + 4H^+ + 3e^- \longrightarrow MnO_2 + 2H_2O$	1.68	$2H^+ + 2e^- \longrightarrow H_2$	0.00
$IO_4^- + 2H^+ + 2e^- \longrightarrow IO_3^- + H_2O$	1.60	$Fe^{3+} + 3e^- \longrightarrow Fe$	-0.036
$MnO_4^+ + 8H^+ + 5e^- \longrightarrow Mn^{2+} + 4H_2O$	1.51	$Pb^{2+} + 2e^- \longrightarrow Pb$	-0.13
$Au^{3+} + 3e^- \longrightarrow Au$	1.50	$Sn^{2+} + 2e^- \longrightarrow Sn$	-0.14
$PbO_2 + 4H^+ + 2e^- \longrightarrow Pb^{2+} + 2H_2O$	1.46	$Ni^{2+} + 2e^- \longrightarrow Ni$	-0.23
$Cl_2 + 2e^- \longrightarrow 2Cl^-$	1.36	$PbSO_4 + 2e^- \longrightarrow Pb + SO_4^{2-}$	-0.35
$Cr_2O_7^{2-} + 14H^+ + 6e^- \longrightarrow 2Cr^{3+} + 7H_2O$	1.33	$Cd^{2+} + 2e^- \longrightarrow Cd$	-0.40
$O_2 + 4H^+ + 4e^- \longrightarrow 2H_2O$	1.23	$Fe^{2+} + 2e^- \longrightarrow Fe$	-0.44
$MnO_2 + 4H^+ + 2e^- \longrightarrow Mn^{2+} + 2H_2O$	1.21	$Cr^{3+} + e^- \longrightarrow Cr^{2+}$	-0.50
$IO_3^- + 6H^+ + 5e^- \longrightarrow \frac{1}{2}I_2 + 3H_2O$	1.20	$Cr^{3+} + 3e^- \longrightarrow Cr$	-0.73
$Br_2 + 2e^- \longrightarrow 2Br^-$	1.09	$Zn^{2+} + 2e^- \longrightarrow Zn$	-0.76
$VO_2^+ + 2H^+ + e^- \longrightarrow VO^{2+} + H_2O$	1.00	$2H_2O + 2e^- \longrightarrow H_2 + 2OH^-$	-0.83
$AuCl_4^- + 3e^- \longrightarrow Au + 4Cl^-$	0.99	$Mn^{2+} + 2e^- \longrightarrow Mn$	-1.18
$NO_3^- + 4H^+ + 3e^- \longrightarrow NO + 2H_2O$	0.96	$Al^{3+} + 3e^- \longrightarrow Al$	-1.66
$ClO_2 + e^- \longrightarrow ClO_2^-$	0.954	$H_2 + 2e^- \longrightarrow 2H^-$	-2.23
$2Hg^{2+} + 2e^- \longrightarrow Hg_2^{2+}$	0.91	$Mg^{2+} + 2e^- \longrightarrow Mg$	-2.37
$Ag^+ + e^- \longrightarrow Ag$	0.80	$La^{3+} + 3e^- \longrightarrow La$	-2.37
$Hg_2^{2+} + 2e^- \longrightarrow 2Hg$	0.80	$Na^+ + e^- \longrightarrow Na$	-2.71
$Fe^{3+} + e^- \longrightarrow Fe^{2+}$	0.77	$Ca^{2+} + 2e^- \longrightarrow Ca$	-2.76
$O_2 + 2H^+ + 2e^- \longrightarrow H_2O_2$	0.68	$Ba^{2+} + 2e^- \longrightarrow Ba$	-2.90
$MnO_4^- + e^- \longrightarrow MnO_4^{2-}$	0.56	$K^+ + e^- \longrightarrow K$	-2.92
$I_2 + 2e^- \longrightarrow 2I^-$	0.54	$Li^+ + e^- \longrightarrow Li$	-3.05
$Cu^+ + e^- \longrightarrow Cu$	0.52		

Glossary

Note to the Student: The Glossary includes brief definitions of some of the fundamental terms used in chemistry. It does not include complex concepts that require detailed explanation for understanding. Please refer to the appropriate sections of the text for complete discussion of particular topics or concepts.

Accuracy: the agreement of a particular value with the true value. (A1.5)

Acid: a substance that produces hydrogen ions in solution; a proton donor. (4.2)

Acid–base indicator: a substance that marks the endpoint of an acid–base titration by changing color. (8.6)

Acid dissociation constant (K_a): the equilibrium constant for a reaction in which a proton is removed from an acid by H_2O to form the conjugate base and H_3O^+. (7.1)

Acid rain: a result of air pollution by sulfur dioxide. (5.11)

Actinide series: a group of 14 elements following actinium in the periodic table, in which the $5f$ orbitals are being filled. (12.13; 18.1)

Activated complex (transition state): the arrangement of atoms found at the top of the potential energy barrier as a reaction proceeds from reactants to products. (15.8)

Activation energy: the threshold energy that must be overcome to produce a chemical reaction. (15.8)

Addition polymerization: a type of polymerization in which the monomers simply add together to form the polymer, with no other products. (21.5)

Addition reaction: a reaction in which atoms add to a carbon–carbon multiple bond. (21.2)

Adiabatic process: a process that occurs without the transfer of energy as heat. (10.14)

Adsorption: the collection of one substance on the surface of another. (15.9)

Air pollution: contamination of the atmosphere, mainly by the gaseous products of transportation and production of electricity. (5.11)

Alcohol: an organic compound in which the hydroxyl group is a substituent on a hydrocarbon. (21.4)

Aldehyde: an organic compound containing the carbonyl group bonded to at least one hydrogen atom. (21.4)

Alkali metal: a Group 1A metal. (2.8; 18.2)

Alkaline earth metal: a Group 2A metal. (2.8; 18.4)

Alkane: a saturated hydrocarbon with the general formula C_nH_{2n+2}. (21.1)

Alkene: an unsaturated hydrocarbon containing a carbon–carbon double bond. The general formula is C_nH_{2n}. (21.2)

Alkyne: an unsaturated hydrocarbon containing a triple carbon–carbon bond. The general formula is C_nH_{2n-2}. (21.2)

Alloy: a substance that contains a mixture of elements and has metallic properties. (16.4)

Alloy steel: a form of steel containing carbon plus other metals such as chromium, cobalt, manganese, and molybdenum. (19.2)

Alpha (α) particle: a helium nucleus. (20.1)

Alpha-particle production: a common mode of decay for radioactive nuclides in which the mass number changes. (20.1)

Amine: an organic base derived from ammonia in which one or more of the hydrogen atoms are replaced by organic groups. (7.6; 21.4)

α-Amino acid: an organic acid in which an amino group and an R group are attached to the carbon atom next to the carboxyl group. (21.6)

Amorphous solid: a solid with considerable disorder in its structure. (16.3)

Ampere: the unit of electric current equal to one coulomb of charge per second. (11.7)

Amphoteric substance: a substance that can behave either as an acid or as a base. (7.2)

Angular momentum quantum number (ℓ): the quantum number relating to the shape of an atomic orbital, which can assume any integral value from 0 to $n - 1$ for each value of n. (12.9)

Anion: a negative ion. (2.7)

Anode: the electrode in a galvanic cell at which oxidation occurs. (11.1)

Antibonding molecular orbital: an orbital higher in energy than the atomic orbitals of which it is composed. (14.2)

Aqueous solution: a solution in which water is the dissolving medium or solvent. (4)

Aromatic hydrocarbon: one of a special class of cyclic unsaturated hydrocarbons, the simplest of which is benzene. (21.3)

Arrhenius concept: a concept postulating that acids produce hydrogen ions in aqueous solution, whereas bases produce hydroxide ions. (7.1)

Arrhenius equation: the equation representing the rate constant as $k = Ae^{-E_a/RT}$ where A represents the product of the collision frequency and the steric factor, and $e^{-E_a/RT}$ is the fraction of collisions with sufficient energy to produce a reaction. (15.8)

Atmosphere: the mixture of gases that surrounds the earth's surface. (5.11)

Atomic mass (average): the weighted average mass of the atoms in a naturally occurring element. (2.3)

Atomic number: the number of protons in the nucleus of an atom. (2.6)

Atomic radius: half the distance between the nuclei in a molecule consisting of identical atoms. (12.15)

Atomic solid: a solid that contains atoms at the lattice points. (16.3)

Aufbau principle: the principle stating that as protons are added one by one to the nucleus to build up the elements, electrons are similarly added to hydrogenlike orbitals. (12.13)

Autoionization: the transfer of a proton from one molecule to another of the same substance. (7.2)

Avogadro's law: equal volumes of gases at the same temperature and pressure contain the same number of particles. (5.2)

Avogadro's number: the number of atoms in exactly 12 grams of pure ^{12}C, equal to 6.022×10^{23}. (3.2)

Ball-and-stick model: a molecular model that distorts the sizes of atoms, but shows bond relationships clearly. (2.7)

Band model: a molecular model for metals in which the electrons are assumed to travel around the metal crystal in molecular orbitals formed from the valence atomic orbitals of the metal atoms. (16.4)

Barometer: a device for measuring atmospheric pressure. (5.1)

Base: a substance that produces hydroxide ions in aqueous solution, a proton acceptor. (7.2)

Base dissociation constant (K_b):   the equilibrium constant for the reaction of a base with water to produce the conjugate acid and hydroxide ion. (7.6)

Basic oxide: an ionic oxide that dissolves in water to produce a basic solution. (18.4)

Battery: a group of galvanic cells connected in series. (11.5)

Beta (β) particle: an electron produced in radioactive decay. (20.1)

Beta-particle production: a decay process for radioactive nuclides in which the mass number remains constant and the atomic number changes. The net effect is to change a neutron to a proton. (20.1)

Bidentate ligand: a ligand that can form two bonds to a metal ion. (19.3)

Bimolecular step: a reaction involving the collision of two molecules. (15.6)

Binary compound: a two-element compound. (2.9)

Binding energy (nuclear):   the energy required to decompose a nucleus into its component nucleons. (20.5)

Biomolecule: a molecule responsible for maintaining and/or reproducing life. (22)

Bond energy: the energy required to break a given chemical bond. (13.1)

Bond length: the distance between the nuclei of the two atoms connected by a bond; the distance where the total energy of a diatomic molecule is minimal. (13.1)

Bond order: the difference between the number of bonding electrons and the number of antibonding electrons, divided by two. It is an index of bond strength. (14.2)

Bonding molecular orbital: an orbital lower in energy than the atomic orbitals of which it is composed. (14.2)

Bonding pair: an electron pair found in the space between two atoms. (13.9)

Borane: a covalent hydride of boron. (18.5)

Boyle's law: the volume of a given sample of gas at constant temperature varies inversely with the pressure. (5.2)

Breeder reactor: a nuclear reactor in which fissionable fuel is produced while the reactor runs. (20.6)

Brønsted–Lowry definition (model):   a model proposing that an acid is a proton donor, and a base is a proton acceptor. (7.1)

Buffer capacity: the ability of a buffered solution to absorb protons or hydroxide ions without a significant change in pH; determined by the magnitudes of [HA] and [A⁻] in the solution. (8.4)

Buffered solution: a solution that resists a change in its pH when either hydroxide ions or protons are added. (8.2)

Calorimetry: the science of measuring heat flow. (9.4)

Capillary action: the spontaneous rising of a liquid in a narrow tube. (16.2)

Carbohydrate: a polyhydroxyl ketone or polyhydroxyl aldehyde or a polymer composed of these. (21.6)

Carboxyhemoglobin: a stable complex of hemoglobin and carbon monoxide that prevents normal oxygen uptake in the blood. (19.8)

Carboxyl group: the —COOH group in an organic acid. (7.2; 21.4)

Carboxylic acid: an organic compound containing the carboxyl group; an acid with the general formula RCOOH. (21.4)

Catalyst: a substance that speeds up a reaction without being consumed. (15.9)

Cathode: the electrode in a galvanic cell at which reduction occurs. (11.1)

Cathode rays: the "rays" emanating from the negative electrode (cathode) in a partially evacuated tube; a stream of electrons. (2.5)

Cathodic protection: a method in which an active metal, such as magnesium, is connected to steel to protect it from corrosion. (11.6)

Cation: a positive ion. (2.7)

Cell potential (electromotive force):   the driving force in a galvanic cell that pulls electrons from the reducing agent in one compartment to the oxidizing agent in the other. (11.1)

Ceramic: a nonmetallic material made from clay and hardened by firing at high temperature; it contains minute silicate crystals suspended in a glassy cement. (16.5)

Chain reaction (nuclear):   a self-sustaining fission process caused by the production of neutrons that proceed to split other nuclei. (20.6)

Charge balance: the positive and negative charges carried by the ions in an aqueous solution must balance. (7.9)

Charles's law: the volume of a given sample of gas at constant pressure is directly proportional to the temperature in kelvins. (5.2)

Chelating ligand (chelate):   a ligand having more than one atom with a lone pair that can be used to bond to a metal ion. (19.3)

Chemical bond: the energy that holds two atoms together in a compound. (2.7)

Chemical equation: a representation of a chemical reaction showing the relative numbers of reactant and product molecules. (3.6)

Chemical equilibrium: a dynamic reaction system in which the concentrations of all reactants and products remain constant as a function of time. (6)

Chemical formula: the representation of a molecule in which the symbols for the elements are used to indicate the types of atoms present and subscripts are used to show the relative numbers of atoms. (2.7)

Chemical kinetics: the area of chemistry that concerns reaction rates. (15)

Chemical stoichiometry: the calculation of the quantities of material consumed and produced in chemical reactions. (3)

Chirality: the quality of having nonsuperimposable mirror images. (19.4)

Chlor-alkali process: the process for producing chlorine and sodium hydroxide by electrolyzing brine in a mercury cell. (11.8)

Coagulation: the destruction of a colloid by causing particles to aggregate and settle out. (17.8)

Codons: organic bases in sets of three that form the genetic code. (21.6)

Colligative properties: properties of a solution that depend on the number, and not on the identity, of the solute particles. (17.5)

Collision model: a model based on the idea that molecules must collide to react; used to account for the observed characteristics of reaction rates. (15.8)

Colloid: a suspension of particles in a dispersing medium. (17.8)

Combustion reaction: the vigorous and exothermic reaction that takes place between certain substances, particularly organic compounds, and oxygen. (21.1)

Common ion effect: the shift in an equilibrium position caused by the addition or presence of an ion involved in the equilibrium reaction. (8.1)

Complete ionic equation: an equation that shows all substances that are strong electrolytes as ions. (4.6)

Complex ion: a charged species consisting of a metal ion surrounded by ligands. (8.9; 19.1)

Compound: a substance with constant composition that can be broken down into elements by chemical processes. (2.7)

Concentration cell: a galvanic cell in which both compartments contain the same components, but at different concentrations. (11.4)

Condensation: the process by which vapor molecules re-form a liquid. (16.10)

Condensation polymerization: a type of polymerization in which the formation of a small molecule, such as water, accompanies the extension of the polymer chain. (21.5)

Condensed states of matter: liquids and solids. (16.1)

Conduction bands: the molecular orbitals that can be occupied by mobile electrons, which are free to travel throughout a metal crystal to conduct electricity or heat. (16.4)

Conjugate acid: the species formed when a proton is added to a base. (7.1)

Conjugate acid–base pair: two species related to each other by the donating and accepting of a single proton. (7.1)

Conjugate base: what remains of an acid molecule after a proton is lost. (7.1)

Continuous spectrum: a spectrum that exhibits all the wavelengths of visible light. (12.3)

Control rods: rods in a nuclear reactor composed of substances that absorb neutrons. These rods regulate the power level of the reactor. (20.6)

Coordinate covalent bond: a metal–ligand bond resulting from the interaction of a Lewis base (the ligand) and a Lewis acid (the metal ion). (19.3)

Coordination compound: a compound composed of a complex ion and counter ions sufficient to give no net charge. (19.3)

Coordination isomerism: isomerism in a coordination compound in which the composition of the coordination sphere of the metal ion varies. (19.4)

Coordination number: the number of bonds formed between the metal ion and the ligands in a complex ion. (19.3)

Copolymer: a polymer formed from the polymerization of more than one type of monomer. (21.5)

Core electron: an inner electron in an atom; one not in the outermost (valence) principal quantum level. (12.13)

Corrosion: the process by which metals are oxidized in the atmosphere. (11.6)

Coulomb's law: $E = 2.31 \times 10^{-19} (Q_1Q_2/r)$, where E is the energy of interaction between a pair of ions, expressed in joules; r is the distance between the ion centers in nm; and Q_1 and Q_2 are the numerical ion charges. (13.1)

Counter ions: anions or cations that balance the charge on the complex ion in a coordination compound. (19.3)

Covalent bonding: a type of bonding in which electrons are shared by atoms. (2.7; 13.1)

Critical mass: the mass of fissionable material required to produce a self-sustaining chain reaction. (20.6)

Critical point: the point on a phase diagram at which the temperature and pressure have their critical values; the endpoint of the liquid–vapor line. (16.11)

Critical pressure: the minimum pressure required to produce liquefaction of a substance at the critical temperature. (16.11)

Critical reaction (nuclear):   a reaction in which exactly one neutron from each fission event causes another fission event, thus sustaining the chain reaction. (20.6)

Critical temperature: the temperature above which vapor cannot be liquefied, no matter what pressure is applied. (16.11)

Crosslinking: the existence of bonds between adjacent chains in a polymer, thus adding strength to the material. (21.5)

Crystal field model: a model used to explain the magnetism and colors of coordination complexes through the splitting of the d orbital energies. (19.6)

Crystalline solid: a solid with a regular arrangement of its components. (16.3)

Cubic closest packed (ccp) structure: a solid modeled by the closest packing of spheres with an *abcabc* arrangement of layers; the unit cell is face-centered cubic. (16.4)

Cyclotron: a type of particle accelerator in which an ion introduced at the center is accelerated in an expanding spiral path by use of alternating electric fields in the presence of a magnetic field. (20.3)

Cytochromes: a series of iron-containing species composed of heme and a protein. Cytochromes are the principal electron-transfer molecules in the respiratory chain. (19.8)

Dalton's law of partial pressures: for a mixture of gases in a container, the total pressure exerted is the sum of the pressures that each gas would exert if it were alone. (5.5)

Degenerate orbitals: a group of orbitals with the same energy. (12.9)

Dehydrogenation reaction: a reaction in which two hydrogen atoms are removed from adjacent carbons of a saturated hydrocarbon, giving an unsaturated hydrocarbon. (21.1)

Delocalization: the condition where the electrons in a molecule are not localized between a pair of atoms but can move throughout the molecule. (13.9)

Denaturation: the breaking down of the three-dimensional structure of a protein resulting in the loss of its function. (21.6)

Denitrification: the return of nitrogen from decomposed matter to the atmosphere by bacteria that change nitrates to nitrogen gas. (18.8)

Deoxyribonucleic acid (DNA): a huge nucleotide polymer having a double-helical structure with complementary bases on the two strands. Its major functions are protein synthesis and the storage and transport of genetic information. (21.6)

Desalination: the removal of dissolved salts from an aqueous solution. (17.6)

Dialysis: a phenomenon in which a semipermeable membrane allows transfer of both solvent molecules and small solute molecules and ions. (17.6)

Diamagnetism: a type of magnetism, associated with paired electrons, that causes a substance to be repelled from the inducing magnetic field. (14.3)

Differential rate law: an expression that gives the rate of a reaction as a function of concentrations; often called the rate law. (15.2)

Diffraction: the scattering of light from a regular array of points or lines, producing constructive and destructive interference. (12.2)

Diffusion: the mixture of gases. (5.7)

Dilution: the process of adding solvent to lower the concentration of solute in a solution. (4.3)

Dimer: a molecule formed by the joining of two identical monomers. (21.5)

Dipole–dipole attraction: the attractive force resulting when polar molecules line up so that the positive and negative ends are close to each other. (16.1)

Dipole moment: a property of a molecule whose charge distribution can be represented by a center of positive charge and a center of negative charge. (13.3)

Disaccharide: a sugar formed from two monosaccharides joined by a glycoside linkage. (21.6)

Disproportionation reaction: a reaction in which a given element is both oxidized and reduced. (18.13)

Disulfide linkage: a S—S bond that stabilizes the tertiary structure of many proteins. (21.6)

Double bond: a bond in which two pairs of electrons are shared by two atoms. (13.8)

Downs cell: a cell used for electrolyzing molten sodium chloride. (11.8)

Dry cell battery: a common battery used in calculators, watches, radios, and portable audio players. (11.5)

Dual nature of light: the statement that light exhibits both wave and particulate properties. (12.2)

$E = mc^2$: Einstein's equation proposing that energy has mass; E is energy, m is mass, and c is the speed of light. (12.2)

Effective nuclear charge: the apparent nuclear charge exerted on a particular electron, equal to the actual nuclear charge minus the effect of electron repulsions. (12.11)

Effusion: the passage of a gas through a tiny orifice into an evacuated chamber. (5.7)

Electrical conductivity: the ability to conduct an electric current. (4.2)

Electrochemistry: the study of the interchange of chemical and electrical energy. (11)

Electrolysis: a process that involves forcing a current through a cell to cause a nonspontaneous chemical reaction to occur. (11.7)

Electrolyte: a material that dissolves in water to give a solution that conducts an electric current. (4.2)

Electrolytic cell: a cell that uses electrical energy to produce a chemical change that would otherwise not occur spontaneously. (11.7)

Electromagnetic radiation: radiant energy that exhibits wavelike behavior and travels through space at the speed of light in a vacuum. (12.1)

Electron: a negatively charged particle that moves around the nucleus of an atom. (2.5)

Electron affinity: the energy change associated with the addition of an electron to a gaseous atom. (12.15)

Electron capture: a process in which one of the inner-orbital electrons in an atom is captured by the nucleus. (20.1)

Electron sea model: a model for metals postulating a regular array of cations in a "sea" of electrons. (16.4)

Electron spin quantum number: a quantum number representing one of the two possible values for the electron spin; either $+\frac{1}{2}$ or $-\frac{1}{2}$. (12.10)

Electronegativity: the tendency of an atom in a molecule to attract shared electrons to itself. (13.2)

Element: a substance that cannot be decomposed into simpler substances by chemical or physical means. (2.1)

Elementary step: a reaction whose rate law can be written from its molecularity. (15.6)

Empirical formula: the simplest whole number ratio of atoms in a compound. (3.5)

Enantiomers: isomers that are nonsuperimposable mirror images of each other. (19.4)

Endpoint: the point in a titration at which the indicator changes color. (4.9)

Endothermic: refers to a reaction where energy (as heat) flows into the system. (9.1)

Energy: the capacity to do work or to cause heat flow. (9.1)

Enthalpy: a property of a system equal to $E + PV$, where E is the internal energy of the system, P is the pressure of the system, and V is the volume of the system. At constant pressure, where only PV work is allowed, the change in enthalpy equals the energy flow as heat. (9.2)

Enthalpy of fusion: the enthalpy change that occurs to melt a solid at its melting point. (16.10)

Entropy: a thermodynamic function that measures randomness or disorder. (10.1)

Enzyme: a large molecule, usually a protein, that catalyzes biological reactions. (15.9)

Equilibrium (thermodynamic definition): the position where the free energy of a reaction system has its lowest possible value. (10.11)

Equilibrium constant: the value obtained when equilibrium concentrations of the chemical species are substituted in the equilibrium expression. (6.2)

Equilibrium expression: the expression (from the law of mass action) obtained by multiplying the product concentrations and dividing by the multiplied reactant concentrations, with each concentration raised to a power represented by the coefficient in the balanced equation. (6.2)

Equilibrium position: a particular set of equilibrium concentrations. (6.2)

Equivalence point (stoichiometric point): the point in a titration when enough titrant has been added to react exactly with the substance in solution being titrated. (4.9; 8.4)

Exothermic: refers to a reaction where energy (as heat) flows out of the system. (9.1)

Exponential notation: expresses a number as $N \times 10^M$, a convenient method for representing a very large or very small number and for easily indicating the number of significant figures. (A1.1)

Faraday: a constant representing the charge on one mole of electrons; 96,485 coulombs. (11.3)

First law of thermodynamics: the energy of the universe is constant; same as the law of conservation of energy. (9.1)

Fission: the process of using a neutron to split a heavy nucleus into two nuclei with smaller mass numbers. (20.6)

Formal charge: the charge assigned to an atom in a molecule or polyatomic ion derived from a specific set of rules. (13.12)

Formation constant (stability constant): the equilibrium constant for each step of the formation of a complex ion by the addition of an individual ligand to a metal ion or complex ion in aqueous solution. (8.9)

Fossil fuel: coal, petroleum, or natural gas; consists of carbon-based molecules derived from decomposition of once-living organisms. (9.7)

Frasch process: the recovery of sulfur from underground deposits by melting it with hot water and forcing it to the surface by air pressure. (18.12)

Free energy: a thermodynamic function equal to the enthalpy (H) minus the product of the entropy (S) and the kelvin temperature (T); $G = H - TS$. Under certain conditions the change in free energy for a process is equal to the maximum useful work. (10.7)

Free radical: a species with an unpaired electron. (21.5)

Frequency: the number of waves (cycles) per second that pass a given point in space. (12.1)

Fuel cell: a galvanic cell for which the reactants are continuously supplied. (11.5)

Functional group: an atom or group of atoms in hydrocarbon derivatives that contains elements in addition to carbon and hydrogen. (21.4)

Fusion: the process of combining two light nuclei to form a heavier, more stable nucleus. (20.6)

Galvanic cell: a device in which chemical energy from a spontaneous redox reaction is changed to electrical energy that can be used to do work. (11.1)

Galvanizing: a process in which steel is coated with zinc to prevent corrosion. (11.6)

Gamma (γ) ray: a high-energy photon. (20.1)

Geiger-Müller counter (Geiger counter): an instrument that measures the rate of radioactive decay based on the ions and electrons produced as a radioactive particle passes through a gas-filled chamber. (20.4)

Gene: a given segment of the DNA molecule that contains the code for a specific protein. (21.6)

Geometrical (*cis-trans*) isomerism: isomerism in which atoms or groups of atoms can assume different positions around a rigid ring or bond. (19.4; 21.2)

Glass: an amorphous solid obtained when silica is mixed with other compounds, heated above its melting point, and then cooled rapidly. (16.5)

Glass electrode: an electrode for measuring pH from the potential difference that develops when it is dipped into an aqueous solution containing H^+ ions. (11.4)

Glycosidic linkage: a C—O—C bond formed between the rings of two cyclic monosaccharides by the elimination of water. (21.6)

Graham's law of effusion: the rate of effusion of a gas is inversely proportional to the square root of the mass of its particles. (5.7)

Gravimetric analysis: a method for determining the amount of a given substance in a solution by precipitation, filtration, drying, and weighing. (4.8)

Greenhouse effect: a warming effect exerted by the earth's atmosphere (particularly CO_2 and H_2O) due to thermal energy retained by absorption of infrared radiation. (9.7)

Ground state: the lowest possible energy state of an atom or molecule. (12.4)

Group (of the periodic table): a vertical column of elements having the same valence electron configuration and showing similar properties. (2.8)

Haber process: the manufacture of ammonia from nitrogen and hydrogen, carried out at high pressure and high temperature with the aid of a catalyst. (3.9; 6.1; 18.8)

Half-life (of a radioactive sample): the time required for the number of nuclides in a radioactive sample to reach half of the original value. (20.2)

Half-life (of a reaction): the time required for a reactant to reach half of its original concentration. (15.4)

Half-reactions: the two parts of an oxidation–reduction reaction, one representing oxidation, the other reduction. (4.11; 11.1)

Halogen: a Group 7A element. (2.8; 18.13)

Halogenation: the addition of halogen atoms to unsaturated hydrocarbons. (21.2)

Hard water: water from natural sources that contains relatively large concentrations of calcium and magnesium ions. (18.4)

Heat: energy transferred between two objects caused by a temperature difference between them. (9.1)

Heat capacity: the amount of energy required to raise the temperature of an object by one degree Celsius. (9.4)

Heat of fusion: the enthalpy change that occurs to melt a solid at its melting point. (16.10)

Heat of hydration: the enthalpy change associated with placing gaseous molecules or ions in water; the sum of the energy needed to expand the solvent and the energy released from the solvent–solute interactions. (17.2)

Heat of solution: the enthalpy change associated with dissolving a solute in a solvent; the sum of the energies needed to expand both solvent and solute in a solution and the energy released from the solvent–solute interactions. (17.2)

Heat of vaporization: the energy required to vaporize one mole of a liquid at a pressure of one atmosphere. (16.10)

Heating curve: a plot of temperature versus time for a substance where energy is added at a constant rate. (16.10)

Heisenberg uncertainty principle: a principle stating that there is a fundamental limitation to how precisely both the position and momentum of a particle can be known at a given time. (12.5)

Heme: an iron complex. (19.8)

Hemoglobin: a biomolecule composed of four myoglobin-like units (proteins plus heme) that can bind and transport four oxygen molecules in the blood. (19.8)

Henderson–Hasselbalch equation: an equation giving the relationship between the pH of an acid–base system and the concentrations of base and acid

$$\text{pH} = \text{p}K_a + \log\left(\frac{[\text{base}]}{[\text{acid}]}\right). \quad (8.2)$$

Henry's law: the amount of a gas dissolved in a solution is directly proportional to the pressure of the gas above the solution. (17.3)

Hess's law: in going from a particular set of reactants to a particular set of products, the enthalpy change is the same whether the reaction takes place in one step or in a series of steps; in summary, enthalpy is a state function. (9.5)

Heterogeneous equilibrium: an equilibrium involving reactants and/or products in more than one phase. (6.5)

Hexagonal closest packed (hcp) structure: a structure composed of closest packed spheres with an *ababab* arrangement of layers; the unit cell is hexagonal. (16.4)

Homogeneous equilibrium: an equilibrium system where all reactants and products are in the same phase. (6.5)

Homopolymer: a polymer formed from the polymerization of only one type of monomer. (21.5)

Hund's rule: the lowest-energy configuration for an atom is the one having the maximum number of unpaired electrons allowed by the Pauli exclusion principle in a particular set of degenerate orbitals, with all unpaired electrons having parallel spins. (12.13)

Hybrid orbitals: a set of atomic orbitals adopted by an atom in a molecule different from those of the atom in the free state. (14.1)

Hybridization: a mixing of the native orbitals on a given atom to form special atomic orbitals for bonding. (14.1)

Hydration: the interaction between solute particles and water molecules. (4.1)

Hydride: a binary compound containing hydrogen. The hydride ion, H^-, exists in ionic hydrides. The three classes of hydrides are covalent, interstitial, and ionic. (18.3)

Hydrocarbon: a compound composed of carbon and hydrogen. (23.1)

Hydrocarbon derivative: an organic molecule that contains one or more elements in addition to carbon and hydrogen. (21.4)

Hydrogen bonding: unusually strong dipole–dipole attractions that occur among molecules in which hydrogen is bonded to a highly electronegative atom. (16.1)

Hydrogenation reaction: a reaction in which hydrogen is added, with a catalyst present, to a carbon–carbon multiple bond. (21.2)

Hydrohalic acid: an aqueous solution of a hydrogen halide. (18.13)

Hydronium ion: the H_3O^+ ion; a hydrated proton. (7.1)

Hypothesis: one or more assumptions put forth to explain the observed behavior of nature. (1.3)

Ideal gas: a gas that obeys the equation, $PV = nRT$. (5.2)

Ideal gas law: an equation of state for a gas, where the state of the gas is its condition at a given time; expressed by $PV = nRT$, where P = pressure, V = volume, n = moles of the gas, R = the universal gas constant, and T = absolute temperature. This equation expresses behavior approached by real gases at high T and low P. (5.3)

Ideal solution: a solution whose vapor pressure is directly proportional to the mole fraction of solvent present. (17.4)

Indicator: a chemical that changes color and is used to mark the endpoint of a titration. (4.9; 8.5)

Inert pair effect: the tendency for the heavier Group 3A elements to exhibit the +1 as well as the expected +3 oxidation states, and Group 4A elements to exhibit the +2 as well as the +4 oxidation states. (18.5)

Integrated rate law: an expression that shows the concentration of a reactant as a function of time. (15.2)

Intermediate: a species that is neither a reactant nor a product but that is formed and consumed in the reaction sequence. (15.6)

Intermolecular forces: relatively weak interactions that occur between molecules. (16.1)

Internal energy: a property of a system that can be changed by a flow of work, heat, or both; $\Delta E = q + w$, where ΔE is the change in the internal energy of the system, q is heat, and w is work. (9.1)

Ion: an atom or a group of atoms that has a net positive or negative charge. (2.7)

Ion exchange (water softening): the process in which an ion-exchange resin removes unwanted ions (for example, Ca^{2+} and Mg^{2+}) and replaces them with Na^+ ions, which do not interfere with soap and detergent action. (18.4)

Ion pairing: a phenomenon occurring in solution when oppositely charged ions aggregate and behave as a single particle. (17.7)

Ion-product constant (K_w): the equilibrium constant for the autoionization of water; $K_w = [H^+][OH^-]$. At 25°C, K_w equals 1.0×10^{-14}. (7.2)

Ion-selective electrode: an electrode sensitive to the concentration of a particular ion in solution. (11.4)

Ionic bonding: the electrostatic attraction between oppositely charged ions. (2.7; 13.1)

Ionic compound (binary): a compound that results when a metal reacts with a nonmetal to form a cation and an anion. (13.1)

Ionic solid: a solid containing cations and anions that dissolves in water to give a solution containing the separated ions, which are mobile and thus free to conduct electric current. (16.3)

Ionization energy: the quantity of energy required to remove an electron from a gaseous atom or ion. (12.15)

Irreversible process: any real process. When a system undergoes the changes State 1 → State 2 → State 1 by any real pathway, the universe is different than before the cyclic process took place in the system. (10.2)

Isoelectronic ions: ions containing the same number of electrons. (13.4)

Isomers: species with the same formula but different properties. (19.4)

Isothermal process: a process in which the temperature remains constant. (10.2)

Isotonic solutions: solutions having identical osmotic pressures. (17.6)

Isotopes: atoms of the same element (the same number of protons) with different numbers of neutrons. They have identical atomic numbers but different mass numbers. (2.6)

Ketone: an organic compound containing the carbonyl group

bonded to two carbon atoms. (21.4)

Kinetic energy ($\frac{1}{2} mv^2$)**:** energy resulting from the motion of an object; dependent on the mass of the object and the square of its velocity. (9.1)

Kinetic molecular theory: a model that assumes that an ideal gas is composed of tiny particles (molecules) in constant motion. (5.6)

Lanthanide contraction: the decrease in the atomic radii of the lanthanide series elements, going from left to right in the periodic table. (19.1)

Lanthanide series: a group of 14 elements following lanthanum in the periodic table, in which the $4f$ orbitals are being filled. (12.13; 18.1; 19.1)

Lattice: a three-dimensional system of points designating the positions of the centers of the components of a solid (atoms, ions, or molecules). (16.3)

Lattice energy: the energy change occurring when separated gaseous ions are packed together to form an ionic solid. (13.5)

Law of conservation of energy: energy can be converted from one form to another but can be neither created nor destroyed. (9.1)

Law of conservation of mass: mass is neither created nor destroyed. (2.2)

Law of definite proportion: a given compound always contains exactly the same proportion of elements by mass. (2.2)

Law of mass action: a general description of the equilibrium condition; it defines the equilibrium constant expression. (6.2)

Law of multiple proportions: when two elements form a series of compounds, the ratios of the masses of the second element that combine with one gram of the first element can always be reduced to small whole numbers. (2.2)

Lead storage battery: a battery (used in cars) in which the anode is lead, the cathode is lead coated with lead dioxide, and the electrolyte is a sulfuric acid solution. (11.5)

Le Châtelier's principle: if a change is imposed on a system at equilibrium, the position of the equilibrium will shift in a direction that tends to reduce the effect of that change. (6.8)

Lewis acid: an electron-pair acceptor. (19.3)

Lewis base: an electron-pair donor. (19.3)

Lewis structure: a diagram of a molecule showing how the valence electrons are arranged among the atoms in the molecule. (13.10)

Ligand: a neutral molecule or ion having a lone pair of electrons that can be used to form a bond to a metal ion; a Lewis base. (19.3)

Lime-soda process: a water-softening method in which lime and soda ash are added to water to remove calcium and magnesium ions by precipitation. (7.6)

Limiting reactant (limiting reagent): the reactant that is completely consumed when a reaction is run to completion. (3.9)

Line spectrum: a spectrum showing only certain discrete wavelengths. (12.3)

Linear accelerator: a type of particle accelerator in which a changing electric field is used to accelerate a positive ion along a linear path. (20.3)

Linkage isomerism: isomerism involving a complex ion where the ligands are all the same but the point of attachment of at least one of the ligands differs. (19.4)

Liquefaction: the transformation of a gas into a liquid. (18.1)

Localized electron (LE) model: a model that assumes that a molecule is composed of atoms that are bound together by sharing pairs of electrons using the atomic orbitals of the bound atoms. (13.9)

London dispersion forces: the forces, existing among noble gas atoms and nonpolar molecules, that involve an accidental dipole that induces a momentary dipole in a neighbor. (16.1)

Lone pair: an electron pair that is localized on a given atom; an electron pair not involved in bonding. (13.9)

Magnetic quantum number (m_ℓ)**:** the quantum number relating to the orientation of an orbital in space relative to the other orbitals with the same ℓ quantum number. It can have integral values between ℓ and $-\ell$, including zero. (12.9)

Main-group (representative) elements: elements in the groups labeled 1A, 2A, 3A, 4A, 5A, 6A, 7A, and 8A in the periodic table. The group number gives the sum of valence s and p electrons. (12.13; 18.1)

Major species: the components present in relatively large amounts in a solution. (7.4)

Manometer: a device for measuring the pressure of a gas in a container. (5.1)

Mass defect: the change in mass occurring when a nucleus is formed from its component nucleons. (20.5)

Mass number: the total number of protons and neutrons in the atomic nucleus of an atom. (2.6)

Mass percent: the percent by mass of a component of a mixture (17.1) or of a given element in a compound. (3.4)

Mass spectrometer: an instrument used to determine the relative masses of atoms by the deflection of their ions in a magnetic field. (3.1)

Matter: the material of the universe.

Mean free path: the average distance a molecule in a given gas sample travels between collisions with other molecules. (5.6; 5.9)

Measurement: a quantitative observation. (A1.5)

Messenger RNA (mRNA): a special RNA molecule built in the cell nucleus that migrates into the cytoplasm and participates in protein synthesis. (21.6)

Metal: an element that gives up electrons relatively easily and is lustrous, malleable, and a good conductor of heat and electricity. (2.8)

Metalloids (semimetals): elements along the division line in the periodic table between metals and nonmetals. These elements exhibit both metallic and nonmetallic properties. (12.16; 18.1)

Metallurgy: the process of separating a metal from its ore and preparing it for use. (18.1)

Millimeters of mercury (mm Hg): a unit of pressure, also called a torr; 760 mm Hg = 760 torr = 101,325 Pa = 1 standard atmosphere. (5.1)

Mixture: a material of variable composition that contains two or more substances.

Model (theory): a set of assumptions put forth to explain the observed behavior of matter. The models of chemistry usually involve assumptions about the behavior of individual atoms or molecules. (1.3)

Moderator: a substance used in a nuclear reactor to slow down the neutrons. (20.6)

Molal boiling-point elevation constant: a constant characteristic of a particular solvent that gives the change in boiling point as a function of solution molality; used in molecular weight determinations. (17.5)

Molal freezing-point depression constant: a constant characteristic of a particular solvent that gives the change in freezing point as a function of the solution molality; used in molecular weight determinations. (17.5)

Molality: the number of moles of solute per kilogram of solvent in a solution. (17.1)

Molar heat capacity: the energy required to raise the temperature of one mole of a substance by one degree Celsius. (9.3; 9.4)

Molar mass: the mass in grams of one mole of molecules or formula units of a substance; also called molecular weight. (3.3)

Molar volume: the volume of one mole of an ideal gas; equal to 22.42 liters at STP. (5.4)

Molarity: moles of solute per volume of solution in liters. (4.3; 17.1)

Mole (mol): the number equal to the number of carbon atoms in exactly 12 grams of pure ^{12}C; Avogadro's number. One mole represents 6.022×10^{23} units. (3.2)

Mole fraction: the ratio of the number of moles of a given component in a mixture to the total number of moles in the mixture. (5.5; 17.1)

Mole ratio (stoichiometry): the ratio of moles of one substance to moles of another substance in a balanced chemical equation. (3.8)

Molecular equation: an equation representing a reaction in solution showing the reactants and products in undissociated form, whether they are strong or weak electrolytes. (4.6)

Molecular formula: the exact formula of a molecule, giving the types of atoms and the number of each type. (3.5)

Molecular orbital (MO) model: a model that regards a molecule as a collection of nuclei and electrons, where the electrons are assumed to occupy orbitals much as they do in atoms, but having the orbitals extend over the entire molecule. In this model the electrons are assumed to be delocalized rather than always located between a given pair of atoms. (14.2)

Molecular orientations (kinetics): orientations of molecules during collisions, some of which can lead to a reaction and some of which cannot. (15.8)

Molecular solid: a solid composed of neutral molecules at the lattice points. (16.3)

Molecular structure: the three-dimensional arrangement of atoms in a molecule. (13.13)

Molecular weight: the mass in grams of one mole of molecules or formula units of a substance; also called molar mass. (3.3)

Molecularity: the number of species that must collide to produce the reaction represented by an elementary step in a reaction mechanism. (15.6)

Molecule: a bonded collection of two or more atoms of the same or different elements. (2.7)

Monodentate (unidentate) ligand: a ligand that can form one bond to a metal ion. (19.3)

Monoprotic acid: an acid with one acidic proton. (7.2)

Monosaccharide (simple sugar): a polyhydroxy ketone or aldehyde containing from three to nine carbon atoms. (21.6)

Myoglobin: an oxygen-storing biomolecule consisting of a heme complex and a protein. (19.8)

Natural law: a statement that expresses generally observed behavior. (1.3)

Nernst equation: an equation relating the potential of an electrochemical cell to the concentrations of the cell components

$$\mathscr{E} = \mathscr{E}^\circ - \frac{0.0591}{n} \log(Q) \text{ at } 25°C. \quad (11.4)$$

Net ionic equation: an equation for a reaction in solution, where strong electrolytes are written as ions, showing only those components that are directly involved in the chemical change. (4.6)

Network solid: an atomic solid containing strong directional covalent bonds. (16.5)

Neutralization reaction: an acid–base reaction. (4.9)

Neutron: a particle in the atomic nucleus with mass virtually equal to the proton's but with no charge. (2.6)

Nitrogen cycle: the conversion of N_2 to nitrogen-containing compounds, followed by the return of nitrogen gas to the atmosphere by natural decay processes. (18.8)

Nitrogen fixation: the process of transforming N_2 to nitrogen-containing compounds useful to plants. (18.8)

Nitrogen-fixing bacteria: bacteria in the root nodules of plants that can convert atmospheric nitrogen to ammonia and other nitrogen-containing compounds useful to plants. (18.8)

Noble gas: a Group 8A element. (2.8; 18.14)

Node: an area of an orbital having zero electron probability. (12.9)

Nonelectrolyte: a substance that, when dissolved in water, gives a nonconducting solution. (4.2)

Nonmetal: an element not exhibiting metallic characteristics. Chemically, a typical nonmetal accepts electrons from a metal. (2.8)

Normal boiling point: the temperature at which the vapor pressure of a liquid is exactly one atmosphere. (16.10)

Normal melting point: the temperature at which the solid and liquid states have the same vapor pressure under conditions where the total pressure on the system is one atmosphere. (16.10)

Normality: the number of equivalents of a substance dissolved in a liter of solution. (17.1)

Nuclear atom: an atom having a dense center of positive charge (the nucleus) with electrons moving around the outside. (2.5)

Nuclear transformation: the change of one element into another. (20.3)

Nucleon: a particle in an atomic nucleus, either a neutron or a proton. (2.6)

Nucleotide: a monomer of the nucleic acids composed of a five-carbon sugar, a nitrogen-containing base, and phosphoric acid. (21.6)

Nucleus: the small, dense center of positive charge in an atom. (2.5)

Nuclide: the general term applied to each unique atom; represented by $^A_Z X$, where X is the symbol for a particular element. (20.2)

Octet rule: the observation that atoms of nonmetals tend to form the most stable molecules when they are surrounded by eight electrons (to fill their valence orbitals). (13.10)

Optical isomerism: isomerism in which the isomers have opposite effects on plane-polarized light. (19.4)

Orbital: a specific wave function for an electron in an atom. The square of this function gives the probability distribution for the electron. (12.5)

d-Orbital splitting: a splitting of the *d* orbitals of the metal ion in a complex such that the orbitals pointing at the ligands have higher energies than those pointing between the ligands. (19.6)

Order (of reactant): the positive or negative exponent, determined by experiment, of the reactant concentration in a rate law. (15.2)

Organic acid: an acid with a carbon-atom backbone; often contains the carboxyl group. (7.2)

Organic chemistry: the study of carbon-containing compounds (typically chains of carbon atoms) and their properties. (21)

Osmosis: the flow of solvent into a solution through a semipermeable membrane. (17.6)

Osmotic pressure (π): the pressure that must be applied to a solution to stop osmosis; $= MRT$. (17.6)

Ostwald process: a commercial process for producing nitric acid by the oxidation of ammonia. (18.8)

Oxidation: an increase in oxidation state (a loss of electrons). (4.10; 11.1)

Oxidation–reduction (redox) reaction: a reaction in which one or more electrons are transferred. (4.4; 4.10; 11.1)

Oxidation states: a concept that provides a way to keep track of electrons in oxidation–reduction reactions according to certain rules. (4.10)

Oxidizing agent (electron acceptor): a reactant that accepts electrons from another reactant. (4.10; 11.1)

Oxyacid: an acid in which the acidic proton is attached to an oxygen atom. (7.2)

Ozone: O_3, the form of elemental oxygen in addition to the much more common O_2. (18.11)

Paramagnetism: a type of induced magnetism, associated with unpaired electrons, that causes a substance to be attracted into the inducing magnetic field. (14.3)

Partial pressures: the independent pressures exerted by different gases in a mixture. (5.5)

Particle accelerator: a device used to accelerate nuclear particles to very high speeds. (20.3)

Pascal: the SI unit of pressure; equal to newtons per meter squared. (5.1)

Pauli exclusion principle: in a given atom no two electrons can have the same set of four quantum numbers. (12.10)

Penetration effect: the effect whereby a valence electron penetrates the core electrons, thus reducing the shielding effect and increasing the effective nuclear charge. (12.14)

Peptide linkage: the bond resulting from the condensation reaction between amino acids; represented by

$$\overset{O}{\underset{}{-\overset{\|}{C}}}-\overset{H}{\underset{}{\overset{|}{N}}}-\qquad (22.6)$$

Percent dissociation: the ratio of the amount of a substance that is dissociated at equilibrium to the initial concentration of the substance in a solution, multiplied by 100. (7.5)

Percent yield: the actual yield of a product as a percentage of the theoretical yield. (3.9)

Periodic table: a chart showing all the elements arranged in columns with similar chemical properties. (2.8)

pH curve (titration curve): a plot showing the pH of a solution being analyzed as a function of the amount of titrant added. (8.5)

pH scale: a log scale based on 10 and equal to $-\log[H^+]$; a convenient way to represent solution acidity. (7.3)

Phase diagram: a convenient way of representing the phases of a substance in a closed system as a function of temperature and pressure. (16.11)

Phenyl group: the benzene molecule minus one hydrogen atom. (21.3)

Photochemical smog: air pollution produced by the action of light on oxygen, nitrogen oxides, and unburned fuel from auto exhaust to form ozone and other pollutants. (5.11)

Photon: a quantum of electromagnetic radiation. (12.2)

Physical change: a change in the form of a substance, but not in its chemical composition; chemical bonds are not broken in a physical change.

Pi (π) bond: a covalent bond in which parallel p orbitals share an electron pair occupying the space above and below the line joining the atoms. (14.1)

Planck's constant: the constant relating the change in energy for a system to the frequency of the electromagnetic radiation absorbed or emitted; equal to 6.626×10^{-34} J s. (12.2)

Polar covalent bond: a covalent bond in which the electrons are not shared equally because one atom attracts them more strongly than the other. (13.1)

Polar molecule: a molecule that has a permanent dipole moment. (4.1)

Polyatomic ion: an ion containing a number of atoms. (2.7)

Polyelectronic atom: an atom with more than one electron. (12.11)

Polymer: a large, usually chainlike molecule built from many small molecules (monomers). (21.5)

Polymerization: a process in which many small molecules (monomers) are joined together to form a large molecule. (21.2)

Polypeptide: a polymer formed from amino acids joined together by peptide linkages. (21.6)

Polyprotic acid: an acid with more than one acidic proton. It dissociates in a stepwise manner, one proton at a time. (7.7)

Porous disk: a disk in a tube connecting two different solutions in a galvanic cell that allows ion flow without extensive mixing of the solutions. (11.1)

Porphyrin: a planar ligand with a central ring structure and various substituent groups at the edges of the ring. (19.8)

Positional probability: a type of probability that depends on the number of arrangements in space that yield a particular state. (10.1)

Positron production: a mode of nuclear decay in which a particle is formed having the same mass as an electron but opposite charge. The net effect is to change a proton to a neutron. (20.1)

Potential energy: energy resulting from position or composition. (9.1)

Precipitation reaction: a reaction in which an insoluble substance forms and separates from the solution. (4.5)

Precision: the degree of agreement among several measurements of the same quantity; the reproducibility of a measurement. (A1.5)

Primary structure (of a protein): the order (sequence) of amino acids in the protein chain. (21.6)

Principal quantum number: the quantum number relating to the size and energy of an orbital; it can have any positive integer value. (12.9)

Probability distribution: the square of the wave function indicating the probability of finding an electron at a particular point in space. (12.8)

Product: a substance resulting from a chemical reaction. It is shown to the right of the arrow in a chemical equation. (3.6)

Protein: a natural high-molecular-weight polymer formed by condensation reactions between amino acids. (21.6)

Proton: a positively charged particle in an atomic nucleus. (2.6; 20)

Qualitative analysis: the separation and identification of individual ions from a mixture. (4.7; 8.9)

Quantization: the concept that energy can occur only in discrete units called quanta. (12.2)

Rad: a unit of radiation dosage corresponding to 10^{-2} J of energy deposited per kilogram of tissue (from *r*adiation *a*bsorbed *d*ose). (20.7)

Radioactive decay (radioactivity): the spontaneous decomposition of a nucleus to form a different nucleus. (20.1)

Radiocarbon dating (carbon-14 dating): a method for dating ancient wood or cloth based on the rate of radioactive decay of the nuclide $^{14}_{6}C$. (20.4)

Radiotracer: a radioactive nuclide, introduced into an organism for diagnostic purposes, whose pathway can be traced by monitoring its radioactivity. (20.4)

Random error: an error that has an equal probability of being high or low. (A1.5)

Raoult's law: the vapor pressure of a solution is directly proportional to the mole fraction of solvent present. (17.4)

Rate constant: the proportionality constant in the relationship between reaction rate and reactant concentrations. (15.2)

Rate of decay: the change in the number of radioactive nuclides in a sample per unit time. (20.2)

Rate-determining step: the slowest step in a reaction mechanism, the one determining the overall rate. (15.6)

Rate law (differential rate law): an expression that shows how the rate of reaction depends on the concentration of reactants. (15.2)

Reactant: a starting substance in a chemical reaction. It appears to the left of the arrow in a chemical equation. (3.6)

Reaction mechanism: the series of elementary steps involved in a chemical reaction. (15.6)

Reaction quotient: a quotient obtained by applying the law of mass action to initial concentrations rather than to equilibrium concentrations. (6.6)

Reaction rate: the change in concentration of a reactant or product per unit time. (15.1)

Reactor core: the part of a nuclear reactor where the fission reaction takes place. (20.6)

Reducing agent (electron donor): a reactant that donates electrons to another substance to reduce the oxidation state of one of its atoms. (4.10; 11.1)

Reduction: a decrease in oxidation state (a gain of electrons). (4.10; 11.1)

Rem: a unit of radiation dosage that accounts for both the energy of the dose and its effectiveness in causing biological damage (from *r*oentgen *e*quivalent for *m*an). (20.7)

Resonance: a condition occurring when more than one valid Lewis structure can be written for a particular molecule. The actual electronic structure is not represented by any one of the Lewis structures but by the average of all of them. (13.11)

Reverse osmosis: the process occurring when the external pressure on a solution causes a net flow of solvent through a semipermeable membrane from the solution to the solvent. (17.6)

Reversible process: a cyclic process carried out by a hypothetical pathway, which leaves the universe exactly the same as it was before the process. No real process is reversible. (10.2)

Ribonucleic acid (RNA): a nucleotide polymer that transmits the genetic information stored in DNA to the ribosomes for protein synthesis. (21.6)

Root mean square velocity: the square root of the average of the squares of the individual velocities of gas particles. (5.6)

Salt: an ionic compound. (7.8)

Salt bridge: a U-tube containing an electrolyte that connects the two compartments of a galvanic cell, allowing ion flow without extensive mixing of the different solutions. (11.1)

Scientific method: the process of studying natural phenomena, involving observations, forming laws and theories, and testing of theories by experimentation. (1.3)

Scintillation counter: an instrument that measures radioactive decay by sensing the flashes of light produced in a substance by the radiation. (20.4)

Second law of thermodynamics: in any spontaneous process, there is always an increase in the entropy of the universe. (10.5)

Secondary structure (of a protein): the three-dimensional structure of the protein chain (for example, α-helix, random coil, or pleated sheet). (21.6)

Selective precipitation: a method of separating metal ions from an aqueous mixture by using a reagent whose anion forms a precipitate with only one or a few of the ions in the mixture. (4.7; 8.8)

Semiconductor: a substance conducting only a slight electric current at room temperature, but showing increased conductivity at higher temperatures. (16.5)

Semipermeable membrane: a membrane that allows solvent but not solute molecules to pass through. (17.6)

Shielding: the effect by which the other electrons screen, or shield, a given electron from some of the nuclear charge. (12.14)

SI units: International System of units based on the metric system and units derived from the metric system. (A2.1)

Side chain (of amino acid): the hydrocarbon group on an amino acid represented by H, CH_3, or a more complex substituent. (21.6)

Sigma (σ) bond: a covalent bond in which the electron pair is shared in an area centered on a line running between the atoms. (14.1)

Significant figures: the certain digits and the first uncertain digit of a measurement. (A1.5)

Silica: the fundamental silicon–oxygen compound, which has the empirical formula SiO_2, and forms the basis of quartz and certain types of sand. (16.5)

Silicates: salts that contain metal cations and polyatomic silicon–oxygen anions that are usually polymeric. (16.5)

Single bond: a bond in which one pair of electrons is shared by two atoms. (13.8)

Solubility: the amount of a substance that dissolves in a given volume of solvent at a given temperature. (4.2)

Solubility product constant: the constant for the equilibrium expression representing the dissolving of an ionic solid in water. (8.8)

Solute: a substance dissolved in a liquid to form a solution. (4.2; 17.1)

Solution: a homogeneous mixture. (17)

Solvent: the dissolving medium in a solution. (4.2)

Somatic damage: radioactive damage to an organism resulting in its sickness or death. (20.7)

Space-filling model: a model of a molecule showing the relative sizes of the atoms and their relative orientations. (2.7)

Specific heat capacity: the energy required to raise the temperature of one gram of a substance by one degree Celsius. (9.4)

Spectator ions: ions present in solution that do not participate directly in a reaction. (4.6)

Spectrochemical series: a listing of ligands in order based on their ability to produce d-orbital splitting. (19.6)

Spectroscopy: the study of the interaction of electromagnetic radiation within matter. (14.7)

Spontaneous fission: the spontaneous splitting of a heavy nuclide into two lighter nuclides. (20.1)

Spontaneous process: a process that occurs without outside intervention. (10.1)

Standard atmosphere: a unit of pressure equal to 760 mm Hg. (5.1)

Standard enthalpy of formation: the enthalpy change that accompanies the formation of one mole of a compound at 25°C from its elements, with all substances in their standard states at that temperature. (9.6)

Standard free energy change: the change in free energy that will occur for one unit of reaction if the reactants in their standard states are converted to products in their standard states. (10.9)

Standard free energy of formation: the change in free energy that accompanies the formation of one mole of a substance from its constituent elements with all reactants and products in their standard states. (10.9)

Standard hydrogen electrode: a platinum conductor in contact with 1 M H^+ ions and bathed by hydrogen gas at one atmosphere. (11.2)

Standard reduction potential: the potential of a half-reaction under standard state conditions, as measured against the potential of the standard hydrogen electrode. (11.2)

Standard solution: a solution whose concentration is accurately known. (4.3)

Standard state: a reference state for a specific substance defined according to a set of conventional definitions. (9.6)

Standard temperature and pressure (STP): the condition 0°C and 1 atm of pressure. (5.4)

Standing wave: a stationary wave as on a string of a musical instrument; in the wave mechanical model, the electron in the hydrogen atom is considered to be a standing wave. (12.5)

State function: a property that is independent of the pathway. (9.1)

States of matter: the three different forms in which matter can exist: solid, liquid, and gas. (5)

Stereoisomerism: isomerism in which all the bonds in the isomers are the same but the spatial arrangements of the atoms are different. (19.4)

Steric factor: the factor (always less than one) that reflects the fraction of collisions with orientations that can produce a chemical reaction. (15.8)

Stoichiometric quantities: quantities of reactants mixed in exactly the correct amounts so that all are used up at the same time. (3.9)

Strong acid: an acid that completely dissociates to produce a H^+ ion and the conjugate base. (4.2; 7.2)

Strong base: a metal hydroxide salt that completely dissociates into its ions in water. (4.2; 7.6)

Strong electrolyte: a material that, when dissolved in water, gives a solution that conducts an electric current very efficiently. (4.2)

Structural formula: the representation of a molecule in which the relative positions of the atoms are shown and the bonds are indicated by lines. (2.7)

Structural isomerism: isomerism in which the isomers contain the same atoms but one or more bonds differ. (19.4; 21.1)

Subcritical reaction (nuclear): a reaction in which less than one neutron causes another fission event and the process dies out. (20.6)

Sublimation: the process by which a substance goes directly from the solid to the gaseous state without passing through the liquid state. (16.10)

Subshell: a set of orbitals with a given angular momentum quantum number. (12.9)

Substitution reaction (hydrocarbons): a reaction in which an atom, usually a halogen, replaces a hydrogen atom in a hydrocarbon. (21.1)

Supercooling: the process of cooling a liquid below its freezing point without its changing to a solid. (16.10)

Supercritical reaction (nuclear): a reaction in which more than one neutron from each fission event causes another fission event. The process rapidly escalates to a violent explosion. (20.6)

Superheating: the process of heating a liquid above its boiling point without its boiling. (16.10)

Superoxide: a compound containing the O_2^- anion. (18.2)

Surface tension: the resistance of a liquid to an increase in its surface area. (16.2)

Surroundings: everything in the universe surrounding a thermodynamic system. (9.1)

Syngas: synthetic gas, a mixture of carbon monoxide and hydrogen, obtained by coal gasification. (9.8)

System (thermodynamic): that part of the universe on which attention is to be focused. (9.1)

Systematic error: an error that always occurs in the same direction. (A1.5)

Termolecular step: a reaction involving the simultaneous collision of three molecules. (15.6)

Tertiary structure (of a protein): the overall shape of a protein, long and narrow or globular, maintained by different types of intramolecular interactions. (21.6)

Theoretical yield: the maximum amount of a given product that can be formed when the limiting reactant is completely consumed. (3.9)

Theory: a set of assumptions put forth to explain some aspect of the observed behavior of matter. (1.3)

Thermal pollution: the oxygen-depleting effect on lakes and rivers of using water for industrial cooling and returning it to its natural source at a higher temperature. (17.3)

Thermodynamic stability (nuclear): the potential energy of a particular nucleus as compared with the sum of the potential energies of its component protons and neutrons. (20.1)

Thermodynamics: the study of energy and its interconversions. (9.1)

Third law of thermodynamics: the entropy of a perfect crystal at 0 K is zero. (10.8)

Titration: a technique in which one solution is used to analyze another. (4.9)

Torr: another name for millimeter of mercury (mm Hg). (5.1)

Transfer RNA (tRNA): a small RNA fragment that finds specific amino acids and attaches them to the protein chain as dictated by the codons in mRNA. (21.6)

Transition metals: several series of elements in which inner orbitals (d or f orbitals) are being filled. (12.13; 18.1)

Transuranium elements: the elements beyond uranium that are made artificially by particle bombardment. (20.3)

Triple bond: a bond in which three pairs of electrons are shared by two atoms. (13.8)

Triple point: the point on a phase diagram at which all three states of a substance are present. (16.11)

Tyndall effect: the scattering of light by particles in a suspension. (17.8)

Uncertainty (in measurement): the characteristics that any measurement involves estimates and cannot be exactly reproduced. (A1.5)

Unimolecular step: a reaction step involving only one molecule. (15.6)

Unit cell: the smallest repeating unit of a lattice. (16.3)

Unit factor: an equivalence statement between units used for converting from one unit to another. (A2.2)

Universal gas constant: the combined proportionality constant in the ideal gas law; 0.08206 L atm/K mol or 8.3145 J/K mol. (5.3)

Valence electrons: the electrons in the outermost principal quantum level of an atom. (12.13)

Valence shell electron-pair repulsion (VSEPR) model: a model whose main postulate is that the structure around a given atom in a molecule is determined principally by minimizing electron-pair repulsions. (13.13)

van der Waals's equation: a mathematical expression for describing the behavior of real gases. (5.10)

van't Hoff factor: the ratio of moles of particles in solution to moles of solute dissolved. (17.7)

Vapor pressure: the pressure of the vapor over a liquid at equilibrium. (16.10)

Vaporization: the change in state that occurs when a liquid evaporates to form a gas. (16.10)

Viscosity: the resistance of a liquid to flow. (16.2)

Volt: the unit of electrical potential defined as one joule of work per coulomb of charge transferred. (11.1)

Voltmeter: an instrument that measures cell potential by drawing electric current through a known resistance. (11.1)

Volumetric analysis: a process involving titration of one solution with another. (4.9)

Wave function: a function of the coordinates of an electron's position in three-dimensional space that describes the properties of the electron. (12.5)

Wave mechanical model: a model for the hydrogen atom in which the electron is assumed to behave as a standing wave. (12.7)

Wavelength: the distance between two consecutive peaks or troughs in a wave. (12.1)

Weak acid: an acid that dissociates only slightly in aqueous solution. (4.2; 7.2)

Weak base: a base that reacts with water to produce hydroxide ions to only a slight extent in aqueous solution. (4.2; 7.6)

Weak electrolyte: a material that, when dissolved in water, gives a solution that conducts only a small electric current. (4.2)

Weight: the force exerted on an object by gravity. (2.3)

Work: force acting over a distance. (9.1)

X-ray diffraction: a technique for establishing the structures of crystalline solids by directing X rays of a single wavelength at a crystal and obtaining a diffraction pattern from which interatomic spaces can be determined. (16.3)

Zone of nuclear stability: the area encompassing the stable nuclides on a plot of their positions as a function of the number of protons and the number of neutrons in the nucleus. (20.1)

Index

Student Solutions Manual To Accompany

General Chemistry 162

TO THE STUDENT: HOW TO USE THIS GUIDE

Solutions to odd-numbered chapter exercises are in this manual. This "Solutions Guide" can be a valuable resource if you use it properly. The way <u>NOT</u> to use it is to look at an exercise in the book and then immediately check the solution, often saying to yourself, "That's easy, I can do it." Developing problem solving skills takes practice. Don't look up a solution to a problem until you have tried to work it on your own. If you are completely stuck, see if you can find a similar problem in the Sample Exercises in the chapter. Only look up the solution as a last resort. If you do this for a problem, look for a similar problem in the end of chapter exercises and try working it. The more problems you do, the easier chemistry becomes. It is also in your self interest to try to work as many problems as possible. Most exams that you will take in chemistry will involve a lot of problem solving. If you have worked several problems similar to the ones on an exam, you will do much better than if the exam is the first time you try to solve a particular type of problem. No matter how much you read and study the text, or how well you think you understand the material, you don't really understand it until you have taken the information in the text and applied the principles to problem solving. You will make mistakes, but the good students learn from their mistakes.

In this manual we have worked problems as in the textbook. We have shown intermediate answers to the correct number of significant figures and used the rounded answer in later calculations. Thus, some of your answers may differ slightly from ours. When we have not followed this convention, we have usually noted this in the solution. The most common exception is when working with the natural logarithm (ln) function, where we usually carried extra significant figures in order to reduce round-off error. In addition, we tried to use constants and conversion factors reported to at least one more significant figure as compared to numbers given in the problem. For some problems, this required the use of more precise atomic masses for H, C, N, and O as given in Chapter 3. This practice of carrying one extra significant figure in constants helps minimize round-off error.

TJH
SSZ

v

CHAPTER 13

BONDING: GENERAL CONCEPTS

Chemical Bonds and Electronegativity

11.   Electronegativity is the ability of an atom in a molecule to attract electrons to itself. Electronegativity is a bonding term. Electron affinity is the energy change when an electron is added to a substance. Electron affinity deals with isolated atoms in the gas phase.

A covalent bond is a sharing of electron pair(s) in a bond between two atoms. An ionic bond is a complete transfer of electrons from one atom to another to form ions. The electrostatic attraction of the oppositely charged ions is the ionic bond.

A pure covalent bond is an equal sharing of shared electron pair(s) in a bond. A polar covalent bond is an unequal sharing.

Ionic bonds form when there is a large difference in electronegativity between the two atoms bonding together. This usually occurs when a metal with a small electronegativity is bonded to a nonmetal having a large electronegativity. A pure covalent bond forms between atoms having identical or nearly identical eletronegativities. A polar covalent bond forms when there is an intermediate electronegativity difference. In general, nonmetals bond together by forming covalent bonds, either pure covalent or polar covalent.

Ionic bonds form due to the strong electrostatic attraction between two oppositely charged ions. Covalent bonds form because the shared electrons in the bond are attracted to two different nuclei, unlike the isolated atoms where electrons are only attracted to one nuclei. The attraction to another nuclei overrides the added electron-electron repulsions.

13.

	(IE – EA)	(IE – EA)/502	EN (text)	2006/502 = 4.0
F	2006 kJ/mol	4.0	4.0	
Cl	1604 kJ/mol	3.2	3.0	
Br	1463 kJ/mol	2.9	2.8	
I	1302 kJ/mol	2.6	2.5	

The values calculated from IE and EA show the same trend as (and agree fairly closely) with the values given in the text.

15.   Using the periodic table, we expect the general trend for electronegativity to be:

　　1. Increase as we go from left to right across a period

　　2. Decrease as we go down a group

　　a. $C < N < O$　　　　b. $Se < S < Cl$　　　　c. $Sn < Ge < Si$

　　d. $Tl < Ge < S$　　　　e. $Rb < K < Na$　　　　f. $Ga < B < O$

17.   The general trends in electronegativity used in Exercises 13.15 and 13.16 are only rules of thumb. In this exercise we use experimental values of electronegativities and can begin to see several exceptions. The order of EN using Figure 13.3 is:

　　a. $C (2.5) < N (3.0) < O (3.5)$ same as predicted

　　b. $Se (2.4) < S (2.5) < Cl (3.0)$ same

　　c. $Si (1.8) = Ge (1.8) = Sn (1.8)$ different   d. $Tl (1.8) = Ge (1.8) < S (2.5)$ different

　　e. $Rb (0.8) = K (0.8) < Na (0.9)$ different   f. $Ga (1.6) < B (2.0) < O (3.5)$ same

Most polar bonds using actual EN values:

　　a. Si–F and Ge–F (Ge–F predicted)　　　b. P–Cl (same as predicted)

　　c. S–F (same as predicted)　　　　　　d. Ti–Cl (same as predicted)

　　e. Si–H and Sn–H (Sn–H predicted)　　　f. Al–Br (Tl–Br predicted)

19.   Ionic character is proportional to the difference in electronegativity values between the two elements forming the bond. Using the trend in electronegativity, the order will be:

　　Br–Br < N–O < C–F < Ca–O < K–F
　　least   most
　　ionic character   ionic character

Note that Br–Br, N–O and C–F bonds are all covalent bonds since the elements are all non-metals. The Ca–O and K–F bonds are ionic, as is generally the case when a metal forms a bond with a nonmetal.

21.   Of the compounds listed, P_2O_5 is the only compound containing only covalent bonds. $(NH_4)_2SO_4$, $Ca_3(PO_4)_2$, K_2O, and KCl are all compounds composed of ions, so they exhibit ionic bonding. The polyatomic ions in $(NH_4)_2SO_4$ are NH_4^+ and SO_4^{2-}. Covalent bonds exist between the N and H atoms in NH_4^+ and between the S and O atoms in SO_4^{2-}. Therefore, $(NH_4)_2SO_4$ contains both ionic and covalent bonds. The same is true for $Ca_3(PO_4)_2$. The bonding is ionic between the Ca^{2+} and PO_4^{3-} ions and covalent between the P and O atoms in PO_4^{3-}. Therefore, $(NH_4)_2SO_4$ and $Ca_3(PO_4)_2$ are the compounds with both ionic and covalent bonds.

Ions and Ionic Compounds

23.   Anions are larger than the neutral atom, and cations are smaller than the neutral atom. For anions, the added electrons increase the electron-electron repulsions. To counteract this, the size of the electron cloud increases, placing the electrons further apart from one another. For cations, as electrons are removed, there are fewer electron-electron repulsions, and the electron cloud can be pulled closer to the nucleus.

Isoelectronic: same number of electrons. Two variables, the number of protons and the number of electrons, determine the size of an ion. Keeping the number of electrons constant, we only have to consider the number of protons to predict trends in size. The ion with the most protons attracts the same number of electrons most strongly, resulting in a smaller size.

25.   a. $Cu > Cu^+ > Cu^{2+}$ b. $Pt^{2+} > Pd^{2+} > Ni^{2+}$ c. $O^{2-} > O^- > O$

       d. $La^{3+} > Eu^{3+} > Gd^{3+} > Yb^{3+}$ e. $Te^{2-} > I^- > Cs^+ > Ba^{2+} > La^{3+}$

For answer a, as electrons are removed from an atom, size decreases. Answers b and d follow the radius trend. For answer c, as electrons are added to an atom, size increases. Answer e follows the trend for an isoelectronic series, i.e., the smallest ion has the most protons.

27. Rb^+: $[Ar]4s^23d^{10}4p^6$; Ba^{2+}: $[Kr]5s^24d^{10}5p^6$; Se^{2-}: $[Ar]4s^23d^{10}4p^6$

       I^-: $[Kr]5s^24d^{10}5p^6$

29.   a. Cs_2S is composed of Cs^+ and S^{2-}. Cs^+ has the same electron configuration as Xe, and S^{2-} has the same configuration as Ar.

       b. SrF_2; Sr^{2+} has the Kr electron configuration, and F^- has the Ne configuration.

       c. Ca_3N_2; Ca^{2+} has the Ar electron configuration, and N^{3-} has the Ne configuration.

       d. $AlBr_3$; Al^{3+} has the Ne electron configuration, and Br^- has the Kr configuration.

31. Se^{2-}, Br^-, Rb^+, Sr^{2+}, Y^{3+}, and Zr^{4+} are some ions that are isoelectronic with Kr (36 electrons). In terms of size, the ion with the most protons will hold the electrons tightest and will be the smallest. The size trend is:

$$Zr^{4+} < Y^{3+} < Sr^{2+} < Rb^+ < Br^- < Se^{2-}$$
       smallest   largest

33.   a. Al^{3+} and S^{2-} are the expected ions. The formula of the compound would be Al_2S_3 (aluminum sulfide).

       b. K^+ and N^{3-}; K_3N, potassium nitride

       c. Mg^{2+} and Cl^-; $MgCl_2$, magnesium chloride

       d. Cs^+ and Br^-; $CsBr$, cesium bromide

35.

$$K(s) \rightarrow K(g) \qquad \Delta H = 90. \text{ kJ} \quad \text{(sublimation)}$$
$$K(g) \rightarrow K^+(g) + e^- \qquad \Delta H = 419 \text{ kJ} \quad \text{(ionization energy)}$$
$$1/2 \, Cl_2(g) \rightarrow Cl(g) \qquad \Delta H = 239/2 \text{ kJ (bond energy)}$$
$$Cl(g) + e^- \rightarrow Cl^-(g) \qquad \Delta H = -349 \text{ kJ} \quad \text{(electron affinity)}$$
$$K^+(g) + Cl^-(g) \rightarrow KCl(s) \qquad \Delta H = -690. \text{ kJ} \quad \text{(lattice energy)}$$

$$K(s) + 1/2 \, Cl_2(g) \rightarrow KCl(s) \qquad \Delta H^\circ_f = -411 \text{ kJ/mol}$$

37.   Use Figure 13.11 as a template for this problem.

$$Li(s) \rightarrow Li(g) \qquad \Delta H_{sub} = ?$$
$$Li(g) \rightarrow Li^+(g) + e^- \qquad \Delta H = 520. \text{ kJ}$$
$$1/2 \, I_2(g) \rightarrow I(g) \qquad \Delta H = 151/2 \text{ kJ}$$
$$I(g) + e^- \rightarrow I^-(g) \qquad \Delta H = -295 \text{ kJ}$$
$$Li^+(g) + I^-(g) \rightarrow LiI(s) \qquad \Delta H = -753 \text{ kJ}$$

$$Li(s) + 1/2 \, I_2(g) \rightarrow LiI(s) \qquad \Delta H = -292 \text{ kJ}$$

$\Delta H_{sub} + 520. + 151/2 - 295 - 753 = -292, \ \Delta H_{sub} = 161 \text{ kJ}$

39.   a. From the data given, less energy is required to produce $Mg^+(g) + O^-(g)$ than to produce $Mg^{2+}(g) + O^{2-}(g)$. However, the lattice energy for $Mg^{2+}O^{2-}$ will be much more exothermic than for Mg^+O^- (due to the greater charges in $Mg^{2+}O^{2-}$). The favorable lattice energy term will dominate and $Mg^{2+}O^{2-}$ forms.

        b. Mg^+ and O^- both have unpaired electrons. In Mg^{2+} and O^{2-} there are no unpaired electrons. Hence Mg^+O^- would be paramagnetic; $Mg^{2+}O^{2-}$ would be diamagnetic. Paramagnetism can be detected by measuring the mass of a sample in the presence and absence of a magnetic field. The apparent mass of a paramagnetic substance will be larger in a magnetic field because of the force between the unpaired electrons and the field.

41. Ca^{2+} has a greater charge than Na^+, and Se^{2-} is smaller than Te^{2-}. The effect of charge on the lattice energy is greater than the effect of size. We expect the trend from most exothermic to least exothermic to be:

        $$CaSe \ > \ CaTe \ > \ Na_2Se \ > \ Na_2Te$$

        $(-2862) \quad (-2721) \quad (-2130) \quad (-2095 \text{ kJ/mol}) \qquad \text{This is what we observe.}$

Bond Energies

43.   a.   H——H + Cl——Cl ⟶ 2 H—Cl

Bonds broken: Bonds formed:

1 H–H (432 kJ/mol)   2 H–Cl (427 kJ/mol)
1 Cl–Cl (239 kJ/mol)

$\Delta H = \Sigma D_{broken} - \Sigma D_{formed}$, $\Delta H = 432$ kJ $+ 239$ kJ $- 2(427)$ kJ $= -183$ kJ

b.   N≡N + 3 H——H ⟶ 2 H—N—H
                                    |
                                    H

Bonds broken: Bonds formed:

1 N ≡ N (941 kJ/mol)   6 N–H (391 kJ/mol)
3 H–H (432 kJ/mol)

$\Delta H = 941$ kJ $+ 3(432)$ kJ $- 6(391)$ kJ $= -109$ kJ

c.   Sometimes some of the bonds remain the same between reactants and products. To save time, only break and form bonds that are involved in the reaction.

H—C≡N + 2 H——H ⟶ H—C—N with H H on C and H H on N

Bonds broken: Bonds formed:

1 C≡N (891 kJ/mol)   1 C–N (305 kJ/mol)
2 H–H (432 kJ/mol)   2 C–H (413 kJ/mol)
                                  2 N–H (391 kJ/mol)

$\Delta H = 891$ kJ $+ 2(432$ kJ$) - [305$ kJ $+ 2(413$ kJ$) + 2(391$ kJ$)] = -158$ kJ

d.   H₂N–NH₂ type structure + 2 F——F ⟶ 4 H——F + N≡N

Bonds broken: Bonds formed:

1 N–N (160. kJ/mol)   4 H–F (565 kJ/mol)
4 N–H (391 kJ/mol)   1 N≡N (941 kJ/mol)
2 F–F (154 kJ/mol)

$\Delta H = 160.$ kJ $+ 4(391$ kJ$) + 2(154$ kJ$) - [4(565$ kJ$) + 941$ kJ$] = -1169$ kJ

45.

Bonds broken: 1 C–N (305 kJ/mol)   Bonds formed: 1 C–C (347 kJ/mol)

$\Delta H = \Sigma D_{broken} - \Sigma D_{formed}$, $\Delta H = 305 - 347 = -42$ kJ

Note: Sometimes some of the bonds remain the same between reactants and products. To save time, only break and form bonds that are involved in the reaction.

47.   H–C≡C–H + 5/2 O=O → 2 O=C=O + H–O–H

Bonds broken: Bonds formed:

   2 C–H (413 kJ/mol)   2 × 2 C=O (799 kJ/mol)
   1 C≡C (839 kJ/mol)   2 O–H (467 kJ/mol)
   5/2 O=O (495 kJ/mol)

   $\Delta H = 2(413 \text{ kJ}) + 839 \text{ kJ} + 5/2 (495 \text{ kJ}) - [4(799 \text{ kJ}) + 2(467 \text{ kJ})] = -1228$ kJ

49.

Bonds broken: Bonds formed:

   9 N–N (160. kJ/mol)   24 O–H (467 kJ/mol)
   4 N–C (305 kJ/mol)   9 N≡N (941 kJ/mol)
   12 C–H (413 kJ/mol)   8 C=O (799 kJ/mol)
   12 N–H (391 kJ/mol)
   10 N=O (607 kJ/mol)
   10 N–O (201 kJ/mol)

   $\Delta H = 9(160.) + 4(305) + 12(413) + 12(391) + 10(607) + 10(201)$

                                     $- [24(467) + 9(941) + 8(799)]$

   $\Delta H = 20{,}388 \text{ kJ} - 26{,}069 \text{ kJ} = -5681$ kJ

51.   Because both reactions are highly exothermic, the high temperature is not needed to provide energy. It must be necessary for some other reason. The reason is to increase the speed of the reaction. This will be discussed in Chapter 15 on kinetics.

53.   a. $HF(g) \rightarrow H(g) + F(g)$ $\Delta H = 565$ kJ
            $H(g) \rightarrow H^+(g) + e^-$ $\Delta H = 1312$ kJ
            $F(g) + e^- \rightarrow F^-(g)$ $\Delta H = -327.8$ kJ

            $HF(g) \rightarrow H^+(g) + F^-(g)$ $\Delta H = 1549$ kJ

       b. $HCl(g) \rightarrow H(g) + Cl(g)$ $\Delta H = 427$ kJ
            $H(g) \rightarrow H^+(g) + e^-$ $\Delta H = 1312$ kJ
            $Cl(g) + e^- \rightarrow Cl^-(g)$ $\Delta H = -348.7$ kJ

            $HCl(g) \rightarrow H^+(g) + Cl^-(g)$ $\Delta H = 1390.$ kJ

       c. $HI(g) \rightarrow H(g) + I(g)$ $\Delta H = 295$ kJ
            $H(g) \rightarrow H^+(g) + e^-$ $\Delta H = 1312$ kJ
            $I(g) + e^- \rightarrow I^-(g)$ $\Delta H = -295.2$ kJ

            $HI(g) \rightarrow H^+(g) + I^-(g)$ $\Delta H = 1312$ kJ

       d. $H_2O(g) \rightarrow OH(g) + H(g)$ $\Delta H = 467$ kJ
            $H(g) \rightarrow H^+(g) + e^-$ $\Delta H = 1312$ kJ
            $OH(g) + e^- \rightarrow OH^-(g)$ $\Delta H = -180.$ kJ

            $H_2O(g) \rightarrow H^+(g) + OH^-(g)$ $\Delta H = 1599$ kJ

55. $NH_3(g) \rightarrow N(g) + 3\ H(g)$

       $\Delta H^\circ = 3D_{NH} = 472.7$ kJ $+ 3(216.0$ kJ$) - (-46.1$ kJ$) = 1166.8$ kJ

       $D_{NH} = \dfrac{1166.8\ \text{kJ}}{3\ \text{mol NH bonds}} = 388.93$ kJ/mol

       $D_{calc} = 389$ kJ/mol compared with 391 kJ/mol in the table. There is good agreement.

Lewis Structures and Resonance

57.   Drawing Lewis structures is mostly trial and error. However, the first two steps are always the same. These steps are (1) count the valence electrons available in the molecule/ion, and (2) attach all atoms to each other with single bonds (called the skeletal structure). Unless noted otherwise, the atom listed first is assumed to be the atom in the middle, called the central atom, and all other atoms in the formula are attached to this atom. The most notable exceptions to the rule are formulas that begin with H, e.g., H_2O, H_2CO, etc. Hydrogen can never be a central atom since this would require H to have more than two electrons. In these compounds, the atom listed second is assumed to be the central atom.

After counting valence electrons and drawing the skeletal structure, the rest is trial and error. We place the remaining electrons around the various atoms in an attempt to satisfy the octet rule (or duet rule for H). Keep in mind that practice makes perfect. After practicing, you can (and will) become very adept at drawing Lewis structures.

a. HCN has $1 + 4 + 5 = 10$ valence electrons.

b. PH_3 has $5 + 3(1) = 8$ valence electrons.

Skeletal structure	Lewis structure	Skeletal structure	Lewis structure

Skeletal structure uses 4 e⁻; 6 e⁻ remain

Skeletal structures uses 6 e⁻; 2 e⁻ remain

c. $CHCl_3$ has $4 + 1 + 3(7) = 26$ valence electrons.

d. NH_4^+ has $5 + 4(1) ! 1 = 8$ valence electrons.

Skeletal structure	Lewis structure	Lewis structure

Note: Subtract valence electrons for positive charged ions.

e. H_2CO has $2(1) + 4 + 6 = 12$ valence electrons.

f. SeF_2 has $6 + 2(7) = 20$ valence electrons.

g. CO_2 has $4 + 2(6) = 16$ valence electrons.

h. O_2 has $2(6) = 12$ valence electrons.

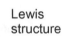

i. HBr has $1 + 7 = 8$ valence electrons.

H —Br:

59. Molecules/ions that have the same number of valence electrons and the same number of atoms will have similar Lewis structures.

61.   Ozone: O_3 has 3(6) = 18 valence electrons. Two resonance structures can be drawn.

Sulfur dioxide: SO_2 has 6 + 2(6) = 18 valence electrons. Two resonance structures are possible.

Sulfur trioxide: SO_3 has 6 + 3(6) = 24 valence electrons. Three resonance structures are possible.

63. CH_3NCO has 4 + 3(1) + 5 + 4 + 6 = 22 valence electrons. The order of the elements in the formula give the skeletal structure.

65.   Benzene has 6(4) + 6(1) = 30 valence electrons. Two resonance structures can be drawn for benzene. The actual structure of benzene is an average of these two resonance structures; i.e., all carbon-carbon bonds are equivalent with a bond length and bond strength somewhere between a single and a double bond.

67.   Borazine ($B_3N_3H_6$) has $3(3) + 3(5) + 6(1) = 30$ valence electrons. The possible resonance structures are similar to those of benzene in Exercise 13.65.

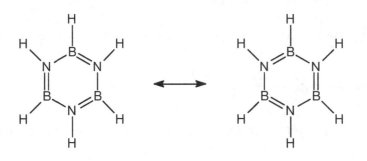

69.   Statements a and c are true. For statement a, XeF_2 has 22 valence electrons and it is impossible to satisfy the octet rule for all atoms with this number of electrons. The best Lewis structure is:

$$:\ddot{F}-\ddot{X}\ddot{e}-\ddot{F}:$$

For statement c, NO^+ has 10 valence electrons, whereas NO^- has 12 valence electrons. The Lewis structures are:

$$\left[:N\equiv O:\right]^+ \qquad \left[\ddot{N}=\ddot{O}\right]^-$$

Because a triple bond is stronger than a double bond, NO^+ has a stronger bond.

For statement b, SF_4 has five electron pairs around the sulfur in the best Lewis structure; it is an exception to the octet rule. Because OF_4 has the same number of valence electrons as SF_4, OF_4 would also have to be an exception to the octet rule. However, Row 2 elements such as O never have more than 8 electrons around them, so OF_4 does not exist. For statement d, two resonance structures can be drawn for ozone:

When resonance structures can be drawn, the actual bond lengths and strengths are all equal to each other. Even though each Lewis structure implies the two O–O bonds are different, this is not the case in real life. In real life, both of the O–O bonds are equivalent. When resonance structures can be drawn, you can think of the bonding as an average of all of the resonance structures.

71.   PF$_5$, 5 +5(7) = 40 valence electrons   SF$_4$, 6 + 4(7) = 34 e$^-$

ClF$_3$, 7 + 3(7) = 28 e$^-$ Br$_3^-$, 3(7) + 1 = 22 e$^-$

Row 3 and heavier nonmetals can have more than 8 electrons around them when they have to. Row 3 and heavier elements have empty d orbitals that are close in energy to valence s and p orbitals. These empty d orbitals can accept extra electrons.

For example, P in PF$_5$ has its five valence electrons in the 3s and 3p orbitals. These s and p orbitals have room for three more electrons, and if it has to, P can use the empty 3d orbitals for any electrons above 8.

73.   CO$_3^{2-}$ has 4 + 3(6) + 2 = 24 valence electrons.

Three resonance structures can be drawn for CO$_3^{2-}$. The actual structure for CO$_3^{2-}$ is an average of these three resonance structures. That is, the three C–O bond lengths are all equivalent, with a length somewhere between a single and a double bond. The actual bond length of 136 pm is consistent with this resonance view of CO$_3^{2-}$.

75.   H$_2$NOH (14 e$^-$):   H—N—O—H   Single bond between N and O
                                            |
                                            H

N_2O (16 e⁻):   N̈=N=Ö̈ ⟷ :N≡N–Ö̈: ⟷ :N̈–N≡O:

Average of a double bond between N and O

NO^+ (10 e⁻): $\left[:N≡O: \right]^+$ Triple bond between N and O

NO_2^- (18 e⁻): $\left[Ö̈=N̈–Ö̈: \right]^-$ ⟷ $\left[:Ö̈–N̈=Ö̈ \right]^-$

Average of 1 1/2 bond between N and O

NO_3^- (24 e⁻):

Average of 1 1/3 bond between N and O

From the Lewis structures, the order from shortest → longest N–O bond is:

$$NO^+ < N_2O < NO_2^- < NO_3^- < H_2NOH$$

Formal Charge

77.   :C≡O: Carbon: FC = 4 – 2 – 1/2(6) = –1; oxygen: FC = 6 – 2 – 1/2(6) = +1

Electronegativity predicts the opposite polarization. The two opposing effects seem to partially cancel to give a much less polar molecule than expected.

79.   See Exercise 13.58a for the Lewis structures of $POCl_3$, SO_4^{2-}, ClO_4^- and PO_4^{3-}. All of these compounds/ions have similar Lewis structures to those of SO_2Cl_2 and XeO_4 shown below.

a. $POCl_3$: P, FC = 5 – 1/2(8) = +1   b. SO_4^{2-}: S, FC = 6 – 1/2(8) = +2

c. ClO_4^-: Cl, FC = 7 – 1/2(8) = +3   d. PO_4^{3-}: P, FC = 5 – 1/2(8) = +1

e. SO_2Cl_2, 6 + 2(6) + 2(7) = 32 e⁻   f. XeO_4, 8 + 4(6) = 32 e⁻

S, FC = 6 – 1/2(8) = +2   Xe, FC = 8 – 1/2(8) = +4

g. ClO_3^-, $7 + 3(6) + 1 = 26$ e$^-$ h. NO_4^{3-}, $5 + 4(6) + 3 = 32$ e$^-$

Cl, FC $= 7 - 2 - 1/2(6) = +2$ N, FC $= 5 - 1/2(8) = +1$

81.   SCl, $6 + 7 = 13$; the formula could be SCl (13 valence electrons), S_2Cl_2 (26 valence
      electrons), S_3Cl_3 (39 valence electrons), etc. For a formal charge of zero on S, we will need
      each sulfur in the Lewis structure to have two bonds to it and two lone pairs [FC $= 6 - 4 -$
      $1/2(4) = 0$]. Cl will need one bond and three lone pairs for a formal charge of zero [FC $= 7 -$
      $6 - 1/2(2) = 0$]. Since chlorine wants only one bond to it, it will not be a central atom here.
      With this in mind, only S_2Cl_2 can have a Lewis structure with a formal charge of zero on all
      atoms. The structure is:

$$:\overset{..}{\underset{..}{Cl}}\!-\!\overset{..}{\underset{..}{S}}\!-\!\overset{..}{\underset{..}{S}}\!-\!\overset{..}{\underset{..}{Cl}}:$$

83. O_2F_2 has $2(6) + 2(7) = 26$ valence e$^-$. The formal charge and oxidation number (state) of
      each atom is below the Lewis structure of O_2F_2.

$$:\overset{..}{\underset{..}{F}}\!-\!\overset{..}{\underset{..}{O}}\!-\!\overset{..}{\underset{..}{O}}\!-\!\overset{..}{\underset{..}{F}}:$$

Formal Charge	0	0	0	0
Oxid. Number	-1	+1	+1	-1

Oxidation states are more useful when accounting for the reactivity of O_2F_2. We are forced to
assign +1 as the oxidation state for oxygen due to the bonding to fluorine. Oxygen is very
electronegative, and +1 is not a stable oxidation state for this element.

Molecular Structure and Polarity

85.   a.   V-shaped or bent   b.   see-saw   c.   trigonal pyramid

      d.   trigonal bipyramid   e.   tetrahedral

87.   The first step always is to draw a valid Lewis structure when predicting molecular structure.
      When resonance is possible, only one of the possible resonance structures is necessary to
      predict the correct structure because all resonance structures give the same structure. The
      Lewis structures are in Exercises 13.57, 13.58 and 13.60. The structures and bond angles for
      each follow.

      13.57   a.   HCN: linear, 180°   b.   PH$_3$: trigonal pyramid, <109.5°

c. $CHCl_3$: tetrahedral, 109.5°

d. NH_4^+: tetrahedral, 109.5°

e. H_2CO: trigonal planar, 120°

f. SeF_2: V-shaped or bent, <109.5°

g. CO_2: linear, 180°

h and i. O_2 and HBr are both linear, but there is no bond angle in either.

Note: PH_3 and SeF_2 both have lone pairs of electrons on the central atom, which result in bond angles that are something less than predicted from a tetrahedral arrangement (109.5°). However, we cannot predict the exact number. For these cases we will just insert a less than sign to indicate this phenomenon.

13.58   a. All are tetrahedral; 109.5°

b. All are trigonal pyramid; <109.5°

c. All are V-shaped; <109.5°

13.60   a. NO_2^-: V-shaped, ≈120°; NO_3^-: trigonal planar, 120°

N_2O_4: trigonal planar, 120° about both N atoms

b. OCN^-, SCN^-, and N_3^- are all linear with 180° bond angles.

89.   From the Lewis structures (see Exercise 13.71), Br_3^- would have a linear molecular structure, ClF_3 would have a T-shaped molecular structure, and SF_4 would have a see-saw molecular structure. For example, consider ClF_3 (28 valence electrons):

The central Cl atom is surrounded by five electron pairs, which requires a trigonal bipyramid geometry. Since there are three bonded atoms and two lone pairs of electrons about Cl, we describe the molecular structure of ClF_3 as T-shaped with predicted bond angles of about 90°. The actual bond angles will be slightly less than 90° due to the stronger repulsive effect of the lone pair electrons as compared to the bonding electrons.

91.   a. $XeCl_2$ has 8 + 2(7) = 22 valence electrons.

There are five pairs of electrons about the central Xe atom. The structure will be based on a trigonal bipyramid geometry. The most stable arrangement of the atoms in $XeCl_2$ is a linear molecular structure with a 180° bond angle.

b. ICl_3 has 7 + 3(7) = 28 valence electrons.

T-shaped; The ClICl angles are ≈ 90°. Since the lone pairs will take up more space, the ClICl bond angles will probably be slightly less than 90°.

c. TeF_4 has $6 + 4(7) = 34$
valence electrons.

d. PCl_5 has $5 + 5(7) = 40$
valence electrons.

See-saw or teeter-totter
or distorted tetrahedron

Trigonal bipyramid

All the species in this exercise have five pairs of electrons around the central atom. All the structures are based on a trigonal bipyramid geometry, but only in PCl_5 are all the pairs bonding pairs. Thus PCl_5 is the only one we describe the molecular structure as trigonal bipyramid. Still, we had to begin with the trigonal bipyramid geometry to get to the structures (and bond angles) of the others.

93.   Let us consider the molecules with three pairs of electrons around the central atom first; these molecules are SeO_3 and SeO_2, and both have a trigonal planar arrangement of electron pairs. Both these molecules have polar bonds, but only SeO_2 has an overall net dipole moment. The net effect of the three bond dipoles from the three polar Se–O bonds in SeO_3 will be to cancel each other out when summed together. Hence SeO_3 is nonpolar since the overall molecule has no resulting dipole moment. In SeO_2, the two Se–O bond dipoles do not cancel when summed together; hence SeO_2 has a net dipole moment (is polar). Since O is more electronegative than Se, the negative end of the dipole moment is between the two O atoms, and the positive end is around the Se atom. The arrow in the following illustration represents the overall dipole moment in SeO_2. Note that to predict polarity for SeO_2, either of the two resonance structures can be used.

The other molecules in Exercise 13.88 (PCl_3, SCl_2, and SiF_4) have a tetrahedral arrangement of electron pairs. All have polar bonds; in SiF_4 the individual bond dipoles cancel when summed together, and in PCl_3 and SCl_2 the individual bond dipoles do not cancel. Therefore, SiF_4 has no net dipole moment (is nonpolar), and PCl_3 and SCl_2 have net dipole moments (are polar). For PCl_3, the negative end of the dipole moment is between the more electronegative chlorine atoms, and the positive end is around P. For SCl_2, the negative end is between the more electronegative Cl atoms, and the positive end of the dipole moment is around S.

95.   The two general requirements for a polar molecule are:

1. Polar bonds

2. A structure such that the bond dipoles of the polar bonds do not cancel

CF_4, $4 + 4(7) = 32$ valence electrons XeF_4, $8 + 4(7) = 36$ e$^-$

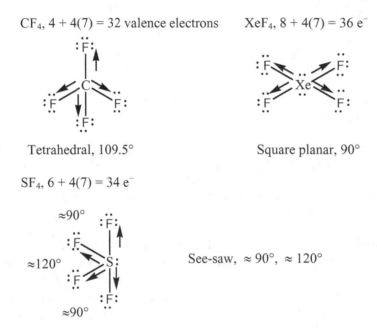

Tetrahedral, 109.5°   Square planar, 90°

SF_4, $6 + 4(7) = 34$ e$^-$

See-saw, ≈ 90°, ≈ 120°

The arrows indicate the individual bond dipoles in the three molecules (the arrows point to the more electronegative atom in the bond, which will be the partial negative end of the bond dipole). All three of these molecules have polar bonds. To determine the polarity of the overall molecule, we sum the effect of all of the individual bond dipoles. In CF_4, the fluorines are symmetrically arranged about the central carbon atom. The net result is for all the individual C–F bond dipoles to cancel each other out, giving a nonpolar molecule. In XeF_4, the 4 Xe–F bond dipoles are also symmetrically arranged, and XeF_4 is also nonpolar. The individual bond dipoles cancel out when summed together. In SF_4, we also have four polar bonds. But in SF_4 the bond dipoles are not symmetrically arranged, and they do not cancel each other out. SF_4 is polar. It is the positioning of the lone pair that disrupts the symmetry in SF_4.

CO_2, $4 + 2(6) = 16$ e$^-$ COS, $4 + 6 + 6 = 16$ e$^-$

CO_2 and COS both have a linear molecular structure with a 180° bond angle. CO_2 is nonpolar because the individual bond dipoles cancel each other out, but COS is polar. By replacing an O with a less electronegative S atom, the molecule is not symmetric any more. The individual bond dipoles do not cancel because the C–S bond dipole is smaller than the C–O bond dipole resulting in a polar molecule.

97. Only statement c is true. The bond dipoles in CF_4 and KrF_4 are arranged in a manner that they all cancel each other out, making them nonpolar molecules (CF_4 has a tetrahedral molecular structure, whereas KrF_4 has a square planar molecular structure). In SeF_4 the bond dipoles in this see-saw molecule do not cancel each other out, so SeF_4 is polar. For statement a, all the molecules have either a trigonal planar geometry or a trigonal bipyramid geometry, both of which have 120° bond angles. However, $XeCl_2$ has three lone pairs and two bonded chlorine atoms around it. $XeCl_2$ has a linear molecular structure with a 180° bond angle. With three lone pairs, we no longer have a 120° bond angle in $XeCl_2$. For statement b, SO_2 has a V-shaped molecular structure with a bond angle of about 120°. CS_2 is linear with a 180° bond angle and SCl_2 is V-shaped but with an approximate 109.5° bond angle. The three compounds do not have the same bond angle. For statement d, central atoms adopt a geometry to minimize electron repulsions, not maximize them.

99. The formula is EF_2O^{2-}, and the Lewis structure has 28 valence electrons.

   $28 = x + 2(7) + 6 + 2$, $x = 6$ valence electrons for element E

   Element E must belong to the Group 6A elements since E has six valence electrons. E must also be a Row 3 or heavier element since this ion has more than eight electrons around the central E atom (Row 2 elements never have more than eight electrons around them). Some possible identities for E are S, Se and Te. The ion has a T-shaped molecular structure (see Exercise 13.89) with bond angles of ≈ 90°.

101. Molecules that have an overall dipole moment are called polar molecules, and molecules that do not have an overall dipole moment are called nonpolar molecules.

   a. OCl_2, $6 + 2(7) = 20$ e⁻ $\qquad\qquad\qquad$ KrF_2, $8 + 2(7) = 22$ e⁻

   V-shaped, polar; OCl_2 is polar because the two O–Cl bond dipoles don't cancel each other. The resulting dipole moment is shown in the drawing.

   Linear, nonpolar; The molecule is nonpolar because the two Kr–F bond dipoles cancel each other.

   BeH_2, $2 + 2(1) = 4$ e⁻ $\qquad\qquad\qquad$ SO_2, $6 + 2(6) = 18$ e⁻

   H —Be—H

   Linear, nonpolar; Be–H bond dipoles are equal and point in opposite directions. They cancel each other. BeH_2 is nonpolar.

   V-shaped, polar; The S–O bond dipoles do not cancel, so SO_2 is polar (has a net dipole moment). Only one resonance structure is shown.

Note: All four species contain three atoms. They have different structures because the number of lone pairs of electrons around the central atom are different in each case.

b. SO_3, $6 + 3(6) = 24$ e⁻ NF_3, $5 + 3(7) = 26$ e⁻

Trigonal planar, nonpolar;   Trigonal pyramid, polar;
bond dipoles cancel. Only one   bond dipoles do not cancel.
resonance structure is shown.

IF_3 has $7 + 3(7) = 28$ valence electrons.

        T-shaped, polar; bond dipoles do not cancel.

Note: Each molecule has the same number of atoms but different structures because of differing numbers of lone pairs around each central atom.

c. CF_4, $4 + 4(7) = 32$ e⁻ SeF_4, $6 + 4(7) = 34$ e⁻

Tetrahedral, nonpolar;   See-saw, polar;
bond dipoles cancel.   bond dipoles do not cancel.

KrF_4, $8 + 4(7) = 36$ valence electrons

        Square planar, nonpolar;
bond dipoles cancel.

Note: Again, each molecule has the same number of atoms but different structures because of differing numbers of lone pairs around the central atom.

d.   IF$_5$, $7 + 5(7) = 42$ e$^-$ AsF$_5$, $5 + 5(7) = 40$ e$^-$

Square pyramid, polar;   Trigonal bipyramid, nonpolar;
bond dipoles do not cancel.   bond dipoles cancel.

Note: Yet again, the molecules have the same number of atoms but different structures
because of the presence of differing numbers of lone pairs.

103.   All these molecules have polar bonds that are symmetrically arranged about the central
atoms. In each molecule the individual bond dipoles cancel to give no net overall dipole
moment. All these molecules are nonpolar even though they all contain polar bonds.

Additional Exercises

105.   CO$_3^{2-}$ has $4 + 3(6) + 2 = 24$ valence electrons.

HCO$_3^-$ has $1 + 4 + 3(6) + 1 = 24$ valence electrons.

H$_2$CO$_3$ has $2(1) + 4 + 3(6) = 24$ valence electrons.

The Lewis structures for the reactants and products are:

Bonds broken:

  2 C–O (358 kJ/mol)
  1 O–H (467 kJ/mol)

Bonds formed:

  1 C=O (799 kJ/mol)
  1 O–H (467 kJ/mol)

$\Delta H = 2(358) + 467 - (799 + 467) = -83$ kJ; the carbon-oxygen double bond is stronger than two carbon-oxygen single bonds; hence CO_2 and H_2O are more stable than H_2CO_3.

107.   As the halogen atoms get larger, it becomes more difficult to fit three halogen atoms around the small nitrogen atom, and the NX_3 molecule becomes less stable.

109.   The stable species are:

a.   NaBr: In $NaBr_2$, the sodium ion would have a 2+ charge, assuming that each bromine has a 1– charge. Sodium doesn't form stable Na^{2+} compounds.

b. ClO_4^-: ClO_4 has 31 valence electrons, so it is impossible to satisfy the octet rule for all atoms in ClO_4. The extra electron from the 1– charge in ClO_4^- allows for complete octets for all atoms.

c. XeO_4: We can't draw a Lewis structure that obeys the octet rule for SO_4 (30 electrons), unlike with XeO_4 (32 electrons).

d. SeF_4: Both compounds require the central atom to expand its octet. O is too small and doesn't have low-energy d orbitals to expand its octet (which is true for all Row 2 elements).

111.   a.   Radius: $N^+ < N < N^-$; IE: $N^- < N < N^+$

N$^+$ has the fewest electrons held by the seven protons in the nucleus whereas N$^-$ has the most electrons held by the seven protons. The seven protons in the nucleus will hold the electrons most tightly in N$^+$ and least tightly in N$^-$. Therefore, N$^+$ has the smallest radius with the largest ionization energy (IE), and N$^-$ is the largest species with the smallest IE.

b.   Radius: $Cl^+ < Cl < Se < Se^-$; IE: $Se^- < Se < Cl < Cl^+$

The general trends tell us that Cl has a smaller radius than Se and a larger IE than Se. Cl$^+$, with fewer electron-electron repulsions than Cl, will be smaller than Cl and have a larger IE. Se$^-$, with more electron-electron repulsions than Se, will be larger than Se and have a smaller IE.

c. Radius: $Sr^{2+} < Rb^+ < Br^-$; IE: $Br^- < Rb^+ < Sr^{2+}$

These ions are isoelectronic. The species with the most protons (Sr^{2+}) will hold the electrons most tightly and will have the smallest radius and largest IE. The ion with the fewest protons (Br^-) will hold the electrons least tightly and will have the largest radius and smallest IE.

113. Assuming 100.00 g of compound: $42.81 \text{ g F} \times \dfrac{1 \text{ mol F}}{19.00 \text{ g F}} = 2.253 \text{ mol F}$

The number of moles of X in XF_5 is: $2.253 \text{ mol F} \times \dfrac{1 \text{ mol X}}{5 \text{ mol F}} = 0.4506 \text{ mol X}$

This number of moles of X has a mass of 57.19 g (= 100.00 g – 42.81 g). The molar mass of X is:

$\dfrac{57.19 \text{ g X}}{0.4506 \text{ mol X}} = 126.9 \text{ g/mol};$ This is element I.

IF_5, $7 + 5(7) = 42 \text{ e}^-$

The molecular structure is square pyramid.

115. Yes, each structure has the same number of effective pairs around the central atom, giving the same predicted molecular structure for each compound/ion. (A multiple bond is counted as a single group of electrons.)

Challenge Problems

117. KrF_2, $8 + 2(7) = 22 \text{ e}^-$; from the Lewis structure, we have a trigonal bipyramid arrangement of electron pairs with a linear molecular structure.

Hyperconjugation assumes that the overall bonding in KrF_2 is a combination of covalent and ionic contributions (see Section 13.12 of the text for discussion of hyperconjugation). Using hyperconjugation, two resonance structures are possible that keep the linear structure.

119. $2 \, Li^+(g) + 2 \, Cl^-(g) \rightarrow 2 \, LiCl(s)$ $\Delta H = 2(-829 \text{ kJ})$
        $2 \, Li(g) \rightarrow 2 \, Li^+(g) + 2 \, e^-$ $\Delta H = 2(520. \text{ kJ})$
        $2 \, Li(s) \rightarrow 2 \, Li(g)$ $\Delta H = 2(166 \text{ kJ})$
        $2 \, HCl(g) \rightarrow 2 \, H(g) + 2 \, Cl(g)$ $\Delta H = 2(427 \text{ kJ})$
        $2 \, Cl(g) + 2 \, e^- \rightarrow 2 \, Cl^-(g)$ $\Delta H = 2(-349 \text{ kJ})$
        $2 \, H(g) \rightarrow H_2(g)$ $\Delta H = -(432 \text{ kJ})$
        _____
        $2 \, Li(s) + 2 \, HCl(g) \rightarrow 2 \, LiCl(s) + H_2(g)$ $\Delta H = -562 \text{ kJ}$

121.   a. $N(NO_2)_2^-$ contains $5 + 2(5) + 4(6) + 1 = 40$ valence electrons.

        The most likely structures are:

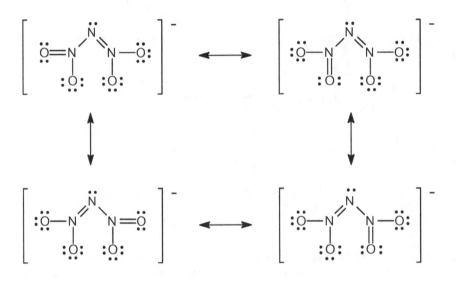

        There are other possible resonance structures, but these are most likely.

        b.   The NNN and all ONN and ONO bond angles should be about 120°.

        c. $NH_4N(NO_2)_2(s) \rightarrow 2 \, N_2(g) + 2 \, H_2O(g) + O_2(g)$; break and form all bonds.

        Bonds broken: Bonds formed:

        4 N–H (391 kJ/mol)   2 N≡N (941 kJ/mol)
        1 N–N (160. kJ/mol)   4 H–O (467 kJ/mol)
        1 N=N (418 kJ/mol)   1 O=O (495 kJ/mol)
        3 N–O (201 kJ/mol)   _____
        1 N=O (607 kJ/mol)
                                         $\Sigma D_{formed} = 4245 \text{ kJ}$
        _____

        $\Sigma D_{broken} = 3352 \text{ kJ}$

        $\Delta H = \Sigma D_{broken} - \Sigma D_{formed} = 3352 \text{ kJ} - 4245 \text{ kJ} = -893 \text{ kJ}$

d. To estimate ΔH, we completely ignored the ionic interactions between NH_4^+ and $N(NO_2)_2^-$ in the solid phase. In addition, we assumed the bond energies in Table 13.6 applied to the $N(NO_2)^-$ bonds in any one of the resonance structures above. This is a bad assumption since molecules that exhibit resonance generally have stronger overall bonds than predicted. All these assumptions give an estimated ΔH value which is too negative.

123.   a.   i. $C_6H_6N_{12}O_{12} \rightarrow 6\ CO + 6\ N_2 + 3\ H_2O + 3/2\ O_2$

The NO_2 groups have one N–O single bond and one N=O double bond, and each carbon atom has one C–H single bond. We must break and form all bonds.

Bonds broken:

3 C–C (347 kJ/mol)
6 C–H (413 kJ/mol)
12 C–N (305 kJ/mol)
6 N–N (160. kJ/mol)
6 N–O (201 kJ/mol)
6 N=O (607 kJ/mol)
_____

ΣD_{broken} = 12,987 kJ

Bonds formed:

6 C≡O (1072 kJ/mol)
6 N≡N (941 kJ/mol)
6 H–O (467 kJ/mol)
3/2 O=O (495 kJ/mol)
_____

ΣD_{formed} = 15,623 kJ

$\Delta H = \Sigma D_{broken} - \Sigma D_{formed}$ = 12,987 kJ – 15,623 kJ = –2636 kJ

ii. $C_6H_6N_{12}O_{12} \rightarrow 3\ CO + 3\ CO_2 + 6\ N_2 + 3\ H_2O$

Note: The bonds broken will be the same for all three reactions.

Bonds formed:

3 C≡O (1072 kJ/mol)
6 C=O (799 kJ/mol)
6 N≡N (941 kJ/mol)
6 H–O (467 kJ/mol)
_____

ΣD_{formed} = 16,458 kJ

ΔH = 12,987 kJ – 16,458 kJ = –3471 kJ

iii. $C_6H_6N_{12}O_{12} \rightarrow 6\ CO_2 + 6\ N_2 + 3\ H_2$

Bonds formed:

12 C=O (799 kJ/mol)
6 N≡N (941 kJ/mol)
3 H–H (432 kJ/mol)
_____

ΣD_{formed} = 16,530. kJ

ΔH = 12,987 kJ – 16,530. kJ = –3543 kJ

b. Reaction iii yields the most energy per mole of CL-20, so it will yield the most energy per kilogram.

$$\frac{-3543\,\text{kJ}}{\text{mol}} \times \frac{1\,\text{mol}}{438.23\,\text{g}} \times \frac{1000\,\text{g}}{\text{kg}} = -8085\,\text{kJ/kg}$$

125. The reaction is: $1/2\ I_2(s) + 1/2\ Cl_2(g) \rightarrow ICl(g)$ $\Delta H_f^\circ = ?$

Using Hess's law:

$1/2\ I_2(s) \rightarrow 1/2\ I_2(g)$	$\Delta H = 1/2\ (62\ \text{kJ})$	(Appendix 4)
$1/2\ I_2(g) \rightarrow I\,(g)$	$\Delta H = 1/2\ (149\ \text{kJ})$	(Table 13.6)
$1/2\ Cl_2(g) \rightarrow Cl(g)$	$\Delta H = 1/2\ (239\ \text{kJ})$	(Table 13.6)
$I(g) + Cl(g) \rightarrow ICl(g)$	$\Delta H = -208\ \text{kJ}$	(Table 13.6)

$1/2\ I_2(s) + 1/2\ Cl_2(g) \rightarrow ICl(g)$ $\Delta H = 17\ \text{kJ so}\ \Delta H_f^\circ = 17\ \text{kJ/mol}$

CHAPTER 14

COVALENT BONDING: ORBITALS

The Localized Electron Model and Hybrid Orbitals

9.   The valence orbitals of the nonmetals are the s and p orbitals. The lobes of the p orbitals are 90° and 180° apart from each other. If the p orbitals were used to form bonds, then all bond angles should be 90° or 180°. This is not the case. In order to explain the observed geometry (bond angles) that molecules exhibit, we need to make up (hybridize) orbitals that point to where the bonded atoms and lone pairs are located. We know the geometry; we hybridize orbitals to explain the geometry.

Sigma bonds have shared electrons in the area centered on a line joining the atoms. The orbitals that overlap to form the sigma bonds must overlap head to head or end to end. The hybrid orbitals about a central atom always are directed at the bonded atoms. Hybrid orbitals will always overlap head to head to form sigma bonds.

11.   We use d orbitals when we have to, i.e., we use d orbitals when the central atom on a molecule has more than eight electrons around it. The d orbitals are necessary to accommodate the electrons over eight. Row 2 elements never have more than eight electrons around them, so they never hybridize d orbitals. We rationalize this by saying there are no d orbitals close in energy to the valence 2s and 2p orbitals (2d orbitals are forbidden energy levels). However, for Row 3 and heavier elements, there are 3d, 4d, 5d, etc. orbitals that will be close in energy to the valence s and p orbitals. It is Row 3 and heavier nonmetals that hybridize d orbitals when they have to.

For sulfur, the valence electrons are in 3s and 3p orbitals. Therefore, 3d orbitals are closest in energy and are available for hybridization. Arsenic would hybridize 4d orbitals to go with the valence 4s and 4p orbitals, whereas iodine would hybridize 5d orbitals since the valence electrons are in $n = 5$.

13. H_2O has $2(1) + 6 = 8$ valence electrons.

H_2O has a tetrahedral arrangement of the electron pairs about the O atom that requires sp^3 hybridization. Two of the four sp^3 hybrid orbitals are used to form bonds to the two hydrogen atoms, and the other two sp^3 hybrid orbitals hold the two lone pairs on oxygen. The two O–H bonds are formed from overlap of the sp^3 hybrid orbitals from oxygen with the 1s atomic orbitals from the hydrogen atoms. Each O–H covalent bond is called a sigma (σ) bond since the shared electron pair in each bond is centered in an area on a line running between the two atoms.

15.   Ethane, C_2H_6, has $2(4) + 6(1) = 14$ valence electrons. The Lewis structure is:

The carbon atoms are sp^3 hybridized. The six C–H sigma bonds are formed from overlap of the sp^3 hybrid orbitals on C with the 1s atomic orbitals from the hydrogen atoms. The carbon-carbon sigma bond is formed from overlap of an sp^3 hybrid orbital on each C atom.

Ethanol, C_2H_6O has $2(4) + 6(1) + 6 = 20$ e⁻

The two C atoms and the O atom are sp^3 hybridized. All bonds are formed from overlap with these sp^3 hybrid orbitals. The C–H and O–H sigma bonds are formed from overlap of sp^3 hybrid orbitals with hydrogen 1s atomic orbitals. The C–C and C–O sigma bonds are formed from overlap of the sp^3 hybrid orbitals on each atom.

17.   See Exercises 13.57, 13.58, and 13.60 for the Lewis structures. To predict the hybridization, first determine the arrangement of electron pairs about each central atom using the VSEPR model, then utilize the information in Figure 14.24 of the text to deduce the hybridization required for that arrangement of electron pairs.

13.57   a.   HCN; C is sp hybridized.   b. PH_3; P is sp^3 hybridized.

        c. $CHCl_3$; C is sp^3 hybridized.   d. NH_4^+; N is sp^3 hybridized.

        e. H_2CO; C is sp^2 hybridized.   f. SeF_2; Se is sp^3 hybridized.

        g. CO_2; C is sp hybridized.   h. O_2; Each O atom is sp^2 hybridized.

        i.   HBr; Br is sp^3 hybridized.

13.58   a.   All the central atoms are sp^3 hybridized.

        b.   All the central atoms are sp^3 hybridized.

        c.   All the central atoms are sp^3 hybridized.

13.60   a.   In NO_2^- and NO_3^-, N is sp^2 hybridized. In N_2O_4, both central N atoms are also sp^2 hybridized.

b.   In OCN^- and SCN^-, the central carbon atoms in each ion are sp hybridized, and in N_3^-, the central N atom is also sp hybridized.

19.   The two nitrogen atoms in urea both have a tetrahedral arrangement of electron pairs, so both of these atoms are sp^3 hybridized. The carbon atom has a trigonal planar arrangement of electron pairs, so C is sp^2 hybridized. O is also sp^2 hybridized because it also has a trigonal planar arrangement of electron pairs.

Each of the four N–H sigma bonds are formed from overlap of an sp^3 hybrid orbital from nitrogen with a 1s orbital from hydrogen. Each of the two N–C sigma bonds are formed from an sp^3 hybrid orbital from N with an sp^2 hybrid orbital from carbon. The double bond between carbon and oxygen consists of one σ and one π bond. The σ bond in the double bond is formed from overlap of a carbon sp^2 hybrid orbital with an oxygen sp^2 hybrid orbital. The π bond in the double bond is formed from overlap of the unhybridized p atomic orbitals. Carbon and oxygen each have one unhybridized p atomic orbital, and they are assumed to be parallel to each other. When two parallel p atomic orbitals overlap side to side, a π bond results.

21.   a.

b.

| tetrahedral | sp^3 |
| 109.5° | nonpolar |

| trigonal pyramid | sp^3 |
| < 109.5° | polar |

The angles in NF_3 should be slightly less than 109.5° because the lone pair requires more space than the bonding pairs.

c.

d.

| V-shaped | sp^3 |
| < 109.5° | polar |

| trigonal planar | sp^2 |
| 120° | nonpolar |

e.

linear   sp
180°   nonpolar

f.

see-saw   dsp^3
a) ≈120°, b) ≈90°   polar

g.

trigonal bipyramid   dsp^3
a) 90°,   b) 120°   nonpolar

h.

linear   dsp^3
180°   nonpolar

i.

square planar   d^{2}sp^3
90°   nonpolar

j.

octahedral   d^{2}sp^3
90°   nonpolar

k.

square pyramid   d^{2}sp^3
≈90°   polar

l.

T-shaped   dsp^3
≈90°   polar

23.

For the p orbitals to properly line up to form the π bond, all six atoms are forced into the same plane. If the atoms are not in the same plane, then the π bond could not form since the p orbitals would no longer be parallel to each other.

25.   To complete the Lewis structures, just add lone pairs of electrons to satisfy the octet rule for the atoms with fewer than eight electrons.

Biacetyl ($C_4H_6O_2$) has $4(4) + 6(1) + 2(6) = 34$ valence electrons.

All CCO angles are 120°. The six atoms are not forced to lie in the same plane because of free rotation about the carbon-carbon single (sigma) bonds. There are 11 σ and 2 π bonds in biacetyl.

Acetoin ($C_4H_8O_2$) has $4(4) + 8(1) + 2(6) = 36$ valence electrons.

The carbon with the doubly bonded O is sp^2 hybridized. The other 3 C atoms are sp^3 hybridized. Angle a = 120° and angle b = 109.5°. There are 13 σ and 1 π bonds in acetoin.

Note: All single bonds are σ bonds, all double bonds are one σ and one π bond, and all triple bonds are one σ and two π bonds.

27.   To complete the Lewis structure, just add lone pairs of electrons to satisfy the octet rule for the atoms that have fewer than eight electrons.

a. 6   b. 4   c.   The center N in −N=N=N group

d. 33 σ   e. 5 π   f.   180°   g. ≈109.5°   h. sp^3

29.   a.   Add lone pairs to complete octets for each O and N.

Azodicarbonamide   methyl cyanoacrylate

Note: NH_2, CH_2 (H_2C), and CH_3 are shorthand for nitrogen or carbon atoms singly bonded to hydrogen atoms.

b.   In azodicarbonamide, the two carbon atoms are sp^2 hybridized, the two nitrogen atoms with hydrogens attached are sp^3 hybridized, and the other two nitrogens are sp^2 hybridized. In methyl cyanoacrylate, the CH_3 carbon is sp^3 hybridized, the carbon with the triple bond is sp hybridized, and the other three carbons are sp^2 hybridized.

c.   Azodicarbonamide contains three π bonds and methyl cyanoacrylate contains four π bonds.

d. a) ≈109.5°   b) 120°   c) ≈120°   d) 120°   e) 180°

f) 120°   g) ≈109.5°   h) 120°

31.   CO, $4 + 6 = 10 \text{ e}^-$; CO_2, $4 + 2(6) = 16 \text{ e}^-$; C_3O_2, $3(4) + 2(6) = 24 \text{ e}^-$

:C≡O: Ö=C=Ö   Ö=C=C=C=Ö

There is no molecular structure for the diatomic CO molecule. The carbon in CO is sp hybrid-ized. CO_2 is a linear molecule, and the central carbon atom is sp hybridized. C_3O_2 is a linear molecule with all the central carbon atoms exhibiting sp hybridization.

The Molecular Orbital (MO) Model

33.   a.

σ_p

When p orbitals are combined head-to-head and the phases are the same sign (the orbital lobes have the same sign), a sigma bonding molecular orbital is formed.

b.

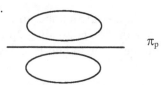

π_p

When parallel p orbitals are combined in-phase (the signs match up), a pi bonding molecular orbital is formed.

c.

σ_p^*

When p orbitals are combined head-to-head and the phases are opposite (the orbital lobes have opposite signs), a sigma antibonding molecular orbital is formed.

d.

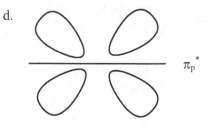

π_p^*

When parallel p orbitals are combined out-of-phase (the orbital lobes have opposite signs), a pi antibonding molecular orbital is formed.

35.   From experiment, B_2 is paramagnetic. If the σ_{2p} MO is lower in energy than the two degenerate π_{2p} MOs, the electron configuration for B_2 would have all electrons paired. Experiment tells us we must have unpaired electrons. Therefore, the MO diagram is modified to have the π_{2p} orbitals lower in energy than the σ_{2p} orbitals. This gives two unpaired electrons in the electron configuration for B_2, which explains the paramagnetic properties of B_2. The model allowed for s and p orbitals to mix, which shifted the energy of the σ_{2p} orbital to above that of the π_{2p} orbitals.

37.   a. H_2 has two valence electrons to put in the MO diagram, whereas He_2 has four valence electrons.

H_2: $(\sigma_{1s})^2$ Bond order = B.O. = (2–0)/2 = 1
He_2: $(\sigma_{1s})^2(\sigma_{1s}*)^2$ B.O. = (2–2)/2 = 0

H_2 has a nonzero bond order, so MO theory predicts it will exist. The H_2 molecule is stable with respect to the two free H atoms. He_2 has a bond order of zero, so it should not form. The He_2 molecule is not more stable than the two free He atoms.

b.   See Figure 14.41 for the MO energy-level diagrams of B_2, C_2, N_2, O_2, and F_2. B_2 and O_2 have unpaired electrons in their electron configuration, so they are predicted to be paramagnetic. C_2, N_2, and F_2 have no unpaired electrons in the MO diagrams; they are all diamagnetic.

c.   From the MO energy diagram in Figure 14.41, N_2 maximizes the number of electrons in the lower-energy bonding orbitals and has no electrons in the antibonding 2p molecular orbitals. N_2 has the highest possible bond order of three, so it should be a very strong (stable) bond.

d. NO^+ has 5 + 6 – 1 = 10 valence electrons to place in the MO diagram, and NO^- has 5 + 6 + 1 = 12 valence electrons. The MO diagram for these two ions is assumed to be the same as that used for N_2.

NO^+: $(\sigma_{2s})^2(\sigma_{2s}*)^2(\pi_{2p})^4(\sigma_{2p})^2$ B.O. = (8 – 2)/2 = 3
NO^-: $(\sigma_{2s})^2(\sigma_{2s}*)^2(\pi_{2p})^4(\sigma_{2p})^2(\pi_{2p}*)^2$ B.O. = (8 – 4)/2 = 2

NO^+ has a larger bond order than NO^-, so NO^+ should be more stable than NO^-.

39.

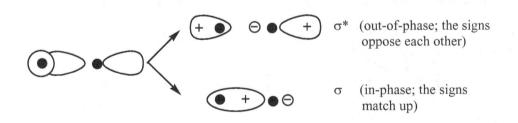

$\sigma*$ (out-of-phase; the signs oppose each other)

σ (in-phase; the signs match up)

These molecular orbitals are sigma MOs because the electron density is cylindrically symmetric about the internuclear axis.

41. N_2: $(\sigma_{2s})^2(\sigma_{2s}*)^2(\pi_{2p})^4(\sigma_{2p})^2$ B.O. = (8 – 2)/2 = 3

We need to decrease the bond order from 3 to 2.5. There are two ways to do this. One is to add an electron to form N_2^-. This added electron goes into one of the π_{2p}^* orbitals, giving a bond order of (8 – 3)/2 = 2.5. We could also remove a bonding electron to form N_2^+. The bond order for N_2^+ is also 2.5 [= (7 – 2)/2].

43.   CN: $(\sigma_{2s})^2(\sigma_{2s}*)^2(\pi_{2p})^4(\sigma_{2p})^1$

NO: $(\sigma_{2s})^2(\sigma_{2s}*)^2(\pi_{2p})^4(\sigma_{2p})^2(\pi_{2p}*)^1$

O_2^{2+}: $(\sigma_{2s})^2(\sigma_{2s}*)^2(\sigma_{2p})^2(\pi_{2p})^4$

N_2^{2+}: $(\sigma_{2s})^2(\sigma_{2s}*)^2(\pi_{2p})^4$

If the added electron goes into a bonding orbital, the bond order would increase, making the species more stable and more likely to form. Between CN and NO, CN would most likely form CN^- since the bond order increases (unlike NO^-, where the added electron goes into an antibonding orbital). Between O_2^{2+} and N_2^{2+}, N_2^+ would most likely form since the bond order increases (unlike O_2^{2+} going to O_2^+).

45.   The π bonds between S atoms and between C and S atoms are not as strong. The atomic orbitals do not overlap with each other as well as the smaller atomic orbitals of C and O overlap.

47.   Side-to-side overlap of these d orbitals would produce a π molecular orbital. There would be no probability of finding an electron on the axis joining the two nuclei, which is characteristic of π MOs.

49.   a.   The electron density would be closer to F on average. The F atom is more electro-negative than the H atom, and the 2p orbital of F is lower in energy than the 1s orbital of H.

b.   The bonding MO would have more fluorine 2p character since it is closer in energy to the fluorine 2p atomic orbital.

c.   The antibonding MO would place more electron density closer to H and would have a greater contribution from the higher-energy hydrogen 1s atomic orbital.

51.   Molecules that exhibit resonance have delocalized π bonding. This is a fancy way of saying that the π electrons are not permanently stationed between two specific atoms but instead can roam about over the surface of a molecule. We use the concept of delocalized π electrons to explain why molecules that exhibit resonance have equal bonds in terms of strength. Because the π electrons can roam about over the entire surface of the molecule, the π electrons are shared by all the atoms in the molecule, giving rise to equal bond strengths.

The classic example of delocalized π electrons is benzene (C_6H_6). Figure 14.50 shows the π molecular orbital system for benzene. Each carbon in benzene is sp^2 hybridized, leaving one unhybridized p atomic orbital. All six of the carbon atoms in benzene have an unhybridized p orbital pointing above and below the planar surface of the molecule. Instead of just two unhybridized p orbitals overlapping, we say all six of the unhybridized p orbitals overlap, resulting in delocalized π electrons roaming about above and below the entire surface of the benzene molecule.

SO_2, $6 + 2(6) = 18$ e$^-$

In SO_2 the central sulfur atom is sp^2 hybridized. The unhybridized p atomic orbital on the central sulfur atom will overlap with parallel p orbitals on each adjacent O atom. All three of these p orbitals overlap together, resulting in the π electrons moving about above and below the surface of the SO_2 molecule. With the delocalized π electrons, the S–O bond lengths in SO_2 are equal (and not different, as each individual Lewis structure indicates).

53.   The Lewis structures for CO_3^{2-} are (24 e$^-$):

In the localized electron view, the central carbon atom is sp^2 hybridized; the sp^2 hybrid orbitals are used to form the three sigma bonds in CO_3^{2-}. The central C atom also has one unhybridized p atomic orbital that overlaps with another p atomic orbital from one of the oxygen atoms to form the π bond in each resonance structure. This localized π bond moves (resonates) from one position to another. In the molecular orbital model for CO_3^{2-}, all four atoms in CO_3^{2-} have a p atomic orbital that is perpendicular to the plane of the ion. All four of these p orbitals overlap at the same time to form a delocalized π bonding system where the π electrons can roam above and below the entire surface of the ion. The π molecular orbital system for CO_3^{2-} is analogous to that for NO_3^- which is shown in Figure 14.51 of the text.

Spectroscopy

55.   reduced mass $= \mu = \dfrac{m_1 m_2}{m_1 + m_2} = \dfrac{(1.0078)(78.918)}{1.0078 + 78.918}$ amu $\times \dfrac{1.66054 \times 10^{-27} \text{ kg}}{\text{amu}}$

$= 1.6524 \times 10^{-27}$ kg

$\nu_o = \dfrac{1}{2\pi} \sqrt{\dfrac{k}{\mu}} = \dfrac{c}{\lambda} = 2.9979 \times 10^{10}$ cm s$^{-1} \times 2650.$ cm$^{-1} = 7.944 \times 10^{13}$ s^{-1}

$$7.944 \times 10^{13} \text{ s}^{-1} = \frac{1}{2\pi} \sqrt{\frac{k}{\mu}} = \frac{1}{2\pi} \sqrt{\frac{k}{1.6524 \times 10^{-27} \text{ kg}}}$$

Solving for k, the force constant: $k = 411.7 \text{ kg s}^{-2} = 411.7 \text{ N m}^{-1}$

Note: one newton = 1 N = 1 kg m s^{-2}.

57. a. $\Delta E = 2hB(J_i + 1) = h\nu = \dfrac{hc}{\lambda}, \ \dfrac{c}{\lambda} = 2B(J_i + 1)$

$$\frac{c}{\lambda} = 2B(0 + 1) = 2B = \frac{2.998 \times 10^8 \text{ m s}^{-1}}{2.60 \times 10^{-3} \text{ m}} = 1.15 \times 10^{11} \text{ s}^{-1}$$

$$B = \frac{1.15 \times 10^{-11} \text{ s}^{-1}}{2} = 5.75 \times 10^{10} \text{ s}^{-1}$$

$$I = \frac{h}{8\pi^2 B} = \frac{6.626 \times 10^{-34} \text{ J s}}{8\pi^2 (5.75 \times 10^{10} \text{ s}^{-1})} = 1.46 \times 10^{-46} \text{ kg m}^2$$

$$I = \mu R_e^2, \ \mu = \frac{m_1 m_2}{m_1 + m_2} = \frac{(12.000)(15.995)}{12.000 + 15.995} \text{ amu} \times \frac{1.66054 \times 10^{-27} \text{ kg}}{\text{amu}}$$
$$= 1.1385 \times 10^{-26} \text{ kg}$$

$$R_e^2 = \frac{I}{\mu} = \frac{1.46 \times 10^{-46} \text{ kg m}^2}{1.1385 \times 10^{-26} \text{ kg}} = 1.28 \times 10^{-20} \text{ m}^2, \ R_e = \text{bond length} = 1.13 \times 10^{-10} \text{ m}$$
$$= 113 \text{ pm}$$

b. $\nu = \dfrac{\Delta E}{h} = 2B(J_i + 1) = 2B(2 + 1) = 6B$

From part a, $B = 5.75 \times 10^{10} \text{ s}^{-1}$, so: $\nu = 6(5.75 \times 10^{10} \text{ s}^{-1}) = 3.45 \times 10^{11} \text{ s}^{-1}$

59. a. The $-CH_2$ group neighbors a $-CH_3$ group, so a quartet of peaks should result (iv).

b. The $-CH_3$ H atoms are separated by more than three sigma bonds from other H atoms, so no spin-spin coupling should occur. A singlet peak should result (i).

c. The $-CH_2$ H atoms neighbor two H atoms, so a triplet peak should result (iii).

d. The two H atoms in the $-CH_2F$ group neighbor one H atom, so a doublet peak should result (ii).

Additional Exercises

61.   a. XeO_3, $8 + 3(6) = 26$ e⁻

b. XeO_4, $8 + 4(6) = 32$ e⁻

trigonal pyramid; sp^3

tetrahedral; sp^3

c. $XeOF_4$, $8 + 6 + 4(7) = 42$ e⁻

d. $XeOF_2$, $8 + 6 + 2(7) = 28$ e⁻

square pyramid; d^2sp^3

T-shaped; dsp^3

e. XeO_3F_2 has $8 + 3(6) + 2(7) = 40$ valence electrons.

trigonal bipyramid; dsp^3

63.   a.   No, some atoms are in different places. Thus these are not resonance structures; they are different compounds.

b.   For the first Lewis structure, all nitrogens are sp^3 hybridized and all carbons are sp^2 hybridized. In the second Lewis structure, all nitrogens and carbons are sp^2 hybridized.

c.   For the reaction:

Bonds broken: Bonds formed:

3 C=O (745 kJ/mol)   3 C=N (615 kJ/mol)
3 C–N (305 kJ/mol)   3 C–O (358 kJ/mol)
3 N–H (391 kJ/mol)   3 O–H (467 kJ/mol)

$\Delta H = 3(745) + 3(305) + 3(391) - [3(615) + 3(358) + 3(467)]$

$\Delta H = 4323 \text{ kJ} - 4320 \text{ kJ} = 3 \text{ kJ}$

The bonds are slightly stronger in the first structure with the carbon-oxygen double bonds since ΔH for the reaction is positive. However, the value of ΔH is so small that the best conclusion is that the bond strengths are comparable in the two structures.

65.

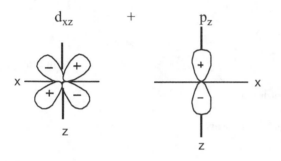

The two orbitals will overlap side-to-side, so when the orbitals are in-phase, a π bonding molecular orbital would form.

67.   Molecule A has a tetrahedral arrangement of electron pairs because it is sp^3 hybridized. Molecule B has 6 electron pairs about the central atom, so it is d^2sp^3 hybridized. Molecule C has two σ and two π bonds to the central atom, so it either has two double bonds to the central atom (as in CO_2) or one triple bond and one single bond (as in HCN). Molecule C is consistent with a linear arrangement of electron pairs exhibiting sp hybridization. There are many correct possibilities for each molecule; an example of each is:

Molecule A: CH$_4$ Molecule B: XeF$_4$ Molecule C: CO_2 or HCN

tetrahedral; 109.5°; sp^3 square planar; 90°; d^2sp^3 linear; 180°; sp

69. a. BH_3 has $3 + 3(1) = 6$ valence electrons.

trigonal planar, nonpolar, 120°, sp^2

b. N_2F_2 has $2(5) + 2(7) = 24$ valence electrons.

Can also be:

V-shaped about both N's;
≈120° about both N's;
both N atoms: sp^2

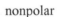

polar

nonpolar

These are distinctly different molecules.

c. C_4H_6 has $4(4) + 6(1) = 22$ valence electrons.

All C atoms are trigonal planar with 120° bond angles and sp^2 hybridization. Because C and H have about equal electronegativities, the C–H bonds are essentially nonpolar, so the molecule is nonpolar. All neutral compounds composed of only C and H atoms are nonpolar.

d. ICl_3 has $7 + 3(7) = 28$ valence electrons.

≈ 90°

≈ 90°

T-shaped, polar
≈90°, dsp^3

71.   For carbon, nitrogen, and oxygen atoms to have formal charge values of zero, each C atom will form four bonds to other atoms and have no lone pairs of electrons, each N atom will form three bonds to other atoms and have one lone pair of electrons, and each O atom will form two bonds to other atoms and have two lone pairs of electrons. The Lewis structure for caffeine that has a formal charge of zero for all atoms is:

The three C atoms each bonded to three H atoms are sp^3 hybridized (tetrahedral geometry); the other five C atoms with trigonal planar geometry are sp^2 hybridized. The one N atom with the double bond is sp^2 hybridized, and the other three N atoms are sp^3 hybridized. The answers to the questions are:

- 6 total C and N atoms are sp^2 hybridized
- 6 total C and N atoms are sp^3 hybridized
- 0 C and N atoms are sp hybridized (linear geometry)
- 25 σ bonds and 4 π bonds

73.   a.   The Lewis structures for NNO and NON are:

The NNO structure is correct. From the Lewis structures we would predict both NNO and NON to be linear. However, we would predict NNO to be polar and NON to be nonpolar. Since experiments show N_2O to be polar, then NNO is the correct structure.

b.   Formal charge = number of valence electrons of atoms – [(number of lone pair electrons) + 1/2 (number of shared electrons)].

$$\ddot{N}=N=\ddot{O} \longleftrightarrow :N\equiv N-\ddot{\ddot{O}}: \longleftrightarrow :\ddot{\ddot{N}}-N\equiv O:$$

-1   +1   0   0   +1   -1   -2   +1   +1

The formal charges for the atoms in the various resonance structures are below each atom. The central N is sp hybridized in all the resonance structures. We can probably ignore the third resonance structure on the basis of the relatively large formal charges as compared to the first two resonance structures.

c.   The sp hybrid orbitals from the center N overlap with atomic orbitals (or appropriate hybrid orbitals) from the other two atoms to form the two sigma bonds. The remaining two unhybridized p orbitals from the center N overlap with two p orbitals from the peripheral N atom to form the two π bonds.

Challenge Problems

75.   a. $F_2^-(g) \rightarrow F(g) + F^-(g)$ $\Delta H = F_2^-$ bond energy; using Hess's law:

$$F_2^-(g) \rightarrow F_2(g) + e^-\qquad \Delta H = 290.\ kJ\ (IE\ for\ F_2^-)$$
$$F_2(g) \rightarrow 2\ F(g)\qquad \Delta H = 154\ kJ\ (BE\ for\ F_2\ from\ Table\ 13.6)$$
$$F(g) + e^- \rightarrow F^-(g)\qquad \Delta H = -327.8\ kJ\ (EA\ for\ F\ from\ Table\ 12.8)$$

$$F_2^-(g) \rightarrow F(g) + F^-(g)\qquad \Delta H = 116\ kJ;\ \ BE\ for\ F_2^- = 116\ kJ/mol$$

Note that F_2^- has a smaller bond energy than F_2.

b. F_2: $(\sigma_{2s})^2(\sigma_{2s}*)^2(\sigma_{2p})^2(\pi_{2p})^4(\pi_{2p}*)^4$ B.O. = (8 – 6)/2 = 1
     F_2^-: $(\sigma_{2s})^2(\sigma_{2s}*)^2(\sigma_{2p})^2(\pi_{2p})^4(\pi_{2p}*)^4(\sigma_{2p}*)^1$ B.O. = (8 – 7)/2 = 0.5

MO theory predicts that F_2 should have a stronger bond than F_2^- because F_2 has the larger bond order. As determined in part a, F_2 indeed has a stronger bond because the F_2 bond energy (154 kJ/mol) is greater than the F_2^- bond energy (116 kJ/mol).

77.   a. $E = \dfrac{hc}{\lambda} = \dfrac{(6.626 \times 10^{-34}\ J\ s)(2.998 \times 10^8\ m/s)}{25 \times 10^{-9}\ m} = 7.9 \times 10^{-18}\ J$

$$7.9 \times 10^{-18}\ J \times \frac{6.022 \times 10^{23}}{mol} \times \frac{1\ kJ}{1000\ J} = 4800\ kJ/mol$$

Using ΔH values from the various reactions, 25-nm light has sufficient energy to ionize N_2 and N and to break the triple bond. Thus N_2, N_2^+, N, and N^+ will all be present, assuming excess N_2.

b. To produce atomic nitrogen but no ions, the range of energies of the light must be from 941 kJ/mol to just below 1402 kJ/mol.

$$\frac{941\,kJ}{mol} \times \frac{1\,mol}{6.022 \times 10^{23}} \times \frac{1000\,J}{1\,kJ} = 1.56 \times 10^{-18}\ J/photon$$

$$\lambda = \frac{hc}{E} = \frac{(6.6261 \times 10^{-34}\ J\,s)(2.998 \times 10^8\ m/s)}{1.56 \times 10^{-18}\ J} = 1.27 \times 10^{-7}\ m = 127\ nm$$

$$\frac{1402\,kJ}{mol} \times \frac{1\,mol}{6.0221 \times 10^{23}} \times \frac{1000\,J}{kJ} = 2.328 \times 10^{-18}\ J/photon$$

$$\lambda = \frac{hc}{E} = \frac{(6.6261 \times 10^{-34}\ J\,s)(2.9979 \times 10^8\ m/s)}{2.328 \times 10^{-18}\ J} = 8.533 \times 10^{-8}\ m = 85.33\ nm$$

Light with wavelengths in the range of 85.33 nm $< \lambda \le$ 127 nm will produce N but no ions.

c. N_2: $(\sigma_{2s})^2(\sigma_{2s}*)^2(\pi_{2p})^4(\sigma_{2p})^2$; the electron removed from N_2 is in the σ_{2p} molecular orbital, which is lower in energy than the 2p atomic orbital from which the electron in atomic nitrogen is removed. Because the electron removed from N_2 is lower in energy than the electron removed from N, the ionization energy of N_2 is greater than that for N.

79.   The complete Lewis structure follows. All but two of the carbon atoms are sp^3 hybridized. The two carbon atoms that contain the double bond are sp^2 hybridized (see *).

No; most of the carbons are not in the same plane since a majority of carbon atoms exhibit the non-planar tetrahedral structure. *Note*: CH, CH$_2$, H$_2$C, and CH$_3$ are shorthand for carbon atoms singly bonded to hydrogen atoms.

81.   a.   The CO bond is polar with the negative end around the more electronegative oxygen atom. We would expect metal cations to be attracted to and to bond to the oxygen end of CO on the basis of electronegativity.

       b.

      :C≡O: FC (carbon) = 4 − 2 − 1/2(6) = −1

                  FC (oxygen) = 6 − 2 − 1/2(6) = +1

From formal charge, we would expect metal cations to bond to the carbon (with the negative formal charge).

       c.   In molecular orbital theory, only orbitals with proper symmetry overlap to form bonding orbitals. The metals that form bonds to CO are usually transition metals, all of which have outer electrons in the d orbitals. The only molecular orbitals of CO that have proper symmetry to overlap with d orbitals are the π_{2p}* orbitals, whose shape is similar to the d orbitals (see Figure 14.36). Since the antibonding molecular orbitals have more carbon character, one would expect the bond to form through carbon.

83.   One of the resonance structures for benzene is:

To break C$_6$H$_6$(g) into C(g) and H(g) requires the breaking of 6 C−H bonds, 3 C=C bonds and 3 C−C bonds:

    C$_6$H$_6$(g) → 6 C(g) + 6 H(g)   ΔH = 6D$_{C−H}$ + 3D$_{C=C}$ + 3D$_{C−C}$

    ΔH = 6(413 kJ) + 3(614 kJ) + 3(347 kJ) = 5361 kJ

The question asks for ΔH$_f^{\circ}$ for C$_6$H$_6$(g), which is ΔH for the reaction:

    6 C(s) + 3 H$_2$(g) → C$_6$H$_6$(g)   ΔH = ΔH$_{f,\ C_6H_6(g)}^{\circ}$

To calculate ΔH for this reaction, we will use Hess's law along with the value ΔH$_f^{\circ}$ for C(g) and the bond energy value for H$_2$ (D$_{H_2}$ = 432 kJ/mol).

$$6\ C(g) + 6\ H(g) \rightarrow C_6H_6(g) \qquad \Delta H_1 = -5361\ kJ$$
$$6\ C(s) \rightarrow 6\ C(g) \qquad \Delta H_2 = \ 6(717\ kJ)$$
$$3\ H_2(g) \rightarrow 6\ H(g) \qquad \Delta H_3 = \ 3(432\ kJ)$$

$$6\ C(s) + 3\ H_2(g) \rightarrow C_6H_6(g) \qquad \Delta H = \Delta H_1 + \Delta H_2 + \Delta H_3 = 237\ kJ;\ \Delta H^{\circ}_{f,\ C_6H_6(g)} = 237\ kJ/mol$$

The experimental ΔH°_f for $C_6H_6(g)$ is more stable (lower in energy) by 154 kJ than the ΔH°_f calculated from bond energies $(83 - 237 = -154\ kJ)$. This extra stability is related to benzene's ability to exhibit resonance. Two equivalent Lewis structures can be drawn for benzene. The π bonding system implied by each Lewis structure consists of three localized π bonds. This is not correct because all C–C bonds in benzene are equivalent. We say the π electrons in benzene are delocalized over the entire surface of C_6H_6 (see Section 14.5 of the text). The large discrepancy between ΔH°_f values is due to the delocalized π electrons, whose effect was not accounted for in the calculated ΔH°_f value. The extra stability associated with benzene can be called resonance stabilization. In general, molecules that exhibit resonance are usually more stable than predicted using bond energies.

85.   The two isomers having the formula C_2H_6O are:

The first structure has three types of hydrogens (*a*, *b*, and *c*), so the signals should be seen in three different regions of the NMR spectra. The overall relative areas of the three signals should be in a 3:2:1 ratio due to the number of *a*, *b*, and *c* hydrogens. The signal for the *a* hydrogens will be split into a triplet signal due to the two neighboring *b* hydrogens. The signal for the *b* hydrogens should be split into a quintet signal due to the three neighboring *a* hydrogens plus the neighboring *c* hydrogen (four total protons). The *c* hydrogen signal should be split into a triplet signal due to the two neighboring *b* hydrogens. In practice, however, the *c* hydrogen bonded to the oxygen does not behave "normally". This O–H hydrogen generally behaves as if it was more than three sigma bonds apart from the *b* hydrogens. Therefore, the spectrum will most likely have a triplet signal for the *a* hydrogens, a quartet signal for the *b* hydrogens, and a singlet signal for the *c* hydrogen.

In the second structure, all six hydrogens are equivalent, so only one signal will appear in the NMR spectrum. This signal will be a singlet signal because the hydrogens in the two –CH$_3$ groups are more than three sigma bonds apart from each other (no splitting occurs).

CHAPTER 15

CHEMICAL KINETICS

Reaction Rates

11. $0.0120/0.0080 = 1.5$; reactant B is used up 1.5 times faster than reactant A. This corresponds to a 3 to 2 mole ratio between B and A in the balanced equation. $0.0160/0.0080 = 2$; product C is produced twice as fast as reactant A is used up. So the coefficient for C is twice the coefficient for A. A possible balanced equation is $2A + 3B \rightarrow 4C$.

13. Using the coefficients in the balanced equation to relate the rates:

$$\frac{d[H_2]}{dt} = 3\frac{d[N_2]}{dt} \text{ and } \frac{d[NH_3]}{dt} = -2\frac{d[N_2]}{dt}$$

$$\text{So}: \frac{1}{3}\frac{d[H_2]}{dt} = -\frac{1}{2}\frac{d[NH_3]}{dt} \text{ or } \frac{d[NH_3]}{dt} = -\frac{2}{3}\frac{d[H_2]}{dt}$$

Ammonia is produced at a rate equal to 2/3 of the rate of consumption of hydrogen.

15. $\text{Rate} = k[Cl]^{1/2}[CHCl_3]$, $\dfrac{mol}{L\,s} = k\left(\dfrac{mol}{L}\right)^{1/2}\left(\dfrac{mol}{L}\right)$; k must have units of $L^{1/2}\,mol^{-1/2}\,s^{-1}$.

Rate Laws from Experimental Data: Initial Rates Method

17. a. In the first two experiments, [NO] is held constant and [Cl_2] is doubled. The rate also doubled. Thus the reaction is first order with respect to Cl_2. Or mathematically: $\text{Rate} = k[NO]^x[Cl_2]^y$

$$\frac{0.36}{0.18} = \frac{k(0.10)^x(0.20)^y}{k(0.10)^x(0.10)^y} = \frac{(0.20)^y}{(0.10)^y}, \ 2.0 = 2.0^y, \ y = 1$$

We can get the dependence on NO from the second and third experiments. Here, as the NO concentration doubles (Cl_2 concentration is constant), the rate increases by a factor of four. Thus, the reaction is second order with respect to NO. Or mathematically:

304

$$\frac{1.45}{0.36} = \frac{k(0.20)^x(0.20)}{k(0.10)^x(0.20)} = \frac{(0.20)^x}{(0.10)^x}, \quad 4.0 = 2.0^x, \quad x = 2; \quad \text{so, Rate} = k[NO]^2[Cl_2].$$

Try to examine experiments where only one concentration changes at a time. The more variables that change, the harder it is to determine the orders. Also, these types of problems can usually be solved by inspection. In general, we will solve using a mathematical approach, but keep in mind that you probably can solve for the orders by simple inspection of the data.

b.   The rate constant k can be determined from the experiments. From experiment 1:

$$\frac{0.18\ mol}{L\ min} = k\left(\frac{0.10\ mol}{L}\right)^2\left(\frac{0.10\ mol}{L}\right), \quad k = 180\ L^2\ mol^{-2}\ min^{-1}$$

From the other experiments:

$$k = 180\ L^2\ mol^{-2}\ min^{-1} \text{ (second exp.); } k = 180\ L^2\ mol^{-2}\ min^{-1} \text{ (third exp.)}$$

The average rate constant is $k_{mean} = 1.8 \times 10^2\ L^2\ mol^{-2}\ min^{-1}$.

19.   a.   Rate $= k[NOCl]^n$; using experiments two and three:

$$\frac{2.66 \times 10^4}{6.64 \times 10^3} = \frac{k(2.0 \times 10^{16})^n}{k(1.0 \times 10^{16})^n}, \quad 4.01 = 2.0^n, \quad n = 2; \quad \text{Rate} = k[NOCl]^2$$

b. $$\frac{5.98 \times 10^4\ molecules}{cm^3\ s} = k\left(\frac{3.0 \times 10^{16}\ molecules}{cm^3}\right)^2, \quad k = 6.6 \times 10^{-29}\ cm^3\ molecules^{-1}\ s^{-1}$$

The other three experiments give (6.7, 6.6, and 6.6) $\times 10^{-29}\ cm^3\ molecules^{-1}\ s^{-1}$, respectively. The mean value for k is $6.6 \times 10^{-29}\ cm^3\ molecules^{-1}\ s^{-1}$.

c. $$\frac{6.6 \times 10^{-29}\ cm^3}{molecules\ s} \times \frac{1\ L}{1000\ cm^3} \times \frac{6.022 \times 10^{23}\ molecules}{mol} = \frac{4.0 \times 10^{-8}\ L}{mol\ s}$$

21.   a.   Rate $= k[ClO_2]^x[OH^-]^y$; From the first two experiments:

$$2.30 \times 10^{-1} = k(0.100)^x(0.100)^y \text{ and } 5.75 \times 10^{-2} = k(0.0500)^x(0.100)^y$$

Dividing the two rate laws: $4.00 = \dfrac{(0.100)^x}{(0.0500)^x} = 2.00^x, \quad x = 2$

Comparing the second and third experiments:

$$2.30 \times 10^{-1} = k(0.100)(0.100)^y \text{ and } 1.15 \times 10^{-1} = k(0.100)(0.0500)^y$$

Dividing: $2.00 = \dfrac{(0.100)^y}{(0.050)^y} = 2.0^y$, $y = 1$

The rate law is: $\text{Rate} = k[ClO_2]^2[OH^-]$

2.30×10^{-1} mol L^{-1} s^{-1} $= k(0.100$ mol/L$)^2(0.100$ mol/L$)$, $k = 2.30 \times 10^2$ L^2 mol^{-2} s^{-1}
$= k_{mean}$

b. $\text{Rate} = \dfrac{2.30 \times 10^2 \ L^2}{mol^2 \ s} \times \left(\dfrac{0.175 \ mol}{L}\right)^2 \times \dfrac{0.0844 \ mol}{L} = 0.594$ mol L^{-1} s^{-1}

23. $\text{Rate} = k[H_2SeO_3]^x[H^+]^y[I^-]^z$; comparing the first and second experiments:

$\dfrac{3.33 \times 10^{-7}}{1.66 \times 10^{-7}} = \dfrac{k(2.0 \times 10^{-4})^x(2.0 \times 10^{-2})^y(2.0 \times 10^{-2})^z}{k(1.0 \times 10^{-4})^x(2.0 \times 10^{-2})^y(2.0 \times 10^{-2})^z}$, $2.01 = 2.0^x$, $x = 1$

Comparing the first and fourth experiments:

$\dfrac{6.66 \times 10^{-7}}{1.66 \times 10^{-7}} = \dfrac{k(1.0 \times 10^{-4})(4.0 \times 10^{-2})^y(2.0 \times 10^{-2})^z}{k(1.0 \times 10^{-4})(2.0 \times 10^{-2})^y(2.0 \times 10^{-2})^z}$, $4.01 = 2.0^y$, $y = 2$

Comparing the first and sixth experiments:

$\dfrac{13.2 \times 10^{-7}}{1.66 \times 10^{-7}} = \dfrac{k(1.0 \times 10^{-4})(2.0 \times 10^{-2})^2(4.0 \times 10^{-2})^z}{k(1.0 \times 10^{-4})(2.0 \times 10^{-2})^2(2.0 \times 10^{-2})^z}$

$7.95 = 2.0^z$, $\log(7.95) = z \log(2.0)$, $z = \dfrac{\log(7.95)}{\log(2.0)} = 2.99 \approx 3$

$\text{Rate} = k[H_2SeO_3][H^+]^2[I^-]^3$

Experiment 1:

$\dfrac{1.66 \times 10^{-7} \ mol}{L \ s} = k\left(\dfrac{1.0 \times 10^{-4} \ mol}{L}\right)\left(\dfrac{2.0 \times 10^{-2} \ mol}{L}\right)^2\left(\dfrac{2.0 \times 10^{-2} \ mol}{L}\right)^3$

$k = 5.19 \times 10^5$ L^5 mol^{-5} s^{-1} $= 5.2 \times 10^5$ L^5 mol^{-5} s^{-1} $= k_{mean}$

25. $\text{Rate} = k[I^-]^x[OCl^-]^y[OH^-]^z$; Comparing the first and second experiments:

$\dfrac{18.7 \times 10^{-3}}{9.4 \times 10^{-3}} = \dfrac{k(0.0026)^x(0.012)^y(0.10)^z}{k(0.0013)^x(0.012)^y(0.10)^z}$, $2.0 = 2.0^x$, $x = 1$

Comparing the first and third experiments:

$$\frac{9.4 \times 10^{-3}}{4.7 \times 10^{-3}} = \frac{k(0.0013)(0.012)^y(0.10)^z}{k(0.0013)(0.0060)^y(0.10)^z}, \quad 2.0 = 2.0^y, \ y = 1$$

Comparing the first and sixth experiments:

$$\frac{4.8 \times 10^{-3}}{9.4 \times 10^{-3}} = \frac{k(0.0013)(0.012)(0.20)^z}{k(0.0013)(0.012)(0.10)^z}, \quad 1/2 = 2.0^z, \ z = -1$$

$\text{Rate} = \dfrac{k[I^-][OCl^-]}{[OH^-]}$; the presence of OH^- decreases the rate of the reaction.

For the first experiment:

$$\frac{9.4 \times 10^{-3}\ \text{mol}}{L\ s} = k\frac{(0.0013\ \text{mol}/L)(0.012\ \text{mol}/L)}{(0.10\ \text{mol}/L)}, \quad k = 60.3\ s^{-1} = 60.\ s^{-1}$$

For all experiments, $k_{mean} = 60.\ s^{-1}$.

Integrated Rate Laws

27.   Zero order: $t_{1/2} = \dfrac{[A]_0}{2k}$;   first order: $t_{1/2} = \dfrac{\ln 2}{k}$;   second order: $t_{1/2} = \dfrac{1}{k[A]_0}$

For a first-order reaction, if the first half-life equals 20. s, the second half-life will also be 20. s because the half-life for a first-order reaction is concentration-independent. The second half-life for a zero-order reaction will be 1/2(20.) = 10. s. This is because the half-life for a zero-order reaction has a direct relationship with concentration (as the concentration decreases by a factor of 2, the half-life decreases by a factor of 2). Because a second-order reaction has an inverse relationship between $t_{1/2}$ and $[A]_0$, the second half-life will be 40. s (twice the first half-life value).

29.   a.   Because the $\ln[A]$ versus time plot was linear, the reaction is first order in A. The slope of the $\ln[A]$ versus time plot equals $-k$. Therefore, the rate law, the integrated rate law, and the rate constant value are:

$$\text{Rate} = k[A]; \ \ln[A] = -kt + \ln[A]_0; \ k = 2.97 \times 10^{-2}\ \text{min}^{-1}$$

b.   The half-life expression for a first order rate law is:

$$t_{1/2} = \frac{\ln 2}{k} = \frac{0.6931}{k}, \quad t_{1/2} = \frac{0.6931}{2.97 \times 10^{-2}\ \text{min}^{-1}} = 23.3\ \text{min}$$

c. 2.50×10^{-3} M is 1/8 of the original amount of A present initially, so the reaction is 87.5% complete. When a first-order reaction is 87.5% complete (or 12.5% remains), then the reaction has gone through 3 half-lives:

$$100\% \;\; \rightarrow \;\; 50.0\% \;\; \rightarrow \;\; 25.0\% \;\; \rightarrow \;\; 12.5\%; \quad t = 3 \times t_{1/2} = 3 \times 23.3 \text{ min} = 69.9 \text{ min}$$
$$\qquad\quad t_{1/2} \qquad\quad t_{1/2} \qquad\quad t_{1/2}$$

Or we can use the integrated rate law:

$$\ln\!\left(\frac{[A]}{[A]_0}\right) = -kt, \;\; \ln\!\left(\frac{2.50 \times 10^{-3} \, M}{2.00 \times 10^{-2} \, M}\right) = -(2.97 \times 10^{-2} \text{ min}^{-1})t$$

$$t = \frac{\ln(0.125)}{-2.97 \times 10^{-2} \text{ min}^{-1}} = 70.0 \text{ min}$$

31.   The first assumption to make is that the reaction is first order. For a first order reaction, a graph of $\ln[H_2O_2]$ versus time will yield a straight line. If this plot is not linear, then the reaction is not first order, and we make another assumption.

Time (s)	[H_2O_2] (mol/L)	$\ln[H_2O_2]$
0	1.00	0.000
120.	0.91	−0.094
300.	0.78	−0.25
600.	0.59	−0.53
1200.	0.37	−0.99
1800.	0.22	−1.51
2400.	0.13	−2.04
3000.	0.082	−2.50
3600.	0.050	−3.00

Note: We carried extra significant figures in some of the natural log values in order to reduce round-off error. For the plots, we will do this most of the time when the natural log function is involved.

The plot of $\ln[H_2O_2]$ versus time is linear. Thus the reaction is first order. The differential rate law and integrated rate law are Rate $= \dfrac{-d[H_2O_2]}{dt} = k[H_2O_2]$ and $\ln[H_2O_2] = -kt + \ln[H_2O_2]_0$.

We determine the rate constant k by determining the slope of the $\ln[H_2O_2]$ versus time plot (slope = −k). Using two points on the curve gives:

$$\text{slope} = -k = \frac{\Delta y}{\Delta x} = \frac{0 - (3.00)}{0 - 3600.} = -8.3 \times 10^{-4} \text{ s}^{-1}, \ k = 8.3 \times 10^{-4} \text{ s}^{-1}$$

To determine $[H_2O_2]$ at 4000. s, use the integrated rate law, where $[H_2O_2]_0 = 1.00 \ M$.

$$\ln[H_2O_2] = -kt + \ln[H_2O_2]_0 \quad \text{or} \quad \ln\left(\frac{[H_2O_2]}{[H_2O_2]_0}\right) = -kt$$

$$\ln\left(\frac{[H_2O_2]}{1.00}\right) = -8.3 \times 10^{-4} \text{ s}^{-1} \times 4000. \text{ s}, \quad \ln[H_2O_2] = -3.3, \quad [H_2O_2] = e^{-3.3} = 0.037 \ M$$

33.   Assume the reaction is first order and see if the plot of $\ln[NO_2]$ versus time is linear. If this isn't linear, try the second order plot of $1/[NO_2]$ versus time. The data and plots follow.

Time (s)	$[NO_2] \ (M)$	$\ln[NO_2]$	$1/[NO_2] \ (M^{-1})$
0	0.500	−0.693	2.00
1.20×10^3	0.444	−0.812	2.25
3.00×10^3	0.381	−0.965	2.62
4.50×10^3	0.340	−1.079	2.94
9.00×10^3	0.250	−1.386	4.00
1.80×10^4	0.174	−1.749	5.75

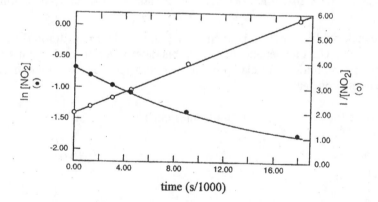

The plot of $1/[NO_2]$ versus time is linear. The reaction is second order in NO_2. The differential rate law and integrated rate law are $\text{Rate} = k[NO_2]^2$ and $\dfrac{1}{[NO_2]} = kt + \dfrac{1}{[NO_2]_0}$.

The slope of the plot $1/[NO_2]$ versus time gives the value of k. Using a couple of points on the plot:

$$\text{slope} = k = \frac{\Delta y}{\Delta x} = \frac{(5.75 - 2.00) \ M^{-1}}{(1.80 \times 10^4 - 0) \text{ s}} = 2.08 \times 10^{-4} \text{ L mol}^{-1} \text{ s}^{-1}$$

To determine $[NO_2]$ at 2.70×10^4 s, use the integrated rate law, where $1/[NO_2]_0 = 1/0.500\ M = 2.00\ M^{-1}$.

$$\frac{1}{[NO_2]} = kt + \frac{1}{[NO_2]_0}, \quad \frac{1}{[NO_2]} = \frac{2.08 \times 10^{-4}\ L}{mol\ s} \times 2.70 \times 10^4\ s + 2.00\ M^{-1}$$

$$\frac{1}{[NO_2]} = 7.62, \quad [NO_2] = 0.131\ M$$

35.   From the data, the pressure of C_2H_5OH decreases at a constant rate of 13 torr for every 100. s. Since the rate of disappearance of C_2H_5OH is not dependent on concentration, the reaction is zero order in C_2H_5OH.

$$k = \frac{13\ torr}{100.\ s} \times \frac{1\ atm}{760\ torr} = 1.7 \times 10^{-4}\ atm/s$$

The rate law and integrated rate law are:

$$Rate = k = 1.7 \times 10^{-4}\ atm/s; \quad P_{C_2H_5OH} = -kt + 250.\ torr \left(\frac{1\ atm}{760\ torr}\right) = -kt + 0.329\ atm$$

At 900. s:

$$P_{C_2H_5OH} = -1.7 \times 10^{-4}\ atm/s \times 900.\ s + 0.329\ atm = 0.176\ atm = 0.18\ atm = 130\ torr$$

37.   a.   We check for first-order dependence by graphing ln[concentration] versus time for each set of data. The rate dependence on NO is determined from the first set of data since the ozone concentration is relatively large compared to the NO concentration, so it is effectively constant.

Time (ms)	[NO] (molecules/cm³)	ln[NO]
0	6.0×10^8	20.21
100.	5.0×10^8	20.03
500.	2.4×10^8	19.30
700.	1.7×10^8	18.95
1000.	9.9×10^7	18.41

Because ln[NO] versus t is linear, the reaction is first order with respect to NO.

We follow the same procedure for ozone using the second set of data. The data and plot are:

Time (ms)	$[O_3]$ (molecules/cm^3)	ln$[O_3]$
0	1.0×10^{10}	23.03
50.	8.4×10^9	22.85
100.	7.0×10^9	22.67
200.	4.9×10^9	22.31
300.	3.4×10^9	21.95

The plot of ln$[O_3]$ versus t is linear. Hence the reaction is first order with respect to ozone.

b.   Rate = k[NO][O$_3$] is the overall rate law.

c.   For NO experiment, Rate = k′[NO] and k′ = –(slope from graph of ln[NO] versus t).

$$k' = -\text{slope} = -\frac{18.41 - 20.21}{(1000. - 0) \times 10^{-3} \text{ s}} = 1.8 \text{ s}^{-1}$$

For ozone experiment, Rate = k″[O$_3$] and k″ = –(slope from ln[O$_3$] versus t).

$$k'' = -\text{slope} = -\frac{(21.95 - 23.03)}{(300. - 0) \times 10^{-3} \text{ s}} = 3.6 \text{ s}^{-1}$$

d.   From NO experiment, Rate = k[NO][O$_3$] = k′[NO] where k′ = k[O$_3$].

$k' = 1.8 \text{ s}^{-1} = k(1.0 \times 10^{14} \text{ molecules/cm}^3)$, $k = 1.8 \times 10^{-14} \text{ cm}^3 \text{ molecules}^{-1} \text{ s}^{-1}$

We can check this from the ozone data. Rate = k″[O$_3$] = k[NO][O$_3$], where k″ = k[NO].

$k'' = 3.6 \text{ s}^{-1} = k(2.0 \times 10^{14} \text{ molecules/cm}^3)$, $k = 1.8 \times 10^{-14} \text{ cm}^3 \text{ molecules}^{-1} \text{ s}^{-1}$

Both values of k agree.

39.   Because $[V]_0 >> [AV]_0$, the concentration of V is essentially constant in this experiment. We have a pseudo-first-order reaction in AV:

$$\text{Rate} = k[AV][V] = k'[AV], \text{ where } k' = k[V]_0$$

The slope of the $\ln[AV]$ versus time plot is equal to $-k'$.

$$k' = -\text{slope} = 0.32 \text{ s}^{-1}; \quad k = \frac{k'}{[V]_0} = \frac{0.32 \text{ s}^{-1}}{0.20 \text{ mol/L}} = 1.6 \text{ L mol}^{-1} \text{ s}^{-1}$$

41.   For a first-order reaction, the integrated rate law is $\ln([A]/[A]_0) = -kt$. Solving for k:

$$\ln\left(\frac{0.250 \text{ mol/L}}{1.00 \text{ mol/L}}\right) = -k \times 120. \text{ s}, \quad k = 0.0116 \text{ s}^{-1}$$

$$\ln\left(\frac{0.350 \text{ mol/L}}{2.00 \text{ mol/L}}\right) = -0.0116 \text{ s}^{-1} \times t, \quad t = 150. \text{ s}$$

43.   Comparing experiments 1 and 2, as the concentration of AB is doubled, the initial rate increases by a factor of 4. The reaction is second order in AB.

$$\text{Rate} = k[AB]^2, \quad 3.20 \times 10^{-3} \text{ mol L}^{-1} \text{s}^{-1} = k_1 (0.200 \text{ } M)^2$$

$$k = 8.00 \times 10^{-2} \text{ L mol}^{-1} \text{s}^{-1} = k_{mean}$$

For a second-order reaction:

$$t_{1/2} = \frac{1}{k[AB]_0} = \frac{1}{8.00 \times 10^{-2} \text{ L mol}^{-1} \text{s}^{-1} \times 1.00 \text{ mol/L}} = 12.5 \text{ s}$$

45.   a. When a reaction is 75.0% complete (25.0% of reactant remains), this represents two half-lives (100% → 50% → 25%). The first-order half-life expression is $t_{1/2} = (\ln 2)/k$. Because there is no concentration dependence for a first-order half-life, 320. s = two half-lives, $t_{1/2} = 320./2 = 160.$ s. This is both the first half-life, the second half-life, etc.

        b. $t_{1/2} = \dfrac{\ln 2}{k}, \quad k = \dfrac{\ln 2}{t_{1/2}} = \dfrac{\ln 2}{160. \text{ s}} = 4.33 \times 10^{-3} \text{ s}^{-1}$

        At 90.0% complete, 10.0% of the original amount of the reactant remains, so $[A] = 0.100[A]_0$.

$$\ln\left(\frac{[A]}{[A]_0}\right) = -kt, \quad \ln\frac{0.100[A]_0}{[A]_0} = -(4.33 \times 10^{-3} \text{ s}^{-1})t, \quad t = \frac{\ln(0.100)}{-4.33 \times 10^{-3} \text{ s}^{-1}} = 532 \text{ s}$$

47.   a.   The integrated rate law for this zero-order reaction is $[HI] = -kt + [HI]_0$.

$$[HI] = -kt + [HI]_0, \ [HI] = -\left(\frac{1.20 \times 10^{-4} \text{ mol}}{\text{L s}}\right) \times \left(25 \text{ min} \times \frac{60 \text{ s}}{\text{min}}\right) + \frac{0.250 \text{ mol}}{\text{L}}$$

$[HI] = -0.18 \text{ mol/L} + 0.250 \text{ mol/L} = 0.07 \ M$

b. $[HI] = 0 = -kt + [HI]_0, \ kt = [HI]_0, \ t = \dfrac{[HI]_0}{k}$

$$t = \frac{0.250 \text{ mol/L}}{1.20 \times 10^{-4} \text{ mol L}^{-1} \text{ s}^{-1}} = 2080 \text{ s} = 34.7 \text{ min}$$

49.   The consecutive half-life values of 24 hours, then 12 hours, show a direct relationship with concentration; as the concentration decreases, the half-life decreases. Assuming the drug reaction is either zero, first, or second order, only a zero order reaction shows this direct relationship between half-life and concentration. Therefore, assume the reaction is zero order in the drug.

$$t_{1/2} = \frac{[A]_0}{2k}, \ k = \frac{[A]_0}{2t_{1/2}} = \frac{2.0 \times 10^{-3} \text{ mol/L}}{2(24 \text{ h})} = 4.2 \times 10^{-5} \text{ mol L}^{-1} \text{ h}^{-1}$$

51.   a.   Because $[A]_0 \ll [B]_0$ or $[C]_0$, the B and C concentrations remain constant at $1.00 \ M$ for this experiment. Thus, rate $= k[A]^2[B][C] = k'[A]^2$ where $k' = k[B][C]$.

For this pseudo-second-order reaction:

$$\frac{1}{[A]} = k't + \frac{1}{[A]_0}, \ \frac{1}{3.26 \times 10^{-5} \ M} = k'(3.00 \text{ min}) + \frac{1}{1.00 \times 10^{-4} \ M}$$

$k' = 6890 \text{ L mol}^{-1} \text{ min}^{-1} = 115 \text{ L mol}^{-1} \text{ s}^{-1}$

$$k' = k[B][C], \ k = \frac{k'}{[B][C]}, \ k = \frac{115 \text{ L mol}^{-1} \text{ s}^{-1}}{(1.00 \ M)(1.00 \ M)} = 115 \text{ L}^3 \text{ mol}^{-3} \text{ s}^{-1}$$

b.   For this pseudo-second-order reaction:

$$\text{Rate} = k'[A]^2, \ t_{1/2} = \frac{1}{k'[A]_0} = \frac{1}{115 \text{ L mol}^{-1} \text{ s}^{-1}(1.00 \times 10^{-4} \text{ mol/L})} = 87.0 \text{ s}$$

c. $\dfrac{1}{[A]} = k't + \dfrac{1}{[A]_0} = 115 \text{ L mol}^{-1} \text{ s}^{-1} \times 600. \text{ s} + \dfrac{1}{1.00 \times 10^{-4} \text{ mol/L}} = 7.90 \times 10^4 \text{ L/mol}$

$[A] = 1/7.90 \times 10^4 \text{ L/mol} = 1.27 \times 10^{-5} \text{ mol/L}$

From the stoichiometry in the balanced reaction, 1 mol of B reacts with every 3 mol of A.

Amount A reacted = $1.00 \times 10^{-4}\ M - 1.27 \times 10^{-5}\ M = 8.7 \times 10^{-5}\ M$

Amount B reacted = 8.7×10^{-5} mol/L $\times \dfrac{1\ \text{mol B}}{3\ \text{mol A}} = 2.9 \times 10^{-5}\ M$

[B] = $1.00\ M - 2.9 \times 10^{-5}\ M = 1.00\ M$

As we mentioned in part a, the concentration of B (and C) remain constant because the A concentration is so small compared to the B (or C) concentration.

Reaction Mechanisms

53.   In a unimolecular reaction, a single reactant molecule decomposes to products. In a bimolecular reaction, two molecules collide to give products. The probability of the simultaneous collision of three molecules with enough energy and the proper orientation is very small, making termolecular steps very unlikely.

55.   For elementary reactions, the rate law can be written using the coefficients in the balanced equation to determine the orders.

   a.   Rate = $k[CH_3NC]$ b.   Rate = $k[O_3][NO]$

   c.   Rate = $k[O_3]$ d.   Rate = $k[O_3][O]$

   e.   Rate = $k\left[{}^{14}_{6}C\right]$ or Rate = kN, where N = the number of ${}^{14}_{6}C$ atoms (convention)

57.   A mechanism consists of a series of elementary reactions in which the rate law for each step can be determined using the coefficients in the balanced equations. For a plausible mechanism, the rate law derived from a mechanism must agree with the rate law determined from experiment. To derive the rate law from the mechanism, the rate of the reaction is assumed to equal the rate of the slowest step in the mechanism.

   Because step 1 is the rate determining step, the rate law for this mechanism is Rate = $k[C_4H_9Br]$. To get the overall reaction, we sum all the individual steps of the mechanism. Summing all steps gives:

$$C_4H_9Br \rightarrow C_4H_9^+ + Br^-$$
$$C_4H_9^+ + H_2O \rightarrow C_4H_9OH_2^+$$
$$C_4H_9OH_2^+ + H_2O \rightarrow C_4H_9OH + H_3O^+$$

$$\overline{C_4H_9Br + 2\ H_2O \rightarrow C_4H_9OH + Br^- + H_3O^+}$$

   Intermediates in a mechanism are species that are neither reactants nor products but that are formed and consumed during the reaction sequence in the mechanism. The intermediates for this mechanism are $C_4H_9^+$ and $C_4H_9OH_2^+$.

59.   Let's determine the rate law for each mechanism. If the rate law derived from the mechanism is the same as the experimental rate law, then the mechanism is possible (assuming the sum of all the steps in the mechanism gives the overall balanced equation). When deriving rate laws from a mechanism, we must substitute for all intermediate concentrations.

   a.   Rate = $k_1[NO][O_2]$;   not possible

   b.   Rate = $k_2[NO_3][NO]$ and $k_1[NO][O_2] = k_{-1}[NO_3]$ or $[NO_3] = \dfrac{k_1}{k_{-1}}[NO][O_2]$

        Rate = $\dfrac{k_2 k_1}{k_{-1}}[NO]^2[O_2]$;   possible

   c.   Rate = $k_1[NO]^2$;   not possible   d.   Rate = $k_2[N_2O_2]$ and $[N_2O_2] = \dfrac{k_1}{k_{-1}}[NO]^2$

                                                             Rate = $\dfrac{k_2 k_1}{k_{-1}}[NO]^2$;   not possible

   Only the mechanism in b is consistent, so only mechanism b is a possible mechanism for this reaction.

61.   Rate = $k_3[Br^-][H_2BrO_3^+]$; we must substitute for the intermediate concentration. Because steps 1 and 2 are fast-equilibrium steps, rate forward reaction = rate reverse reaction.

   $k_2[HBrO_3][H^+] = k_{-2}[H_2BrO_3^+]$; $k_1[BrO_3^-][H^+] = k_{-1}[HBrO_3]$

   $[HBrO_3] = \dfrac{k_1}{k_{-1}}[BrO_3^-][H^+]$; $[H_2BrO_3^+] = \dfrac{k_2}{k_{-2}}[HBrO_3][H^+] = \dfrac{k_2 k_1}{k_{-2}k_{-1}}[BrO_3^-][H^+]^2$

   Rate = $\dfrac{k_3 k_2 k_1}{k_{-2}k_{-1}}[Br^-][BrO_3^-][H^+]^2 = k[Br^-][BrO_3^-][H^+]^2$

63.   Rate = $k_2[I^-][HOCl]$; from the fast-equilibrium first step:

        $k_1[OCl^-] = k_{-1}[HOCl][OH^-]$, $[HOCl] = \dfrac{k_1[OCl^-]}{k_{-1}[OH^-]}$; substituting into the rate equation:

        Rate = $\dfrac{k_2 k_1[I^-][OCl^-]}{k_{-1}[OH^-]} = \dfrac{k[I^-][OCl^-]}{[OH^-]}$

65.   a. $MoCl_5^-$

       b.   Rate = $\dfrac{d[NO_2^-]}{dt} = k_2[NO_3^-][MoCl_5^-]$ (Only the last step contains NO_2^-.)

            We use the steady-state assumption to substitute for the intermediate concentration in the rate law. The steady-state approximation assumes that the concentration of an intermediate remains constant; i.e., d[intermediate]/dt = 0. To apply the steady-state assumption, we write rate laws for all steps where the intermediate is produced and equate the sum of these rate laws to the sum of the rate laws where the intermediate is consumed. Applying the steady-state approximation to $MoCl_5^-$:

$$\frac{d[MoCl_5^-]}{dt} = 0, \text{ so } k_1[MoCl_6^{2-}] = k_{-1}[MoCl_5^-][Cl^-] + k_2[NO_3^-][MoCl_5^-]$$

$$[MoCl_5^-] = \frac{k_1[MoCl_6^{2-}]}{k_{-1}[Cl^-] + k_2[NO_3^-]} ; \quad \text{Rate} = \frac{d[NO_2^-]}{dt} = \frac{k_1k_2[NO_3^-][MoCl_6^{2-}]}{k_{-1}[Cl^-] + k_2[NO_3^-]}$$

67.   a. $\text{Rate} = \dfrac{d[E]}{dt} = k_2[B^*]$; assume $\dfrac{d[B^*]}{dt} = 0$, then $k_1[B]^2 = k_{-1}[B][B^*] + k_2[B^*]$.

$[B^*] = \dfrac{k_1[B]^2}{k_{-1}[B] + k_2}$; the rate law is: $\text{Rate} = \dfrac{d[E]}{dt} = \dfrac{k_1k_2[B]^2}{k_{-1}[B] + k_2}$

b.   When $k_2 \ll k_{-1}[B]$, then $\text{Rate} = \dfrac{d[E]}{dt} = \dfrac{k_1k_2[B]^2}{k_{-1}[B]} = \dfrac{k_1k_2}{k_{-1}}[B]$.

The reaction is first order when the rate of the second step is very slow (when k_2 is very small).

c.   Collisions between B molecules only transfer energy from one B to another. This occurs at a much faster rate than the decomposition of an energetic B molecule (B^*).

Temperature Dependence of Rate Constants and the Collision Model

69.   Two reasons are:

1)   The collision must involve enough energy to produce the reaction; i.e., the collision energy must be equal to or exceed the activation energy.

2)   The relative orientation of the reactants when they collide must allow formation of any new bonds necessary to produce products.

71.   a. $T_2 > T_1$; as temperature increases, the distribution of collision energies shifts to the right. That is, as temperature increases, there are fewer collision energies with small energies and more collisions with large energies.

b.   As temperature increases, more of the collisions have the required activation energy necessary to convert reactants into products. Hence, the rate of the reaction increases with increasing temperature.

73. $k = A \exp(-E_a/RT)$ or $\ln k = \dfrac{-E_a}{RT} + \ln A$ (the Arrhenius equation)

For two conditions: $\ln\left(\dfrac{k_2}{k_1}\right) = \dfrac{E_a}{R}\left(\dfrac{1}{T_1} - \dfrac{1}{T_2}\right)$ (Assuming A is temperature independent.)

Let $k_1 = 3.52 \times 10^{-7}$ L mol^{-1}s^{-1}, $T_1 = 555$ K; $k_2 = ?$, $T_2 = 645$ K; $E_a = 186 \times 10^3$ J/mol

$$\ln\left(\frac{k_2}{3.52 \times 10^{-7}}\right) = \frac{1.86 \times 10^5 \text{ J/mol}}{8.3145 \text{ J K}^{-1}\text{ mol}^{-1}}\left(\frac{1}{555 \text{ K}} - \frac{1}{645 \text{ K}}\right) = 5.6$$

$$\frac{k_2}{3.52 \times 10^{-7}} = e^{5.6} = 270, \quad k_2 = 270(3.52 \times 10^{-7}) = 9.5 \times 10^{-5} \text{ L mol}^{-1}\text{ s}^{-1}$$

75. $\ln\left(\dfrac{k_2}{k_1}\right) = \dfrac{E_a}{R}\left(\dfrac{1}{T_1} - \dfrac{1}{T_2}\right)$; $\dfrac{k_2}{k_1} = 7.00$, $T_1 = 295$ K, $E_a = 54.0 \times 10^3$ J/mol

$$\ln(7.00) = \frac{54.0 \times 10^3 \text{ J/mol}}{8.3145 \text{ J K}^{-1}\text{ mol}^{-1}}\left(\frac{1}{295 \text{ K}} - \frac{1}{T_2}\right), \quad \frac{1}{295 \text{ K}} - \frac{1}{T_2} = 3.00 \times 10^{-4}$$

$$\frac{1}{T_2} = 3.09 \times 10^{-3}, \quad T_2 = 324 \text{ K} = 51°\text{C}$$

77.   From the Arrhenius equation in logarithmic form ($\ln k = -E_a/RT + \ln A$), a graph of ln k versus. 1/T should yield a straight line with a slope equal to $-E_a/R$ and a y intercept equal to ln A.

a.   Slope $= -E_a/R$, $E_a = 1.10 \times 10^4$ K $\times \dfrac{8.3145 \text{ J}}{\text{K mol}} = 9.15 \times 10^4$ J/mol $= 91.5$ kJ/mol

b.   The units for A are the same as the units for k (s^{-1}).

   y intercept $= \ln A$, $A = e^{33.5} = 3.54 \times 10^{14}$ s^{-1}

c. $\ln k = -E_a/RT + \ln A$ or $k = A \exp(-E_a/RT)$

$$k = 3.54 \times 10^{14}\,\text{s}^{-1} \times \exp\left(\frac{-9.15 \times 10^{-4} \text{ J/mol}}{8.3145 \text{ J K}^{-1}\text{ mol}^{-1} \times 298 \text{ K}}\right) = 3.24 \times 10^{-2} \text{ s}^{-1}$$

79.   The Arrhenius equation is $k = A\exp(-E_a/RT)$ or, in logarithmic form, $\ln k = -E_a/RT + \ln A$. Hence a graph of ln k versus 1/T should yield a straight line with a slope equal to $-E_a/R$ since the logarithmic form of the Arrhenius equation is in the form of a straight-line equation, $y = mx + b$. *Note*: We carried one extra significant figure in the following ln k values in order to reduce round-off error.

T (K)	1/T (K^{-1})	k (L mol^{-1} s^{-1})	ln k
195	5.13×10^{-3}	1.08×10^9	20.80
230.	4.35×10^{-3}	2.95×10^9	21.81
260.	3.85×10^{-3}	5.42×10^9	22.41
298	3.36×10^{-3}	12.0×10^9	23.21
369	2.71×10^{-3}	35.5×10^9	24.29

Using a couple of points on the plot:

$$\text{slope} = \frac{20.95 - 23.65}{5.00 \times 10^{-3} - 3.00 \times 10^{-3}} = \frac{-2.70}{2.00 \times 10^{-3}} = -1.35 \times 10^3 \text{ K} = \frac{-E_a}{R}$$

$E_a = 1.35 \times 10^3 \text{ K} \times 8.3145 \text{ J K}^{-1} \text{ mol}^{-1} = 1.12 \times 10^4 \text{ J/mol} = 11.2 \text{ kJ/mol}$

From the best straight line (by calculator): slope $= -1.43 \times 10^3$ K and $E_a = 11.9$ kJ/mol

81.   In the following reaction profiles R = reactants, P = products, E_a = activation energy, ΔE = overall energy change for the reaction, and RC = reaction coordinate, which is the same as reaction progress.

The second reaction profile represents a two-step reaction since an intermediate plateau appears between the reactants and the products. This plateau (see I in plot) represents the energy of the intermediate. The general reaction mechanism for this reaction is:

R → I
I → P
─────
R → P

In a mechanism, the rate of the slowest step determines the rate of the reaction. The activation energy for the slowest step will be the largest energy barrier that the reaction must overcome. Since the second hump in the diagram is at the highest energy, the second step has the largest activation energy and will be the rate determining step (the slow step).

83.

The activation energy for the reverse reaction is E_R in the diagram.

$E_R = 167 - 28 = 139$ kJ/mol

Catalysis

85.   a.   The blue plot is the catalyzed pathway. The catalyzed pathway has the lower activation. This is why the catalyzed pathway is faster.

b. ΔE_1 represents the activation energy for the uncatalyzed pathway.

c. ΔE_2 represents the energy difference between the reactants and products. Note that ΔE_2 is the same for both the catalyzed and the uncatalyzed pathways. It is the activation energy that is different for a catalyzed pathway versus an uncatalyzed pathway.

d.   Because the products have a higher total energy as compared to reactants, this is an endothermic reaction.

87.   a.   W because it has a lower activation energy than the Os catalyst.

b. $k_w = A_w \exp[-E_a(W)/RT]$; $k_{uncat} = A_{uncat} \exp[-E_a(uncat)/RT]$; assume $A_w = A_{uncat}$.

$$\frac{k_w}{k_{uncat}} = \exp\left(\frac{-E_a(W)}{RT} + \frac{E_a(uncat)}{RT}\right)$$

$$\frac{k_w}{k_{uncat}} = \exp\left(\frac{-163,000 \text{ J}/\text{mol} + 335,000 \text{ J}/\text{mol}}{8.3145 \text{ J K}^{-1} \text{ mol}^{-1} \times 298 \text{ K}}\right) = 1.41 \times 10^{30}$$

The W-catalyzed reaction is approximately 10^{30} times faster than the uncatalyzed reaction.

c.   Because $[H_2]$ is in the denominator of the rate law, the presence of H_2 decreases the rate of the reaction. For the decomposition to occur, NH_3 molecules must be adsorbed on the surface of the catalyst. If H_2 is also adsorbed on the catalyst surface, then there are fewer sites for NH_3 molecules to be adsorbed, and the rate decreases.

89.   The mechanism for the chlorine catalyzed destruction of ozone is:

$$O_3 + Cl \rightarrow O_2 + ClO \quad \text{(slow)}$$
$$ClO + O \rightarrow O_2 + Cl \qquad \text{(fast)}$$
$$\overline{\rule{5cm}{0pt}}$$
$$O_3 + O \rightarrow 2\,O_2$$

Because the chlorine atom-catalyzed reaction has a lower activation energy, the Cl-catalyzed rate is faster. Hence Cl is a more effective catalyst. Using the activation energy, we can estimate the efficiency that Cl atoms destroy ozone compared to NO molecules (see Exercise 15.88c).

At 25°C: $\dfrac{k_{Cl}}{k_{NO}} = \exp\left[\dfrac{-E_a(Cl)}{RT} + \dfrac{E_a(NO)}{RT}\right] = \exp\left[\dfrac{(-2100 + 11{,}900)\,J/mol}{(8.3145 \times 298)\,J/mol}\right] = e^{3.96} = 52$

At 25°C, the Cl catalyzed reaction is roughly 52 times faster than the NO-catalyzed reaction, assuming the frequency factor A is the same for each reaction.

91.   At high [S], the enzyme is completely saturated with substrate. Once the enzyme is completely saturated, the rate of decomposition of ES can no longer increase, and the overall rate remains constant.

93. $\text{Rate} = \dfrac{-d[A]}{dt} = k[A]^x$

Assuming the catalyzed and uncatalyzed reaction have the same form and orders and because concentrations are assumed equal, rate $\propto 1/\Delta t$, where $\Delta t = \Delta \text{time}$.

$$\dfrac{\text{Rate}_{cat}}{\text{Rate}_{un}} = \dfrac{\Delta t_{un}}{\Delta t_{cat}} = \dfrac{2400\ yr}{\Delta t_{cat}} \quad \text{and} \quad \dfrac{\text{rate}_{cat}}{\text{rate}_{un}} = \dfrac{k_{cat}}{k_{un}}$$

$$\dfrac{\text{Rate}_{cat}}{\text{Rate}_{un}} = \dfrac{k_{cat}}{k_{un}} = \dfrac{A\exp[-E_a(cat)/RT]}{A\exp[-E_a(un)/RT]} = \exp\left[\dfrac{-E_a(cat) + E_a(un)}{RT}\right]$$

$$\dfrac{k_{cat}}{k_{un}} = \exp\left(\dfrac{-5.90 \times 10^4\ J/mol + 1.84 \times 10^5\ J/mol}{8.3145\ J\,K^{-1}\,mol^{-1} \times 600.\ K}\right) = 7.62 \times 10^{10}$$

$$\dfrac{\Delta t_{un}}{\Delta t_{cat}} = \dfrac{\text{rate}_{cat}}{\text{rate}_{un}} = \dfrac{k_{cat}}{k_{un}}, \quad \dfrac{2400\ yr}{\Delta t_{cat}} = 7.62 \times 10^{10}, \quad \Delta t_{cat} = 3.15 \times 10^{-8}\ yr \approx 1\ s$$

Additional Exercises

95.   The most common method to experimentally determine the differential rate law is the method of initial rates. Once the differential rate law is determined experimentally, the integrated rate law can be derived. However, sometimes it is more convenient and more accurate to collect concentration versus time data for a reactant. When this is the case, then we do "proof" plots to determine the integrated rate law. Once the integrated rate law is determined, the differential rate law can be determined. Either experimental procedure allows determination of both the integrated and the differential rate law; and which rate law is determined by experiment and which is derived is usually decided by which data are easiest and most accurately collected.

97.   Rate = $k[DNA]^x[CH_3I]^y$; comparing the second and third experiments:

$$\frac{1.28 \times 10^{-3}}{6.40 \times 10^{-4}} = \frac{k(0.200)^x(0.200)^y}{k(0.100)^x(0.200)^y}, \ 2.00 = 2.00^x, \ x = 1$$

Comparing the first and second experiments:

$$\frac{6.40 \times 10^{-4}}{3.20 \times 10^{-4}} = \frac{k(0.100)(0.200)^y}{k(0.100)(0.100)^y}, \ 2.00 = 2.00^y, \ y = 1$$

The rate law is Rate = $k[DNA][CH_3I]$.

Mechanism I is possible because the derived rate law from the mechanism (Rate = $k[DNA][CH_3I]$) agrees with the experimentally determined rate law. The derived rate law for Mechanism II will equal the rate of the slowest step. This is step 1 in the mechanism giving a derived rate law that is Rate = $k[CH_3I]$. Because this rate law does not agree with experiment, Mechanism II would not be a possible mechanism for the reaction.

99.

Heating Time	Untreated		Deacidifying		Antioxidant	
(days)	s	ln s	s	ln s	s	ln s
0.00	100.0	4.605	100.1	4.606	114.6	4.741
1.00	67.9	4.218	60.8	4.108	65.2	4.177
2.00	38.9	3.661	26.8	3.288	28.1	3.336
3.00	16.1	2.779	–	–	11.3	2.425
6.00	6.8	1.92	–	–	–	–

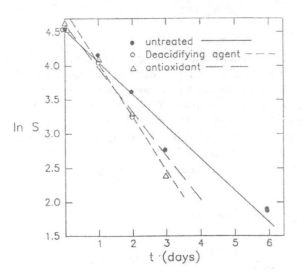

a. We used a calculator to fit the data by least squares. The results follow.

Untreated: ln s = –(0.465)t + 4.55, k = 0.465 d^{-1}

Deacidifying agent: ln s = –(0.659)t + 4.66, k = 0.659 d^{-1}

Antioxidant: ln s = –(0.779)t + 4.84, k = 0.779 d^{-1}

b. No, the silk degrades more rapidly with the additives since k increases.

c. $t_{1/2}$ = (ln 2)/k; untreated: $t_{1/2}$ = 1.49 day; deacidifying agent: $t_{1/2}$ = 1.05 day;

antioxidant: $t_{1/2}$ = 0.890 day.

101. Carbon cannot form the fifth bond necessary for the transition state because of the small atomic size of carbon and because carbon doesn't have low-energy d orbitals available to expand the octet.

103. a.

t (s)	$[C_4H_6]$ (M)	$\ln[C_4H_6]$	$1/[C_4H_6]$ (M^{-1})
0	0.01000	–4.6052	1.000×10^2
1000.	0.00629	–5.069	1.59×10^2
2000.	0.00459	–5.384	2.18×10^2
3000.	0.00361	–5.624	2.77×10^2

The plot of $1/[C_4H_6]$ versus t is linear, thus the reaction is second order in butadiene. From the plot (not included), the integrated rate law is:

$$\frac{1}{[C_4H_6]} = (5.90 \times 10^{-2} \text{ L mol}^{-1} \text{ s}^{-1})t + 100.0 \, M^{-1}$$

b. When dimerization is 1.0% complete, 99.0% of C_4H_6 is left.

$[C_4H_6] = 0.990(0.01000) = 0.00990\ M$; $\dfrac{1}{0.00990} = (5.90 \times 10^{-2})t + 100.0$

t = 17.1 s ≈ 20 s

c. 2.0% complete, $[C_4H_6] = 0.00980\ M$; $\dfrac{1}{0.00980} = (5.90 \times 10^{-2})t + 100.0$,

t = 34.6 s ≈ 30 s

d. $\dfrac{1}{[C_4H_6]} = kt + \dfrac{1}{[C_4H_6]_0}$; $[C_4H_6]_0 = 0.0200\ M$; at t = $t_{1/2}$, $[C_4H_6] = 0.0100\ M$.

$\dfrac{1}{0.0100} = (5.90 \times 10^{-2})t_{1/2} + \dfrac{1}{0.0200}$, $t_{1/2} = 847\ s = 850\ s$

Or: $t_{1/2} = \dfrac{1}{k[A]_0} = \dfrac{1}{(5.90 \times 10^{-2}\ \text{L mol}^{-1}\ \text{s}^{-1})(2.00 \times 10^{-2}\ M)} = 847\ s$

e. From Exercise 15.32, k = 1.4 × 10⁻² L mol⁻¹ s⁻¹ at 500. K. From this problem, k = 5.90 × 10⁻² L mol⁻¹ s⁻¹ at 620. K.

$\ln\!\left(\dfrac{k_2}{k_1}\right) = \dfrac{E_a}{R}\!\left(\dfrac{1}{T_1} - \dfrac{1}{T_2}\right)$, $\ln\!\left(\dfrac{5.90 \times 10^{-2}}{1.4 \times 10^{-2}}\right) = \dfrac{E_a}{8.3145\ \text{J K}^{-1}\ \text{mol}^{-1}}\!\left(\dfrac{1}{500.\,K} - \dfrac{1}{620.\,K}\right)$

$12 = E_a(3.9 \times 10^{-4})$, $E_a = 3.1 \times 10^4$ J/mol = 31 kJ/mol

105. $k = A\exp(-E_a/RT)$; $\dfrac{k_{cat}}{k_{uncat}} = \dfrac{A_{cat}\exp(-E_{a,cat}/RT)}{A_{uncat}\exp(-E_{a,uncat}/RT)} = \exp\!\left(\dfrac{-E_{a,cat} + E_{a,uncat}}{RT}\right)$

$2.50 \times 10^3 = \dfrac{k_{cat}}{k_{uncat}} = \exp\!\left(\dfrac{-E_{a,cat} + 5.00 \times 10^4\ \text{J/mol}}{8.3145\ \text{J K}^{-1}\ \text{mol}^{-1} \times 310.\,K}\right)$

$\ln(2.50 \times 10^3) \times 2.58 \times 10^3$ J/mol $= -E_{a,cat} + 5.00 \times 10^4$ J/mol

$E_{a,cat} = 5.00 \times 10^4$ J/mol $- 2.02 \times 10^4$ J/mol $= 2.98 \times 10^4$ J/mol $= 29.8$ kJ/mol

107. a.

T (K)	1/T (K⁻¹)	k (min⁻¹)	ln k
298.2	3.353 × 10⁻³	178	5.182
293.5	3.407 × 10⁻³	126	4.836
290.5	3.442 × 10⁻³	100.	4.605

A plot of ln k versus 1/T gives a straight line (plot not included). The equation for the straight line is:

$$\ln k = -6.48 \times 10^3(1/T) + 26.9$$

For the ln k versus 1/T plot, slope $= -E_a/R = -6.48 \times 10^3$ K.

$$-6.48 \times 10^3 \text{ K} = -E_a/8.3145 \text{ J K}^{-1} \text{ mol}^{-1}, \quad E_a = 5.39 \times 10^4 \text{ J/mol} = 53.9 \text{ kJ/mol}$$

b. $\ln k = -6.48 \times 10^3(1/288.2) + 26.9 = 4.42, \quad k = e^{4.42} = 83 \text{ min}^{-1}$

About 83 chirps per minute per insect. Note: We carried extra significant figures.

c.   k gives the number of chirps per minute. The number or chirps in 15 s is k/4.

T (°C)	T (°F)	k (min^{-1})	42 + 0.80(k/4)
25.0	77.0	178	78° F
20.3	68.5	126	67°F
17.3	63.1	100.	62°F
15.0	59.0	83	59°F

The rule of thumb appears to be fairly accurate, almost $\pm 1°$F.

109.   Rate $= \dfrac{d[Cl_2]}{dt} = k_2[NO_2Cl][Cl]$; Assume $\dfrac{d[Cl]}{dt} = 0$, then:

$$k_1[NO_2Cl] = k_{-1}[NO_2][Cl] + k_2[NO_2Cl][Cl], \quad [Cl] = \frac{k_1[NO_2Cl]}{k_{-1}[NO_2] + k_2[NO_2Cl]}$$

$$\text{Rate} = \frac{d[Cl_2]}{dt} = \frac{k_1k_2[NO_2Cl]^2}{k_{-1}[NO_2] + k_2[NO_2Cl]}$$

Challenge Problems

111.   a.   Rate $= k[CH_3X]^x[Y]^y$; for experiment 1, [Y] is in large excess, so its concentration will be constant. Rate $= k'[CH_3X]^x$, where $k' = k(3.0 \text{ } M)^y$.

A plot (not included) of $\ln[CH_3X]$ versus t is linear ($x = 1$). The integrated rate law is:

$$\ln[CH_3X] = -(0.93)t - 3.99; \quad k' = 0.93 \text{ h}^{-1}$$

For experiment 2, [Y] is again constant, with Rate $= k''[CH_3X]^x$, where $k'' = k(4.5 \text{ } M)^y$. The natural log plot is linear again with an integrated rate law:

$$\ln[CH_3X] = -(0.93)t - 5.40; \quad k'' = 0.93 \text{ h}^{-1}$$

Dividing the rate-constant values: $\dfrac{k'}{k''} = \dfrac{0.93}{0.93} = \dfrac{k(3.0)^y}{k(4.5)^y}, \quad 1.0 = (0.67)^y, \quad y = 0$

Reaction is first order in CH_3X and zero order in Y. The overall rate law is:

Rate = $k[CH_3X]$, where $k = 0.93$ h^{-1} at 25°C

b. $t_{1/2} = (\ln 2)/k = 0.6931/(7.88 \times 10^8$ $h^{-1}) = 8.80 \times 10^{-10}$ hour

c. $\ln\left(\dfrac{k_2}{k_1}\right) = \dfrac{E_a}{R}\left(\dfrac{1}{T_1} - \dfrac{1}{T_2}\right)$, $\ln\left(\dfrac{7.88 \times 10^8}{0.93}\right) = \dfrac{E_a}{8.3145 \text{ J K}^{-1}\text{ mol}^{-1}}\left(\dfrac{1}{298 \text{ K}} - \dfrac{1}{358 \text{ K}}\right)$

$E_a = 3.0 \times 10^5$ J/mol $= 3.0 \times 10^2$ kJ/mol

d. From part a, the reaction is first order in CH_3X and zero order in Y. From part c, the activation energy is close to the C-X bond energy. A plausible mechanism that explains the results in parts a and c is:

$CH_3X \rightarrow CH_3 + X$ (slow)

$CH_3 + Y \rightarrow CH_3Y$ (fast)

Note: This is a possible mechanism because the derived rate law is the same as the experimental rate law (and the sum of the steps gives the overall balanced equation).

113. $\dfrac{-d[A]}{dt} = k[A]^3$, $\displaystyle\int_{[A]_0}^{[A]_t} \dfrac{d[A]}{[A]^3} = -\int_0^t k \, dt$

$\displaystyle\int x^n \, dx = \dfrac{x^{n+1}}{n+1}$; so: $-\dfrac{1}{2[A]^2}\Big|_{[A]_0}^{[A]_t} = -kt$, $-\dfrac{1}{2[A]_t^2} + \dfrac{1}{2[A]_0^2} = -kt$

For the half-life equation, $[A]_t = 1/2[A]_0$:

$-\dfrac{1}{2\left(\dfrac{1}{2}[A]_0\right)^2} + \dfrac{1}{2[A]_0^2} = -kt_{1/2}$, $-\dfrac{4}{2[A]_0^2} + \dfrac{1}{2[A]_0^2} = -kt_{1/2}$

$-\dfrac{3}{2[A]_0^2} = -kt_{1/2}$, $t_{1/2} = \dfrac{3}{2[A]_0^2 k}$

The first half-life is $t_{1/2} = 40.$ s and corresponds to going from $[A]_0$ to $1/2[A]_0$. The second half-life corresponds to going from $1/2$ $[A]_0$ to $1/4$ $[A]_0$.

First half-life $= \dfrac{3}{2[A]_0^2 k}$; second half-life $= \dfrac{3}{2\left(\dfrac{1}{2}[A]_0\right)^2 k} = \dfrac{6}{[A]_0^2 k}$

$$\frac{\text{First half} - \text{life}}{\text{Second half} - \text{life}} = \frac{\dfrac{3}{2[A]_0^2\,k}}{\dfrac{6}{[A]_0^2\,k}} = 3/12 = 1/4$$

Because the first half-life is 40. s, the second half-life will be four times this, or 160 s.

115.   Rate = $k[A]^x[B]^y[C]^z$; during the course of experiment 1, [A] and [C] are essentially constant, and Rate = $k'[B]^y$, where $k' = k[A]_0^x[C]_0^z$.

[B] (M)	time (s)	ln[B]	1/[B] (M^{-1})
1.0×10^{-3}	0	−6.91	1.0×10^3
2.7×10^{-4}	1.0×10^5	−8.22	3.7×10^3
1.6×10^{-4}	2.0×10^5	−8.74	6.3×10^3
1.1×10^{-4}	3.0×10^5	−9.12	9.1×10^3
8.5×10^{-5}	4.0×10^5	−9.37	12×10^3
6.9×10^{-5}	5.0×10^5	−9.58	14×10^3
5.8×10^{-5}	6.0×10^5	−9.76	17×10^3

A plot of 1/[B] versus t is linear (plot not included). The reaction is second order in B, and the integrated rate equation is:

$$1/[B] = (2.7 \times 10^{-2}\ \text{L mol}^{-1}\ \text{s}^{-1})t + 1.0 \times 10^3\ M^{-1};\ \ k' = 2.7 \times 10^{-2}\ \text{L mol}^{-1}\ \text{s}^{-1}$$

For experiment 2, [B] and [C] are essentially constant, and Rate = $k''[A]^x$, where $k'' = k[B]_0^y[C]_0^z = k[B]_0^2[C]_0^z$.

[A] (M)	time (s)	ln[A]	1/[A] (M^{-1})
1.0×10^{-2}	0	−4.61	1.0×10^2
8.9×10^{-3}	1.0	−4.72	110
7.1×10^{-3}	3.0	−4.95	140
5.5×10^{-3}	5.0	−5.20	180
3.8×10^{-3}	8.0	−5.57	260
2.9×10^{-3}	10.0	−5.84	340
2.0×10^{-3}	13.0	−6.21	5.0×10^2

A plot of ln[A] versus t is linear. The reaction is first order in A, and the integrated rate law is:

$$\ln[A] = -(0.123\ \text{s}^{-1})t - 4.61;\ \ k'' = 0.123\ \text{s}^{-1}$$

Note: We will carry an extra significant figure in k''.

Experiment 3:   [A] and [B] are constant; Rate = $k'''[C]^z$

The plot of [C] versus t is linear. Thus $z = 0$.

The overall rate law is Rate = $k[A][B]^2$.

From experiment 1 (to determine k):

$$k' = 2.7 \times 10^{-2} \text{ L mol}^{-1} \text{ s}^{-1} = k[A]_0^x[C]_0^z = k[A]_0 = k(2.0 \text{ M}), \ k = 1.4 \times 10^{-2} \text{ L}^2 \text{ mol}^{-2} \text{ s}^{-1}$$

From experiment 2: $k'' = 0.123 \text{ s}^{-1} = k[B]_0^2$, $k = \dfrac{0.123 \text{ s}^{-1}}{(3.0 \text{ M})^2} = 1.4 \times 10^{-2} \text{ L}^2 \text{ mol}^{-2} \text{ s}^{-1}$

Thus Rate = $k[A][B]^2$ and $k = 1.4 \times 10^{-2} \text{ L}^2 \text{ mol}^{-2} \text{ s}^{-1}$.

117.   Rate = $\dfrac{-d[N_2O_5]}{dt} = k_1[M][N_2O_5] - k_{-1}[NO_3][NO_2][M]$

Assume $d[NO_3]/dt = 0$, so $k_1[N_2O_5][M] = k_{-1}[NO_3][NO_2][M] + k_2[NO_3][NO_2] +$

$$k_3[NO_3][NO].$$

$$[NO_3] = \frac{k_1[N_2O_5][M]}{k_{-1}[NO_2][M] + k_2[NO_2] + k_3[NO]}$$

Assume $\dfrac{d[NO]}{dt} = 0$, so $k_2[NO_3][NO_2] = k_3[NO_3][NO]$, $[NO] = \dfrac{k_2}{k_3}[NO_2]$.

Substituting: $[NO_3] = \dfrac{k_1[N_2O_5][M]}{k_{-1}[NO_2][M] + k_2[NO_2] + \dfrac{k_2 k_3}{k_3}[NO_2]} = \dfrac{k_1[N_2O_5][M]}{[NO_2](k_{-1}[M] + 2k_2)}$

Solving for the rate law:

$$\text{Rate} = \frac{-d[N_2O_5]}{dt} = k_1[N_2O_5][M] - \frac{k_{-1}k_1[NO_2][N_2O_5][M]^2}{[NO_2](k_{-1}[M] + 2k_2)} = k_1[N_2O_5][M]$$

$$- \frac{k_{-1}k_1[M]^2[N_2O_5]}{k_{-1}[M] + 2k_2}$$

$$\text{Rate} = \frac{-d[N_2O_5]}{dt} = \left(k_1 - \frac{k_{-1}k_1[M]}{k_{-1}[M] + 2k_2} \right)[N_2O_5][M]; \text{ simplifying:}$$

$$\text{Rate} = \frac{-d[N_2O_5]}{dt} = \frac{2k_1k_2[M][N_2O_5]}{k_{-1}[M] + 2k_2}$$

119.   a.   Rate $= (k_1 + k_2[H^+])[I^-]^m[H_2O_2]^n$

In all the experiments the concentration of H_2O_2 is small compared to the concentrations of I^- and H^+. Therefore, the concentrations of I^- and H^+ are effectively constant, and the rate law reduces to:

Rate $= k_{obs}[H_2O_2]^n$, where $k_{obs} = (k_1 + k_2[H^+])[I^-]^m$

Because all plots of $\ln[H_2O_2]$ versus time are linear, the reaction is first order with respect to H_2O_2 ($n = 1$). The slopes of the $\ln[H_2O_2]$ versus time plots equal $-k_{obs}$, which equals $-(k_1 + k_2[H^+])[I^-]^m$. To determine the order of I^-, compare the slopes of two experiments in which I^- changes and H^+ is constant. Comparing the first two experiments:

$$\frac{\text{slope (exp. 2)}}{\text{slope (exp. 1)}} = \frac{-0.360}{-0.120} = \frac{-[k_1 + k_2(0.0400\ M)](0.3000\ M)^m}{-[k_1 + k_2(0.0400\ M)](0.1000\ M)^m}$$

$$3.00 = \left(\frac{0.3000\ M}{0.1000\ M}\right)^m = (3.000)^m,\ \ m = 1$$

The reaction is also first order with respect to I^-.

b.   The slope equation has two unknowns, k_1 and k_2. To solve for k_1 and k_2, we must have two equations. We need to take one of the first set of three experiments and one of the second set of three experiments to generate the two equations in k_1 and k_2.

Experiment 1: slope $= -(k_1 + k_2[H^+])[I^-]$

   -0.120 min$^{-1} = -[k_1 + k_2(0.0400\ M)](0.1000\ M)$ or $1.20 = k_1 + k_2(0.0400)$

Experiment 4:

   -0.0760 min$^{-1} = -[k_1 + k_2(0.0200\ M)](0.0750\ M)$ or $1.01 = k_1 + k_2(0.0200)$

Subtracting 4 from 1:

$$\begin{array}{rl} 1.20 = & k_1 + k_2(0.0400) \\ -1.01 = & -k_1 - k_2(0.0200) \\ \hline 0.19 = & k_2(0.0200), \ \ k_2 = 9.5\ L^2\ mol^{-2}\ min^{-1} \end{array}$$

$1.20 = k_1 + 9.5(0.0400)$, $k_1 = 0.82\ L\ mol^{-1}\ min^{-1}$

c.   There are two pathways, one involving H^+ with rate $= k_2[H^+][I^-][H_2O_2]$ and another not involving H^+ with rate $= k_1[I^-][H_2O_2]$. The overall rate of reaction depends on which of these two pathways dominates, and this depends on the H^+ concentration.

CHAPTER 16

LIQUIDS AND SOLIDS

Intermolecular Forces and Physical Properties

11.   Intermolecular forces are the relatively weak forces between molecules that hold the molecules together in the solid and liquid phases. Intramolecular forces are the forces within a molecule. These are the covalent bonds in a molecule. Intramolecular forces (covalent bonds) are much stronger than intermolecular forces.

Dipole forces are the forces that act between polar molecules. The electrostatic attraction between the partial positive end of one polar molecule and the partial negative end of another is the dipole force. Dipole forces are generally weaker than hydrogen bonding. Both of these forces are due to dipole moments in molecules. Hydrogen bonding is given a separate name from dipole forces because hydrogen bonding is a particularly strong dipole force. Any neutral molecule that has a hydrogen covalently bonded to N, O, or F exhibits the relatively strong hydrogen bonding intermolecular forces.

London dispersion forces are accidental-induced dipole forces. Like dipole forces, London dispersion forces are electrostatic in nature. Dipole forces are the electrostatic forces between molecules having a permanent dipole. London dispersion forces are the electrostatic forces between molecules having an accidental or induced dipole. All covalent molecules (polar and nonpolar) have London dispersion forces, but only polar molecules (those with permanent dipoles) exhibit dipole forces.

13.   Fusion refers to a solid converting to a liquid, and vaporization refers to a liquid converting to a gas. Only a fraction of the hydrogen bonds are broken in going from the solid phase to the liquid phase. Most of the hydrogen bonds are still present in the liquid phase and must be broken during the liquid to gas phase transition. Thus the enthalpy of vaporization is much larger than the enthalpy of fusion since more intermolecular forces are broken during the vaporization process.

15.   Ionic compounds have ionic forces. Covalent compounds all have London dispersion (LD) forces, whereas polar covalent compounds have dipole forces and/or hydrogen-bonding forces. For hydrogen bonding (H-bonding) forces, the covalent compound must have either a N–H, O–H, or F–H bond in the molecule.

   a. LD only   b. dipole, LD   c. H-bonding, LD

   d. ionic   e. LD only (CH_4 in a nonpolar covalent compound.)

329

f. dipole, LD   g. ionic   h. ionic

i. LD mostly; C–F bonds are polar, but polymers such as teflon are so large that LD forces are the predominant intermolecular forces.

j. LD   k. dipole, LD   l. H-bonding, LD

m. dipole, LD   n. LD only

17.   Boiling points and freezing points are assumed directly related to the strength of the intermolecular forces, whereas vapor pressure is inversely related to the strength of the intermolecular forces.

a. HBr; HBr is polar, whereas Kr and Cl_2 are nonpolar. HBr has dipole forces unlike Kr and Cl_2. So HBr has the stronger intermolecular forces and the highest boiling point.

b. NaCl; the ionic forces in NaCl are much stronger than the intermolecular forces for molecular substances, so NaCl has the highest melting point.

c. I_2; all are nonpolar, so the largest molecule (I_2) will have the strongest LD (London Dispersion) forces and the lowest vapor pressure.

d. N_2; nonpolar and smallest, so it has the weakest intermolecular forces.

e. CH_4; smallest, nonpolar molecule, so it has the weakest LD forces.

f. HF; HF can form relatively strong H-bonding interactions, unlike the others.

g. $CH_3CH_2CH_2OH$; H-bonding, unlike the others, so it has strongest intermolecular forces.

19.   a. Neopentane is more compact than n-pentane. There is less surface-area contact among neopentane molecules. This leads to weaker LD (London Dispersion) forces and a lower boiling point.

b. HF is capable of H-bonding; HCl is not.

c. LiCl is ionic, and HCl is a molecular solid with only dipole forces and LD forces. Ionic forces are much stronger than the forces for molecular solids.

d. n-Hexane is a larger molecule, so it has stronger LD forces.

21.   Ar exists as individual atoms that are held together in the condensed phases by London dispersion forces. The molecule that will have a boiling point closest to Ar will be a nonpolar substance with about the same molar mass as Ar (39.95 g/mol); this same size nonpolar substance will have about equivalent strength of London dispersion forces. Of the choices, only Cl_2 (70.90 g/mol) and F_2 (38.00 g/mol) are nonpolar. Because F_2 has a molar mass closest to that of Ar, one would expect the boiling point of F_2 to be close to that of Ar.

23.   The electrostatic potential diagrams indicate that ethanol and acetone are polar substances, and that propane is a nonpolar substance. Ethanol, with the O–H covalent bond, will exhibit relatively strong hydrogen bonding intermolecular forces in addition to London dispersion forces. The polar acetone will exhibit dipole forces in addition to London dispersion forces,

and the nonpolar propane will only exhibit London dispersion (LD) forces. Because all three compounds have about the same molar mass, the relative strengths of the LD forces should be about the same. Therefore, ethanol (with the H-bonding capacity) should have the highest boiling point, with polar acetone having the next highest boiling point, and the nonpolar propane, with the weakest intermolecular forces, will have the lowest boiling point.

25.   A single hydrogen bond in H_2O has a strength of 21 kJ/mol. Each H_2O molecule forms two H-bonds. Thus it should take 42 kJ/mol of energy to break all of the H-bonds in water. Consider the phase transitions:

$$\text{Solid} \xrightarrow{\text{6.0 kJ}} \text{liquid} \xrightarrow{\text{40.7 kJ}} \text{vapor} \qquad \Delta H_{sub} = \Delta H_{fus} + \Delta H_{vap}$$

It takes a total of 46.7 kJ/mol to convert solid H_2O to vapor (ΔH_{sub}). This would be the amount of energy necessary to disrupt all of the intermolecular forces in ice. Thus $(42 \div 46.7) \times 100 = 90.\%$ of the attraction in ice can be attributed to H-bonding.

Properties of Liquids

27.   a.   Surface tension: the resistance of a liquid to an increase in its surface area.

       b.   Viscosity: the resistance of a liquid to flow.

       c.   Melting point: the temperature (at constant pressure) where a solid converts entirely to a liquid as long as heat is applied. A more detailed definition is the temperature at which the solid and liquid states have the same vapor pressure under conditions where the total pressure is constant.

       d.   Boiling point: the temperature (at constant pressure) where a liquid converts entirely to a gas as long as heat is applied. The detailed definition is the temperature at which the vapor pressure of the liquid is exactly equal to the external pressure.

       e.   Vapor pressure: the pressure of the vapor over a liquid at equilibrium.

       As the strengths of intermolecular forces increase, surface tension, viscosity, melting point, and boiling point increase, whereas vapor pressure decreases.

29.   Water is a polar substance, and wax is a nonpolar substance; they are not attracted to each other. A molecule at the surface of a drop of water is subject to attractions only by water molecules below it and to each side. The effect of this uneven pull on the surface water molecules tends to draw them into the body of the water and causes the droplet to assume the shape that has the minimum surface area, a sphere.

31.   The structure of H_2O_2 is $H - O - O - H$, which produces greater hydrogen bonding than in water. Thus the intermolecular forces are stronger in H_2O_2 than in H_2O resulting in a higher normal boiling point for H_2O_2 and a lower vapor pressure.

Structures and Properties of Solids

33. a. Crystalline solid: Regular, repeating structure

         Amorphous solid: Irregular arrangement of atoms or molecules

     b. Ionic solid: Made up of ions held together by ionic bonding.

         Molecular solid: Made up of discrete covalently bonded molecules held together in the solid phase by weaker forces (LD, dipole or hydrogen bonds).

     c. Molecular solid: Discrete, individual molecules

         Covalent network solid: No discrete molecules; a covalent network solid is one large molecule; the interparticle forces are the covalent bonds between atoms.

     d. Metallic solid: Completely delocalized electrons, conductor of electricity (ions in a sea of electrons)

         Covalent network solid: Localized electrons; insulator or semiconductor

35. a. Both forms of carbon are network solids. In diamond, each carbon atom is surrounded by a tetrahedral arrangement of other carbon atoms to form a huge molecule. Each carbon atom is covalently bonded to four other carbon atoms.

         The structure of graphite is based on layers of carbon atoms arranged in fused six-membered rings. Each carbon atom in a particular layer of graphite is surrounded by three other carbons in a trigonal planar arrangement. This requires sp^2 hybridization. Each carbon has an unhybridized p atomic orbital; all of these p orbitals in each six-membered ring overlap with each other to form a delocalized π electron system.

     b. Silica is a network solid having an empirical formula of SiO_2. The silicon atoms are singly bonded to four oxygens. Each silicon atom is at the center of a tetrahedral arrangement of oxygen atoms that are shared with other silicon atoms. The structure of silica is based on a network of SiO_4 tetrahedra with shared oxygen atoms rather than discrete SiO_2 molecules.

         Silicates closely resemble silica. The structure is based on interconnected SiO_4 tetrahedra. However, in contrast to silica, where the O/Si ratio is 2:1, silicates have O/Si ratios greater than 2:1 and contain silicon-oxygen anions. To form a neutral solid silicate, metal cations are needed to balance the charge. In other words, silicates are salts containing metal cations and polyatomic silicon-oxygen anions.

         When silica is heated above its melting point and cooled rapidly, an amorphous (disordered) solid called glass results. Glass more closely resembles a very viscous solution than it does a crystalline solid. To affect the properties of glass, several different additives are thrown into the mixture. Some of these additives are Na_2CO_3, B_2O_3, and K_2O, with each compound serving a specific purpose relating to the properties of glass.

37.   A crystalline solid will have the simpler diffraction pattern because a regular, repeating arrangement is necessary to produce planes of atoms that will diffract the X rays in regular patterns. An amorphous solid does not have a regular repeating arrangement and will produce a complicated diffraction pattern.

39. $\lambda = \dfrac{2d \sin \theta}{n} = \dfrac{2 \times 1.36 \times 10^{-10} \text{ m} \times \sin 15.0°}{1} = 7.04 \times 10^{-11} \text{ m} = 0.704 \text{ Å}$

41. $n\lambda = 2d \sin \theta,\ \ d = \dfrac{n\lambda}{2 \sin \theta} = \dfrac{1 \times 1.54 \text{ Å}}{2 \times \sin 14.22°} = 3.13 \text{ Å} = 3.13 \times 10^{-10} \text{ m} = 313 \text{ pm}$

43.   A cubic closest packed structure has a face-centered cubic unit cell. In a face-centered cubic unit, there are:

$$8 \text{ corners} \times \dfrac{1/8 \text{ atom}}{\text{corner}} + 6 \text{ faces} \times \dfrac{1/2 \text{ atom}}{\text{face}} = 4 \text{ atoms}$$

The atoms in a face-centered cubic unit cell touch along the face diagonal of the cubic unit cell. Using the Pythagorean formula, where l = length of the face diagonal and r = radius of the atom:

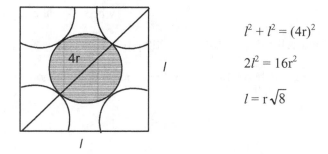

$l^2 + l^2 = (4r)^2$

$2l^2 = 16r^2$

$l = r\sqrt{8}$

$l = r\sqrt{8} = 197 \times 10^{-12} \text{ m} \times \sqrt{8} = 5.57 \times 10^{-10} \text{ m} = 5.57 \times 10^{-8} \text{ cm}$

Volume of a unit cell = $l^3 = (5.57 \times 10^{-8} \text{ cm})^3 = 1.73 \times 10^{-22} \text{ cm}^3$

Mass of a unit cell = $4 \text{ Ca atoms} \times \dfrac{1 \text{ mol Ca}}{6.022 \times 10^{23} \text{ atoms}} \times \dfrac{40.08 \text{ g Ca}}{\text{mol Ca}} = 2.662 \times 10^{-22} \text{ g Ca}$

Density = $\dfrac{\text{mass}}{\text{volume}} = \dfrac{2.662 \times 10^{-22} \text{ g}}{1.73 \times 10^{-22} \text{ cm}^3} = 1.54 \text{ g/cm}^3$

45.   There are four Ni atoms in each unit cell: For a unit cell:

$$\text{density} = \dfrac{\text{mass}}{\text{volume}} = 6.84 \text{ g/cm}^3 = \dfrac{4 \text{ Ni atoms} \times \dfrac{1 \text{ mol Ni}}{6.022 \times 10^{23} \text{ atoms}} \times \dfrac{58.69 \text{ g Ni}}{\text{mol Ni}}}{l^3}$$

Solving: $l = 3.85 \times 10^{-8}$ cm = cube edge length

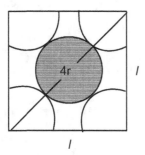

For a face centered cube:

$$(4r)^2 = l^2 + l^2 = 2l^2$$

$$r\sqrt{8} = l, \; r = l / \sqrt{8}$$

$$r = 3.85 \times 10^{-8} \text{ cm}/\sqrt{8}$$

$$r = 1.36 \times 10^{-8} \text{ cm} = 136 \text{ pm}$$

47.   For a body-centered unit cell: 8 corners $\times \dfrac{1/8 \text{ Ti}}{\text{corner}} + 1$ Ti at body center = 2 Ti atoms

All body-centered unit cells have two atoms per unit cell. For a unit cell:

$$\text{density} = 4.50 \text{ g/cm}^3 = \frac{2 \text{ atoms Ti } \times \dfrac{1 \text{ mol Ti}}{6.022 \times 10^{23} \text{ atoms}} \times \dfrac{47.88 \text{ g Ti}}{\text{mol Ti}}}{l^3},$$

where l = cube edge length

Solving: l = edge length of unit cell = 3.28×10^{-8} cm = 328 pm

Assume Ti atoms just touch along the body diagonal of the cube, so body diagonal = 4 × radius of atoms = 4r.

The triangle we need to solve is:

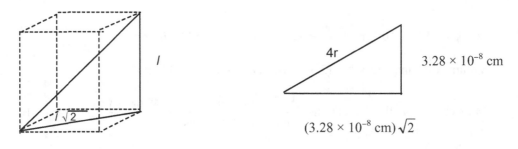

$(4r)^2 = (3.28 \times 10^{-8} \text{ cm})^2 + [(3.28 \times 10^{-8} \text{ cm}) \sqrt{2}\,]^2$, $r = 1.42 \times 10^{-8}$ cm = 142 pm

For a body-centered cubic unit cell, the radius of the atom is related to the cube edge length by $4r = l\sqrt{3}$ or $l = 4r/\sqrt{3}$.

49.   If gold has a face-centered cubic structure, then there are four atoms per unit cell, and from Exercise 16.43:

$$2l^2 = 16r^2$$

$$l = r\sqrt{8} = (144 \text{ pm})\sqrt{8} = 407 \text{ pm}$$

$$l = 407 \times 10^{-12} \text{ m} = 4.07 \times 10^{-8} \text{ cm}$$

$$\text{Density} = \frac{4 \text{ atoms Au} \times \dfrac{1 \text{ mol Au}}{6.022 \times 10^{23} \text{ atoms}} \times \dfrac{197.0 \text{ g Au}}{\text{mol Au}}}{(4.07 \times 10^{-8} \text{ cm})^3} = 19.4 \text{ g/cm}^3$$

If gold has a body-centered cubic structure, then there are two atoms per unit cell, and from Exercise 16.47:

$$16r^2 = l^2 + 2l^2$$

$$l = 4r/\sqrt{3} = 333 \text{ pm} = 333 \times 10^{-12} \text{ m}$$

$$l = 333 \times 10^{-10} \text{ cm} = 3.33 \times 10^{-8} \text{ cm}$$

$$\text{Density} = \frac{2 \text{ atoms Au} \times \dfrac{1 \text{ mol Au}}{6.022 \times 10^{23} \text{ atoms}} \times \dfrac{197.0 \text{ g Au}}{\text{mol Au}}}{(3.33 \times 10^{-8} \text{ cm})^3} = 17.7 \text{ g/cm}^3$$

The measured density of gold is consistent with a face-centered cubic unit cell.

51.   Conductor: The energy difference between the filled and unfilled molecular orbitals is minimal. We call this energy difference the band gap. Because the band gap is minimal, electrons can easily move into the conduction bands (the unfilled molecular orbitals).

        Insulator: Large band gap; electrons do not move from the filled molecular orbitals to the conduction bands since the energy difference is large.

        Semiconductor: Small band gap; the energy difference between the filled and unfilled molecular orbitals is smaller than in insulators, so some electrons can jump into the conduction bands. The band gap, however, is not as small as with conductors, so semiconductors have intermediate conductivity.

a.   As the temperature is increased, more electrons in the filled molecular orbitals have sufficient kinetic energy to jump into the conduction bands (the unfilled molecular orbitals).

b.   A photon of light is absorbed by an electron that then has sufficient energy to jump into the conduction bands.

c.   An impurity either adds electrons at an energy near that of the conduction bands (n-type) or creates holes (unfilled energy levels) at energies in the previously filled molecular orbitals (p-type). Both n-type and p-type semiconductors increase conductivity by creating an easier path for electrons to jump from filled to unfilled energy levels.

In conductors, electrical conductivity is inversely proportional to temperature. Increases in temperature increase the motions of the atoms, which gives rise to increased resistance (decreased conductivity). In a semiconductor, electrical conductivity is directly proportional to temperature. An increase in temperature provides more electrons with enough kinetic energy to jump from the filled molecular orbitals to the conduction bands, increasing conductivity.

53.   A rectifier is a device that produces a current that flows in one direction from an alternating current that flows in both directions. In a p-n junction, a p-type and an n-type semi-conductor are connected. The natural flow of electrons in a p-n junction is for the excess electrons in the n-type semiconductor to move to the empty energy levels (holes) of the p-type semiconductor. Only when an external electric potential is connected so that electrons flow in this natural direction will the current flow easily (forward bias). If the external electric potential is connected in reverse of the natural flow of electrons, no current flows through the system (reverse bias). A p-n junction only transmits a current under forward bias, thus converting the alternating current to direct current.

55.   In has fewer valence electrons than Se. Thus Se doped with In would be a p-type semiconductor.

57. $E_{gap} = 2.5 \text{ eV} \times 1.6 \times 10^{-19} \text{ J/eV} = 4.0 \times 10^{-19} \text{ J}$; we want $E_{gap} = E_{light}$.

$$E_{light} = \frac{hc}{\lambda}, \quad \lambda = \frac{hc}{E} = \frac{(6.63 \times 10^{-34} \text{ J s})(3.00 \times 10^8 \text{ m/s})}{4.0 \times 10^{-19} \text{ J}} = 5.0 \times 10^{-7} \text{ m} = 5.0 \times 10^2 \text{ nm}$$

59.   Sodium chloride structure: $8 \text{ corners} \times \dfrac{1/8 \text{ Cl}^-}{\text{corner}} + 6 \text{ faces} \times \dfrac{1/2 \text{ Cl}^-}{\text{face}} = 4 \text{ Cl}^- \text{ ions}$

$12 \text{ edges} \times \dfrac{1/4 \text{ Na}^+}{\text{edge}} + 1 \text{ Na}^+ \text{ at body center} = 4 \text{ Na}^+ \text{ ions; NaCl is the formula.}$

Cesium chloride structure: $1 \text{ Cs}^+ \text{ ion at body center};$ $8 \text{ corners} \times \dfrac{1/8 \text{ Cl}^-}{\text{corner}} = 1 \text{ Cl}^- \text{ ion; CsCl}$ is the formula.

Zinc sulfide structure: There are four Zn^{2+} ions inside the cube.

$$8 \text{ corners} \times \frac{1/8\, S^{2-}}{\text{corner}} + 6 \text{ faces} \times \frac{1/2\, S^{2-}}{\text{face}} = 4\, S^{2-} \text{ ions};\quad \text{ZnS is the formula.}$$

Titanium oxide structure: $8 \text{ corners} \times \dfrac{1/8\, Ti^{4+}}{\text{corner}} + 1\, Ti^{4+} \text{ at body center} = 2\, Ti^{4+}$ ions

$$4 \text{ faces} \times \frac{1/2\, O^{2-}}{\text{face}} + 2\, O^{2-} \text{ inside cube} = 4\, O^{2-} \text{ ions};\quad \text{TiO}_2 \text{ is the formula.}$$

61.   The structures of most binary ionic solids can be explained by the closest packing of spheres. Typically, the larger ions, usually the anions, are packed in one of the closest packing arrangements, and the smaller cations fit into holes among the closest packed anions. There are different types of holes within the closest packed anions that are determined by the number of spheres that form them. Which of the three types of holes are filled usually depends on the relative size of the cation to the anion. Ionic solids will always try to maximize electrostatic attractions among oppositely charged ions and minimize the repulsions among ions with like charges.

The structure of sodium chloride can be described in terms of a cubic closest packed array of Cl^- ions with Na^+ ions in all of the octahedral holes. An octahedral hole is formed between six Cl^- anions. The number of octrahedral holes is the same as the number of packed ions. So in the face-centered unit cell of sodium chloride, there are four net Cl^- ions and four net octahedral holes. Because the stoichiometry dictates a 1:1 ratio between the number of Cl^- anions and Na^+ cations, all of the octahedral holes must be filled with Na^+ ions.

In zinc sulfide, the sulfide anions also occupy the lattice points of a cubic closest packing arrangement. But instead of having the cations in octahedral holes, the Zn^{2+} cations occupy tetrahedral holes. A tetrahedral hole is the empty space created when four spheres are packed together. There are twice as many tetrahedral holes as packed anions in the closest packed structure. Therefore, each face-centered unit cell of sulfide anions contains four net S^{2-} ions and eight net tetrahedral holes. For the 1:1 stoichiometry to work out, only one-half of the tetrahedral holes are filled with Zn^{2+} ions. This gives four S^{2-} ions and four Zn^{2+} ions per unit cell for an empirical formula of ZnS.

63.   There is one octahedral hole per closest packed anion in a closest packed structure. If one-half of the octahedral holes are filled, then there is a 2:1 ratio of fluoride ions to cobalt ions in the crystal. The formula is CoF_2.

65.   Mn ions at 8 corners: $8(1/8) = 1$ Mn ion; F ions at 12 edges: $12(1/4) = 3$ F ions; the formula is MnF_3. Assuming fluoride is 1– charged, then the charge on Mn is 3+.

67.   CsCl is a simple cubic array of Cl^- ions with Cs^+ in the middle of each unit cell. There is one Cs^+ and one Cl^- ion in each unit cell. Cs^+ and Cl^- touch along the body diagonal.

Body diagonal $= 2r_{Cs^+} + 2r_{Cl^-} = \sqrt{3}\, l,\quad l = $ length of cube edge

In each unit cell:

$$\text{mass} = 1 \text{ CsCl unit}(1 \text{ mol}/6.022 \times 10^{23} \text{ units})(168.4 \text{ g/mol}) = 2.796 \times 10^{-22} \text{ g}$$

$$\text{volume} = l^3 = \text{mass/density} = 2.796 \times 10^{-22} \text{ g}/3.97 \text{ g cm}^{-3} = 7.04 \times 10^{-23} \text{ cm}^3$$

$$l^3 = 7.04 \times 10^{-23} \text{ cm}^3, \; l = 4.13 \times 10^{-8} \text{ cm} = 413 \text{ pm} = \text{length of cube edge}$$

$$2r_{Cs^+} + 2r_{Cl^-} = \sqrt{3}\, l = \sqrt{3}\,(413 \text{ pm}) = 715 \text{ pm}$$

The distance between ion centers $= r_{Cs^+} + r_{Cl^-} = 715 \text{ pm}/2 = 358 \text{ pm}$.

From ionic radius: $r_{Cs^+} = 169 \text{ pm}$ and $r_{Cl^-} = 181 \text{ pm}$; $r_{Cs^+} + r_{Cl^-} = 169 + 181 = 350. \text{ pm}$

The distance calculated from the density is 8 pm (2.3%) greater than that calculated from tables of ionic radii.

69.   For a cubic hole to be filled, the cation to anion radius ratio is between $0.732 < r_+/r_- < 1.00$.

CsBr: Cs^+ radius $= 169 \text{ pm}$, Br^- radius $= 195 \text{ pm}$; $r_+/r_- = 169/195 = 0.867$

From the radius ratio, Cs^+ should occupy cubic holes. The structure should be the CsCl structure. The actual structure is the CsCl structure.

KF: K^+ radius $= 133 \text{ pm}$, F^- radius $= 136 \text{ pm}$; $r_+/r_- = 133/136 = 0.978$

Again, we would predict a structure similar to CsCl, i.e., cations in the middle of a simple cubic array of anions. The actual structure is the NaCl structure.

The radius ratio rules fail for KF. Exceptions are common for crystal structures.

71.   Al: 8 corners $\times \dfrac{1/8 \text{ Al}}{\text{corner}} = 1 \text{ Al}$; Ni: 6 face centers $\times \dfrac{1/2 \text{ Ni}}{\text{face center}} = 3 \text{ Ni}$

The composition of the specific phase of the superalloy is $AlNi_3$.

73.   With a cubic closest packed array of oxygen ions, we have 4 O^{2-} ions per unit cell. We need to balance the total 8– charge of the anions with a 8+ charge from the Al^{3+} and Mg^{2+} cations. The only simple combination of ions that gives a 8+ charge is 2 Al^{3+} ions and 1 Mg^{2+} ion. The formula is Al_2MgO_4.

There are an equal number of octahedral holes as anions (4) in a cubic closest packed array and twice the number of tetrahedral holes as anions in a cubic closest packed array. For the stoichiometry to work out, we need 2 Al^{3+} and 1 Mg^{2+} per unit cell. Hence one-half the octahedral holes are filled with Al^{3+} ions, and one-eighth the tetrahedral holes are filled with Mg^{2+} ions.

75.   a.   Y: 1 Y in center; Ba: 2 Ba in center

Cu: 8 corners × $\dfrac{1/8\,Cu}{corner}$ = 1 Cu, 8 edges × $\dfrac{1/4\,Cu}{edge}$ = 2 Cu, total = 3 Cu atoms

O: 20 edges × $\dfrac{1/4\,O}{edge}$ = 5 oxygen, 8 faces × $\dfrac{1/2\,O}{face}$ = 4 oxygen, total = 9 O atoms

Formula: $YBa_2Cu_3O_9$

b.   The structure of this superconductor material follows the alternative perovskite structure described in Exercise 16.74b. The $YBa_2Cu_3O_9$ structure is three of these cubic perovskite unit cells stacked on top of each other. The oxygen atoms are in the same places, Cu takes the place of Ti, two of the calcium atoms are replaced by two barium atoms, and one Ca is replaced by Y.

c.   Y, Ba, and Cu are the same. Some oxygen atoms are missing.

12 edges × $\dfrac{1/4\,O}{edge}$ = 3 O, 8 faces × $\dfrac{1/2\,O}{face}$ = 4 O, total = 7 O atoms

Superconductor formula is $YBa_2Cu_3O_7$.

Phase Changes and Phase Diagrams

77.   A volatile liquid is one that evaporates relatively easily. Volatile liquids have large vapor pressures because the intermolecular forces that prevent evaporation are relatively weak.

79.   a.   As the intermolecular forces increase, the rate of evaporation decreases.

b.   As temperature increases, the rate of evaporation increases.

c.   As surface area increases, the rate of evaporation increases.

81. $C_2H_5OH(l) \rightarrow C_2H_5OH(g)$ is an endothermic process. Heat is absorbed when liquid ethanol vaporizes; the internal heat from the body provides this heat, which results in the cooling of the body.

83.   The mathematical equation that relates the vapor pressure of a substance to temperature is:

$$\ln P_{vap} = -\dfrac{\Delta H_{vap}}{R}\left(\dfrac{1}{T}\right) + C$$
$$\quad y \qquad\quad m \quad x \;+\; b$$

As shown above, this equation is in the form of the straight-line equation. If one plots $\ln P_{vap}$ versus $1/T$ with temperature in Kelvin, the slope of the straight line is $-\Delta H_{vap}/R$. Because ΔH_{vap} is always positive, the slope of the straight line will be negative.

85. $\ln\left(\dfrac{P_1}{P_2}\right) = \dfrac{\Delta H_{vap}}{R}\left(\dfrac{1}{T_2} - \dfrac{1}{T_1}\right)$, $\ln\left(\dfrac{836\ \text{torr}}{213\ \text{torr}}\right) = \dfrac{\Delta H_{vap}}{8.3145\ \text{J K}^{-1}\ \text{mol}^{-1}}\left(\dfrac{1}{313\ \text{K}} - \dfrac{1}{353\ \text{K}}\right)$

Solving: $\Delta H_{vap} = 3.1 \times 10^4$ J/mol; for the normal boiling point, P = 1.00 atm = 760. torr.

$\ln\left(\dfrac{760.\ \text{torr}}{213\ \text{torr}}\right) = \dfrac{3.1 \times 10^4\ \text{J/mol}}{8.3145\ \text{J K}^{-1}\ \text{mol}^{-1}}\left(\dfrac{1}{313\ \text{K}} - \dfrac{1}{T_1}\right)$, $\dfrac{1}{313} - \dfrac{1}{T_1} = 3.4 \times 10^{-4}$

$T_1 = 350.\ \text{K} = 77°C$; the normal boiling point of CCl_4 is 77°C.

87. If we graph $\ln P_{vap}$ versus $1/T$ with temperature in Kelvin, the slope of the resulting straight line will be $-\Delta H_{vap}/R$.

P_{vap}	$\ln P_{vap}$	T (Li)	1/T	T (Mg)	1/T
1 torr	0	1023 K	$9.775 \times 10^{-4}\ \text{K}^{-1}$	893 K	$11.2 \times 10^{-4}\ \text{K}^{-1}$
10.	2.3	1163	8.598×10^{-4}	1013	9.872×10^{-4}
100.	4.61	1353	7.391×10^{-4}	1173	8.525×10^{-4}
400.	5.99	1513	6.609×10^{-4}	1313	7.616×10^{-4}
760.	6.63	1583	6.317×10^{-4}	1383	7.231×10^{-4}

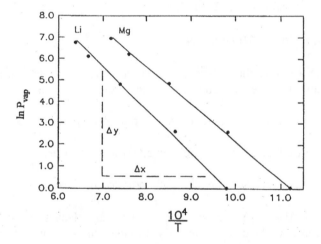

For Li:

We get the slope by taking two points (x, y) that are on the line we draw. For a line, slope = $\Delta y/\Delta x$; or we can determine the straight-line equation using a calculator. The general straight-line equation is $y = mx + b$ where m = slope and $b = y$ intercept.

The equation of the Li line is: $\ln P_{vap} = -1.90 \times 10^4 (1/T) + 18.6$, slope = -1.90×10^4 K

Slope = $-\Delta H_{vap}/R$, $\Delta H_{vap} = -\text{slope} \times R = 1.90 \times 10^4\ \text{K} \times 8.3145\ \text{J K}^{-1}\ \text{mol}^{-1}$

$\Delta H_{vap} = 1.58 \times 10^5$ J/mol = 158 kJ/mol

For Mg:

The equation of the line is: $\ln P_{vap} = -1.67 \times 10^4 (1/T) + 18.7$, slope $= -1.67 \times 10^4$ K

$\Delta H_{vap} = -\text{slope} \times R = 1.67 \times 10^4$ K $\times 8.3145$ J K^{-1} mol^{-1}

$\Delta H_{vap} = 1.39 \times 10^5$ J/mol $= 139$ kJ/mol

The bonding is stronger in Li because ΔH_{vap} is larger for Li.

89.

Slope 5 > Slope 3 > Slope 1

Time 4 = 4 × Time 2

91.   To calculate q_{total}, break up the heating process into five steps.

$H_2O(s, -20.°C) \rightarrow H_2O(s, 0°C)$, $\Delta T = 20.°C$

$$q_1 = s_{ice} \times m \times \Delta T = \frac{2.1\,J}{g\,°C} \times 5.00 \times 10^2\,g \times 20.°C = 2.1 \times 10^4\,J = 21\,kJ$$

$H_2O(s, 0°C) \rightarrow H_2O(l, 0°C)$, $q_2 = 5.00 \times 10^2\,g\,H_2O \times \dfrac{1\,mol}{18.02\,g} \times \dfrac{6.01\,kJ}{mol} = 167\,kJ$

$H_2O(l, 0°C) \rightarrow H_2O(l, 100.°C)$, $q_3 = \dfrac{4.2\,J}{g\,°C} \times 5.00 \times 10^2\,g \times 100.°C = 2.1 \times 10^5\,J = 210\,kJ$

$H_2O(l, 100.°C) \rightarrow H_2O(g, 100.°C)$, $q_4 = 5.00 \times 10^2\,g \times \dfrac{1\,mol}{18.02\,g} \times \dfrac{40.7\,kJ}{mol} = 1130\,kJ$

$H_2O(g, 100.°C) \rightarrow H_2O(g, 250.°C)$, $q_5 = \dfrac{2.0\,J}{g\,°C} \times 5.00 \times 10^2\,g \times 150.°C = 1.5 \times 10^5\,J$

$= 150$ kJ

$q_{total} = q_1 + q_2 + q_3 + q_4 + q_5 = 21 + 167 + 210 + 1130 + 150 = 1680$ kJ

93.   Heat released $= 0.250$ g Na $\times \dfrac{1\,\text{mol}}{22.99\,\text{g}} \times \dfrac{368\,\text{kJ}}{2\,\text{mol}} = 2.00$ kJ

To melt 50.0 g of ice requires: 50.0 g ice $\times \dfrac{1\,\text{mol}\,H_2O}{18.02\,\text{g}} \times \dfrac{6.01\,\text{kJ}}{\text{mol}} = 16.7$ kJ

The reaction doesn't release enough heat to melt all of the ice. The temperature will remain at $0^{\circ}C$.

95.   Total mass $H_2O = 18$ cubes $\times \dfrac{30.0\,\text{g}}{\text{cube}} = 540.$ g; $540.$ g $H_2O \times \dfrac{1\,\text{mol}\,H_2O}{18.02\,\text{g}} = 30.0$ mol H_2O

Heat removed to produce ice at $-5.0^{\circ}C$:

$$\left(\dfrac{4.18\,\text{J}}{\text{g}\,^{\circ}C} \times 540.\,\text{g} \times 22.0\,^{\circ}C\right) + \left(\dfrac{6.01 \times 10^3\,\text{J}}{\text{mol}} \times 30.0\,\text{mol}\right) + \left(\dfrac{2.08\,\text{J}}{\text{g}\,^{\circ}C} \times 540.\,\text{g} \times 5.0\,^{\circ}C\right)$$

$$= 4.97 \times 10^4\,\text{J} + 1.80 \times 10^5\,\text{J} + 5.6 \times 10^3\,\text{J} = 2.35 \times 10^5\,\text{J}$$

$2.35 \times 10^5\,\text{J} \times \dfrac{1\,\text{g}\,CF_2Cl_2}{158\,\text{J}} = 1.49 \times 10^3$ g CF_2Cl_2 must be vaporized.

97.   See Figures 16.55 and 16.58 for the phase diagrams of H_2O and CO_2. Most substances exhibit only three different phases: solid, liquid, and gas. This is true for H_2O and CO_2. Also typical of phase diagrams is the positive slopes for both the liquid-gas equilibrium line and the solid-gas equilibrium line. This is also true for both H_2O and CO_2. The solid-liquid equilibrium line also generally has a positive slope. This is true for CO_2 but not for H_2O. In the H_2O phase diagram, the slope of the solid-liquid line is negative. The determining factor for the slope of the solid-liquid line is the relative densities of the solid and liquid phases. The solid phase is denser than the liquid phase in most substances; for these substances, the slope of the solid-liquid equilibrium line is positive. For water, the liquid phase is denser than the solid phase, which corresponds to a negative-sloping solid-liquid equilibrium line. Another difference between H_2O and CO_2 is the normal melting points and normal boiling points. The term normal just dictates a pressure of 1 atm. H_2O has a normal melting point ($0^{\circ}C$) and a normal boiling point ($100^{\circ}C$), but CO_2 does not. At 1 atm pressure, CO_2 only sublimes (goes from the solid phase directly to the gas phase). There are no temperatures at 1 atm for CO_2 where the solid and liquid phases are in equilibrium or where the liquid and gas phases are in equilibrium. There are other differences, but those discussed above are the major ones.

The relationship between melting points and pressure is determined by the slope of the solid-liquid equilibrium line. For most substances (CO_2 included), the positive slope of the solid-liquid line shows a direct relationship between the melting point and pressure. As pressure increases, the melting point increases. Water is just the opposite since the slope of the solid-liquid line in water is negative. Here, the melting point of water is inversely related to the pressure.

For boiling points, the positive slope of the liquid-gas equilibrium line indicates a direct relationship between the boiling point and pressure. This direct relationship is true for all substances, including H_2O and CO_2.

The critical temperature for a substance is defined as the temperature above which the vapor cannot be liquefied no matter what pressure is applied. The critical temperature, like the boiling-point temperature, is directly related to the strength of the intermolecular forces. Since H_2O exhibits relatively strong hydrogen bonding interactions and CO_2 only exhibits London dispersion forces, one would expect a higher critical temperature for H_2O than for CO_2.

99.   The critical temperature is the temperature above which the vapor cannot be liquefied no matter what pressure is applied. Since N_2 has a critical temperature below room temperature (~22°C), it cannot be liquefied at room temperature. NH_3, with a critical temperature above room temperature, can be liquefied at room temperature.

101.   A: solid;   B: liquid;   C: vapor

        D: solid + vapor;   E: solid + liquid + vapor

        F: liquid + vapor;   G: liquid + vapor;   H: vapor

        triple point: E;   critical point: G

Normal freezing point: temperature at which solid-liquid line is at 1.0 atm (see following plot).

Normal boiling point: temperature at which liquid-vapor line is at 1.0 atm (see following plot).

Because the solid-liquid equilibrium line has a positive slope, the solid phase is denser than the liquid phase.

103.   a. two

        b. Higher-pressure triple point: graphite, diamond, and liquid; lower-pressure triple point at $\sim10^7$ Pa: graphite, liquid, and vapor

        c. It is converted to diamond (the more dense solid form).

        d. Diamond is more dense, which is why graphite can be converted to diamond by applying pressure.

105.   Because the density of the liquid phase is greater than the density of the solid phase, the slope of the solid-liquid boundary line is negative (as in H_2O). With a negative slope, the melting points increase with a decrease in pressure, so the normal melting point of X should be greater than 225°C.

107.

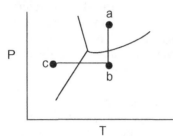

As P is lowered, we go from a to b on the phase diagram. The water boils. The evaporation of the water is endothermic, and the water is cooled (b → c), forming some ice. If the pump is left on, the ice will sublime until none is left. This is the basis of freeze drying.

Additional Exercises

109.   The strength of intermolecular forces determines relative boiling points. The types of intermolecular forces for covalent compounds are London dispersion forces, dipole forces, and hydrogen bonding. Because the three compounds are assumed to have similar molar mass and shape, the strength of the London dispersion forces will be about equal among the three compounds. One of the compounds will be nonpolar, so it only has London dispersion forces. The other two compounds will be polar, so they have additional dipole forces and will boil at a higher temperature than the nonpolar compound. One of the polar compounds probably has an H covalently bonded to either N, O, or F. This gives rise to the strongest type of covalent intermolecular forces, hydrogen bonding. The compound that hydrogen bonds will have the highest boiling point, whereas the polar compound with no hydrogen bonding will boil at a temperature in the middle of the other compounds.

111.   If TiO_2 conducts electricity as a liquid, then it is an ionic solid; if not, then TiO_2 is a network solid.

113. B_2H_6: This compound contains only nonmetals, so it is probably a molecular solid with covalent bonding. The low boiling point confirms this.

        SiO_2: This is the empirical formula for quartz, which is a network solid.

        CsI: This is a metal bonded to a nonmetal, which generally form ionic solids. The electrical conductivity in aqueous solution confirms this.

        W: Tungsten is a metallic solid as the conductivity data confirms.

115.

R = radius of the sphere

r = radius of trigonal hole

For a right-angle triangle (opposite side not drawn in):

$$\cos 30° = \frac{\text{adjacent}}{\text{hypotenuse}} = \frac{R}{R + r}, \ 0.866 = \frac{R}{R + r}$$

$$(0.866)r = R - (0.866)R, \ r = \left(\frac{0.134}{0.866}\right) \times R = (0.155)R$$

The cation must have a radius that is 0.155 times the radius of the spheres to just fit into the trigonal hole.

117.   Ar is cubic closest packed. There are four Ar atoms per unit cell and with a face-centered unit cell, the atoms touch along the face diagonal. Let l = length of cube edge.

Face diagonal $= 4r = l\sqrt{2}$, $\ l = 4(190.\ \text{pm})/\sqrt{2} = 537\ \text{pm} = 5.37 \times 10^{-8}\ \text{cm}$

$$\text{Density} = \frac{\text{mass}}{\text{volume}} = \frac{4\ \text{atoms} \times \dfrac{1\ \text{mol}}{6.022 \times 10^{23}\ \text{atoms}} \times \dfrac{39.95\ \text{g}}{\text{mol}}}{(5.37 \times 10^{-8}\ \text{cm})^3} = 1.71\ \text{g/cm}^3$$

119.   Assuming 100.00 g: $28.31\ \text{g O} \times \dfrac{1\ \text{mol}}{15.999\ \text{g}} = 1.769\ \text{mol O};\ 71.69\ \text{g Ti} \times \dfrac{1\ \text{mol}}{47.88\ \text{g}}$

$$= 1.497\ \text{mol Ti}$$

Dividing one mole quantity by the other, gives formulas of $TiO_{1.182}$ or $Ti_{0.8462}O$.

For $Ti_{0.8462}O$, let $x = Ti^{2+}$ per mol O^{2-} and $y = Ti^{3+}$ per mol O^{2-}. Setting up two equations and solving:

$x + y = 0.8462$ and $2x + 3y = 2$; $2x + 3(0.8462 - x) = 2$

$x = 0.539\ \text{mol Ti}^{2+}/\text{mol O}^{2-}$ and $y = 0.307\ \text{mol Ti}^{3+}/\text{mol O}^{2-}$

$\dfrac{0.539}{0.8462} \times 100 = 63.7\%$ of the titanium is Ti^{2+} and 36.3% is Ti^{3+}.

121.   For a face-centered unit cell, the radius r of an atom is related to the length of a cube edge l by the equation $l = r\sqrt{8}$ (see Exercise 43).

Radius $= r = l / \sqrt{8} = 392 \times 10^{-12}\ \text{m} / \sqrt{8} = 1.39 \times 10^{-10}\ \text{m} = 1.39 \times 10^{-8}\ \text{cm}$

The volume of a unit cell is l^3, so the mass of the unknown metal (X) in a unit cell is:

$$\text{volume} \times \text{density} = (3.92 \times 10^{-8} \text{ cm})^3 \times \frac{21.45 \text{ g X}}{\text{cm}^3} = 1.29 \times 10^{-21} \text{ g X}$$

Because each face-centered unit cell contains four atoms of X:

$$\text{mol X in unit cell} = 4 \text{ atoms X} \times \frac{1 \text{ mol X}}{6.022 \times 10^{23} \text{ atoms X}} = 6.642 \times 10^{-24} \text{ mol X}$$

Therefore, each unit cell contains 1.29×10^{-21} g X, which is equal to 6.642×10^{-24} mol X. The molar mass of X is:

$$\frac{1.29 \times 10^{-21} \text{ g X}}{6.642 \times 10^{-24} \text{ mol X}} = 194 \text{ g/mol}$$

The atomic mass would be 194 amu. From the periodic table, the best choice for the metal is platinum.

123.   Assuming K^+ and Cl^- just touch along the cube edge l:

$$l = 2(314 \text{ pm}) = 628 \text{ pm} = 6.28 \times 10^{-8} \text{ cm}$$

Volume of unit cell $= l^3 = (6.28 \times 10^{-8} \text{ cm})^3$

The unit cell contains four K^+ and four Cl^- ions. For a unit cell:

$$\text{density} = \frac{4 \text{ KCl formula units} \times \dfrac{1 \text{ mol KCl}}{6.022 \times 10^{23} \text{ formula units}} \times \dfrac{74.55 \text{ g KCl}}{\text{mol KCl}}}{(6.28 \times 10^{-8} \text{ cm})^3}$$

$$= 2.00 \text{ g/cm}^3$$

125. $24.7 \text{ g C}_6\text{H}_6 \times \dfrac{1 \text{ mol}}{78.11 \text{ g}} = 0.316 \text{ mol C}_6\text{H}_6$

$$P_{C_6H_6} = \frac{nRT}{V} = \frac{0.316 \text{ mol} \times \dfrac{0.08296 \text{ L atm}}{\text{K mol}} \times 293.2 \text{ K}}{100.0 \text{ L}} = 0.0760 \text{ atm, or } 57.8 \text{ torr}$$

127. $w = -P\Delta V$;   assume constant P of 1.00 atm.

$$V_{373} = \frac{nRT}{P} = \frac{1.00 \,(0.08206)(373)}{1.00} = 30.6 \text{ L for 1 mol of water vapor}$$

Because the density of $H_2O(l)$ is 1.00 g/cm^3, 1.00 mol of $H_2O(l)$ occupies 18.0 cm^3 or 0.0180 L.

w = –1.00 atm (30.6 L – 0.0180 L) = –30.6 L atm

w = –30.6 L atm × 101.3 J L^{-1} atm^{-1} = –3.10 × 10^3 J = –3.10 kJ

ΔE = q + w = 41.16 kJ – 3.10 kJ = 38.06 kJ

$\dfrac{38.06}{41.16}$ × 100 = 92.47% of the energy goes to increase the internal energy of the water.

The remainder of the energy (7.53%) goes to do work against the atmosphere.

129.   The three sheets of B's form a cube. In this cubic unit cell there are B atoms at every face, B atoms at every edge, B atoms at every corner, and one B atom in the center. A representation of this cube is:

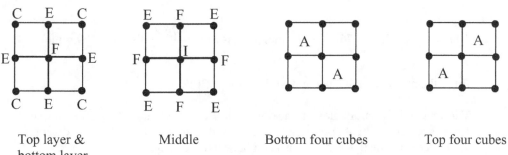

| Top layer & bottom layer | Middle | Bottom four cubes | Top four cubes |

C = corner;   E = edge;   F = face;   I = inside

Each unit cell of B atoms contains four A atoms. The number of B atoms in each unit cell is:

(8 corners × 1/8) + (6 faces × 1/2) + (12 edges × 1/4) + (1 middle B) = 8 B atoms

The empirical formula is AB_2.

Each A atom is in a cubic hole of B atoms, so eight B atoms surround each A atom. This will also be true in the extended lattice. The structure of B atoms in the unit cell is a cubic arrangement with B atoms at every face, edge, corner, and center of the cube.

Challenge Problems

131. $E = \dfrac{h^2(n_x^2 + n_y^2 + n_z^2)}{8mL^2}$; $E_{111} = \dfrac{3h^2}{8mL^2}$; $E_{112} = \dfrac{6h^2}{8mL^2}$; $\Delta E = E_{112} - E_{111} = \dfrac{3h^2}{8mL^2}$

$\Delta E = \dfrac{hc}{\lambda} = \dfrac{(6.626 \times 10^{-34} \text{ J s})(2.998 \times 10^8 \text{ m/s})}{9.50 \times 10^{-9} \text{ m}} = 2.09 \times 10^{-17}$ J

$$L^2 = \frac{3h^2}{8m\Delta E}, \quad L = \left(\frac{3h^2}{8m\Delta E}\right)^{1/2} = \left[\frac{3(6.626 \times 10^{-34} \text{ J s})^2}{8(9.109 \times 10^{-31} \text{ kg})(2.09 \times 10^{-17} \text{ J})}\right]^{1/2}$$

$L = 9.30 \times 10^{-11}$ m $= 93.0$ pm

The sphere that fits in this cube will touch the cube at the center of each face. The diameter of the sphere will equal the length of the cube. So:

$2r = L, \ r = 93.0/2 = 46.5$ pm

133.   Assuming 100.00 g of MO_2:

$$23.72 \text{ g O} \times \frac{1 \text{ mol O}}{16.00 \text{ g O}} = 1.483 \text{ mol O}$$

$$1.483 \text{ mol O} \times \frac{1 \text{ mol M}}{2 \text{ mol O}} = 0.7415 \text{ mol M}$$

$100.00 \text{ g} - 23.72 \text{ g} = 76.28 \text{ g M}; \quad \text{molar mass M} = \dfrac{76.28 \text{ g}}{0.7415 \text{ mol}} = 102.9 \text{ g/mol}$

From the periodic table, element M is rhodium (Rh).

The unit cell for cubic closest packing is face-centered cubic (4 atoms/unit cell). The atoms for a face-centered cubic unit cell are assumed to touch along the face diagonal of the cube, so the face diagonal = 4r. The distance between the centers of touching Rh atoms will be the distance of 2r where r = radius of Rh atom.

Face diagonal = $\sqrt{2} \ l$, where l = cube edge.

Face diagonal = 4r = $2 \times 269.0 \times 10^{-12}$ m $= 5.380 \times 10^{-10}$ m

$\sqrt{2} \ l = 4r = 5.38 \times 10^{-10}$ m, $l = \dfrac{5.38 \times 10^{-10} \text{ m}}{\sqrt{2}} = 3.804 \times 10^{-10}$ m $= 3.804 \times 10^{-8}$ cm

$$\text{Density} = \frac{4 \text{ atoms Rh} \times \dfrac{1 \text{ mol Rh}}{6.0221 \times 10^{23} \text{ atoms}} \times \dfrac{102.9 \text{ g Rh}}{\text{mol Rh}}}{(3.804 \times 10^{-8} \text{ cm})^3} = 12.42 \text{ g/cm}^3$$

135.   For water vapor at 30.0°C and 31.824 torr:

$$\text{density} = \frac{P(\text{molar mass})}{RT} = \frac{\left(\dfrac{31.824 \text{ atm}}{760}\right)\left(\dfrac{18.015 \text{ g}}{\text{mol}}\right)}{\dfrac{0.08206 \text{ L atm}}{\text{K mol}} \times 303.2 \text{ K}} = 0.03032 \text{ g/L}$$

The volume of one molecule is proportional to d^3, where d is the average distance between molecules. For a large sample of molecules, the volume is still proportional to d^3. So:

$$\frac{V_{gas}}{V_{liq}} = \frac{d_{gas}^3}{d_{liq}^3}$$

If we have 0.99567 g H_2O, then V_{liq}= 1.0000 cm^3 = 1.0000×10^{-3} L.

V_{gas} = 0.99567 g × 1 L/0.03032 g = 32.84 L

$$\frac{d_{gas}^3}{d_{liq}^3} = \frac{32.84 \text{ L}}{1.0000 \times 10^{-3} \text{ L}} = 3.284 \times 10^4, \quad \frac{d_{gas}}{d_{liq}} = (3.284 \times 10^4)^{1/3} = 32.02, \quad \frac{d_{liq}}{d_{gas}} = 0.03123$$

137.   a.   Structure a:

Ba: 2 Ba inside unit cell; Tl: 8 corners × $\dfrac{1/8 \text{ Tl}}{\text{corner}}$ = 1 Tl; Cu: 4 edges × $\dfrac{1/4 \text{ Cu}}{\text{edge}}$ = 1 Cu

O: 6 faces × $\dfrac{1/2 \text{ O}}{\text{face}}$ + 8 edges × $\dfrac{1/4 \text{ O}}{\text{edge}}$ = 5 O

Formula = $TlBa_2CuO_5$.

Structure b:

Tl and Ba are the same as in structure a.

Ca: 1 Ca inside unit cell; Cu: 8 edges × $\dfrac{1/4 \text{ Cu}}{\text{edge}}$ = 2 Cu

O: 10 faces × $\dfrac{1/2 \text{ O}}{\text{edge}}$ + 8 edges × $\dfrac{1/4 \text{ O}}{\text{edge}}$ = 7 O

Formula = $TlBa_2CaCu_2O_7$.

Structure c:

Tl and Ba are the same and two Ca atoms are located inside the unit cell.

Cu: 12 edges × $\dfrac{1/4 \text{ Cu}}{\text{edge}}$ = 3 Cu; O: 14 faces × $\dfrac{1/2 \text{ O}}{\text{face}}$ + 8 edges × $\dfrac{1/4 \text{ O}}{\text{edge}}$ = 9 O

Formula = $TlBa_2Ca_2Cu_3O_9$.

Structure d: Following similar calculations, formula = $TlBa_2Ca_3Cu_4O_{11}$.

b. Structure a has one planar sheet of Cu and O atoms and the number increases by one for each of the remaining structures. The order of superconductivity temperature from lowest to highest temperature is a < b < c < d.

c. $TlBa_2CuO_5$: $3 + 2(2) + x + 5(-2) = 0$, $x = +3$
Only Cu^{3+} is present in each formula unit.

$TlBa_2CaCu_2O_7$: $3 + 2(2) + 2 + 2(x) + 7(-2) = 0$, $x = +5/2$
Each formula unit contains 1 Cu^{2+} and 1 Cu^{3+}.

$TlBa_2Ca_2Cu_3O_9$: $3 + 2(2) + 2(2) + 3(x) + 9(-2) = 0$, $x = +7/3$
Each formula unit contains 2 Cu^{2+} and 1 Cu^{3+}.

$TlBa_2Ca_3Cu_4O_{11}$: $3 + 2(2) + 3(2) + 4(x) + 11(-2) = 0$, $x = +9/4$
Each formula unit contains 3 Cu^{2+} and 1 Cu^{3+}.

d. This superconductor material achieves variable copper oxidation states by varying the numbers of Ca, Cu, and O in each unit cell. The mixtures of copper oxidation states is discussed in part c. The superconductor material in Exercise 16.75 achieves variable copper oxidation states by omitting oxygen at various sites in the lattice.

139. For an octahedral hole, the geometry is:

From the diagram: $\cos 45° = \dfrac{adjacent}{hypotenuse} = \dfrac{2R}{2R + 2r} = \dfrac{R}{R + r}$, $0.707 = \dfrac{R}{R + r}$

$R = 0.707(R + r)$, $r = (0.414)R$

LiCl unit cell:

length of cube edge $= 2R + 2r = 514$ pm

$2R + 2(0.414\ R) = 514$ pm, $R = 182$ pm $= Cl^-$ radius

$2(182\ pm) + 2r = 514$ pm, $r = 75$ pm $= Li^+$ radius

From Figure 13.8, the Li^+ radius is 60 pm, and the Cl^- radius is 181 pm. The Li^+ ion is much smaller than calculated. This probably means that the ions are not actually in contact with each other. The octahedral holes are larger than the Li^+ ion.

CHAPTER 17

PROPERTIES OF SOLUTIONS

Solution Composition

13.　a.　$HNO_3(l) \rightarrow H^+(aq) + NO_3^-(aq)$

　　b.　$Na_2SO_4(s) \rightarrow 2\ Na^+(aq) + SO_4^{2-}(aq)$

　　c.　$Al(NO_3)_3(s) \rightarrow Al^{3+}(aq) + 3\ NO_3^-(aq)$

　　d.　$SrBr_2(s) \rightarrow Sr^{2+}(aq) + 2\ Br^-(aq)$

　　e.　$KClO_4(s) \rightarrow K^+(aq) + ClO_4^-(aq)$

　　f.　$NH_4Br(s) \rightarrow NH_4^+(aq) + Br^-(aq)$

　　g.　$NH_4NO_3(s) \rightarrow NH_4^+(aq) + NO_3^-(aq)$

　　h.　$CuSO_4(s) \rightarrow Cu^{2+}(aq) + SO_4^{2-}(aq)$

　　i.　$NaOH(s) \rightarrow Na^+(aq) + OH^-(aq)$

15.　$$\text{Molality} = \frac{40.0\ \text{g EG}}{60.0\ \text{g H}_2\text{O}} \times \frac{1000\ \text{g}}{\text{kg}} \times \frac{1\ \text{mol EG}}{62.07\ \text{g}} = 10.7\ \text{mol/kg}$$

$$\text{Molarity} = \frac{40.0\ \text{g EG}}{100.0\ \text{g solution}} \times \frac{1.05\ \text{g}}{\text{cm}^3} \times \frac{1000\ \text{cm}^3}{\text{L}} \times \frac{1\ \text{mol}}{62.07\ \text{g}} = 6.77\ \text{mol/L}$$

$$40.0\ \text{g EG} \times \frac{1\ \text{mol}}{62.07\ \text{g}} = 0.644\ \text{mol EG};\ \ 60.0\ \text{g H}_2\text{O} \times \frac{1\ \text{mol}}{18.02\ \text{g}} = 3.33\ \text{mol H}_2\text{O}$$

$$\chi_{EG} = \frac{0.644}{3.33 + 0.644} = 0.162 = \text{mole fraction ethylene glycol}$$

17.　$$50.0\ \text{mL toluene} \times \frac{0.867\ \text{g}}{\text{mL}} = 43.4\ \text{g toluene};\ \ 125\ \text{mL benzene} \times \frac{0.874\ \text{g}}{\text{mL}} = 109\ \text{g benzene}$$

$$\text{Mass \% toluene} = \frac{\text{mass of toluene}}{\text{total mass}} \times 100 = \frac{43.4\ \text{g}}{43.4\ \text{g} + 109\ \text{g}} \times 100 = 28.5\%$$

$$\text{Molarity} = \frac{43.4\ \text{g toluene}}{175\ \text{mL soln}} \times \frac{1000\ \text{mL}}{\text{L}} \times \frac{1\ \text{mol toluene}}{92.13\ \text{g toluene}} = 2.69\ \text{mol/L}$$

$$\text{Molality} = \frac{43.4\,\text{g toluene}}{109\,\text{g benzene}} \times \frac{1000\,\text{g}}{\text{kg}} \times \frac{1\,\text{mol toluene}}{92.13\,\text{g toluene}} = 4.32\,\text{mol/kg}$$

$$43.4\,\text{g toluene} \times \frac{1\,\text{mol}}{92.13\,\text{g}} = 0.471\,\text{mol toluene}$$

$$109\,\text{g benzene} \times \frac{1\,\text{mol benzene}}{78.11\,\text{g benzene}} = 1.40\,\text{mol benzene}; \quad \chi_{\text{toluene}} = \frac{0.471}{0.471 + 1.40} = 0.252$$

19.   If we have 1.00 L of solution:

$$1.37\,\text{mol citric acid} \times \frac{192.1\,\text{g}}{\text{mol}} = 263\,\text{g citric acid}$$

$$1.00 \times 10^3\,\text{mL solution} \times \frac{1.10\,\text{g}}{\text{mL}} = 1.10 \times 10^3\,\text{g solution}$$

$$\text{Mass \% of citric acid} = \frac{263\,\text{g}}{1.10 \times 10^3\,\text{g}} \times 100 = 23.9\%$$

In 1.00 L of solution, we have 263 g citric acid and $(1.10 \times 10^3 - 263) = 840$ g of H_2O.

$$\text{Molality} = \frac{1.37\,\text{mol citric acid}}{0.84\,\text{kg}\,H_2O} = 1.6\,\text{mol/kg}$$

$$840\,\text{g}\,H_2O \times \frac{1\,\text{mol}}{18.0\,\text{g}} = 47\,\text{mol}\,H_2O; \quad \chi_{\text{citric acid}} = \frac{1.37}{47 + 1.37} = 0.028$$

21.   Because the density of water is 1.00 g/mL, 100.0 mL of water has a mass of 100. g.

$$\text{Density} = \frac{\text{mass}}{\text{volume}} = \frac{10.0\,\text{g}\,H_3PO_4 + 100.\,\text{g}\,H_2O}{104\,\text{mL}} = 1.06\,\text{g/mL} = 1.06\,\text{g/cm}^3$$

$$\text{Mol}\,H_3PO_4 = 10.0\,\text{g} \times \frac{1\,\text{mol}}{97.99\,\text{g}} = 0.102\,\text{mol}\,H_3PO_4$$

$$\text{Mol}\,H_2O = 100.\,\text{g} \times \frac{1\,\text{mol}}{18.02\,\text{g}} = 5.55\,\text{mol}\,H_2O$$

$$\text{Mole fraction of}\,H_3PO_4 = \frac{0.102\,\text{mol}\,H_3PO_4}{(0.102 + 5.55)\,\text{mol}} = 0.0180$$

$$\chi_{H_2O} = 1.0000 - 0.0180 = 0.9820$$

$$\text{Molarity} = \frac{0.102 \text{ mol H}_3\text{PO}_4}{0.104 \text{ L soln}} = 0.981 \text{ mol/L}$$

$$\text{Molality} = \frac{0.102 \text{ mol H}_3\text{PO}_4}{0.100 \text{ kg solvent}} = 1.02 \text{ mol/kg}$$

Thermodynamics of Solutions and Solubility

23. "Like dissolves like" refers to the nature of the intermolecular forces. Polar solutes and ionic solutes dissolve in polar solvents because the types of intermolecular forces present in solute and solvent are similar. When they dissolve, the strengths of the intermolecular forces in solution are about the same as in pure solute and pure solvent. The same is true for nonpolar solutes in nonpolar solvents. The strengths of the intermolecular forces (London dispersion forces) are about the same in solution as in pure solute and pure solvent. In all cases of like dissolves like, the magnitude of ΔH_{soln} is either a small positive number (endothermic) or a small negative number (exothermic), with a value close to zero. For polar solutes in nonpolar solvents and vice versa, ΔH_{soln} is a very large, unfavorable value (very endothermic). Because the energetics are so unfavorable, polar solutes do not dissolve in nonpolar solvents, and vice versa.

25. Although the enthalpy change is endothermic when NaCl dissolves in water, the magnitude of ΔH_{soln} will be a value close to zero ($\Delta H_{soln} \approx 0$). This is typical for soluble ionic compounds.   So energy is not the reason why ionic solids like NaCl are so soluble in water. The answer lies in nature's tendency toward the higher probability of the mixed state; solutions form due to an increase in entropy ($\Delta S_{soln} > 0$). In the mixed state, the Na^+ and Cl^- ions have access to a larger volume and therefore have more positions available to them. When a solution forms, positional probability increases, which translates into an increase in entropy. The positive ΔS_{soln} furnishes the driving force for NaCl to dissolve in water.

27. Using Hess's law:

$$\text{NaI(s)} \rightarrow \text{Na}^+(g) + \text{I}^-(g) \qquad\qquad \Delta H = -\Delta H_{LE} = -(-686 \text{ kJ/mol})$$
$$\text{Na}^+(g) + \text{I}^-(g) \rightarrow \text{Na}^+(aq) + \text{I}^-(aq) \qquad \Delta H = \Delta H_{hyd} = -694 \text{ kJ/mol}$$

$$\overline{\qquad\text{NaI(s)} \rightarrow \text{Na}^+(aq) + \text{I}^-(aq) \qquad\qquad \Delta H_{soln} = -8 \text{ kJ/mol}\qquad}$$

ΔH_{soln} refers to the heat released or gained when a solute dissolves in a solvent. Here, an ionic compound dissolves in water.

29. Both $Al(OH)_3$ and NaOH are ionic compounds. Because the lattice energy is proportional to the charge of the ions, the lattice energy of aluminum hydroxide is greater than that of sodium hydroxide. The attraction of water molecules for Al^{3+} and OH^- cannot overcome the larger lattice energy, and $Al(OH)_3$ is insoluble. For NaOH, the favorable hydration energy is large enough to overcome the smaller lattice energy, and NaOH is soluble.

31.   Water exhibits H-bonding in the pure state and is classified as a polar solvent. Water will dissolve other polar solutes and ionic solutes.

   a. NH_3; similar to water, NH_3 is capable of H-bonding, unlike PH_3.

   b. CH_3CN; CH_3CN is polar, while CH_3CH_3 is nonpolar.

   c. CH_3CO_2H; CH_3CO_2H is capable of H-bonding, unlike the other compound.

33.   As the length of the hydrocarbon chain increases, the solubility decreases. The $-OH$ end of the alcohols can hydrogen-bond with water. The hydrocarbon chain, however, is basically nonpolar and interacts poorly with water. As the hydrocarbon chain gets longer, a greater portion of the molecule cannot interact with the water molecules, and the solubility decreases; i.e., the effect of the $-OH$ group decreases as the alcohols get larger.

35.   Structure effects refer to solute and solvent having similar polarities in order for solution formation to occur. Hydrophobic solutes are mostly nonpolar substances that are "water-fearing." Hydrophilic solutes are mostly polar or ionic substances that are "water-loving." Pressure has little effect on the solubilities of solids or liquids; it does significantly affect the solubility of a gas. Henry's law states that the amount of a gas dissolved in a solution is directly proportional to the pressure of the gas above the solution ($C = kP$). The equation for Henry's law works best for dilute solutions of gases that do not dissociate in or react with the solvent. $HCl(g)$ does not follow Henry's law because it dissociates into $H^+(aq)$ and $Cl^-(aq)$ in solution (HCl is a strong acid). For O_2 and N_2, Henry's law works well since these gases do not react with the water solvent.

        An increase in temperature can either increase or decrease the solubility of a solid solute in water. It is true that a solute dissolves more rapidly with an increase in temperature, but the amount of solid solute that dissolves to form a saturated solution can either decrease or increase with temperature. The temperature effect is difficult to predict for solid solutes. However, the temperature effect for gas solutes is easier to predict because the solubility of a gas typically decreases with increasing temperature.

37. $P_{gas} = kC$, $0.790 \text{ atm} = k \times \dfrac{8.21 \times 10^{-4} \text{ mol}}{L}$, $k = 962 \text{ L atm/mol}$

        $P_{gas} = kC$, $1.10 \text{ atm} = \dfrac{962 \text{ L atm}}{mol} \times C$, $C = 1.14 \times 10^{-3} \text{ mol/L}$

39.   As the temperature increases the gas molecules will have a greater average kinetic energy. A greater fraction of the gas molecules in solution will have a kinetic energy greater than the attractive forces between the gas molecules and the solvent molecules. More gas molecules are able to escape to the vapor phase and the solubility of the gas decreases.

Vapor Pressures of Solution

41. $P_{soln} = \chi_{C_2H_5OH} P^{\circ}_{C_2H_5OH}$; $\chi_{C_2H_5OH} = \dfrac{\text{mol } C_2H_5OH \text{ in solution}}{\text{total mol in solution}}$

53.6 g $C_3H_8O_3$ × $\dfrac{1 \text{ mol } C_3H_8O_3}{92.09 \text{ g}}$ = 0.582 mol $C_3H_8O_3$

133.7 g C_2H_5OH × $\dfrac{1 \text{ mol } C_2H_5OH}{46.07 \text{ g}}$ = 2.90 mol C_2H_5OH; total mol = 0.582 + 2.90 = 3.48 mol

113 torr = $\dfrac{2.90 \text{ mol}}{3.48 \text{ mol}}$ × $P^{\circ}_{C_2H_5OH}$, $P^{\circ}_{C_2H_5OH}$ = 136 torr

43. $P = \chi P^{\circ}$; 710.0 torr = χ(760.0 torr), χ = 0.9342 = mole fraction of methanol

45. $P_B = \chi_B P^{\circ}_B$, $\chi_B = P_B / P^{\circ}_B$ = 0.900 atm/0.930 atm = 0.968

0.968 = $\dfrac{\text{mol benzene}}{\text{total mol}}$; mol benzene = 78.11 g C_6H_6 × $\dfrac{1 \text{ mol}}{78.11 \text{ g}}$ = 1.000 mol

Let x = mol solute; then: χ_B = 0.968 = $\dfrac{1.000 \text{ mol}}{1.000 + x}$, 0.968 + (0.968)x = 1.000, x = 0.033 mol

Molar mass = $\dfrac{10.0 \text{ g}}{0.033 \text{ mol}}$ = 303 g/mol ≈ 3.0 × 10^2 g/mol

47.   a.   25 mL C_5H_{12} × $\dfrac{0.63 \text{ g}}{\text{mL}}$ × $\dfrac{1 \text{ mol}}{72.15}$ = 0.22 mol C_5H_{12}

45 mL C_6H_{14} × $\dfrac{0.66 \text{ g}}{\text{mL}}$ × $\dfrac{1 \text{ mol}}{86.17}$ = 0.34 mol C_6H_{14}; total mol = 0.22 + 0.34 = 0.56 mol

$\chi^L_{pen} = \dfrac{\text{mol pentane in solution}}{\text{total mol in solution}} = \dfrac{0.22 \text{ mol}}{0.56 \text{ mol}}$ = 0.39, χ^L_{hex} = 1.00 − 0.39 = 0.61

$P_{pen} = \chi^L_{pen} P^{\circ}_{pen}$ = 0.39(511 torr) = 2.0 × 10^2 torr; P_{hex} = 0.61(150. torr) = 92 torr

$P_{total} = P_{pen} + P_{hex}$ = 2.0 × 10^2 + 92 = 292 torr = 290 torr

b.   From Chapter 5 on gases, the partial pressure of a gas is proportional to the number of moles of gas present. For the vapor phase:

$\chi^V_{pen} = \dfrac{\text{mol pentane in vapor}}{\text{total mol vapor}} = \dfrac{P_{pen}}{P_{total}} = \dfrac{2.0 \times 10^2 \text{ torr}}{290 \text{ torr}}$ = 0.69

Note: In the *Solutions Guide*, we added V or L to the mole fraction symbol to emphasize which value we are solving. If the L or V is omitted, then the liquid phase is assumed.

49. $P_{total} = P_{meth} + P_{prop}$,   174 torr = $\chi^L_{meth}(303 \text{ torr}) + \chi^L_{prop}(44.6 \text{ torr})$; $\chi^L_{prop} = 1.000 - \chi^L_{meth}$

$174 = 303\chi^L_{meth} + (1.000 - \chi^L_{meth})44.6 \text{ torr}$, $\dfrac{129}{258} = \chi^L_{meth} = 0.500$

$\chi^L_{prop} = 1.000 - 0.500 = 0.500$

51.   50.0 g $CH_3COCH_3 \times \dfrac{1 \text{ mol}}{58.08 \text{ g}} = 0.861$ mol acetone

50.0 g $CH_3OH \times 1$ mol/32.04 g $= 1.56$ mol methanol

$\chi^L_{acetone} = \dfrac{0.861}{0.861 + 1.56} = 0.356$; $\chi^L_{methanol} = 1.000 - \chi^L_{acetone} = 0.644$

$P_{total} = P_{methanol} + P_{acetone} = 0.644(143 \text{ torr}) + 0.356(271 \text{ torr}) = 92.1 \text{ torr} + 96.5 \text{ torr}$

$= 188.6$ torr

Because partial pressures are proportional to the moles of gas present, in the vapor phase:

$\chi^V_{acetone} = \dfrac{P_{acetone}}{P_{total}} = \dfrac{96.5 \text{ torr}}{188.6 \text{ torr}} = 0.512$; $\chi^V_{methanol} = 1.000 - 0.512 = 0.488$

The actual vapor pressure of the solution (161 torr) is less than the calculated pressure assuming ideal behavior (188.6 torr). Therefore, the solution exhibits negative deviations from Raoult's law. This occurs when the solute-solvent interactions are stronger than in pure solute and pure solvent.

53.   No, the solution is not ideal. For an ideal solution, the strengths of intermolecular forces in the solution are the same as in pure solute and pure solvent. This results in $\Delta H_{soln} = 0$ for an ideal solution. ΔH_{soln} for methanol-water is not zero. Because $\Delta H_{soln} < 0$, this solution exhibits negative deviation from Raoult's law.

55.   Solutions of A and B have vapor pressures less than ideal (see Figure 17.11 of the text), so this plot shows negative deviations from Rault's law. Negative deviations occur when the intermolecular forces are stronger in solution than in pure solvent and solute. This results in an exothermic enthalpy of solution. The only statement that is false is e. A substance boils when the vapor pressure equals the external pressure. Because $\chi_B = 0.6$ has a lower vapor pressure at the temperature of the plot than either pure A or pure B, one would expect this solution to require the highest temperature in order for the vapor pressure to reach the external pressure. Therefore, the solution with $\chi_B = 0.6$ will have a higher boiling point than either pure A or pure B. (Note that because $P_B^o > P_A^o$, B is more volatile than A.)

Colligative Properties

57. $\pi = MRT$, $M = \dfrac{\pi}{RT} = \dfrac{15 \text{ atm}}{0.08206 \text{ L atm K}^{-1} \text{ mol}^{-1} \times 295 \text{ K}} = 0.62$ M

$$\frac{0.62 \text{ mol}}{L} \times \frac{342.30 \text{ g}}{\text{mol } C_{12}H_{22}O_{11}} = 212 \text{ g/L} \approx 210 \text{ g/L}$$

Dissolve 210 g of sucrose in some water and dilute to 1.0 L in a volumetric flask. To get 0.62 ±0.01 mol/L, we need 212 ±3 g sucrose.

59.   Molality $= m = \dfrac{\text{mol solute}}{\text{kg solvent}} = \dfrac{27.0 \text{ g } N_2H_4CO}{150.0 \text{ g } H_2O} \times \dfrac{1000 \text{ g}}{\text{kg}} \times \dfrac{1 \text{ mol } N_2H_4CO}{60.06 \text{ g } N_2H_4CO} = 3.00 \text{ molal}$

$\Delta T_b = K_b m = \dfrac{0.51\,^{\circ}C}{\text{molal}} \times 3.00 \text{ molal} = 1.5^{\circ}C$

The boiling point is raised from 100.0°C to 101.5°C (assuming P = 1 atm).

61.   Molality $= m = \dfrac{50.0 \text{ g } C_2H_6O_2}{50.0 \text{ g } H_2O} \times \dfrac{1000 \text{ g}}{\text{kg}} \times \dfrac{1 \text{ mol}}{62.07 \text{ g}} = 16.1 \text{ mol/kg}$

$\Delta T_f = K_f m = 1.86\ ^{\circ}C/\text{molal} \times 16.1 \text{ molal} = 29.9^{\circ}C; \ T_f = 0.0^{\circ}C - 29.9^{\circ}C = -29.9^{\circ}C$

$\Delta T_b = K_b m = 0.51^{\circ}C/\text{molal} \times 16.1 \text{ molal} = 8.2^{\circ}C; \ T_b = 100.0^{\circ}C + 8.2^{\circ}C = 108.2^{\circ}C$

63. $m = \dfrac{24.0 \text{ g} \times \dfrac{1 \text{ mol}}{58.0 \text{ g}}}{0.600 \text{ kg}} = 0.690 \text{ mol/kg}; \ \Delta T_b = K_b m = 0.51^{\circ}C \text{ kg/mol} \times 0.690 \text{ mol/kg} = 0.35^{\circ}C$

$T_b = 99.725^{\circ}C + 0.35^{\circ}C = 100.08^{\circ}C$

65. $\Delta T_b = 77.85^{\circ}C - 76.50^{\circ}C = 1.35^{\circ}C; \ m = \dfrac{\Delta T_b}{K_b} = \dfrac{1.35\ ^{\circ}C}{5.03\ ^{\circ}C \text{ kg/mol}} = 0.268 \text{ mol/kg}$

Mol biomolecule $= 0.0150 \text{ kg solvent} \times \dfrac{0.268 \text{ mol hydrocarbon}}{\text{kg solvent}} = 4.02 \times 10^{-3} \text{ mol}$

From the problem, 2.00 g biomolecule was used, which must contain 4.02×10^{-3} mol biomolecule. The molar mass of the biomolecule is:

$$\frac{2.00 \text{ g}}{4.02 \times 10^{-3} \text{ mol}} = 498 \text{ g/mol}$$

67. $\Delta T_f = K_f m, \ m = \dfrac{\Delta T_f}{K_f} = \dfrac{0.300^{\circ}C}{5.12\ ^{\circ}C \text{ kg/mol}} = \dfrac{5.86 \times 10^{-2} \text{ mol thyroxine}}{\text{kg benzene}}$

The moles of thyroxine present are:

$$0.0100 \text{ kg benzene} \times \frac{5.86 \times 10^{-2} \text{ mol thyroxine}}{\text{kg benzene}} = 5.86 \times 10^{-4} \text{ mol thyroxine}$$

From the problem, 0.455 g thyroxine was used; this must contain 5.86×10^{-4} mol thyroxine. The molar mass of the thyroxine is:

$$\text{molar mass} = \frac{0.455 \text{ g}}{5.86 \times 10^{-4} \text{ mol}} = 776 \text{ g/mol}$$

69. $M = \dfrac{1.0 \text{ g}}{\text{L}} \times \dfrac{1 \text{ mol}}{9.0 \times 10^4 \text{ g}} = 1.1 \times 10^{-5}$ mol/L; $\pi = MRT$

At 298 K: $\pi = \dfrac{1.1 \times 10^{-5} \text{ mol}}{\text{L}} \times \dfrac{0.08206 \text{ L atm}}{\text{K mol}} \times 298 \text{ K} \times \dfrac{760 \text{ torr}}{\text{atm}}$, $\pi = 0.20$ torr

Because d = 1.0 g/cm^3, 1.0 L of solution has a mass of 1.0 kg. Because only 1.0 g of protein is present per liter solution, 1.0 kg of H_2O is present, and molality equals molarity to the correct number of significant figures.

$$\Delta T_f = K_f m = \frac{1.86 \text{ }^\circ\text{C}}{\text{molal}} \times 1.1 \times 10^{-5} \text{ molal} = 2.0 \times 10^{-5} \text{ }^\circ\text{C}$$

71. $\pi = MRT = \dfrac{0.1 \text{ mol}}{\text{L}} \times \dfrac{0.08206 \text{ L atm}}{\text{K mol}} \times 298 \text{ K} = 2.45 \text{ atm} \approx 2$ atm

$\pi = 2 \text{ atm} \times \dfrac{760 \text{ mm Hg}}{\text{atm}} \approx 2000 \text{ mm} \approx 2$ m

The osmotic pressure would support a mercury column of approximately 2 m. The height of a fluid column in a tree will be higher because Hg is more dense than the fluid in a tree. If we assume the fluid in a tree is mostly H_2O, then the fluid has a density of 1.0 g/cm^3. The density of Hg is 13.6 g/cm^3.

Height of fluid $\approx$ 2 m $\times$ 13.6 $\approx$ 30 m

73.   With addition of salt or sugar, the osmotic pressure inside the fruit cells (and bacteria) is less than outside the cell. Water will leave the cells, which will dehydrate any bacteria present, causing them to die.

Properties of Electrolyte Solutions

75. $P = \chi P^\circ$; 19.6 torr = $\chi_{H_2O}(23.8 \text{ torr})$, $\chi_{H_2O} = 0.824$; $\chi_{\text{solute}} = 1.000 - 0.824 = 0.176$

0.176 is the mole fraction of all the solute particles present. Because NaCl dissolves to produce two ions in solution (Na^+ and Cl^-), 0.176 is the mole fraction of Na^+ and Cl^- ions present. The mole fraction of NaCl is 1/2 (0.176) = 0.0880 = χ_{NaCl}.

At 45°C, $P_{\text{soln}} = 0.824(71.9 \text{ torr}) = 59.2$ torr.

77. $Na_3PO_4(s) \rightarrow 3\ Na^+(aq) + PO_4^{3-}(aq)$, $i = 4.0$; $CaBr_2(s) \rightarrow Ca^{2+}(aq) + 2\ Br^-(aq)$, $i = 3.0$

$KCl(s) \rightarrow K^+(aq) + Cl^-(aq)$, $i = 2.0$

The effective particle concentrations of the solutions are (assuming complete dissociation):

4.0(0.010 molal) = 0.040 molal for the Na_3PO_4 solution; 3.0(0.020 molal) = 0.060 molal for the $CaBr_2$ solution; 2.0(0.020 molal) = 0.040 molal for the KCl solution; slightly greater than 0.020 molal for the HF solution because HF only partially dissociates in water (it is a weak acid).

a.   The 0.010 m Na_3PO_4 solution and the 0.020 m KCl solution both have effective particle concentrations of 0.040 m (assuming complete dissociation), so both of these solutions should have the same boiling point as the 0.040 m $C_6H_{12}O_6$ solution (a nonelectrolyte).

b. $P = \chi P°$; as the solute concentration decreases, the solvent's vapor pressure increases because χ increases. Therefore, the 0.020 m HF solution will have the highest vapor pressure because it has the smallest effective particle concentration.

c. $\Delta T = K_f m$; the 0.020 m $CaBr_2$ solution has the largest effective particle concentration, so it will have the largest freezing point depression (largest ΔT).

79.   There are six cations and six anions in the illustration which indicates six solute formula units initially. There are a total of 10 solute particles in solution (a combined ion pair counts as one solute particle). So the value for the van't Hoff factor is:

$$i = \frac{\text{moles of particles in solution}}{\text{moles of solute dissolved}} = \frac{10}{6} = 1.67$$

81.   For $CaCl_2$: $i = \dfrac{\Delta T_f}{K_f m} = \dfrac{0.440°C}{1.86\ °C/molal \times 0.091\ molal} = 2.6$

Percent $CaCl_2$ ionized $= \dfrac{2.6 - 1.0}{3.0 - 1.0} \times 100 = 80.\%$; 20.% ion association occurs.

For CsCl: $i = \dfrac{\Delta T_f}{K_f m} = \dfrac{0.320°C}{1.86\ °C/molal \times 0.091\ molal} = 1.9$

Percent CsCl ionized $= \dfrac{1.9 - 1.0}{2.0 - 1.0} \times 100 = 90.\%$; 10% ion association occurs.

The ion association is greater in the $CaCl_2$ solution.

83. $NaCl(s) \rightarrow Na^+(aq) + Cl^-(aq)$, $i = 2.0$

$$\pi = iMRT = 2.0 \times \frac{0.10\ mol}{L} \times \frac{0.08206\ L\ atm}{K\ mol} \times 293\ K = 4.8\ atm$$

A pressure greater than 4.8 atm should be applied to ensure purification by reverse osmosis.

85.   a. $MgCl_2$, i (observed) = 2.7

$\Delta T_f = iK_f m = 2.7 \times 1.86 \,°C/molal \times 0.050 \,molal = 0.25°C; \;\; T_f = -0.25°C$

$\Delta T_b = iK_b m = 2.7 \times 0.51 \,°C/molal \times 0.050 \,molal = 0.069°C; \;\; T_b = 100.069°C$

    b. $FeCl_3$, i (observed) = 3.4

$\Delta T_f = iK_f m = 3.4 \times 1.86 \,°C/molal \times 0.050 \,molal = 0.32°C; \;\; T_f = -0.32°C$

$\Delta T_b = iK_b m = 3.4 \times 0.51°C/molal \times 0.050 \,molal = 0.087°C; \;\; T_b = 100.087°C$

87. $\pi = iMRT, \;\; M = \dfrac{\pi}{iRT} = \dfrac{2.50 \text{ atm}}{2.00 \times \dfrac{0.08206 \text{ L atm}}{\text{K mol}} \times 298 \text{ K}} = 5.11 \times 10^{-2} \text{ mol/L}$

Molar mass of compound $= \dfrac{0.500 \text{ g}}{0.1000 \text{ L} \times \dfrac{5.11 \times 10^{-2} \text{ mol}}{\text{L}}} = 97.8 \text{ g/mol}$

Additional Exercises

89.   Both solutions and colloids have suspended particles in some medium. The major difference between the two is the size of the particles. A colloid is a suspension of relatively large particles compared to a solution. Because of this, colloids will scatter light, whereas solutions will not. The scattering of light by a colloidal suspension is called the Tyndall effect.

91.   Coagulation is the destruction of a colloid by the aggregation of many suspended particles to form a large particle that settles out of solution.

93.   A 92 proof ethanol solution is 46% C_2H_5OH by volume. Assuming 100.0 mL of solution:

mol ethanol $= 46 \text{ mL } C_2H_5OH \times \dfrac{0.79 \text{ g}}{\text{mL}} \times \dfrac{1 \text{ mol } C_2H_5OH}{46.07 \text{ g}} = 0.79 \text{ mol } C_2H_5OH$

molarity $= \dfrac{0.79 \text{ mol}}{0.1000 \text{ L}} = 7.9 \; M \text{ ethanol}$

95. $\Delta T = K_f m, \;\; m = \dfrac{\Delta T}{K_f} = \dfrac{2.79°\text{C}}{1.86 \,°C/molal} = 1.50 \text{ molal}$

    a. $\Delta T = K_b m, \;\; \Delta T = 0.51°C/molal \times 1.50 \text{ molal} = 0.77°C, \;\; T_b = 100.77°C$

    b. $P_{soln} = \chi_{water} P_{water}^{o}, \;\; \chi_{water} = \dfrac{\text{mol } H_2O}{\text{mol } H_2O + \text{mol solute}}$

Assuming 1.00 kg of water, we have 1.50 mol solute, and:

$$mol\ H_2O = 1.00 \times 10^3\ g\ H_2O \times \frac{1\ mol\ H_2O}{18.02\ g\ H_2O} = 55.5\ mol\ H_2O$$

$$\chi_{water} = \frac{55.5\ mol}{1.50 + 55.5} = 0.974;\quad P_{soln} = (0.974)(23.76\ mm\ Hg) = 23.1\ mm\ Hg$$

c.   We assumed ideal behavior in solution formation, we assumed the solute was nonvolatile, and we assumed i = 1 (no ions formed).

97.   Benzoic acid is capable of hydrogen-bonding, but a significant part of benzoic acid is the nonpolar benzene ring.   In benzene, a hydrogen-bonded dimer forms.

The dimer is relatively nonpolar and thus more soluble in benzene than in water. Because benzoic acid forms dimers in benzene, the effective solute particle concentration will be less than 1.0 molal. Therefore, the freezing-point depression would be less than 5.12°C   ($\Delta T_f = K_f m$).

99.   a. $NH_4NO_3(s) \rightarrow NH_4^+(aq) + NO_3^-(aq)$ $\Delta H_{soln} = ?$

Heat gain by dissolution process = heat loss by solution; We will keep all quantities positive in order to avoid sign errors. Because the temperature of the water decreased, the dissolution of NH_4NO_3 is endothermic (ΔH is positive). Mass of solution = 1.60 + 75.0 = 76.6 g

$$\text{Heat loss by solution} = \frac{4.18\ J}{°C\ g} \times 76.6\ g \times (25.00°C - 23.34°C) = 532\ J$$

$$\Delta H_{soln} = \frac{532\ J}{1.60\ g\ NH_4NO_3} \times \frac{80.05\ g\ NH_4NO_3}{mol\ NH_4NO_3} = 2.66 \times 10^4\ J/mol = 26.6\ kJ/mol$$

b.   We will use Hess's law to solve for the lattice energy. The lattice energy equation is:

$NH_4^+(g) + NO_3^-(g) \rightarrow NH_4NO_3(s)$ ΔH = lattice energy

$NH_4^+(g) + NO_3^-(g) \rightarrow NH_4^+(aq) + NO_3^-(aq)$ $\Delta H = \Delta H_{hyd} = -630.\ kJ/mol$
$NH_4^+(aq) + NO_3^-(aq) \rightarrow NH_4NO_3(s)$ $\Delta H = -\Delta H_{soln} = -26.6\ kJ/mol$

_____

$NH_4^+(g) + NO_3^-(g) \rightarrow NH_4NO_3(s)$ $\Delta H = \Delta H_{hyd} - \Delta H_{soln} = -657\ kJ/mol$

101. $\chi_{pen}^{V} = 0.15 = \dfrac{P_{pen}}{P_{total}}$; $P_{pen} = \chi_{pen}^{L} P_{pen}^{o}$; $P_{total} = P_{pen} + P_{hex} = \chi_{pen}^{L}(511) + \chi_{hex}^{L}(150.)$

Because $\chi_{hex}^{L} = 1.000 - \chi_{pen}^{L}$: $P_{total} = \chi_{pen}^{L}(511) + (1.000 - \chi_{pen}^{L})(150.) = 150. + 361\chi_{pen}^{L}$

$\chi_{pen}^{V} = \dfrac{P_{pen}}{P_{total}}$, $0.15 = \dfrac{\chi_{pen}^{L}(511)}{150. + 361\chi_{pen}^{L}}$, $0.15(150. + 361\chi_{pen}^{L}) = 511\chi_{pen}^{L}$

$23 + 54\chi_{pen}^{L} = 511\chi_{pen}^{L}$, $\chi_{pen}^{L} = \dfrac{23}{457} = 0.050$

103. $14.2 \text{ mg CO}_2 \times \dfrac{12.01 \text{ mg C}}{44.01 \text{ mg CO}_2} = 3.88 \text{ mg C}$; $\% \text{ C} = \dfrac{3.88 \text{ mg}}{4.80 \text{ mg}} \times 100 = 80.8\% \text{ C}$

$1.65 \text{ mg H}_2\text{O} \times \dfrac{2.016 \text{ mg H}}{18.02 \text{ mg H}_2\text{O}} = 0.185 \text{ mg H}$; $\% \text{ H} = \dfrac{0.185 \text{ mg}}{4.80 \text{ mg}} \times 100 = 3.85\% \text{ H}$

Mass % O = $100.00 - (80.8 + 3.85) = 15.4\%$ O

Out of 100.00 g:

$80.8 \text{ g C} \times \dfrac{1 \text{ mol}}{12.01 \text{ g}} = 6.73 \text{ mol C}$; $\dfrac{6.73}{0.963} = 6.99 \approx 7$

$3.85 \text{ g H} \times \dfrac{1 \text{ mol}}{1.008 \text{ g}} = 3.82 \text{ mol H}$; $\dfrac{3.82}{0.963} = 3.97 \approx 4$

$15.4 \text{ g O} \times \dfrac{1 \text{ mol}}{16.00 \text{ g}} = 0.963 \text{ mol O}$; $\dfrac{0.963}{0.963} = 1.00$

Therefore, the empirical formula is C_7H_4O.

$\Delta T_f = K_f m$, $m = \dfrac{\Delta T_f}{K_f} = \dfrac{22.3 \,^{\circ}C}{40. \,^{\circ}C / \text{molal}} = 0.56$ molal

Mol anthraquinone = $0.0114 \text{ kg camphor} \times \dfrac{0.56 \text{ mol anthraquinone}}{\text{kg camphor}} = 6.4 \times 10^{-3}$ mol

Molar mass = $\dfrac{1.32 \text{ g}}{6.4 \times 10^{-3} \text{ mol}} = 210$ g/mol

The empirical mass of C_7H_4O is $7(12) + 4(1) + 16 \approx 104$ g/mol. Because the molar mass is twice the empirical mass, the molecular formula is $C_{14}H_8O_2$.

105.   a. $m = \dfrac{\Delta T_f}{K_f} = \dfrac{1.32\,°C}{5.12\,°C\ kg/mol} = 0.258$ mol/kg

Mol unknown $= 0.01560$ kg $\times \dfrac{0.258\ \text{mol unknown}}{\text{kg}} = 4.02 \times 10^{-3}$ mol

Molar mass of unknown $= \dfrac{1.22\ g}{4.02 \times 10^{-3}\ \text{mol}} = 303$ g/mol

Uncertainty in temperature $= \dfrac{0.04}{1.32} \times 100 = 3\%$

A 3% uncertainty in 303 g/mol = 9 g/mol. So, molar mass = 303 ±9 g/mol.

b.   No, codeine could not be eliminated since its molar mass is in the possible range including the uncertainty.

c.   We would like the uncertainty to be ±1 g/mol. We need the freezing-point depression to be about 10 times what it was in this problem. Two possibilities are:

1.   make the solution 10 times more concentrated (may be solubility problem)

2.   use a solvent with a larger K_f value, e.g., camphor

107. $M_3X_2(s) \quad \rightarrow \quad 3\ M^{2+}(aq) \quad + \quad 2\ X^{3-}(aq) \qquad K_{sp} = [M^{2+}]^3[X^{3-}]^2$

Initial $s =$ solubility (mol/L)   0   0
Equil. $3s$ $2s$

$K_{sp} = (3s)^3(2s)^2 = 108s^5$; total ion concentration $= 3s + 2s = 5s$.

$\pi = iMRT,\ iM =$ total ion concentration $= \dfrac{\pi}{RT} = \dfrac{2.64 \times 10^{-2}\ \text{atm}}{0.08206\ \text{L atm K}^{-1}\ \text{mol}^{-1} \times 298\ \text{K}}$

$= 1.08 \times 10^{-3}$ mol/L

$5s = 1.08 \times 10^{-3}$ mol/L, $s = 2.16 \times 10^{-4}$ mol/L

$K_{sp} = 108s^5 = 108(2.16 \times 10^{-4})^5 = 5.08 \times 10^{-17}$

109. $m = \dfrac{0.100\ g \times \dfrac{1\ \text{mol}}{100.0\ g}}{0.5000\ \text{kg}} = 2.00 \times 10^{-3}$ mol/kg $\approx 2.00 \times 10^{-3}$ mol/L   (dilute solution)

$\Delta T_f = iK_f m$, $0.0056°C = i \times 1.86\ °C/\text{molal} \times 2.00 \times 10^{-3}$ molal, $i = 1.5$

If i = 1.0, percent dissociation = 0%, and if i = 2.0, percent dissociation = 100%. Because i = 1.5, the weak acid is 50.% dissociated.

$$HA \rightleftharpoons H^+ + A^- \qquad K_a = \frac{[H^+][A^-]}{[HA]}$$

Because the weak acid is 50.% dissociated:

$$[H^+] = [A^-] = [HA]_o \times 0.50 = 2.00 \times 10^{-3}\,M \times 0.50 = 1.0 \times 10^{-3}\,M$$

$$[HA] = [HA]_0 - \text{amount HA reacted} = 2.00 \times 10^{-3}\,M - 1.0 \times 10^{-3}\,M = 1.0 \times 10^{-3}\,M$$

$$K_a = \frac{[H^+][A^-]}{[HA]} = \frac{(1.0 \times 10^{-3})(1.0 \times 10^{-3})}{1.0 \times 10^{-3}} = 1.0 \times 10^{-3}$$

111. $$iM = \frac{\pi}{RT} = \frac{0.3950\,\text{atm}}{0.08206\,\text{L atm K}^{-1}\,\text{mol}^{-1}(298.2\,\text{K})} = 0.01614\,\text{mol/L} = \text{total ion concentration}$$

$$0.01614\,\text{mol/L} = M_{Mg^{2+}} + M_{Na^+} + M_{Cl^-};\quad M_{Cl^-} = 2M_{Mg^{2+}} + M_{Na^+} \text{ (charge balance)}$$

Combining: $0.01614 = 3M_{Mg^{2+}} + 2M_{Na^+}$

Let x = mass $MgCl_2$ and y = mass NaCl; then $x + y = 0.5000$ g.

$$M_{Mg^{2+}} = \frac{x}{95.218} \text{ and } M_{Na^+} = \frac{y}{58.443} \quad \text{(Because V = 1.000 L.)}$$

Total ion concentration $= \dfrac{3x}{95.218} + \dfrac{2y}{58.443} = 0.01614\,\text{mol/L}$

Rearranging: $3x + (3.2585)y = 1.537$

Solving by simultaneous equations:

$$\begin{array}{rcl} 3x + (3.2585)y &=& 1.537 \\ -3(x + \quad y) &=& -3(0.5000) \\ \hline (0.2585)y &=& 0.037, \qquad y = 0.14\,\text{g NaCl} \end{array}$$

Mass $MgCl_2 = 0.5000$ g $- 0.14$ g $= 0.36$ g; mass % $MgCl_2 = \dfrac{0.36\,\text{g}}{0.5000\,\text{g}} \times 100 = 72\%$

Challenge Problems

113.   From the problem, $\chi_{C_6H_6}^L = \chi_{CCl_4}^L = 0.500$. We need the pure vapor pressures (P^o) in order to calculate the vapor pressure of the solution.

$$C_6H_6(l) \rightleftharpoons C_6H_6(g) \quad K = P_{C_6H_6} = P_{C_6H_6}^o \text{ at } 25°C$$

$$\Delta G^\circ_{rxn} = \Delta G^\circ_{f, C_6H_6(g)} - \Delta G^\circ_{f, C_6H_6(l)} = 129.66 \text{ kJ/mol} - 124.50 \text{ kJ/mol} = 5.16 \text{ kJ/mol}$$

$$\Delta G^\circ = -RT \ln K, \quad \ln K = \frac{-\Delta G^\circ}{RT} = \frac{-5.16 \times 10^3 \text{ J/mol}}{(8.3145 \text{ J K}^{-1} \text{ mol}^{-1})(298 \text{ K})} = -2.08$$

$$K = P^\circ_{C_6H_6} = e^{-2.08} = 0.125 \text{ atm}$$

For CCl$_4$: $\Delta G^\circ_{rxn} = \Delta G^\circ_{f, CCl_4(g)} - \Delta G^\circ_{f, CCl_4(l)} = -60.59 \text{ kJ/mol} - (-65.21 \text{ kJ/mol})$

$$= 4.62 \text{ kJ/mol}$$

$$K = P^\circ_{CCl_4} = \exp\left(\frac{-\Delta G^\circ}{RT}\right) = \exp\left(\frac{-4620 \text{ J/mol}}{8.3145 \text{ J K}^{-1} \text{ mol}^{-1} \times 298 \text{ K}}\right) = 0.155 \text{ atm}$$

$$P_{C_6H_6} = \chi^L_{C_6H_6} P^\circ_{C_6H_6} = 0.500(0.125 \text{ atm}) = 0.0625 \text{ atm}; \quad P_{CCl_4} = 0.500(0.155 \text{ atm})$$

$$= 0.0775 \text{ atm}$$

$$\chi^V_{C_6H_6} = \frac{P_{C_6H_6}}{P_{total}} = \frac{0.0625 \text{ atm}}{0.0625 \text{ atm} + 0.0775 \text{ atm}} = \frac{0.0625}{0.1400} = 0.446; \quad \chi^V_{CCl_4} = 1.000 - 0.446$$

$$= 0.554$$

115.   For the second vapor collected, $\chi^V_{B, 2} = 0.714$ and $\chi^V_{T, 2} = 0.286$. Let $\chi^L_{B, 2}$ = mole fraction of benzene in the second solution and $\chi^L_{T, 2}$ = mole fraction of toluene in the second solution.

$$\chi^L_{B, 2} + \chi^L_{T, 2} = 1.000$$

$$\chi^V_{B, 2} = 0.714 = \frac{P_B}{P_{total}} = \frac{P_B}{P_B + P_T} = \frac{\chi^L_{B, 2}(750.0 \text{ torr})}{\chi^L_{B, 2}(750.0 \text{ torr}) + (1.000 - \chi^L_{B, 2})(300.0 \text{ torr})}$$

Solving: $\chi^L_{B, 2} = 0.500 = \chi^L_{T, 2}$

This second solution came from the vapor collected from the first (initial) solution, so, $\chi^V_{B, 1} = \chi^V_{T, 1} = 0.500$. Let $\chi^L_{B, 1}$ = mole fraction benzene in the first solution and $\chi^L_{T, 1}$ = mole fraction of toluene in first solution. $\chi^L_{B, 1} + \chi^L_{T, 1} = 1.000$.

$$\chi^V_{B, 1} = 0.500 = \frac{P_B}{P_{total}} = \frac{P_B}{P_B + P_T} = \frac{\chi^L_{B, 1}(750.0 \text{ torr})}{\chi^L_{B, 1}(750.0 \text{ torr}) + (1.000 - \chi^L_{B, 1})(300.0 \text{ torr})}$$

Solving: $\chi^L_{B, 1} = 0.286$; the original solution had $\chi_B = 0.286$ and $\chi_T = 0.714$.

117.   a.   Assuming MgCO$_3$(s) does not dissociate, the solute concentration in water is:

$$\frac{560 \text{ μg MgCO}_3(s)}{\text{mL}} = \frac{560 \text{ mg}}{\text{L}} = \frac{560 \times 10^{-3} \text{ g}}{\text{L}} \times \frac{1 \text{ mol MgCO}_3}{84.32 \text{ g}}$$

$$= 6.6 \times 10^{-3} \text{ mol MgCO}_3/\text{L}$$

An applied pressure of 8.0 atm will purify water up to a solute concentration of:

$$M = \frac{\pi}{RT} = \frac{8.0 \text{ atm}}{0.08206 \text{ L atm K}^{-1} \text{ mol}^{-1} \times 300. \text{ K}} = \frac{0.32 \text{ mol}}{L}$$

When the concentration of $MgCO_3(s)$ reaches 0.32 mol/L, the reverse osmosis unit can no longer purify the water. Let V = volume (L) of water remaining after purifying 45 L of H_2O. When V + 45 L of water has been processed, the moles of solute particles will equal:

$$6.6 \times 10^{-3} \text{ mol/L} \times (45 \text{ L} + \text{V}) = 0.32 \text{ mol/L} \times \text{V}$$

Solving: $0.30 = (0.32 - 0.0066) \times \text{V}, \quad \text{V} = 0.96 \text{ L}$

The minimum total volume of water that must be processed is 45 L + 0.96 L = 46 L.

Note: If $MgCO_3$ does dissociate into Mg^{2+} and CO_3^{2-} ions, then the solute concentration increases to 1.3×10^{-2} M, and at least 47 L of water must be processed.

b. No; a reverse osmosis system that applies 8.0 atm can only purify water with a solute concentration of less than 0.32 mol/L. Salt water has a solute concentration of 2(0.60 M) = 1.2 mol/L ions. The solute concentration of salt water is much too high for this reverse osmosis unit to work.

119. a. Assuming no ion association between $SO_4^{2-}(aq)$ and $Fe^{3+}(aq)$, then i = 5 for $Fe_2(SO_4)_3$.

$\pi = iMRT = 5 \times 0.0500 \text{ mol/L} \times 0.08206 \text{ L atm K}^{-1} \text{ mol}^{-1} \times 298 \text{ K} = 6.11 \text{ atm}$

b. $Fe_2(SO_4)_3(aq) \rightarrow 2 \text{ Fe}^{3+}(aq) + 3 \text{ SO}_4^{2-} (aq)$

Under ideal circumstances, 2/5 of π calculated above results from Fe^{3+} and 3/5 results from SO_4^{2-}. The contribution to π from SO_4^{2-} is $3/5 \times 6.11$ atm = 3.67 atm. Because SO_4^{2-} is assumed unchanged in solution, the SO_4^{2-} contribution in the actual solution will also be 3.67 atm. The contribution to the actual π from the $Fe(H_2O)_6^{3+}$ dissociation reaction is 6.73 − 3.67 = 3.06 atm.

The initial concentration of $Fe(H_2O)_6^{2+}$ is 2(0.0500) = 0.100 M. The setup for the weak acid problem is:

$$Fe(H_2O)_6^{3+} \quad \rightarrow \quad H^+ \quad + \quad Fe(OH)(H_2O)_5^{2+} \qquad K_a = \frac{[H^+][Fe(OH)(H_2O)_5^{2+}]}{[Fe(H_2O)_6^{3+}]}$$

Initial 0.100 M   ~0   0
         x mol/L of $Fe(H_2O)_6^{3+}$ reacts to reach equilibrium
Equil. 0.100 − x   x   x

$$\text{Total ion concentration} = iM = \frac{\pi}{RT} = \frac{3.06 \text{ atm}}{0.08206 \text{ L atm K}^{-1} \text{ mol}^{-1}(298 \text{ K})} = 0.125 \text{ M}$$

$0.125\ M = 0.100 - x + x + x = 0.100 + x,\ x = 0.025\ M$

$$K_a = \frac{[H^+][Fe(OH)(H_2O)_5^{2+}]}{[Fe(H_2O)_6^{3+}]} = \frac{x^2}{0.100 - x} = \frac{(0.025)^2}{(0.100 - 0.025)} = \frac{(0.025)^2}{0.075} = 8.3 \times 10^{-3}$$

121.   a. $\pi = iMRT,\ iM = \dfrac{\pi}{RT} = \dfrac{7.83\ \text{atm}}{0.08206\ \text{L atm K}^{-1}\ \text{mol}^{-1} \times 298\ \text{K}} = 0.320\ \text{mol/L}$

Assuming 1.000 L of solution:

total mol solute particles = mol Na^+ + mol Cl^- + mol NaCl = 0.320 mol

mass solution = 1000. mL $\times \dfrac{1.071\ \text{g}}{\text{mL}} = 1071$ g solution

mass NaCl in solution = 0.0100×1071 g = 10.7 g NaCl

mol NaCl added to solution = 10.7 g $\times \dfrac{1\ \text{mol}}{58.44\ \text{g}} = 0.183$ mol NaCl

Some of this NaCl dissociates into Na^+ and Cl^- (two moles of ions per mole of NaCl), and some remains undissociated. Let x = mol undissociated NaCl = mol ion pairs.

Mol solute particles = 0.320 mol = $2(0.183 - x) + x$

$0.320 = 0.366 - x,\ x = 0.046$ mol ion pairs

Fraction of ion pairs = $\dfrac{0.046}{0.183} = 0.25$, or 25%

b. $\Delta T = K_f m$, where $K_f = 1.86$ °C kg/mol; from part a, 1.000 L of solution contains 0.320 mol of solute particles. To calculate the molality of the solution, we need the kilograms of solvent present in 1.000 L of solution.

Mass of 1.000 L solution = 1071 g; mass of NaCl = 10.7 g

Mass of solvent in 1.000 L solution = 1071 g – 10.7 g = 1060. g

$\Delta T = 1.86$ °C kg/mol $\times \dfrac{0.320\ \text{mol}}{1.060\ \text{kg}} = 0.562$°C

Assuming water freezes at 0.000°C, then $T_f = -0.562$°C.

CHAPTER 18

THE REPRESENTATIVE ELEMENTS

Group 1A Elements

1. The gravity of the earth is not strong enough to keep the light H_2 molecules in the atmosphere.

3. a. $\Delta H° = 2(-46 \text{ kJ}) = -92 \text{ kJ}$; $\Delta S° = 2(193 \text{ J/K}) - [3(131 \text{ J/K}) + 192 \text{ J/K}] = -199 \text{ J/K}$

    $\Delta G° = \Delta H° - T\Delta S° = -92 \text{ kJ} - 298 \text{ K}(-0.199 \text{ kJ/K}) = -33 \text{ kJ}$

    b. Because $\Delta G°$ is negative, this reaction is spontaneous at standard conditions.

    c. $\Delta G° = 0$ when $T = \dfrac{\Delta H°}{\Delta S°} = \dfrac{-92 \text{ kJ}}{-0.199 \text{ kJ/K}} = 460 \text{ K}$

    At T < 460 K and standard pressures, the favorable $\Delta H°$ term dominates, and the reaction is spontaneous ($\Delta G° < 0$).

5. The first illustration is an example of a covalent hydride like H_2O. Covalent hydrides are just binary covalent compounds formed between hydrogen and some other nonmetal and exists as individual molecules. The middle illustration represents interstitial (or metallic) hydrides. In interstitial hydrides, hydrogen atoms occupy the holes of a transition metal crystal. These hydrides are more like solid solutions than true compounds. The third illustration represents ionic (or salt-like) hydrides like LiH. Ionic hydrides form when hydrogen reacts with a metal from Group 1A or 2A. The metals lose electrons to form cations and the hydrogen atoms gain electrons to form the hydride anions (H^-). These are just ionic compounds formed between a metal and hydrogen.

7. Alkali metals have a ns^1 valence shell electron configuration. Alkali metals lose this valence electron with relative ease to form M^+ cations when in ionic compounds. They all are easily oxidized. Therefore, in order to prepare the pure metals, alkali metals must be produced in the absence of materials (H_2O, O_2) that are capable of oxidizing them. The method of preparation is electrochemical processes, specifically, electrolysis of molten chloride salts and reduction of alkali salts with Mg and H_2. In all production methods, H_2O and O_2 must be absent.

9. Hydrogen forms many compounds in which the oxidation state is +1, as do the Group 1A elements. For example, H_2SO_4 and HCl as compared to Na_2SO_4 and NaCl. On the other hand, hydrogen forms diatomic H_2 molecules and is a nonmetal, whereas the Group 1A elements are metals. Hydrogen also forms compounds with a −1 oxidation state, which is not characteristic of Group 1A metals, e.g., NaH.

11. $4 \text{ Li(s)} + O_2(g) \rightarrow 2 \text{ Li}_2O(s)$

$16 \text{ Li(s)} + S_8(s) \rightarrow 8 \text{ Li}_2S(s);\ \ 2 \text{ Li(s)} + Cl_2(g) \rightarrow 2 \text{ LiCl(s)}$

$12 \text{ Li(s)} + P_4(s) \rightarrow 4 \text{ Li}_3P(s);\ \ 2 \text{ Li(s)} + H_2(g) \rightarrow 2 \text{ LiH(s)}$

$2 \text{ Li(s)} + 2 \text{ H}_2O(l) \rightarrow 2 \text{ LiOH(aq)} + H_2(g);\ \ 2 \text{ Li(s)} + 2 \text{ HCl(aq)} \rightarrow 2 \text{ LiCl(aq)} + H_2(g)$

Group 2A Elements

13. $MgCl_2$ is composed of Mg^{2+} ions; Mg^{2+} gains 2 electrons to form magnesium metal in electrolysis.

$$1.00 \times 10^6 \text{ g Mg} \times \frac{1 \text{ mol Mg}}{24.31 \text{ g Mg}} \times \frac{2 \text{ mol e}^-}{1 \text{ mol Mg}} \times \frac{96{,}485 \text{ C}}{1 \text{ mol e}^-} \times \frac{1 \text{ s}}{5.00 \times 10^4 \text{ C}} \times \frac{1 \text{ h}}{3600 \text{ s}}$$
$$= 44.1 \text{ hours}$$

15.   The alkaline earth ions that give water the hard designation are Ca^{2+} and Mg^{2+}. These ions interfere with the action of detergents and form unwanted precipitates with soaps. Large-scale water softeners remove Ca^{2+} by precipitating out the calcium ions as $CaCO_3$. In homes, Ca^{2+} and Mg^{2+} (plus other cations) are removed by ion exchange. See Figure 18.6 for a schematic of a typical cation exchange resin.

17. $CaCO_3(s) + H_2SO_4(aq) \rightarrow CaSO_4(aq) + H_2O(l) + CO_2(g)$

19. $\dfrac{1 \text{ mg F}^-}{\text{L}} \times \dfrac{1 \text{ g}}{1000 \text{ mg}} \times \dfrac{1 \text{ mol F}^-}{19.0 \text{ g F}^-} = 5.3 \times 10^{-5} M \text{ F}^- = 5 \times 10^{-5} M \text{ F}^-$

$CaF_2(s) \rightleftharpoons Ca^{2+}(aq) + 2 \text{ F}^-(aq)\ \ K_{sp} = [Ca^{2+}][F^-]^2 = 4.0 \times 10^{-11}$; precipitation will occur when $Q > K_{sp}$. Let's calculate $[Ca^{2+}]$ so that $Q = K_{sp}$.

$Q = 4.0 \times 10^{-11} = [Ca^{2+}]_0[F^-]_0^2 = [Ca^{2+}]_0(5 \times 10^{-5})^2,\ \ [Ca^{2+}]_0 = 2 \times 10^{-2} M$

$CaF_2(s)$ will precipitate when $[Ca^{2+}]_0 > 2 \times 10^{-2} M$. Therefore, hard water should have a calcium ion concentration of less than $2 \times 10^{-2} M$ to avoid precipitate formation.

Group 3A Elements

21.   The valence electron configuration of Group 3A elements is ns^2np^1. The lightest Group 3A element, boron, is a nonmetal because most of its compounds are covalent. Aluminum, although commonly thought of as a metal, does have some nonmetallic properties because its bonds to other nonmetals have significant covalent character. The other Group 3A elements have typical metal characteristics; their compounds formed with nonmetals are ionic. From this discussion, metallic character increases as the Group 3A elements get larger.

As discussed above, boron is a nonmetal in both properties and compounds formed. However aluminum has physical properties of metals, such as high thermal and electrical conductivities and a lustrous appearance. The compounds of aluminum with other nonmetals, however, do have some nonmetallic properties because the bonds have significant covalent character.

23. $B_2H_6(g) + 3\ O_2(g) \rightarrow 2\ B(OH)_3(s)$

25. $2\ Ga(s) + 3\ F_2(g) \rightarrow 2\ GaF_3(s);\ \ 4\ Ga(s) + 3\ O_2(g) \rightarrow 2\ Ga_2O_3(s)$

       $16\ Ga(s) + 3\ S_8(s) \rightarrow 8\ Ga_2S_3(s)$

       $2\ Ga(s) + 6\ HCl(aq) \rightarrow 2\ GaCl_3(aq) + 3\ H_2(g)$

Group 4A Elements

27.   The valence electron configuration of Group 4A elements is ns^2np^2. The two most important elements on earth are both Group 4A elements. They are carbon, found in all biologically important molecules, and silicon, found in most of the compounds that make up the earth's crust. They are important because they are so prevalent in compounds necessary for life and the geologic world.

       Group 4A shows an increase in metallic character as the elements get heavier. Carbon is a typical nonmetal, silicon and germanium have properties of both metals and nonmetals so they are classified as semimetals, and tin and lead have typical metallic characteristics.

29. $\ddot{O}\!=\!\!=\!\!C\!=\!\!=\!\ddot{O}$

       The darker green orbitals about carbon are sp hybrid orbitals. The lighter green orbitals about each oxygen are sp^2 hybrid orbitals, and the gold orbitals about all of the atoms are unhybridized p atomic orbitals. In each double bond in CO_2, one sigma and one π bond exists. The two carbon-oxygen sigma bonds are formed from overlap of sp hybrid orbitals from carbon with a sp^2 hybrid orbital from each oxygen. The two carbon-oxygen π bonds are formed from side-to-side overlap of the unhybridized p atomic orbitals from carbon with an unhybridized p atomic orbital from each oxygen. These two π bonds are oriented perpendicular to each other as illustrated in the figure.

31.   White tin is stable at normal temperatures. Gray tin is stable at temperatures below 13.2°C. Thus, for the phase change: Sn(gray) → Sn(white), ΔG is negative at T > 13.2°C and ΔG is positive at T < 13.2°C. This is only possible if ΔH is positive and ΔS is positive. Therefore, gray tin has the more ordered structure (has the smaller positional probability).

33. $Sn(s) + 2F_2(g) \rightarrow SnF_4(s)$, tin(IV) fluoride; $Sn(s) + F_2(g) \rightarrow SnF_2(s)$, tin(II) fluoride

35. Pb_3O_4: we assign –2 for the oxidation state of O. The sum of the oxidation states of Pb must be +8. We get this if two of the lead atoms are Pb(II) and one is Pb(IV). Therefore, the mole ratio of lead(II) to lead(IV) is 2:1.

Group 5A Elements

37. NO_4^{3-}

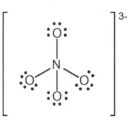

Both NO_4^{3-} and PO_4^{3-} have 32 valence electrons so both have similar Lewis structures. From the Lewis structure for NO_4^{3-}, the central N atom has a tetrahedral arrangement of electron pairs. N is small. There is probably not enough room for all four oxygen atoms around N. P is larger; thus PO_4^{3-} is stable.

PO_3^-

PO_3^- and NO_3^- both have 24 valence electrons, so both have similar Lewis structures. From the Lewis structure, PO_3^- has a trigonal arrangement of electron pairs about the central P atom (two single bonds and one double bond). P=O bonds are not particularly stable, whereas N=O bonds are stable. Thus NO_3^- is stable.

39. N: $1s^2 2s^2 2p^3$; the extremes of the oxidation states for N can be rationalized by examining the electron configuration of N. Nitrogen is three electrons short of the stable Ne electron configuration of $1s^2 2s^2 2p^6$. Having an oxidation state of -3 makes sense. The $+5$ oxidation state corresponds to N "losing" its five valence electrons. In compounds with oxygen, the N–O bonds are polar covalent, with N having the partial positive end of the bond dipole. In the world of oxidation states, electrons in polar covalent bonds are assigned to the more electronegative atom; this is oxygen in N–O bonds. N can form enough bonds to oxygen to give it a $+5$ oxidation state. This loosely corresponds to losing all the valence electrons.

41. This is due to nitrogen's ability to form strong π bonds, whereas heavier group 5A elements do not form strong π bonds. Therefore, P_2, As_2, and Sb_2 do not form since two π bonds are required to form these diatomic substances.

43.   a. NO_2, $5 + 2(6) = 17\ e^-$ N_2O_4, $2(5) + 4(6) = 34\ e^-$

        plus other resonance structures   plus other resonance structures

b. BF_3, $3 + 3(7) = 24$ e⁻ NH_3, $5 + 3(1) = 8$ e⁻

BF_3NH_3, $24 + 8 = 32$ e⁻

:F:
   | H
   | |
:F—B—N—H
   | |
:F: H

In reaction a, NO_2 has an odd number of electrons, so it is impossible to satisfy the octet rule. By dimerizing to form N_2O_4, the odd electron on two NO_2 molecules can pair up, giving a species whose Lewis structure can satisfy the octet rule. In general, odd-electron species are very reactive.   In reaction b, BF_3 can be considered electron-deficient; boron has only six electrons around it. By forming BF_3NH_3, the boron atom satisfies the octet rule by accepting a lone pair of electrons from NH_3 to form a fourth bond.

45.   As temperature increases, the value of K decreases. This is consistent with an exothermic reaction. In an exothermic reaction, heat is a product, and an increase in temperature shifts the equilibrium to the reactant side (as well as lowering the value of K).

47.

Bonds broken: Bonds formed:

1 N–N (160. kJ/mol)   4 H–F (565 kJ/mol)
4 N–H (391 kJ/mol)   1 N≡N (941 kJ/mol)
2 F–F (154 kJ/mol)

$\Delta H = 160. + 4(391) + 2(154) - [4(565) + 941] = 2032$ kJ $- 3201$ kJ $= -1169$ kJ

49.   Production of bismuth:

$2 Bi_2S_3(s) + 9 O_2(g) \rightarrow 2 Bi_2O_3(s) + 6 SO_2(g); 2 Bi_2O_3(s) + 3 C(s) \rightarrow 4 Bi(s) + 3 CO_2(g)$

Production of antimony:

$2 Sb_2S_3(s) + 9 O_2(g) \rightarrow 2 Sb_2O_3(s) + 6 SO_2(g); 2 Sb_2O_3(s) + 3 C(s) \rightarrow 4 Sb(s) + 3 CO_2(g)$

51.   TSP = Na_3PO_4; PO_4^{3-} is the conjugate base of the weak acid HPO_4^{2-} ($K_a = 4.8 \times 10^{-13}$). All conjugate bases of weak acids are effective bases ($K_b = K_w/K_a = 1.0 \times 10^{-14}/4.8 \times 10^{-13} = 2.1 \times 10^{-2}$). The weak base reaction of PO_4^{3-} with H_2O is $PO_4^{3-}(aq) + H_2O(l) \rightleftharpoons HPO_4^{2-}(aq) + OH^-(aq)$.

53. $4 As(s) + 3 O_2(g) \rightarrow As_4O_6(s)$; $4 As(s) + 5 O_2(g) \rightarrow As_4O_{10}(s)$

       $As_4O_6(s) + 6 H_2O(l) \rightarrow 4 H_3AsO_3(aq)$; $As_4O_{10}(s) + 6 H_2O(l) \rightarrow 4 H_3AsO_4(aq)$

55. $1/2 N_2(g) + 1/2 O_2(g) \rightarrow NO(g)$ $\Delta G° = \Delta G^{\circ}_{f, NO} = 87$ kJ/mol; by definition, ΔG°_f for a compound equals the free energy change that would accompany the formation of 1 mole of that compound from its elements in their standard states. NO (and some other oxides of nitrogen) have weaker bonds than the triple bond of N_2 and the double bond of O_2. Because of this, NO (and some other oxides of nitrogen) have higher (positive) standard free energies of formation than the relatively stable N_2 and O_2 molecules.

57.   The pollution provides sources of nitrogen and phosphorus nutrients so that the algae can grow. The algae consume oxygen, which decrease the dissolved oxygen levels below that required for other aquatic life to survive, and fish die.

59. $5 N_2O_4(l) + 4 N_2H_3CH_3(l) \rightarrow 12 H_2O(g) + 9 N_2(g) + 4 CO_2(g)$

$$\Delta H° = \left[12 \text{ mol}\left(\frac{-242 \text{ kJ}}{\text{mol}} \right) + 4 \text{ mol}\left(\frac{-393.5 \text{ kJ}}{\text{mol}} \right) \right]$$

$$- \left[5 \text{ mol}\left(\frac{-20. \text{ kJ}}{\text{mol}} \right) + 4 \text{ mol}\left(\frac{54 \text{ kJ}}{\text{mol}} \right) \right] = -4594 \text{ kJ}$$

61.   Hydrazine also can hydrogen bond because it has covalent N–H bonds as well as having a lone pair of electrons on each N. The high boiling point for hydrazine's relatively small size supports this.

Group 6A Elements

63.   The two allotropic forms of oxygen are O_2 and O_3.

       O_2, 2(6) = 12 e^- O_3, 3(6) = 18 e^-

The MO electron configuration of O_2 has two unpaired electrons in the degenerate pi antibonding (π^*_{2p}) orbitals (see Figure 14.41). A substance with unpaired electrons is paramagnetic. Ozone has a V-shape molecular structure with a bond angle of 117°, slightly less than the predicted 120° trigonal planar bond angle.

65.   In the upper atmosphere, O_3 acts as a filter for ultraviolet (UV) radiation:

$$O_3 \xrightarrow{hv} O_2 + O \quad \text{(See Exercise 18.64.)}$$

O_3 is also a powerful oxidizing agent.   It irritates the lungs and eyes, and at high concentration, it is toxic. The smell of a "spring thunderstorm" is O_3 formed during lightning discharges. Toxic materials don't necessarily smell bad. For example, HCN smells like almonds.

67.   +6 oxidation state: SO_4^{2-}, SO_3, SF_6

+4 oxidation state: SO_3^{2-}, SO_2, SF_4

+2 oxidation state: SCl_2

 0 oxidation state: S_8 and all other elemental forms of sulfur

−2 oxidation state: H_2S, Na_2S

69. $H_2SeO_4(aq) + 3\ SO_2(g) \rightarrow Se(s) + 3\ SO_3(g) + H_2O(l)$

Group 7A Elements

71. O_2F_2 has $2(6) + 2(7) = 26$ valence e^-.

$$:\!F\!-\!\overset{..}{\underset{..}{O}}\!-\!\overset{..}{\underset{..}{O}}\!-\!F\!:$$

Formal charge   0   0   0   0

Oxidation state   −1   +1   +1   −1

Oxidation states (numbers) are more useful. We are forced to assign +1 as the oxidation state for oxygen. Oxygen is very electronegative, and +1 is not a stable oxidation state for this element.

73.   Fluorine is the most reactive of the halogens because it is the most electronegative atom, and the bond in the F_2 molecule is very weak.

75.

$$ClO^- + H_2O + 2\ e^- \rightarrow 2\ OH^- + Cl^- \qquad E^\circ_c = 0.90\ V$$
$$2\ NH_3 + 2\ OH^- \rightarrow N_2H_4 + 2\ H_2O + 2\ e^- \qquad -E^\circ_a = 0.10\ V$$

$$ClO^-(aq) + 2\ NH_3(aq) \rightarrow Cl^-(aq) + N_2H_4(aq) + H_2O(l) \qquad E^\circ_{cell} = 1.00\ V$$

Because E°_{cell} is positive for this reaction, ClO^-, at standard conditions, can spontaneously oxidize NH_3 to the somewhat toxic N_2H_4.

77.   a. $AgCl(s) \xrightarrow{hv} Ag(s) + Cl$; the reactive chlorine atom is trapped in the crystal. When light is removed, Cl reacts with silver atoms to re-form AgCl; that is, the reverse reaction occurs. In pure AgCl, the Cl atoms escape, making the reverse reaction impossible.

        b.   Over time chlorine is lost, and the presence of the dark silver metal is permanent.

Group 8A Elements

79.   Helium is unreactive and doesn't combine with any other elements. It is a very light gas and would easily escape the earth's gravitational pull as the planet was formed.

81. $10.0 \text{ m} \times 10.0 \text{ m} \times 10.0 \text{ m} = 1.00 \times 10^3 \text{ m}^3$; from Table 18.22, volume percent of Ar = 0.9%.

$$1.00 \times 10^3 \text{ m}^3 \times \left(\frac{10 \text{ dm}}{\text{m}}\right)^3 \times \frac{1 \text{ L}}{\text{dm}^3} \times \frac{0.9 \text{ L Ar}}{100 \text{ L air}} = 9 \times 10^3 \text{ L of Ar in the room}$$

$$PV = nRT, \quad n = \frac{PV}{RT} = \frac{(1.0 \text{ atm})(9 \times 10^3 \text{ L})}{(0.08206 \text{ L atm K}^{-1} \text{ mol}^{-1})(298 \text{ K})} = 4 \times 10^2 \text{ mol Ar}$$

$$4 \times 10^2 \text{ mol Ar} \times \frac{39.95 \text{ g}}{\text{mol}} = 2 \times 10^4 \text{ g Ar in the room}$$

$$4 \times 10^2 \text{ mol Ar} \times \frac{6.022 \times 10^{23} \text{ atoms}}{\text{mol}} = 2 \times 10^{26} \text{ atoms Ar in the room}$$

A 2-L breath contains: $2 \text{ L air} \times \dfrac{0.9 \text{ L Ar}}{100 \text{ L air}} = 2 \times 10^{-2} \text{ L Ar}$

$$n = \frac{PV}{RT} = \frac{(1.0 \text{ atm})(2 \times 10^{-2} \text{ L})}{(0.08206 \text{ L atm K}^{-1} \text{ mol}^{-1})(298 \text{ K})} = 8 \times 10^{-4} \text{ mol Ar}$$

$$8 \times 10^{-4} \text{ mol Ar} \times \frac{6.022 \times 10^{23} \text{ atoms}}{\text{mol}} = 5 \times 10^{20} \text{ atoms of Ar in a 2-L breath}$$

Because Ar and Rn are both noble gases, both species will be relatively unreactive. However, all nuclei of Rn are radioactive, unlike most nuclei of Ar. The radioactive decay products of Rn can cause biological damage when inhaled.

83.   One would expect RnF_2 and RnF_4 to form in fashion similar to XeF_2 and XeF_4. The chemistry of radon is difficult to study because radon isotopes are all radioactive. The hazards of dealing with radioactive materials are immense.

Additional Exercises

85.   Solids have stronger intermolecular forces than liquids. In order to maximize the hydrogen bonding in the solid phase, ice is forced into an open structure. This open structure is why $H_2O(s)$ is less dense than $H_2O(l)$.

87.   Strontium and calcium are both alkaline earth metals, so both have similar chemical properties. Because milk is a good source of calcium, strontium could replace some calcium in milk without much difficulty.

89. $Tl^{3+} + 2 e^- \rightarrow Tl^+$ $E_c^\circ = 1.25$ V
           $3 I^- \rightarrow I_3^- + 2 e^-$ $-E_a^\circ = -0.55$ V
       _____

       $Tl^{3+} + 3 I^- \rightarrow Tl^+ + I_3^-$ $E_{cell}^\circ = 0.70$ V   (Spontaneous because $E_{cell}^\circ > 0$.)

       In solution, Tl^{3+} can oxidize I^- to I_3^-. Thus we expect TlI_3 to be thallium(I) triiodide.

91.   The inert pair effect refers to the difficulty of removing the pair of s electrons from some of the elements in the fifth and sixth periods of the periodic table. As a result, multiple oxidation states are exhibited for the heavier elements of Groups 3A and 4A. In^+, In^{3+}, Tl^+, and Tl^{3+} oxidation states are all important to the chemistry of In and Tl.

93. 15 kWh $= \dfrac{15000 \, J \, h}{s} \times \dfrac{60 \, s}{min} \times \dfrac{60 \, min}{h} = 5.4 \times 10^7$ J or 5.4×10^4 kJ   (Hall process)

       To melt 1.0 kg Al requires: 1.0×10^3 g Al $\times \dfrac{1 \, mol \, Al}{26.98 \, g} \times \dfrac{10.7 \, kJ}{mol \, Al} = 4.0 \times 10^2$ kJ

       It is feasible to recycle Al by melting the metal because, in theory, it takes less than 1% of the energy required to produce the same amount of Al by the Hall process.

95.   The bonds in SnX_4 compounds have a large covalent character. SnX_4 acts as discrete molecules held together by weak London dispersion forces. SnX_2 compounds are ionic and are held in the solid state by strong ionic forces. Because the intermolecular forces are weaker for SnX_4 compounds, they are more volatile (have a lower boiling point).

97.   Carbon cannot form the fifth bond necessary for the transition state because carbon doesn't have low-energy d orbitals available to expand its octet of valence electrons.

99.   a.   The Lewis structures for NNO and NON are (16 valence electrons each):

       The NNO structure is correct. From the Lewis structures we would predict both NNO and NON to be linear. However, we would predict NNO to be polar and NON to be nonpolar. Becase experiments show N_2O to be polar, then NNO is the correct structure.

b. Formal charge = number of valence electrons of atoms - [(number of lone pair electrons) + 1/2 (number of shared electrons)].

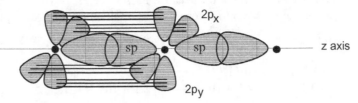

-1   +1   0   0   +1   -1   -2   +1   +1

The formal charges for the atoms in the various resonance structures appear below each atom. The central N is sp hybridized in all the resonance structures. We can probably ignore the third resonance structure on the basis of the relatively large formal charges on the various atoms in N_2O as compared with the first two resonance structures.

c. The sp hybrid orbitals on the center N overlap with atomic orbitals (or hybrid orbitals) on the other two atoms to form the two sigma bonds. The remaining two unhybridized p orbitals on the center N overlap with two p orbitals on the peripheral N to form the two π bonds.

101.   For a buffer solution: $pH = pK_a + \log\dfrac{[\text{base}]}{[\text{acid}]}$; $pH = -\log(6.2 \times 10^{-8}) + \log\dfrac{[HPO_4^{2-}]}{[H_2PO_4^-]}$

From the problem, $\dfrac{[H_2PO_4^-]}{[HPO_4^{2-}]} = 1.1$, so: $pH = 7.21 + \log\dfrac{1}{1.1}$, $pH = 7.21 - 0.041 = 7.17$

Challenge Problems

103.   a. Mol $In(CH_3)_3 = \dfrac{PV}{RT} = \dfrac{2.00\,\text{atm} \times 2.56\,\text{L}}{0.08206\,\text{L atm K}^{-1}\,\text{mol}^{-1} \times 900.\,\text{K}} = 0.0693\,\text{mol}$

Mol $PH_3 = \dfrac{PV}{RT} = \dfrac{3.00\,\text{atm} \times 1.38\,\text{L}}{0.08206\,\text{L atm K}^{-1}\,\text{mol}^{-1} \times 900.\,\text{K}} = 0.0561\,\text{mol}$

Because the reaction requires a 1 : 1 mole ratio between these reactants, the reactant with the small number of moles (PH_3) is limiting.

$0.0561\,\text{mol}\,PH_3 \times \dfrac{1\,\text{mol InP}}{\text{mol}\,PH_3} \times \dfrac{145.8\,\text{g InP}}{\text{mol InP}} = 8.18\,\text{g InP}$

The actual yield of InP is $0.87 \times 8.18\,\text{g} = 7.1\,\text{g InP}$.

b. $\lambda = \dfrac{hc}{E} = \dfrac{6.626 \times 10^{-34}\,\text{J s} \times 2.998 \times 10^8\,\text{m/s}}{2.03 \times 10^{-19}\,\text{J}} = 9.79 \times 10^{-7}\,\text{m} = 979\,\text{nm}$

From the Figure 12.3 of the text, visible light has wavelengths between 4×10^{-7} and 7×10^{-7} m. Therefore, this wavelength is not visible to humans; it is in the infrared region of the electromagnetic radiation spectrum.

c. $[Kr]5s^2 4d^{10} 5p^4$ is the electron configuration for tellurium, Te. Because Te has more valence electrons than P, this would form an n-type semiconductor (n-type doping).

105. $Mg^{2+} + P_3O_{10}^{5-} \rightleftharpoons MgP_3O_{10}^{3-}$ pK = −8.60; $[Mg^{2+}]_0 = \dfrac{50. \times 10^{-3} \text{ g}}{L} \times \dfrac{1 \text{ mol}}{24.3 \text{ g}} = 2.1 \times 10^{-3} \ M$

$[P_3O_{10}^{5-}]_0 = \dfrac{40. \text{ g } Na_5P_3O_{10}}{L} \times \dfrac{1 \text{ mol}}{367.9 \text{ g}} = 0.11 \ M$

Assume the reaction goes to completion because K is large (K = $10^{8.60}$ = 4.0×10^8). Then solve the back-equilibrium problem to determine the small amount of Mg^{2+} present.

$$Mg^{2+} \quad + \quad P_3O_{10}^{5-} \quad \rightleftharpoons \quad MgP_3O_{10}^{3-}$$

Before	$2.1 \times 10^{-3} \ M$	0.11 M	0
Change	-2.1×10^{-3}	$-2.1 \times 10^{-3} \rightarrow$	$+2.1 \times 10^{-3}$ Reacts completely
After	0	0.11	2.1×10^{-3} New initial

x mol/L $MgP_3O_{10}^{3-}$ dissociates to reach equilibrium

Change	$+x$	$+x \quad \leftarrow$	$-x$
Equil.	x	$0.11 + x$	$2.1 \times 10^{-3} - x$

$K = 4.0 \times 10^8 = \dfrac{[MgP_3O_{10}^{3-}]}{[Mg^{2+}][P_3O_{10}^{5-}]} = \dfrac{2.1 \times 10^{-3} - x}{x(0.11 + x)}$ (assume $x \ll 2.1 \times 10^{-3}$)

$4.0 \times 10^8 \approx \dfrac{2.1 \times 10^{-3}}{x(0.11)}$, $x = [Mg^{2+}] = 4.8 \times 10^{-11} \ M$;   assumptions good.

107. $3 \ O_2(g) \rightleftharpoons 2 \ O_3(g)$; $\Delta H° = 2(143) = 286$ kJ; $\Delta G° = 2(163) = 326$ kJ

$\ln K_p = \dfrac{-\Delta G°}{RT} = \dfrac{-326 \times 10^3 \text{ J}}{(8.3145 \text{ J K}^{-1} \text{ mol}^{-1})(298 \text{ K})} = -131.573, \ K_p = e^{-131.573} = 7.22 \times 10^{-58}$

Note: We carried extra significant figures for the K_p calculation.

We need the value of K at 230. K. From Section 10.11 of the text: $\ln K = \dfrac{-\Delta H°}{RT} + \dfrac{\Delta S°}{R}$

For two sets of K and T:

$$\ln K_1 = \dfrac{-\Delta H°}{R}\left(\dfrac{1}{T_1}\right) + \dfrac{\Delta S°}{R}; \quad \ln K_2 = \dfrac{-\Delta H°}{R}\left(\dfrac{1}{T_2}\right) + \dfrac{\Delta S°}{R}$$

Subtracting the first expression from the second:

$$\ln K_2 - \ln K_1 = \frac{\Delta H^\circ}{R}\left(\frac{1}{T_1} - \frac{1}{T_2}\right) \quad \text{or} \quad \ln\frac{K_2}{K_1} = \frac{\Delta H^\circ}{R}\left(\frac{1}{T_1} - \frac{1}{T_2}\right)$$

Let $K_2 = 7.22 \times 10^{-58}$, $T_2 = 298$; $K_1 = K_{230}$, $T_1 = 230.\ K$; $\Delta H^\circ = 286 \times 10^3\ J$

$$\ln\frac{7.22 \times 10^{-58}}{K_{230}} = \frac{286 \times 10^3}{8.3145}\left(\frac{1}{230.} - \frac{1}{298}\right) = 34.13 \qquad \text{(Carrying extra sig. figs.)}$$

$$\frac{7.22 \times 10^{-58}}{K_{230}} = e^{34.13} = 6.6 \times 10^{14},\ \ K_{230} = 1.1 \times 10^{-72}$$

$$K_{230} = 1.1 \times 10^{-72} = \frac{P_{O_3}^2}{P_{O_2}^3} = \frac{P_{O_3}^2}{(1.0 \times 10^{-3}\ \text{atm})^3},\ \ P_{O_3} = 3.3 \times 10^{-41}\ \text{atm}$$

The volume occupied by one molecule of ozone is:

$$V = \frac{nRT}{P} = \frac{(1/6.022 \times 10^{23}\ \text{mol})(0.08206\ \text{L atm K}^{-1}\ \text{mol}^{-1})(230.\,K)}{(3.3 \times 10^{-41}\ \text{atm})},\ V = 9.5 \times 10^{17}\ L$$

Equilibrium is probably not maintained under these conditions. When only two ozone molecules are in a volume of 9.5×10^{17} L, the reaction is not at equilibrium. Under these conditions, Q > K, and the reaction shifts left. But with only two ozone molecules in this huge volume, it is extremely unlikely that they will collide with each other. At these conditions, the concentration of ozone is not large enough to maintain equilibrium.

109.   a.   The sum of the two steps gives the overall balanced equation.

$$O_3(g) + NO(g) \rightarrow NO_2(g) + O_2(g)$$

$$\underline{NO_2(g) + O(g) \rightarrow NO(g)\ + O_2(g)}$$

$$O_3(g)\ +\ O(g)\ \rightarrow 2\ O_2(g) \qquad\qquad \text{overall equation}$$

b.   NO is the catalyst. NO is present in the first step of the mechanism on the reactant side, but it is not a reactant because it is regenerated in the second step and does not appear in the overall balanced equation.

c. NO_2 is an intermediate. It is produced in the first step, but is consumed in the second step. Intermediates also never appear in the overall balanced equation. In a mechanism, intermediates always appear first on the product side, while catalysts always appear first on the reactant side.

d.   The rate of the slow step in a mechanism gives the rate law for the reaction. From the problem, the rate determining step (the slow step) is step 1. The derived rate law is:

Rate = $k[O_3][NO]$

Because NO is a catalyst and not a proposed intermediate, it can appear in the rate law.

e. The mechanism for the chlorine-catalyzed destruction of ozone is:

$$O_3(g) + Cl(g) \rightarrow O_2(g) + ClO(g) \quad \text{slow step 1}$$
$$ClO(g) + O(g) \rightarrow O_2(g) + Cl(g) \quad \text{fast step 2}$$

$$O_3(g) + O(g) \rightarrow 2\ O_2(g) \qquad \text{overall equation}$$

111. $$Pb^{2+} \quad + \quad H_2EDTA^{2-} \quad \rightleftharpoons \quad PbEDTA^{2-} \quad + \quad 2\ H^+$$

Before	0.0050 M	0.075 M	0	$1.0 \times 10^{-7}\ M$	(Buffer, $[H^+]$ constant)
Change	−0.0050	−0.0050	$\rightarrow$ +0.0050	No change	Reacts completely
After	0	0.070	0.0050	1.0×10^{-7}	New initial conditions

x mol/L $PbEDTA^{2-}$ dissociates to reach equilibrium

Change	+x	+x	$\leftarrow$ −x		
Equil.	x	$0.070 + x$	$0.0050 − x$	1.0×10^{-7}	(Buffer)

$$K = 6.7 \times 10^{21} = \frac{[PbEDTA^{2-}][H^+]^2}{[Pb^{2+}][H_2EDTA^{2-}]} = \frac{(0.0050 - x)(1.0 \times 10^{-7})^2}{(x)(0.070 + x)}$$

$$6.7 \times 10^{21} \approx \frac{(0.0050)(1.0 \times 10^{-14})}{(x)(0.070)}, \quad x = [Pb^{2+}] = 1.1 \times 10^{-37}\ M; \ \text{assumptions good.}$$

113.   a. K^+(blood) $\rightleftharpoons$ K^+(muscle) $\Delta G° = 0$; $\Delta G = RT \ln\left(\dfrac{[K^+]_m}{[K^+]_b}\right)$; $\Delta G = w_{max}$

$$\Delta G = \frac{8.3145\ J}{K\ mol}(310.\ K) \ln\left(\frac{0.15}{0.0050}\right), \ \Delta G = 8.8 \times 10^3\ J/mol = 8.8\ kJ/mol$$

At least 8.8 kJ of work must be applied to transport 1 mol K^+.

b. Other ions will have to be transported in order to maintain electroneutrality. Either anions must be transported into the cells, or cations (Na^+) in the cell must be transported to the blood. The latter is what happens: $[Na^+]$ in blood is greater than $[Na^+]$ in cells as a result of this pumping.

c. $\Delta G° = -RT \ln K = -8.3145\ J\ K^{-1}\ mol^{-1} \times 310.\ K \times \ln(1.7 \times 10^5) = -3.1 \times 10^4\ J/mol$
$$= -31\ kJ/mol$$

The hydrolysis of ATP (at standard conditions) provides 31 kJ/mol of energy to do work. We need 8.8 kJ of work to transport 1.0 mol of K^+.

$$8.8\ kJ \times \frac{1\ mol\ ATP}{31\ kJ} = 0.28\ mol\ ATP\ \text{must be hydrolyzed}$$

CHAPTER 19

TRANSITION METALS AND COORDINATION CHEMISTRY

Transition Metals

7. Cr and Cu are exceptions to the normal filling order of electrons.

a. Cr: $[Ar]4s^1 3d^5$

Cr^{2+}: $[Ar]3d^4$

Cr^{3+}: $[Ar]3d^3$

b. Cu: $[Ar]4s^1 3d^{10}$

Cu$^+$: $[Ar]3d^{10}$

Cu^{2+}: $[Ar]3d^9$

c. V: $[Ar]4s^2 3d^3$

V^{2+}: $[Ar]3d^3$

V^{3+}: $[Ar]3d^2$

9. The lanthanide elements are located just before the 5d transition metals. The lanthanide contraction is the steady decrease in the atomic radii of the lanthanide elements when going from left to right across the periodic table. As a result of the lanthanide contraction, the sizes of the 4d and 5d elements are very similar (see the following exercise). This leads to a greater similarity in the chemistry of the 4d and 5d elements in a given vertical group.

11. a. molybdenum(IV) sulfide; molybdenum(VI) oxide

b. MoS_2, +4; MoO_3, +6; $(NH_4)_2Mo_2O_7$, +6; $(NH_4)_6Mo_7O_{24} \bullet 4\ H_2O$, +6

13. TiF_4: ionic compound containing Ti^{4+} ions and F^- ions. $TiCl_4$, $TiBr_4$, and TiI_4: covalent compounds containing discrete, tetrahedral TiX_4 molecules. As these covalent molecules get larger, the boiling points and melting points increase because the London dispersion forces increase. TiF_4 has the highest boiling point because the interparticle forces are stronger in ionic compounds than in covalent compounds.

15. $H^+ + OH^- \rightarrow H_2O$; sodium hydroxide (NaOH) will react with the H^+ on the product side of the reaction. This effectively removes H^+ from the equilibrium, which will shift the reaction to the right to produce more H^+ and CrO_4^{2-}. As more CrO_4^{2-} is produced, the solution turns yellow.

17. Because transition metals form bonds to species that donate lone pairs of electrons, transition metals are Lewis acids (electron pair acceptors). The Lewis bases in coordination compounds are the ligands, all of which have an unshared pair of electrons to donate. The coordinate covalent bond between the ligand and the transition metal just indicates that both electrons in the bond originally came from one of the atoms in the bond. Here, the electrons in the bond come from the ligand.

19.   The complex ion is $PtCl_4^{2-}$, which is composed of Pt^{2+} and four Cl^- ligands. Pt^{2+}: $[Xe]4f^{14}5d^8$. With square planar geometry, geometric (cis-trans) isomerism is possible. Cisplatin is the cis isomer of the compound and has the following structural formula.

21.   To determine the oxidation state of the metal, you must know the charges of the various common ligands (see Table 19.13 of the text).

   a.   hexacyanomanganate(II) ion

   b.   cis-tetraamminedichlorocobalt(III) ion

   c.   pentaamminechlorocobalt(II) ion

23.   To determine the oxidation state of the metal, you must know the charges of the various common ligands (see Tables 19.13 and 19.14 of the text).

   a.   pentaamminechlororuthenium(III) ion   b.   hexacyanoferrate(II) ion

   c.   tris(ethylenediamine)manganese(II) ion   d.   pentaamminenitrocobalt(III) ion

25.   a. $K_2[CoCl_4]$ b. $[Pt(H_2O)(CO)_3]Br_2$

   c. $Na_3[Fe(CN)_2(C_2O_4)_2]$ d. $[Cr(NH_3)_3Cl(NH_2CH_2CH_2NH_2)]I_2$

27. $BaCl_2$ gives no precipitate, so SO_4^{2-} must be in the coordination sphere ($BaSO_4$ is insoluble). A precipitate with $AgNO_3$ means the Cl^- is not in the coordination sphere, that is, Cl^- is a counter ion. Because there are only four ammonia molecules in the coordination sphere, SO_4^{2-} must be acting as a bidentate ligand. The structure is:

29.   Because each compound contains an octahedral complex ion, the formulas for the compounds are $[Co(NH_3)_6]I_3$, $[Pt(NH_3)_4I_2]I_2$, $Na_2[PtI_6]$, and $[Cr(NH_3)_4I_2]I$. Note that in some cases the I^- ions are ligands bound to the transition metal ion as required for a coordination number of 6, whereas in other cases the I^- ions are counter ions required to balance the charge of the complex ion. The $AgNO_3$ solution will only precipitate the I^- counter ions and will not

precipitate the I^- ligands.   Therefore, 3 mol AgI will precipitate per mole of $[Co(NH_3)_6]I_3$, 2 mol AgI will precipitate per mole of $[Pt(NH_3)_4I_2]I_2$, 0 mol AgI will precipitate per mole of $Na_2[PtI_6]$, and 1 mol AgI will precipitate per mole of $[Cr(NH_3)_4I_2]I$.

31.   a.   Isomers: species with the same formulas but different properties; they are different compounds. See the text for examples of the following types of isomers.

       b.   Structural isomers: isomers that have one or more bonds that are different.

       c.   Stereoisomers: isomers that contain the same bonds but differ in how the atoms are arranged in space.

       d.   Coordination isomers: structural isomers that differ in the atoms that make up the complex ion.

       e.   Linkage isomers: structural isomers that differ in how one or more ligands are attached to the transition metal.

       f.   Geometric isomers: (cis-trans isomerism); stereoisomers that differ in the positions of atoms with respect to a rigid ring, bond, or each other.

       g.   Optical isomers: stereoisomers that are nonsuperimposable mirror images of each other; that is, they are different in the same way that our left and right hands are different.

33.   a.

cis   trans

Note: $C_2O_4^{2-}$ is a bidentate ligand. Bidentate ligands bond to the metal at two positions that are 90° apart from each other in octahedral complexes. Bidentate ligands do not bond to the metal at positions 180° apart from each other.

b.

cis

trans

c.

cis

trans

d.

Note: is an abbreviation for the bidentate en ligand (ethylenediamine, $NH_2CH_2CH_2NH_2$).

35.

mirror

trans
(mirror image is
superimposable)

cis

The mirror image of the cis
isomer is also superimposable.

No; both the trans and the cis forms of $Co(NH_3)_4Cl_2^+$ have mirror images that are superimposable. For the cis form, the mirror image only needs a $90°$ rotation to produce the original structure. Hence neither the trans nor cis form is optically active.

37.

M = transition metal ion

39.   Linkage isomers differ in the way that the ligand bonds to the metal. SCN^- can bond through the sulfur or through the nitrogen atom. NO_2^- can bond through the nitrogen or through the oxygen atom. OCN^- can bond through the oxygen or through the nitrogen atom. N_3^-, $NH_2CH_2CH_2NH_2$ and I^- are not capable of linkage isomerism.

41.   Similar to the molecules discussed in Figures 19.17 and 19.18 of the text, $Cr(acac)_3$ and cis-$Cr(acac)_2(H_2O)_2$ are optically active. The mirror images of these two complexes are nonsuperimposable. There is a plane of symmetry in trans-$Cr(acac)_2(H_2O)_2$, so it is not optically active. A molecule with a plane of symmetry is never optically active because the mirror images are always superimposable. A plane of symmetry is a plane through a molecule where one side exactly reflects the other side of the molecule.

43.   There are four geometrical isomers (labeled i-iv). Isomers iii and iv are optically active, and the nonsuperimposable mirror images are shown.

iv.

optically active   mirror   mirror image of iv
                                                      (nonsuperimposable)

Bonding, Color, and Magnetism in Coordination Compounds

45.   a.   Ligand that will give complex ions with the maximum number of unpaired electrons.

       b.   Ligand that will give complex ions with the minimum number of unpaired electrons.

       c.   Complex with a minimum number of unpaired electrons (low spin = strong field).

       d.   Complex with a maximum number of unpaired electrons (high spin = weak field).

47. Sc^{3+} has no electrons in d orbitals. Ti^{3+} and V^{3+} have d electrons present. The color of transition metal complexes results from electron transfer between split d orbitals. If no d electrons are present, no electron transfer can occur, and the compounds are not colored.

49.   The metal ions are both d^5 (Fe^{3+}: $[Ar]d^5$ and Mn^{2+}: $[Ar]d^5$). One of the diagrams (a) is for a weak-field (high-spin) d^5 complex ion while the other diagram (b) is for a strong-field (low-spin) d^5 complex ion. From the spectrochemical series, CN^- is a strong-field ligand while H_2O is in the middle of the series. Because the iron complex ion has CN^- for the ligands as well as having a higher metal ion charge (3+ vs. 2+), one would expect $[Fe(CN)_6]^{3-}$ to have the strong-field diagram in b, while $[Mn(H_2O)_6]^{2+}$ would have the weak-field diagram in a.

51.   a. Fe^{2+}: $[Ar]3d^6$

High spin, small Δ Low spin, large Δ

b. Fe^{3+}: $[Ar]3d^5$

↑   ↑

↑   ↑   ↑

High spin, small Δ

c. Ni^{2+}: $[Ar]3d^8$

↑   ↑

↑↓   ↑↓   ↑↓

d. Zn^{2+}: $[Ar]3d^{10}$

↑↓   ↑↓

↑↓   ↑↓   ↑↓

e. Co^{2+}: $[Ar]3d^7$

↑   ↑   ↑   —

↑↓   ↑↓   ↑   ↑↓   ↑↓   ↑↓

High spin, small Δ Low spin, large Δ

53.   To determine the crystal field diagrams, you need to determine the oxidation state of the transition metal, which can only be determined if you know the charges of the ligands (see Table 19.13). The electron configurations and the crystal field diagrams follow.

a. Ru^{2+}: $[Kr]4d^6$, no unpaired e⁻

—   —

↑↓   ↑↓   ↑↓

Low spin, large Δ

b. Ni^{2+}: $[Ar]3d^8$, 2 unpaired e⁻

↑   ↑

↑↓   ↑↓   ↑↓

c. V^{3+}: $[Ar]3d^2$, 2 unpaired e⁻

—   —

↑   ↑   —

Note: Ni^{2+} must have two unpaired electrons, whether high spin or low spin, and V^{3+} must have two unpaired electrons, whether high spin or low spin.

55.   Replacement of water ligands by ammonia ligands resulted in shorter wavelengths of light being absorbed. Energy and wavelength are inversely related, so the presence of the NH_3 ligands resulted in a larger d-orbital splitting (larger Δ). Therefore, NH_3 is a stronger-field ligand than H_2O.

57.   From Table 19.16 of the text, the violet complex ion absorbs yellow-green light ($\lambda \approx 570$ nm), the yellow complex ion absorbs blue light ($\lambda \approx 450$ nm), and the green complex ion absorbs red light ($\lambda \approx 650$ nm). The spectrochemical series shows that NH_3 is a stronger-field ligand than H_2O, which is a stronger-field ligand than Cl^-. Therefore, $Cr(NH_3)_6^{3+}$ will have the largest d-orbital splitting and will absorb the lowest wavelength electromagnetic radiation ($\lambda \approx 450$ nm) because energy and wavelength are inversely related ($\lambda = hc/E$).   Thus the yellow solution contains the $Cr(NH_3)_6^{3+}$ complex ion.   Similarly, we would expect the $Cr(H_2O)_4Cl_2^+$ complex ion to have the smallest d-orbital splitting because it contains the weakest-field ligands.   The green solution with the longest wavelength of absorbed light contains the $Cr(H_2O)_4Cl_2^+$ complex ion.   This leaves the violet solution, which contains the $Cr(H_2O)_6^{3+}$ complex ion.   This makes sense because we would expect $Cr(H_2O)_6^{3+}$ to absorb light of a wavelength between that of $Cr(NH_3)_6^{3+}$ and $Cr(H_2O)_4Cl_2^+$.

59.   a. $Ru(phen)_3^{2+}$ exhibits optical isomerism [similar to $Co(en)_3^{3+}$ in Figure 19.17 of the text].

    b. Ru^{2+}: $[Kr]4d^6$; because there are no unpaired electrons, Ru^{2+} is a strong-field (low-spin) case.

large Δ

61.   The crystal field diagrams are different because the geometries of where the ligands point are different. The tetrahedrally oriented ligands point differently in relationship to the d orbitals than do the octahedrally oriented ligands. Also, we have more ligands in an octahedral complex.

    See Figure 19.28 for the tetrahedral crystal field diagram. Notice that the orbitals are reverse of that in the octahedral crystal field diagram. The degenerate d_{z^2} and $d_{x^2-y^2}$ are at a lower energy than the degenerate d_{xy}, d_{xz}, and d_{yz} orbitals. Again, the reason for this is that tetrahedral ligands are oriented differently than octahedral field ligands, so the interactions with specifically oriented d orbitals are different. Also notice that the difference in magnitude of the d-orbital splitting for the two geometries. The d-orbital splitting in tetrahedral complexes is less than one-half the d-orbital splitting in octahedral complexes. There are no known ligands powerful enough to produce the strong-field case; hence all tetrahedral complexes are weak field or high spin.

63. $CoBr_6^{4-}$ has an octahedral structure, and $CoBr_4^{2-}$ has a tetrahedral structure (as do most Co^{2+} complexes with four ligands).   Coordination complexes absorb electromagnetic radiation (EMR) of energy equal to the energy difference between the split d orbitals. Because the tetrahedral d-orbital splitting is less than one-half the octahedral d-orbital splitting, tetrahedral complexes will absorb lower-energy EMR, which corresponds to longer-wavelength EMR ($E = hc/\lambda$). Therefore, $CoBr_6^{4-}$ will absorb EMR having a wavelength shorter than 3.4×10^{-6} m.

Additional Exercises

65. $Hg^{2+}(aq) + 2\,I^-(aq) \rightarrow HgI_2(s)$, orange precipitate

$HgI_2(s) + 2\,I^-(aq) \rightarrow HgI_4^{2-}(aq)$, soluble complex ion

Hg^{2+} is a d^{10} ion. Color is the result of electron transfer between split d orbitals. This cannot occur for the filled d orbitals in Hg^{2+}. Therefore, we would not expect Hg^{2+} complex ions to form colored solutions.

67. $Ni(CO)_4$ is composed of 4 CO molecules and Ni. Thus nickel has an oxidation state of zero.

69.   At high altitudes, the oxygen content of air is lower, so less oxyhemoglobin is formed, which diminishes the transport of oxygen in the blood. A serious illness called high-altitude sickness can result from the decrease of O_2 in the blood. High-altitude acclimatization is the phenomenon that occurs with time in the human body in response to the lower amounts of oxyhemoglobin in the blood. This response is to produce more hemoglobin and hence, increase the oxyhemoglobin in the blood. High-altitude acclimatization takes several weeks to take hold for people moving from lower altitudes to higher altitudes.

71.   i. $0.0203\ \text{g CrO}_3 \times \dfrac{52.00\ \text{g Cr}}{100.0\ \text{g CrO}_3} = 0.0106\ \text{g Cr};\ \%\ \text{Cr} = \dfrac{0.0106\ \text{g}}{0.105\ \text{g}} \times 100 = 10.1\%\ \text{Cr}$

ii. $32.93\ \text{mL HCl} \times \dfrac{0.100\ \text{mmol HCl}}{\text{mL}} \times \dfrac{1\ \text{mmol NH}_3}{\text{mmol HCl}} \times \dfrac{17.03\ \text{mg NH}_3}{\text{mmol}} = 56.1\ \text{mg NH}_3$

$\%\ \text{NH}_3 = \dfrac{56.1\ \text{mg}}{341\ \text{mg}} \times 100 = 16.5\%\ \text{NH}_3$

iii. $73.53\% + 16.5\% + 10.1\% = 100.1\%$; the compound must be composed of only Cr, NH_3, and I.

Out of 100.00 g of compound:

$10.1\ \text{g Cr} \times \dfrac{1\ \text{mol}}{52.00\ \text{g}} = 0.194\ \text{mol};$ $\qquad \dfrac{0.194}{0.194} = 1.00$

$16.5\ \text{g NH}_3 \times \dfrac{1\ \text{mol}}{17.03\ \text{g}} = 0.969\ \text{mol};$ $\qquad \dfrac{0.969}{0.194} = 4.99$

$73.53\ \text{g I} \times \dfrac{1\ \text{mol}}{126.9\ \text{g}} = 0.5794\ \text{mol};$ $\qquad \dfrac{0.5794}{0.194} = 2.99$

$Cr(NH_3)_5I_3$ is the empirical formula. Cr^{3+} forms octahedral complexes. So compound A is made of the octahedral $[Cr(NH_3)_5I]^{2+}$ complex ion and two I^- ions as counter ions; the formula is $[Cr(NH_3)_5I]I_2$. Lets check this proposed formula using the freezing-point data.

iv. $\Delta T_f = iK_f m$; for $[Cr(NH_3)_5I]I_2$, $i = 3.0$ (assuming complete dissociation).

$$\text{Molality} = m = \frac{0.601\,\text{g complex}}{1.000 \times 10^{-2}\,\text{kg H}_2\text{O}} \times \frac{1\,\text{mol complex}}{517.9\,\text{g complex}} = 0.116\,\text{mol/kg}$$

$\Delta T_f = 3.0 \times 1.86\,°\text{C kg/mol} \times 0.116\,\text{mol/kg} = 0.65°\text{C}$

Because ΔT_f is close to the measured value, this is consistent with the formula $[Cr(NH_3)_5I]I_2$.

73.   M = metal ion

75.   No; in all three cases, six bonds are formed between Ni^{2+} and nitrogen, so ΔH values should be similar. $\Delta S°$ for formation of the complex ion is most negative for 6 NH_3 molecules reacting with a metal ion (seven independent species become one). For penten reacting with a metal ion, two independent species become one, so $\Delta S°$ is least negative for this reaction compared to the other reactions. Thus the chelate effect occurs because the more bonds a chelating agent can form to the metal, the less unfavorable $\Delta S°$ is for the formation of the complex ion, and the larger the formation constant.

77. $\overset{\text{II} \qquad \text{III}}{(H_2O)_5Cr-Cl-Co(NH_3)_5} \rightarrow \overset{\text{III} \qquad \text{II}}{(H_2O)_5Cr-Cl-Co(NH_3)_5} \rightarrow Cr(H_2O)_5Cl^{2+} + Co(II)\ \text{complex}$

Yes; this is consistent. After the oxidation, the ligands on Cr(III) won't exchange. Because Cl^- is in the coordination sphere, it must have formed a bond to Cr(II) before the electron transfer occurred (as proposed through the formation of the intermediate).

79.   a. $Fe(H_2O)_6{}^{3+} + H_2O \rightleftharpoons Fe(H_2O)_5(OH)^{2+} + H_3O^+$

Initial   0.10 M 0   ~0
Equil. $0.10 - x$ x x

$$K_a = \frac{[Fe(H_2O)_5(OH)^{2+}][H_3O^+]}{[Fe(H_2O)_6^{3+}]} = 6.0 \times 10^{-3} = \frac{x^2}{0.10 - x} \approx \frac{x^2}{0.10}$$

$x = 2.4 \times 10^{-2}$; assumption is poor (x is 24% of 0.10). Using successive approximations:

$$\frac{x^2}{0.10 - 0.024} = 6.0 \times 10^{-3}, \ x = 0.021$$

$$\frac{x^2}{0.10 - 0.021} = 6.0 \times 10^{-3}, \ x = 0.022; \quad \frac{x^2}{0.10 - 0.022} = 6.0 \times 10^{-3}, \ x = 0.022$$

$$x = [H^+] = 0.022 \ M; \ pH = 1.66$$

b. Because of the lower charge, $Fe^{2+}(aq)$ will not be as strong an acid as $Fe^{3+}(aq)$. A solution of iron(II) nitrate will be less acidic (have a higher pH) than a solution with the same concentration of iron(III) nitrate.

81. a. In the lungs, there is a lot of O_2, and the equilibrium favors $Hb(O_2)_4$. In the cells, there is a lower concentration of O_2, and the equilibrium favors HbH_4^{4+}.

b. CO_2 is a weak acid in water; $CO_2 + H_2O \rightleftharpoons HCO_3^- + H^+$. Removing CO_2 essentially decreases H^+, which causes the hemoglobin reaction to shift right. $Hb(O_2)_4$ is then favored, and O_2 is not released by hemoglobin in the cells. Breathing into a paper bag increases $[CO_2]$ in the blood, thus increasing $[H^+]$, which shifts the hemoglobin reaction left.

c. CO_2 builds up in the blood, and it becomes too acidic, driving the equilibrium to the left. Hemoglobin can't bind O_2 as strongly in the lungs. Bicarbonate ion acts as a base in water and neutralizes the excess acidity.

Challenge Problems

83.

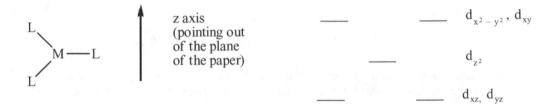

The $d_{x^2 - y^2}$ and d_{xy} orbitals are in the plane of the three ligands and should be destabilized the most. The amount of destabilization should be about equal when all the possible interactions are considered. The d_{z^2} orbital has some electron density in the xy plane (the doughnut) and should be destabilized a lesser amount than the $d_{x^2 - y^2}$ and d_{xy} orbitals. The d_{xz} and d_{yz} orbitals have no electron density in the plane and should be lowest in energy.

85.

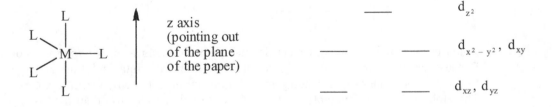

The d_{z^2} orbital will be destabilized much more than in the trigonal planar case (see Exercise 19.83). The d_{z^2} orbital has electron density on the z axis directed at the two axial ligands. The $d_{x^2-y^2}$ and d_{xy} orbitals are in the plane of the three trigonal planar ligands and should be destabilized a lesser amount than the d_{z^2} orbital; only a portion of the electron density in the $d_{x^2-y^2}$ and d_{xy} orbitals is directed at the ligands. The d_{xz} and d_{yz} orbitals will be destabilized the least since the electron density is directed between the ligands.

87.   a.   Consider the following electrochemical cell:

$$Co^{3+} + e^- \rightarrow Co^{2+} \qquad\qquad E_c^\circ = 1.82\ V$$
$$\underline{Co(en)_3^{2+} \rightarrow Co(en)_3^{3+} + e^- \qquad\qquad -E_a^\circ = ?}$$
$$Co^{3+} + Co(en)_3^{2+} \rightarrow Co^{2+} + Co(en)_3^{3+} \qquad\qquad E_{cell}^\circ = 1.82 - E_a^\circ$$

The equilibrium constant for this overall reaction is:

$$Co^{3+} + 3\ en \rightarrow Co(en)_3^{3+} \qquad\qquad K_1 = 2.0 \times 10^{47}$$
$$\underline{Co(en)_3^{2+} \rightarrow Co^{2+} + 3\ en \qquad\qquad K_2 = 1/1.5 \times 10^{12}}$$
$$Co^{3+} + Co(en)_3^{2+} \rightarrow Co(en)_3^{3+} + Co^{2+} \qquad K = K_1K_2 = \frac{2.0 \times 10^{47}}{1.5 \times 10^{12}} = 1.3 \times 10^{35}$$

From the Nernst equation for the overall reaction:

$$E_{cell}^\circ = \frac{0.0591}{n} \log K = \frac{0.0591}{1} \log(1.3 \times 10^{35}), \quad E_{cell}^\circ = 2.08\ V$$

$$E_{cell}^\circ = 1.82 - E_a^\circ = 2.08\ V, \quad -E_a^\circ = 2.08\ V - 1.82\ V = 0.26\ V, \text{ so } E_c^\circ = -0.26\ V$$

b.   The stronger oxidizing agent will be the more easily reduced species and will have the more positive standard reduction potential. From the reduction potentials, Co^{3+} ($E^\circ = 1.82\ V$) is a much stronger oxidizing agent than $Co(en)_3^{3+}$ ($E^\circ = -0.26\ V$).

c.   In aqueous solution, Co^{3+} forms the hydrated transition metal complex $Co(H_2O)_6^{3+}$. In both complexes, $Co(H_2O)_6^{3+}$ and $Co(en)_3^{3+}$, cobalt exists as Co^{3+}, which has six d electrons. Assuming a strong-field case for each complex ion, the d-orbital splitting diagram for each is:

$$\underline{\quad}\ \ \underline{\quad} \qquad\qquad e_g$$

$$\uparrow\downarrow \quad \uparrow\downarrow \quad \uparrow\downarrow \qquad\qquad t_{2g}$$

When each complex gains an electron, the electron enters a higher-energy e_g orbital. Because en is a stronger-field ligand than H_2O, the d-orbital splitting is larger for $Co(en)_3^{3+}$, and it takes more energy to add an electron to $Co(en)_3^{3+}$ than to $Co(H_2O)_6^{3+}$. Therefore, it is more favorable for $Co(H_2O)_6^{3+}$ to gain an electron than for $Co(en)_3^{3+}$ to gain an electron.

89.   a. $AgBr(s) \rightleftharpoons Ag^+ + Br^-$ $K_{sp} = [Ag^+][Br^-] = 5.0 \times 10^{-13}$

Initial s = solubility (mol/L)   0   0
Equil. s s

$K_{sp} = 5.0 \times 10^{-13} = s^2$, $s = 7.1 \times 10^{-7}$ mol/L

b. $AgBr(s) \rightleftharpoons Ag^+ + Br^-$ $K_{sp} = 5.0 \times 10^{-13}$
               $Ag^+ + 2\ NH_3 \rightleftharpoons Ag(NH_3)_2^+$ $K_f = 1.7 \times 10^7$

$AgBr(s) + 2\ NH_3(aq) \rightleftharpoons Ag(NH_3)_2^+(aq) + Br^-(aq)$ $K = K_{sp} \times K_f = 8.5 \times 10^{-6}$

$AgBr(s)$ + $2\ NH_3$ $\rightleftharpoons$ $Ag(NH_3)_2^+$ + Br^-

Initial   3.0 M 0   0
             s mol/L of AgBr(s) dissolves to reach equilibrium = molar solubility
Equil.   3.0 − 2s s s

$K = \dfrac{[Ag(NH_3)_2^+][Br^-]}{[NH_3]^2} = \dfrac{s^2}{(3.0 - 2s)^2}$, $8.5 \times 10^{-6} \approx \dfrac{s^2}{(3.0)^2}$, $s = 8.7 \times 10^{-3}$ mol/L

Assumption good.

c.   The presence of NH_3 increases the solubility of AgBr. Added NH_3 removes Ag^+ from solution by forming the complex ion $Ag(NH_3)_2^+$. As Ag^+ is removed, more AgBr(s) will dissolve to replenish the Ag^+ concentration.

d.   Mass AgBr = 0.2500 L $\times \dfrac{8.7 \times 10^{-3} \text{ mol AgBr}}{\text{L}} \times \dfrac{187.8 \text{ g AgBr}}{\text{mol AgBr}} = 0.41$ g AgBr

e.   Added HNO_3 will have no effect on the AgBr(s) solubility in pure water. Neither H^+ nor NO_3^- reacts with Ag^+ or Br^- ions. Br^- is the conjugate base of the strong acid HBr, so it is a terrible base. Added H^+ will not react with Br^- to any great extent. However, added HNO_3 will reduce the solubility of AgBr(s) in the ammonia solution. NH_3 is a weak base ($K_b = 1.8 \times 10^{-5}$). Added H^+ will react with NH_3 to form NH_4^+. As NH_3 is removed, a smaller amount of the $Ag(NH_3)_2^+$ complex ion will form, resulting in a smaller amount of AgBr(s) that will dissolve.

CHAPTER 20

THE NUCLEUS: A CHEMIST'S VIEW

Radioactive Decay and Nuclear Transformations

1. a. Thermodynamic stability: the potential energy of a particular nucleus compared to the sum of the potential energies of its component protons and neutrons.

    b. Kinetic stability: the probability that a nucleus will undergo decomposition to form a different nucleus.

    c. Radioactive decay: a spontaneous decomposition of a nucleus to form a different nucleus.

    d. Beta-particle production: a decay process for radioactive nuclides where an electron is produced; the mass number remains constant and the atomic number changes.

    e. Alpha-particle production: a common mode of decay for heavy radioactive nuclides where a helium nucleus is produced, causing the atomic number and the mass number to change.

    f. Positron production: a mode of nuclear decay in which a particle is formed having the same mass as an electron but opposite in charge.

    g. Electron capture: a process in which one of the inner-orbital electrons in an atom is captured by the nucleus.

    h. Gamma-ray emissions; the production of high-energy photons (gamma rays) that frequently accompany nuclear decays and particle reactions.

3. All nuclear reactions must be charge balanced and mass balanced. To charge balance, balance the sum of the atomic numbers on each side of the reaction, and to mass balance, balance the sum of the mass numbers on each side of the reaction.

    a. $^{238}_{92}\text{U} \rightarrow {}^{4}_{2}\text{He} + {}^{234}_{90}\text{Th}$; this is alpha-particle production.

    b. $^{234}_{90}\text{Th} \rightarrow {}^{234}_{91}\text{Pa} + {}^{0}_{-1}\text{e}$; this is β-particle production.

5. All nuclear reactions must be charge-balanced and mass-balanced. To charge-balance, balance the sum of the atomic numbers on each side of the reaction, and to mass-balance, balance the sum of the mass numbers on each side of the reaction.

a. $^{51}_{24}\text{Cr} + ^{0}_{-1}\text{e} \rightarrow ^{51}_{23}\text{V}$ b. $^{131}_{53}\text{I} \rightarrow ^{0}_{-1}\text{e} + ^{131}_{54}\text{Xe}$

c. $^{32}_{15}\text{P} \rightarrow ^{0}_{-1}\text{e} + ^{32}_{16}\text{S}$

7. a. $^{68}_{31}\text{Ga} + ^{0}_{-1}\text{e} \rightarrow ^{68}_{30}\text{Zn}$ b. $^{62}_{29}\text{Cu} \rightarrow ^{0}_{+1}\text{e} + ^{62}_{28}\text{Ni}$

c. $^{212}_{87}\text{Fr} \rightarrow ^{4}_{2}\text{He} + ^{208}_{85}\text{At}$ d. $^{129}_{51}\text{Sb} \rightarrow ^{0}_{-1}\text{e} + ^{129}_{52}\text{Te}$

9. $^{247}_{97}\text{Bk} \rightarrow ^{207}_{82}\text{Pb} + ? ^{4}_{2}\text{He} + ? ^{0}_{-1}\text{e}$; The change in mass number (247 - 207 = 40) is due ex-exclusively to the alpha particles. A change in mass number of 40 requires 10 $^{4}_{2}\text{He}$ particles to be produced. The atomic number only changes by 97 − 82 = 15. The 10 alpha particles change the atomic number by 20, so 5 $^{0}_{-1}\text{e}$ (five beta particles) are produced in the decay series of ^{247}Bk to ^{207}Pb.

11. Reference Table 20.2 of the text for potential radioactive decay processes. ^{17}F and ^{18}F contain too many protons or too few neutrons. Electron capture and positron production are both possible decay mechanisms that increase the neutron-to-proton ratio. Alpha-particle production also increases the neutron-to-proton ratio, but it is not likely for these light nuclei. ^{21}F contains too many neutrons or too few protons. Beta-particle production lowers the neutron-to-proton ratio, so we expect ^{21}F to be a β-emitter.

13. a. $^{249}_{98}\text{Cf} + ^{18}_{8}\text{O} \rightarrow ^{263}_{106}\text{Sg} + 4^{1}_{0}\text{n}$ b. $^{259}_{104}\text{Rf}$; $^{263}_{106}\text{Sg} \rightarrow ^{4}_{2}\text{He} + ^{259}_{104}\text{Rf}$

Kinetics of Radioactive Decay

15. $k = \dfrac{\ln 2}{t_{1/2}} = \dfrac{0.69315}{433\,\text{yr}} \times \dfrac{1\,\text{yr}}{365\,\text{d}} \times \dfrac{1\,\text{d}}{24\,\text{h}} \times \dfrac{1\,\text{h}}{3600\,\text{s}} = 5.08 \times 10^{-11}\,\text{s}^{-1}$

Rate $= kN = 5.08 \times 10^{-11}\,\text{s}^{-1} \times 5.00\,\text{g} \times \dfrac{1\,\text{mol}}{241\,\text{g}} \times \dfrac{6.022 \times 10^{23}\,\text{nuclei}}{\text{mol}} = 6.35 \times 10^{11}$ decays/s

6.35×10^{11} alpha particles are emitted each second from a 5.00-g ^{241}Am sample.

17. a. $k = \dfrac{\ln 2}{t_{1/2}} = \dfrac{0.6931}{12.8\,\text{d}} \times \dfrac{1\,\text{d}}{24\,\text{h}} \times \dfrac{1\,\text{h}}{3600\,\text{s}} = 6.27 \times 10^{-7}\,\text{s}^{-1}$

b. Rate $= kN = 6.27 \times 10^{-7}\,\text{s}^{-1} \left(28.0 \times 10^{-3}\,\text{g} \times \dfrac{1\,\text{mol}}{64.0\,\text{g}} \times \dfrac{6.022 \times 10^{23}\,\text{nuclei}}{\text{mol}} \right)$

Rate $= 1.65 \times 10^{14}$ decays/s

c. 25% of the ^{64}Cu will remain after 2 half-lives (100% decays to 50% after one half-life which decays to 25% after a second half-life). Hence 2(12.8 days) = 25.6 days is the time frame for the experiment.

19. $t = 67.0 \text{ yr}; \ k = \dfrac{\ln 2}{t_{1/2}}; \ \ln\left(\dfrac{N}{N_0}\right) = -kt = \dfrac{-(0.6931)67.0 \text{ yr}}{28.9 \text{ yr}} = -1.61, \ \left(\dfrac{N}{N_0}\right) = e^{-1.61} = 0.200$

20.0% of the ^{90}Sr remains as of July 16, 2012.

21. $175 \text{ mg Na}_3{}^{32}\text{PO}_4 \times \dfrac{32.0 \text{ mg } {}^{32}\text{P}}{165.0 \text{ mg Na}_3{}^{32}\text{PO}_4} = 33.9 \text{ mg } {}^{32}\text{P}; \ k = \dfrac{\ln 2}{t_{1/2}}$

$\ln\left(\dfrac{N}{N_0}\right) = -kt = \dfrac{-(0.6931)t}{t_{1/2}}, \ \ln\left(\dfrac{m}{33.9 \text{ mg}}\right) = \dfrac{-0.6931(35.0 \text{ d})}{14.3 \text{ d}}; \ \text{carrying extra sig. figs.:}$

   $\ln(m) = -1.696 + 3.523 = 1.827, \ m = e^{1.827} = 6.22 \text{ mg } {}^{32}\text{P remains}$

23.   Plants take in CO_2 during the photosynthesis process, which incorporates carbon, including ^{14}C, into its molecules. As long as the plant is alive, the ^{14}C/^{12}C ratio in the plant will equal the ratio in the atmosphere. When the plant dies, ^{14}C is not replenished because ^{14}C decays by beta-particle production. By measuring the ^{14}C activity today in the artifact and comparing this to the assumed ^{14}C activity when the plant died to make the artifact, an age can be determined for the artifact. The assumptions are that the ^{14}C level in the atmosphere is constant or that the ^{14}C level at the time the plant died can be calculated. A constant ^{14}C level is a pure assumption, and accounting for variation is complicated. Another problem is that some of the material must be destroyed to determine the ^{14}C level.

25. $t_{1/2} = 5730 \text{ y}; \ k = (\ln 2)/t_{1/2}; \ \ln (N/N_0) = -kt; \ \ln\dfrac{15.1}{15.3} = \dfrac{-(\ln 2)t}{5730 \text{ yr}}, \ t = 109 \text{ years}$

No; from ^{14}C dating, the painting was produced during the early 1900s.

27. $\ln\left(\dfrac{N}{N_0}\right) = -kt = \dfrac{-(\ln 2)t}{12.3 \text{ yr}}, \ \ln\left(\dfrac{0.17 \times N_0}{N_0}\right) = -(5.64 \times 10^{-2})t, \ t = 31.4 \text{ years}$

It takes 31.4 years for the tritium to decay to 17% of the original amount. Hence the watch stopped fluorescing enough to be read in 1975 (1944 + 31.4).

29.   Assuming 1.000 g ^{238}U present in a sample, then 0.688 g ^{206}Pb is present. Because 1 mol ^{206}Pb is produced per mol ^{238}U decayed:

   $^{238}\text{U decayed} = 0.688 \text{ g Pb} \times \dfrac{1 \text{ mol Pb}}{206 \text{ g Pb}} \times \dfrac{1 \text{ mol U}}{\text{mol Pb}} \times \dfrac{238 \text{ g U}}{\text{mol U}} = 0.795 \text{ g } {}^{238}\text{U}$

Original mass ^{238}U present = 1.000 g + 0.795 g = 1.795 g ^{238}U

   $\ln\left(\dfrac{N}{N_0}\right) = -kt = \dfrac{-(\ln 2)t}{t_{1/2}}, \ \ln\left(\dfrac{1.000 \text{ g}}{1.795 \text{ g}}\right) = \dfrac{-(0.693)t}{4.5 \times 10^9 \text{ yr}}, \ t = 3.8 \times 10^9 \text{ years}$

Energy Changes in Nuclear Reactions

31. $\Delta E = \Delta mc^2$, $\Delta m = \dfrac{\Delta E}{c^2} = \dfrac{3.9 \times 10^{23} \text{ kg m}^2/\text{s}^2}{(3.00 \times 10^8 \text{ m/s})^2} = 4.3 \times 10^6 \text{ kg}$

The sun loses 4.3×10^6 kg of mass each second. *Note*: 1 J = 1 kg m^2/s^2.

33.   From the text, the mass of a proton = 1.00728 amu, the mass of a neutron = 1.00866 amu, and the mass of an electron = 5.486×10^{-4} amu.

Mass of $^{56}_{26}$Fe nucleus = mass of atom − mass of electrons = 55.9349 − 26(0.0005486)

$$= 55.9206 \text{ amu}$$

$26\,^1_1\text{H} + 30\,^1_1\text{n} \rightarrow\, ^{56}_{26}\text{Fe}$; $\Delta m = 55.9206$ amu − [26(1.00728) + 30(1.00866)] amu

$$= -0.5285 \text{ amu}$$

$\Delta E = \Delta mc^2 = -0.5285$ amu $\times \dfrac{1.6605 \times 10^{-27} \text{ kg}}{\text{amu}} \times (2.9979 \times 10^8 \text{ m/s})^2 = -7.887 \times 10^{-11}$ J

$\dfrac{\text{Binding energy}}{\text{Nucleon}} = \dfrac{7.887 \times 10^{-11} \text{ J}}{56 \text{ nucleons}} = 1.408 \times 10^{-12}$ J/nucleon

35.   Let m_e = mass of electron; for ^{12}C (6e, 6p, 6n): mass defect = Δm = [mass of ^{12}C nucleus] − [mass of 6 protons + mass of 6 neutrons]. *Note*: Atomic masses given include the mass of the electrons.

$\Delta m = 12.00000$ amu − $6m_e$ − [6(1.00782 − m_e) + 6(1.00866)]; mass of electrons cancel.

$\Delta m = 12.00000$ − [6(1.00782) + 6(1.00866)] = −0.09888 amu

$\Delta E = \Delta mc^2 = -0.09888$ amu $\times \dfrac{1.6605 \times 10^{-27} \text{ kg}}{\text{amu}} \times (2.9979 \times 10^8 \text{ m/s})^2$

$$= -1.476 \times 10^{-11} \text{ J}$$

$\dfrac{\text{Binding energy}}{\text{Nucleon}} = \dfrac{1.476 \times 10^{-11} \text{ J}}{12 \text{ nucleons}} = 1.230 \times 10^{-12}$ J/nucleon

For ^{235}U (92e, 92p, 143n):

$\Delta m = 235.0439 − 92m_e − [92(1.00782 − m_e) + 143(1.00866)] = −1.9139$ amu

$\Delta E = \Delta mc^2 = -1.9139 \times \dfrac{1.66054 \times 10^{-27} \text{ kg}}{\text{amu}} \times (2.99792 \times 10^8 \text{ m/s})^2 = -2.8563 \times 10^{-10}$ J

$\dfrac{\text{Binding energy}}{\text{Nucleon}} = \dfrac{2.8563 \times 10^{-10} \text{ J}}{235 \text{ nucleons}} = 1.2154 \times 10^{-12}$ J/nucleon

Because ^{56}Fe is the most stable known nucleus, the binding energy per nucleon for ^{56}Fe (1.408×10^{-12} J/nucleon) will be larger than that of ^{12}C or ^{235}U (see Figure 20.9 of the text).

37.   Binding energy $= \dfrac{1.326 \times 10^{-12}\ \text{J}}{\text{nucleon}} \times 27$ nucleons $= 3.580 \times 10^{-11}$ J for each ^{27}Mg nucleus

$$\Delta E = \Delta mc^2, \quad \Delta m = \frac{\Delta E}{c^2} = \frac{-3.580 \times 10^{-11}\ \text{J}}{(2.9979 \times 10^8\ \text{m/s})^2} = -3.983\ 10^{-28}\ \text{kg}$$

$$\Delta m = -3.983\ 10^{-28}\ \text{kg} \times \frac{1\ \text{amu}}{1.6605 \times 10^{-27}\ \text{kg}} = -0.2399\ \text{amu} = \text{mass defect}$$

Let m_{Mg} = mass of ^{27}Mg nucleus; an ^{27}Mg nucleus has 12 p and 15 n.

-0.2399 amu $= m_{Mg} - (12m_p + 15m_n) = m_{Mg} - [12(1.00728\ \text{amu}) + 15(1.00866\ \text{amu})]$

$m_{Mg} = 26.9764$ amu

Mass of ^{27}Mg atom $= 26.9764$ amu $+ 12m_e$, $26.9764 + 12(5.49 \times 10^{-4}\ \text{amu}) = 26.9830$ amu (includes mass of 12 e$^-$)

39. $^{2}_{1}\text{H} + ^{3}_{1}\text{H} \rightarrow ^{4}_{2}\text{He} + ^{1}_{0}\text{n}$; mass of electrons cancel when determining Δm for this nuclear reaction.

$\Delta m = [4.00260 + 1.00866 - (2.01410 + 3.01605)]$ amu $= -1.889 \times 10^{-2}$ amu

For the production of 1 mol of $^{4}_{2}\text{He}$: $\Delta m = -1.889 \times 10^{-2}$ g $= -1.889 \times 10^{-5}$ kg

$\Delta E = \Delta mc^2 = -1.889 \times 10^{-5}$ kg $\times (2.9979 \times 10^8\ \text{m/s})^2 = -1.698 \times 10^{12}$ J/mol

For one nucleus of $^{4}_{2}\text{He}$:

$$\frac{-1.698 \times 10^{12}\ \text{J}}{\text{mol}} \times \frac{1\ \text{mol}}{6.0221 \times 10^{23}\ \text{nuclei}} = -2.820 \times 10^{-12}\ \text{J/nucleus}$$

Detection, Uses, and Health Effects of Radiation

41.   The Geiger-Müller tube has a certain response time. After the gas in the tube ionizes to produce a "count," some time must elapse for the gas to return to an electrically neutral state. The response of the tube levels out because at high activities, radioactive particles are entering the tube faster than the tube can respond to them.

43.   Fission: Splitting of a heavy nucleus into two (or more) lighter nuclei.

         Fusion: Combining two light nuclei to form a heavier nucleus.

The maximum binding energy per nucleon occurs at Fe. Nuclei smaller than Fe become more stable by fusing to form heavier nuclei closer in mass to Fe. Nuclei larger than Fe form more stable nuclei by splitting to form lighter nuclei closer in mass to Fe.

45.   Moderator: Slows the neutrons to increase the efficiency of the fission reaction.

Control rods: Absorbs neutrons to slow or halt the fission reaction.

47.   In order to sustain a nuclear chain reaction, the neutrons produced by the fission process must be contained within the fissionable material so that they can go on to cause other fissions. The fissionable material must be closely packed together to ensure that neutrons are not lost to the outside. The critical mass is the mass of material in which exactly one neutron from each fission event causes another fission event so that the process sustains itself. A supercritical situation occurs when more than one neutron from each fission event causes another fission event. In this case the process rapidly escalates, and the heat buildup causes a violent explosion.

49.   A nonradioactive substance can be put in equilibrium with a radioactive substance. The two materials can then be checked to see whether all the radioactivity remains in the original material or if it has been scrambled by the equilibrium.

51.   All evolved oxygen in O_2 comes from water and not from carbon dioxide.

53.   Some factors for the biological effects of radiation exposure are:

a.   The energy of the radiation. The higher the energy, the more damage it can cause.

b.   The penetrating ability of radiation. The ability of specific radiation to penetrate human tissue where it can do damage must be considered.

c.   The ionizing ability of the radiation. When biomolecules are ionized, their function is usually disturbed.

d.   The chemical properties of the radiation source. Specifically, can the radioactive substance be readily incorporated into the body, or is the radiation source inert chemically so that it passes through the body relatively quickly.

^{90}Sr will be incorporated into the body by replacing calcium in the bones. Once incorporated, ^{90}Sr can cause leukemia and bone cancer. Krypton is chemically inert, so it will not be incorporated into the body.

55.   (i) and (ii) mean that Pu is not a significant threat outside the body. Our skin is sufficient to keep out the α particles. If Pu gets inside the body, it is easily oxidized to Pu^{4+} (iv), which is chemically similar to Fe^{3+} (iii). Thus Pu^{4+} will concentrate in tissues where Fe^{3+} is found, including the bone marrow, where red blood cells are produced. Once inside the body, α particles can cause considerable damage.

Additional Exercises

57. $$N = 180 \text{ lb} \times \frac{453.6\text{ g}}{\text{lb}} \times \frac{18\text{ g C}}{100\text{ g body}} \times \frac{1.6 \times 10^{-10}\text{ g }^{14}\text{C}}{100\text{ g C}} \times \frac{1\text{ mol }^{14}\text{C}}{14\text{ g }^{14}\text{C}}$$

$$\times \frac{6.022 \times 10^{23}\text{ nuclei }^{14}\text{C}}{\text{mol }^{14}\text{C}} = 1.0 \times 10^{15}\text{ nuclei }^{14}\text{C}$$

$$\text{Rate} = kN; \ \ k = \frac{\ln 2}{t_{1/2}} = \frac{0.693}{5730\text{ yr}} \times \frac{1\text{ yr}}{365\text{ d}} \times \frac{1\text{ d}}{24\text{ h}} \times \frac{1\text{ h}}{3600\text{ s}} = 3.8 \times 10^{-12}\text{ s}^{-1}$$

$$\text{Rate} = kN; \ \ k = 3.8 \times 10^{-12}\text{ s}^{-1}(1.0 \times 10^{15}\text{ nuclei }^{14}\text{C}) = 3800\text{ decays/s}$$

A typical 180 lb person produces 3800 beta particles each second.

59. $$20{,}000\text{ ton TNT} \times \frac{4 \times 10^{9}\text{ J}}{\text{ton TNT}} \times \frac{1\text{ mol }^{235}\text{U}}{2 \times 10^{13}\text{ J}} \times \frac{235\text{ g }^{235}\text{U}}{\text{mol }^{235}\text{U}} = 940\text{ g }^{235}\text{U} \approx 900\text{ g }^{235}\text{U}$$

This assumes that all of the ^{235}U undergoes fission.

61. The only product in the fast-equilibrium step is assumed to be $N^{16}O^{18}O_2$, where N is the central atom. However, this is a reversible reaction where $N^{16}O^{18}O_2$ will decompose to NO and O_2. Because any two oxygen atoms can leave $N^{16}O^{18}O_2$ to form O_2, we would expect (at equilibrium) one-third of the NO present in this fast equilibrium step to be $N^{16}O$ and two-thirds to be $N^{18}O$. In the second step (the slow step), the intermediate $N^{16}O^{18}O_2$ reacts with the scrambled NO to form the NO_2 product, where N is the central atom in NO_2. Any one of the three oxygen atoms can be transferred from $N^{16}O^{18}O_2$ to NO when the NO_2 product is formed. The distribution of ^{18}O in the product can best be determined by forming a probability table.

	$N^{16}O$ (1/3)	$N^{18}O$ (2/3)
^{16}O (1/3) from $N^{16}O^{18}O_2$	$N^{16}O_2$ (1/9)	$N^{18}O^{16}O$ (2/9)
^{18}O (2/3) from $N^{16}O^{18}O_2$	$N^{16}O^{18}O$ (2/9)	$N^{18}O_2$ (4/9)

From the probability table, 1/9 of the NO_2 is $N^{16}O_2$, 4/9 of the NO_2 is $N^{18}O_2$, and 4/9 of the NO_2 is $N^{16}O^{18}O$ (2/9 + 2/9 = 4/9). *Note*: $N^{16}O^{18}O$ is the same as $N^{18}O^{16}O$. In addition, $N^{16}O^{18}O_2$ is not the only NO_3 intermediate formed; $N^{16}O_2{}^{18}O$ and $N^{18}O_3$ can also form in the fast-equilibrium first step. However, the distribution of ^{18}O in the NO_2 product is the same as calculated above, even when these other NO_3 intermediates are considered.

63.   Assuming that the radionuclide is long lived enough that no significant decay occurs during the time of the experiment, the total counts of radioactivity injected are:

$$0.10 \text{ mL} \times \frac{5.0 \times 10^3 \text{ cpm}}{\text{mL}} = 5.0 \times 10^2 \text{ cpm}$$

Assuming that the total activity is uniformly distributed only in the rat's blood, the blood volume is:

$$V \times \frac{48 \text{ cpm}}{\text{mL}} = 5.0 \times 10^2 \text{ cpm}, \quad V = 10.4 \text{ mL} = 10. \text{ mL}$$

Challenge Problems

65. $k = \dfrac{\ln 2}{t_{1/2}}; \quad \ln\left(\dfrac{N}{N_0}\right) = -kt = \dfrac{-(0.693)t}{t_{1/2}}$

For ^{238}U: $\ln\left(\dfrac{N}{N_0}\right) = \dfrac{-(0.693)(4.5 \times 10^9 \text{ yr})}{4.5 \times 10^9 \text{ yr}} = -0.693, \quad \dfrac{N}{N_0} = e^{-0.693} = 0.50$

For ^{235}U: $\ln\left(\dfrac{N}{N_0}\right) = \dfrac{-(0.693)(4.5 \times 10^9 \text{ yr})}{7.1 \times 10^8 \text{ yr}} = -4.39, \quad \dfrac{N}{N_0} = e^{-4.39} = 0.012$

If we have a current sample of 10,000 uranium nuclei, 9928 nuclei of ^{238}U and 72 nuclei of ^{235}U are present. Now let's calculate the initial number of nuclei that must have been present 4.5×10^9 years ago to produce these 10,000 uranium nuclei.

For ^{238}U: $\dfrac{N}{N_0} = 0.50, \quad N_0 = \dfrac{N}{0.50} = \dfrac{9928 \text{ nuclei}}{0.50} = 2.0 \times 10^4 \ ^{238}\text{U nuclei}$

For ^{235}U: $N_0 = \dfrac{N}{0.012} = \dfrac{72 \text{ nuclei}}{0.012} = 6.0 \times 10^3 \ ^{235}\text{U nuclei}$

So 4.5 billion years ago, the 10,000-nuclei sample of uranium was composed of 2.0×10^4 ^{238}U nuclei and 6.0×10^3 ^{235}U nuclei. The percent composition 4.5 billion years ago would have been:

$$\frac{2.0 \times 10^4 \ ^{238}\text{U nuclei}}{(6.0 \times 10^3 + 2.0 \times 10^4) \text{ total nuclei}} \times 100 = 77\% \ ^{238}\text{U and } 23\% \ ^{235}\text{U}$$

67. $_1^2 H + _1^2 H \rightarrow _2^4 He$; Q for $_1^2 H = 1.6 \times 10^{-19}$ C;   mass of deuterium = 2 amu.

$$E = \frac{9.0 \times 10^9 \text{ J} \bullet \text{m}/\text{C}^2(Q_1 Q_2)}{r} = \frac{9.0 \times 10^9 \text{ J} \bullet \text{m}/\text{C}^2(1.6 \times 10^{-19} \text{ C})^2}{2 \times 10^{-15} \text{ m}}$$

$$= 1 \times 10^{-13} \text{ J per alpha particle}$$

KE = $1/2$ mv^2; 1×10^{-13} J = $1/2$ (2 amu $\times$ 1.66 $\times$ 10^{-27} kg/amu)v^2, v = 8 $\times$ 10^6 m/s

From the kinetic molecular theory discussed in Chapter 5:

$$u_{rms} = \left(\frac{3RT}{M}\right)^{1/2} \text{ where M = molar mass in kilograms = 2} \times 10^{-3} \text{kg/mol for deuterium}$$

$$8 \times 10^6 \text{ m/s} = \left[\frac{3(8.3145 \text{ J K}^{-1} \text{ mol}^{-1})(T)}{2 \times 10^{-3} \text{ kg}}\right]^{1/2}, \quad T = 5 \times 10^9 \text{ K}$$

69. $\text{mol I} = \dfrac{33 \text{ counts}}{\text{min}} \times \dfrac{1 \text{ mol I} \bullet \text{min}}{5.0 \times 10^{11} \text{ counts}} = 6.6 \times 10^{-11} \text{ mol I}$

$$[I^-] = \frac{6.6 \times 10^{-11} \text{ mol I}^-}{0.150 \text{ L}} = 4.4 \times 10^{-10} \text{ mol/L}$$

$$Hg_2I_2(s) \rightarrow Hg_2^{2+}(aq) + 2 I^-(aq) \qquad K_{sp} = [Hg_2^{2+}][I^-]^2$$

Initial   s = solubility (mol/L)   0   0

Equil.   s   2s

From the problem, $2s = 4.4 \times 10^{-10}$ mol/L, $s = 2.2 \times 10^{-10}$ mol/L.

$K_{sp} = (s)(2s)^2 = (2.2 \times 10^{-10})(4.4 \times 10^{-10})^2 = 4.3 \times 10^{-29}$

71.   a.   For a gas, $u_{avg} = \sqrt{8RT/\pi R}$ where M is the molar mass in kg. From the equation, the lighter the gas molecule, the faster is the average velocity. Therefore, $^{235}UF_6$ will have the greater average velocity at a certain temperature because it is the lighter molecule.

        b.   From Graham's law (see Section 5.7 of the text):

$$\frac{\text{diffusion rate for } ^{235}UF_6}{\text{diffusion rate for } ^{238}UF_6} = \sqrt{\frac{M(^{238}UF_6)}{M(^{235}UF_6)}} = \sqrt{\frac{352.05 \text{ g/mol}}{349.03 \text{ g/mol}}} = 1.0043$$

Each diffusion step increases the $^{235}UF_6$ concentration by a factor of 1.0043. To determine the number of steps to get to the desired 3.00% ^{235}U, we use the following formula:

$$\frac{0.700 \ ^{235}UF_6}{99.3 \ ^{238}UF_6} \times (1.0043)^N = \frac{3.00 \ ^{235}UF_6}{97.0 \ ^{238}UF_6}$$

$$\text{original ratio} \qquad\qquad\qquad \text{final ratio}$$

where N represents the number of steps required.

Solving (and carrying extra sig. figs.):

$$(1.0043)^N = \frac{297.9}{67.9} = 4.387, \ \ N\log(1.0043) = \log(4.387)$$

$$N = \frac{0.6422}{1.863 \times 10^{-3}} = 345 \text{ steps}$$

Thus 345 steps are required to obtain the desired enrichment.

c. $\dfrac{^{235}UF_6}{^{238}UF_6} \times (1.0043)^{100} = \dfrac{1526}{1.000 \times 10^5 - 1526}, \ \dfrac{^{235}UF_6}{^{238}UF_6} \times 1.5358 = \dfrac{1526}{98500}$

original ratio   final ratio

$$\frac{^{235}UF_6}{^{238}UF_6} = 1.01 \times 10^{-2} = \text{initial } ^{235}U \text{ to } ^{238}U \text{ atom ratio}$$

CHAPTER 21

ORGANIC CHEMISTRY

Hydrocarbons

1.   A hydrocarbon is a compound composed of only carbon and hydrogen. A saturated hydro-carbon has only carbon-carbon single bonds in the molecule. An unsaturated hydrocarbon has one or more carbon-carbon multiple bonds but may also contain carbon-carbon single bonds. A normal hydrocarbon has one chain of consecutively bonded carbon atoms, with each carbon atom in the chain bonded to one or two other carbon atoms. A branched hydrocarbon has at least one carbon atom in the structure that forms bonds to three or four other carbon atoms; the structure is not one continuous chain of carbon atoms.

3.   In order to form, cyclopropane and cyclobutane are forced to form bond angles much smaller than the preferred 109.5° bond angles. Cyclopropane and cyclobutane easily react in order to obtain the preferred 109.5° bond angles.

5.   A difficult task in this problem is recognizing different compounds from compounds that differ by rotations about one or more C–C bonds (called conformations). The best way to distinguish different compounds from conformations is to name them. Different name = different compound; same name = same compound, so it is not an isomer but instead is a conformation.

   a.

$$CH_3CHCH_2CH_2CH_2CH_2CH_3$$ with CH_3 branch

2-methylheptane

$$CH_3CH_2CHCH_2CH_2CH_2CH_3$$ with CH_3 branch

3-methylheptane

$$CH_3CH_2CH_2CHCH_2CH_2CH_3$$ with CH_3 branch

4-methylheptane

   b.

$$CH_3CCH_2CH_2CH_2CH_3$$ with CH_3 above and CH_3 below

2,2-dimethylhexane

$$CH_3CHCHCH_2CH_2CH_3$$ with CH_3 above and CH_3 below

2,3-dimethylhexane

404

2,4-dimethylhexane

2,5-dimethylhexane

3,3-dimethylhexane

3,4-dimethylhexane

3-ethylhexane

c.

2,2,3-trimethylpentane

2,2,4-trimethylpentane

2,3,3-trimethylpentane

2,3,4-trimethylpentane

3-ethyl-2-methylpentane

3-ethyl-3-methylpentane

d.

CH₃—C—C—CH₃

2,2,3,3-tetramethylbutane

7.   London dispersion (LD) forces are the primary intermolecular forces exhibited by hydrocarbons. The strength of the LD forces depends on the surface-area contact among neighboring molecules. As branching increases, there is less surface-area contact among neighboring molecules, leading to weaker LD forces and lower boiling points.

9.   a.   b.

        c.   d. For 3-isobutylhexane, the longest chain is seven carbons long. The correct name is 4-ethyl-2-methylheptane. For 2-tert-butylpentane, the longest chain is six carbons long. The correct name is 2,2,3-trimethylhexane.

11.   a. 2,2,4-trimethylhexane   b. 5-methylnonane   c. 2,2,4,4-tetramethylpentane

        d. 3-ethyl-3-methyloctane

        Note: For alkanes, always identify the longest carbon chain for the base name first, then number the carbons to give the lowest overall numbers for the substituent groups.

13.   a. 1-butene   b. 2-methyl-2-butene

        c. 2,5-dimethyl-3-heptene   d. 2,3-dimethyl-1-pentene

        e. 1-ethyl-3-methylcyclopentene (double bond assumed between C_1 and C_2)

        f. 4-ethyl-3-methylcyclopentene   g. 4-methyl-2-pentyne

        Note: Multiple bonds are assigned the lowest number possible.

15.   a. 1,3-dichlorobutane   b. 1,1,1-trichlorobutane

        c. 2,3-dichloro-2,4-dimethylhexane   d. 1,2-difluoroethane

        e. 3-iodo-1-butene

        f. 2-bromotoluene (or o-bromotoluene or 1-bromo-2-methylbenzene)

        g. 1-bromo-2-methylcyclohexane

        h. 4-bromo-3-methylcyclohexene (double bond assumed between C_1 and C_2)

17.   isopropylbenzene or 2-phenylpropane

Isomerism

19.   a. 1-sec-butylpropane   b. 4-methylhexane

$$CH_2CH_2CH_3$$
$$|$$
$$CH_3CHCH_2CH_3$$

$$CH_3$$
$$|$$
$$CH_3CH_2CH_2CHCH_2CH_3$$

3-Methylhexane is correct.   3-Methylhexane is correct.

        c. 2-ethylpentane   d. 1-ethyl-1-methylbutane

$$CH_3CHCH_2CH_2CH_3$$
$$|$$
$$CH_2CH_3$$

$$CH_2CH_3$$
$$|$$
$$CHCH_2CH_2CH_3$$
$$|$$
$$CH_3$$

3-Methylhexane is correct.   3-Methylhexane is correct.

        e. 3-methylhexane   f. 4-ethylpentane

$$CH_3CH_2CHCH_2CH_2CH_3$$
$$|$$
$$CH_3$$

$$CH_3CH_2CH_2CHCH_3$$
$$|$$
$$CH_2CH_3$$

This is a correct name.   3-Methylhexane is correct.

        All six of these compounds are the same. They only differ from each other by rotations
        about one or more carbon-carbon single bonds. Only one isomer of C_7H_{16} is present in all
        of these names, 3-methylhexane.

21.   To exhibit cis-trans isomerism, a compound must first have restricted rotation about a carbon-
        carbon bond. This occurs in compounds with double bonds and ring compounds. Second,
        the compound must have two carbons in the restricted rotation environment that each have
        two different groups bonded. For example, the compound in Exercise 21.13a has a double
        bond, but the first carbon in the double bond has two H atoms attached. This compound does
        not exhibit cis-trans isomerism. To see this, let's draw the potential cis-trans isomers:

These are the same compounds; they only differ by a simply rotation of the molecule. Therefore, they are not isomers of each other, but instead, they are the same compound. The only compounds that fulfill the restricted rotation requirement *and* have two different groups attached to carbons in the restricted rotation are compounds c and f. The cis-trans isomerism for these follows.

c.

f.

= out of plane of paper;   ----- = into plane of paper

23.   a.   All these structures have the formula C_5H_8. The compounds with the same physical properties will be the compounds that are identical to each other, i.e., compounds that only differ by rotations of C–C single bonds. To recognize identical compounds, name them. The names of the compounds are:

i.   trans-1,3-pentadiene   ii.   cis-1,3-pentadiene

iii.   cis-1,3-pentadiene   iv.   2-methyl-1,3-butadiene

Compounds ii and iii are identical compounds, so they would have the same physical properties.

b.   Compound i is a trans isomer because the bulkiest groups bonded to the carbon atoms in the $C_3=C_4$ double bond are as far apart as possible.

c.   Compound iv does not have carbon atoms in a double bond that each have two different groups attached. Compound iv does not exhibit cis-trans isomerism.

25.   The cis isomer has the CH_3 groups on the same side of the ring. The trans isomer has the
       CH_3 groups on opposite sides of the ring.

               cis   trans

27.   To help distinguish the different isomers, we will name them.

       cis-1-chloro-1-propene   trans-1-chloro-1-propene

       2-chloro-1-propene   3-chloro-1-propene   chlorocyclopropane

29. C_5H_{10} has the general formula for alkenes, C_nH_{2n}. To distinguish the different isomers from
       each other, we will name them. Each isomer must have a different name.

       $CH_2{=\!\!=}CHCH_2CH_2CH_3$ $CH_3CH{=\!\!=}CHCH_2CH_3$

              1-pentene   2-pentene

       $CH_2{=\!\!=}CCH_2CH_3$ $CH_3C{=\!\!=}CHCH_3$
                | |
               CH_3 CH_3

       2-methyl-1-butene   2-methyl-2-butene

       $CH_3CHCH{=\!\!=}CH_2$
             |
            CH_3

       3-methyl-1-butene

Only 2-pentene exhibits cis-trans isomerism. The isomers are:

cis   trans

The other isomers of C_5H_{10} do not contain carbons in the double bond to which two different groups are attached.

31.   a.   cis-1-bromo-1-propene   b.   cis-4-ethyl-3-methyl-3-heptene

c.   trans-1,4-diiodo-2-propyl-1-pentene

Note: In general, cis-trans designations refer to the relative positions of the largest groups. In compound b, the largest group off the first carbon in the double bond is CH_2CH_3, and the largest group off the second carbon in the double bond is $CH_2CH_2CH_3$. Since their relative placement is on the same side of the double bond, this is the cis isomer.

33.   a.

ortho   meta   para

b.   There are three trichlorobenzenes (1,2,3-trichlorobenzene, 1,2,4-trichlorobenzene, and 1,3,5-trichlorobenzene).

c.   The meta isomer will be very difficult to synthesize.

d.   1,3,5-Trichlorobenzene will be the most difficult to synthesize since all Cl groups are meta to each other in this compound.

Functional Groups

35.

Carboxylic acid   Aldehyde

RCOOH   RCHO

The R designation refers to the rest of the organic molecule beyond the specific functional group indicated in the formula. The R group may be a hydrogen but is usually a hydrocarbon fragment. The major point in the R group designation is that if the R group is an organic fragment, then the first atom in the R group is a carbon atom. What the R group has after the first carbon is not important to the functional group designation.

37.   Reference Table 21.4 for the common functional groups.

     a.   ketone   b.   aldehyde   c.   carboxylic acid   d.   amine

39.   a.

     b.   5 carbons in ring and the carbon in $-CO_2H$: sp^2; the other two carbons: sp^3

     c.   24 sigma bonds; 4 pi bonds

41.   a.   3-chloro-1-butanol; since the carbon containing the OH group is bonded to just one other carbon (one R group), this is a primary alcohol.

     b.   3-methyl-3-hexanol; since the carbon containing the OH group is bonded to three other carbons (three R groups), this is a tertirary alcohol

     c.   2-methylcyclopentanol; secondary alcohol (two R groups bonded to carbon containing the OH group). *Note*: In ring compounds, the alcohol group is assumed to be bonded to C_1, so the number designation is commonly omitted for the alcohol group.

43.

OH
|
CH₃CH₂CH₂CH₂CH₂

1-pentanol

OH
|
CH₃CH₂CH₂CHCH₃

2-pentanol

OH
|
CH₃CH₂CHCH₂CH₃

3-pentanol

OH
|
CH₃CH₂CHCH₂
|
CH₃

2-methyl-1-butanol

OH
|
CH₃CHCH₂CH₂
|
CH₃

3-methyl-1-butanol

OH
|
CH₃CH₂CCH₃
|
CH₃

2-methyl-2-butanol

OH
|
CH₃CHCHCH₃
|
CH₃

3-methyl-2-butanol

CH₃   OH
| |
CH₃—C——CH₂
|
CH₃

2,2-dimethyl-1-propanol

There are six isomeric ethers with formula C₅H₁₂O. The structures follow.

CH₃—O—CH₂CH₂CH₂CH₃

CH₃
|
CH₃—O—CHCH₂CH₃

CH₃
|
CH₃—O—CH₂CHCH₃

CH₃
|
CH₃—O—C—CH₃
|
CH₃

CH₃CH₂—O—CH₂CH₂CH₃

CH₃
|
CH₃CH₂—O—CH
|
CH₃

45.   a.   4,5-dichloro-3-hexanone   b.   2,3-dimethylpentanal

c.   3-methylbenzaldehyde or m-methylbenzaldehyde

47.   a.   b.

O
‖
H——C——H

O
‖
CH₃CH₂CH₂CCH₂CH₂CH₃

c.   d.

O
‖
H——CCH₂CHCH₃
      |
      Cl

O   CH₃
‖ |
CH₃ CCH₂CH₂CCH₃
            |
            CH₃

49. a.   trans-2-butene: , formula = C_4H_8

   or

b.   propanoic acid: $CH_3CH_2\overset{\text{O}}{\overset{\|}{C}}$—OH,   formula = $C_3H_6O_2$

$CH_3\overset{\text{O}}{\overset{\|}{C}}$—O—$CH_3$ or $H\overset{\text{O}}{\overset{\|}{C}}$—O—$CH_2CH_3$

c.   butanal: $CH_3CH_2CH_2\overset{\text{O}}{\overset{\|}{C}}H$,   formula = C_4H_8O

$CH_3CH_2\overset{\text{O}}{\overset{\|}{C}}CH_3$

d.   butylamine: $CH_3CH_2CH_2CH_2NH_2$,   formula = $C_4H_{11}N$:

A secondary amine has two R groups bonded to N.

CH_3—N—H   or CH_3—N—H   or CH_3CH_2—N—H
       | | |
$CH_2CH_2CH_3$ CH_3CHCH_3 CH_2CH_3

e. A tertiary amine has two R groups bonded to N.
    (See answer d for the structure of butylamine.)

CH_3—N—CH_3
       |
CH_2CH_3

f.   2-methyl-2-propanol: $CH_3\overset{CH_3}{\overset{|}{\underset{|}{\underset{OH}{C}}}}CH_3$, formula = $C_4H_{10}O$

g. A secondary alcohol has two R groups attached to the carbon bonded to the OH group. (See answer f for the structure of 2-methyl-2-propanol.)

51.   a. 2-Chloro-2-butyne would have five bonds to the second carbon. Carbon never expands its octet.

b. 2-Methyl-2-propanone would have five bonds to the second carbon.

c. Carbon-1 in 1,1-dimethylbenzene would have five bonds.

d. You cannot have an aldehyde functional group bonded to a middle carbon in a chain. Aldehyde groups, i.e.,

can only be at the beginning and/or the end of a chain of carbon atoms.

e. You cannot have a carboxylic acid group bonded to a middle carbon in a chain. Carboxylic groups, i.e.,

must be at the beginning and/or the end of a chain of carbon atoms.

f. In cyclobutanol, the 1 and 5 positions refer to the same carbon atom. 5,5-Dibromo-1-cyclobutanol would have five bonds to carbon-1. This is impossible; carbon never expands its octet.

Reactions of Organic Compounds

53.   Substitution: An atom or group is replaced by another atom or group.

For example: H in benzene is replaced by Cl.

$$C_6H_6 + Cl_2 \xrightarrow{\text{catalyst}} C_6H_5Cl + HCl$$

Addition: Atoms or groups are added to a molecule.

For example: Cl$_2$ adds to ethene. $CH_2 = CH_2 + Cl_2 \rightarrow CH_2Cl–CH_2Cl$

55.   a.

57.

a.   CH₃CH—CHCH₃   b.   CH₂—CHCHCH—CH

c.   [benzene ring]—Cl + HCl

d.   C₄H₈(g) + 6 O₂(g) → 4 CO₂(g) + 4 H₂O(g)

59.   When CH₂=CH₂ reacts with HCl, there is only one possible product, chloroethane. When Cl₂ is reacted with CH₃CH₃ (in the presence of light), there are six possible products because any number of the six hydrogens in ethane can be substituted for by Cl. The light-catalyzed substitution reaction is very difficult to control; hence it is not a very efficient method of producing monochlorinated alkanes.

61.   Primary alcohols (a, d, and f) are oxidized to aldehydes, which can be oxidized further to carboxylic acids. Secondary alcohols (b, e, and f) are oxidized to ketones, and tertiary alcohols (c and f) do not undergo this type of oxidation reaction. Note that compound f contains a primary, a secondary, and a tertiary alcohol. For the primary alcohols (a, d, and f), we listed both the aldehyde and the carboxylic acid as possible products.

c.   No reaction

63.   KMnO$_4$ will oxidize primary alcohols to aldehydes and then to carboxylic acids. Secondary alcohols are oxidized to ketones by KMnO$_4$. Tertiary alcohols and ethers are not oxidized by KMnO$_4$.

The three isomers and their reactions with KMnO$_4$ are:

The products of the reactions with excess KMnO$_4$ are 2-propanone and propanoic acid.

65.   a.   CH$_3$CH = CH$_2$ + Br$_2$ → CH$_3$CHBrCH$_2$Br (Addition reaction of Br$_2$ with propene)

b.

Oxidation of 2-propanol yields acetone (2-propanone).

c.

Addition of H$_2$O to 2-methylpropene would yield tert-butyl alcohol (2-methyl-2-propanol) as the major product.

d.

Oxidation of 1-propanol would eventually yield propanoic acid. Propanal is produced first in this reaction and is then oxidized to propanoic acid.

67.   When an alcohol is reacted with a carboxylic acid, an ester is produced.

a.

b.

Polymers

69.   a.   Addition polymer: a polymer that forms by adding monomer units together (usually by reacting double bonds). Teflon, polyvinyl chloride, and polyethylene are examples of addition polymers.

b.   Condensation polymer: a polymer that forms when two monomers combine by eliminating a small molecule (usually H_2O or HCl). Nylon and Dacron are examples of condensation polymers.

c.   Copolymer: a polymer formed from more than one type of monomer. Nylon and Dacron are copolymers.

d.   Homopolymer: a polymer formed from the polymerization of only one type of monomer. Polyethylene, Teflon, and polystyrene are examples of homopolymers.

e.   Polyester: a condensation polymer whose monomers link together by formation of the ester functional group. Dacron is a polyester.

f.   Polyamide: a condensation polymer whose monomers link together by formation of the amide functional group. Nylon is a polyamide as are proteins in the human body.

71. a. A polyester forms when an alcohol functional group reacts with a carboxylic acid functional group. The monomer for a homopolymer polyester must have an alcohol functional group and a carboxylic acid functional group present within the structure of the monomer.

     b. A polyamide forms when an amine functional group reacts with a carboxylic acid functional group. For a copolymer polyamide, one monomer would have at least two amine functional groups present, and the other monomer would have at least two carboxylic acid functional groups present. For polymerization to occur, each monomer must have two reactive functional groups present.

     c. To form an addition polymer, a carbon-carbon double bond must be present. Polyesters and polyamides are condensation polymers. To form a polyester, the monomer would need the alcohol and carboxylic acid functional groups present. To form a polyamide, the monomer would need the amine and carboxylic acid functional groups present. The two possibilities are for the monomer to have a carbon-carbon double bond, an alcohol functional group, and a carboxylic acid functional group present or to have a carbon-carbon double bond, an amine functional group, and a carboxylic acid functional group present.

73. The backbone of the polymer contains only carbon atoms, which indicates that Kel-F is an addition polymer. The smallest repeating unit of the polymer and the monomer used to produce this polymer are:

75. a.

     and

     b. Repeating unit:

     The two polymers differ in the substitution pattern on the benzene rings. The Kevlar chain is straighter, and there is more efficient hydrogen bonding between Kevlar chains than between Nomex chains.

77.

"Super glue" is an addition polymer formed by reaction of the C=C bond in methyl cyanoacrylate.

79.   Divinylbenzene is a crosslinking agent. Divinylbenzene has two reactive double bonds that are both reacted when divinylbenzene inserts itself into two adjacent polymer chains during the polymerization process. The chains cannot move past each other because the crosslinks bond adjacent polymer chains together, making the polymer more rigid.

81.   a.

b.   Condensation; HCl is eliminated when the polymer bonds form.

83.   Polyacrylonitrile:

The CN triple bond is very strong and will not easily break in the combustion process. A likely combustion product is the toxic gas hydrogen cyanide, HCN(g).

85.

Two linkages are possible with glycerol. A possible repeating unit with both types of linkages is shown above. With either linkage, there are unreacted OH groups on the polymer chains. These unreacted OH groups on adjacent polymer chains can react with the acid groups of phthalic acid to form crosslinks (bonds) between various polymer chains.

Natural Polymers

87.

 = general amino acid formula

Hydrophilic ("water-loving") and hydrophobic ("water-fearing") refer to the polarity of the R group. When the R group consists of a polar group, then the amino acid is hydrophilic. When the R group consists of a nonpolar group, then the amino acid is hydrophobic.

89.   Denaturation changes the three-dimensional structure of a protein. Once the structure is affected, the function of the protein will also be affected.

91.   a.   Serine, tyrosine, and threonine contain the –OH functional group in the R group.

        b.   Aspartic acid and glutamic acid contain the –COOH functional group in the R group.

        c.   An amine group has a nitrogen bonded to other carbon and/or hydrogen atoms. Histidine, lysine, arginine, and tryptophan contain the amine functional group in the R group.

        d.   The amide functional group is:

        This functional group is formed when individual amino acids bond together to form the peptide linkage. Glutamine and asparagine have the amide functional group in the R group.

93.   a.   Aspartic acid and phenylalanine make up aspartame.

        b.   Aspartame contains the methyl ester of phenylalanine. This ester can hydrolyze to form methanol:

$$R-CO_2CH_3 + H_2O \rightleftharpoons RCO_2H + HOCH_3$$

95.

ser - ala   ala - ser

97.   a.   Six tetrapeptides are possible. From NH_2 to CO_2H end:

phe-phe-gly-gly, gly-gly-phe-phe, gly-phe-phe-gly,

phe-gly-gly-phe, phe-gly-phe-gly, gly-phe-gly-phe

b.   Twelve tetrapeptides are possible. From NH_2 to CO_2H end:

phe-phe-gly-ala, phe-phe-ala-gly, phe-gly-phe-ala,

phe-gly-ala-phe, phe-ala-phe-gly, phe-ala-gly-phe,

gly-phe-phe-ala, gly-phe-ala-phe, gly-ala-phe-phe,

ala-phe-phe-gly, ala-phe-gly-phe, ala-gly-phe-phe

99.   a.   Covalent (forms a disulfide linkage)

b.   Hydrogen bonding (need N-H or O-H bond in side chain)

c.   Ionic (need NH_2 group on side chain of one amino acid with CO_2H group on side chain of the other amino acid)

d.   London dispersion (need amino acids with nonpolar R groups)

101.   Glutamic acid: R = $-CH_2CH_2CO_2H$; valine: R = $-CH(CH_3)_2$; a polar side chain is replaced by a nonpolar side chain. This could affect the tertiary structure of hemoglobin and the ability of hemoglobin to bind oxygen.

103.   Glutamic acid: Monosodium glutamate:

$$H_2N-CH-CO_2H$$
$$CH_2CH_2CO_2H$$

$$H_2N-CH-CO_2H$$
$$CH_2CH_2CO_2^-Na^+$$

One of the two acidic protons in the carboxylic acid groups is lost to form MSG. Which proton is lost is impossible for you to predict.

In MSG, the acidic proton from the carboxylic acid in the R group is lost, allowing formation of the ionic compound.

105.   See Figures 21.30 and 21.31 of the text for examples of the cyclization process.

D-Ribose   D-Mannose

107.   The aldohexoses contain six carbons and the aldehyde functional group. Glucose, mannose, and galactose are aldohexoses. Ribose and arabinose are aldopentoses since they contain five carbons with the aldehyde functional group. The ketohexose (six carbons + ketone functional group) is fructose, and the ketopentose (five carbons + ketone functional group) is ribulose.

109.   A disaccharide is a carbohydrate formed by bonding two monosaccharides (simple sugars) together. In sucrose, the simple sugars are glucose and fructose, and the bond formed between these two monosaccharides is called a glycoside linkage.

111.   The α and β forms of glucose differ in the orientation of a hydroxy group on one specific carbon in the cyclic forms (see Figure 21.31 of the text). Starch is a polymer composed of only α-D-glucose, and cellulose is a polymer composed of only β-D-glucose.

113.   A chiral carbon has four different groups attached to it. A compound with a chiral carbon is optically active. Isoleucine and threonine contain more than the one chiral carbon atom (see asterisks).

isoleucine   threonine

115.   Only one of the isomers is optically active. The chiral carbon in this optically active isomer is marked with an asterisk.

117.   They all contain nitrogen atoms with lone pairs of electrons.

119.   The complementary base pairs in DNA are cytosine (C) and guanine (G), and thymine (T) and adenine (A). The complementary sequence is C-C-A-G-A-T-A-T-G.

121.   Uracil will hydrogen bond to adenine.

123.   Base pair:

        RNA   DNA

        A . . . . T

        G C

        C . . . . G

        U . . . . A

    a. Glu: CTT, CTC   Val: CAA, CAG, CAT, CAC

        Met: TAC   Trp: ACC

        Phe: AAA, AAG   Asp: CTA, CTG

    b. DNA sequence for trp-glu-phe-met:

            ACC – CTT – AAA – TAC
                   or   or
               CTC   AAG

    c. Due to glu and phe, there is a possibility of four different DNA sequences. They are:

            ACC–CTT–AAA–TAC or ACC–CTC–AAA–TAC or

            ACC–CTT–AAG –TAC or ACC–CTC–AAG–TAC

d.

$$T-A-C-C-T-G-A-A-G$$

met   asp   phe

e.   TAC–CTA–AAG; TAC–CTA–AAA; TAC–CTG–AAA

125.   A deletion may change the entire code for a protein, thus giving an entirely different sequence of amino acids. A substitution will change only one single amino acid in a protein.

Additional Exercises

127. $CH_3CH_2CH_2CH_2CH_2CH_2CH_2COOH + OH^- \rightarrow CH_3-(CH_2)_6-COO^- + H_2O$; octanoic acid is more soluble in 1 M NaOH. Added OH⁻ will remove the acidic proton from octanoic acid, creating a charged species. As is the case with any substance with an overall charge, solubility in water increases. When morphine is reacted with H^+, the amine group is protonated, creating a positive charge on morphine $(R_3N + H^+ \rightarrow R_3NH^+)$. By treating morphine with HCl, an ionic compound results that is more soluble in water and in the bloodstream than is the neutral covalent form of morphine.

129.

To substitute for the benzene ring hydrogens, an iron(III) catalyst must be present. Without this special iron catalyst, the benzene ring hydrogens are unreactive. To substitute for an alkane hydrogen, specific wavelengths of light must be present. For toluene, the light-catalyzed reaction substitutes a chlorine for a hydrogen in the methyl group attached to the benzene ring.

131. $85.63 \text{ g C} \times \dfrac{1 \text{ mol C}}{12.011 \text{ g C}} = 7.129 \text{ mol C};\ \ 14.37 \text{ g H} \times \dfrac{1 \text{ mol H}}{1.0079 \text{ g H}} = 14.26 \text{ mol H}$

Because the moles of H to moles of C ratio is 2:1 (14.26/7.129 = 2.000), the empirical formula is CH_2. The empirical formula mass $\approx 12 + 2(1) = 14$. Because $4 \times 14 = 56$ puts the molar mass between 50 and 60, the molecular formula is C_4H_8.

The isomers of C_4H_8 are:

$CH_2{=}CHCH_2CH_3$ $CH_3CH{=}CHCH_3$ $\overset{\displaystyle CH_3}{\overset{|}{CH}}{=}CHCH_3$

1-butene   2-butene   2-methyl-1-propene

cyclobutane   methylcyclopropane

Only the alkenes will react with H_2O to produce alcohols, and only 1-butene will produce a secondary alcohol for the major product and a primary alcohol for the minor product.

$CH_2{=}CHCH_2CH_3 + H_2O \longrightarrow \overset{H\quad OH}{\underset{}{CH_2{-}CHCH_2CH_3}}$
2° alcohol, major product

$CH_2{=}CHCH_2CH_3 + H_2O \longrightarrow \overset{OH\quad H}{\underset{}{CH_2{-}CHCH_2CH_3}}$
1° alcohol, minor product

2-Butene will produce only a secondary alcohol when reacted with H_2O, and 2-methyl-1-propene will produce a tertiary alcohol as the major product and a primary alcohol as the minor product.

133.   a.   The bond angles in the ring are about 60°. VSEPR predicts bond angles close to 109°. The bonding electrons are closer together than they prefer, resulting is strong electron-electron repulsions. Thus ethylene oxide is unstable (reactive).

b.   The ring opens up during polymerization; the monomers link together through the formation of O–C bonds.

$\underbrace{{-}(O{-}CH_2CH_2{-}O{-}CH_2CH_2{-}O{-}CH_2CH_2{-})}_{n}$

135.

137.   The structures, the types of intermolecular forces exerted, and the boiling points for the
        compounds are:

O
‖
$CH_3CH_2CH_2COH$

butanoic acid, 164°C
LD + dipole + H-bonding

$CH_3CH_2CH_2CH_2CH_2OH$

1-pentanol, 137°C
LD + H-bonding

O
‖
$CH_3CH_2CH_2CH_2CH$

pentanal, 103°C
LD + dipole

$CH_3CH_2CH_2CH_2CH_2CH_3$

n-hexane, 69°C
LD only

All these compounds have about the same molar mass. Therefore, the London dispersion
(LD) forces in each are about the same. The other types of forces determine the boiling-point
order. Because butanoic acid and 1-pentanol both exhibit hydrogen-bonding (H–bonding)
interactions, these two compounds will have the two highest boiling points. Butanoic acid
has the highest boiling point since it exhibits H-bonding along with dipole-dipole forces due
to the polar C=O bond.

139.   When addition polymerization of monomers with C=C bonds occurs, the backbone of the
        polymer chain consists of only carbon atoms. Because the backbone contains oxygen atoms,
        this is not an addition polymer; it is a condensation polymer. Because the ester functional
        group is present, we have a polyester condensation polymer. To form an ester functional
        group, we need the carboxylic acid and alcohol functional groups present in the monomers.
        From the structure of the polymer, we have a copolymer formed by the following monomers.

141.   a.

$$CH_3CHCH_3$$
$$|$$
$$CH_2CH_3$$

The longest chain is four carbons long. The correct name is 2-methylbutane.

b.

The longest chain is seven carbons long and we would start the numbering system at the other end for lowest possible numbers. The correct name is 3-iodo-3-methylheptane.

c.

$$CH_3$$
$$|$$
$$CH_3CH_2CH\!=\!C\!-\!CH_3$$

This compound cannot exhibit cis–trans isomerism since one of the double-bonded carbons has the same two groups (CH_3) attached. The numbering system should also start at the other end to give the double bond the lowest possible number. 2-Methyl-2-pentene is correct.

d.

$$Br\ OH$$
$$|\ \ |$$
$$CH_3CHCHCH_3$$

The OH functional group gets the lowest number. 3-Bromo-2-butanol is correct.

143. $\Delta G = \Delta H - T\Delta S$; for the reaction, we break a P–O and O–H bond and form a P–O and O–H bond, so $\Delta H \approx 0$ based on bond dissociation energies. ΔS for this process is negative (unfavorable) because positional probability decreases. $\Delta G = \Delta H - T\Delta S$; thus, $\Delta G > 0$ due to the unfavorable ΔS term, and the reaction is not expected to be spontaneous.

145.   a.   Even though this form of tartaric acid contains two chiral carbon atoms (see asterisks in the following structure), the mirror image of this form of tartaric acid is superimposable. Therefore, it is not optically active. One way to identify optical activity in molecules with two or more chiral carbon atoms is to look for a plane of symmetry in the molecule. If a molecule has a plane of symmetry, then it is never optically active. A plane of symmetry is a plane that bisects the molecule where one side exactly reflects the other side.

symmetry plane

b. The optically active forms of tartaric acid have no plane of symmetry. The structures of the optically active forms of tartaric acid are:

mirror

These two forms of tartaric acid are nonsuperimposable.

147.   For the reaction:

$$^{+}H_3NCH_2CO_2H \rightleftharpoons 2\,H^+ + H_2NCH_2CO_2^{-} \qquad K_{eq} = 7.3 \times 10^{-13} = K_a(-CO_2H) \times K_a(-NH_3^{+})$$

$$7.3 \times 10^{-13} = \frac{[H^+]^2[H_2NCH_2CO_2^{-}]}{[^{+}H_3NCH_2CO_2H]} = [H^+]^2, \quad [H^+] = (7.3 \times 10^{-13})^{1/2}$$

$$[H^+] = 8.5 \times 10^{-7}\,M; \quad pH = -\log[H^+] = 6.07 = \text{isoelectric point}$$

149. 4.2×10^{-3} g K$_2$CrO$_7 \times \dfrac{1\,\text{mol K}_2\text{Cr}_2\text{O}_7}{294.20\,\text{g}} \times \dfrac{1\,\text{mol Cr}_2\text{O}_7^{2-}}{\text{mol K}_2\text{Cr}_2\text{O}_7} \times \dfrac{3\,\text{mol C}_2\text{H}_5\text{OH}}{2\,\text{mol Cr}_2\text{O}_7^{2-}}$

$$= 2.1 \times 10^{-5}\,\text{mol C}_2\text{H}_5\text{OH}$$

$$n_{\text{breath}} = \frac{PV}{RT} = \frac{\left(750.\,\text{mm Hg} \times \dfrac{1\,\text{atm}}{760\,\text{mm Hg}}\right) \times 0.500\,\text{L}}{\dfrac{0.08206\,\text{L atm}}{\text{K mol}} \times 303\,\text{K}} = 0.0198\,\text{mol breath}$$

$$\text{Mol \% C}_2\text{H}_5\text{OH} = \frac{2.1 \times 10^{-5}\,\text{mol C}_2\text{H}_5\text{OH}}{0.0198\,\text{mol total}} \times 100 = 0.11\%\,\text{alcohol}$$

Challenge Problems

151.   Assuming 1.000 L of the hydrocarbon (C$_x$H$_y$), then the volume of products will be 4.000 L and the mass of products (H$_2$O + CO$_2$) will be:

1.391 g/L × 4.000 L = 5.564 g products

$$\text{Mol } C_xH_y = n_{C_xH_y} = \frac{PV}{RT} = \frac{0.959 \text{ atm} \times 1.000 \text{ L}}{\dfrac{0.08206 \text{ L atm}}{\text{K mol}} \times 298 \text{ K}} = 0.0392 \text{ mol}$$

$$\text{Mol products} = n_p = \frac{PV}{RT} = \frac{1.51 \text{ atm} \times 4.000 \text{ L}}{\dfrac{0.08206 \text{ L atm}}{\text{K mol}} \times 375 \text{ K}} = 0.196 \text{ mol}$$

C_xH_y + oxygen $\rightarrow x$ CO_2 + $y/2$ H_2O;   setting up two equations:

$(0.0392)x + 0.0392(y/2) = 0.196$ (moles of products)

$(0.0392)x(44.01 \text{ g/mol}) + 0.0392(y/2)(18.02 \text{ g/mol}) = 5.564 \text{ g}$ (mass of products)

Solving: $x = 2$ and $y = 6$, so the formula of the hydrocarbon is C_2H_6 which is ethane.

153.   a.   The three structural isomers of C_5H_{12} are:

CH$_3$CH$_2$CH$_2$CH$_2$CH$_3$ CH$_3$CHCH$_2$CH$_3$ CH$_3$—C—CH$_3$
                                                                    | |
                                                                  CH$_3$ CH$_3$

        n-pentane   2-methylbutane   2,2-dimethylpropane

n-Pentane will form three different monochlorination products: 1-chloropentane, 2-chloropentane, and 3-chloropentane (the other possible monochlorination products differ by a simple rotation of the molecule; they are not different products from the ones listed). 2,2-Dimethylpropane will only form one monochlorination product: 1-chloro-2,2-dimethylpropane.   2-Methylbutane is the isomer of C_5H_{12} that forms four different monochlorination products: 1-chloro-2-methylbutane, 2-chloro-2-methylbutane, 3-chloro-2-methylbutane (or we could name this compound as 2-chloro-3-methylbutane), and 1-chloro-3-methylbutane.

        b.   The isomers of C_4H_8 are:

                                                                                                            CH$_3$
                                                                                                            |
CH$_2$=CHCH$_2$CH$_3$ CH$_3$CH=CHCH$_3$ CH$_2$=CCH$_3$

        1-butene   2-butene   2-methyl-1-propene or
                                                                                2-methylpropene

                                                            CH$_3$
                                                            |
            ☐   △

        cyclobutane   methylcyclopropane

The cyclic structures will not react with H_2O; only the alkenes will add H_2O to the double bond. From Exercise 21.58, the major product of the reaction of 1-butene and H_2O is 2-butanol (a 2° alcohol). 2-Butanol is also the major (and only) product when 2-butene and H_2O react. 2-Methylpropene forms 2-methyl-2-propanol as the major product when reacted with H_2O; this product is a tertiary alcohol. Therefore, the C_4H_8 isomer is 2-methylpropene.

$$CH_2{=}\overset{\overset{\displaystyle CH_3}{|}}{C}{-}CH_3 \ + \ HOH \ \longrightarrow \ CH_3{-}\overset{\overset{\displaystyle CH_3}{|}}{\underset{\underset{\displaystyle OH}{|}}{C}}{-}CH_3$$

2-methyl-2-propanol (a 3° alcohol, 3 R groups)

c. The structure of 1-chloro-1-methylcyclohexane is:

The addition reaction of HCl with an alkene is a likely choice for this reaction (see Exercise 21.58). The two isomers of C_7H_{12} that produce 1-chloro-1-methylcyclohexane as the major product are:

d. Working backwards, 2° alcohols produce ketones when they are oxidized (1° alcohols produce aldehydes, and then carboxylic acids). The easiest way to produce the 2° alcohol from a hydrocarbon is to add H_2O to an alkene. The alkene reacted is 1-propene (or propene).

propene   acetone

e. The $C_5H_{12}O$ formula has too many hydrogens to be anything other than an alcohol (or an unreactive ether). 1° alcohols are first oxidized to aldehydes, and then to carboxylic acids. Therefore, we want a 1° alcohol. The 1° alcohols with formula $C_5H_{12}O$ are:

$$
\begin{array}{cccc}
\text{OH} & \text{CH}_3 & \text{CH}_3 & \text{CH}_3 \\
| & | & | & | \\
\text{CH}_2\text{CH}_2\text{CH}_2\text{CH}_2\text{CH}_3 & \text{CH}_2\text{CHCH}_2\text{CH}_3 & \text{CH}_3\text{CHCH}_2\text{CH}_2 & \text{CH}_2\!\!-\!\!\text{C}\!\!-\!\!\text{CH}_3 \\
 & | & | & |\quad| \\
 & \text{OH} & \text{OH} & \text{OH}\;\;\text{CH}_3
\end{array}
$$

| 1-pentanol | 2-methyl-1-butanol | 3-methyl-1-butanol | 2,2-dimethyl-1-propanol |

There are other alcohols with formula $C_5H_{12}O$, but they are all 2° or 3° alcohols, which do not produce carboxylic acids when oxidized.

155.   Treat this problem like a diprotic acid (H_2A) titration. The K_{a_1} and K_{a_2} reactions are:

$$^+NH_3CH_2COOH \rightleftharpoons\ ^+NH_3CH_2COO^- + H^+ \quad K_{a_1} = \frac{[^+NH_3CH_2COO^-][H^+]}{[^+NH_3CH_2COOH]} = 4.3 \times 10^{-3}$$

$$^+NH_3CH_2COO^- \rightleftharpoons\ NH_2CH_2COO^- + H^+ \quad K_{a_2} = \frac{[NH_2CH_2COO^-][H^+]}{[^+NH_3CH_2COO^-]}$$

$$K_{a_2} = K_w/K_b = 1.0 \times 10^{-14}/6.0 \times 10^{-5} = 1.7 \times 10^{-10}$$

As OH⁻ is added, it reacts completely with the best acid present. From 0–50.0 mL of OH⁻ added, the reaction is:

$$^+NH_3CH_2COOH + OH^- \rightarrow\ ^+NH_3CH_2COO^- + H_2O$$

At 50.0 mL OH⁻ added (the first equivalence point), all of the $^+NH_3CH_2COOH$ has been converted into $^+NH_3CH_2COO^-$. This is an amphoteric species. To determine the pH when an amphoteric species is the major species present, we use the formula $pH = (pK_{a_1} + pK_{a_2})/2$. From 50.1–100.0 mL of OH⁻ added, the reaction that occurs is:

$$^+NH_3CH_2COO^- + OH^- \rightarrow\ NH_2CH_2COO^- + H_2O$$

100.0 mL of OH⁻ added represents the second equivalence point where $H_2NCH_2COO^-$ is the major amino acid species present.

a. 25.0 mL of OH⁻ added represents the first halfway point to equivalence. Here, $[^+NH_3CH_2COOH] = [^+NH_3CH_2COO^-]$. This is a buffer solution where $pH = pK_{a_1}$.

At 25.0 mL OH⁻ added:

$$pH = pK_{a_1} = -\log(4.3 \times 10^{-3}) = 2.37$$

50.0 mL of OH⁻ added represents the first equivalence point. Here, $^+$NH$_3$CH$_2$COO⁻ is the major amino acid species present. This is amphoteric species. At 50.0 mL OH⁻ added:

$$pH = \frac{pK_{a_1} + pK_{a_2}}{2} = \frac{2.37 - \log(1.7 \times 10^{-10})}{2} = \frac{2.37 + 9.77}{2} = 6.07$$

75.0 mL of OH⁻ added represents the second halfway point to equivalence. Here, $[^+NH_3CH_2COO^-] = [NH_2CH_2COO^-]$ and $pH = pK_{a_2}$. At 75.0 mL OH⁻ added:

$$pH = pK_{a_2} = -\log(1.7 \times 10^{-10}) = 9.77$$

b.

Volume of OH⁻ added

The major amino acid species present are:

point A (0.0 mL OH⁻): $^+$NH$_3$CH$_2$COOH

point B (25.0 mL OH⁻): $^+$NH$_3$CH$_2$COOH and $^+$NH$_3$CH$_2$COO⁻

point C (50.0 mL OH⁻): $^+$NH$_3$CH$_2$COO⁻

point D (75.0 mL OH⁻): $^+$NH$_3$CH$_2$COO⁻ and NH$_2$CH$_2$COO⁻

point E (100.0 mL OH⁻):   NH$_2$CH$_2$COO⁻

c.   The various charged amino acid species are:

$^+NH_3CH_2COOH$ net charge = +1

$^+NH_3CH_2COO^-$ net charge = 0

$NH_2CH_2COO^-$ net charge = −1

The net charge is zero at the pH when the major amino acid species present is the $^+NH_3CH_2COO^-$ form; this happens at the first equivalence point in our titration problem. From part a, this occurs at pH = 6.07 (the isoelectric point).

d.   The net charge is +1/2 when = $[^+NH_3CH_2COOH] = [^+NH_3CH_2COO^-]$; net charge = (+1 + 0)/2 = +1/2. This occurs at the first halfway point to equivalence, where pH = pK_{a_1} = 2.37. The net charge is −1/2 when $[^+NH_3CH_2COO^-] = [NH_2CH_2COO^-]$; net charge = (0 − 1)/2 = −1/2. This occurs at the second halfway point to equivalence, where pH = pK_{a_2} = 9.77.

Page Numbers of Some Important Tables

Physical Constants

Constant	Symbol	Value
Atomic mass unit	amu	1.66054×10^{-27} kg
Avogadro's number	N	6.02214×10^{23} mol^{-1}
Bohr radius	a_0	5.292×10^{-11} m
Boltzmann's constant	k	1.38066×10^{-23} J K^{-1}
Charge of an electron	e	1.60218×10^{-19} C
Faraday's constant	F	96,485 C mol^{-1}
Gas constant	R	8.31451 J K^{-1} mol^{-1}
		0.08206 L atm K^{-1} mol^{-1}
Mass of an electron	m_e	9.10939×10^{-31} kg
		5.48580×10^{-4} amu
Mass of a neutron	m_n	1.67493×10^{-27} kg
		1.00866 amu
Mass of a proton	m_p	1.67262×10^{-27} kg
		1.00728 amu
Planck's constant	h	6.62608×10^{-34} J s
Speed of light	c	2.99792458×10^8 m s^{-1}